There was light in a vacuum-enclosed filament of carbon, when fed an electrical current. It took a genius to find just how to do it. Thomas Edison's discovery (1879) led to the first power stations. Charles Parsons' steam turbine (1884) and the great Niagara Falls Hydroelectric station (1893) were pioneering events in the evolution of electrical engineering.

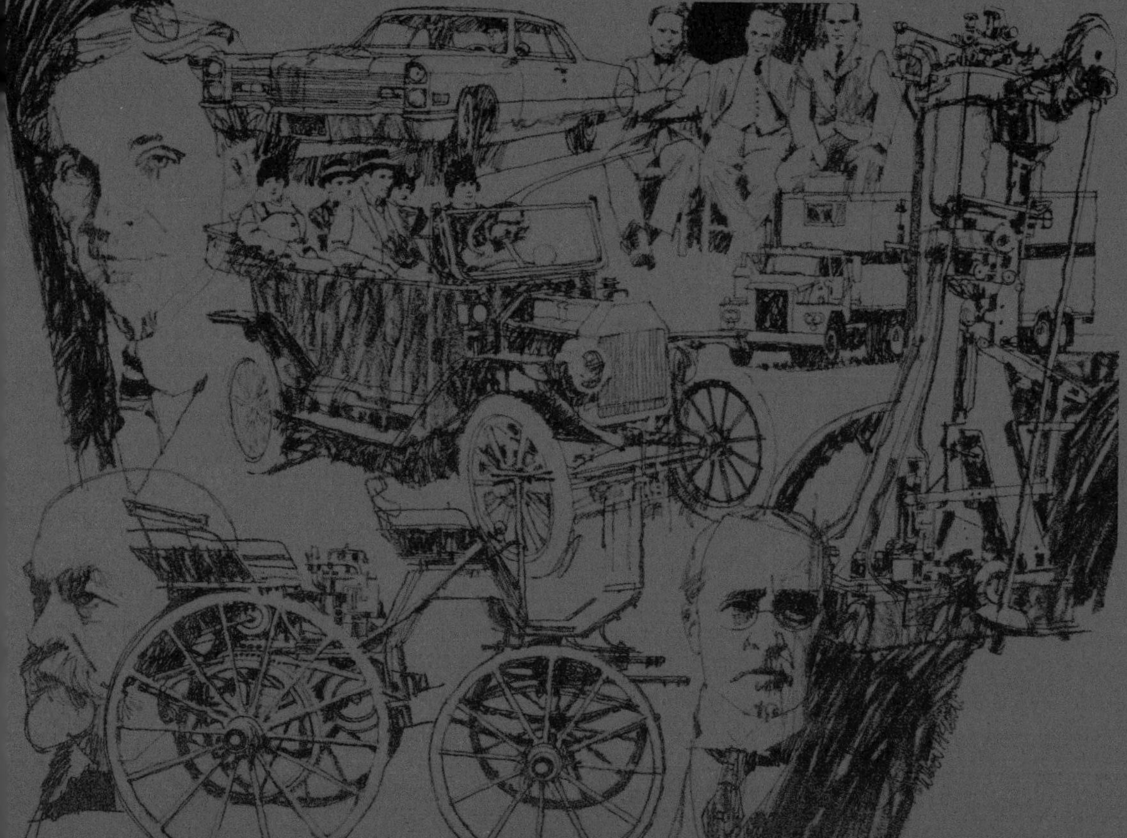

Automotive engineering really began to roll about 1885, when Gottlieb Daimler's first internal-combustion car appeared. Henry Ford's genius was to create mass-production —Model T's for the millions. Rudolph Diesel developed his famed work-horse engine in 1892. Civil engineers set out to build roads fast enough to keep up with the drivers. That race isn't over yet.

engineering design graphics

SECOND EDITION

JAMES H. EARLE, Texas A&M University

engineering design graphics

SECOND EDITION

ADDISON-WESLEY PUBLISHING COMPANY
Reading, Massachusetts
Menlo Park, California · London · Don Mills, Ontario

Chapter opening illustrations are reproduced through the courtesy of Mattel, Inc. ("Decision" photo) and the National Aeronautics and Space Administration (all other photos).

Endpaper drawings are reproduced through the courtesy of Keuffel & Esser Co.

Second printing May 1973

Printed in the United States of America. Published simultaneously in Canada. Library of Congress Catalog Card No. 72–9499.

HA 4/73 01718

Dedicated to my father
Hubert Lewis Earle
October 25, 1900—October 22, 1967

PREFACE

Design is a major function of the engineer and technician, and engineering graphics and descriptive geometry principles are the fundamental tools of the design process. It is this interrelationship of graphical methods in engineering design that has been used as the theme for this textbook. The material in the text has been organized to conform to a sequence of the design process — identification, preliminary ideas, refinement, analysis, decision, and finally, implementation. These six steps represent an orderly approach to the solution of any problem requiring innovation and creativity. However, they are not intended to serve as a rigid constraint on creativity; they are merely suggested as guides to the designer who wishes to organize his approach to a problem in an orderly manner, knowing that he will thereby increase his chances of obtaining satisfactory solutions and improve his production.

This first revision represents a major modification of several chapters. Statistical figures pertaining to the various engineering professions (Chapter 1) have been updated. Beginning with Chapter 3, more detailed attention has been given to methods of scheduling and planning team projects; additional scheduling suggestions are included throughout the book. Added emphasis has been placed on more traditional principles related to the preparation of working drawings in Chapter 5. Many new figures have been added in this chapter, and most of the previous ones have been redrawn to incorporate the latest principles and to make use of better drafting techniques than are found in the current standards, which were used as the basis of many of these figures. Many new problems have been added to this chapter also.

Additional articles have been included in Chapters 8 and 9 to give a broader coverage of descriptive geometry principles. Chapter 15 represents a major revision with considerable improvement of the coverage of data analysis and construction of charts and graphs. The section on empirical data and equations has been expanded, both in text and in figures, and the section on cams has also been enlarged.

An important inclusion in Chapter 16 is material on the preparation of written technical reports that is important to the technician and engineer. Sample sheets of typical pages from a written report are included to give actual examples to assist the student with his class assignments. The coverage of pictorials in Chapter 17 has been broadened. Chapter 19 is the most completely modified chapter of this revision. Essentially all the drawings of this chapter have been redrawn to make them more readable and more germane to the principles that they represent. Threaded fasteners receive a more complete coverage, as do working drawings and introductory shop processes. Material on gears is introduced. This chapter gives a complete coverage of basic fundamentals of dimensioning as well as the more advanced principles of geometric tolerancing and the preparation of final working drawings.

Most of these revisions were suggested by instructors who have adopted this book for use in their classes. We are grateful for their many suggestions that have been incorporated in this version.

The graphical principles presented in this text are closely related to actual engineering design problems. It is important to emphasize that engineering graphics and descriptive geometry, as presented here, are not the same as mechanical drafting, since this discipline is only a minor aspect of graphics. Instead, engineering graphics encompasses the total effort made by the design team, the engineer, technician, and designer, to solve graphically engineering problems. Our concept of engineering graphics motivates the student by exposing him to engineering examples taken from real life situations. Instead of boring the student with synthetic projects, the approach chosen in this text has proved to stimulate his interest in engineering as a creative profession.

Several techniques of presentation have been used in this text that improve the exposition and help the student to understand the concepts and procedures discussed. Many of these techniques allow the student to grasp principles on his own, thus requiring less of the instructor's time while allowing the average student to cover more material than in the conventional course. For greater clarity, a second color has been introduced to highlight significant steps and notes in the illustrations. More complex problems are solved by the *step method*, i.e., steps leading to the solution of a problem are presented in sequence with the instructional text closely related to each step. Since this method of developing a solution by steps shows the actual progression of graphical construction, the student can review the procedure and theory involved in a problem while studying alone without the help of an instructor. To determine the effectiveness of the step method*, it was tested throughout a semester's work and the results were compared with those obtained by conventional textbook methods. A statistical comparison of 2800 experimental samples showed that the step method was 20 percentage points superior to the conventional approach. This result prompted the author to introduce the step method in this volume.

Enough material is included in this text for two separate courses—engineering graphics and descriptive geometry—and either could serve as an introductory engineering course.

---

*Earle, James H., *An Experimental Comparison of Three Self-Instruction Formats for Descriptive Geometry*. Unpublished dissertation, Texas A&M University, College Station, Texas, 1964.

Although the material is arranged within the framework of the design process, with which it is partially integrated, it is sufficiently independent from it to be readily extracted for use in two separate courses, with some chapters being common to both. Where two courses are offered, it is suggested that the design aspects be a prominent part of both.

The problems at the end of each chapter vary widely in form, ranging from reports and models to working drawings. The problems are structured to be difficult enough to be interesting, but not so difficult as to be beyond the ability of a freshman student.

A number of problem books are available that can supplement the problems provided at the end of each chapter. Twelve problem books authored by the Engineering Design Graphics Department of Texas A&M University have been published by Addison-Wesley Publishing Company. The authors of this series are James H. Earle, Samuel M. Cleland, Lawrence E. Stark, John P. Oliver, Paul M. Mason, North B. Bardell, Richard F. Vogel, J. Tim Coppinger, and Michael P. Guerard. Five volumes each of *Engineering Graphics and Design Problems* (1, 2, 3, 4 and 5) and *Design and Descriptive Geometry Problems* (1, 2, 3, 4 and 5) are available. Also available are two problem books for schools offering a single combined course in graphics. These two problem books are *Engineering Design Graphics Problems* C and *D*. Each of these problem books is completely different from the others in the series. All contain design problems and industrial applications of problems to be solved by graphical methods. Also available are teacher's guides and solution booklets which provide solutions, course outlines, and quizzes. This continuing series provides the instructor with a different set of problems for each semester.

Thanks are due to the hundreds of industries who have provided photographs, drawings, and examples included in this text. Special thanks are given to Mr. Howard Gibbons and the staff of NASA for their review and approval of Chapter 2, as well as for the many photographs provided by the Agency. Appreciation is also expressed to Professor Michael P. Guerard of Texas A&M University for his assistance in preparing the section on nomography, and to the Whitney Library of Design and Mr. Henry Dreyfuss for generously granting permission to reproduce excerpts from their book, *The Measure of Man*. Credits would not be complete without mentioning the encouragement, confidence, and assistance given to the author by the staff of Addison-Wesley Publishing Company. They have been instrumental in recognizing the need for a book of this type and in expediting its publication.

College Station, Texas J. H. E.
November 1972

CONTENTS

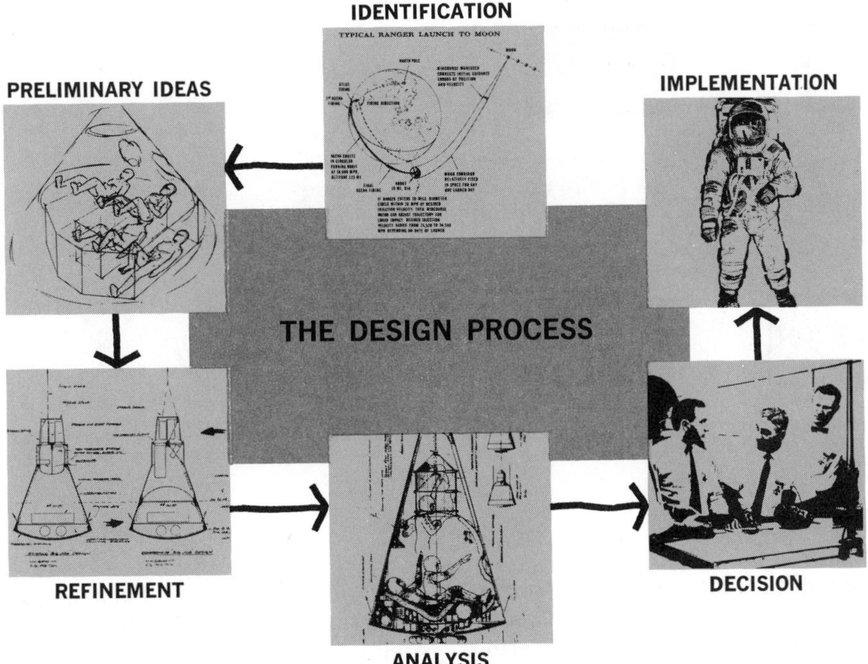

1 INTRODUCTION TO ENGINEERING AND DESIGN

1-1 INTRODUCTION

Engineering has made significant contributions to the advancement of our standard of living—probably more than any other profession. Essentially all our daily activities are assisted by products, systems, and services made possible by the engineer. Our utilities, heating and cooling equipment, automobiles, machinery, and consumer products have been provided at an economical rate to the bulk of our national population by the engineering profession.

The engineer must function as a member of a team composed of other related, and sometimes unrelated, disciplines. Many engineers have been responsible for innovations of life-saving mechanisms used in medicine which were designed in cooperation with members of the medical profession. Other engineers are technical representatives or salesmen who explain and demonstrate applications of technical products to a specialized segment of the market. Even though there is a wide range of activities within the broad definition of engineering, the engineer is basically a *designer.* This is the activity that most distinguishes him from other associated members of the technological team.

This book is devoted to the introduction of elementary design concepts related to the field of engineering and to the application of engineering graphics and descriptive geometry to the design process. Examples are given which have an engineering problem at the core, and which require organization, analysis, problem solving, graphical principles, communication, and skill (Fig. 1-1). Problems which require a minimum of technical background are presented, emphasizing the organization, conceptualization, and

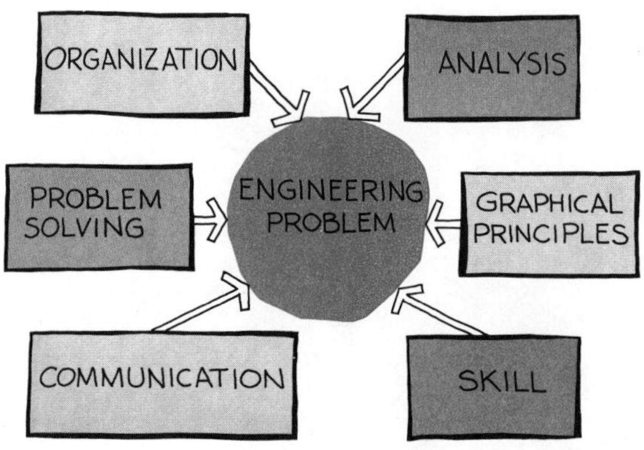

Fig. 1–1. Problems in this text require a total engineering approach with the engineering problem as the central theme.

Fig. 1–2. Albert Einstein, the famous physicist, said, "Imagination is more important than knowledge . . ."

development of a design solution with graphical methods used as the primary method of solution. Extensive illustrations of engineering applications are included to relate the theoretical principles to actual engineering situations. These illustrations will introduce the student to various fields of engineering and familiarize him with the wide variety of applications of graphical principles in the design and solution of problems.

Creativity and imagination are encouraged by this textbook as essential ingredients in the engineer's professional activities. All principles presented are structured to emphasize the importance of innovation and experimentation in solving elementary engineering problems. A systematic approach to developing a design solution has been used as the format for the entire volume, carrying the process from problem identification to final implementation by successive chapters. Albert Einstein, the famous physicist, said that "Imagination is more important than knowledge, for knowledge is limited, whereas imagination embraces the entire world . . . stimulating progress, giving birth to evolution . . ." (Fig. 1–2).

This chapter will define the activities of the members of the engineering team—scientist, engineer, technician, craftsman, designer, stylist, and draftsman. Each major field of engineering will be discussed to familiarize the student with these fields and their technical societies. The design process, used as the framework for the remaining chapters, will be introduced in general terms.

1–2 ENGINEERING GRAPHICS

Engineering graphics is usually considered to be the total field of graphical problem solving and includes two major areas of specialization, descriptive geometry and working drawings. Other areas that can be utilized for a wide variety of scientific and engineering applications are also included within the field. These are nomography, graphical mathematics, empirical equations, technical illustration, vector analysis, data analysis, and other graphical applications associated with each of the different engineering industries. Engineering graphics should not be confused with drafting, since it is considerably more extensive than the communication of an idea in the form of a working drawing. Graphical methods are the primary means of creating a solution to a problem requiring innovations not already available to the designer. Graphics is the designer's method

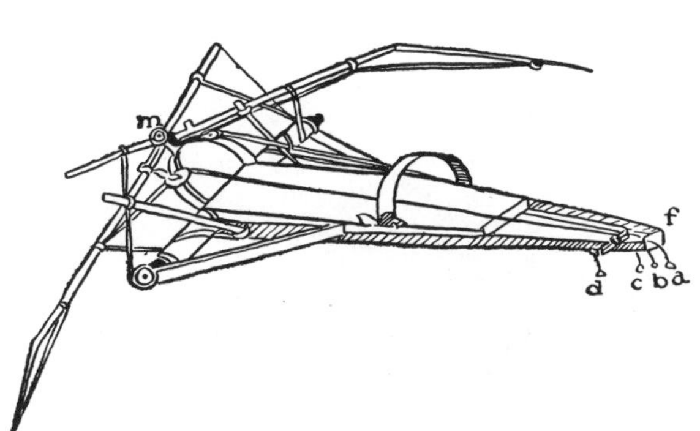

Fig. 1–3. Leonardo da Vinci developed many creative designs through the use of graphical methods.

Fig. 1–4. Gaspard Monge, the "father of descriptive geometry."

of thinking, solving, and communicating his ideas throughout the design process. Man's progress can be attributed to a great extent to the area of engineering graphics. Even the simplest of structures could not have been designed or built without drawings, diagrams, and details that explained their construction (Fig. 1–3). For many years technical drawings, such as they were, were confined to two dimensions, usually a plan view. Supplemental sketches and pictorials were used to explain other dimensions of the project being depicted. Gradually, graphical methods were developed to show three related views of an object to simulate its three-dimensional representation. A most significant development in the engineering graphics area was descriptive geometry as introduced by Gaspard Monge (Fig. 1–4).

Descriptive Geometry. Gaspard Monge (1746–1818) is considered the "father of descriptive geometry." Young Monge used this graphical method of solving design problems related to fortifications and battlements while a military student in France. He was scolded by his headmaster for not solving a problem by the usual, long, tedious mathematical process traditionally used for problems of this type. It was only after long explanations and comparisons of the solutions of both methods that he was able to convince the faculty that his graphical methods could be used to solve the problem in considerably less time. This was such an improvement over the mathematical solution that it was kept a military secret for 15 years before it was allowed to be taught as part of the technical curriculum. Monge became a scientific and mathematical aide to Napoleon during his reign as general and emperor of France.

Descriptive geometry has been simplified from the "indirect" method introduced by Monge to the "direct" method used today. In the "indirect" method, the first angle of projection is used primarily, with the front view projected above the top view, and the projections are revolved onto the projection planes to obtain the desired relationships (Fig. 1–5). The "direct" method utilizes the third angle, with the top view projected over the front view, and auxiliary views are projected directly to auxiliary planes in succession until the required geometric relationships are found.

Descriptive geometry can be defined as the projection of three-dimensional figures onto a two-dimensional plane of paper in such a manner as to allow geometric manipulations to determine lengths, angles, shapes, and other descriptive information concerning the figures.

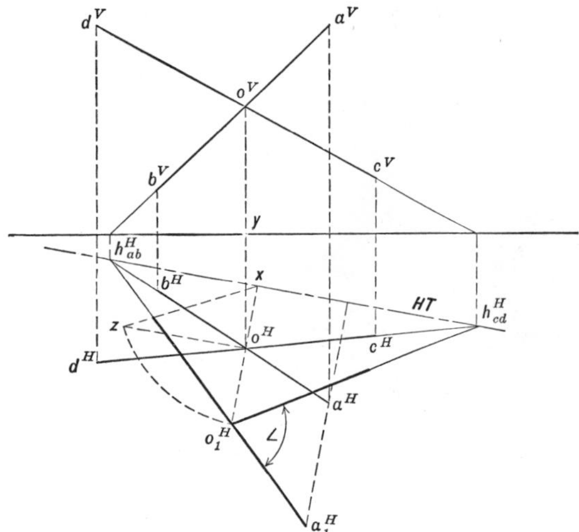

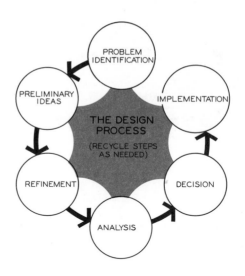

Fig. 1–5. An indirect solution to a descriptive geometry utilizing the Mongean method. (Courtesy of C. H. Schumann, Jr., *Descriptive Geometry*, 3rd Edition, Van Nostrand, 1938.)

Fig. 1–6. The steps of the design process.

The type of problems lending themselves to solution by descriptive geometry, although very common, are usually considerably more difficult to solve by mathematics. The simple determination of the angle between planes is a basic descriptive geometry problem, but is difficult to determine mathematically when the plane of the angle does not appear true size in the given views.

1–3 THE DESIGN PROCESS

The act of devising an original solution to a problem by a combination of principles, resources, and products is design. As we stated at the beginning of this chapter, design is the most distinguishing responsibility that separates the engineer from the scientist and the technician. His solutions may involve a combination of existing components in a different arrangement to provide a more efficient result or they may involve the development of an entirely new product; but in either case his work is referred to as the act of designing. This process is not an inspirational phenomenon that is experienced by only a few, but is the result of a systematic, disciplined approach to the needs of the problem.

The design process is the usual pattern of activities that are followed by the designer in arriving at the solution of a technological problem. Many combinations of steps have been suggested to enable one to achieve design objectives. This book emphasizes a six-step design process that is a composite of the sequences most commonly employed in solving problems. The six steps are: (1) Problem identification, (2) Preliminary ideas, (3) Problem refinement, (4) Analysis, (5) Decision, and (6) Implementation (Fig. 1–6). Although the designer will sequentially work from step to step, he may recycle to previous steps as he progresses.

Engineering graphics and descriptive geometry have been integrated into these steps to stress their role in the creative process of designing. These areas are probably more critical to the design process than any other single field of study. The following articles present the design process while succeeding chapters illustrate the applications of graphics to the design process.

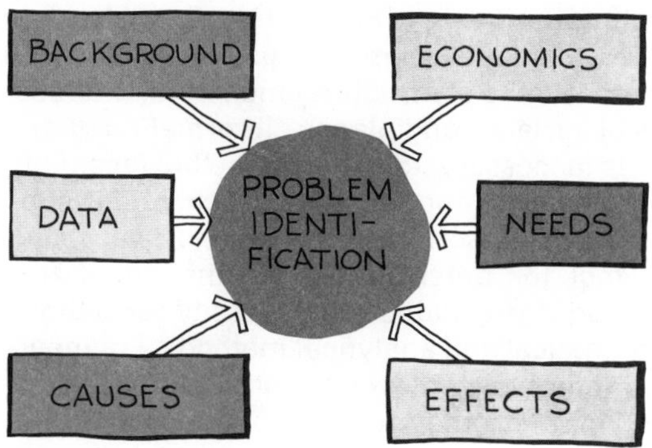

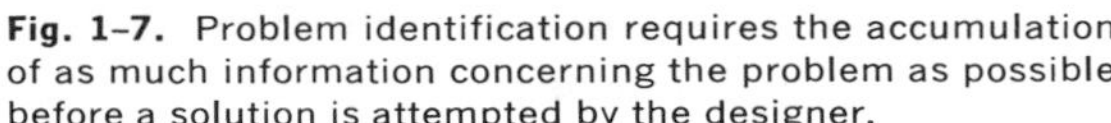
Fig. 1–7. Problem identification requires the accumulation of as much information concerning the problem as possible before a solution is attempted by the designer.

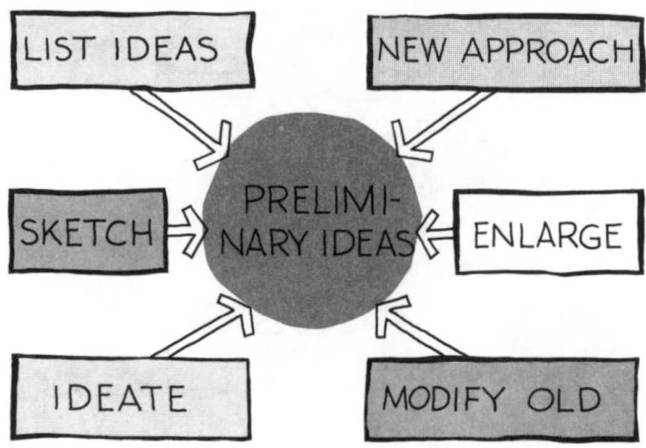

Fig. 1–8. Preliminary ideas are developed after the identification step has been completed. All possibilities should be listed and sketched to give the designer a broad selection of ideas from which to work.

Problem Identification. Many engineering problems are not clearly defined nor do they have apparent solutions. As in any problem situation, it is necessary that the problem be identified and understood before an attempt should be made to solve it (Fig. 1–7). For example, a prominent concern today is air pollution. If you were assigned to find ways of reducing air pollution, you would first have to identify the problem. We know that many impurities are released into the atmosphere that are unhealthy and cause general discomfort. But is the problem the control of the sources of the impurities, their elimination, the control of atmospheric conditions that harbor impurities, or the creation of an artificial atmosphere that is free of the polluted air?

Assume that there is a bad intersection where traffic is unusually congested. What is the problem? Is it too many cars for the capacity of the road, is it poorly synchronized signals, is it poorly routed traffic, or is it visual obstructions resulting in congestion of traffic? The answers to questions such as these would be very helpful in identifying the problem and consequently arriving at a conclusion. Field data gathered at the site can provide valuable information that will serve to identify the problem.

Preliminary Ideas. Once the problem has been identified, the next step is to accumulate as many ideas for solution as possible (Fig. 1–8). Preliminary ideas can be gathered by individual or group approaches. Preliminary ideas should be sufficiently broad to allow for unique solutions that could revolutionize present methods. All ideas should be recorded in written form. Many rough sketches of preliminary ideas should be made and retained as a means of generating original ideas and stimulating the design process. Ideas and comments should be noted on the sketches as a basis for further preliminary designs.

Preliminary ideas can be gathered from several commonly used methods, including brainstorming, market analysis, or research of present designs. These methods are explained in detail in later chapters. All work is most useful if completed in graphical form for easy analysis.

Problem Refinement. Several of the better preliminary ideas are selected for further refinement to determine their true merits. Rough sketches are converted to scale drawings that will permit space analysis, critical measurements, and the calculation of areas and volumes

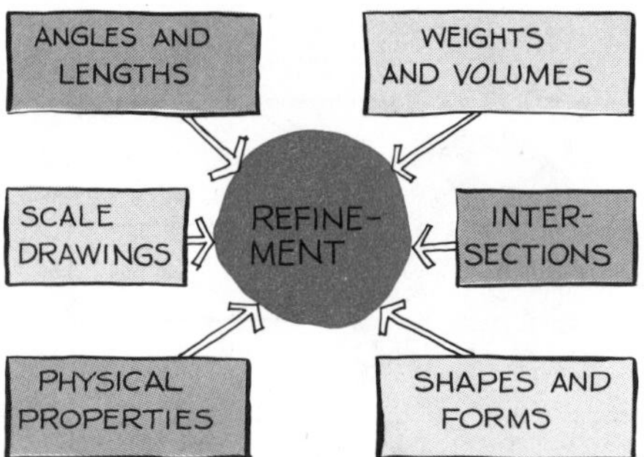

Fig. 1–9A. Refinement begins with construction of scale drawings of the better preliminary ideas. Descriptive geometry and graphical methods are used to find necessary geometric characteristics.

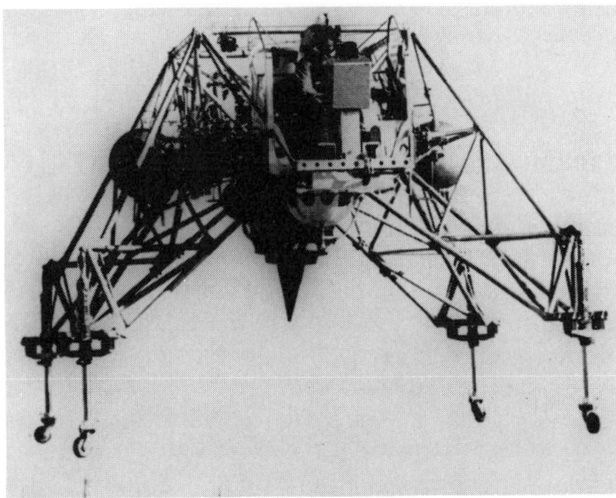

Fig. 1–9B. The refinement of the lunar vehicle required the use of descriptive geometry and other graphical methods. (Courtesy of Ryan Aircraft Corporation.)

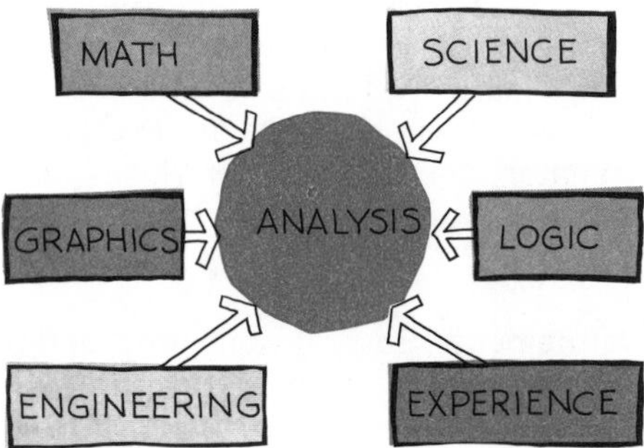

Fig. 1–10. The analysis phase of the design process is the application of all available technological methods from science to graphics in evaluating the refined designs.

affecting the design (Fig. 1–9A). Consideration is given to spatial relationships, angles between planes, lengths of structural members, intersections of surfaces and planes. Information of this type is necessary to determine the feasibility of manufacture and the physical characteristics of a design. Descriptive geometry is a very valuable tool for determining information of this type, and it precludes the necessity for tedious mathematical and analytical methods. Engineering graphics is employed to construct the necessary views of the design so that it can be analyzed for its spatial characteristics with descriptive geometry.

An example of a problem of this type is illustrated in the landing gear of the lunar vehicle shown in Fig. 1–9B. It was necessary for the designer to make many freehand sketches of the design and finally a scale drawing to establish clearances with the landing surface. The configuration of the landing gear was drawn to scale in the descriptive views of the landing craft. It was necessary, at this point, to determine certain fundamental lengths, angles, and specifications that are related to the fabrication of the gear. The length of each leg of the landing apparatus and the angles between the members at the point of junction had to be found to design a connector, and the angles the legs made with the body of the spacecraft had to be known in order to design these joints. All of this information was easily and quickly determined with the use of descriptive geometry. The employment of descriptive geometry as a preliminary means of determining this information facilitates the application of analytical principles to convert this information into equations for mathematical solutions. Chapters 6 through 12 are devoted to graphical methods of problem refinements.

Analysis. Analysis is the step of the design process where engineering and scientific principles are used most (Fig. 1–10). Analysis involves the study of the best designs to determine the comparative merits of each with respect to cost, strength, function, and market appeal. Graphical principles can also be applied to analysis to a considerable extent. The determination of stress is somewhat simpler with graphical vectors than with the analytical method. Functional relationships between moving parts will also provide data that can be obtained graphically more easily than by analytical methods. Graphical solutions to analytical problems offer a readily available means of checking the solution, therefore reducing checking time. Graphical methods can also be applied to the conversion of functions of mechanisms to a graphical format that will permit the designer to convert this action into an equation form that will be easy to utilize. Data can be gathered and graphically analyzed that would otherwise be difficult to analyze by mathematical means. For instance, empirical curves that do not fit a normal equation are often integrated graphically when the mathematical process would involve unwieldy equations.

Graphical methods are vital supplements to the engineering sciences when applied to the analysis procedure. These methods should be well understood by the engineer, technician, or designer, to afford him every available aid to effectively solve a problem in the minimum time. Chapters 13, 14, and 15 cover this phase of the design process. Human factors are the basis for a design and are given as an introduction to this important area of consideration.

Models constructed at reduced scales are valuable to the analysis of a design to establish relationships of moving parts and outward appearances, and to evaluate other design characteristics. Full-scale prototypes are often constructed after the scale models have been studied for function. This provides a tangible model for further development prior to extensive manufacture on a large volume basis. Graphical methods are applied as tools for modifying designs at each revision.

Decision. A decision must be made at this stage to select a single design that will be accepted as the solution of the design problem (Fig. 1–11). Each of the several designs that have been refined and analyzed will offer unique features, and it will probably not be possible to include all of these in a single final solution. In many cases, the final design is a compromise that offers as many of the best features as possible.

The decision may be made by the designer on an independent, unassisted basis, or it may be made by a group of associates. Regardless of the size of the group making the decision as to which design will be accepted, graphics is a primary means of presenting the proposed designs for a decision. The outstanding aspects of each design usually lend themselves to presentation in the form of graphs which compare costs of manufacturing, weights, operational characteristics, and other data that would be considered in arriving at the final decision. Pictorial sketches or formal pictorials are excellent methods of graphically studying different designs before arriving at a decision.

When working on a small project, the designer must communicate with himself through these methods if he is to make the decision independently. When the approval of a design is made by a group of associates or people unfamiliar with the technical aspects of his work, different forms of graphics that will satisfy the needs of the audience are used to aid in the decision process. More detailed schematics, graphs, and pictorials are used to communicate the advantages and disadvantages of each design in as clear a format as possible. Chapter 18 elaborates on this portion of the design process.

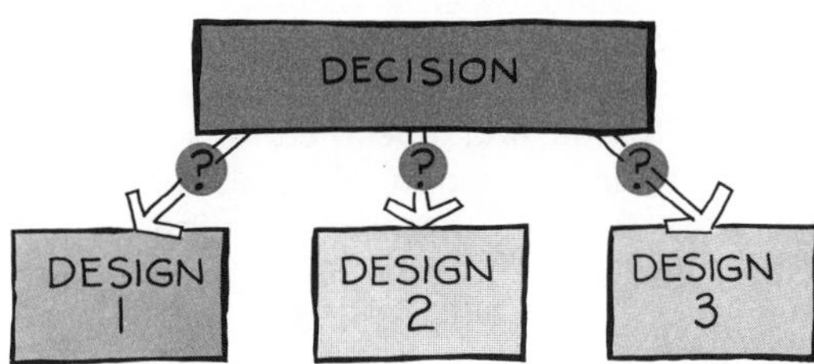

Fig. 1–11. Decision is the selection of the best design or design features to be implemented.

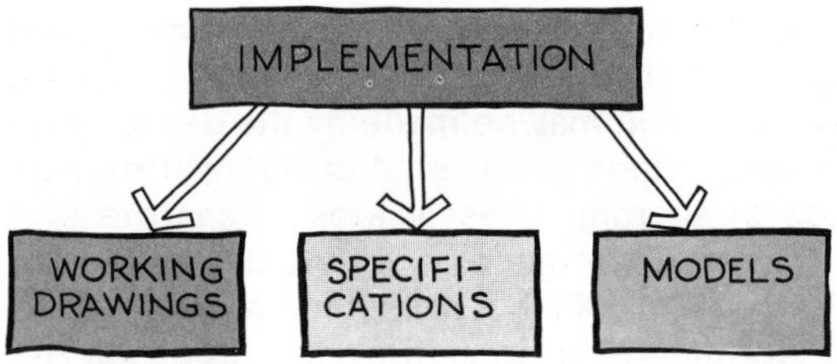

IMPLEMENTATION

WORKING DRAWINGS | SPECIFI-CATIONS | MODELS

Fig. 1–12. Implementation is the final step of the design process, where drawings and specifications are prepared from which the final product can be constructed.

Implementation. The final design concept must be presented in a workable form after the best design has been selected and decided upon. This type of presentation refers primarily to the working drawings and specifications that are used as the actual instruments for the fabrication of the product, whether it is a small piece of hardware or a bridge (Fig. 1–12). Engineering graphics fundamentals must be used to convert all preliminary designs and data into the language of the manufacturer who will be responsible for the conversion of the ideas into a reality. Workmen must have complete detailed instructions for the manufacture of each single part, measured to a thousandth of an inch to facilitate its proper manufacture. Working drawings must be sufficiently detailed and explicit to provide a legal basis for a contract which will be the document for the contractor's bid on the job.

Plans are usually executed by draftsmen and technicians who are specialists in this area. The designer or engineer must be sufficiently knowledgeable in graphical presentation to be able to supervise the preparation of working drawings even though he may not be involved in the mechanics of producing them. He must approve all plans and specifications prior to their release for production. This responsibility necessitates that he be well-rounded in all aspects of graphical techniques to enable him to approve the plans with assurance. This step of the design process is probably less creative than the subsequent steps, but it is no less important than any other step.

Fig. 1–14. A scientist studies the thin membrane of cellulose acetate as part of a reverse osmosis technique to screen out salt in the exploration of new methods of desalination of salt and brackish waters. (Courtesy of General Dynamics.)

Fig. 1–15. A scientist reads the pressure gauges that measure gas flow into a furnace used to grow single crystals of gallium phosphide. These crystals are necessary to the investigation of chemiluminescence. (Courtesy of Bell Telephone Laboratories.)

Fig. 1–16. A scientist adjusts gas flow into a new high-powered gas laser. This laser (which mixes helium, carbon dioxide, and nitrogen) has produced continuous outputs of more than 106 watts—the highest continuous output obtained from any laser to date. (Courtesy of Bell Telephone Laboratories.)

Fig. 1–17. Scientists work on one of the most modern of discoveries, the laser, as they conduct a study of the helium-neon laser to determine the relationship of power output to the length of the cavity. (Courtesy of Bell Telephone Laboratories.)

Fig. 1–18. The successful application of scientific principles to practical problems is evidenced by the erection of the Hoover Dam. This famous dam, built in 1932, is one of engineering's finest achievements. (Courtesy of the Bureau of Reclamation.)

Fig. 1–19. An engineer must apply experience and judgment in the application of engineering principles to the solution of a problem. (Courtesy of AT&T.)

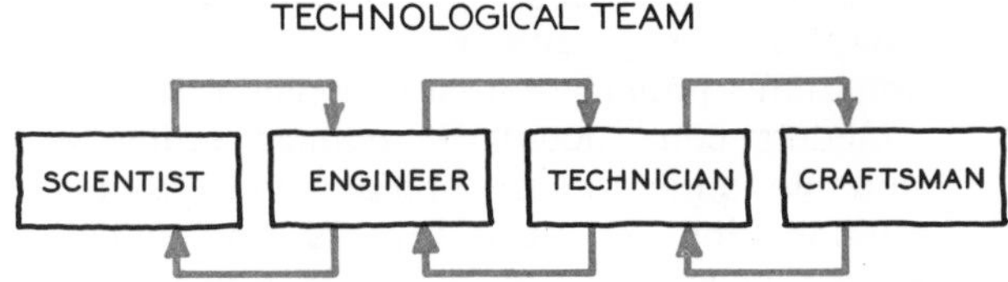

Fig. 1–13. The technological team.

1–4 THE TECHNOLOGICAL TEAM

The profession of engineering has broadened at a rapid rate during recent years with the introduction of many new processes and fields of specialty unheard of a decade ago. With the increasing complexity of technology, it has become necessary for professional responsibilities to be performed by highly qualified people with specialized training. Thus technology has

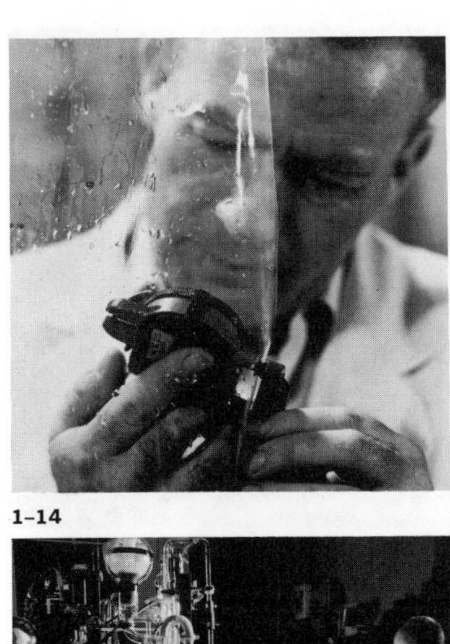

1–14

1–15

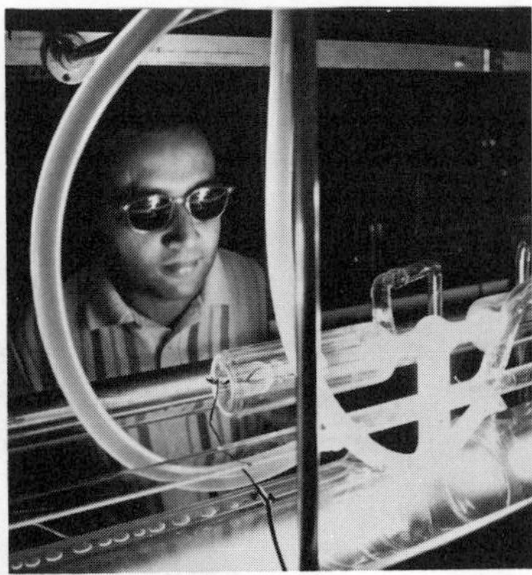

1–16

1–17

1–18

1–19

become a team effort involving the scientist, engineer, technician, and craftsman (Fig. 1-13). A project may include mechanical design, an advanced electronics system, a structure, and chemical processes, and therefore it may require many engineers, technicians, and craftsmen to complete the design. This changing complexion of industrial technology requires that engineering teams function as a composite unit. The members of the technological team are listed below.

The Scientist. The scientist is primarily a researcher who is seeking to establish new theories and principles through experimentation and testing (Figs. 1–14 through 1–17). Often he has little concern for the application of specific principles that are being developed, but is merely interested in isolating significant relationships. Scientific discoveries are used as the basis for related research and the development of practical applications for the discoveries which may not come into existence until years after the initial discovery.

The Engineer. The engineer's training in areas of science and mathematics, in addition to industrial processes, prepares him to apply the basic principles discovered by the scientist to practical problems (Fig. 1–18). He is concerned with the conversion of raw materials and power sources into needed products and services. The

1-20

1-21

1-22

Fig. 1-20. Engineers must analyze the costs and profits that will result from a project before it can be recommended for implementation. (Courtesy of AT&T Long Lines.)

Fig. 1-21. Reactor fuel is weighed prior to its being formed into compacts for a high-temperature gas-cooled reactor. Many duties of this type may be performed by trained technicians who assist an engineer or scientist. (Courtesy of General Dynamics.)

Fig. 1-22. Craftsmen are assembling a CO_2 sand-casting mold to produce a transmission housing weighing 186 pounds. The shape in the foreground is part of the mold assembly. (Courtesy of ALCOA.)

emphasis on practical application of principles distinguishes the engineer from the scientist. The application of these principles to new products or systems is the process of designing, which is the engineer's most unique function, requiring the highest degree of creativity. Engineers must always be concerned with efficiency and economy in their designs to provide the greatest service to society (Fig. 1-19). In general terms, the engineer practices the art of using available principles and resources to achieve a practical end at a reasonable cost (Fig. 1-20). Additional information on specific fields of engineering will be covered in Articles 1-6 through 1-15.

The Technician. The technician is a specially trained individual who assists the engineer at a semiprofessional level. His work may vary from technical laboratory experiments to the supervision of production (Fig. 1-21). In general, the technician works as a liaison between the engineer and the craftsman who will actually construct the design. The technician must exercise a large degree of judgment and imagination in his work and he must assume responsibilities beyond that of the craftsman, who is concerned with carrying out the specifications with the minimum of variation.

The Craftsman. The craftsman is a vital member of the engineering team since he must see that the engineering design is implemented by producing it according to the specifications of the engineer (Fig. 1-22). He may be a machinist

Fig. 1–23. Thomas A. Edison had essentially no formal education, but he gave the world some of its most creative designs, which have never been equaled by a single individual.

who fabricates the various components of the product or an electrical craftsman who assembles electrical components. Craftsmen are no less important than other members of the team since they supply a technical skill that cannot be provided by the engineer or the technician. The ability to produce a given part in accordance with design specifications is as necessary as the act of designing the part. Craftsmen include electricians, welders, machinists, fabricators, draftsmen, and many other types.

The Designer. The designer is that individual who has special talents for creating solutions to technological problems. Often a designer may be wrongly referred to as a person with aesthetic or artistic abilities who is concerned primarily with the appearance of a design. This is an area of design that is filled by the "stylist." The designer may be an engineer, an inventor, or a person who has special talents for devising creative solutions, even though he may not have an engineering background. This is often the case in young areas of technology where little precedent has been established by previous experience. Thomas A. Edison (Fig. 1–23) had very little formal education, but he possessed an exceptional ability to design and perfect some of the world's most significant designs. Engineers may find that their formal backgrounds inhibit their design abilities. They may be too quick to label a particular approach as impossible, when in reality it can be solved by a designer who did not know better than to try.

A designer must define the problem on the basis of needs, and develop and analyze solutions based on factors affecting the requirements. He must be concerned with cost, manufacturing, human factors, simplicity, workability, and appearance. The designer of a household appliance, for example, must first determine what type of product is needed. He must understand the consumer for whom he is designing so that he may arrive at the cost of the item that would be acceptable, i.e., he must know the potential market. He must design the method of operation, the source of power, and a package for the system, and determine its capacities and limits of operation.

The Stylist. The person who is concerned with the outward appearance of a product rather than the development of a functional design is referred to as a stylist (Fig. 1–24). A stylist may be concerned with the design of an automobile body or the configuration of an electric iron. He will be concerned with developing an appropriate design that will be functional with respect to its use, but he will not be concerned with the design of the total product. The stylist must have a high degree of aesthetic awareness plus a feel for the consumer's acceptance of his designs.

A stylist who designs an automobile body considers the functional requirements of the body, including driver vision, enclosure of passengers, space for the power unit, etc. However, he does not concern himself with the design of such items as the engine or the steering linkage. He is more interested in an outward appearance of the automobile which will conform to the limitations imposed by the operational systems involved in the unit. The refinement of systems has permitted the evolution of body styles into lower and more streamlined bodies (Fig. 1–25).

1-24

1-25

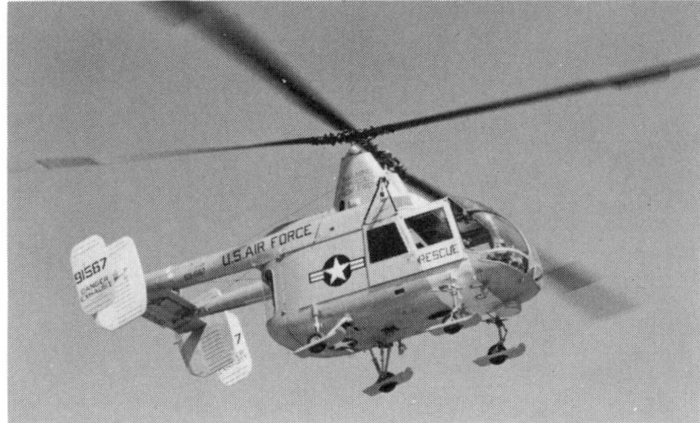

1-26

Fig. 1-24. The stylist is more concerned with the outward appearance of a product than the functional aspects of its design. (Courtesy of Ford Motor Company.)

Fig. 1-25. This experimental body, designed by a stylist, is a prototype of new bodies that may be seen on the general market in the near future. (Courtesy of Rohm and Haas Company.)

Fig. 1-26. The aerospace engineer is responsible for the design and testing of aircraft to determine the most efficient craft possible. (Courtesy of Kaman Aircraft Corporation.)

1-5 THE ENGINEERING FIELDS

The following articles briefly outline the more prominent areas of engineering and describe the duties of engineers employed in these fields of the profession. Each of the areas discussed is considerably broader than the description given, since only the more basic activities are listed. The addresses of the professional societies associated with each field are given at the end of this chapter as sources for additional information concerning the opportunities and challenges of each branch.

The new field of technology is also described to provide an insight into this rapidly developing area of industry. The technician has established himself as an indispensable member of the engineering team. The area of the draftsman is included to identify this occupation and give its relationship to that of the engineer and the technician, who also use the graphical process but in a different manner with different objectives.

1-6 AEROSPACE ENGINEERING

The advent of space exploration has played a vital role in the development and expansion of the field of aerospace engineering. Aerospace engineers have also made considerable contributions to the growth of air transportation.

Engineers in the space exploration branch of this profession work on all types of aircraft and spacecraft, including missiles, rockets, and conventional propeller-driven and jet-powered planes.[1*] The responsibilities include the development of aerospace products from initial planning and design to the final manufacture and testing (Fig. 1-26).

The aerospace field currently employs more people in the United States than any other industry. Second only to the auto industry in sales, the aerospace industry contributes immeasurably to national defense and the national econ-

* Numbers in superscript refer to the Bibliography.

omy.[2] There is a growing need for additional engineers to conceive, design, and build aerospace equipment for defense, for scientific research, and for transportation. The future for aeronautical engineers appears to offer rewarding and challenging opportunities in the years ahead.

Aerospace engineering deals with flight in all aspects—at all speeds and all altitudes. Aerospace engineering assignments range from complex vehicles traveling 350 million miles to Mars to hovering aircraft used in deep sea exploration. This broad field of engineering encompasses many specialized disciplines. As a result, most aerospace engineers usually specialize in a particular area of work. Specialized areas are (1) aerodynamics, (2) structural design, (3) instrumentation, (4) propulsion systems, (5) materials, (6) reliability testing, and (7) production methods. They may also specialize in a particular product, such as conventional power planes, jet-powered military aircraft, rockets, satellites, or manned space capsules (Figs. 1–27 and 1–28).

In the broadest sense, aerospace engineering can be divided into two major areas: research

Fig. 1–27. Aerospace engineers are closely involved in the development of new flying devices in conjunction with the space program. This one-man flying device, which would be used by astronauts on the moon's surface, is being tested to establish its feasibility. It is tested under a controlled system that simulates lunar gravity forces. (Courtesy of the National Aeronautics and Space Administration.)

Fig. 1–28. The one-man flying device, "POGO," by Bell Aerosystems Company, is shown in a sequence photograph during its test operation. (Courtesy of National Aeronautics and Space Administration.)

1–27

1–28

engineering and design engineering. The research engineer is concerned with the exploration of known principles in search of new ideas and concepts. On the other hand, the design engineer translates the new concepts developed by the researcher into workable applications for the improvement of the existing state of the art. Engineers in each of these two areas must approach the unknowns of their fields with creativity, skill, and knowledge. This approach has elevated the field of aerospace engineering from the Wright Brothers' first flight at Kittyhawk, N. C., in 1903 to the penetration of outer space with an unlimited future (Fig. 1–29).

Related engineering specialists are vital members of the aerospace engineering team. Many of these specialist areas are new to the field of engineering. A few of these areas are: (1) avionics—the study of electronic, computerized communication and flight-control systems; (2) equipment—the design and installation of equipment for navigation, hydraulic, armament, survival, electrical, and comfort control related to the functional operation of the aircraft; (3) materials and processes—the development, testing, and evaluation of new materials, such as plastics, to determine their applications to aircraft designs; (4) metallurgy—the evaluation and testing of new and specially treated metals to determine the most efficient metals for aerospace use.

The aerospace engineer can devote his career to the study of a wide variety of engineering systems within this large and ever-expanding field of engineering. The challenges of the aerospace field offer unlimited opportunities for imaginative engineers who are seeking the excitement of exploration in this young and promising area of technology.

The professional society of the aeronautical engineer, the American Institute of Aeronautics and Astronautics (AIAA), has a membership of approximately 36,000 scientists and engineers. Student branches of this association are located on most college campuses offering degrees in aeronautical engineering. Where student chapters do not exist, interested students can join the AIAA by applying to the national headquarters. Professional society addresses are listed at the end of this chapter.

1–29

1–30

1–7 AGRICULTURAL ENGINEERING

Agricultural engineers are trained to serve the world's largest industry—agriculture. Engineering problems of agriculture deal with the production, processing, and handling of food and fiber.[3] The four major areas of specialization of agriculture are: mechanical power and machinery, farm structures, electrical power and processing equipment, and soil and water control and conservation.[4]

Fig. 1–29. Aerospace engineers enjoy unlimited challenges in designing equipment for the penetration of space, one of the youngest fields of engineering. (Courtesy of National Aeronautics and Space Administration.)

Fig. 1–30. An agricultural engineer is responsible for the design and testing of new agricultural devices that will improve production and reduce cost. (Courtesy of the U.S. Department of Agriculture.)

Fig. 1–31. The agricultural engineer improves production by designing irrigation systems. This irrigation chute is $3\frac{1}{4}$ miles long. (Courtesy of the Bureau of Reclamation.)

1–31

Mechanical Power. The agricultural engineer who works with one of the more than 800 manufacturers of farm equipment will be concerned with gasoline and diesel engine equipment such as pumps, irrigation machinery, and tractors. The farm machinery designed by agricultural engineers has been responsible for the increased production of agriculture at a higher degree of efficiency (Fig. 1–30). Machinery must be designed for the electrical curing of hay, milk processing and pasteurizing, fruit processing, and artificially heated environments in which to raise animals and poultry.

Farm Structures. The construction of barns, shelters, silos, granaries, processing centers, and other agricultural buildings requires specialists in agricultural engineering. The design of buildings of this type requires that the engineer understand heating, ventilation, and chemical changes that affect the storage of crops. He may also supervise research that will improve methods of design and construction of farm structures.

Electrical Power. A high percentage of the equipment used for agricultural purposes is driven by electrical power. The agricultural engineer designs electrical systems and selects equipment that will provide efficient operation to meet the requirements of the specific situation. He may serve as a consultant or a designer for a manufacturer or large processor of agricultural products. His knowledge improves living and working conditions connected with rural activities.

Soil and Water Control. The agricultural engineer is responsible for devising systems for improving drainage and irrigation systems, resurfacing fields, and constructing water reservoirs (Fig. 1–31). These activities may be performed in association with the U. S. Department of Agriculture or the Department of Interior, with state agricultural colleges, with consulting engineering firms, or with irrigation companies.

Most of the 12,000 agricultural engineers are employed in private industry, especially by manufacturers of heavy farm equipment and specialized lines of field, barnyard, and household equipment; electrical service companies; and distributors of farm equipment and supplies.[1] Agricultural engineering is not limited to work in rural areas. Most agricultural engineers live in cities where the leading farm equipment and manufacturing centers are located. Although he need not live on a farm or be involved in agriculture, it is helpful if he has a clear understanding of agricultural problems, farmwork, crops, animals, and people involved in farming. The agricultural engineer has much the same background in engineering fundamentals as that required in other fields of engineering.

The future of agricultural engineering is expected to continue to grow with the increase of agricultural needs due to population increases and the mechanization of all phases of the agricultural process. Agricultural engineers will be involved in the problems of conservation of resources and the introduction of new agricultural products in the future. Agricultural engineering has been instrumental in raising the farmer's efficiency so much that one farmer today raises enough food for 32 people, whereas he was capable of supplying only four other people 100 years ago. The future offers many opportunities in agricultural engineering.

The professional society of the agricultural engineer is the American Society for Agricultural Engineers.

Fig. 1–32. The chemical engineer conducts experiments on new refinery methods to improve the quality of products. (Courtesy of Humble Oil and Refining Company.)

1–8 CHEMICAL ENGINEERING

Chemical engineering involves the design and selection of equipment that will facilitate the processing and manufacturing of chemicals in large quantities.[1] These designs are closely related to the principles of chemistry and those of other engineering fields that aid in the economic and efficient production of chemical products. Products made possible through chemical engineering have contributed much to our high standard of living (Fig. 1–32).

Chemical engineers design unit operations, including fluid transportation through ducts or pipelines, solid material transportation through pipes or conveyors, heat transfer from one fluid or substance to another fluid or substance through plate or tube walls, absorption of gases by bubbling them through liquids, evaporation of liquids to increase concentration of solutions, distillation under carefully controlled temperatures to separate mixed liquids, and many other similar chemical processes. They may employ chemical reactions of raw products such as oxidation, hydrogenation, reduction, chlorination, nitration, sulfonation, pyrolysis, and polymerization (Fig. 1–33). From these reactions come new materials and products.[5]

Fig. 1–33. The last stop a new process makes en route from its birthplace—the scientist's laboratory—to the chemical engineer for development and construction on a commercial scale is the "pilot plant." These range in size from table-top models capable of making a cupful of product per day to massive 10-story plants whose daily output is measured in tons. Thus they provide the engineers with another means of checking the efficiency of the process, of arriving at the right combination of pressure, temperature, and other variables that will ensure the trouble-free, economical manufacture of high-quality products. (Courtesy of Esso Research and Engineering Company.)

Process control and instrumentation have developed as important specialties in chemical engineering. The handling and control of large quantities of materials must be possible with a high degree of accuracy and precision. Process control is designed for fully automatic operation with the measurement of quality and quantity by fully automatic instrumentation. In many cases, these instruments must be designed by the chemical engineer for the processing of new products.

Chemical engineers develop and process chemicals such as acids, alkalies, salts, coal-tar products, dyes, synthetic chemicals, plastics, insecticides, fungicides, and many others for industrial and domestic uses. He is associated with drugs and medicine, cosmetics, explosives, ceramics, cements, paints, petroleum products, lubricants, synthetic fibers, rubber, and detergents (Fig. 1–34). He also designs equipment for food preparation and canning plants.[5]

The chemical engineer works with metallurgical and mining engineers in designing processing equipment, and in designing and laying out complete plants. He must be well versed in chemistry and must be able to discuss plant design and operation with the plant operator. This combination requires that the chemical engineer be well-rounded in a number of disciplines which enable him to select several specialties in which to work.

Approximately 80 percent of the more than 50,000 chemical engineers work in the manufacturing industries—primarily in the chemical industry.[1] The remainder work for government agencies, independent research institutes, and as independent consulting engineers. New fields that require chemical engineers are nuclear sciences, rocket fuels, and environmental pollution areas. The development of new drugs, fertilizers, paints, and chemicals is expected to increase the demand for chemical engineers in the coming years.

The professional society for chemical engineers is the American Institute of Chemical Engineers (AIChE). This organization is the collective voice of all chemical engineers and is responsible for establishing ethics of the profession and standards of competence. Publications, research projects, and other activities sponsored by the society serve as guidelines for chemical engineering students and the professional practicing chemical engineer.

Fig. 1–34. The chemical engineer's efforts, in conjunction with other engineering fields, are finalized in the construction and operation of a completed refinery producing vital products for our economy and needs. (Courtesy of Esso Research and Engineering Company.)

1–9 CIVIL ENGINEERING

Civil engineering, the oldest branch of engineering, is closely related to practically all of our daily activities. The buildings we live in and work in, the transportation facilities we use, the water we drink, and the drainage and sewage systems are the results of civil engineering.[5] Civil engineers design and supervise the construction of roads, harbors, airfields, tunnels, bridges, water supply and sewage systems, and many other types of structures.[1] Civil engineers can specialize in a number of areas within the field, with the following being the most prominent: construction, city planning, structural engineering, hydraulic engineering, transportation, highways, and sanitation.[5]

Construction engineers are responsible for the management of resources, manpower, finances, and materials necessary for construction projects. These projects may vary from the erection of skyscrapers to the movement of concrete and earth (Fig. 1–35).

1–35

Fig. 1–35. Civil engineers specializing in construction supervise projects such as the erection of the U. S. Pavilion at Expo 67 in Canada. This geodesic dome, which has a diameter of 250 ft, is being enclosed with acrylic plastic panels. (Courtesy of Rohm and Haas Company.)

Fig. 1–36. Civil engineers design bridges, dams, and other superstructures common to our contemporary way of life. (Courtesy of the Bureau of Reclamation.)

Fig. 1–37. Transportation requires the services of a civil engineer. This master plan of the Port of Oakland will become a major responsibility of civil engineers who will develop the area, surfaces, waterways, and utilities. (Courtesy of Kaiser Engineers.)

Fig. 1–38. City planning and traffic management is an area requiring imagination and creativity on the part of the civil engineer to provide adequate systems for keeping pace with the problems caused by increasing needs. (Courtesy of California Division of Highways.)

1–36

1–37

1–38

City planners develop plans for the future growth of cities and the various systems related to their operation. Street planning, zoning, and industrial site development are problems encountered in the field of city planning.

Structural engineers are responsible for the design and supervision of the erection of structural systems, including buildings, dams, powerhouses, stadiums, bridges, and numerous other structures (Fig. 1-36). Strength and appearances are considered in designing structures of this type to economically serve the required needs.

Hydraulic engineers work with the behavior of water from its conservation to its transportation. They design wells, canals, dams, pipelines, drainage systems, and other methods of controlling and utilizing water and petroleum products (Fig. 1-37).

Transportation engineers work with the development and improvement of railroads and airlines in all phases of their operations. Railroads are built, modified, and maintained under the supervision of civil engineers. Design and construction of airport runways, control towers, passenger and freight stations, and aircraft hangars are performed by civil engineers who specialize in the field of transportation.

Highway engineers develop the complex network of highways and interchanges for moving the masses of automobile traffic common to daily life. These systems require the design of tunnels, culverts, and traffic control systems (Fig. 1-38).

Sanitary engineers assist in maintaining public health through the purification of water, control of water pollution, and sewage control. Such systems involve the design of pipelines, treatment plants, dams, and related systems.

The activities of the civil engineer are very diversified, with opportunities in a variety of locations from city centers to remote construction sites. Due to their experience in management and the solution of environmental problems, many civil engineers find positions in administration and municipal management. About 180,000 civil engineers were employed in 1964, with the majority associated with federal, state, and local governmental agencies and the construction industry. Many worked as consulting engineers for architectural firms and independent consulting engineering firms. The remainder worked for public utilities, railroads, educational institutions, steel industries, and other manufacturing industries.[1]

The employment future of civil engineers will continue to increase through the 1970's; however, it is not expected to increase at the same rate as the relatively new fields of engineering. Problems of increased population, housing needs, urban development, and water pollution will result in the need for greater numbers of engineers. It is estimated that 3500 civil engineers will be needed annually to fill vacancies in civil engineering. This number is expected to rise slowly in the future.[1]

The professional society for civil engineering is the American Society of Civil Engineers, founded in 1852, the oldest engineering society in the United States. Colleges offering degrees in civil engineering usually have student branches of this society to introduce the student to the professional aspects of civil engineering. A monthly periodical, *Civil Engineering,* is published by the ASCE for communication with members of the profession and related disciplines.

1-10 ELECTRICAL ENGINEERING

Electrical engineering is concerned with the utilization and distribution of electrical energy for the improvement of industrial and domestic functions. The two main divisions of electrical engineering are (1) power and (2) electronics. Power deals with the control of large amounts of energy used by cities and large industries, whereas electronics deals with small amounts of power used for communications and automated operations that have become integral parts of our everyday lives.[5]

These two major divisions of electrical engineering have many areas of specialization. A few of these are given below.[5]

Power generation poses many electrical engineering problems from the development of transmission equipment to the design of generators for producing electricity. Modern methods of power transmission and generation have made it possible for electrical power to be the most economical source of industrial energy (Fig. 1–39).

Power applications are numerous in typical homes where toasters, washers, dryers, vacuum cleaners, and lights are used on a continuing basis. Only about one-quarter of the total energy consumed is used in the home. Industry uses about half of all energy for metal refining, heating, motor drives, welding, machinery controls, chemical processes, plating, and electrolysis.

Transportation industries require electrical engineers to develop electrical systems for automobiles, aircraft, and other forms of transportation. These systems are used for starting ignition, lighting, and instrumentation. Locomotives and ships may power their own generators, which supply electrical power to turn their driving wheels or propellers. The sophisticated signal systems necessary for all forms of transportation require electrical engineers.

Illumination is required at all levels of man's activities and environment. The improvement of illumination systems and the economy of illumination energy are challenging areas of study for the electrical engineer.

Industrial electronics has enabled sensitive manufacturing operations to be performed more accurately with less effort than when done by a human operator. Computerized operations have reduced the need for the tedious human effort that might result in more errors at higher cost (Figs. 1–40 and 1–41). This area is also closely related to instrumentation and communications.

Communications is the field devoted to the improvement of radio, telephone, telegraph, and television systems, which are the nerve centers of most industrial operations. Communications is vital in the dispatching of a taxicab, the control of ships and aircrafts, and in the many other everyday personal and industrial applications.

Fig. 1–39. The design of power transmission systems is the responsibility of the electrical engineer. A helicopter is used to patrol this 1800-mile long Parker-Davis project in Arizona. (Courtesy of the Bureau of Reclamation.)

Fig. 1–40. Electrical engineers have played prominent roles in the development and utilization of computer systems used to perform complicated operations in minutes. This computer can be used to simulate the operation of a new refinery or chemical process before the refinery is built or the process is put into production. (Courtesy of Esso Research and Engineering Company.)

Instrumentation is the study of systems of electronic instruments used in the precise measuring of industrial processes. Extensive use has been made of the cathode-ray tube and the electronic amplifier in industrial applications and atomic power reactors. Instrumentation has been increasingly applied to medicine for diagnosis and therapy.

Military electronics is utilized in practically all areas of military weapons and tactical systems from the walkie-talkie to the distant radar networks for detecting enemy aircraft. Remote-

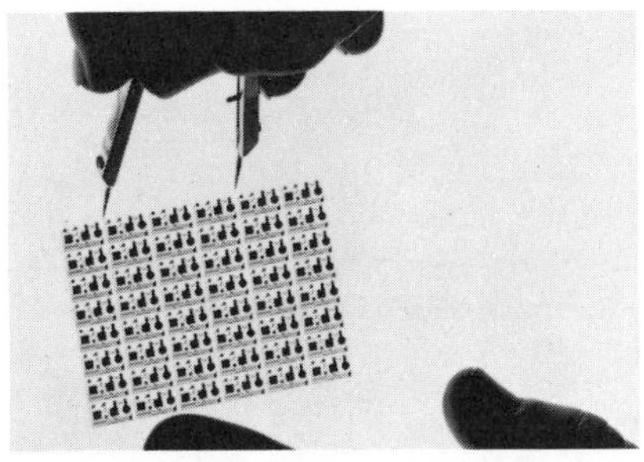

Fig. 1-41. Electrical engineers have made components smaller, lighter, and more efficient. Microminiature components, printed wiring, and advanced encapsulation techniques all combine to reduce complete circuits to fractions of their former size. (Courtesy of General Dynamics.)

Fig. 1-42. Industrial engineers lay out and design complex industrial facilities to provide efficient production. This plant produces light gauge aluminum sheet for rigid containers and other applications. (Courtesy of ALCOA.)

controlled electronic systems are used for navigation and interception of guided missiles. Many revolutionary advancements are expected to continue in fields of military applications of electrical engineering.

More electrical engineers are employed than any other type of engineer in the profession. More than 230,000 electrical engineers are employed in the United States. They are employed chiefly by manufacturers of electrical and electronic equipment, aircraft and parts, business machines, and professional and scientific equipment. The increased need for electrical equipment for automation and computerized systems are expected to contribute to the growth of this field during the coming years.[1]

The professional society for electrical engineers is the Institute of Electrical and Electronic Engineers (IEEE). This is the world's largest technical society, and it was founded in 1884. Present membership in this organization is approximately 150,000. A periodical, *IEEE Student Journal,* is published especially for college electrical engineering students.

1-11 INDUSTRIAL ENGINEERING

Industrial engineering, one of the newer branches of the engineering profession, is defined by the National Professional Society of Industrial Engineers as follows:

> "Industrial Engineering is concerned with the design, improvement, and installation of integrated systems of men, materials, and equipment. It draws upon specialized knowledge and skill in the mathematical, physical, and social sciences together with the principles and methods of engineering analysis and design to specify, predict, and evaluate the results to be obtained from such systems."

Industrial engineering is related to all areas of engineering and business. This field differs from other areas of engineering in that it is more closely related to people and their performance and working conditions (Fig. 1-42). Consequently, in many instances the industrial engineer is a manager who is interested in the men, machines, materials, methods, money, and markets involved.[5]

The industrial engineer may be assigned the responsibility of plant layout, the development of plant processes, or the determination of operating standards that will improve the efficiency of a plant operation. He may be responsible for quality control and cost analysis, two operations which are essential to a profitable manufacturing industry.

Fig. 1–43. The industrial engineer applies his capabilities to industrial problems to increase efficiency and provide a better analysis of operation. (Courtesy of International Business Machines Corporation.)

Fig. 1–44. These five 75,000-kilowatt generators are typical of projects developed by mechanical engineers. (Courtesy of the Bureau of Reclamation.)

Several specific areas of industrial engineering are: management, plant design and engineering, electronic data processing, systems analysis and design, control of production and quality, performance standards and measurements, and research. In order for the industrial engineer to work in these areas, he must act as a member of a team composed of engineers from other branches of the profession.[6] He must view the overall operations of industry and the factors affecting its efficiency rather than be concerned with isolated areas within the total structure (Fig. 1–43).

People-oriented areas include the development of wage incentive systems, job evaluation, work measurement, and the design of environmental systems. The industrial engineer is often involved in management-labor agreements that affect the operation and production of an industry. He designs and supervises systems for the improved safety and production of the working forces employed in an industry.

More than two-thirds of an estimated 120,000 industrial engineers are employed in manufacturing industries. Others work for insurance companies, construction and mining firms, public utilities, large businesses, and governmental agencies. With the increasing complexities of industrial operations and the expansion of automated processes, the field of industrial engineering is expected to grow in numbers. Approximately 1300 industrial engineers will be needed on an annual basis to fill vacancies and to assume new positions that occur in the field.

The professional society of industrial engineers is the American Institute of Industrial Engineers (AIIE), which was organized in 1948. Its address is listed at the end of this chapter.

1–12 MECHANICAL ENGINEERING

Mechanical engineers are concerned with the production, transmission, and use of power through a wide variety of activities. The major areas of specialization of the mechanical engineer are: power generation, transportation, aeronautics, marine vessels, manufacturing, power services, and atomic energy. Activities within each of these specialties are outlined below.[5]

Power generation requires that prime movers be developed to power electrical generators that will produce electrical energy in stationary power plants. The mechanical engineers will design and supervise the operation of steam

Fig. 1–45. Mechanical engineers design and modify manufacturing equipment to provide mass production methods at reduced costs. This temper mill operates at speeds up to 4500 ft/min and delivers steel coils weighing up to 60,000 lb. (Courtesy of Jones & Laughlin Steel Corporation.)

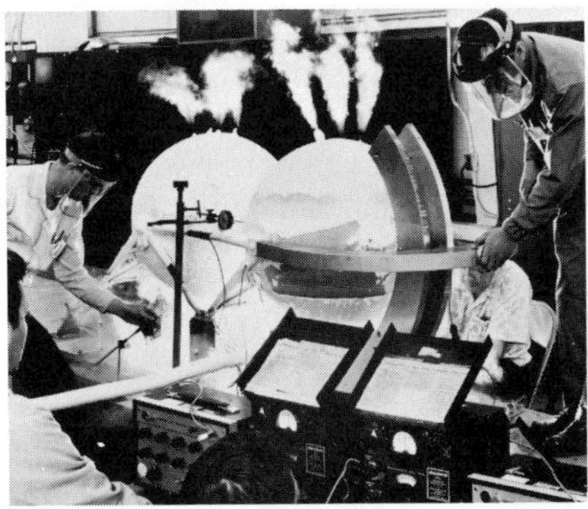

Fig. 1–46. Mechanical engineering research includes the study of the movement of liquids and gases at different temperatures. Here, cryogenic experiments are being carried on by using compressed gases such as nitrogen or helium to bring temperatures down to supercloud levels. (Courtesy of General Dynamics.)

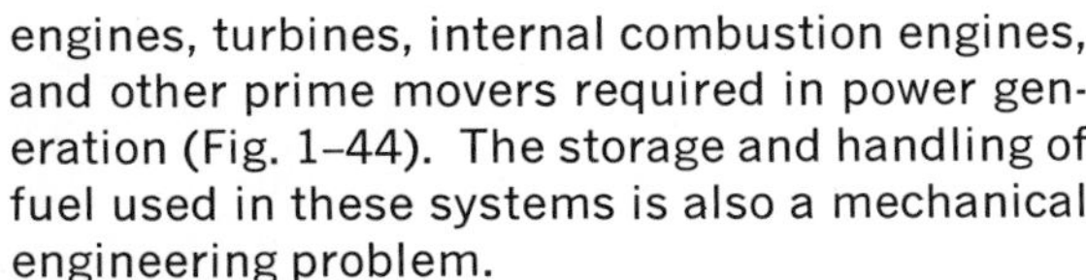

engines, turbines, internal combustion engines, and other prime movers required in power generation (Fig. 1–44). The storage and handling of fuel used in these systems is also a mechanical engineering problem.

Transportation conveyances are designed and manufactured by mechanical engineers. Automobiles, trucks, buses, locomotives, marine vessels, and aircraft are designed and produced through the efforts of mechanical engineers. He must design the power systems of transportation vehicles as well as the structural and fuel systems.

Aeronautics is a specialized field requiring the mechanical engineer to develop engines to power aircraft. The controls and environmental systems of aircraft are also problems solved by mechanical engineers. The fabrication of the aircraft requires a close coordination between the mechanical and aerospace engineer.

Marine vessels are powered by steam, diesel, or gas-generated engines designed by the mechanical engineer. He is also responsible for supplying power services throughout the vessel, including light, water, refrigeration, and ventilation.

Manufacturing is a challenging field that requires the mechanical engineer to design new products and new factories in which to build them. He works closely with the industrial engineer in the management of a wide variety of machines. Economy of manufacturing and the achievement of a uniform level of product quality is a major function of this area of mechanical engineering (Fig. 1–45).

Power services include the movement of liquid and gases through pipelines, refrigeration systems, elevators, and escalators (Fig. 1–46). In applying the principles of mechanical engineering, the mechanical engineer must have a knowledge of pumps, ventilation equipment, fans, and compressors.

Atomic energy development has used mechanical engineers for the development and handling of protective equipment and materials. Nuclear reactors, which provide nuclear power for various applications, are constructed as a joint effort with the mechanical engineer playing an important role in this young field.

More than 215,000 mechanical engineers are employed in the United States with nearly three-quarters of this group employed in manufacturing industries. Others are employed by governmental agencies, educational institutions, and consulting engineering firms. The employment outlook indicates that the number of mechanical engineers will continue to grow with an estimated 3000 engineers needed each year to fill vacancies and new positions.[1]

The professional society of the mechanical engineering field is the American Society of Mechanical Engineers (ASME). Student and professional chapters are organized to distribute information about current developments in the field to its members. There are about 60,000 members of the Society with 10,000 members from 170 student sections throughout the nation.

Fig. 1–47. The metallurgical engineer develops new materials and methods of production. This wire is being woven for use in a 1000-mile communication network for the Colorado River Storage Project. (Courtesy of General Dynamics.)

1–13 MINING AND METALLURGICAL ENGINEERING

Mining and metallurgical engineers are often grouped together as a common profession although their functions are somewhat separate. The mining engineer is responsible for the extraction of minerals from the earth and for the preparation of minerals for use by the manufacturing industries (Fig. 1–47). He works with geologists to locate ore deposits, which must be exploited through the construction of extensive tunnels and underground operations, necessitating an understanding of safety, ventilation, water supply, and communications (Fig. 1–48).

Fig. 1–48. This gold mining operation of the U. S. Smelting, Refining & Mining Company is the responsibility of mining engineers. (Courtesy of the U. S. Forest Service.)

The metallurgical engineer develops methods of processing and converting metals into useful products. Two main areas of metallurgical engineering are extractive and physical. Extractive metallurgy is concerned with the extraction of metal from raw ores to form pure metals. Physical metallurgy is the development of new products and alloys that are beneficial to new industrial applications.

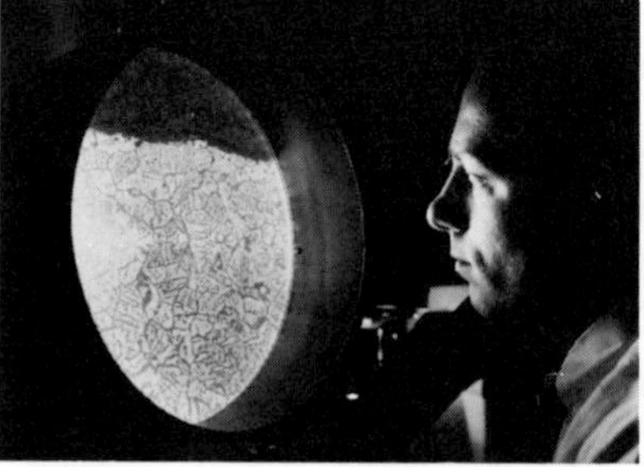

Fig. 1–49. A metallograph is used to show the structure of an alloy that may be used in the construction of a refinery unit. Materials are specially developed for specific applications by the metallurgical engineer. (Courtesy of Esso Research and Engineering Company.)

Approximately 10,000 metallurgical engineers are employed, with an estimated 50 percent of these associated with the iron, steel, and nonferrous metals industries. Many metallurgical engineers work on development of machinery for electrical equipment and in the aircraft and aircraft parts industries. With the development of new materials for space flight vehicles, jet aircraft, missiles, and satellites, new lightweight, high-strength materials will increase the need for additional metallurgical engineers (Fig. 1–49). They will also be needed to develop economical methods for extracting metal from low-grade ore when the high-grade ore has been depleted.[1]

Three-quarters of the estimated 5000 mining engineers employed are associated with the mining and petroleum industries. Those who work at mining sites are usually employed near small communities or in out-of-the-way places, while those in research and consulting are often located in metropolitan areas. Employment is expected to increase at a slower pace in mining engineering than in other areas of engineering. However, the supply of mining engineers is so limited it is not expected to keep pace with the vacancies caused by retirements within the field. The development of new alloys is expected to increase the need for mining engineers for the recovery of relatively little-used ores.[1]

The professional society of this field of engineering is the American Institute of Mining, Metallurgical, and Petroleum Engineering (AIME). Additional information concerning this broad profession can be obtained from the society. Technical reports and surveys are available to provide a better understanding of professional trends.

1–14 NUCLEAR ENGINEERING

The relatively new field of nuclear engineering has been confined to graduate studies until recent years, when undergraduate programs were developed to provide a more continuous curriculum. This branch of engineering promises to be a spectacular contributor to our future way of life.

The earliest work in the nuclear field has been for military applications and defense purposes. However, the utilization of nuclear power for domestic needs is being developed for a number of areas (Fig. 1–50). Present applications of

Fig. 1–50 The nuclear engineer is harnessing atomic energy for domestic uses to provide many new applications. This is a dual-purpose nuclear-powered desalination plant. The Israel facility would have the capacity of 100 million gallons of desalted water per day and 200,000 kilowatts of useable power. (Courtesy of Kaiser Engineers.)

nuclear energy can be seen in the medical profession, and in various other fields as a power source for propulsion.

Although nuclear engineering degrees are now offered at the bachelor's level, advanced degrees are recommended for this area of engineering. Advanced degrees can provide the additional specialization especially important in the field. Peaceful applications in the nuclear field are divided into two major areas—radiation and nuclear power reactors. Radiation is the propagation of energy through matter or space in the form of waves. In atomic physics this term has been extended to include fast-moving particles (alpha and beta rays, free neutrons, etc.), gamma rays, and x-rays. Of particular interest in atomic physics is electromagnetic radiation, in which energy is propagated in pockets called photons.[7] Nuclear science is closely associated with botany, chemistry, medicine, and biology (Fig. 1–51).

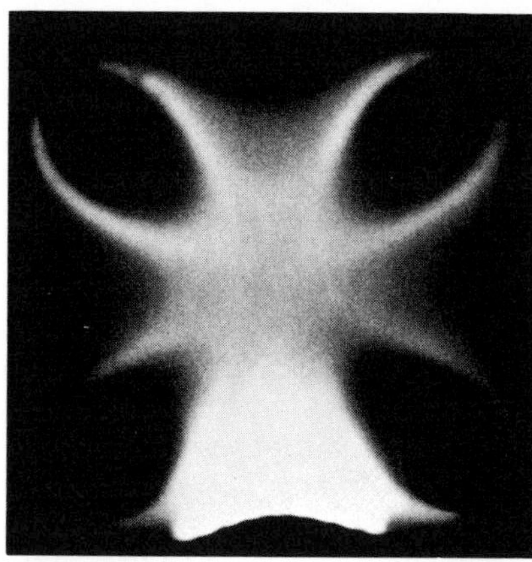

Fig. 1–51. In a fusion research program aimed at harnessing thermonuclear energy, plasma is contained by convex lines of magnetic forces. (Courtesy of General Dynamics).

The production of nuclear power in the form of mechanical or electrical power has become a major area of the peaceful utilization of nuclear energy, involving nuclear engineers and many other branches of engineering as well. For the production of electrical power, nuclear energy is used as the fuel for producing steam that will drive a turbine generator in the conventional manner. Nuclear energy is released by certain reactions involving the atom's nucleus, such as fission, neutron capture, and radioactive decay, or by fusion, which is limited to changes in the electron structure surrounding the nucleus.[7] The fission process is initiated, maintained, and controlled in a device called a nuclear reactor (Fig. 1–52). This source of power is expected to reduce the expenditure of our depleting supply of coal, oil, and gas presently being used in great quantities for power production.[8]

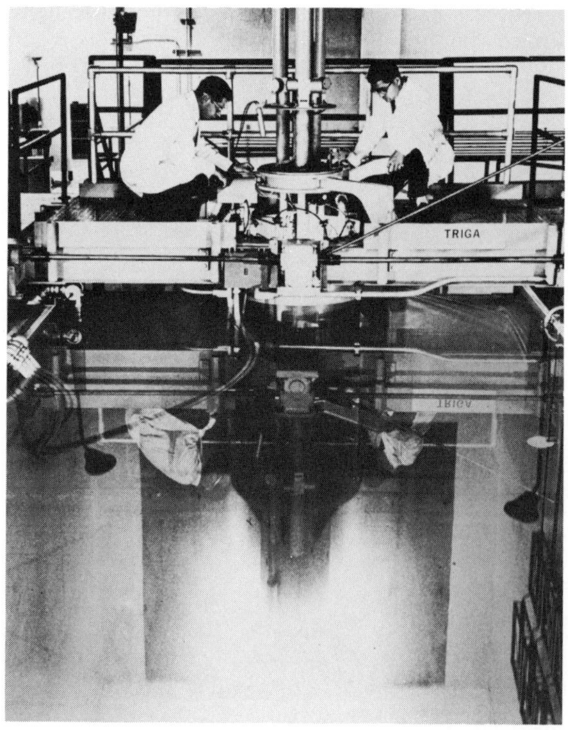

Fig. 1–52. This pulsing reactor is being operated by a nuclear engineer to test the effect of extremely high radiation on delicate equipment. (Courtesy of General Dynamics.)

Due to its newness, nuclear engineering is a field with many unexplored frontiers. Most training is centered around the design, construction, and operation of nuclear reactors. Other areas include the processing of nuclear fuels, thermonuclear engineering, and the utilization of various nuclear by-products.

Total employment in atomic energy work is reported as 135,000. About 101,000 of these were employed in Atomic Energy Commission facilities, while the remaining 34,000 were employed in privately owned facilities. Approximately two-thirds of those employed by private firms were associated with peaceful uses of atomic energy. These figures include all levels of employees, of which nuclear engineers are a part.[9]

Further information concerning nuclear engineering may be obtained by writing the American Nuclear Society.

1–15 PETROLEUM ENGINEERING

Petroleum engineering is the application of engineering to the development and recovery of petroleum resources. The petroleum engineer's primary concern is the recovery of petroleum and gases; however, he must also develop methods for the transportation and separation of various products. He is responsible for the improvement of drilling equipment and its economy of operation when drilling is being carried out at excessive depths, sometimes as great as four miles (Fig. 1–53).

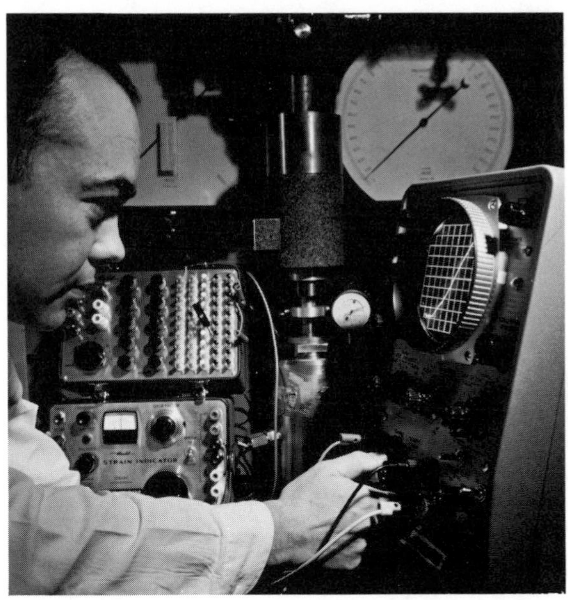

Fig. 1–53. The petroleum engineer is concerned with developing new and improved methods of extracting petroleum from the earth. Here, a researcher seeks faster drilling methods as he studies rock failure mechanisms. Hydraulic pressure is used to simulate the weight of overlying formations. (Courtesy of Humble Oil and Refining Company.)

Conservation of petroleum reservoirs has gained increased emphasis with greater consumption each year. New uses for petroleum and petroleum products are being investigated by petroleum engineer researchers. New processes have been developed in recent years for recovering increasing amounts of petroleum from dormant oil reservoirs that had previously been abandoned (Fig. 1–54).

Fig. 1–54. Downtown Kilgore, Texas is a reminder of one of the world's richest oil strikes in 1930. Buildings were torn down to make room for more wells.

The production phase of petroleum engineering requires the cooperation of practically all branches of engineering, due to the wide variety of knowledge and skills demanded. Many new industries have emerged from new petroleum products that have been developed through production methods and research.

The petroleum engineer is assisted by the geologist in the exploration stages of searching for petroleum. Geologists use advanced devices such as the airborne magnetometer, which gives readings on the earth's subsurfaces, indicating where uplifts that could hold oil or gas are located. If these findings are favorable, seismo-

Fig. 1-55. Petroleum engineers are closely associated with methods of processing and refining petroleum products. This refinery was designed to manufacture high-density polyethylene. (Courtesy of E. I. du Pont de Nemours and Company.)

Fig. 1-56. Technicians are important members of the engineering team and provide vital assistance to the engineer. This technician operates a "tape recorder" console in an area office where seismic records that were taped in the field are converted to visual records. (Courtesy of Humble Oil and Refining Company.)

graph crews measure the depths of particular layers of the subsurface. The only sure way of determining whether oil or gas does exist after preliminary surveys have been made is to drill a well. A typical wildcat oil well costs between $50,000 and $80,000.[10]

Oil well drilling is supervised by the petroleum engineer, who also develops the drilling equipment with members of other branches of engineering to offer the most efficient method of oil removal. When oil is found, the petroleum engineer must design piping systems to remove the oil and transport it to its next point of processing. The processing itself is a joint project in which chemical engineers work with petroleum engineers (Fig. 1-55).

The future of petroleum engineering appears to be very promising, with extensive exploration going on in many countries that are relatively new to oil and gas production. Petroleum engineers will also be required to stimulate new sources of petroleum when present fields have been depleted.

Further information about petroleum engineering may be obtained by writing to the Society of Petroleum Engineers. This society is a branch of AIME, which includes mining and metallurgical engineers and geologists. This society was founded in 1871 to serve members of this vital field of engineering.

1-16 TECHNICIAN

The technician has gained separate identification as a member of the engineering team. As technology has expanded to include more disciplines, materials, and systems, it has become impractical for one individual to understand and perform all the steps required in the implementation of design. Instead, it has been a more efficient application of manpower resources to have trained specialists responsible for specific areas of technology.

The expansion of the field of engineering, caused by the introduction of new theories and the development of additional new systems, has left a sizable void between the engineer and the craftsman who will fabricate the engineer's design. This void is being filled by the technician, who has capabilities in engineering funda-

Fig. 1-57. These technicians are making a cartographic survey. Data from the tellurometer are being recorded in a notebook. (Courtesy of the U. S. Forest Service.)

Fig. 1-58. In nuclear physics a technician may work in conjunction with both engineers and scientists. This team is working on a Van de Graaff particle accelerator. (Courtesy of Los Alamos Scientific Laboratory.)

mentals and areas of production. Technicians serve as a liaison between engineering and production (Fig. 1-56).

Technicians assist engineers in a wide variety of jobs that range from technical writing to maintenance problems. Much of their work might otherwise have been done by engineers. Their assistance in relieving the engineer from these necessary duties has enabled the engineer to better utilize his talents in broadening the field of engineering. The specific activities performed by the technician will be determined by his industrial field. Opportunities for the technician are available in all fields of engineering (Fig. 1-57).

Technicians may be responsible for conducting laboratory experiments, operating instruments, making calculations, developing experimental models, and preparing drawings and specifications under the supervision of an engineer (Fig. 1-58). Their work usually follows the procedure prescribed by an engineer, but with a minimum degree of supervision. Some well-established areas of technology are aeronautical technology, chemical technology, civil engineering technology, and electronic technology.

Training for the technician usually includes a minimum of two years of specialized training in a technical institute or junior college. A recent trend is toward a four-year technical institute program which gives more extensive preparation in areas of technology. Instruction includes laboratory techniques, science, mathematics, and engineering with subject matter related to practical problems. Additional on-the-job training is necessary to provide the technician with a working knowledge of his duty assignments. Training for technology may be provided by departments of Technology or Industrial Education on university campuses. This training may be for two years or four years.

Approximately 620,000 engineering and science technicians (exclusive of draftsmen) are employed in all industries. Twelve percent of these are women. Almost 450,000 technicians are employed in private industry.[11] The more prominent employing industries are producers of electrical equipment, machinery, chemicals, aircraft, missiles, and spacecraft (Fig. 1-59).

Fig. 1-59. Technicians prepare a prototype Plexiglas acrylic plastic dome for a detailed structural load test. These domes were used as part of the U. S. Pavilion at Expo 67. (Courtesy of Rohm and Haas Company.)

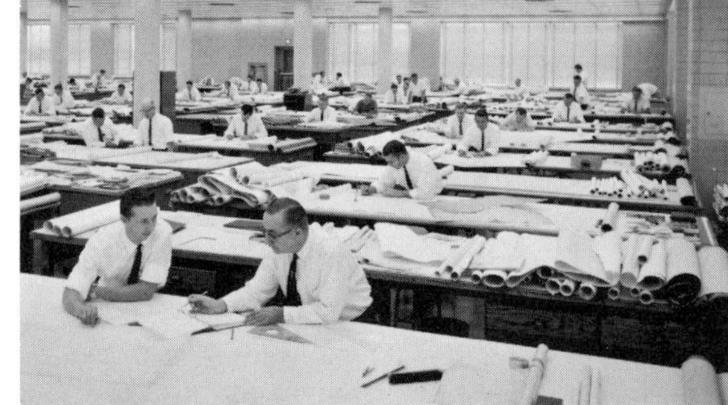

Fig. 1-60. Over 1200 draftsmen design chassis and body parts at Chrysler Corporation. Each year, blueprints produced from their drawings would cover an area of approximately 700 acres. (Courtesy of Chrysler Corporation.)

Approximately 85,000 are employed by federal agencies as engineering aides and technicians, with the largest number in the Department of Defense.

The technician field has been one of the fastest growing occupational groups during recent decades, and a continued increase is expected with the expansion of industry. More than 10,000 per year will be required to fill vacancies arising in the present work force. Starting salaries range from $6000 to $8000 per year, depending upon industrial qualifications, with excellent prospects for increases in earning with additional experience.[11] Additional information concerning technicians can be obtained from the American Society for Engineering Education, whose address is given at the end of this chapter.

1-17 DRAFTSMAN

An early definition of a draftsman was an employee who was responsible for tracing or copying rough sketches made by the engineer into an acceptable form from which the design could be implemented. This definition is somewhat outdated, since industry has improved its methods by reproduction to the point of eliminating the need for a draftsman who only traced drawings. Engineers no longer have time to devote to the more routine developments of drawings from which the draftsmen could make tracings. Consequently, the draftsman's position now involves increased responsibility and he is usually called a *detailer* or *detail draftsman*. The detailer is an expert in the production of working drawings for the layout drawings that will be released for manufacturing. He may make simple decisions, but he generally receives explicit instructions from an engineer or technician. He must be well-founded in dimensioning practices and in the fundamentals of depicting designs.[12]

The *layout draftsman* is a technician who transforms sketches, models, or verbal instructions into drawings that will be detailed by the detailer. The layout draftsman requires a two-year technical school education with a knowledge of tolerances, algebra, geometry, and trigonometry. It is desirable that he have previous experience as a detailer in order that he can work more closely with this member of the engineering team.

The *senior draftsman* is often referred to as a designer, since he will contribute to the development of the finished product rather than being concerned solely with the expression of an idea in graphic form. He has a combination of experiences in the drafting area, as well as technical know-how accumulated through years of experience.

Drafting is a semiprofessional activity that is closely related to the engineer's conceptualization of the design (Fig. 1–60). The engineer must rely on the senior draftsman to assist him in reviewing the preliminary sketches of a design, which may be in the form of freehand sketches. The senior draftsman works with the layout draftsman in developing a general layout of the graphical details of the design, which will be reviewed and perhaps modified by the engineer. This interrelationship will continue in this manner until certain components have been sufficiently refined to require the preparation of detail drawings by the detailer. The completed drawings must be closely checked by all members of the drafting team from detailer to senior draftsman and engineer. The ultimate responsibility for the correctness of a set of drawings lies with the engineer, who must have a complete understanding of the drafting requirements on a project.

Approximately 300,000 draftsmen and designers are employed by industry, and a very critical need for these specialists is foreseen for the next decade. The need for draftsmen is expected to increase at a rate of 5.2 percent per year if technology increases at the same rate. A number of technological changes and simplifications of technique are expected to take place in the drafting occupation in the late 1970's.[12] Many computerized drawing systems are expected to be in operation in larger industries with heavy drafting requirements. With the draftsman working at a console, these systems will alleviate the need for as many men on the board as in the past. This will not lessen the need for a knowledge of drafting and graphical principles by the draftsman or engineer, but will provide a different medium of expression. The need for detailers may decrease after twenty years but the draftsman-designer who is associated with the development of a product or a design will be less affected. Areas of drafting least affected will be those involving many dimensions and mechanical design.

1–18 SUMMARY

This chapter attempted to relate the field of engineering graphics and design to the total field of engineering. Engineering graphics is an essential area to the engineer, technician, craftsman, designer, and stylist, as well as to the draftsman. This is the medium through which an idea is developed from the conceptual stage to the final production. Production would be all but impossible without the use of engineering graphics as the language and tool of the engineering designer.

The design process as introduced in this chapter will be used as the central theme for the presentation of graphical principles that follow in successive chapters. Many industrial examples will be given to relate as many engineering applications as possible throughout the book. Each principle of graphical theory is presented in simplified form to establish the fundamentals and each is related to practical applications which are illustrated by engineering projects and products. Many problems are presented in sequential steps, utilizing color to clarify complicated problems.

Engineering graphics and descriptive geometry are vital tools that must be used by the engineer if he is to function at his fullest capacity. To this end, graphics is presented in this text in association with the design process as approached by an engineer developing design solutions. Essentially all designs are drawn utilizing spatial relationships that must be considered in arriving at the final solution. Examples of graphical solutions to engineering design problems are given throughout this volume.

1–19 SOLUTION OF PROBLEMS

The problems at the end of each chapter are provided to afford the student an opportunity to test his understanding of the principles covered in the preceding text. Most problems deal with an understanding of the theoretical concepts rather than specific applications. An understanding of theoretical concepts will enable the student to solve comprehensive problems involving engineering applications, such as those in Chapter 20.

Most problems are to be solved on $8\frac{1}{2}'' \times 11''$ paper, using instruments or drawing freehand as specified. The paper can be printed with a $\frac{1}{4}$-in. grid to assist in laying out the problems, or plain paper can be used with the layout made with a 16 scale (architect's scale). The grid of the given problems in later chapters represents

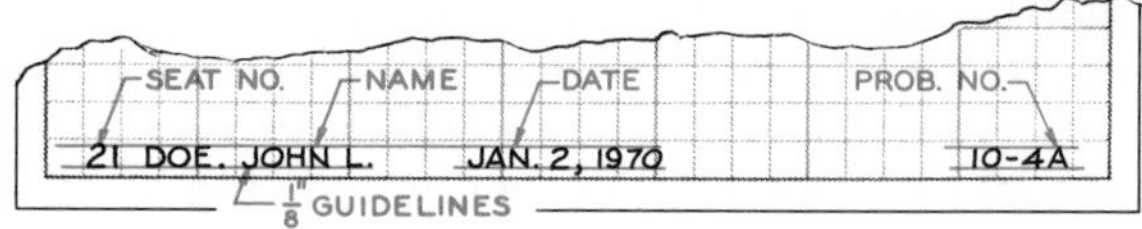

Figure 1–61

$\frac{1}{4}$-in. intervals that can be counted and transferred to a like grid paper or scaled on plain paper. Each problem sheet should be endorsed as shown in Fig. 1–61. The endorsement should include the student's seat number, and name, the date, and the problem number. Guidelines should be drawn with a straightedge to aid in lettering, using $\frac{1}{8}$-in. letters. All points, lines, and planes should be lettered using $\frac{1}{8}$-in. letters with guidelines in all cases. Reference planes should be noted appropriately when applicable. Most problems have a minimum of lettering and notations given, which requires the student to provide the necessary notations in keeping with the instructions of each chapter.

Problems of an essay type, as in this chapter, should have their answers lettered, using approved, single-stroke, Gothic lettering, as introduced in Chapter 5. Guidelines should be used to assist in alignment and uniformity of lettering. Each page should be numbered and stapled in the upper left corner if turned in for review by the instructor. All solved problems should be maintained in the student's notebook for future reference during the course and other courses later in his college curriculum.

PROBLEMS

1. Assume that you are responsible for designing a car jack that would be more serviceable than present models. Review the six steps of the design process given in Article 1–3 and make a brief outline of what you would do to apply these steps to your attempt to design a jack. Write the sequential steps and the methods that would be used to carry out each step. List the subject areas that would be used for each step and indicate the more difficult problems that you would anticipate at each step. Keep your outline brief, but thorough. Freehand letter your paper.

2. As an introductory problem to the steps of the design process, design a door stop that could be used to prevent a door from slamming into a wall. This stop could be attached to the floor or the door and should be as simple as possible. Make sketches and notes as necessary to give tangible evidence that you have proceeded through the six steps and label each step. Your work should be entirely freehand and rapid. Do not spend longer than 30 minutes on this problem. Indicate any information you would need in a final design approach that may not be accessible to you now.

3. List areas that you must consider during the problem identification phase of a design project for the following products: a new skillet design for the housewife, a lock for a bicycle, a handle for a piece of luggage, an escape from prison, a child's toy, a stadium seat, a desk lamp, an improved umbrella, a hotdog stand.

4. Make a series of rough, freehand sketches to indicate your preliminary ideas for the solution of the following problems: a functional powdered soap dispenser for washing hands, a protector for a football player with an injured elbow, a method of positioning the cross-bar at a pole vault pit, a portable seat for waiting in long lines, a method of protecting windshields of parked cars during freezing weather, a pet-proof garbage can, a bicycle rack, a door knob, a seat to support a small child in a bathtub.

5. Evaluate the sketches made in Exercise 4 above and briefly outline in narrative form the information that would be needed to refine your design into a workable form. Use freehand lettering, striving for a neat, readable paper.

6. Many automobiles are available on the market. Explain your decision for selecting the one that would be most appropriate for the activities listed below: a trip on a sightseeing tour in the mountains, a hunting trip in a wooded area for several days, a trip from coast to coast, the delivering of groceries, a business trip downtown. List the type of vehicle, model, its features and why you made your decision to select it.

7. Write a report of not more than 10 typewritten pages that outlines the specific duties and relationships between the scientist, engineer, craftsman, designer, and stylist in an engineering field of your choice. For example, explain this relationship for an engineering team involved in an aspect of civil engineering. Your report should be supported by factual information obtained from interviews, brochures, or library references.

8. Write a report that investigates the employment opportunities, job requirements, professional challenges and activities of your chosen branch of engineering or technology. Write this report in compliance with the engineering report format given in Chapter 16. Illustrate this report with charts and graphs where possible for easy interpretation. Compare your personal abilities and interests with those required by the profession.

9. Arrange a personal interview with a practicing engineer or technician in the field of your interest. Discuss with him the general duties and responsibilities of his position to gain a better understanding of this field. Summarize your interview in a written report.

10. Write to the professional society of your field of study for information concerning this area. Prepare a notebook of these materials for easy reference. Include in the notebook a list of books that would provide career information for the engineering student.

BIBLIOGRAPHY

1. U. S. Department of Labor, *Employment Outlook for Engineers,* Bulletin No. 1650-23. Washington: U. S. Government Printing Office, 1970.
2. R. Paul Harrington, *Your Career as an Aerospace Engineer.* New York: American Institute of Aeronautics and Astronautics.
3. *Agricultural Engineering.* St. Joseph, Mich.: American Society of Agricultural Engineers.
4. *Occupational Briefs—Agricultural Engineers.* Chicago: Science Research Associates, Inc.
5. *Engineering—A Creative Profession.* New York: Engineers' Council for Professional Development, Inc., 1963.
6. *Industrial Engineering—The Profession with a Future.* New York: The American Institute of Industrial Engineers, Inc.

7. *Nuclear Terms—A Brief Glossary,* Oak Ridge, Tenn.: United States Atomic Energy Commission, 1964.

8. Lyerly, Ray L., and Walter Mitchell III, *Nuclear Power Plants.* Washington, D.C.: U. S. Atomic Energy Commission, 1966.

9. United States Atomic Energy Commission, *The Nuclear Industry.* Washington: U. S. Government Printing Office, 1967.

10. Weaver, Elbert C., *The Story of Gas.* New York: American Gas Association, 1964.

11. U. S. Department of Labor, *Occupational Outlook Handbook—Employment Outlook of Technicians,* Bulletin No. 1650-27. Washington: U. S. Government Printing Office, 1970.

12. U. S. Department of Labor, *Technology and Manpower in Design and Drafting,* 1965–75. Washington: U. S. Government Printing Office, 1966.

SUGGESTED READING

Engineering: General

Accredited Curricula Leading to First Degrees in Engineering in the United States (published annually), Engineers' Council for Professional Development, 345 East 47th St., New York, N. Y. 10017. (25¢)

Accredited Engineering Technology Curricula in the United States (published annually), Engineers' Council for Professional Development, 345 East 47th St., New York, N. Y. 10017. (25¢)

Engineering—A Career of Opportunity, National Society of Professional Engineers, 2029 K St. N.W., Washington, D. C., 20006.

Should you Be an Engineer?, by T. Keith Glennan, Career Information Service, New York Life Insurance Company, Box 51, Madison Square Station, New York, N. Y. 10010.

After High School What?, Engineers' Council for Professional Development, 345 East 47th Street, New York, N. Y. 10017.

Women in Engineering Careers, Society of Women Engineers, 345 East 47th St., New York, N. Y. 10017.

Fields of Engineering

Aerospace Engineering

Your Career as an Aerospace Engineer, American Institute of Aeronautics and Astronautics, 1290 Avenue of the Americas, New York, N. Y. 10019.

Agricultural Engineering

The Profession with a Future, American Society of Agricultural Engineers, 420 Main St., St. Joseph, Mich. 49085.

Ceramic Engineering

For Career Opportunities Explore the Wonder World of Ceramics, American Ceramic Society, 4055 North High St., Columbus, Ohio 43214.

Chemical Engineering

Will You Be a Chemical Engineer?, American Institute of Chemical Engineers, 345 East 47th St., New York, N. Y. 10017.

Civil Engineering

A Definitive Study of Your Future in Civil Engineering, by Alfred R. Golze, American Society of Civil Engineers, 345 East 47th St., New York, N. Y. 10017.

Electrical and Electronics Engineering

Your Challenge in Electrical Engineering, Institute of Electrical and Electronics Engineers, Inc., 345 East 47th St., New York, N. Y. 10017. (25¢)

Industrial Engineering

Industrial Engineering—The Profession with a Future, American Institute of Industrial Engineers, 345 East 47th St., New York, N. Y. 10017.

Mechanical Engineering

Mechanical Engineering, American Society of Mechanical Engineers, 345 East 47th St., New York, N. Y. 10017. (25¢)

Metallurgical Engineering

Careers in Metallurgy and Metallurgical Engineering, Metallurgical Society of AIME, 345 East 47th St., New York, N. Y. 10017.

Mining Engineering

Opportunities Unlimited—Careers in the Mineral Industry, Society of Mining Engineers of AIME, 345 East 47th St., New York, N. Y. 10017.

Petroleum Engineering

Careers in Petroleum Engineering, Society of Petroleum Engineers of AIME, 6300 North Central Expressway, Dallas, Tex. 75206.

Engineering Technician Careers

Technician Career Opportunities in Engineering Technology, American Society of Engineering Education, 1346 Connecticut Ave., N.W., Washington, D. C. 20036. (25¢)

Can I Be a Technician? Let's Find Out, by Public Relations Staff, General Motors Corporation, Detroit, Mich. 48202.

The JETS Program, The Junior Engineering Technical Society, 345 East 47th St., New York, N. Y. 10017.

Careers in Engineering

The World of Engineering, John R. Whinnery, ed., McGraw-Hill, 330 West 42nd St., New York, N. Y. 10036. ($5.95)

Engineering as a Career Today, by B. H. Amstead and Wilbourn McNutt, Dodd, Mead & Co., 432 Park Ave., New York, N. Y. 10022. ($3.75)

Listen to Leaders in Engineering, Albert Love and James S. Childers, ed., McKay Co., 750 Third Ave., New York, N. Y. 10017. ($6.95)

ADDRESSES FOR PROFESSIONAL SOCIETIES

The American Institute of Aeronautics and Astronautics
1290 Avenue of the Americas, New York, N.Y. 10019

American Institute of Chemical Engineers
345 East 47th Street, New York, N.Y. 10017

The American Institute of Industrial Engineers
345 East 47th St., New York, N.Y. 10017

American Institute of Mining, Metallurgical, and Petroleum Engineering
345 East 47th Street, New York, N.Y. 10017

American Nuclear Society
244A East Ogden Avenue, Hinsdale, Ill. 60521

American Society of Agricultural Engineers
420 Main Street, St. Joseph, Mich. 49085

American Society of Civil Engineers
345 East 47th Street, New York, N.Y. 10017

American Society for Engineering Education, Technical Institute Division
1346 Connecticut Avenue, Washington, D.C. 20036

American Society of Mechanical Engineers
345 East 47th Street, New York, N.Y. 10017

The Institute of Electrical and Electronic Engineers
345 East 47th Street, New York, N.Y. 10017

Society of Petroleum Engineers (AIME)
6300 North Central Expressway, Dallas, Tex. 75206

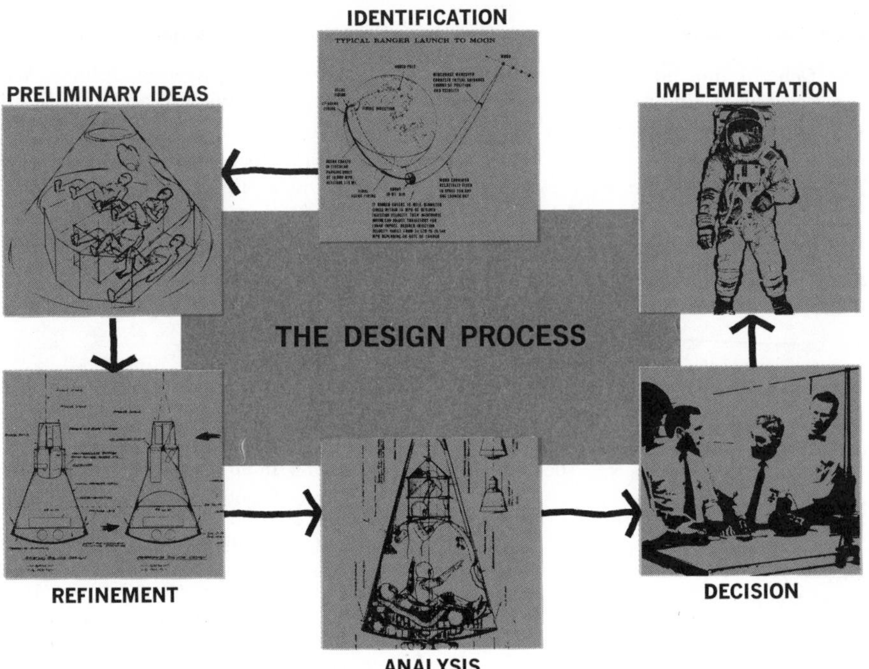

2 THE DESIGN PROCESS

2-1 INTRODUCTION

The fields of engineering and technology have been defined in Chapter 1 as creative fields which are responsible for the development of new applications of scientific principles to fit specific needs. A knowledge of scientific and engineering principles is of little value in the field of design if these disciplines cannot be harnessed to obtain a tangible end that will fulfill the needs of a given situation. For an engineer to function to his fullest extent, he must exercise imagination combined with knowledge and curiosity.

Engineering graphics and descriptive geometry provide methods of solving technical problems, just as other engineering courses do. If this area of study were applied without creativity, the result would be merely a repetitious drawing or a spatial problem analysis which could be performed by a machine. Likewise, a mathematical problem solved with no regard for its significance or effect on a given result is a noncreative activity of a clerical nature. However, when an engineer applies mathematics to the solution of an engineering problem to attain a design solution, he is being creative. An engineer who is developing a design solution must make many sketches and drawings to develop his preliminary ideas before he can communicate with his associates. Used in this manner, graphical methods are creative tools.

This chapter will define the basic steps of the design process suggested for application to a problem. These steps will offer a plan of action that will aid the designer in organizing his efforts. Succeeding chapters will develop each of these design steps with greater detail.

2-2 CREATIVITY

Creativity is as important to the engineer as it is to the artist, although creativity is more commonly associated with the arts than with technology. Artistic creativity has fewer restrictions than technology does. The engineer or designer must be creative within certain limits of physical and scientific laws which cannot be violated. His design must function and serve a worthwhile purpose at an economical cost, and he must originate solutions within this strict framework. Consequently, in many respects he must be more creative than the artistically creative person who has essentially no restrictions or functional products to produce.

In technology, creativity can also be described as the relationship of innovations to an applied problem. The solution of any problem in a different way is an act of creativity. Of course, the degree to which one solution is more creative than the next may be difficult to ascertain unless one design is considerably superior to the others. If economy is the prime criterion, an engine that provides adequate power at the lowest operational rate is obviously the superior design. The engineer can also express himself aesthetically through his designs although the designs may be truly functional with no frills or intricacies of ornamentation. A well-designed bridge will be as aesthetically acceptable to the tastes of the artist as would a piece of art. A functional design often yields the most attractive design. Most of today's utensils, appliances, and products are examples of eye appeal through simplified presentation of functional systems, rather than through an attempt to force the function of a design to fit a preconceived form.

Creativity is present in varying degrees in all people, with some being more creative than others. Many claim that creativity cannot be taught; however, research has indicated that this ability can be developed as can most other personal talents. All individuals should strive to develop their capacities for creativity in order to achieve satisfaction and contribute to the growth of our expanding technology.

2-3 TYPES OF DESIGN PROBLEMS

Design problems are numerous and take many forms; however, most fall in one of two categories: *systems design* and *product design*. These two types of design problems will be referred to throughout this textbook as the basic types of design problems. The distinct separation of these types of problems is often difficult, due to an overlap of certain characteristics. The following descriptions are given to define systems design and product development in general.

2-4 SYSTEMS DESIGN

A systems problem is one that involves an interaction of related components and principles which form a composite that functions as a unit. A residential building is a complex system made up of component systems and products. For example, the typical residence has a heating-cooling system, a utility system, a plumbing system, a gas system, an electrical system, and many other systems that form the overall composite system (Fig. 2-1). These component systems are also called systems because they are composed of a number of individual parts that can be used for other applications. The

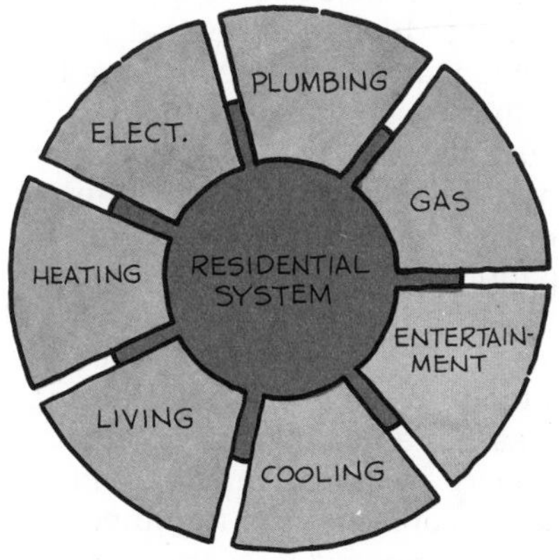

Fig. 2-1. The typical residence is a system composed of many component systems.

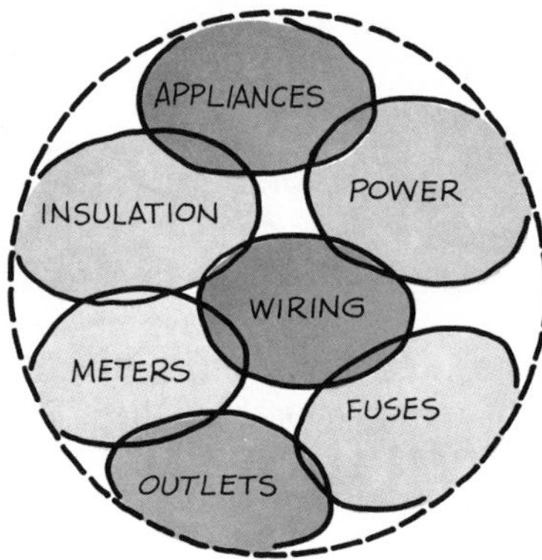

Fig. 2-2. An electrical system of a residence is a composite of related components.

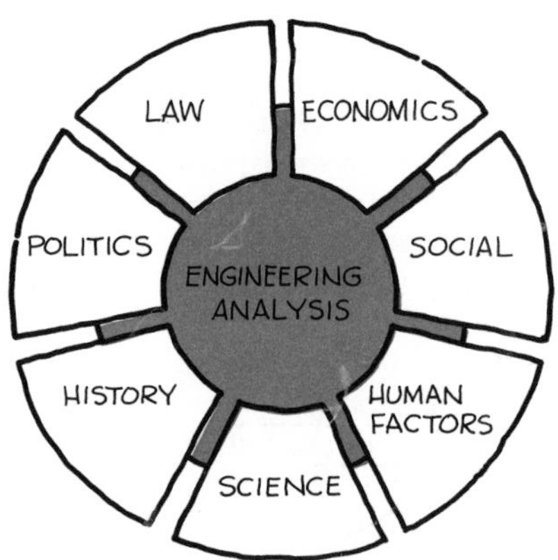

Fig. 2-3. An engineering system may be a complex interaction of many professions, with the engineering function holding the primary area of emphasis. An example of a system of this type is a traffic design problem.

electrical system involves wiring, insulation, electrical components, light bulbs, meters, controls, switches, and related items (Fig. 2-2). Each of these parts can be used in other systems in an infinite number of combinations. However, the specific arrangement used in a residence is unique to that application and is not adaptable in all respects to a nonresidential application.

A number of systems, such as those cited above, can be joined together to give a more complex system that involves many more factors than simply technological systems. An engineering project which requires that a traffic system be developed for a particular need will overlap into other disciplines (Fig. 2-3). The engineering function will be the primary area that will support the project; however, the project will also involve legal problems, economical principles, historical data, human factors, social considerations, scientific principles, and political limitations. The engineer can, of course, design a suitable driving surface, drainage system, overpasses, and other components of the traffic system by application of engineering principles without consideration for other areas and the limitations imposed by them. However, there are always limitations which make this an unrealistic situation. The engineer must adhere to a specific budget in essentially all projects in which he is involved, and the budget is closely related to legal and political problems. Traffic laws, zoning ordinances, right-of-way possession, and liability clearances are other legal areas that must be considered.

Planning for the future is based on past needs and trends, which introduces historical data as a design consideration. Human factors involve driver characteristics, safety features, and other factors that would affect the function of the traffic system. Social problems are associated with traffic systems. Heavily traveled highways will attract commercial establishments, shopping centers, and filling stations, which will affect the adjacent property. The entire complexion of a given neighborhood might be changed from residential to commercial in a short period of time. Scientific principles developed through laboratory research can be applied by the engineer in building more durable roads, cheaper bridges, and a more functional system. Pressures from special interest groups may conflict with interests of other groups and result in limiting the engineer's freedom of approach. The future of the total project may depend upon a compromise of different ideas to form an acceptable solution that will be suitable for the need.

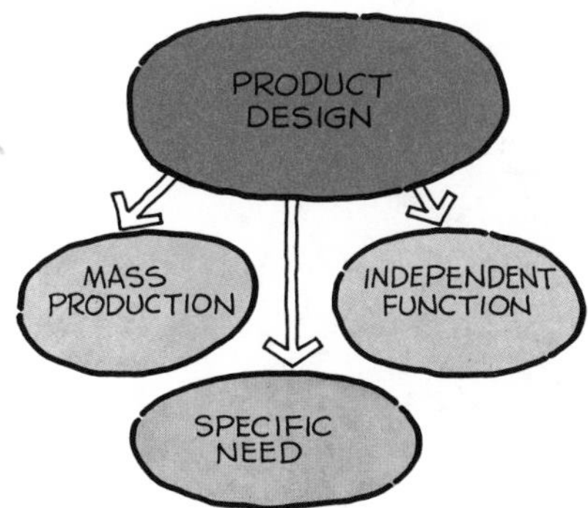

Fig. 2-4. Product design is more limited in scope than systems design.

The engineer must have a background in these areas in addition to his traditional engineering background. The need for a broader background for engineers has resulted in the inclusion of more liberal arts courses and humanities in the engineering curriculum, for these enable the engineer to grasp the broadness of his profession as it relates to other professions.

An Example System Problem. The following problem is given as an example of a rather simple system design that can be used to illustrate the various steps of the design process. This particular problem requires a minimum of theoretical engineering principles.

Select a building on your campus that is in need of an improved parking lot to accommodate the people who are housed in the building. This may be a dormitory, office building, or classroom building. Design a combination traffic and parking system that will be adequate for the requirements of the building. The solution of this problem must adhere to existing limitations, regulations, and policies of your campus in order for the problem to be as realistic as possible.

2-5 PRODUCT DESIGN

Product design is concerned with the design, testing, manufacture, and sale of an item that will perform a specific function. Such a product can be an appliance, a tool, a system component, a toy, or a similar item that can be purchased as a commercial unit. Because of its more limited function, product development is considerably more specific than systems design. A coffee pot, for example, is limited in its application to the preparation of coffee.

The distinction between a system and a product is not always clearly apparent. An automotive system has a primary function of providing transportation. However, the automobile must also furnish its passengers with communications, illumination, comfort, and safety, and these would classify it as a system. Nevertheless, the automobile is thought of as a product, since it is mass-produced for a large consumer market. On the other hand, a petroleum refinery is definitely a system, composed of many interrelated functions and components. All refineries will have certain processes in common, but no two can be considered alike in all respects. Consequently, refineries cannot be purchased as if they were units or products, but instead, they must be constructed from stock components and originally designed components. Likewise, a water system for a community must be designed to utilize many existing elements and conditions; these variables make each system different and inappropriate for mass-production as if it were a product.

The definition of a product, as used in this textbook, will be considered to be an item that has been mass-produced for a rather general market to meet a specific need and that can be used independently to serve a given function (Fig. 2-4). In this definition, an automobile, airplane, television set, or similar product available on the retail market can be considered a product. The examples covered in this volume will be considerably more simple to be within the grasp of the typical student beginning his studies in engineering or technology.

Product design is not as closely related to the general professional areas illustrated in Fig. 2-3 as systems design. Product design is more

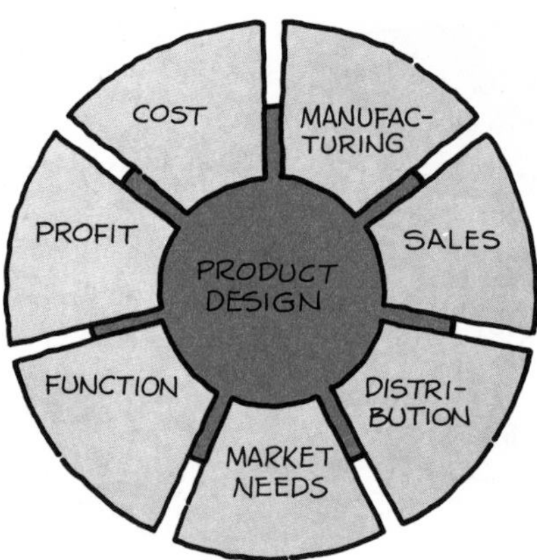

Fig. 2-5. Areas associated with product design are related to the manufacture and sale of the completed product.

related to the current market needs, cost of production, function, sales, method of distribution, and profit predictions (Fig. 2-5). Although this is the initial concern when approaching product design, this concept may be broadened to encompass an entire system that will have sweeping changes of a social and economic nature. An example of this transition from a product to a system is the automobile, whose function has had a significant effect on our way of life. This product has expanded to a system including highways, service stations, repair shops, parking lots, drive-in businesses, residential garages, traffic enforcement, and endless other related components.

An Example Product Design Problem. The product problem given below is an example of the type of problem that may be assigned as a class project. This problem exhibits typical conditions from which a new product is developed to fill a need for a given market.

Many hunters, especially deer hunters, hunt from trees to obtain a vantage point. Sitting in a tree for several hours can be uncomfortable and hazardous to the hunter, which indicates a need for a hunting seat that could be used to improve this situation. Design a seat that would provide the hunter with comfort and safety while hunting from a tree, and meet the general requirements of economy and hunting limitations.

2-6 THE DESIGN PROCESS

The design process is a general outline of steps that can be followed to give a degree of direction to the designer. Many combinations of steps and procedures of design are used by various designers, with no single combination being the best. This is due to the complexity of design and the many ways in which different designers achieve success. Adherence to strict rules of design cannot ensure success of design, and may even inhibit the designer to the point of containing his freedom of imagination. Nevertheless, the design process is believed to be an effective means for introducing a method of design to the beginner. The steps of the design process will give him a sequence of tasks that will familiarize him with the considerations of a design problem. An understanding of these steps will enable him to devise his own method of designing in some other combination or sequence of steps.

The steps of the design process are: (1) Problem identification, (2) Preliminary ideas, (3) Problem refinement, (4) Analysis, (5) Decision, and (6) Implementation. These steps are part of any design process regardless of the variations in approach that may be used. They can be applied to the formulation of any type of problem requiring an original solution, from planning a weekend to designing an appliance. The following articles will expand the definitions of these steps and illustrate their application to the complex problem of developing a system for traveling to the moon.

2-7 PROBLEM IDENTIFICATION

All designs are based on needs that exist. Weapons are designed to win wars; can openers are designed to open cans. It is important in any constructive activity to have a clear definition of the objectives so as to provide a target for all efforts. This is very true of the design process. To justify its manufacture, the designer must identify the need and the function which the product must provide if it is to satisfy the need. The identification of the needs for a design may be based on data of several types: field data, opinion surveys, historical records, personal observations, experimental data, or projections of present concepts.

These methods of problem identification are illustrated below as they apply to the problem of designing a system to carry man to the moon. It is possible to discuss only generalities in a problem of this degree of complexity.

Mission to the Moon—Problem Identification. The concept of traveling to the moon is based on an identification of *why* the trip should be undertaken and, secondly, *how* the trip will be possible. Planners and designers responsible for this system must develop hardware components and devise sophisticated systems that will launch and guide the spacecraft and communicate with it in flight. Scientific curiosity is usually the basic reason for wanting to travel to the moon. Secondary reasons may be the exploitation of needed resources, enlargement of living space, and discovery of an improved environment, to name a few.

The identification of the problems related to *how* the mission can become a reality is the more difficult part of the design process. Consideration must be given to physical and natural systems that will affect the flight. Figure 2–6 illustrates an area on the moon's surface where test vehicles will photograph an area of the moon to determine its suitability as a landing site. Such criteria as the distance from the earth to the moon, the gravitational fields of each, the availability of propulsion for the spacecraft, the number of crew required, their living conditions during flight, the method of returning to earth, and guidance systems must be investigated. A preliminary, unmanned launch to the moon is illustrated in Fig. 2–7 with supplementary notes and information to identify various details of the mission. It is obvious that many other considerations of this type are necessary for an understanding of the problem requirements, to

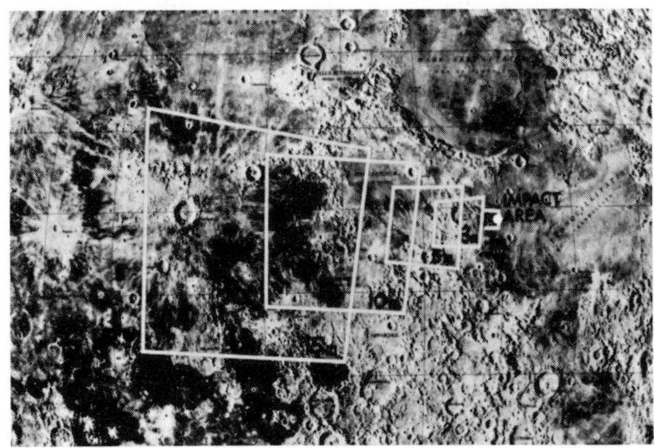

Fig. 2–6. During the last 15 minutes of flight, an experimental spacecraft will provide camera coverage of the areas on the moon's surface that are outlined here in white. (Courtesy of the National Aeronautics and Space Administration.)

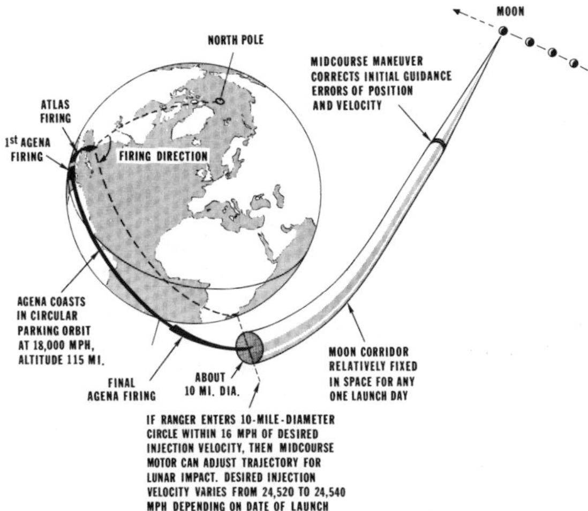

Fig. 2–7. This graphical schematic illustrates a proposed test flight to the moon by an unmanned spacecraft, Ranger, prior to manned flight. Information gained from this mission will be valuable to later manned missions. (Courtesy of the National Aeronautics and Space Administration.)

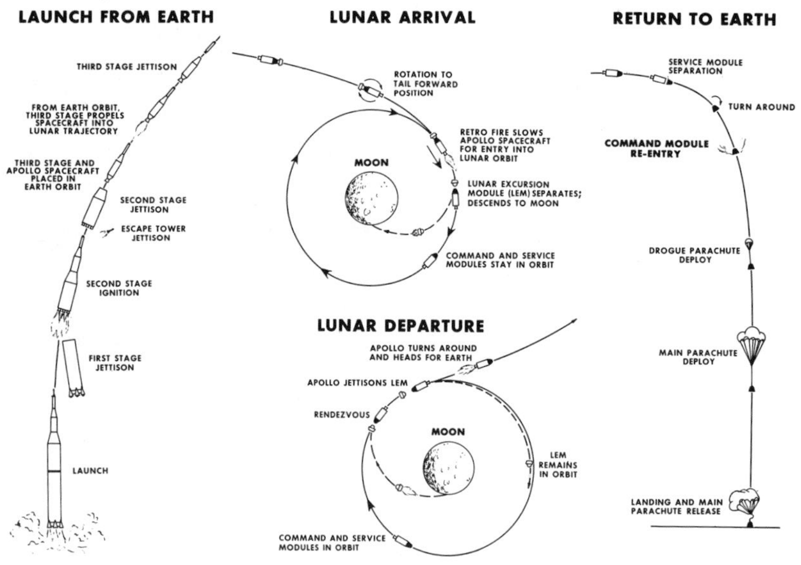

Fig. 2-8. A four-stage sketch is used to identify specific problems that must be solved in landing a man on the moon and returning him to the earth. (Courtesy of the National Aeronautics and Space Administration.)

prevent an important concept from being overlooked.

Information pertaining to the identification of a problem can be more easily understood and interpreted if presented graphically, as in Fig. 2-8. Tabular data showing variations of related factors can be graphed for evaluation. The reduction of gravitational force with respect to the distance from the earth is an example of this type of information. Estimates of the funds required for the project must be tabulated and graphed. A further extension of the cost of the mission, the determination of a source of funds, and the method of gaining necessary financing will also be required. A government-supported system introduces problems of a political nature. These need to be evaluated.

All information and data that serve to identify a design problem should be presented in written and graphical form. This information should be maintained as a permanent record of the identification stage. If the problem identification is no more than writing out several statements that describe the problem requirements, this should be done to solidify the problem rather than relying on impression or intuition. This is especially important when the design process is attempted by a team working toward a common goal. Unless the problem is clearly defined, there may be different interpretations of the design objectives by different members of the team. Problem identification will be explained in greater detail in Chapter 3.

2-8 PRELIMINARY IDEAS

Once the problem has been defined and clearly stated, it is necessary to collect preliminary ideas from which design concepts can be assimilated. This is probably the most creative stage of the entire design process. Since only general limitations have been set in the problem identification step, the designer is free to let his imagination consider any idea that comes to mind. These ideas should not be evaluated for feasibility as they are developed in hopes that a positive attitude will stimulate other related ideas in a chain reaction.

The most useful means for developing preliminary ideas is by freehand sketching. This quick way of recording an idea will be more meaningful to the designer when he is reviewing

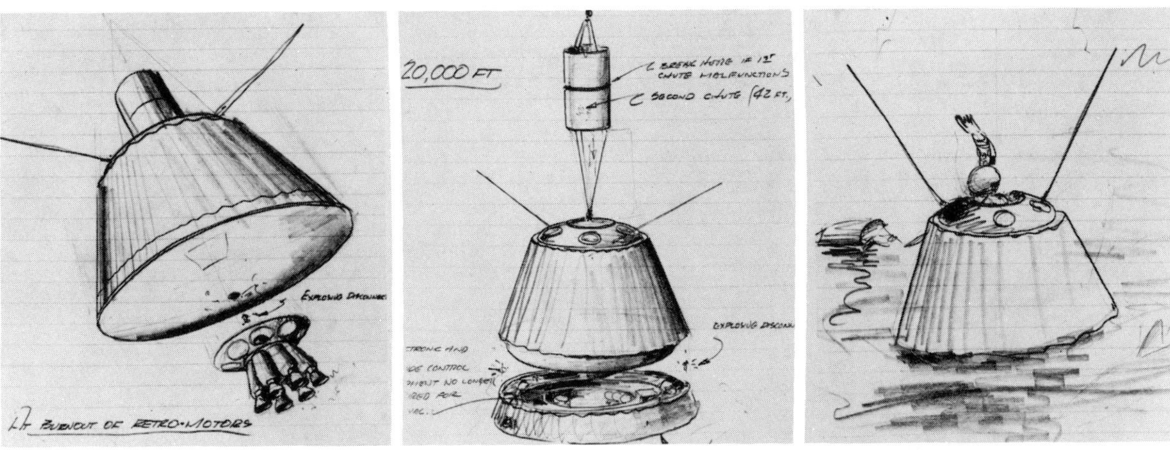

2–9 2–10 2–11

various ideas for refinement in the succeeding step of the design process. His sketches need not be detailed or in final form but should be rapidly drawn to express an idea for a hardware design or a schematic relationship between concepts or functions. General notes can be used to supplement these rough sketches and to clarify details that are not apparent in the sketches.

An attempt to evaluate and pass judgment on each preliminary idea will reduce the possibility of arriving at a unique solution. Evaluation in a negative sense leads to inhibitions that retard the free flow of ideas. The important concept of the accumulation of ideas is to gather as many as possible, varying from adaptations of old ideas to new ideas. All ideas should be listed and sketched so they can be reviewed for further development.

Mission to the Moon—Preliminary Ideas. The complexity of the problem of traveling to the moon requires preliminary ideas in a large number of separate areas. The primary problem is that of providing a power unit to propel the spacecraft. The design of the spacecraft itself and its integral systems is the next problem. The method of landing the vehicle on the lunar surface and returning it to earth must also be determined.

Fig. 2–9. An early sketch suggests a method of separating the retro-motors from the Mercury spacecraft following their use in slowing down the craft upon reentering the earth's atmosphere. (Courtesy of the National Aeronautics and Space Administration.)

Fig. 2–10. This sketch depicts the capsule's deceleration by a parachute as it reenters the earth's atmosphere. (Courtesy of the National Aeronautics and Space Administration.)

Fig. 2–11. A final step is illustrated with the capsule safely afloat awaiting pick up. (Courtesy of the National Aeronautics and Space Administration.)

The sketches shown in Figs. 2–9, 2–10, and 2–11 were used to develop ideas for a spacecraft to carry astronauts to the moon. (These Mercury sketches were preliminary only and do not reflect the final specifications.) Many of these ideas were considered too radical and extreme a few years ago to be anything more than comic-strip material. Changing times and technology have converted "wild" ideas into reasonable solutions to engineering and scientific problems.

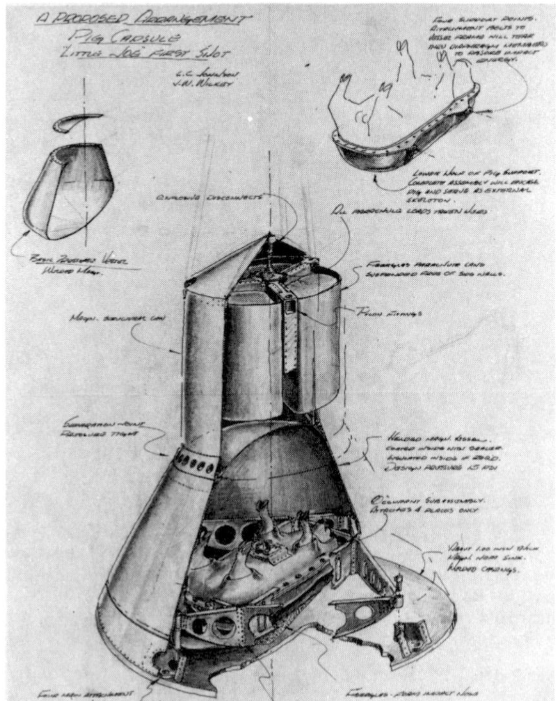

Fig. 2-12. A preliminary sketch of the spacecraft for Project Mercury illustrates a possible configuration for the capsule. A pig was initially considered for experimental tests, but was later rejected. (Courtesy of the National Aeronautics and Space Administration.)

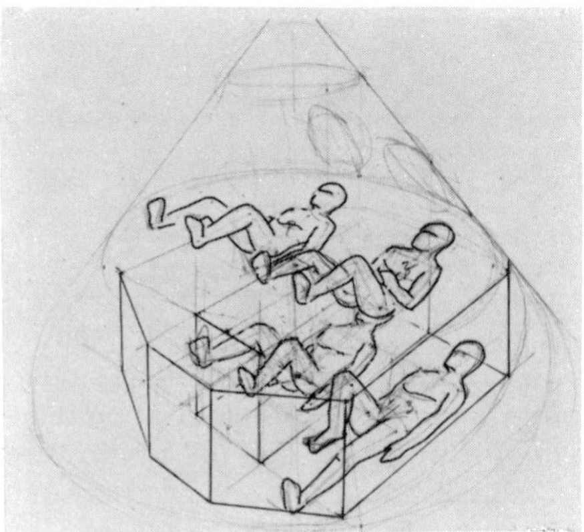

Fig. 2-13. This sketch developed preliminary ideas for the seating arrangement for Project Apollo. (Courtesy of the National Aeronautics and Space Administration.)

Figure 2-12 is a sketch of an experimental spacecraft, designed for Project Mercury, which was to use a pig to determine the effects of space flight on an animal. Pigs were eliminated from the experiment when it was discovered that they could not survive on their backs for an appreciable length of time. A preliminary sketch of the command module shown in Fig. 2-13 led to the final seating arrangement in Project Apollo.

Thousands of sketches of the types described above were necessary to develop ideas that would contribute to a space program which would enable man to travel to the moon. Some concepts were modifications of existing systems, while others displayed a high degree of imagination and creativity that extended beyond existing concepts. All significant ideas and sketches were saved for reference in succeeding projects.

Preliminary ideas will be discussed in more detail in Chapter 4. There, sketching and other graphical techniques will be explained that will aid in the preparation of preliminary ideas.

2-9 PROBLEM REFINEMENT

The preliminary idea stage of the design process has few restraints to limit imagination and creativity. Problem refinement is the initial stage of the evaluation of preliminary ideas, and it deals more closely with an analysis of limitations. All rough sketches and notes are reviewed, combined, and refined to determine several reasonable solutions to the problem. Consideration should be given to limitations and restrictions that will affect the final design. Rough sketches can be more valuable if drawn to scale, where relative sizes and clearances can be developed, so that lengths, weights, angles, and shapes can be determined by application of descriptive geometry methods and analytical drawings. These physical characteristics must be determined at an early stage of the design, since they may affect the final design.

The designer should periodically refer to his preliminary sketches in search of a worthy idea that he may have overlooked and that will assist

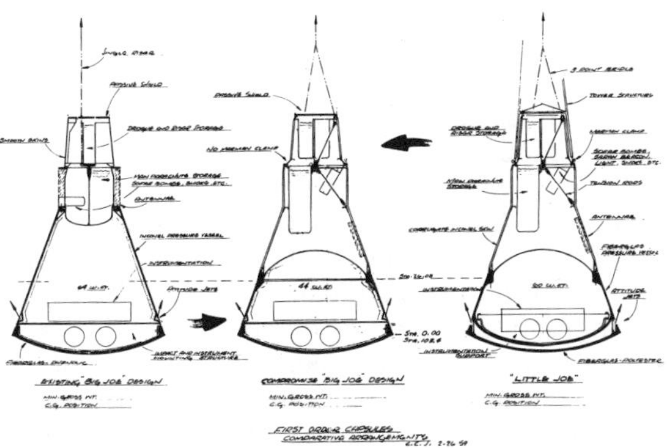

Fig. 2-14. Scale drawings were used to refine the final design of the "Big Joe" spacecraft by incorporating the best preliminary ideas. (Courtesy of the National Aeronautics and Space Administration.)

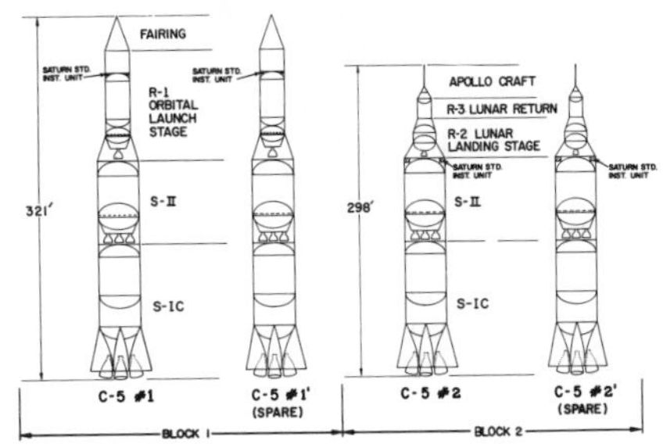

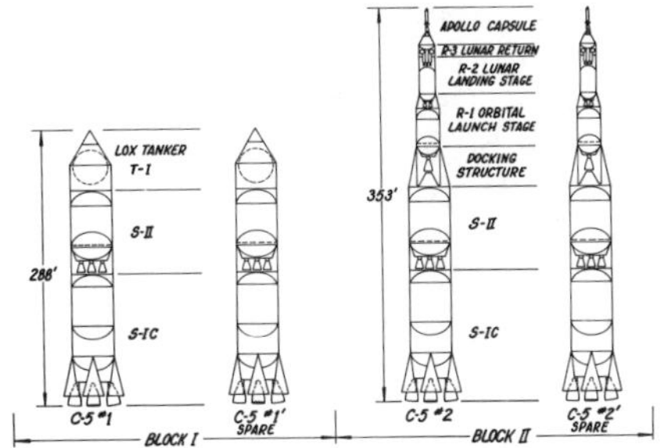

Fig. 2-15. Various spacecraft assemblies are compared in these drawings. (Courtesy of the National Aeronautics and Space Administration.)

him in refining his solutions. He should not become involved with a particular idea to such an extent that he does not feel free to drop the idea and develop an entirely different concept. Changes in solution are much easier here than later when more time has been invested.

Mission to the Moon—Problem Refinement. The preliminary sketches of the spacecraft are developed and refined to offer alternative configurations of the capsule. Three designs are depicted in scale drawings in Fig. 2-14. Each design incorporates the general ideas arrived at through the previous step; however, each configuration offers a different solution to the problem. Notes are used to identify differences in each design. Figure 2-15 illustrates a comparison of spacecraft assemblies for various stages of the program.

The refinement of the Apollo Control Capsule is shown in Fig. 2-16. This drawing has been drawn to scale to give a clear understanding of the space requirements and the clearances

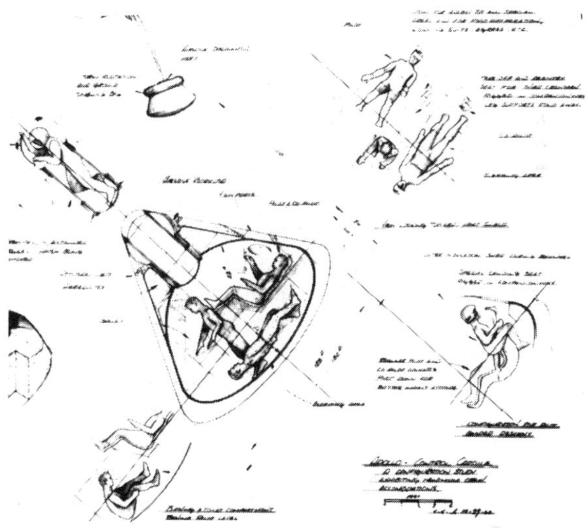

Fig. 2-16. Scale drawings were used to refine the clearances and working areas within the Apollo capsule. By refining his drawings to scale, the designer can determine critical measurements and estimate weights and volumes. (Courtesy of the National Aeronautics and Space Administration.)

required within its environment during flight. Auxiliary views and sketches are used to develop and refine the basic design. A scale drawing permits the designer to measure critical dimensions, estimate weights, volumes, and areas, and study the function of the craft in relationship to its passengers.

Consideration is given to the known limitations of equipment, physical and scientific principles, and related systems during the early stages of the design process. However, graphical methods are the designer's most helpful tools in developing a design. Rough sketches and diagrams aid him in arranging his ideas in a preliminary form. Scale drawings are used to assist the evolution process from a rough idea to a refined concept. Descriptive geometry and spatial analysis can be employed to determine from scaled drawings critical information that will influence further development. Problem refinement and its relation to graphical methods will be covered in greater detail in Chapter 6.

2-10 ANALYSIS

Analysis is the portion of the design process that is best understood in a general sense. Analysis involves the review and evaluation of a design for human factors, market appeal, strength, function, physical quantities, and economics to meet the needs of the design. Most of an engineer's formal training is centered around these areas of study. Mathematics, physics, chemistry, and other engineering sciences are utilized more in this phase of the design process than at any other time. The analysis of a design is critical to the design process; however, this is probably the least creative step. This is true because a solution must be designed before it can be analyzed. If by analysis the proposed design is found to be inadequate for its needs, the designer must return to his earlier ideas and look for a modification that will be workable, or even seek an entirely new solution which will be analyzed after it has been refined. Scale models and full-size prototypes are usually constructed and tested as a method of analyzing advanced design concepts. Laboratory data gathered from these tests can be analyzed to learn more of the design's characteristics.

Analysis serves to provide the designer and engineer with a means of evaluating a design, but it cannot offer a solution to a design problem. The designer who is experienced in engineering principles and methods of analysis can profit from his knowledge in designing creative products and systems while adhering to the standards of analysis that will be used to measure his completed designs. Again, graphical methods have definite applications to design analysis. Chapters 13, 14, and 15 elaborate on the applications of graphical and descriptive geometry principles to this important step of the design process.

Mission to the Moon—Analysis. The analysis of a mission to the moon requires a detailed study of scientific principles, utilizing advanced mathematics and other disciplines related to a project of this complexity. The thrust of the rocket system must be tested extensively to determine whether the propulsion system is adequate. Communications and guidance systems are analyzed through field tests and simulated missions such as the unmanned Surveyor spacecraft mission illustrated in Fig. 2-17. Environmental systems are tested with animals to determine the systems' ability to maintain the conditions required for manned flight.

Graphical analysis of the interior design of a proposed spacecraft is shown in Fig. 2-18. This drawing is used as a means of analyzing the configuration and function of the interior of the capsule. The location of the controls and other manually operated systems can be analyzed to determine the feasibility of their location and function. The size of the astronaut is a primary factor affecting the size of the craft. A further analysis of human factors can be seen in the sketch shown in Fig. 2-19. The astronaut's position suggested by the couch principle was analyzed and tested. It was found that an astronaut could withstand the required g-loads present at launch and at reentry at the end of the flight. This particular method of fabrication was later discarded after further analysis.

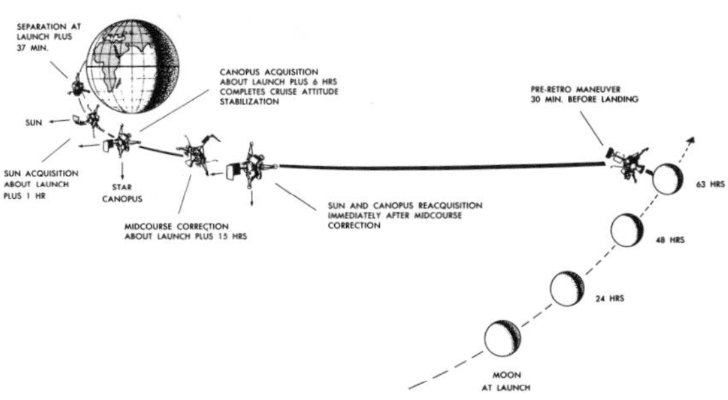

2–17

Fig. 2–17. The problems of landing man on the moon were analyzed by reviewing data gathered through unmanned spacecraft such as Surveyor, shown in this flight profile. This vehicle provided information on soft landings on the lunar surface. (Courtesy of the National Aeronautics and Space Administration.)

Fig. 2–18. The Mercury spacecraft is presented graphically to analyze the relationships between various interior units and human factors that are required for effective functioning. (Courtesy of the National Aeronautics and Space Administration.)

Fig. 2–19. An analysis of a couch support for an astronaut is shown in this sketch and scale drawing. This position was adopted, but the method of fabrication was discarded. (Courtesy of the National Aeronautics and Space Administration.)

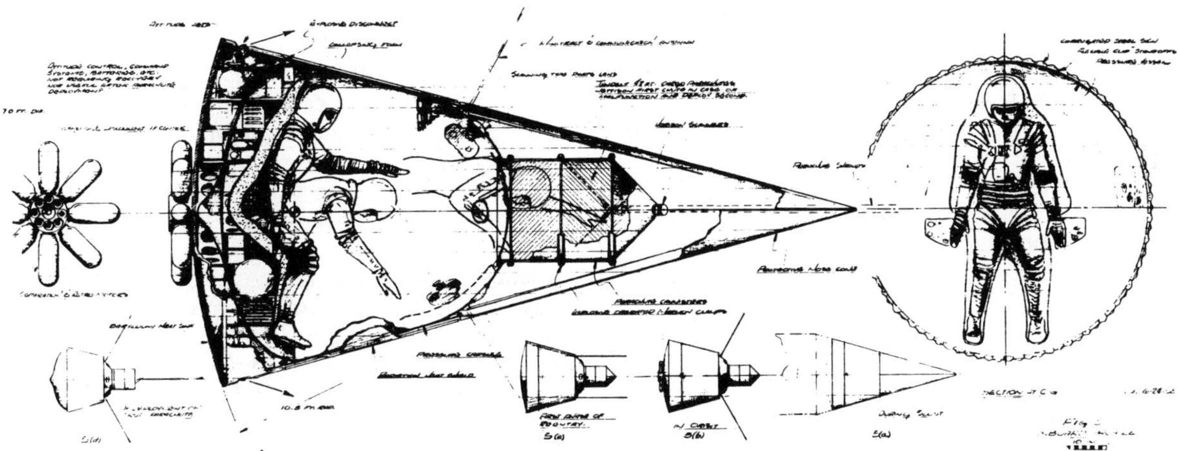

2–18

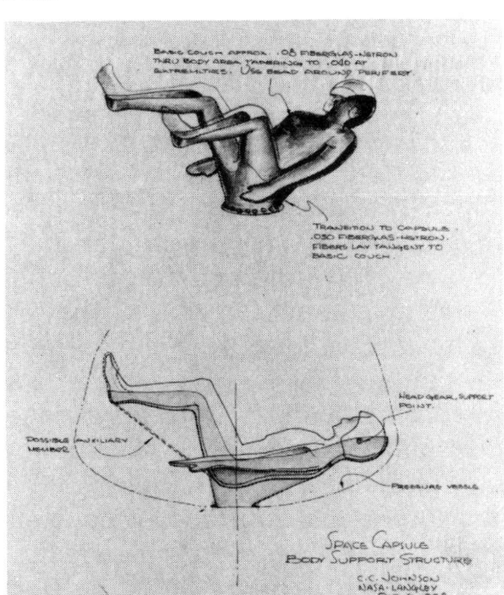

2–19

The other analyses conducted on the space program are indeed too numerous to mention. The analytical evaluation of the proposed designs were tested and evaluated by hundreds of engineers, scientists, and technicians working as members of different teams.

2–11 DECISION

The decision step is the portion of the design process in which a design must be accepted or rejected, in part or in whole. Several ideas may have been developed, refined, and analyzed. Each may offer advantages over the others, with no single design being clearly superior to the others. The decision as to which design will be the best for a particular requirement must be determined through engineering experience and factual information. There is always a chance for error in any decision, but a well-thought-out design will evaluate the problem to such an extent as to lessen the possibility of overlooking an important consideration, as could occur in an impulsive solution.

The decision process may be the responsibility of the designer, a group of associates, or a group of administrative officials. In any case, the designer should assemble all design information he has accumulated into a presentable form that would assist in the decision. Charts, graphs, pictorials, diagrams, and schematics are helpful in condensing this accumulation of information into a form for easy interpretation. Models are helpful in illustrating spatial relationships in complicated designs.

When a designer completes a design he usually writes a report outlining his findings and recommendations for further action, if any, on the project. In a smaller company, he may give a presentation to his associates and superiors, using any visual aids that will communicate his ideas to the group. The designer with a greater proficiency for writing and speaking will have an advantage in communicating his ideas and recommendations. It is not the purpose of the presentation to deceive the reviewing panel, but instead, to present a complete picture of the total project, including its weaknesses and advantages. An engineer who is weak in communicating his ideas, either orally or in writing, may not effectively present a good design idea and, consequently, his ideas may be rejected.

Mission to the Moon—Decision. Decisions must continually be made when designing for a trip to the moon. Each individual component, system, and design concept must be decided upon by a number of groups and individuals. The decision process in a relatively new, experimental field of this type is more crucial to the outcome, since there are more unknowns in an unexplored field. A wrong decision can hinder the program and disrupt the entire planning schedule.

Decisions in all areas must be made by groups of experts qualified in specialized areas. No single individual or group is capable of making all of the decisions required. The diversity of the backgrounds of the scientists, engineers, and other specialists makes communication of all concepts more critical than when working with a relatively homogeneous group within a small industry. These specialists must communicate their ideas to each other in order for the best use to be made of all talents involved in the project.

Fig. 2-20. Oral presentations should be accompanied with sufficient graphical aids to improve communication.

Important decisions are usually made from oral presentations which may follow written reports. Design concepts are presented and discussed by the reviewing panel to better understand the design and to assist in a more valid decision. A presentation is given with graphical aids that will improve communication (Fig. 2-20).

2-12 IMPLEMENTATION

The designer's last step is the preparation and supervision of the final drawings and specifications from which the final design will be constructed. In some cases, the designer may supervise and inspect the implementation of his design, also. When presenting his design in working form, he will be concerned with details of fabrication, methods of assembly, materials used, and other specifications. He may make minor modifications that will improve his design during this step; however, such changes will be relatively minor unless an entirely new concept becomes apparent. In this case, the design process will revert to the initial stages so that the new approach may be developed before it is approved and presented.

Fig. 2–21A. The presentation of completed designs must be in the form of working drawings and specifications; however, supplementary pictorials, models, and other techniques can be used to improve communications. (Courtesy of the National Aeronautics and Space Administration.)

Fig. 2–21B. This exploded pictorial is used to present details of construction of the launch tower of Complex 39, Cape Kennedy. (Courtesy of the National Aeronautics and Space Administration.)

Fig. 2–22. The final result of the design process is the accomplishment of the mission. Man lands on the moon and returns safely home. (Courtesy of the National Aeronautics and Space Administration.)

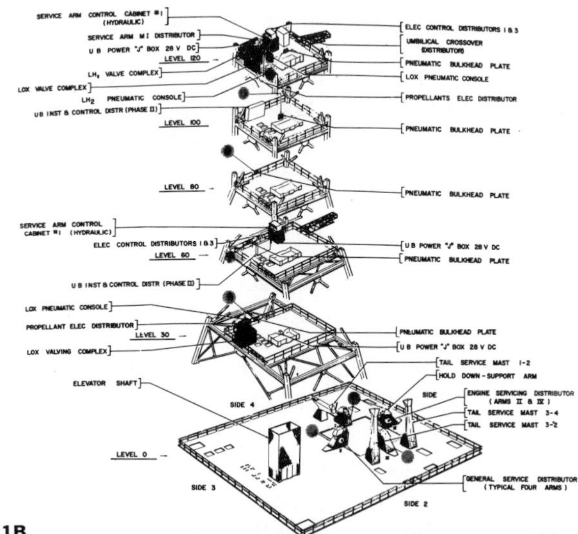

2–21B

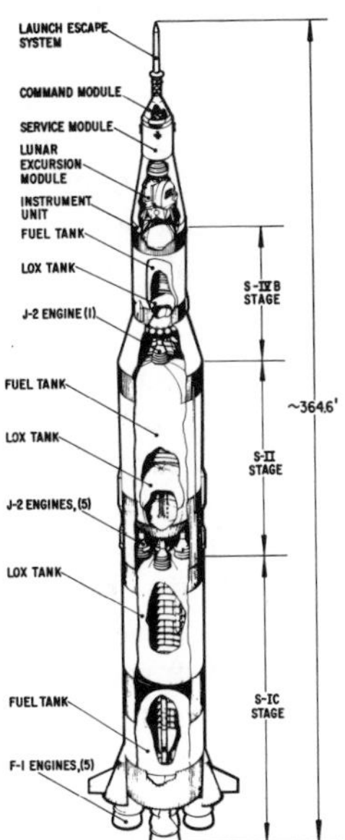

2–21A

2–22

The implementation portion of the design process utilizes the application of graphical methods to a great extent in communicating the details of the completed design. This is the least creative use of graphical methods. This application is merely the presentation of already developed ideas and innovations in the form of working drawings. Draftsmen can perform this service with supervision from the designers and engineers who developed the design solutions.

Mission to the Moon—Implementation. Manufacturers located in different parts of the nation are responsible for producing parts within close tolerances that will function properly when assembled with components produced by other manufacturers. This requires that all designs be presented in great detail with the maximum of clarity. The designer utilizes every method at his disposal to communicate an idea, whether it is a working drawing, a pictorial, or a scale model (Fig. 2–21A). Essentially, it would be impossible to achieve unity of design without employing working drawings and graphical methods in the presentation of design details and specifications. Figure 2–21B is an exploded pictorial, intended to show the construction of a launch tower.

As a final result, the designer will see his plans and specifications implemented and become a reality. Only in the final stage when the actual design is tested will the designer know whether his design will function well enough to be considered satisfactory (Fig. 2–22). Knowledge is gained through failure as well as success. Failure should not be taken to mean the entire project was a failure, but instead, it should provide suggestions for areas to be reevaluated.

2–13 SIMPLIFIED DESIGN PROBLEM

The preceding articles described the steps of the design process in general terms and how they applied to a highly advanced space problem. In order to illustrate these steps as they would be applied to a simple design problem, the following example is given.

Swing Set Anchor Problem. A child's swing set has been found unstable during the peak of the swing. The momentum of the swing causes the A-frame to tilt with a possibility of overturning and causing injury. The swing set has swings attached to accommodate three children at one time. Design a device that will eliminate this hazard and have market appeal for owners of swing sets of this type.

Problem Identification. As a first step, the designer writes down the problem statement (Fig. 2–23) and a statement of need. This overt action stimulates flow of thought and assists him in attacking the problem systematically. The limitations and desirable features are listed with necessary sketches to enable him to communicate with himself and to develop a better understanding of the problem requirements. Much of the information and notes in the problem identification step may be obvious to the designer, but the act of writing statements about the problem and making freehand sketches helps him get off "dead center," which is a common weakness at the beginning of the creative process. He will also find that some of his initial ideas may not be entirely valid when actually listed on paper.

This design problem is simple to the point of requiring more common sense than engineering ability, but common sense should not be overlooked even in engineering design. Many scientifically oriented people may find it difficult to recognize an obvious, workable solution that may be available to them through the application of everyday logic. Engineers, technicians, and designers should develop the ability to have a "feel" for their work so that they can evaluate calculations and findings by inspection and notice any significant errors.

Preliminary Ideas. A second work sheet is used to sketch preliminary ideas that would lead to a possible solution to the problem (Fig. 2–24). This is the most creative part of the process, and the part which has the fewest restraints. The designer makes rough sketches and notes to describe his preliminary thoughts, without dwelling upon a single design. After several ideas have been sketched, he can go over his sketches and make notes in colored pencil to indicate the better points of each design, narrowing down his ideas to those that seem to have the most merit.

Problem Refinement. The best designs—two or more unless one is highly superior to all others—are drawn to scale in a general working drawing, as a means of refining preliminary designs. Sufficient notes are used to describe the design without becoming too involved with details (Fig. 2–25). The refinement provides the physical properties and dimensions that must be considered during the earlier stages of the design process.

Orthographic projection, working drawing principles, and descriptive geometry may be used, depending upon the particular problem being refined. In this example (Fig. 2–25), simple orthographic views with auxiliary views depict the two designs. These drawings, even though refined, are still subject to change throughout the entire process.

Analysis. Once a preliminary design has been refined to establish fundamental dimensions and relationships, the designs must be analyzed to determine their suitability and other criteria. The maximum angles of swing need to be established by observation of a child swinging under average conditions. The force F at the critical angle can be calculated mathematically or estimated by observation (Fig. 2–26). Since three swings may be in use at once, the maximum

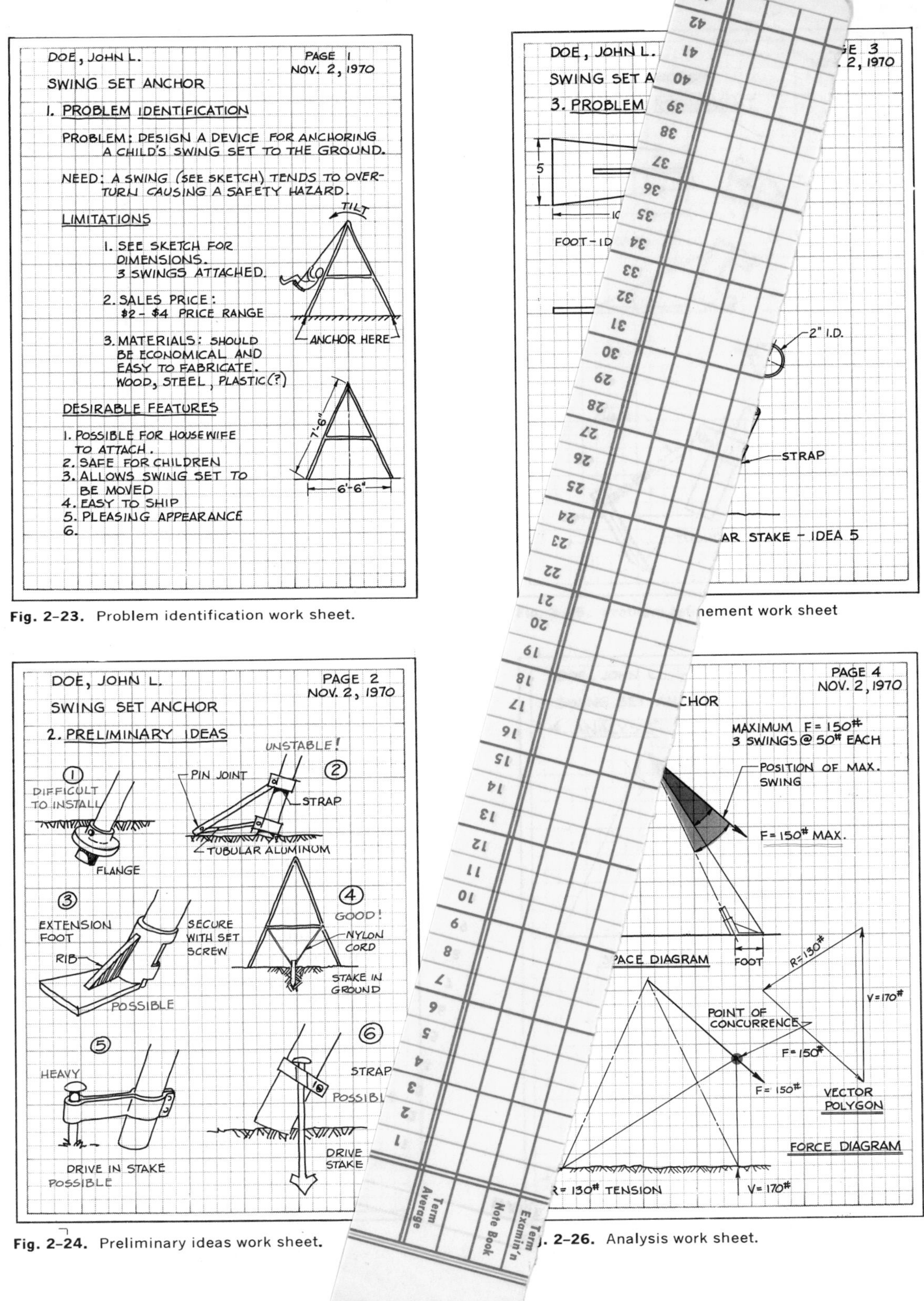

Fig. 2-23. Problem identification work sheet.

Fig. 2-24. Preliminary ideas work sheet.

…nement work sheet

…. 2-26. Analysis work sheet.

DOE, JOHN L. PAGE 5
NOV. 2, 1970

SWING SET ANCHOR

5. DECISION

SUPERIOR FEATURES

FOOT	TUBULAR STAKE
A. EASY TO ATTACH	A. POSITIVE ANCHORING
B. EASY MOVEMENT OF SET	B. EASIER TO PACK
C.	C. CHEAPER
	D. STOCK MATERIALS
	E. SIMPLE DESIGN

DISADVANTAGES

FOOT	TUBULAR STAKE
A. EXPENSIVE CONSTR.	A. SAFETY – PROJECTS OUT OF GROUND
B. BULKY	B. TRIP ON CHAIN ?
C. HEAVY	
D. LIMITED RANGE OF PROTECTION	

CONCLUSION: THE TUBULAR STAKE IS THE SUPERIOR DESIGN. IMPLEMENT.

Fig. 2–27. Decision work sheet.

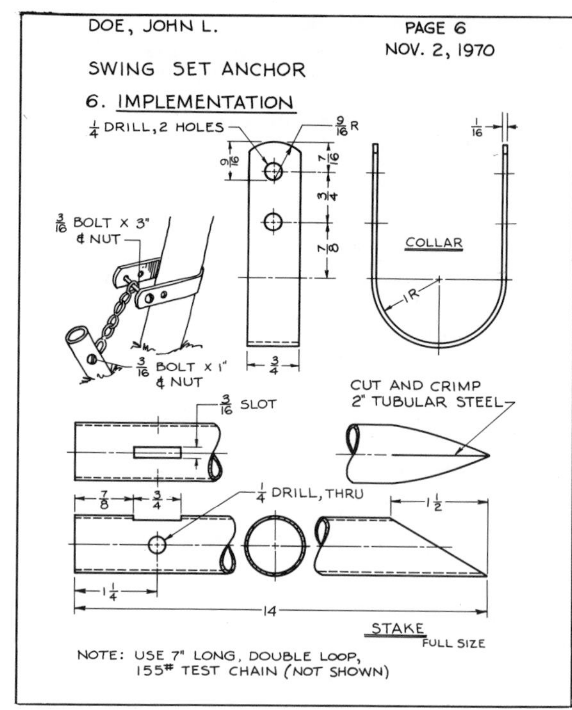

Fig. 2–28. Implementation drawing.

condition will exist when all three swings are in phase, resulting in a triple pull, or 150 lb in this example.

The danger zones are graphically indicated in the space diagram to show the effects of the foot design and to establish the dimension that it must have in order for it to eliminate the tilting tendency at the maximum angle. The force diagram is drawn to scale to analyze the reaction forces at the extreme condition. This diagram gives the direction of reaction, R, but not its magnitude. A vector polygon is drawn with the vectors parallel to the forces in the force diagram, where the only known force is $F = 150$ lb. The magnitude of resultant R is found to be 130 lb, which is the maximum force that must be overcome at the base of the swing set.

Decision. The designs must be evaluated and the better of the two selected for implementation. The designer may wish to repeat the previous process at any point, and develop an entirely different approach to the problem if he sees a need. In this example (Fig. 2–27), the superior features of each design are listed for easy comparison. The disadvantages of each are listed also to prevent any design weakness from being overlooked. These tabulated lists are reviewed and a final conclusion is reached. A decision is made to implement the tubular stake design.

Implementation. The tubular stake design is presented in the form of a working drawing, in which each individual part is detailed and dimensioned, and from which the parts could be made. All principles of graphical presentation are used, including a freehand sketch illustrating how the parts will be assembled (Fig. 2–28). Note that changes have been made since the initial refinement of this design. These changes were believed to be more operational and economical while serving the desired function. Standard parts, such as nuts, bolts, and the chain, need not be drawn, but merely noted, since they are parts that will not be specially fabricated. With this drawing the designer has implemented his design as far as he can without actually building a prototype, model, or the actual part. He may later make modifications in his design, but this is a separate design process very similar to the steps reviewed here.

The following chapters will elaborate on each of the steps of the design process in greater detail. Chapter 3 will discuss a suggested method of preparing work sheets and accumulating a design file to document the development of ideas and final designs. The example work sheets shown in Figs. 2–23 through 2–28 illustrate the typical approach to a simple design problem. It should be noted that most of the design work is directly related to the use of graphical methods. As simple as this problem is, it would be virtually impossible for it to be designed without the utilization of graphical methods.

A photograph of the actual part is shown in Fig. 2–29 as it would be available for the market. It is shown attached to the swing set in Fig. 2–30 with the stake driven into the ground. No mention has been made of a market analysis or an evaluation of the commercial prospects of the item. This would be an ultimate requirement for any device that is produced for consumption by the general market.

2–14 SUMMARY

The design process introduced in this chapter is composed of six steps. These steps are (1) Problem identification, (2) Preliminary ideas, (3) Problem refinement, (4) Analysis, (5) Decision, and (6) Implementation. These six steps must be applied to all design problems to some degree, whether in this sequence or others. The process of designing can take many forms and be approached by a number of methods. The procedure that works best for an individual is the one he should use.

The example problem of a mission to the moon was used to illustrate the application of these steps to a broad engineering problem in general terms. In subsequent chapters, the various steps of the design process will be applied to more simple problems that are within the grasp of the student and typical of class assignments that he might receive.

Graphical methods are necessary tools of the designer striving for a problem solution. These methods have definite applications to every aspect of the design process; therefore graphics and descriptive geometry principles form an indispensable part of the design process. The designer must actually think with a pencil in developing creative designs. Graphics is used more extensively throughout the design process than any other single tool at the designer's disposal.

Fig. 2–29. The completed swing-set anchor.

Fig. 2–30. The anchor attached to a swing set.

PROBLEMS

Problems should be presented on $8\frac{1}{2}'' \times 11''$ paper, grid or plain, using the format presented in Article 1–19. All notes, sketches, drawings, and graphical work should be neatly prepared in keeping with good practices, as introduced in this volume. Written matter should be legibly lettered using $\frac{1}{8}''$ guidelines.

1. List engineering achievements that have demonstrated a high degree of creativity in the following areas: (a) the household, (b) transportation, (c) recreation, (d) educational facilities, (e) construction, (f) agriculture, (g) power, (h) manufacture.

2. Make an outline of your plan of activities for the weekend. Indicate areas in your plans that you feel display a degree of creativity or imagination. Explain why.

3. Write a short report on the engineering achievement or the man who you feel has exhibited the highest degree of creativity. Justify your selection by outlining the creative aspects of your choice. Your report should not exceed three typewritten pages.

4. Test your creativity in recognizing needs for new designs. List as many improvements for the typical automobile as possible. Make suggestions for implementing these improvements. Follow this same procedure in another area of your choice.

5. List as many systems as possible that affect your daily life. Separate several of these systems into component parts or subsystems.

6. Subdivide the following systems into components: (a) a classroom, (b) a wrist watch, (c) a movie theater, (d) an electric motor, (e) a coffee percolator, (f) a golf course, (g) a service station, (h) a bridge.

7. Indicate which of the items in Exercise 6 are systems and which are products. Explain your answers.

8. Make a list of new products that have been introduced within the last five years with which you are familiar.

9. Make a list of products and systems that you would anticipate for life on the moon.

10. Assume that you have been assigned the responsibility for organizing and designing a Go-Kart installation on your campus. This must be a self-supporting enterprise. Write a paragraph on each of the six steps of the design process to explain how the steps would be applied to the problem. For example, what action would you take to identify the problem?

11. You are responsible for designing a motorized wheelbarrow to be marketed for home use. Write a paragraph on each of the six steps of the design process to explain how the steps would be applied to the problem. For example, what action would you take to identify the problem?

12. List and explain a sequence of steps that you feel would be adequate for the design process, yet different from the six given in this chapter. Your version of the design process may contain as many of the steps discussed here as you desire.

13. Assume that you are marooned on a desert island with no tools, supplies, or anything. Identify major problems that you would be required to solve. List factors that would identify the problems in detail. *Example:* Need for food. Determine (a) available sources of food on island, (b) method of storing food supply, (c) method of cooking, (d) method of hunting and trapping or otherwise obtaining food, etc. Although you are not in a position to gather data or supply answers to these questions, list factors of this type that would need to be answered before a solution could be attempted.

14. Can you design a device for holding a fishing pole in a fishing position while you are fishing in a rowboat? This could be a simple device that will allow you freedom while performing other chores in the boat. Make notes and sketches to describe your design.

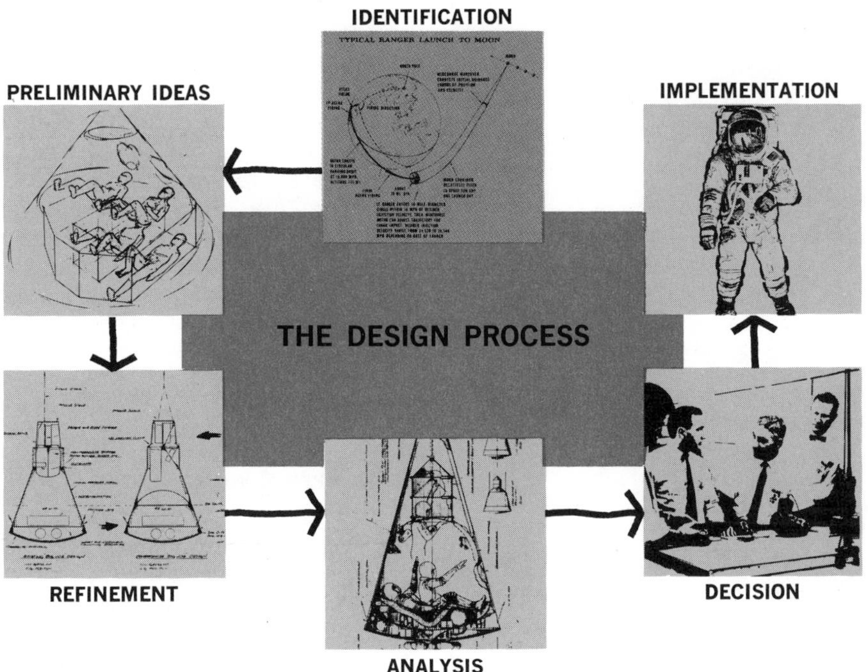

3 PROBLEM IDENTIFICATION

3–1 GENERAL

The initial step in any designer's approach to the solution of a design problem begins with problem identification. Problem identification can be one of two general types: (1) identification of a need, or (2) identification of design criteria (Fig. 3–1). Identification of a need is a common beginning point for a design project. A problem, defect, or shortcoming is recognized in an existing product, system, or environment. The need may be for an improved automobile safety belt, for a solution to air pollution, for a special hunting apparatus, or for a self-opening can (Fig. 3–2). Identification of a need at this stage is not sufficiently thorough to establish the criteria that must be met in solving the problem; the designer merely recognizes the existence of a need for which a design solution is necessary.

The identification of a problem need is the basis for beginning a design problem. This information can be used to state the problem in a proposal, whether in paragraph form or as a several-page report for formal submission. A proposal is a written plan of action that will be taken to solve a problem that has been identified. Formal proposals are written in much the same form as technical reports, which are covered in Chapter 16. Chapter 20 relates the proposal to the design process as applied to a comprehensive problem. In general, a proposal is a statement of action that would serve as a contractual agreement with an administrator, or with your teacher in a classroom situation.

Once approval has been received to proceed with a proposal, the problem is more thoroughly identified to determine the design criteria. This

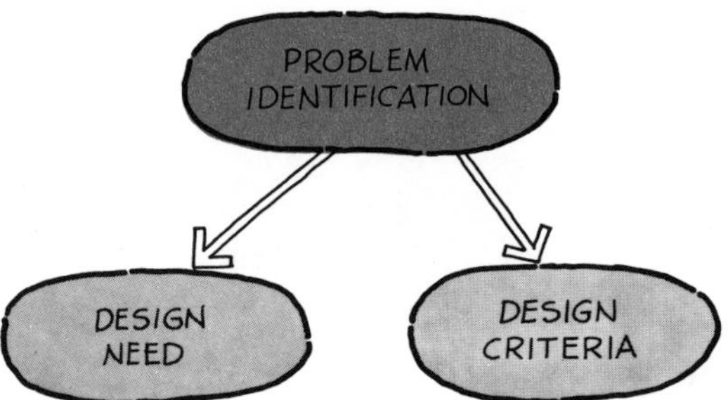

Fig. 3–1. Two basic types of problem identification.

Fig. 3–2. Problem identification may be the recognition of a need for a self-opening can. (Courtesy of Aluminum Company of America.)

Fig. 3–3. Work-sheet materials include pencils, work sheets, and an enveolpe or notebook.

phase may be performed by a team or by an individual designer. Identification of all aspects of a problem and the various related factors that must be considered in its solution is necessary before effort can be scheduled to bring about a completed design within a specified time. It is this type of identification that the remainder of the chapter will develop. Periodic reference should be made to Chapter 20, where the relationship of problem identification with the total design process is applied to comprehensive problems.

3–2 DESIGN WORK SHEETS

Throughout the design process, the designer should make numerous notes and sketches to provide a permanent record of his thinking that will serve as a reference. Periodically, he should review his earlier thoughts and notes to avoid overlooking an important concept. His ideas and thoughts are a vital resource—creativity—that should not be discarded after the solution of an immediate problem. Very often, preliminary design studies are not developed to a final stage for a considerable time after the initial work. Also, rough design sketches can serve as a permanent record to establish priority on a patentable design that may be developed. The following materials and format are suggested to enable the designer to effectively accumulate a record of his thoughts. This method will be used in each and every step of the design process.

Materials. It is beneficial to approach the entire design process in an orderly, organized manner. Orderly work will assist the designer in achieving an orderly sequence of ideas.

1. $8\frac{1}{2} \times 11$*-inch sketchpad.* A sketchpad can be either grid-ruled or plain, depending upon the preference of the designer. Sheets should be punched for insertion in a notebook or file that will contain the accumulation of notes and drawings (Fig. 3–3).

2. *Pencils.* A medium-grade pencil, such as an F pencil, is adequate when used with most papers. A colored pencil can be used beneficially to emphasize special features or ideas.

3. *Binder or envelope.* All work sheets should be maintained in an orderly sequence for easy reference. A binder or envelope is helpful in keeping work sheets in a presentable manner.

Format of Work Sheets. The following suggestions are given to aid the designer in properly utilizing his work sheets to best advantage. These steps are considered to be minimum requirements.

1. *Label each sheet.* Each individual work sheet (Fig. 3–5), should have the following information written in a prominent location:

a) Name or title of the project.
b) Name of the designer.
c) Date (month, day, and year).
d) Page number on each work sheet.

2. *Design work.* All sketches and notes should be presented in a readable form, although precise lettering is not necessary. Notes should be complete to reflect the total thoughts of the designer during the period when his thinking was closely aligned with the problem, thus enabling him to retain his grasp of the problem. Skimpy or brief notes could require the expenditure of valuable time to rediscover lost concepts at a later date. General comments pertaining to an idea or sketch should become a part of the permanent record.

3. *Work sheet accumulation.* All work sheets should be preserved in a binder, folder, or envelope as an accurate record of all steps of the design process. Solutions to future or related problems may emerge from the design problem at hand.

Preliminary notes and sketches are often included in the appendix of an engineering report to document the designer's approach to a final design. The application of these suggestions will be explained further in the examples that follow.

3–3 PROBLEM IDENTIFICATION

The designer usually has a general idea of the problem, the design criteria, and requirements that must be met when he begins a problem. It is easy for him to become prematurely attached to a single solution to the problem before it has been thoroughly analyzed. He may find later that his first impression of the problem was ill-founded or at least inaccurate, due to an incomplete understanding of all factors.

As the first step of the process, a design problem should be identified. Identification is a mental exercise requiring the designer to analyze the requirements, limitations, and other parameters. This mental process is directed toward tangible results, with graphical methods used as a stimulus to motivate thinking. The designer must overtly involve himself in the problem of sketching, writing notes, and doodling with his pencil on work sheets. He must think with his pencil. Graphical notes and sketches permit him to communicate with himself and solidify his thoughts.

Method of Problem Identification. The designer should make every effort to transcribe his thoughts on his work sheets as soon as possible rather than waiting for an inspirational solution. The following (Fig. 3–4) briefly outlines the initial steps in problem identification.

1. *Problem statement.* The problem statement should be written out to begin the thinking process. The statement should be complete and comprehensive, but as concise as possible so that the designer may refer to the statement with a minimum of lengthy, unnecessary reading.

2. *Problem requirements.* Make a list of the positive requirements that must be achieved in the design. Use words or phrases to describe specific and general requirements or features that are important to the solution of the problem. Many of these statements may be questions that will be listed and answered later when data have been gathered.

3. *Problem limitations.* List negative factors that confine the problem to specified limita-

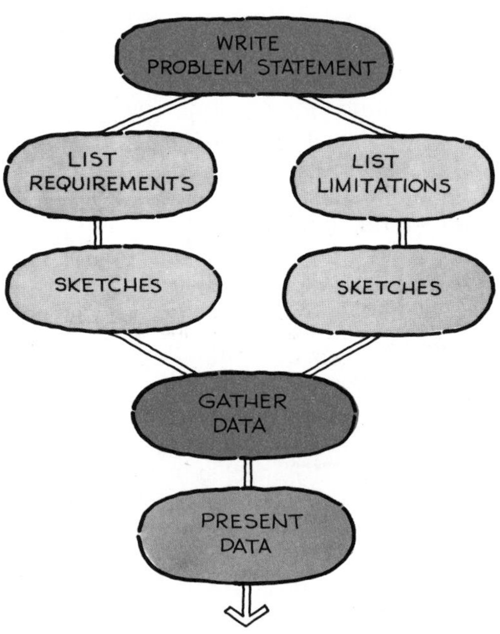

Fig. 3-4. The initial steps of problem identification.

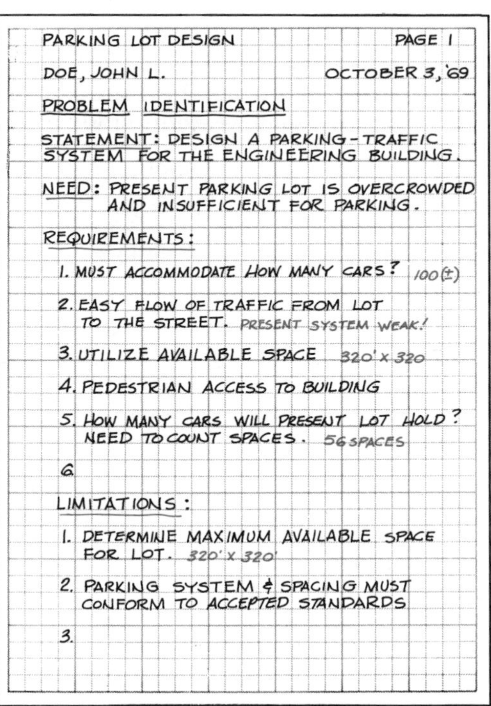

PARKING LOT DESIGN PAGE 1

DOE, JOHN L. OCTOBER 3, '69

PROBLEM IDENTIFICATION

STATEMENT: DESIGN A PARKING-TRAFFIC SYSTEM FOR THE ENGINEERING BUILDING.

NEED: PRESENT PARKING LOT IS OVERCROWDED AND INSUFFICIENT FOR PARKING.

REQUIREMENTS:

1. MUST ACCOMMODATE HOW MANY CARS? 100(±)
2. EASY FLOW OF TRAFFIC FROM LOT TO THE STREET. PRESENT SYSTEM WEAK!
3. UTILIZE AVAILABLE SPACE 320' x 320
4. PEDESTRIAN ACCESS TO BUILDING
5. HOW MANY CARS WILL PRESENT LOT HOLD? NEED TO COUNT SPACES. 56 SPACES
6.

LIMITATIONS:

1. DETERMINE MAXIMUM AVAILABLE SPACE FOR LOT. 320' x 320'
2. PARKING SYSTEM & SPACING MUST CONFORM TO ACCEPTED STANDARDS
3.

Fig. 3-5. A systems problem work sheet.

tions. Example: (1) cannot weigh more than 25 lb, (2) must fit in the trunk of a car, etc.

4. *Sketches.* Make sketches of any physical limitations or requirements that relate to the problem. Add notes or dimensions that would make these sketches more meaningful.

5. *Gather data.* Comprehensive designs may require the study of existing data related to the problem. These data could be population trends, related designs, physical characteristics associated with the problem, or a market analysis, when developing a product for general market utilization. Information of this type should be presented graphically when possible to permit easy analysis, since tabulated information is difficult to evaluate.

The designer may find that his concept of a problem's identity changes as he obtains more background material pertaining to the problem. If this is the case, he should rewrite his statement to more appropriately describe the problem. The first statement should not be discarded; instead, it should be retained as a record of the thinking process. Write a note to indicate that the first problem statement has been revised. A colored pencil would make these secondary notes more meaningful.

The designer should maintain an open mind to permit further modifications of his views of the problem. Every attempt should be made to remain receptive to innovations that might be precluded if the scope of the problem were excessively narrowed.

3-4 SYSTEMS PROBLEM IDENTIFICATION

An understanding of the aspects of problem identification can be seen as they apply to a simple systems problem that was previously stated in Chapter 2. This problem is restated below.

Systems Problem. Select a building on your campus that is in need of an improved parking lot to accommodate the people who are housed in the building. This may be a dormitory, office building, or a classroom building. Design a combination traffic and parking system that will be adequate for the requirements of the building. The solution of this problem must adhere to existing limitations, regulations, and policies of your campus in order for the problem to be as realistic as possible.

The first step in identifying the problem is to write the problem statement on a work sheet (Fig. 3-5). To establish justification for the design effort, the need is also stated. Obviously, no design would be necessary if a need was not apparent. It is important to note that these statements *are written* on the work sheets even though the designer has a complete grasp of the problem statement and the need. The mental act of writing a statement relating to the problem can stimulate a flow of ideas or thoughts that will give impetus to the design process. Reluctance of the designer to list ideas and, in a sense, to communicate with himself, may retard his progress toward a design solution.

The designer should also list the requirements for the lot on the work sheet, rather than attempting to rely on memory. The most important requirement is the number of cars for which the lot will be designed. This requirement statement is written in the form of a question with numbers left blank until the designer can gather data necessary for determination of this information. The designer writes a note to himself stating that it is necessary for him to investigate the needs as part of the identification phase. When data are not readily available, questions are used to outline the information that must be gathered and supplied prior to complete identification of the problem.

It is important that traffic have easy access to main arteries of traffic so as to avoid congestion. Another requirement is the efficient utilization of space and provision for sidewalks to allow passengers and pedestrians to enter the building with the minimum of difficulty. Other ideas may be added to this list. The designer asks

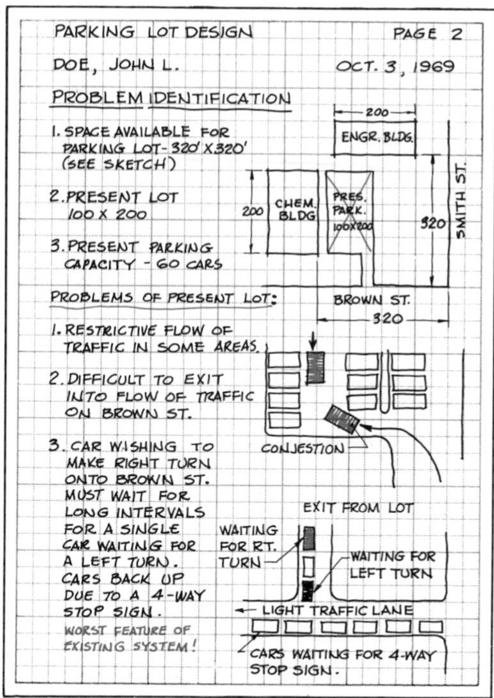

Fig. 3-6. A systems problem work sheet.

himself how many cars the existing lot will accommodate.

Limitations would include the maximum allowable space available for the lot, the existing standards for parking spaces, and the space required to maneuver an automobile in and out of a parking space. In actual practice, limitations will almost always begin with the available sum of money that must not be exceeded in the construction. This limitation is difficult for a class project due to the lack of experience of the average student in construction costs. Consequently, class assignments usually deal with construction costs in very general terms.

A second work sheet (Fig. 3-6) is used to supply answers to a few of the questions the designer asked himself on the first work sheet. Reference to existing campus maps or actual measurement of the site is necessary to gain a better understanding of the problem. The site is sketched freehand to save time while satisfying the immediate needs. Lettering and notes need not be as well executed as on working drawings, but should be sufficient to be readable. These notes are communications of the designer with himself.

Specific problems that may be seen in the present parking system are noted and sketched, as shown in Fig. 3–7, to identify corrections that would be desirable. The act of outlining these problems and sketching their layout helps the designer to better understand the problem.

The designer gathered data when he measured the existing parking lot, counted the number of spaces, and measured the size of the available space for additional parking. But there is additional information that he must gather, since it bears on the problem. It would, for example, be beneficial for him to know the number of people who would need parking accommodations in the buildings served by the lot. In this case, a count has to be made of the teaching staff housed in the chemistry and engineering buildings. The number of secretaries and other staff members should be tabulated. The utilization of the present parking lot during various hours of the day and on various days of the week would be helpful in identifying the peak periods of usage. This could be determined by making periodic spot checks during various scheduled times, counting the cars and tabulating the results.

Other data that must be gathered include physical criteria and standards established for parking automobiles, widths of driveways, turning radii of automobiles, and any other information that will identify problem limitations. Information of this nature can be obtained from published standards, observations, and measurements of existing systems that appear to be functional. Sketches of these physical limitations and general notes are made as they apply to the problem identification. Available population records provide the numbers of faculty members on the campus during the past years and the numbers of cars registered on the campus during these years. Past catalogs can be checked to determine the growth of the engineering and chemistry faculties, who would probably be housed in the two buildings in

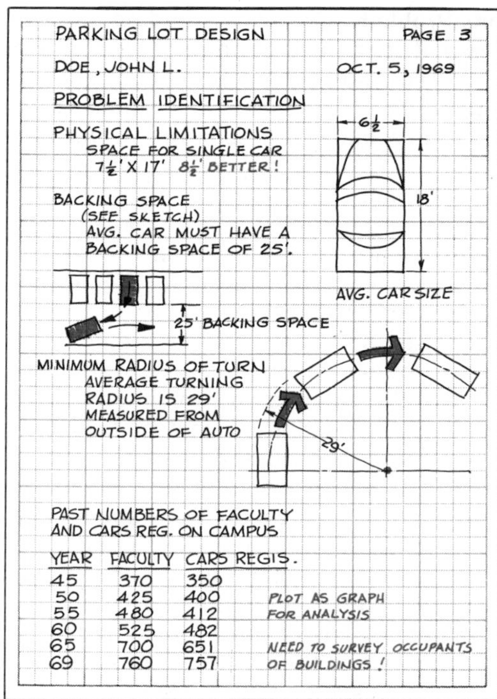

Fig. 3–7. A systems problem work sheet.

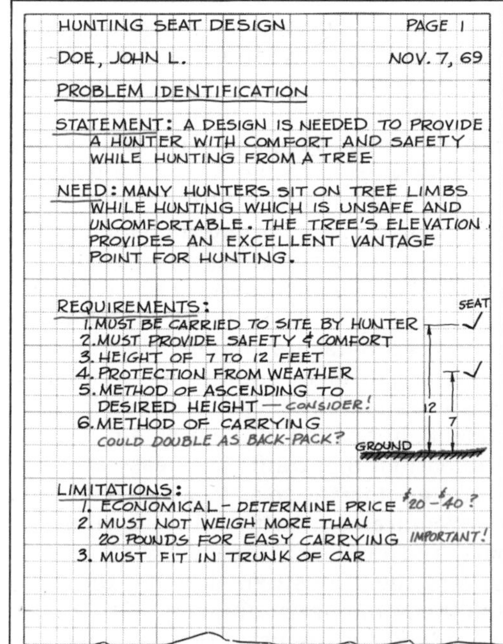

Fig. 3–8. A product development work sheet.

question. These data will establish trends that would be reflected in a design for a parking and traffic system serving these buildings.

This rather simple example of a systems problem illustrates a few of the fundamental steps required to identify the problem before actually suggesting preliminary solution. Information that has been gathered is retained on work sheets as a permanent file, allowing the designer to resume his work on the problem at a later date if the project is shelved for a period of time. His ideas and notes have preserved initial ideas that can be reviewed easily. Graphical notes and sketches are helpful in stimulating a flow of ideas so necessary in attempting a design solution.

3–5 PRODUCT DESIGN PROBLEM IDENTIFICATION

The product design problem is identified in much the same manner as the systems problem, but the type of data will be somewhat different. The following example, previously stated in Chapter 2, will be used to illustrate problem identification for a product design.

Product Design Problem. Many hunters, especially deer hunters, hunt from trees to obtain a better vantage point. Sitting in a tree for several hours can be uncomfortable and hazardous to the hunter; this fact indicates a need for a hunting seat that could be used to improve his situation. Design a seat that would provide the hunter with comfort and safety while hunting from a tree and would meet general requirements of economy and hunting limitations.

The work sheet in Fig. 3–8 is used in much the same manner as the systems problem. The problem is stated and the need identified. Requirements listed on the work sheet include a provision for safety and comfort, a method of carrying the apparatus to the hunting site, a consideration of protection from weather, and a method of attaining the desired height of 7 to 12 feet. The designer does not attempt to offer solutions to the problem, but merely to identify needs that must be met.

Limitations are concerned with the sales price of the item, its weight to permit easy carrying,

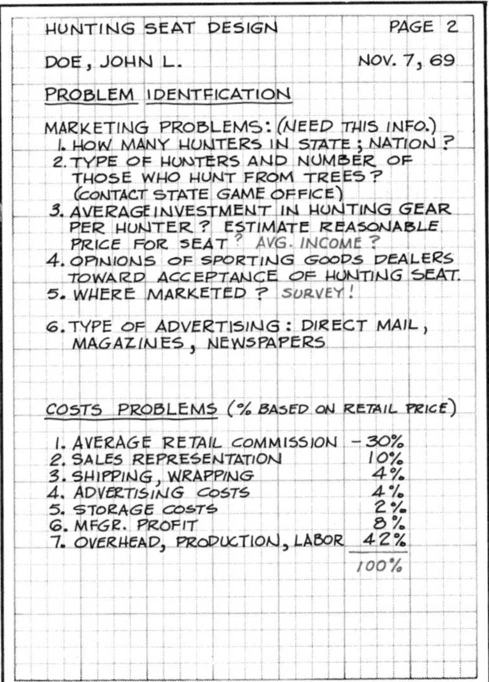
HUNTING SEAT DESIGN PAGE 2

DOE, JOHN L. NOV. 7, 69

PROBLEM IDENTFICATION

MARKETING PROBLEMS: (NEED THIS INFO.)
1. HOW MANY HUNTERS IN STATE ; NATION ?
2. TYPE OF HUNTERS AND NUMBER OF THOSE WHO HUNT FROM TREES ? (CONTACT STATE GAME OFFICE)
3. AVERAGE INVESTMENT IN HUNTING GEAR PER HUNTER ? ESTIMATE REASONABLE PRICE FOR SEAT ? AVG. INCOME ?
4. OPINIONS OF SPORTING GOODS DEALERS TOWARD ACCEPTANCE OF HUNTING SEAT.
5. WHERE MARKETED ? SURVEY !
6. TYPE OF ADVERTISING : DIRECT MAIL, MAGAZINES, NEWSPAPERS

COSTS PROBLEMS (% BASED ON RETAIL PRICE)

1. AVERAGE RETAIL COMMISSION	– 30%
2. SALES REPRESENTATION	10%
3. SHIPPING, WRAPPING	4%
4. ADVERTISING COSTS	4%
5. STORAGE COSTS	2%
6. MFGR. PROFIT	8%
7. OVERHEAD, PRODUCTION, LABOR	42%
	100%

Fig. 3–9. A product development work sheet.

and a size that would fit in most standard car trunks. Other limitations are marketing requirements, as given in Fig. 3–9, the second work sheet. The designer asks himself questions that must be determined by gathering data from available sources. The number of hunters who would be considered the potential market will give an estimate of the prospects of manufacturing the seat. Of even more value would be an estimate of the number of hunters who hunt from trees. This information could be obtained from a state game office or a governmental counterpart. The average income of the hunter could be determined by interviewing sporting goods dealers, hunters, or by personal experience in some cases. This will give an idea of the most marketable price range for such a product on the general market. Sporting goods dealers would be helpful in giving their opinions of a hunting seat as a marketable item. Although the product has not been designed, the designer must think in terms of distribution, advertising, and sales as early as possible to identify the need. Where will the seats be sold? How will they be advertised? What type of sales representative will be required? These questions must be considered from the beginning of the design process.

Cost problems must be identified, since these will impose restrictions on methods of manufacture and design necessary for the price range. If the item is to sell for $25, the designer must determine the actual manufacturing funds available to him for constructing the product. The average markup on an item of this type will be about 30 percent or a wholesale price of about $17.50. The manufacturer must pay about 10 percent of the retail price to sales representatives for establishing dealerships and taking orders, which reduces income to approximately $15. From the remaining $15, he must pay for advertising, shipping costs, and storage of surplus inventories. This is estimated to be about $2.50 per seat, which reduces the sum to $12.50, from which the manufacturer wants a profit of 12 percent of his wholesale price or about $2.10 per seat. This leaves $10.40 to cover the cost of manufacture. This sum will be a definite limitation on the designer in developing his design. The designer must be able to analyze these expenses as part of his design effort in identifying the problem.

Data pertaining to numbers of hunters and licenses sold during recent years are determined by writing letters to agencies who could supply this information. These data are tabulated on work sheets of easy access. The designer may conduct a survey among the hunters he knows to gather firsthand opinions of the merits of a hunting seat on the commercial market. This type of survey is explained in greater detail in Chapter 4. Field data of this type should be tabulated on work sheets similar to the example shown in Fig. 3-10. Answers to questions asked in a previous work sheet (Fig. 3-9) are indicated in colored pencil when determined from the data.

A product designer is more concerned with the details of marketing a product on the open market and its acceptance than the systems designer, who does not design for the consumer market. In both cases, the designer must identify the problem for need, and gather data that relate to it, before he can pursue the succeeding steps of the design process. An investment of effort at this stage will prevent the designer from being unfamiliar with the true requirements of the problem, which may be different from the first impression.

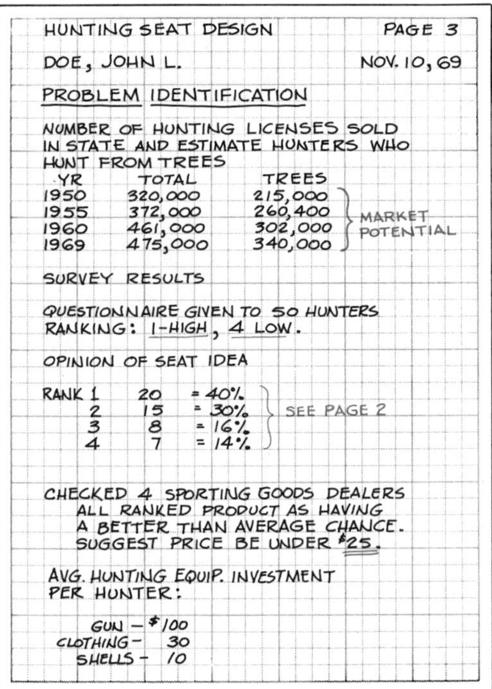

Fig. 3-10. A product development work sheet.

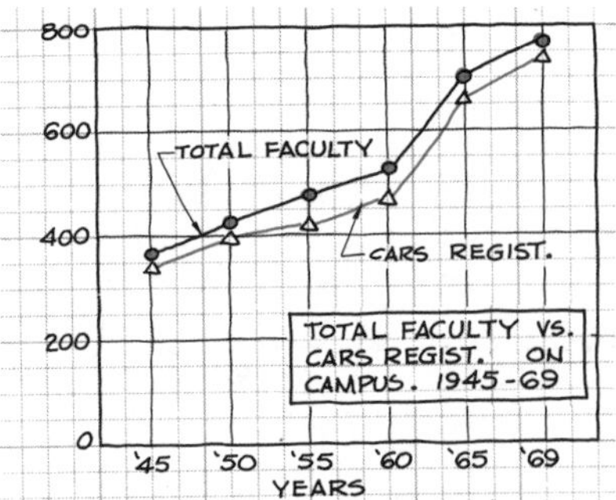

Fig. 3-11. Representation of data by a freehand graph.

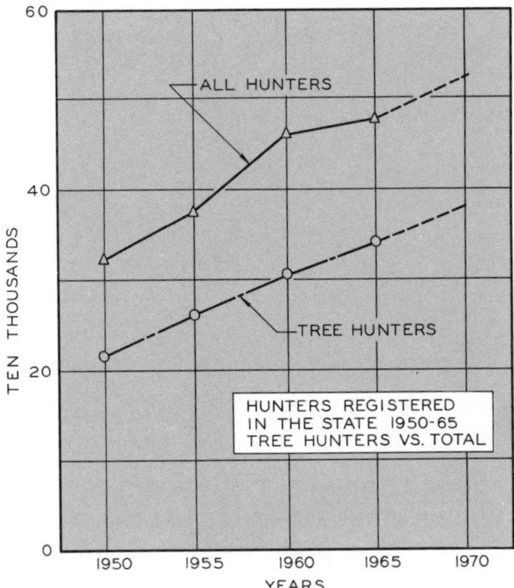

Fig. 3–12. A formal graph of data.

Fig. 3–13. A schematic of this type can be used to illustrate concepts and intangible ideas.

3–6 PRESENTATION OF DATA

The designer has gathered the data used to identify the problem so that he might form a better opinion of the design needs. The data may be rather extensive and difficult to interpret in the tabular form given in the work sheets in the systems problem (Fig. 3–7) and the product design problem (Fig. 3–10). Data are more beneficial to the designer if they are presented in a graph for visual interpretation, with trends clearly emphasized. Methods of preparing charts and graphs are given in Chapter 15, where the methods are used to analyze design data. In effect, the designer is analyzing data as a means of identifying the problem.

The data gathered for the systems problem and the product design problem should be presented in a graph to give a visual impression of the data. These graphs can be rough sketches or finished graphs that can be inserted in the finished report when the design problem has been completed. A rough, freehand graph is shown in Fig. 3–11, where the population figures of the faculty and the cars registered are graphed. It is important that a graph of this type be scaled and noted with adequate legends to fully explain its meaning.

A similar graph is given in Fig. 3–12 in the usual formal layout used in most reports. This figure presents the total number of hunters per year in the state compared with the number per year who hunt from a tree. This graph can be used to estimate future trends based on the figures from previous years. The graphical presentation makes it easy for the designer to grasp the relationship of these data from year to year with the minimum of study. Graphs of this type are also useful in communicating ideas to laymen who may be totally unfamiliar with the data being discussed.

Graphical presentation need not be limited to data, but can also be applied to concepts and intangible ideas for improved comprehension. Figure 3–13 is a graphical illustration showing the initial steps of the problem identification phase of the product design process. A schematic of this type can be used effectively in organizing ideas and concepts for easier interpretation to assist the designer in communicating with others and with himself. The designer must communicate with himself to permit his thinking to evolve from his first ideas to a finished solution. Ideas preserved by notes and sketches may suggest solutions, while a fleeting idea not recorded may be lost forever. The sketches in Fig. 3–7 are examples of how schematics are used to establish design criteria for both reference and interpretation.

A more extensive coverage of the applications of charts and graphs and their presentation is given in Chapter 15. Refer to this chapter to note standards of graphical representation of data and their application to the analysis of data. Standard graph paper is available commercially, which reduces layout time; however, formal reports often require that graphs be specially prepared in ink for reproduction.

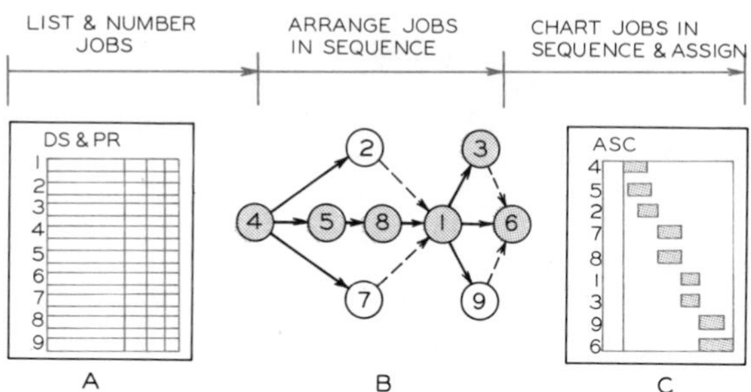

Fig. 3-14. The three steps of planning and scheduling a project.

3-7 ORGANIZATION OF DESIGN EFFORT

The proper organization and scheduling of design effort and related activities is essential to productive results. This is probably more important to projects of a design nature than to more routine assignments. The designer who has anticipated the various activities that must be performed in achieving a solution is much better prepared than his unorganized counterpart.

A schedule of design efforts should be prepared immediately after the identification of a need has been sufficiently established to warrant procedure with the design process. This may come after the approval of a design proposal by an administrator, engineer, or teacher if performed as a class assignment. A more extensive problem identification effort will be a part of the scheduled activities when further plans are made.

A recently developed technique of scheduling project work is "Project Evaluation and Review Technique" (PERT), which was developed by industries participating in certain governmental projects where coordination of many activities within a prescribed time limit was essential to the successful completion of the project. PERT provides a means of scheduling the activities in their appropriate sequence and reviewing the progress being made in their completion. Time is assigned to each task, with periodic adjustments made for savings and overages in time available for each.

The critical-path method of scheduling project activities evolved from PERT, and it is used in conjunction with PERT in most cases. The critical-path method is concerned with the determination of the chain of events that are dependent upon other activities. In other words, some jobs cannot be performed until previous tasks have been completed. The critical path is a sequence of tasks that will require the longest period of time with the minimum of flexibility before the project can be completed. Other activities, not in the critical path, can be scheduled to receive secondary emphasis, since they are not critical to the completion of the project.

An engineer must be responsible for the effective management of time, money, equipment, and personnel, in addition to supplying technical consultation and project guidance. PERT is a systematic method of organization that will aid in the management process cycle.

3-8 PLANNING DESIGN ACTIVITIES

A student design team will find that it can function more effectively if a few of the basic principles of PERT and critical-path scheduling are applied to its planning. Although scheduling is important to an individual in planning his own activities, it is increasingly valuable to a group effort as the size of the group increases.

Figure 3-14 is a flow chart showing the suggested steps for the best results in planning your project. The steps of planning are: (A) List the jobs that must be performed on a form called a Design Schedule and Progress Record. (B) Prepare an Activities Network to place the jobs in sequence. (C) Prepare an Activity Sequence Chart that graphs the jobs in the same sequence as shown in the network.

Design Schedule & Progress Record

USE THIS FORM TO SCHEDULE TEAM ASSIGNMENTS AND TO RECORD PROGRESS. AN ACCURATE RECORD WILL ASSIST YOUR TEAM IN UTILIZING AVAILABLE TIME.

PROJECT: PRODUCT DESIGN #2

DESIGN TEAM: 7 WORK PERIODS: NOV. 8, NOV. 16, NOV. 21

LEADER: BROWN COMPLETION DATE: DEC. 1

JONES MAN HRS: 24

SMITH

WHITE

ASSIGNMENT	ESTIM'D MAN HRS	BEGIN'G DATE	PER CENT COMPLETE 25	50	75	100	COMPL. DATE	ACTUAL MAN HRS
1. WRITE REPORT BROWN & SMITH	4							
2. BRAINSTORM ALL	1/2							
3. WRITE LETTERS JONES	2							
4. GRAPH DATA WHITE	2							
5. MARKET ANALYSIS ALL	3							
6. FIELD DATA SMITH	3							
7. ORGANIZATION ALL	1							

Fig. 3–15. Design Schedule and Progress Record. Typical entries are shown for identifying design tasks.

Design Schedule and Progress Record. A suggested form for this chart is given in Fig. 3–15. Each team member should participate in the listing of the jobs that must be completed to arrive at a final solution to a project. Each job is broken into reasonably small tasks, which are listed on the Design Schedule and Progress Record (DS&PR) form in the order in which they come to mind, with no concern for their sequence. When all of these are listed on the form, an estimate of the time required for each job is listed in the second column. The sum of the times for each job should be adjusted to approximate the total time allotted for the project. Extra time may be left unassigned for emergencies. Each job is given a number to identify it. This number has no relation to the sequence in which the jobs will be completed.

The Activities Network. The numbered jobs listed on the DS&PR must now be arranged in the proper sequence so that they can be completed in the most efficient manner. The method of graphically arranging the jobs is shown in Fig. 3–16. The note form (Fig. 3–16A) lists the events by name. The symbol form (Fig. 3–16B) uses numbers of the jobs from the DS&PR as the events. An *event* is some specific point in the Activities Network. Events do not require time, but are considered to be milestones along the sequence of activities.

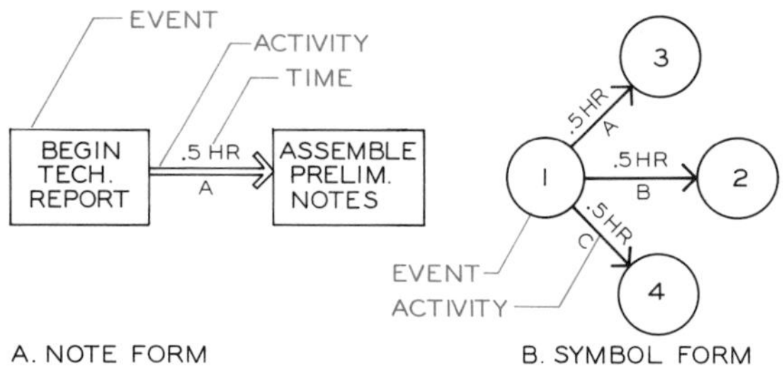

Fig. 3–16. The two forms of preparing an Activities Network, which graphically places the jobs in sequence.

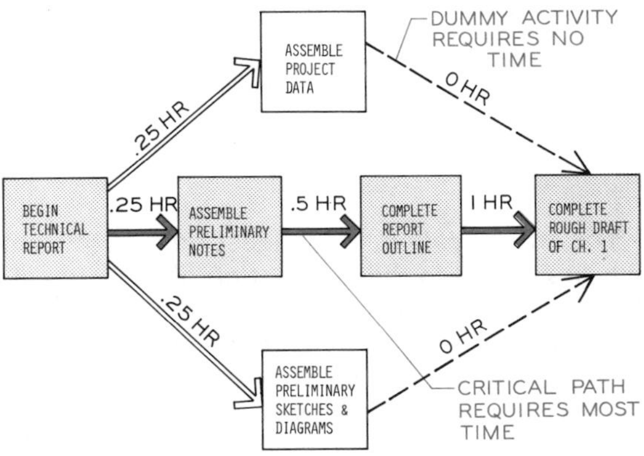

Fig. 3–17. The critical path is the path that requires the most time to arrive at the last event of a project.

Events are connected by arrows that represent the *activities* that consume time from one event to the next. For example, in Fig. 3–16A, it requires 0.5 hour to assemble preliminary notes after beginning the technical report. The time is marked on the activity arrow, and the length of the arrow has no relation to the amount of time.

Dummy activities are often used in completing an Activities Network to indicate a connection between activities even though the dummy activity requires "zero time." All events must be connected by activity arrows that come to the event and also leave the event to connect it with the next successive event, even though no time is required in this step. Two dummy activities are used in the Activities Network in Fig. 3–17 to show a sequential connection but no expenditure of time. Dashed lines are used for dummy activities.

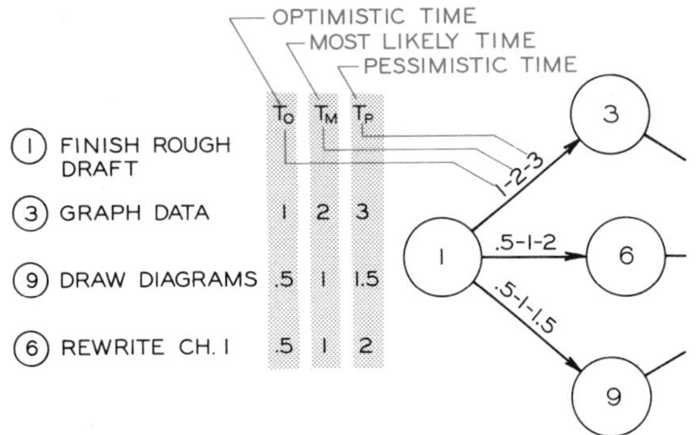

Fig. 3–18. An Activities Network can be constructed to show optimistic, most likely, and pessimistic times on the activity arrows to give a tolerance in the schedule.

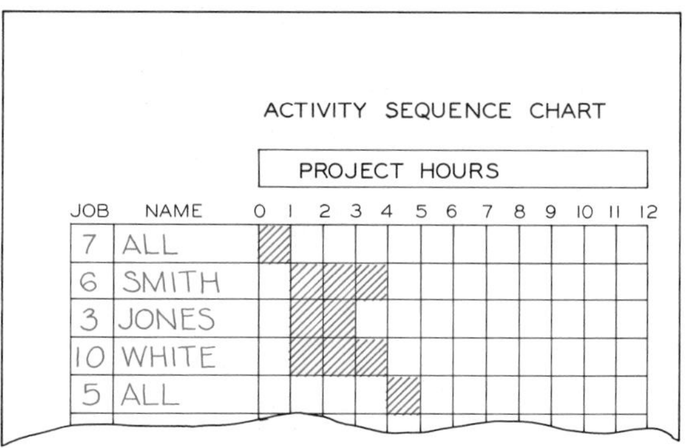

Fig. 3–20. The jobs listed on DS&PR are converted into an Activities Network and are then graphed on an Activity Sequence Chart (ASC) to assign each job to a fixed time schedule in the proper order.

The *critical path* is the longest time path from the first event to the completion of the project. This path is the sequence of jobs that must be concentrated on throughout the project to remain on schedule. The critical path is marked in the portion of the Activity Network shown in Fig. 3–17, where 1.75 hours are required to complete the rough draft of the first chapter of a report after beginning.

A more sophisticated method of estimating the activity times of an Activity Network is shown in Fig. 3–18. Each activity is given an optimistic time, a most likely time, and a pessimistic time. These three times are written on each activity arrow and are used in arriving at critical paths based on each of these estimates. This procedure may enable you to improve your estimate of the time required for the project.

An Activities Network for a project is shown in Fig. 3–19. Different teams will prepare different networks for the same set of activities. However, the more important jobs should be sched-

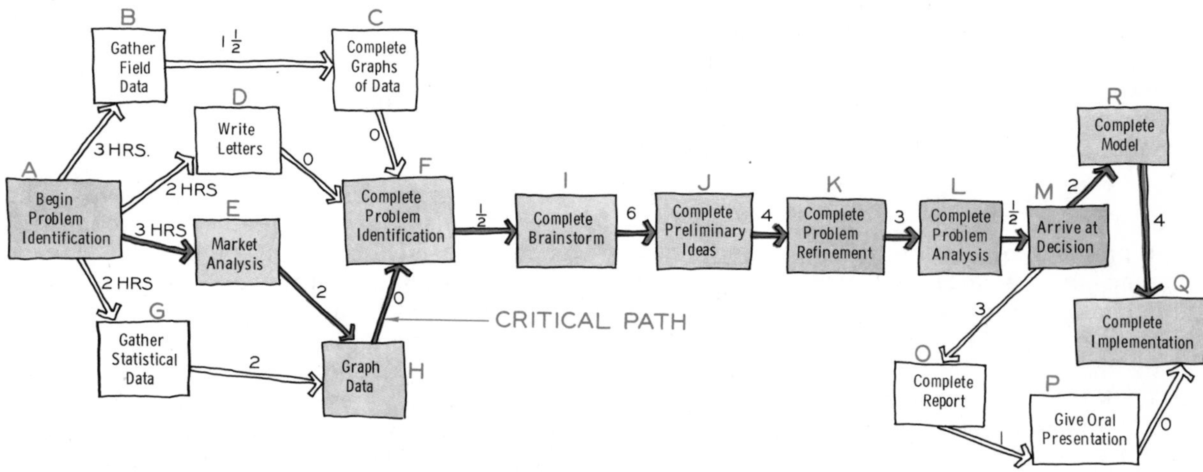

Fig. 3–19. An Activities Network scheduling design effort where the critical path is noted.

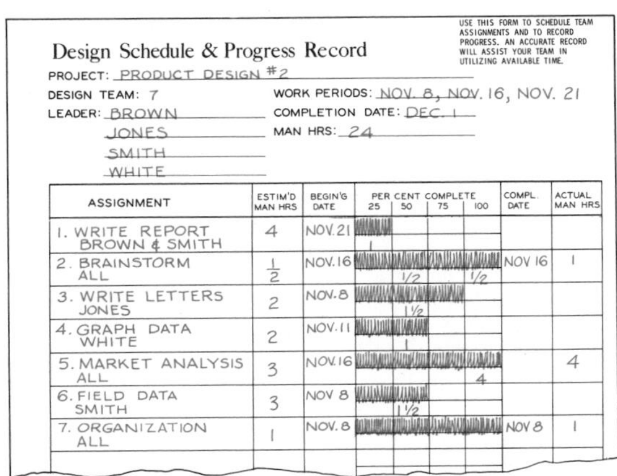

Design Schedule & Progress Record

USE THIS FORM TO SCHEDULE TEAM ASSIGNMENTS AND TO RECORD PROGRESS. AN ACCURATE RECORD WILL ASSIST YOUR TEAM IN UTILIZING AVAILABLE TIME.

PROJECT: PRODUCT DESIGN #2

DESIGN TEAM: 7

WORK PERIODS: NOV. 8, NOV. 16, NOV. 21

LEADER: BROWN

JONES

SMITH

WHITE

COMPLETION DATE: DEC. 1

MAN HRS: 24

ASSIGNMENT	ESTIM'D MAN HRS	BEGIN'G DATE	PER CENT COMPLETE 25	50	75	100	COMPL. DATE	ACTUAL MAN HRS
1. WRITE REPORT BROWN & SMITH	4	NOV. 21	1					
2. BRAINSTORM ALL	1/2	NOV. 16		1/2		1/2	NOV 16	1
3. WRITE LETTERS JONES	2	NOV. 8		1½				
4. GRAPH DATA WHITE	2	NOV. 11		1				
5. MARKET ANALYSIS ALL	3	NOV. 16				4		4
6. FIELD DATA SMITH	3	NOV 8		1½				
7. ORGANIZATION ALL	1	NOV. 8					NOV 8	1

Fig. 3–21. The completion of the Design Schedule and Progress Record to record progress.

uled in generally the same order, and the identification of these is the most important function of the Activities Network.

The Activity Sequence Chart. The jobs of the Activities Network can be listed on the Activity Sequence Chart (ASC). Figure 3–20 is an example of this type of chart. The job numbers are taken from the Network and are listed in sequence and assigned to members of the team. A bar graph is used to graph the time for each job. For example, the first hour of the project will be used to perform job 7, which is "organization," listed on the DS&PR during the first step of planning. This will require the cooperation of the entire team and this must be completed before the next job can begin. This procedure is continued until all the jobs are listed. The project hours across the top of the ASC can be used to schedule the events and to estimate when each event should be reached during the project.

As progress is made with the completion of the jobs, the status of each assignment can be graphed on the DS&PR (Fig. 3–21). When a job is completed, the completion date and the man-hours required are listed in the last two columns. If more time was required than was scheduled, it is helpful to know this as soon as possible so that adjustments can be made in subsequent jobs to compensate for this loss.

You should always refer to the critical path of the ASC to be sure that the jobs on this path receive priority since they will require the most time.

This method of planning and scheduling is closely related to PERT, but it has been simplified to introduce the basic principles in a direct fashion. You may wish to make modifications of this approach that would be more helpful to a specific situation. Additional suggestions for the organization of a team are given in Chapter 20.

3–9 SUMMARY

Problem identification is the first task confronting the designer in any process. The two basic types of identification are (1) identification of a need and (2) identification of design criteria. Identification of a need is the recognition of a correctable problem or weakness. An extension of this recognition could lead to a proposal by a designer whereby the need is outlined and permission is requested to attempt a solution. This proposal could be a simple statement of the need or an extensive proposal which includes an identification of design criteria.

The design criteria phase is concerned with a detailed investigation and study of the problem and its total relationship to factors pertaining to the criteria. The designer conducts a thorough research of the problem from all available sources and records his findings on work sheets that will be maintained in a permanent file. In more simple problems, the identification of design criteria may involve no more than listing a series of ideas and factors that affect the problem. Nevertheless, it is highly important that all notes, ideas, sketches, and doodles be recorded and maintained in a file. Success in designing will come from tangible, orderly work transcribed onto work sheets. Regardless of the degree of creativity a person may possess, he must learn to express his ideas and findings on paper for evaluation and further development.

Data should be graphed where possible to improve the representation of tabular material. The graphs can be rough, freehand graphs or finished graphs for inclusion in the completed technical report when the design project has been completed. Graphical methods should be used to present as many ideas and data as possible, thereby improving comprehension and communication of information. The organization of design effort is the most important part of the initial phase of a design problem. An assessment of the problem requirements and the steps that must be taken to arrive at a satisfactory decision is a necessary basis for scheduling and planning. Articles 13–7 and 13–9 review a method that will assist the student in organizing his effort whether he is working independently or as a member of a design team. This method, or a similar plan, should be employed to reduce lost time and wasted effort due to lack of organization. The schedule should be reviewed and modified to keep pace with progress throughout the design process. This chapter should be reviewed from time to time, to ensure that the principles covered here are being applied.

PROBLEMS

Problems should be presented on $8\frac{1}{2}'' \times 11''$ paper, grid or plain, using the format presented in Articles 1–19 and 3–2. All notes, sketches, drawings, and graphical work should be neatly prepared in keeping with good practices, as introduced in this volume. Written matter should be typed or lettered using $\frac{1}{8}''$ guidelines.

General

1. Identify a need for a design solution that could be used as a short design problem for a class assignment (less than three man-hours for complete solution). This can be a system or a product. Submit a proposal that briefly outlines this need and your general plan for solution. Limit the proposal to two typewritten pages.

2. Assume that you were marooned on a deserted island with no tools, supplies, or anything. Identify major problems that you would be required to solve. List factors that would identify the problems in detail. *Example:* Need for food: determine (a) available sources of food on island, (b) method of storing food supply, (c) method of cooking, (d) method of hunting and trapping or otherwise obtaining food, etc. Although you are not in a position to gather data or supply answers to these questions, list factors of this type that would need to be answered before a solution could be attempted.

3. While walking to class, what irritations or discomforts did you recognize? Identify the problem causing these irritations, using work sheets and writing out the problem statement, recognition of a need, requirements, and limitations.

4. Apply the criteria given in problem 3 above to your living quarters, your classroom, recreational facilities, dining facilities, and other environments with which you are associated.

Product Design Problems

5. Assume that you are attempting to reconstruct the designer's approach to the development of the self-opening can shown in Fig. 3–2. Even though the problem has been solved and completed, follow the identification steps with which the designer was concerned. Using the procedure outlined in Article 3–5, list these on work sheets. After identifying the problem, do you feel that the solution is the most appropriate one or does your identification suggest other designs?

6. Follow the same procedure outlined in problem 5 in identifying the problem of designing a travel iron for pressing clothes. Retain your notes and sketches on work sheets.

7. Identify the problems of designing a motorized wheelbarrow. List your ideas on work sheets.

8. You have noticed the need for a device that, attached to a bicycle, would allow the bicycle to ride over street curbs to sidewalk level. Identify the problem to determine its application to the general market.

9. Identify the problem and need for the development of a portable engineering travel kit that would provide the engineer with on-the-road facilities to make engineering calculations, notes, sketches, and drawings. This may take the form of a case which includes a slide rule, drawing instruments, paper, reference material, etc. Investigate this problem and identify the needs of such a product.

Systems Design Problems

10. Water pollution is a complex systems problem. Use the work-sheet approach to identifying the problem. State the problem and list the need, requirements, and limitations. Data need not be gathered, but indicate the type of data needed and their probable source.

11. Assume that you are assigned the responsibility of planning for the expansion of your campus during the next twenty years. This applies to all aspects of the campus, including classroom buildings, dormitories, traffic, libraries, etc. Although this comprehensive problem would require the assistance of many experts, test your logic by identifying the major aspects of the problem. Without gathering field data, indicate the type of data needed and where they would be found. Prepare work sheets as a record of your effort.

12. Identify the problems of designing a water supply that would serve your campus, assuming that the only source was rainfall over the campus. Gather any data that would contribute to problem identification. Prepare work sheets.

13. Identify the problems of designing an outdoor, drive-in movie installation. Use the work-sheet approach and identify all areas of the problem, including traffic, engineering, and economics.

14. Assume that you are assigned the responsibility of correcting the existing campus system that is in most critical need of modification. List the several systems that you recognize as needing improvement. Select the most critical problem and identify it on work sheets. Gather any necessary data to assist in this identification. Submit a proposal for design if the identification supports the need for a solution.

15. Identify the problems of constructing, equipping, and operating a commercial pistol range. Use work sheets to retain your ideas.

16. Select one of the comprehensive problems given in Chapter 20 and identify the problem on work sheets as the initial step toward a completed design. Retain your work sheets in a binder or envelope. Other work sheets and materials will be added to this file as the design process is applied to the problem with each successive chapter until the design is completed.

17. Using the principles of PERT, introduced in Articles 3–7 and 3–8, prepare a schedule of your activities for a typical class day. Complete the three forms discussed—Design Schedule and Progress Record, Activities Network, and Activity Sequence Chart. Indicate the critical path that exists if recreation and nonproductive activities are eliminated from your schedule.

18. Prepare the forms mentioned in problem 17 to organize your effort for a design project that you might be assigned or one that you select. Prepare these in a final form to be submitted to your instructor for evaluation.

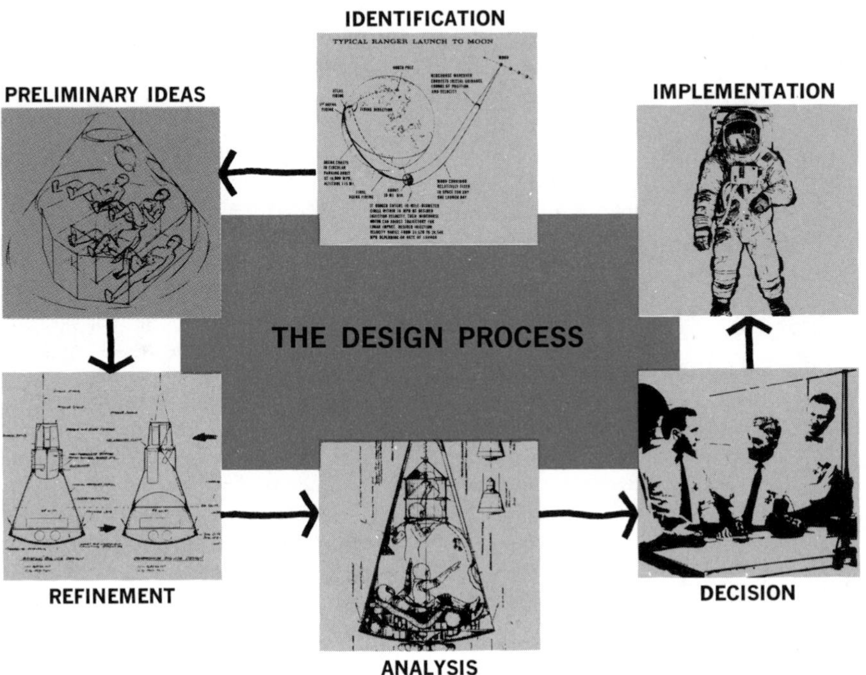

4 PRELIMINARY IDEAS

4-1 GENERAL

The accumulation of preliminary ideas is the second major step of the design process. Graphical methods, and freehand sketching in particular, will be the primary means used by the designer in developing his ideas. The designer should have received a "feel" for the problem during the identification phase and will probably form several ideas for possible solutions as he lists the problem requirements. However, the designer should not allow himself to narrow his efforts to any preliminary ideas that might preclude other possible solutions.

The need for creativity and imagination is greater at the beginning of the design process than during later stages. The final steps of the design process are applied to the refinement and development of the initial ideas with little concern for developing new concepts. The relationship between creativity and data and information development can be seen in Fig. 4-1. This need for a high level of creativity cannot be fulfilled unless the designer avoids negative thoughts. He must cultivate his ideas regardless of how radical they may appear to be initially. He must not attempt to evaluate his ideas at this stage, but instead, he should develop as many ideas as possible and record them with sketches and notes.

Figure 4-2 illustrates an "instant spoon," which began as a radical idea. This spoon contains instant coffee for immediate use with hot water. Bouillon, dry soup mixes, tea, chocolate, and fruit juice concentrates are a few product possibilities for the air-formed packages. This

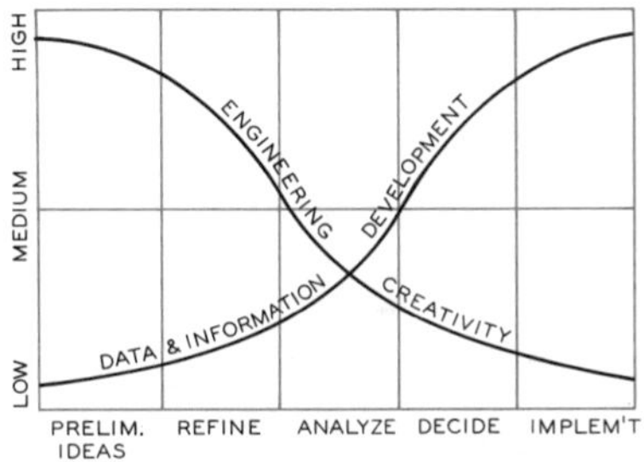

Fig. 4-1. Engineering creativity is highest during the initial stages of the design process, while data and information development increase during the final stages.

Fig. 4-2. A unique design is the "instant spoon," which is used as a package for instant coffee. Bouillon, dry soup mixes, tea, chocolate, and fruit juice concentrates are a few product possibilities for the air-formed packages. (Courtesy of ALCOA.)

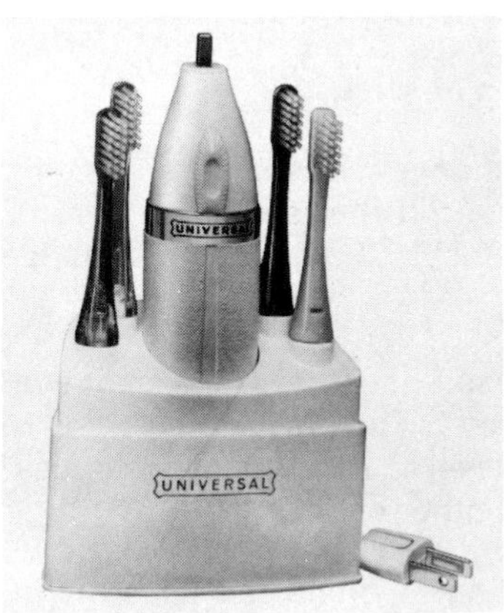

Fig. 4-3. A new design concept is the rechargeable, cordless electric toothbrush. (Courtesy of General Electric Company.)

concept could not have been developed unless the designer had permitted his creativity the freedom to explore all possibilities.

A relatively new product is the electric toothbrush shown in Fig. 4-3. A short time ago, this concept would have been considered as an extravagance with little market appeal; however, it has become a well-accepted household item. It is designed with four interchangeable individual brushes and a recharger wall-stand. This device would not have been designed and manufactured if the designer had become too critical during the formation of his preliminary ideas and had been influenced by an adverse initial reaction to an idea of this type.

Graphical methods are again the best means of sustaining a continued course of action. The designer must not allow himself to lapse into a daydreaming state. He must apply pressure to himself as a means of continuing a fluency of thought. If several ideas come rapidly, he should write these down on his work sheets without hesitating to develop each idea individually lest they be forgotten. Ideas can be converted from notes into sketches of preliminary designs later. Four methods of accumulating preliminary ideas are (1) the individual approach, (2) the team approach, (3) the research method, and (4) the survey method. This chapter will discuss these methods and give examples of how preliminary ideas can be developed utilizing graphical methods.

4-2 INDIVIDUAL APPROACH

The designer who works independently must make as many sketches and notes as he would if he were working as a member of a team. In effect, he must communicate with himself through his sketches and notes (Fig. 4-4). His ideas are recorded graphically with all pertinent notes and explanations. His primary goal is to obtain as many ideas as possible, on the assumption that the better ideas will be more likely to come from a long list than from a short list. He must avoid the temptation of becoming involved with a preliminary idea and attempting to develop it before he has listed as many alternative solutions as possible.

Fig. 4–4. The designer communicates with himself through sketches and notes. This technique enables him to develop his preliminary ideas. (Courtesy of the Ford Motor Company.)

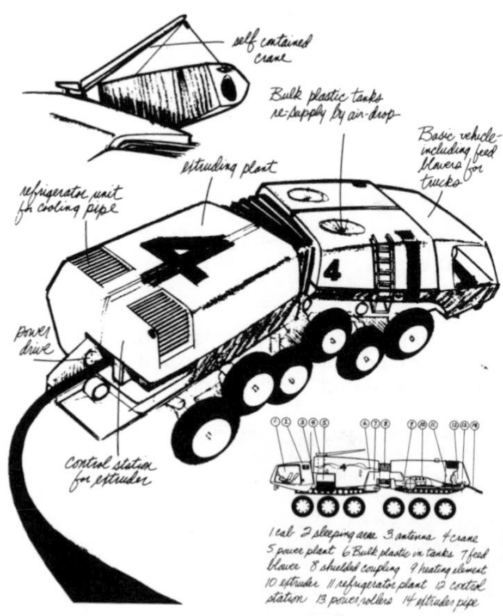

Fig. 4–5. A designer's preliminary design of a self-contained pipelayer, which is intended to facilitate irrigation of large tracts of desert. (Courtesy of Donald Desky Associates, Inc., and Charles Bruning Company.)

Ideas are sketched into possible solutions with notes to explain the sketches. These sketches are not working drawings, but rapid freehand sketches used to retain a possible idea that might otherwise be lost. The procedure for recording these sketches will be discussed in greater detail in Article 4–7. All sketches and notes are retained as a basis for possible adaptations and modifications.

Some preliminary sketches and ideas may not at first appear to have sufficient merit as possible solutions to the problem at hand, but often these ideas can be converted into more valuable solutions when later modified. The designer should familiarize himself with the following checklist by Osborn, since it can be used to improve his preliminary ideas.*

Put to Other Uses? New ways to use as is? Other uses if modified?

Modify? New twist? Change meaning, color, motion, sound, odor, form, shape? Other changes?

Magnify? What to add? More time? Greater frequency? Stronger? Higher? Longer? Thicker? Extra value? Plus ingredient? Duplicate? Multiply? Exaggerate?

Minify? What to subtract? Smaller? Condensed? Miniature? Lower? Shorter? Lighter? Omit? Streamline? Split up? Understate?

Substitute? Who else instead? What else instead? Other ingredient? Other material? Other process? Other power? Other place? Other approach? Other tone of voice?

Rearrange? Interchange components? Other pattern? Other layout? Other sequence? Transpose cause and effect? Change pace? Change schedule?

Reverse? Transpose positive and negative? How about opposites? Turn it backward? Turn it upside down? Reverse roles? Change shoes? Turn tables? Turn other cheek?

Combine? How about a blend, an assortment, an ensemble? Combine units? Combine purposes? Combine appeals? Combine ideas?

---

* From Osborn, Alex F., *Applied Imagination.* New York: Scribner, 1963, p. 286.

If the designer will ask himself these questions about each preliminary idea he develops, he will be able to expand his initial concepts. Figure 4–5 is a designer's preliminary concept of a self-contained pipelayer, which represents a composite of many innovations and unique applications of existing components. These sketches could have been developed by applying the questions in the previous checklist.

The self-contained pipelayer, which may be in use by 1985, is intended to facilitate irrigation of large tracts of desert. It consists of two units. The first unit is the tractor, which includes the cab, sleeping accommodations, radio equipment, power plant, and bulk storage tanks for plastics. The second unit, the van, consists of an extrusion machine, a refrigeration unit, and a control station. The unit is capable of transporting sufficient bulk plastic and machinery to extrude and lay approximately two miles of plastic pipe from each pair of storage tanks. The tanks are discarded when empty and replaced via air drop. Note that sketches and notes have been used to explain the details of this design. In addition to sketches of the conventional working-drawing type, pictorials may also be very helpful in transmitting and developing ideas.

4–3 TEAM APPROACH

Due to the complexity of technology, the team approach is necessary in many of today's problems. Many specialists in a variety of fields must work together toward a common goal. An interaction between team members introduces the problem of communications and human relations. These problems are much the same whether the groups are professionals or students participating in a team project assigned by their instructor. They must work together to overcome personality differences and personal ambitions.

A design team should alternate between individual work and group work. For instance, each team member could individually prepare a series of preliminary ideas for group discussion with the entire team. Most teams perform best if a chief designer is selected by the team members to be responsible for making assignments and moderating all discussions and to ensure that progress is maintained throughout the entire problem.

A unique approach to the team effort is the *brainstorming session,* which is a spontaneous interchange of ideas. This method of ideation will be discussed in detail in Article 4–6. Essentially, all the steps taken by the team are identical to those of an individual working independently; the primary difference is the method that is employed. The strength of a team, in contrast to an individual, is the utilization of the special talents of the team members to best advantage. Consequently, team assignments should be made by the leader so that each team member's unique abilities are exploited.

An example of a system that is being developed by teams of experts is the Airtrans, which is an intra-airport transit system. The development of this system was prompted by the need to improve transportation between airports and downtown areas or college campuses. At present the trip from an airport to a downtown destination may take longer than an inter-city flight.

Figure 4–6 is a map of the airport area showing its proximity to the cities that it is to serve. The Dallas/Fort Worth Airport is to be the world's largest air transportation center and will occupy 18,000 acres. The Airtrans system will serve as a vital link to carparks and to commercial pickup points, and will provide rapid transit for people, goods, and services throughout the 28 square miles of the airport.

The routes, spacings and switchings of the vehicles that carry the passengers and goods will be controlled by a Central Control (Fig. 4–7). This computerized system controls and monitors the power distribution system and provides a systemwide voice and video communications system for vehicle and station surveillance.

Passenger stations are designed to provide graphic directions and clearly understood symbology to guide travelers. Graphic communications on board the vehicles include maps and station information to direct the passengers along their route (Fig. 4–8).

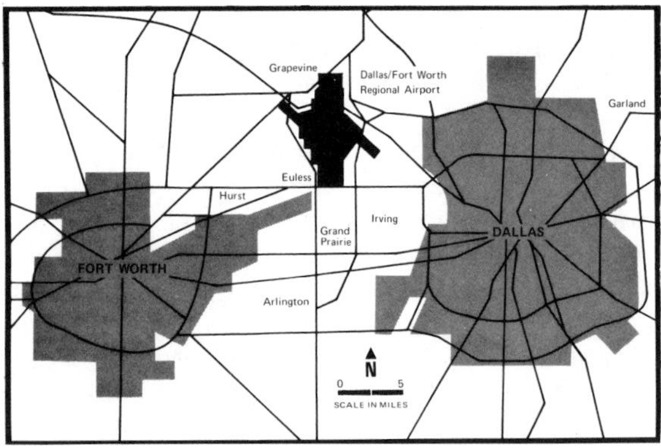

Fig. 4–6. This area map shows the location of the airport to be served by Airtrans. (Courtesy of Vought Aeronautics Company.)

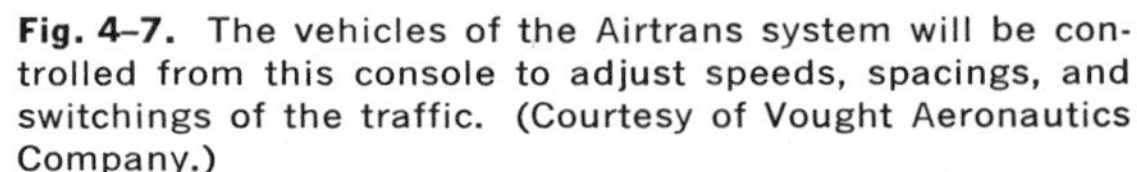

Fig. 4–7. The vehicles of the Airtrans system will be controlled from this console to adjust speeds, spacings, and switchings of the traffic. (Courtesy of Vought Aeronautics Company.)

Fig. 4–8. Station designs include graphic displays to explain the routings to travelers and help them select the correct vehicles. (Courtesy of Vought Aeronautics Company.)

Fig. 4–9. This transportation system has many future adaptations that will broaden its range of service. (Courtesy of Vought Aeronautics Company.)

The vehicles are designed to serve a number of purposes in addition to the transportation of passengers, but all of the vehicle bodies are designed to fit a standard chassis. This makes it possible to standardize the vehicles and thus reduce the cost of manufacturing them. The vehicles will be steered by a U-shaped guideway of reinforced concrete.

Future applications of this system can solve more extensive transit problems. With the addition of independent power to the vehicles and the provision of guideways, the system can be given a longer transportation route (Fig. 4–9). These airport vehicles could also connect the airport with downtown sites and thereby reduce congestion and travel time.

A design problem of this degree of sophistication could not have been solved by a single engineer or specialist, since many disciplines are represented. The team approach is the natural means of attempting a problem of this type. Sketches are used to communicate ideas among team members and also among officials who will be responsible for approving preliminary ideas for further development.

The organization of a team is a critical aspect of a successful project. Suggestions for organizing a team are given in Chapter 20. Scheduling of team assignments and review of activities are covered in Article 3–7 to assist in organizing group effort.

4–4 RESEARCH METHODS

Preliminary ideas can be obtained through research methods where a study is made of similar products and designs that were previously developed. Most design projects are closely related to existing designs which will provide the designer with ideas that can be modified to meet the needs of his problem; this process of applying known principles to new applications is called *synthesis*. There are many sources of references available that provide comparative design solutions for further analysis. Among these are technical magazines, manufacturers' product brochures, current periodicals, patent records, and professional consultants.

Technical Magazines. Libraries contain numerous technical journals that review the current developments for the specific area of specialization covered by the publication. Excellent magazines are available to the engineer or technician at no charge through controlled circulation subscriptions. Such periodicals are supported by the advertisers of products used primarily by the subscribers for whom the periodical was published. Articles in technical periodicals often give complete detailed explanations of unique designs, complete with sketches and photographs. Such articles can be beneficial in supplying general ideas that may be applicable to a given design project. Advertisements in these journals can furnish information on materials and components that may be needed for a design solution. Additional technical specifications can be obtained from the manufacturer by letter.

Manufacturers' Brochures. All manufacturers of products sold on the commercial market put out literature that describes their product. Many of the brochures are quite elaborate and contain extensive information that would be helpful to a designer interested in reviewing related design solutions. Other manufacturers' brochures may be brief—three or four pages in length—but even brief brochures may be sufficient to stimulate a fresh idea. Manufacturers are most accommodating in supplying brochures free of charge upon request. Literature obtained through manufacturers should be retained in permanent files as a source for future reference. Also, many designs will require that certain stock components from manufacturers be combined into a systems design. Students working on a design project would benefit by writing manufacturers for brochures that could assist them with their design development.

General Periodicals. Significant design developments are usually reported in general-market periodicals, such as those subscribed to by most families. Magazines several years old may be as helpful to the designer as current issues in finding an idea. Attention should be directed toward the advertisements, since new products are usually presented in each issue. Advertisers are a source of the manufacturers' brochures mentioned above. Daily newspapers are equally valuable to the designer.

Patents. Patents on file in the U. S. Patent Office can provide many ideas and technical information that would assist the designer in his solution to a problem. Patents are a matter of public record and are available to anyone who desires to receive copies at a cost of 50¢ each. Figure 4–10 is a reproduction of Thomas Edison's patent illustration for the phonograph. Two pages of explanatory text accompany this patent.

A current record of newly issued patents is published weekly in the *Official Gazette*, which is published by the U. S. Patent Office. It contains a claim and a selected figure of the drawings for each patent granted on that day; decisions in patent and trademark cases rendered by the Courts and the Patent Office; notices of patent and trademark suits; indexes of patents and patentees; list of patents available for license or sale; and much general information such as orders, notices, changes in rules, changes in classification, etc. This weekly publication costs $50 per year or $1.25 per single issue. Other manuals and documents are available through the Patent Office to assist the designer in reviewing patents and applying for patents. All correspondence concerning patent laws, subscriptions to the *Official Gazette*, and the ordering of patents should be directed to:

Commissioner of Patents
U. S. Patent Office
Washington, D. C. 20231

The designer or engineer can gain considerable benefit from reviewing patents. Not only will he receive helpful technical information, but he will also know whether or not his ideas are infringing on existing patents. The Patent Office provides a source of over 3,000,000

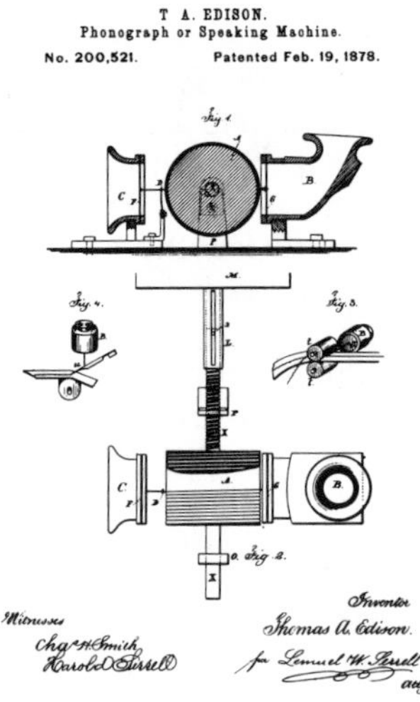

Fig. 4–10. A patent illustration of Thomas Edison's phonograph.

patents that can help the designer. Additional information on patents is included in Article 16–11.

Professional Consultants. The designer should learn to take advantage of the knowledge and experience of specialists as the need arises. Often his design will require an investigation of a field that is foreign to him, thus necessitating consultation with a specialist in this field. Such a person could provide guidance that could circumvent the necessity of rediscovering an existing system; he would also be familiar with methods that are readily available. A consultant may be a technician associated with the designer's firm, an engineer in his office, or any coworker who has a sufficient knowledge of the problem.

A professional consultant or consulting firm may be employed to provide assistance to the designer in reviewing possible solutions. A comprehensive design problem may require a team of specialists in structures, electronics, power systems, and instrumentation. Manufacturers' representatives are available for consultation to assist with many problems that

Fig. 4–11. The design of this flood-control lake and power-generating system required the cooperation of many specialists working as members of a team. (Courtesy of the Bureau of Reclamation.)

Fig. 4–12. Plant layout specialists design and develop facilities to provide maximum efficiency and comfort. (Courtesy of Firestone Tire and Rubber Company.)

are related to services and products provided by the manufacturers. Figure 4–11 illustrates a design system that required the knowledge of many individual specialists working toward the same goal. Planning engineers are shown laying out a manufacturing facility that will provide the highest degree of efficiency, comfort, and economy, in Fig. 4–12. These are specialists who are more qualified to plan a layout than are the operators of the facility.

A student can get assistance with a design project from other students with appropriate backgrounds and from teachers of courses covering the areas of his need. In most communities there are many groups and individuals who can provide information that would conserve time and point toward a solution. Notes should be used to record points of discussion and conclusions reached during a conference with a consultant.

4–5 SURVEY METHODS

Survey methods are used to gather opinions and reactions concerning a completed design, as covered in Chapter 13, or to sample opinions toward a preliminary design during the early stages of the design process. The designer can benefit from a contact with his "customer" or the consumer of his design project. This is especially important when designing a product that will be used by the general market. Survey methods are used to determine the need for a particular design during the problem identification step. Survey methods covered in this article will relate to the consumer's reaction to a specific solution or design that has been proposed.

Opinions. The designer is interested in learning the consumer's attitude toward his design. Is the buyer excited about the product or in desperate need of it, or does he show little interest in it? For example, a golf course would probably not be built unless there was adequate interest in it to indicate that it would be utilized by the residents of the area it was to serve.

Professional agencies are available to perform surveys that will determine general reactions and opinions with regard to a particular situation. Agencies may conduct surveys that would reflect general public feelings or they may obtain opinions of a selected segment of the population. The preference of an item consumed by the total population would involve all age levels and backgrounds, whereas an item used only by machinists would require a survey of these people and their employers. Once the surveyor, who may be either the designer or an agency, has determined the particular group whose opinion would be most essential to his project, he may select one of the following methods of gathering this information: (1) personal interview, (2) telephone interview, (3) mail questionnaire.

The personal interview should be organized to provide uniformity that would yield reliable and unbiased opinions. A list of fundamental questions that require a minimum of explanation and can be easily understood should be printed on a sheet in such a manner that the interviewer can tabulate replies as they are given. Questions should be true-false or multiple choice to facilitate tabulation and the arriving at conclusions after the survey. Questions requiring essay answers become unmanageable and are usually inconclusive. The number of questions should be sufficient to learn as much about the consumer's opinions as possible, without becoming too wordy and repetitious. The interviewer should introduce himself, give the purpose of his interview, and ask for permission to proceed. Questions should be asked as impersonally as possible to avoid influencing responses. Tabulate the replies as they are given and thank the respondent at the close of the interview.

The telephone interview can be conducted by randomly picking names from the directory if the opinions of a general cross section of the public are desired. If the opinions of a select group—for example, sporting goods retailers—would be more valuable, the yellow pages of a large city directory would supply a ready list of leads. The telephone interview should be conducted in the same manner as the personal interview and tabulated in similar fashion.

The mail questionnaire is an economical method of contacting large numbers of people in a wide range of locations. The organization of the questionnaire is very critical to the quality of the responses returned. Many questions appear to be well-stated until the replies are analyzed, and it becomes apparent that one or more questions were misunderstood. Consequently, it is advantageous to test the questionnaire by sending it to a small group as a pilot study to isolate weak questions, in order that they may be revised prior to the final mailing. A self-addressed, stamped envelope should be included in all mailings of this type to improve the response. Questions should be multiple choice where possible as in the previously mentioned methods of opinion surveys. At least twice as many questionnaires should be mailed as the number of replies that you have determined would be sufficient to provide a valid survey of opinions. This will serve to offset a poor return which may result.

Consideration of the sample size is important in an opinion survey, since if the sample is too small, little confidence can be placed in the conclusions; larger samples are more reliable. Likewise, opinions must be obtained from a typical cross section of the population being considered, since opinions often vary geographically and economically. Statistical methods are employed to determine the suitable sample size.

What type of opinions would be helpful to the designer? First he would like to know if there is a need for the product or assignment he is working on. If the consumer is not wholeheartedly sold on the merits of the total product, what features does he like and dislike? What price would he be willing to pay for it? If he is a retailer, what does he think it will sell for? Does size matter? Color? Has he bought similar products before? What does he like about those?

All findings should be presented graphically after tabulation for study and analysis. At this stage the data could be presented in sketch form, prior to presentation for decision, as covered in Chapter 3. Opinions often identify needed and desired characteristics of products that were previously nonexistent. Few of today's common household appliances were in existence 20 years ago. Tomorrow's technology will

Fig. 4–13. The brainstorming session is a group ideation process that may prove helpful to the development of preliminary ideas.

probably introduce an equal proportion of new products. The student can learn much about the gathering of preliminary ideas that influence his design if he surveys opinions of his classmates or local consumers. He must learn to be sensitive to the needs of the market for which he is designing.

4–6 BRAINSTORMING

The brainstorming session is a form of group ideation (the process of gathering ideas) that was developed in the advertising industry and is now used extensively by many other groups in need of problem solution (Fig. 4–13). To "brainstorm" is defined by Webster's Dictionary as follows: "To practice a conference technique by which a group attempts to find a solution for a specific problem by amassing all the ideas spontaneously contributed by its members." This technique of gathering ideas should not be thought of as a final means to an end, but instead, as a means of accumulating possible ideas for further study. Brainstorming is used to take advantage of the combined ideas of a group of people. Although it is commonly agreed that a group of individuals has more ideas than a single individual, it is usually difficult for several people to produce ideas together with any degree of originality. Human nature tends to be analytical and cautious of each idea, and the total result is a rather negative attitude toward unusual ideas.

Rules of Brainstorming. Brainstorming differs from a conventional conference in that no attempt is made to evaluate or analyze any of the ideas that are expressed. Instead, a list of brief spontaneous ideas are accumulated and recorded, and the evaluation is deferred until a later time. Any attempt to discuss the merits of an idea at the time would break the flow of thoughts and consequently return the group to the usual conference format.

The participants in a brainstorming session must adhere to basic guidelines that have been established through experience and research. No brainstorming session should be attempted unless the panel members understand the following rules:*

1) *Criticism is ruled out.* Adverse judgment of ideas must be withheld until later.
2) *"Free-wheeling" is welcomed.* The wilder the idea, the better; it is easier to tame down than to think up.
3) *Quantity is wanted.* The greater the number of ideas, the more likelihood of useful ideas.
4) *Combination and improvement are sought.* Participants should seek ways of improving the ideas of others.

Organization of a Brainstorming Session. The organization of a brainstorming session could be divided into the following segments: (1) selection of the panel, (2) preliminary group work, (3) selection of moderator and recorder, (4) the brainstorming session, and (5) follow-up. Each of these steps is necessary to the effectiveness of this group process, although there are different ways in which the steps can be completed.

The panel who will participate in the brainstorming session may vary from two or three people working jointly on a project to a group of 100 or more. The usually accepted optimum is about 12 panel members. To encourage a variety of ideas, the group should be composed of both people with experience in the area to be brainstormed and people with limited experience. Supervisors or superior officers often

---

* From Osborn, Alex F., *Applied Imagination.* New York: Scribner, 1963, p. 156.

restrict a flow of ideas; consequently, it is desirable that panels be composed of people of much the same rank or professional status. It is important that members feel free to offer any idea without fear of being judged. The presence of this fear would defeat the primary purpose of the session.

Preliminary groundwork is important in preparing the participants for the session. It is helpful for the leader to prepare a one-page outline of the general information pertaining to the brainstorming session and supply copies to the panel approximately two days prior to the session. This will allow the idea process to "incubate" over a short period of time and produce a more fruitful collection of ideas. The rules of a brainstorming session should be included on this sheet if any of the participants are unfamiliar with this process. The actual problem to be brainstormed should be clearly and concisely defined. The problem should be reduced to simple and somewhat specific terms. For example, instead of posing the problem as "How to improve our campus," it would be better to narrow the problem to several more specific components such as "How to improve instruction," or "How to improve the student parking situation." A brief list of topics of this type will help to eliminate frustration and unify the panel toward studying pertinent problems, rather than becoming too general.

A moderator, to take charge of the brainstorming session, and a recorder must be selected by the panel. In some cases, the moderator (or leader) will select the panel when he is in need of ideas to assist him with a problem. In other cases, a team of individuals working together on a common project may decide that a brainstorming session would be beneficial and, as a result, select a member of the group as the leader. The leader will usually be responsible for laying the groundwork and making arrangements for the session. He will ensure that the session adheres to the guidelines of a brainstorming session. The recorder will tabulate a list of the ideas as they are given during the session (Fig. 4–14). These will be reproduced and distributed among the participants afterwards.

Fig. 4–14. A recorder should list all ideas for future reference as they are given.

The brainstorming session should be held in an informal, comfortable atmosphere. The leader should begin by briefly reviewing the problems to be discussed. This might lead to question-and-answer sessions that could serve to warm up the panel members, as well as increase their familiarity with the problem. The leader should review the four basic guidelines of brainstorming and insist that they be followed at all times during the session. He should emphasize that all evaluation of ideas will be deferred.

The leader will toss out the first problem and recognize the first man with an idea to hold up his hand. The man will respond with as few words as possible to communicate his ideas. The next man who holds his hand up will be recognized by the leader for his response and the process will continue in this manner. It is desirable that a suggestion by one member might stimulate a related thought by another panel member. In this case he will "hitch-hike" by supplementing the idea with one of his own. A panel member wishing to hitch-hike will hold his hand up and snap his fingers to be given priority of recognition by the leader (Fig. 4–15). Hitch-hiking can initiate a chain reaction of developments for a single concept. The leader must be sensitive to the flow of ideas. When ideas lag, he should have alternate problems to provoke a new flow of ideas. The leader must discourage individuals from lengthy discussions or other distracting involvements that would be detrimental to the session.

Fig. 4-15. A person who wishes to "hitch-hike" (add to someone else's idea) indicates this by snapping his fingers during a brainstorming session.

A session should move at a brisk pace and be called to a halt when the ideas have slowed to an unproductive rate, after all aspects of the problems have been exploited. An effective session can last between a few minutes to an hour. A 20- or 30-minute session is considered to be about the best length for most.

The follow-up is initiated by the recorder who reproduces the list of ideas gathered during the session for distribution to the participants. Approximately 100 ideas should be gathered during a 25-minute brainstorming session. These ideas should be studied for their possible application to the problem at hand. The person who reviews a list of ideas from a brainstorming session must be cautious in his screening so that he does not overlook possible solutions that might appear extreme at first glance. The list should be pared down to the ideas believed to have the most merit—probably 10 or 12. These can be developed and analyzed for their suitability.

Topics to Be Brainstormed. The brainstorming technique is a supplement to the individual's thinking process and should not be considered as the means of solving problems—it is merely an effective means of gathering ideas and stimulating group effort toward the solution of a problem. Brainstorming can be used to determine possible solutions to a problem, or to identify problems that need to be solved. An attempt to solve a problem might be limited to the modification of a present product that would improve its function and market appeal. The same method could easily be applied to determining areas of need for new products that are not available on the market.

By applying brainstorming techniques, a class of students could easily gather a long list of ideas for design projects that could be solved by teams or individuals. The teacher could effectively serve as the leader to introduce the class to this process during the first session. Problems could either be limited to campus needs or be broadened to any extent. The teacher could review the guidelines and purposes of brainstorming during the period prior to the session. A single-page outline of the session could be given to the class, providing a general outline of the problem areas to be studied. These ideas could be as follows:

1) Methods in improving study environment.
2) Needs that are not being met in recreational facilities.
3) Pedestrian and vehicular problems on the campus.
4) Classroom shortcomings.

Ideas referring to these topics may suggest the need for new products or devices, systems, or modifications of present designs. Design projects could be selected from these ideas for class assignments. The ideas selected should be adequately simple to be fitted within the time schedule available without frustrating the student. It is better to carry problems through from start to finish, than to attempt an overly ambitious project that cannot be finalized in the available time and within the knowledge or capabilities of the student.

Student teams can effectively use brainstorming to assist them in solving projects that have been selected or assigned. A group of three or four students would follow the same procedure in brainstorming as would the larger group. Student teams could work individually to develop their list of ideas by making sketches of each suggestion that appears to have merit. Sketches will assist them in their thinking and creative process and make their group discussions more productive.

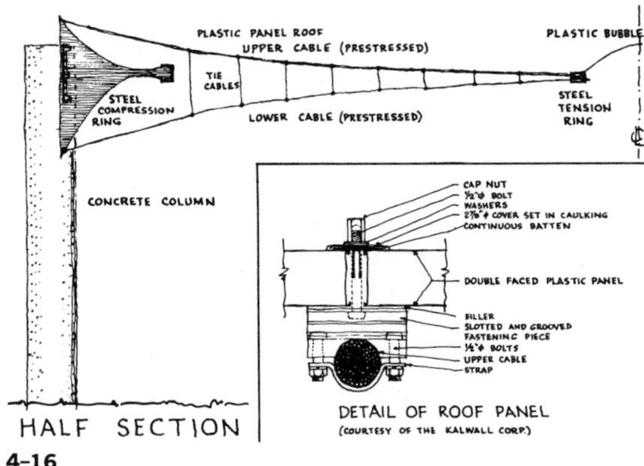

4–16

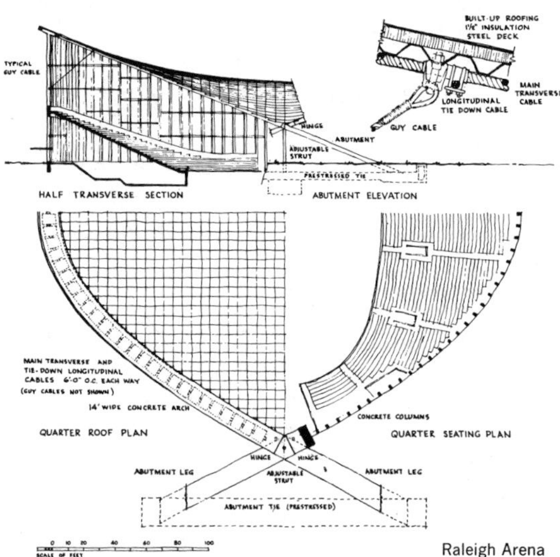

Raleigh Arena

4–17

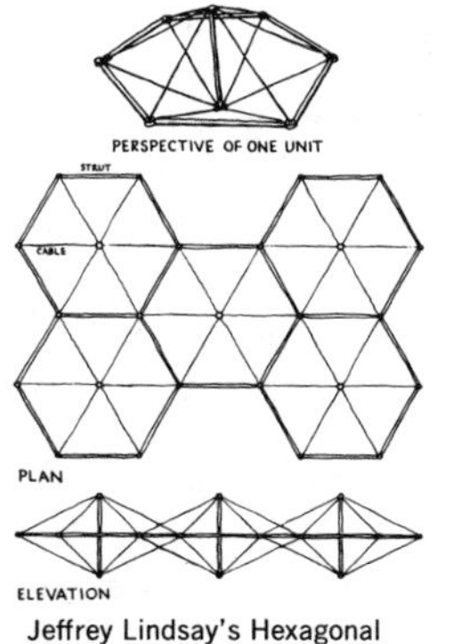

Jeffrey Lindsay's Hexagonal Space-Frame

4–18

Fig. 4–16. Sketches were used to develop structural details of a roof. (Courtesy of U. S. Steel Corporation and H. S. Howard, Jr.)

Fig. 4–17. These sketches are orthographic views which convey a structural idea. (Courtesy of U. S. Steel Corporation and H. S. Howard, Jr.)

Fig. 4–18. Sketches are used effectively to illustrate a space-frame to be used in a structural system. (Courtesy of U. S. Steel Corporation and H. S. Howard, Jr.)

Figs. 4–19 and 4–20. Preliminary sketches of a rear-view mirror design. (Courtesy of the Ford Motor Company.)

Fig. 4–21. Preliminary sketches of a "Transportable Uni-Lodge" for the future. (Courtesy of Lippincott and Margulies, Inc., and Charles Bruning Company.)

Fig. 4–22. The conceptualization of an automatic check-out/packaging unit for a supermarket is shown in a sequence of sketches. (Courtesy of Lester Beall, Inc., and Charles Bruning Company.)

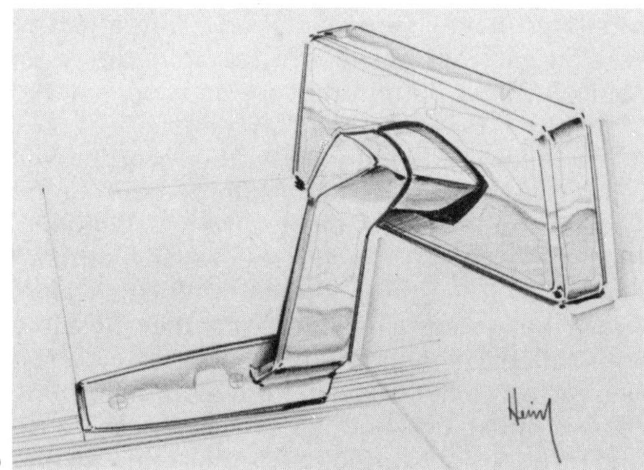

4–19

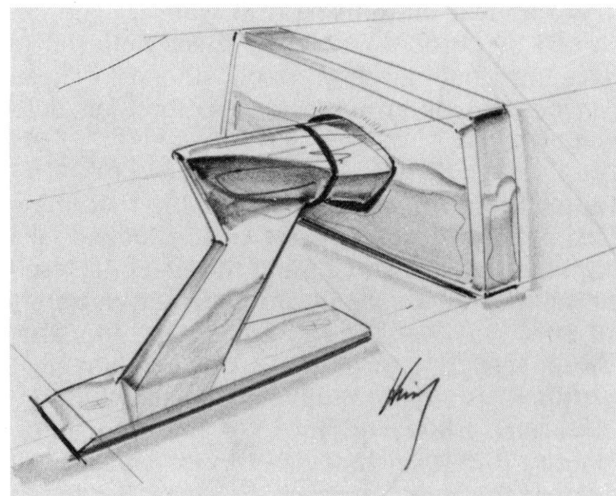

4–20

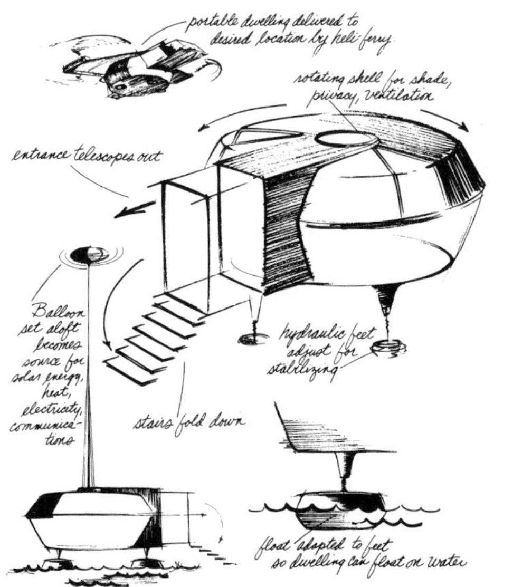

4-21

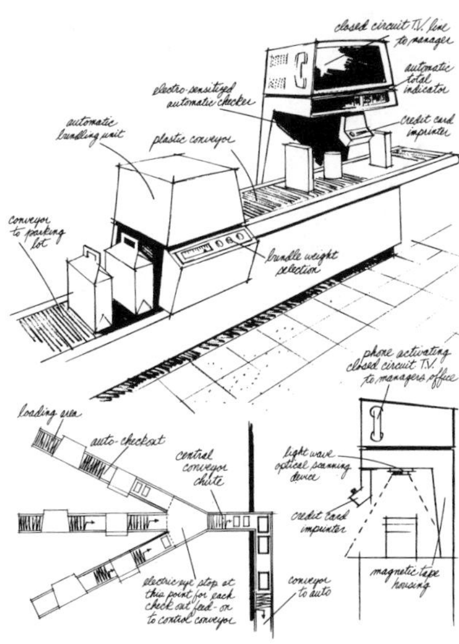

4-22

4-7 DOCUMENTATION OF IDEAS

The designer should strive to maintain all of his preliminary sketches and notes, as emphasized in Article 3-2. Preliminary ideas are important in the documentation of priority in the case of patents. Consequently, a standard format for design sheets, such as that introduced in Chapter 3, should be used for the tabulation of preliminary ideas, and each sheet should be dated and noted with important information.

Sketching is the designer's most vital tool in developing preliminary ideas. Sketches can be very loosely drawn pictorials or sketches of the working-drawing variety. Figures 4-16 and 4-17 are sketches that were used to develop structural concepts, with details to explain important points. The sketch of a space frame shown in Fig. 4-18 combines view drawings and a pictorial to communicate an understanding of the system. Principles of working drawings are covered in detail in Chapter 5, which will assist the designer in preparing freehand sketches during the design process.

Figures 4-19 and 4-20 show sketches that were used to develop preliminary designs for a rear-view mirror for an automobile. These are perspective sketches that can be made easily after reviewing the principles of this type of pictorial in Chapter 17.

The Transportable Uni-Lodge (Fig. 4-21) illustrates the value of sketches in developing and communicating complicated ideas. These sketches represent preliminary ideas for a transportable lodge that may become a reality by 1985. With helicopter service easily available, the Uni-Lodge could be transported to isolated or previously unreachable areas. There are retractable legs with pontoons that permit water travel. Special features: accommodates up to six people; has space for two weeks' food supply and for clothing and bedding; small tank and conversion unit provides water for drinking, shower and toilet facilities; solar power unit supplies electricity for cooking, air conditioning, refrigerator, two-way radio, and even TV. Most of these ideas were indicated on the sketches by means of notes as the ideas occurred. Pictorials and view drawings have been used in combination to depict the entire system. It would be impossible to communicate and develop these ideas without the benefit of sketching and graphical principles.

A similar example of sketching used to develop a new concept is shown in Fig. 4-22, where pictorials and schematics are used to convey the idea. This design involves a total systems concept that could greatly change the usual method of checking and packaging groceries purchased at the supermarket. The shopper sets the machine in operation by inserting her credit card. After the card is scanned (and approved), the customer receives an order number tag, and the conveyor is set into motion. The optical scanner totals items as they pass under it. If the customer has any questions concerning her purchases, she can stop the machine and have TV communication with store personnel by lifting the phone. The totaled items are conveyed directly into a packaging unit where they are enclosed in plastic containers marked with the customer's order number. The customer may now pick up a small order, or let the order be transported by a central conveyor to an exterior pick-up point.

Even though many questions may arise concerning specific details, the sketches in these two examples have successfully explained the designer's ideas. Aside from the communications aspect, sketching was the means of developing the relationship between the components and the configuration of the system. Sketching is a necessary medium of design and development of creative solutions.

4-8 SYSTEMS PROBLEM—PRELIMINARY IDEAS

To illustrate the graphical methods of developing and communicating preliminary ideas, we shall use the example problem introduced in Article 2-4 and later identified in Article 3-4. This problem is restated below:

Systems Problem. Select a building on your campus that is in need of an improved parking lot to accommodate the people who are housed in the building. This may be a dormitory, an office building, or a classroom building. Design a combination traffic and parking system that will be adequate for the requirements of the building. The solution of this problem must adhere to existing limitations, regulations, and policies of your campus in order for the problem to be as realistic as possible.

Preliminary ideas are listed and sketched on work sheets using the format introduced in Article 3-2. These sheets will become a part of the cumulative sequence of design sheets and are numbered in order. The last work sheet in this series, which was covered in Chapter 3, was page 3. The preliminary ideas sheet will therefore be numbered page 4 (Fig. 4-23). The same heading information is placed on each work sheet to identify it and to facilitate the determination of elapsed time between sheets.

Ideas, notes, and sketches are usually drawn with an F or HB pencil, using a grid for approximation of scale. It is unnecessary to strive for a high quality of technique and presentation, since it is more important that sketches be rapidly drawn to keep pace with ideas as they are conceived. It is important that notes and sketches be sufficiently readable to convey the ideas clearly, particularly after a lapse of several days or weeks. The purpose of this approach is to capture a developable idea before it is lost.

The notes concerning each plan are written as they are developed. Here, these notes give such information as the general dimensions of the proposed areas and estimates of the numbers of spaces. The parking spaces are sketched generally to scale, but cannot necessarily be counted to add up to the number of spaces indicated. The actual numbers of spaces are noted on the drawings. The sketching in of spaces provides a quick schematic method of indicating parking. The actual number of spaces in each row can be determined mathematically by dividing the space width into the length. Special details of significance can be enlarged in preliminary sketches to indicate functions, such as the exit detail shown in Fig. 4-23.

The second work sheet of preliminary ideas (Fig. 4-24) develops a third preliminary concept. This idea is sketched in schematics and in pictorial form, showing the parking layout and relationship with the buildings. Each of the three ideas was evaluated to determine the ratio of paving per car required for the addition to the present lot. The total area was divided by the number of the cars provided for. This ratio varied from 194 sq ft in Idea #1 to 326 sq ft in Idea #3. This ratio will be a definite factor when

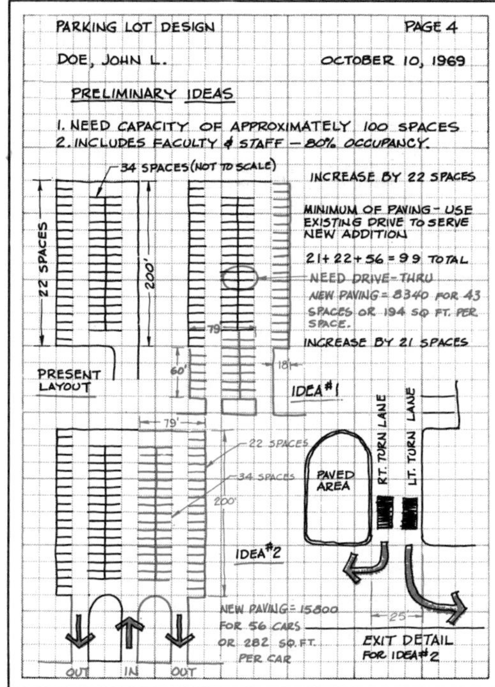

Fig. 4–23. This work sheet is used to develop preliminary ideas for a systems problem. All work is freehand at this stage.

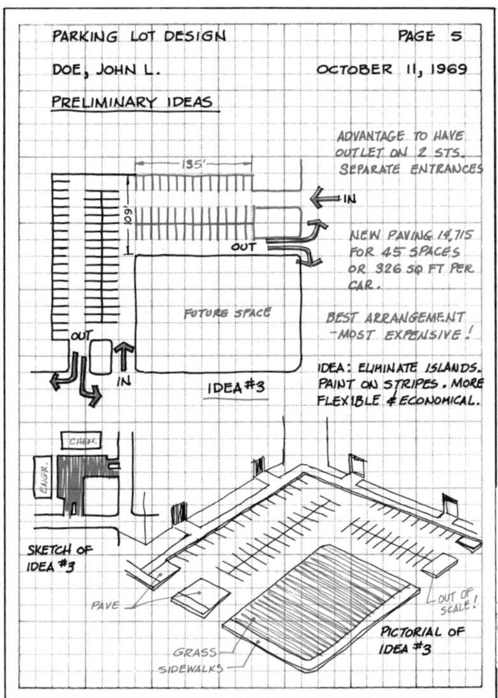

Fig. 4–24. A second work sheet develops a third preliminary concept for the solution of the parking lot system.

the costs of the construction are considered. On the work sheets, these notes were indicated with a colored pencil for emphasis. Notes written in color indicate an emphasis of a point or an evaluation of an idea, and are usually added after all ideas have been recorded and when the designer reviews each concept.

The line weight of freehand sketches should be distinct and sharp. Light gray lines should be avoided as these are difficult to read. Often, rough freehand sketches are given to draftsmen for development of scale drawings, which requires that the designer provide a readable drawing that effectively conveys his concepts. More specific information concerning the mechanical details of sketching and working drawings will be covered in Chapter 5.

The two example work sheets illustrated in Figs. 4–23 and 4–24 do not represent the full extent of preliminary ideas required for a project of this type. These sheets are merely examples which illustrate the initial steps in becoming more familiar with the problem. Additional work must be done to design sidewalks, traffic signals, flow of traffic, and similar considerations. In the examples, primary concern was given to the parking layout, with little attention given the factors mentioned above. The designer developing preliminary ideas is actually communicating with himself when he develops a work sheet of this type.

4-9 PRODUCT DESIGN—PRELIMINARY IDEAS

The product design problem—designing a tree-borne hunting seat—introduced in Chapter 3 is carried through the second phase of the design process, and preliminary ideas for it are developed. In the method of presentation, this example is somewhat similar to the systems

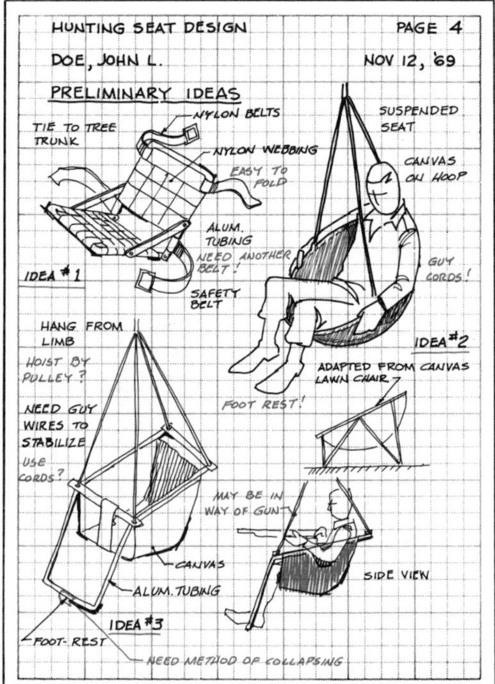

Fig. 4–25. A work sheet for the presentation of preliminary ideas for a product design. Notes and sketches are used to save all thoughts and ideas for reference.

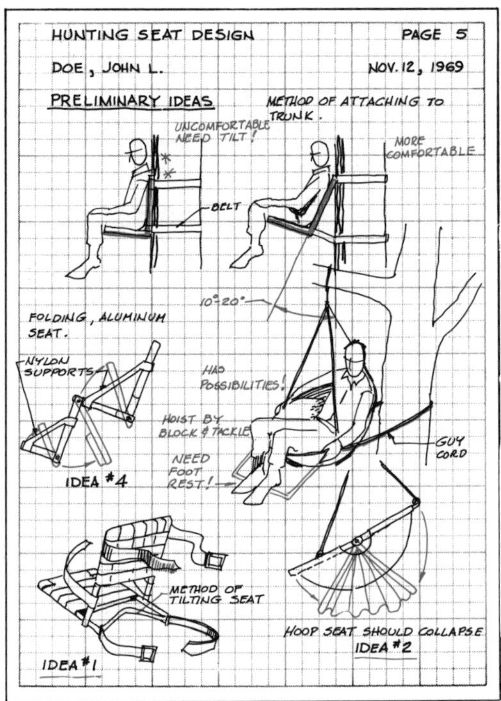

Fig. 4–26. Additional preliminary ideas are recorded to illustrate design concepts for the hunting-seat design problem.

design covered in the previous article. However, here emphasis is placed on hardware design, rather than on the development of concepts as in the system problem. The hunting seat problem is restated below:

Hunting Seat Problem. Many hunters, especially deer hunters, hunt from trees to obtain a better vantage point. Sitting in a tree for several hours can be uncomfortable and hazardous to the hunter; this indicates a need for a hunting seat that could be used to improve his situation. Design a seat that would provide the hunter with comfort and safety while hunting from a tree and that would meet the general requirements of economy and hunting limitations.

A work sheet is used to continue the design sequence begun in Article 3–5. Page 4 of this series of work sheets is shown in Fig. 4–25. The designer gives his name, project title, page number, and other descriptive information of importance on the heading of each sheet. Ideas are sketched freehand in pictorial form and/or as view drawings with supplementary notes. Thoughts or questions that come to mind during this ideation process are noted on the sketches. Lettering and sketching techniques need not be highly detailed nor painstakingly presented; instead, techniques should be rapid but clear.

Each idea is numbered as a means of identifying each concept. Three ideas are shown in Fig. 4–25, varying from a design that attaches to the tree trunk to designs that are suspended from an overhead tree limb. A second work sheet, Fig. 4–26, gives a fourth idea, which is presented as a view drawing. Idea #2 is modified on this sheet to include a footrest and to illustrate a method of guying the seat while suspended. The upper part of the work sheet identifies a problem of tilting the seat for optimum comfort. Idea #1 is revised to include a V-frame for anchoring and tilting the seat.

Many other ideas of this type need to be developed for further study before attempting to refine the designs. These two sheets are representative of the initial ideas that could be considered, but many others should be introduced before leaving the preliminary idea stage of the design process. No ideas are discarded; all are retained as part of the work-sheet file.

After a number of preliminary designs are sketched, they are evaluated for their particular advantages or weaknesses, and notes are added for clarification. These notes are more effective if drawn in color to separate the two phases. Color should be used to denote specific points of importance that should not be overlooked. Design modifications can also be sketched in color with identifying notes to indicate that the modification was a later thought rather than an initial idea. Since the hunter is sketched in several seats, it is not important that the drawings be dimensioned in this problem. Body dimensions give a relative scale to the designs.

4–10 SKETCHING

Freehand sketching is a valuable tool used by the designer and engineer. Sketching ability enables him to make rapid drawings of ideas or designs, which can then be given to a drafting department for development into scale working drawings. The engineer is responsible for reviewing the completed drawings, making the necessary modifications, and accepting or rejecting the drawings.

Sketching saves valuable time and permits the engineer and designer to use their time more effectively. On some occasions, however, the designer may find it easier to develop his own scale drawings from his sketches than to delegate this responsibility to his draftsmen. This is true when his design concepts are complicated and difficult to explain without extensive detailed drawings. The sketches prepared by NASA, shown in Chapter 2, are typical of the application of sketches to the development of advanced designs.

Preliminary ideas that are sketched are usually drawn as view drawings or pictorials. Since view drawings are based on rules of orthographic projection and other working-drawing standards, sketching techniques will be discussed in Chapter 5 where these principles are covered. Working-drawing principles are applied to sketches, but the primary emphasis is on rapid communication of ideas rather than on an attempt to prepare finished instrument drawings.

4–11 SUMMARY

The accumulation of preliminary ideas is the most creative phase of the design process, and is subject to fewer restraints than any other step. Graphical methods are the most commonly used tools in developing and recording ideas, whether the designer works independently or as a member of a design team. Research methods are employed to review the state of the art of a particular problem, and thus to avoid the unnecessary expenditure of time when existing ideas may be helpful in guiding the designer.

Brainstorming can be an effective means of gleaning ideas from a group concerned with the problem being solved. This method cannot serve to solve the problem in its entirety, but it can offer possibilities for consideration. Ideas that are developed or gathered should be recorded and documented by means of notes, sketches, and pictorials. Preliminary ideas should be maintained as a permanent part of the design work sheets that can be referred to at a later date for the possible incorporation of ideas into a related design. These sketches can be used to document a patentable idea and to establish priority of rights if all sheets are dated and other essential information included.

The designer would find it virtually impossible to design without benefit of graphical techniques and freehand sketching in particular. Sketching is not only the most effective means of communicating ideas, but it is also the best method of developing an idea into an acceptable state. The designer uses sketching as a means of communicating with himself and improving his ideas.

Chapter 5 will cover various aspects of preparing working drawings that also have application to sketching techniques. That is, the principles used in working drawings apply equally to sketches. In some cases, the sketch will actually serve as the working drawing from which the part is fabricated.

PROBLEMS

Problems should be presented on $8\frac{1}{2}'' \times 11''$ paper, grid or plain, using the format presented in Article 1–19. Each grid square represents $\frac{1}{4}''$. All notes, sketches, drawings, and graphical work should be neatly prepared in keeping with good practices as introduced in this volume. Written matter should be legibly lettered using $\frac{1}{8}''$ guidelines.

1. Assume that you had been given access to the following items. Select one or several of these and list as many uses as possible. Look for applications that would be unique or unusual.

Empty vegetable cans (3″ diameter × 5″ tall), 2000 sheets of $8\frac{1}{2}'' \times 11''$ bond paper, one cu yd of dirt, three empty oil drums (24″ diameter × 36″ tall), a load of egg cartons, 25 bamboo poles (10′ long), 10 old tires, old newspapers.

2. If you were going to select an ideal team to develop an engineering problem, what would you look for? List these characteristics with your explanations. Letter your response.

3. What are the advantages and the disadvantages of working independently on a project? What are the advantages and the disadvantages of working as a member of a design team? List your reasons and give examples of the types of problems where each approach would have the greater advantage.

4. Conduct a brief research of materials available to you to accumulate information on one of the following design problems or on one of your own selection. You are concerned with costs, methods of construction, dimensions, existing models, estimates of need, and other information of a general nature that will assist you in understanding the problem and deciding whether or not it is a feasible project. List the references you used. Prepare your research in a presentable form that could be reviewed by your instructor.

A one-man canoe, a built-in car jack, an automatic blackboard eraser, a built-in coffee maker for an automobile, a self-opening door to permit a pet to leave or enter the house, an emergency fire escape for a two-story building, a rain protector for persons attending sporting events and other spectator activities, a new household appliance, a home exerciser.

5. List and describe the type of consulting services on an engineering or professional level that would be required in the following design projects:

A zoning system for a city of 20,000 population, a shopping-center development, a go-cart, a water purification facility, a hydroelectrical system, a nuclear fallout disaster plan, a processing plant for refining petroleum products, a drainage system for residential and rural areas.

6. Develop a questionnaire that could be given to the general public to determine its attitude toward a particular product. Select a product and prepare the questionnaire to measure response to its unique features. The questionnaire should be simple and brief and should require mostly multiple-choice answers, with the minimum of subjective answers. Indicate how you would tabulate the information received from your questionnaire.

7. A brainstorming session is a good method of loosening one's imagination and releasing latent ideas. After reviewing the brainstorming session techniques, beginning with Article 4–6, organize a group of associates to brainstorm a selected problem or to determine a problem in need of solution. List all ideas as they are suggested. Write a brief review of the results of this session.

8. Select a systems problem similar to the one covered in Article 4–8 and sketch rough ideas that would improve the existing situation. This may be a traffic intersection on your campus, an area where pedestrian traffic becomes congested during class breaks, improvement of a cafeteria system, improvement of your campus library system, or any other problem of this type. Follow the same general format as that shown in Figs. 4–23 and 4–24.

9. Prepare preliminary sketches and notes of ideas to develop the problems of a systems nature that were identified in Chapter 3, Problems 12–16.

10. Select a product-design problem similar to the one covered in Article 4-9 and sketch rough ideas that might be possible solutions to the problem. Some example problems are a stadium seat, a trailer hitch, a handle for a filing cabinet, a portable clothes rod for installation in a closet, or other products of this nature.

11. Prepare preliminary sketches and notes to develop the product designs which were identified in Chapter 3, Problems 6–9.

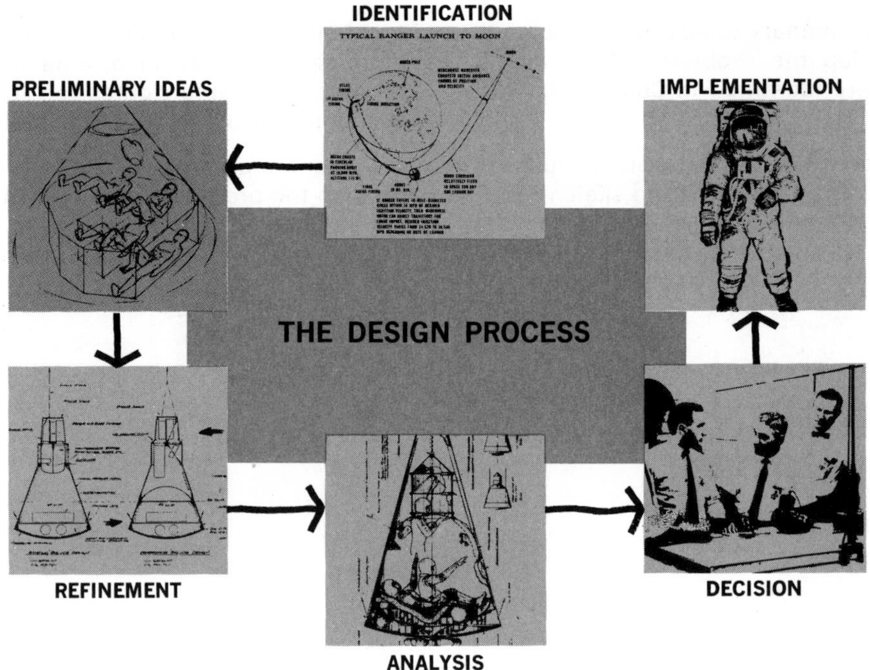

5 ENGINEERING DRAWING STANDARDS

5–1 GENERAL

Chapter 4 stressed the importance of freehand sketching in the development of preliminary ideas during the design process. Freehand sketches can assume practically any form—pictorials, orthographic projections, or schematics—provided that they effectively communicate the designer's thoughts. As the preliminary designs are refined to permit the representation of details of component parts, it becomes advantageous to sketch the parts in the form that will ultimately be used for the preparation of the engineering drawings from which the parts will be constructed. In this case, the same principles generally apply to sketching as to instrument drawing.

The preparation of effective sketches will be easier for the designer if he fully understands the various principles of engineering drawing and the related constructions that are necessary in their preparation. This understanding will enable him to make sketches in the language of engineering, and thus to convey his ideas more easily to the draftsmen for presentation and further refinement. The fundamentals of engineering drawing include (1) geometric construction, (2) lettering, (3) orthographic projection, (4) auxiliary views, (5) sections and conventions, and (6) dimensioning. This chapter will cover all of these except dimensioning, which will be covered in Chapter 19 as the final step, implementation of a finalized design. The engineering drawing principles are based to a considerable extent on standards established by the American National Standards Institute

Fig. 5–1. The design of this advanced traffic interchange is based on the application of geometric constructions. (Courtesy of California Division of Highways.)

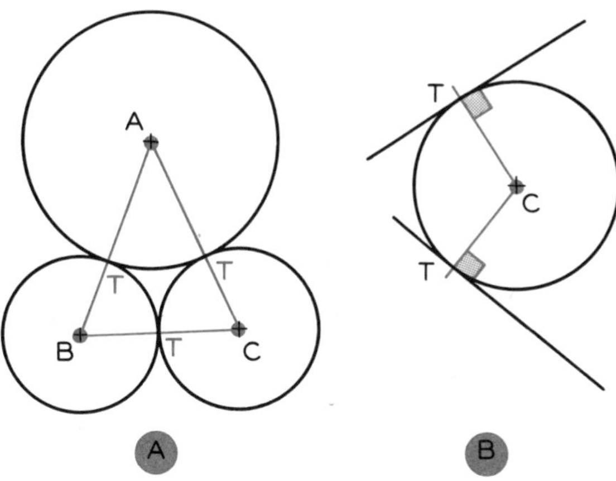

Fig. 5–2. The location of tangent points between tangent circles and between lines and a circle.

(ANSI), and many of the illustrations in this chapter are reproduced from the actual standards.

5–2 GEOMETRIC CONSTRUCTION

The highway interchange shown in Fig. 5–1 is composed of a number of arcs and straight lines which form the total layout of the system. The curves are smooth, permitting the straight segments of road to join curves gradually with no abrupt changes caused by sharp angular intersections. This interchange is an example of a huge geometric construction problem that is based on the simple principle of constructing an arc tangent to a straight line or other arcs. Many other examples of this principle can be seen in products encountered daily. The typical classroom chair shows several examples of arcs that were drawn tangent to lines and arcs when the chair was being designed. It is necessary that these simple principles be understood to design products or systems that make use of arcs tangent to lines and arcs.

The basic principle of tangency problems is the location of the points of tangency between arcs or between arcs and straight lines. The points of tangency between arcs can be found by constructing a line from the center of one tangent arc to the center of the other (Fig. 5–2A). This principle will apply for arcs of equal or unequal size. The points of tangency of an arc with two lines can be found by constructing, from the center of the arc, lines perpendicular to the tangent lines as shown in part B. In both cases, thin lines of this type are shown on the drawing to locate tangent points. These thin lines are drawn with a 4H or 3H pencil through the points of tangency. The lines are especially helpful in preparing finished drawings, since they will serve as guides for ending the arcs drawn with a compass.

5–3 ARC TANGENT TO TWO LINES

An arc of a given radius can be constructed tangent to two nonparallel lines. This construction may be used to round a corner on a product or to design a curb at a traffic intersection. The method of construction is given in Fig. 5–3 in three steps.

Arc Tangent to Perpendicular Lines. The same general procedure covered in the previous example can be employed to construct an arc

FIGURE 5-3. ARC TANGENT TO TWO LINES

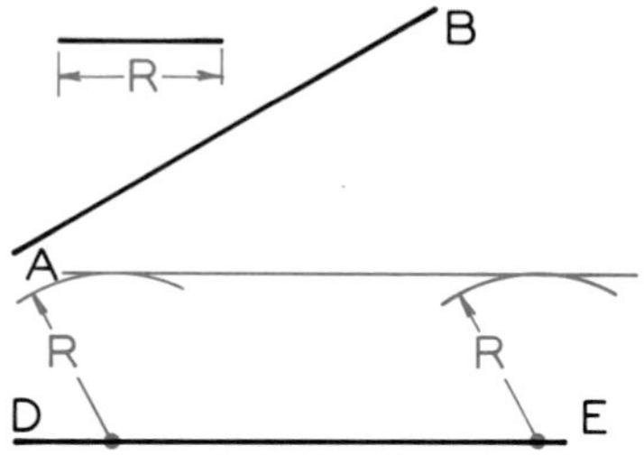

Step 1: A compass is used to construct arcs with radius *R* at two intervals along line *DE*. A construction line is drawn parallel to *DE* and tangent to the two arcs.

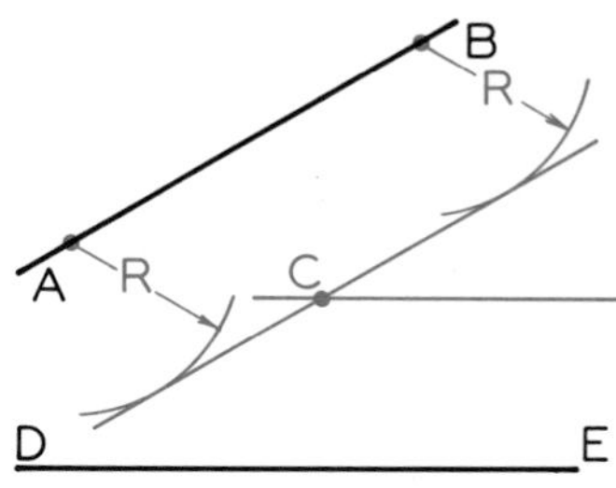

Step 2: A construction line is drawn parallel to line *AB* by the same technique used in step 1. These two construction lines intersect at point *C*.

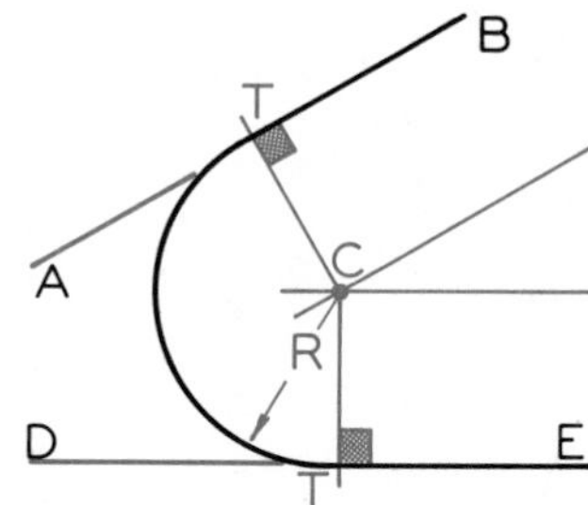

Step 3: Thin lines are drawn from point *C* perpendicular to *AB* and *DE* to locate points of tangency. With point *C* as the center and radius ***R***, an arc is drawn tangent to the two lines.

FIGURE 5-4. ARC TANGENT TO TWO PERPENDICULAR LINES

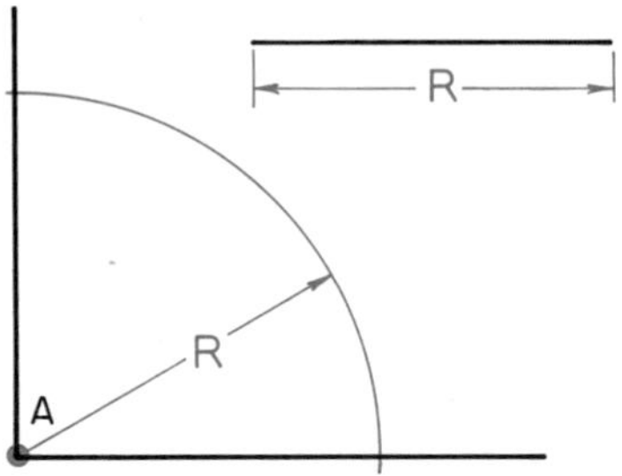

Step 1: Radius *R* is used to construct an arc with its center at *A*. This locates two points of tangency.

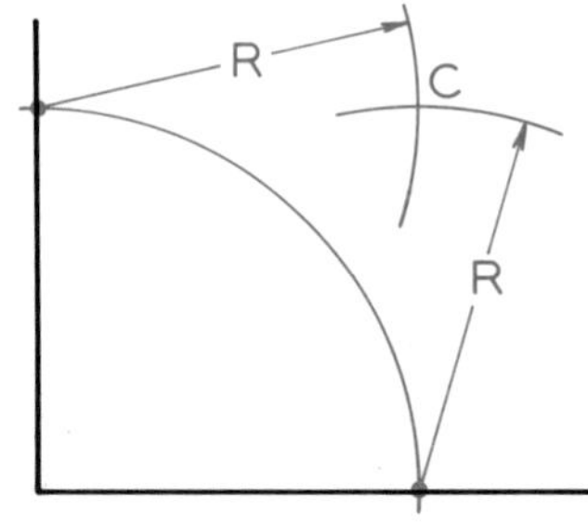

Step 2: Arcs are drawn with centers at each point of tangency. Their intersection will locate center *C*.

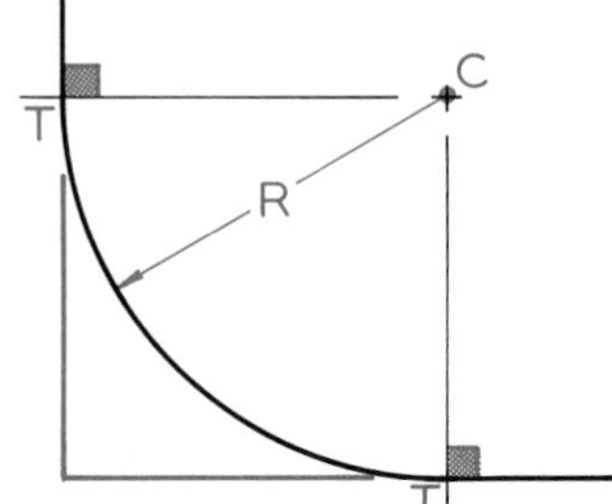

Step 3: Thin center lines are drawn from *C* through the points of tangency. These will be perpendicular to the two lines. The arc is drawn from tangent point to tangent point using center *C* and radius ***R***.

tangent to any two lines, but if the two lines are perpendicular, we can use an alternative method. This is a special case that cannot be applied to nonperpendicular lines.

The steps of constructing an arc tangent to two perpendicular lines are shown in Fig. 5-4. In all cases, the points of tangency should be indicated as part of the construction. These points are shown with either thin lines or center lines, drawn from the center through the points of tangency and extending past them about $\frac{1}{16}''$. The lines are drawn so as to provide a visual means of inspecting the construction to verify its correctness.

FIGURE 5-5. ARC TANGENT TO AN ARC AND A LINE

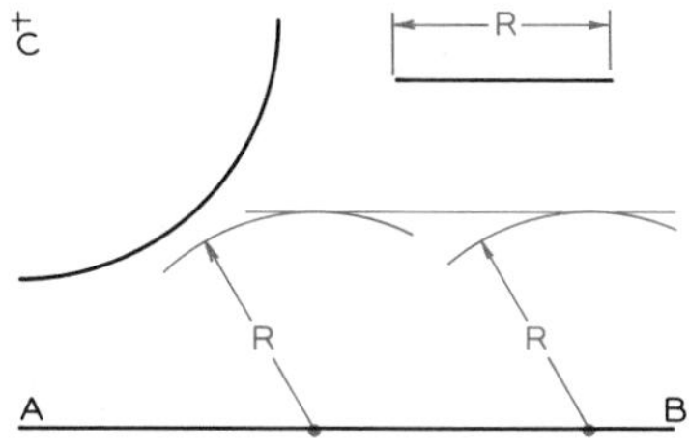

Step 1: A compass is used to construct arcs with radius *R* at two intervals along line *AB*. A construction line is drawn parallel to *AB* and tangent to the arcs.

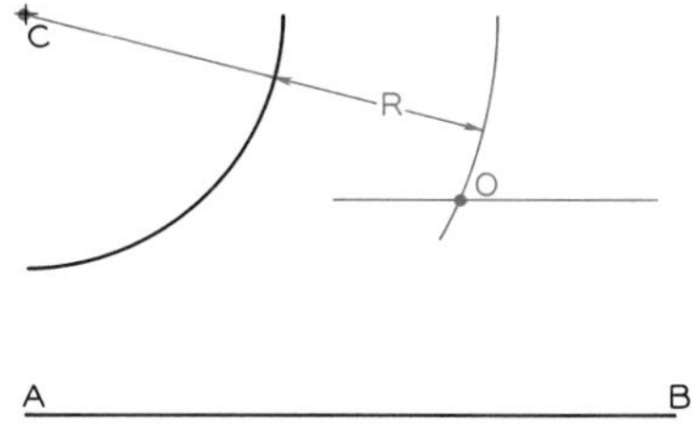

Step 2: Radius *R* is added to the extended radius through point *C*. The extended radius with center *C* is used to locate point *O*.

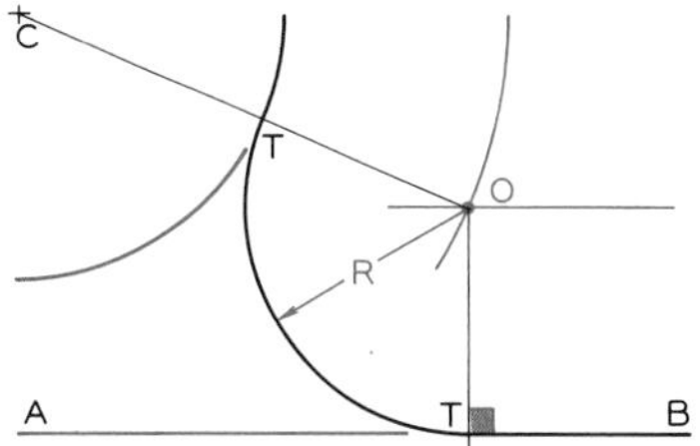

Step 3: Tangent points are located by drawing thin lines from *O* to *C* and from *O* perpendicular to line *AB*. The arc is drawn with center *O* and tangent to the arc and line.

5-4 ARC TANGENT TO AN ARC AND A LINE

It is often necessary for an arc to be drawn with a given radius tangent to an arc and a straight line. Since an infinite number of solutions may be obtained by varying the length of the radius, it is necessary that the radius be given.

Figure 5-5 gives the sequential steps of construction necessary for the solution of this type of problem.

5-5 ARC TANGENT TO TWO ARCS

A detail drawing, Fig. 5-6, illustrates several examples of tangency problems and, in particular, the construction of arcs tangent to given arcs. It was necessary to solve these geometric construction problems before arriving at the finished design. The method of construction is illustrated in Fig. 5-7.

You should note that to solve tangency problems of this type it is necessary to know the centers of the given arcs and the radius of the arc that is to be drawn. Always mark the points of tangency.

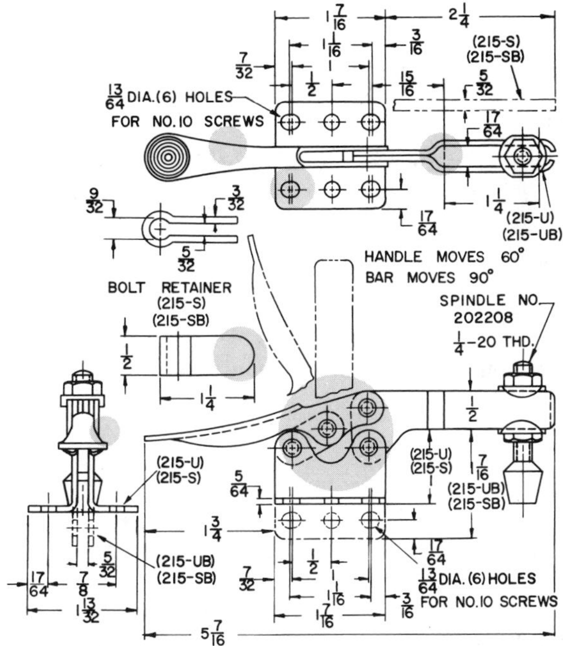

Fig. 5-6. Several examples of tangency problems can be seen in this industrial working drawing. These constructions were necessary in the design of each component. (Courtesy of De-Sta-Co Corporation.)

FIGURE 5-7. ARC TANGENT TO TWO ARCS

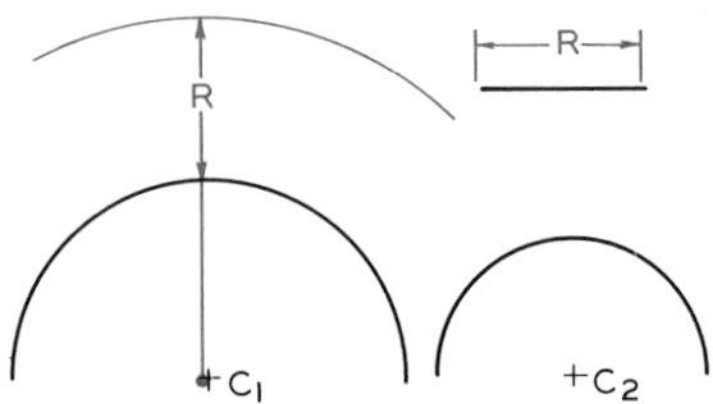

Step 1: The radius from center C_1 is extended and radius *R* is added to this extension. A concentric arc is drawn using the extended radius.

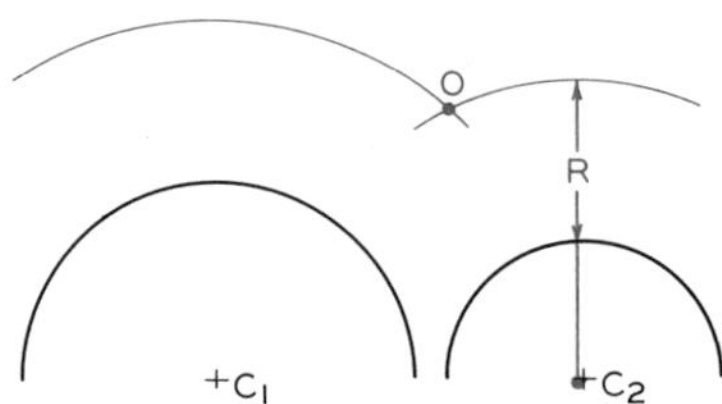

Step 2: The radius from C_2 is extended and radius *R* is added. The extended radius is used to draw a second concentric arc which locates point *O*.

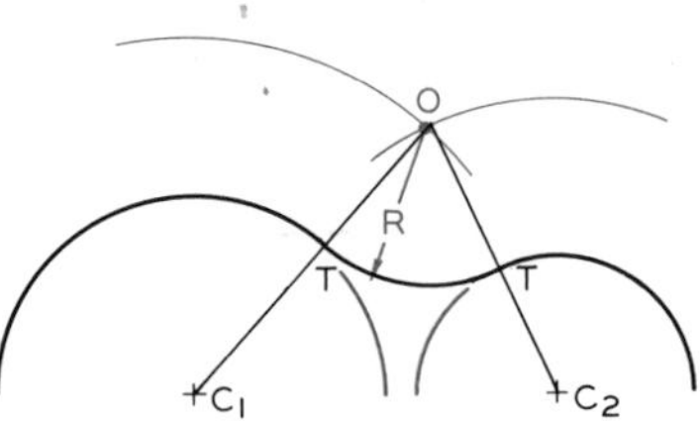

Step 3: Thin lines are drawn from point *O* to points C_1 and C_2, which locate the points of tangency. The arc is drawn with its center at *O*.

FIGURE 5-8. ARC TANGENT TO TWO ARCS

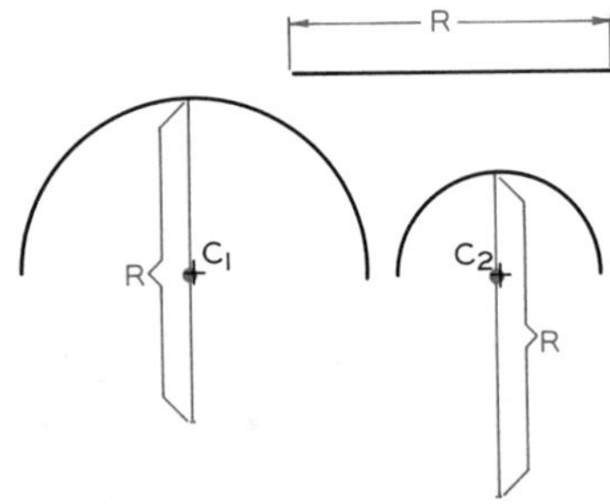

Step 1: Construction lines are drawn from each of the arcs through their centers, C_1 and C_2. The radius *R* is measured off along each of these lines.

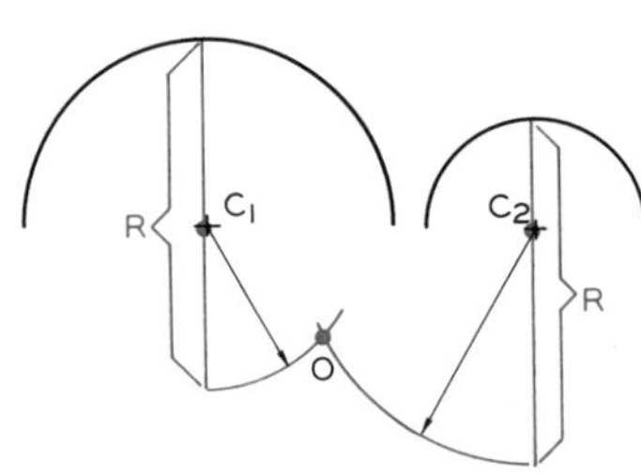

Step 2: The distance from each center to the end of the extended radius is used to construct an arc. The two arcs intersect at point *O*.

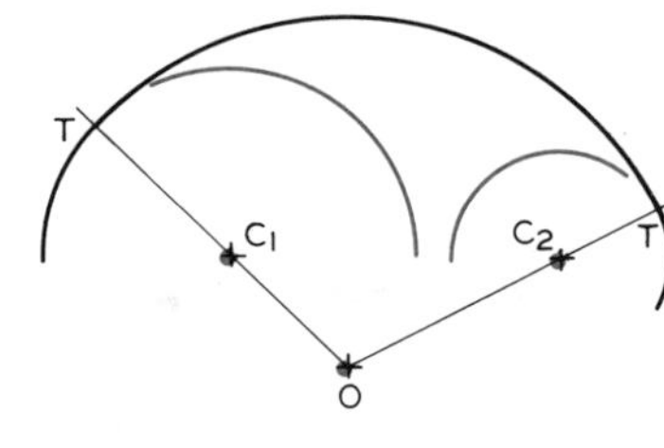

Step 3: Thin lines are drawn from point *O* through centers C_1 and C_2 to the arcs to locate the points of tangency. The arc is drawn using point *O* as the center.

FIGURE 5-9. LINE FROM A POINT TANGENT TO AN ARC

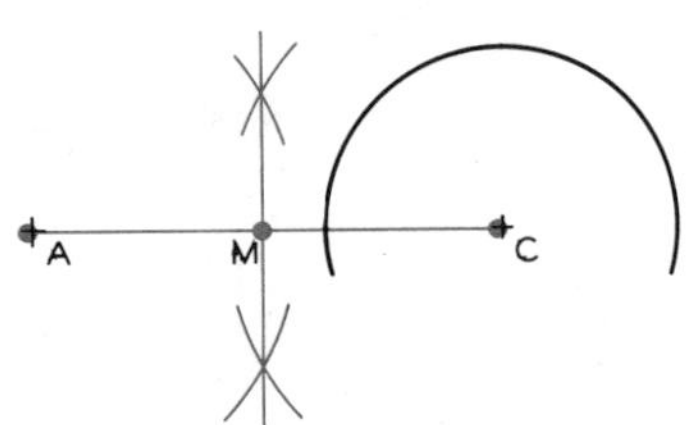

Step 1: A line is to be drawn from *A* tangent to the arc. Line *AC* is drawn and bisected to find midpoint *M*.

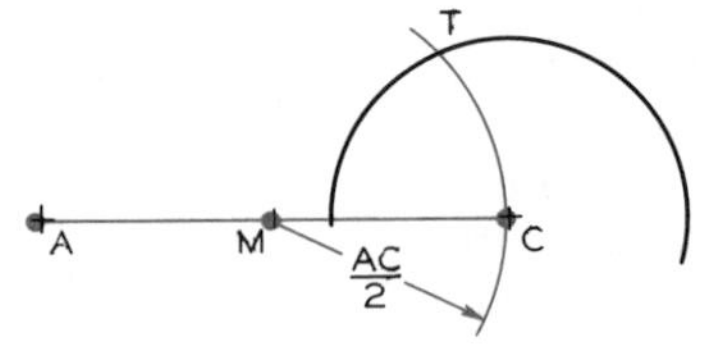

Step 2: Using midpoint *M* as the center and half the length *AC* as the radius, an arc is drawn to locate point *T*, the point of tangency.

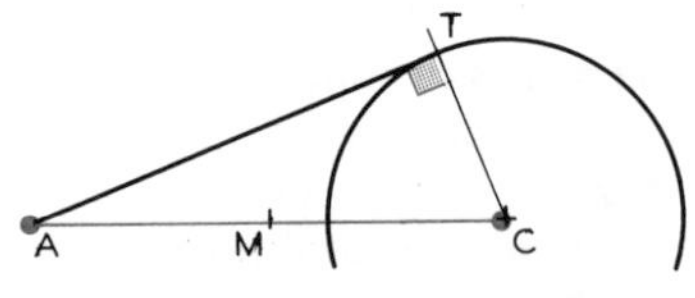

Step 3: The tangent line is drawn from *A* to *T*. Line *CT* will be perpendicular to line *AT*.

Alternative Solution. In cases where the given radius is sufficiently long, two methods are available for constructing an arc tangent to two given arcs. One method was covered in the previous example; the alternative method is illustrated in Fig. 5–8.

5–6 LINE FROM A POINT TANGENT TO AN ARC

A line from a point to an arc can be approximated by eye to serve most uses; however, the exact location of a tangent point can be found by geometric construction. This method is illustrated in Fig. 5–9.

An alternative method of locating the point of tangency involves the use of a triangle and straightedge, as shown in Fig. 5–10. This is a draftsman's technique that requires less time than the former method.

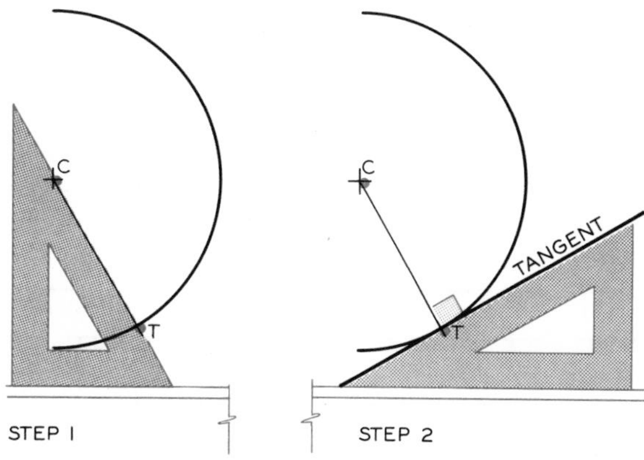

Fig. 5–10. Construction of a line that is tangent to an arc.

5–7 USE OF SCALES

Essentially all engineering drawings will require the measurement of lengths, sizes, and other linear dimensions as an integral part of all construction. This requires a thorough understanding of the scales used to make the drawings and their various applications. A number of scales are available in a variety of scale designations from metric scales to fractional divisions. The most common scales used in engineering drawing are the architects' scale and the engineers' scale. These scales are usually 12 inches long, with some pocket scales being six inches in length.

Architects' Scale. The architects' scale is used to dimension and scale items normally encountered by the architect, which include building designs, cabinet work, interior plumbing, and electrical layouts. In general, most indoor measurements are measured in feet and inches as with an architects' scale. It is obvious that few drawings can be made full size; consequently, scales are used to draw the layouts at proportional, but reduced sizes. For example, the architects' scale has the following graduations:

Full size	$\frac{3}{8}'' = 1'\text{-}0''$
$3'' = 1'\text{-}0''$	$\frac{1}{4}'' = 1'\text{-}0''$
$1\frac{1}{2}'' = 1'\text{-}0''$	$\frac{3}{32}'' = 1'\text{-}0''$
$1'' = 1'\text{-}0''$	$\frac{1}{8}'' = 1'\text{-}0''$
$\frac{3}{4}'' = 1'\text{-}0''$	$\frac{3}{16}'' = 1'\text{-}0''$
$\frac{1}{2}'' = 1'\text{-}0''$	

The architect usually is concerned with rather large drawings of building designs that would be impossible to represent except at a reduced scale. Since he makes measurements in feet and inches, the architects' scale is graduated into inches on one end and feet on the other. The 16 scale is the scale used for making full-size dimensions with each inch divided into sixteenths of an inch. This is the scale found on most yardsticks and tape measurements used by the workmen who will be constructing the finished components from engineering drawings. The full-size scale is used for drawing small parts or enlarging specific details for improved interpretation.

Full size. The use of the 16 scale for measuring a full-size line is shown in Fig. 5–11A. One end of the line is placed at the zero end of the

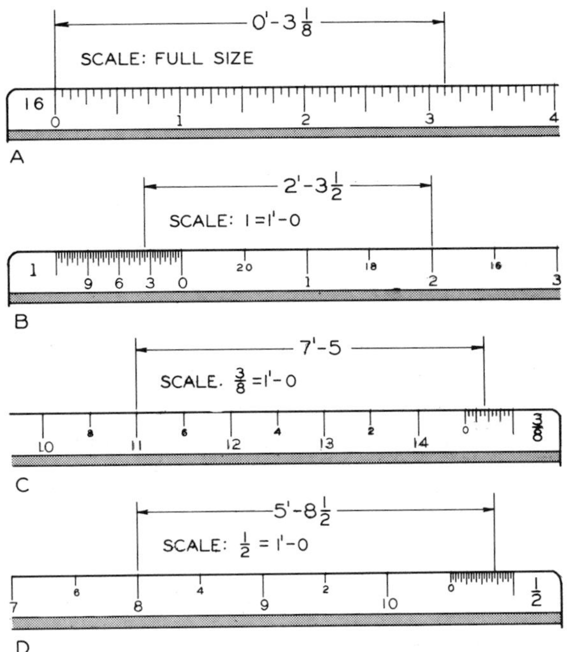

Fig. 5-11. Measurement of lines using the architects' scale.

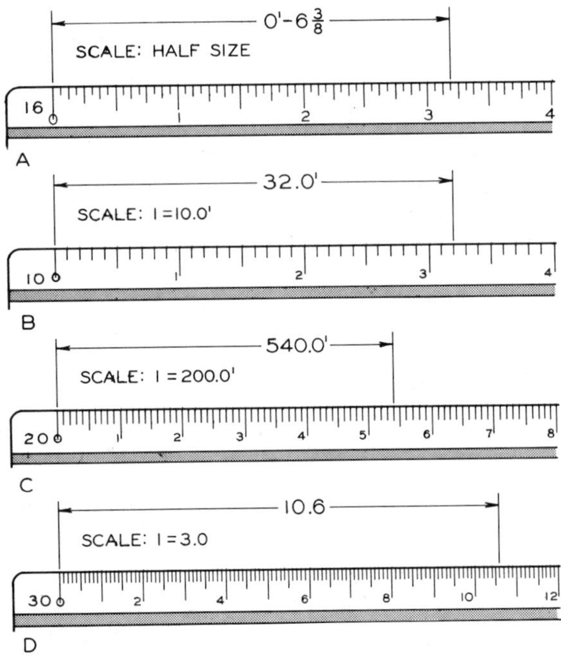

Fig. 5-12. Measurement of lines using the 16-scale and the engineers' scale.

scale, and the reading is made at the other end to the nearest $\frac{1}{16}''$. In this example, it can be seen that the length of the line is $3\frac{1}{8}''$.

Scale: $1'' = 1'$-$0''$. When an architects' scale is used to express feet and inches, it is necessary to measure the line from the nearest whole foot graduation and let the excess length extend into the inch graduations at the end of the scale. This may be at the left or the right end, depending on which scale is being used, since each edge of the architects' scale is used for two scales. The example in Fig. 5-11B gives the measurement of $2'$-$3\frac{1}{2}''$. Note that the right end of the line being measured is aligned with the whole foot unit, $2'$. The other end gives a reading of $3\frac{1}{2}''$.

Scale: $\frac{3}{8}'' = 1'$-$0''$. This scale is used when $\frac{3}{8}''$ is used to represent $12''$ on drawing. In Fig. 5-11C a line is measured to be $7'$-$5''$ long. Note that the 7 does not appear on the scale, but if it did, it would be in the same position as the number 11, which is a unit on the scale running in the opposite direction. Care must be taken not to confuse the numbering on an architects' scale.

Scale: $\frac{1}{2}'' = 1'$-$0''$. The $\frac{1}{2}''$ scale is used to represent one foot or $12''$ by a $\frac{1}{2}''$ distance. A measurement of $5'$-$8\frac{1}{2}''$ is scaled in Fig. 5-11D. Care must be taken to avoid confusing $5'$-$8\frac{1}{2}''$ with $8'$-$8\frac{1}{2}''$. The inch divisions at the end of the scale are not numbered because the divisions are too small to be labeled.

Scale: half size. A drawing may be drawn half size to advantage in some cases. The 16 scale is used for this purpose. Since the drawing is to be made half size, a $6\frac{3}{8}''$ measurement will be drawn $3\frac{3}{16}''$ long (Fig. 5-12A). In other words, the measurement to be drawn is divided by two and drawn with a 16 scale. When a measurement is being taken from a half-size drawing, the measurement is scaled and doubled to give the actual length.

The Engineers' Scale. The engineers' scale is a decimal scale on which each division is divided into multiples of 10 units. This scale is commonly used for engineering drawings of structures or projects that are erected outdoors, such as street systems, drainage systems, and other systems having measurements of rather long dimensions associated with topography and map drawing. Since the divisions are in decimals, it is easy to perform multiplication and division without the complicated conversion of feet and inches as would be the case if the architects' scale were used. Areas and volumes can be found with the minimum of difficulty by use of the engineers' scale. The engineers' scale is divided into scales denoted by 10, 20, 30, 40, 50, and 60, which means that an inch is divided into this number of parts on each scale, respectively. The graduations permit the following scales:

10 scale: $1'' = 0.1''$, $1'' = 1'$, $1'' = 10''$
20 scale: $1'' = 20'$, $1'' = 200'$
30 scale: $1'' = 300'$, $1'' = 3000'$
40 scale: $1'' = 40'$, $1'' = 400'$
50 scale: $1'' = 50'$, $1'' = 500'$
60 scale: $1'' = 600'$, $1'' = 6000'$

These are examples of typical scales that can be read directly from the engineers' scale. Many other combinations may be obtained by increasing or reducing the scales by multiples of ten. For example, the 10 scale can be used for $1'' = 0.0001''$ or $1'' = 10000'$ by simply moving the decimal point as desired.

10 scale. In Fig. 5-12B, the 10 scale is used to measure a line at the scale $1'' = 1.0''$. The zero index is placed at one end of the line and the measurement is read directly at the other end. A line is measured to have a length of 32.0'. Note that the dimensions are written in inches with a decimal. If a line were measured with an engineers' scale to give an even measurement of 2 inches, it would be written as 2.0" to indicate that it was an accurate reading rather than a rounded-off measurement.

20 scale. Each inch is divided into 20 divisions on the 20 scale. Using a scale of $1'' = 200'$ a line is measured to have a length of 540.0' in Fig. 5-12C.

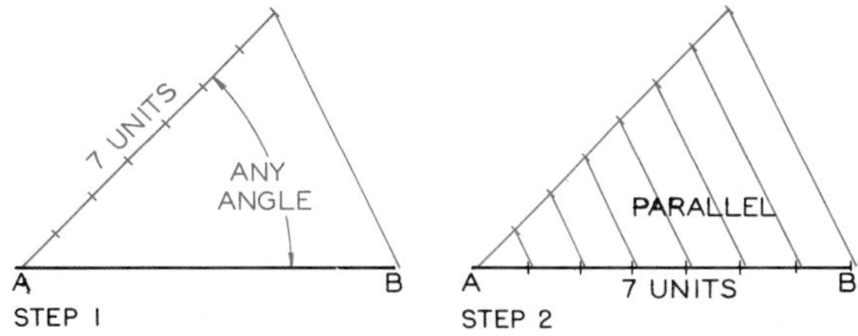

Fig. 5-13. Division of a line into equal segments by geometric construction.

30 scale. A line in Fig. 5-12D is measured to be 10.6" long. Note that a 30 scale was used for this measurement.

5-8 MATHEMATICAL CONSTRUCTION

The use of scales and principles of geometric construction can be combined to provide graphical solutions to mathematical problems to a reasonable degree of accuracy. This is the principle employed in nomography, which will be covered in Article 15-35. This form of problem solution is especially applicable to problems of a repetitive nature where the variable remains constant, thus enabling graphical readings to be taken from the same drawing.

The basis of most construction of this type begins with the division of a line into a given number of parts, as illustrated in Fig. 5-13.

Step 1. Line *AB* is to be divided into seven units by graphical methods. A line is drawn at a convenient angle through point *A*. This line is divided into seven equal segments using dividers or a scale having some convenient number of divisions. The seventh division mark is connected to point *B* with a construction line.

Step 2. Lines are drawn from each division mark parallel to the construction line through point *B*. These lines intersect line *AB*, dividing it into seven equal segments.

5-9 GRAPHICAL MULTIPLICATION

The principle of similar triangles can be used to perform multiplication graphically. This method of geometric construction is shown in Fig. 5-14.

Step 1. Two lines are drawn to intersect at any angle with each other, and each line is divided into equal units. The units on one scale can be different from the units on the other. The units along each scale are numbered to provide a sufficient range for the multiplications that will be performed. If the multiplication is to have a factor of three as a constant multiplier, three units are marked along one of the scales and a unit of one along the other. Since $1 \times 3 = 3$, the answer to this multiplication can be read directly along the horizontal scale by drawing a diagonal connecting one with three.

Step 2. The multiplication of $3 \times 3 =$ can be found by constructing a line through point 3 on the inclined axis parallel to the diagonal through points 1 and 3. This line intersects the horizontal axis at nine units, which is the product. This same procedure can be repeated for 3×4 or any other number multiplied by 3, and the answer can be read on the horizontal scale.

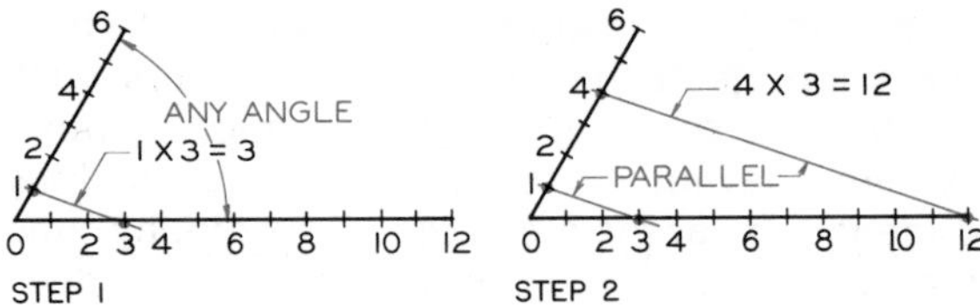

Fig. 5-14. Graphical multiplication.

5-10 GRAPHICAL DIVISION

The reverse procedure is used to divide one number by another, as illustrated in Fig. 5-15. In this example, the axes are drawn perpendicular to each other for convenience.

Step 1. Each scale is divided into units as in the previous example. Since 15 is to be divided by 5, a diagonal is drawn from 15 units on one scale to 5 units on the other.

Step 2. A second diagonal is drawn parallel to this diagonal through unit 1 on the vertical scale. This diagonal intersects the horizontal scale at unit 3, the quotient of 15 divided by 5. These axes could have been constructed at any angle other than perpendicular.

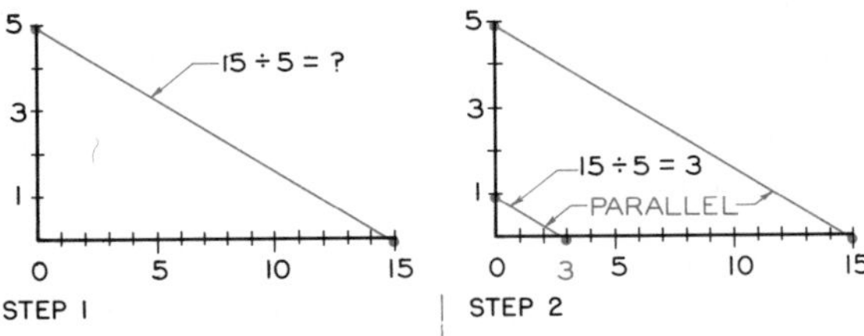

Fig. 5-15. Graphical division.

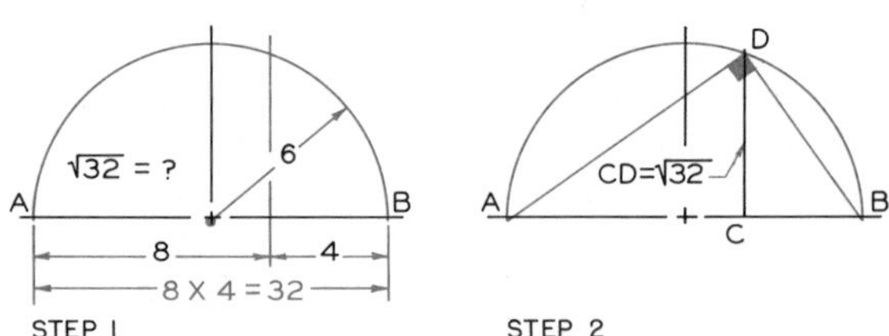

Fig. 5-16. Determination of the square root of 32 by graphical construction.

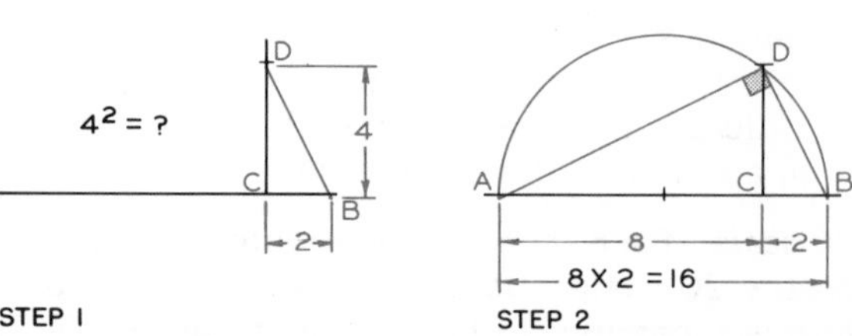

Fig. 5-17. Squaring a number by graphical methods.

5-11 GRAPHICAL SQUARES AND SQUARE ROOTS

The geometric principle that any two lines form a right angle when inscribed in a semicircle is used to find the square root of a number graphically, by construction of a series of similar triangles. This method is illustrated in Fig. 5-16.

Step 1. To find the square root of 32, we divide the number into nearly equal factors—8 and 4 in this case. Selection of factors that are approximately equal will give a higher degree of accuracy in the answer. Unity can also be used as a factor, but it is limited to rather small numbers.

Factors 8 and 4 are added together to give the diameter *AB* of a semicircle, with the midpoint located six units from either end of the diameter. A semicircle with a radius of six units is drawn from the midpoint of the diameter. Point *C* is located to represent the point where the factors 8 and 4 join.

Step 2. A perpendicular line is constructed from point *C* to intersect the arc at point *D*. With the engineers' scale, line *CD* is measured to give the square root of 32, line *AB*. Note that *the same scale must be used throughout the construction process.*

Proof. This relationship can be proved through similar triangles by referring to the following equations and Step 2 of Fig. 5-16:

$$DC : AC = BC : DC$$

or

$$\frac{DC}{AC} = \frac{BC}{DC} \quad \text{or} \quad DC^2 = AC(BC); \qquad (1)$$

therefore

$$DC = \sqrt{AC(BC)} \quad \text{or} \quad DC = \sqrt{8(4)} = \sqrt{32}.$$

Factors of 32 and 1 could have been used with a semicircle diameter of 33; however, the square root would be a very short line in comparison with the other dimensions of the construction. This would result in less accuracy than is obtained when the factors are more nearly equal in length.

A number can be squared in the same manner by reversing the process covered in the previous example. This procedure is illustrated in Fig. 5-17.

Step 1. It is required to find graphically the square of four. A vertical line, *DC*, is drawn four units long with an engineers' scale. A horizontal line is drawn through point *C* perpendicular to line *DC*. Using the same scale for measurement, locate point *B* two units from point *C*. Point *B* is connected to point *D*.

Step 2. A line is drawn from point *D* perpendicular to line *BD*, and it is extended until it intersects the horizontal line at point *A*. As a check, an arc drawn from the midpoint of line *AB* should pass through point *D* if the construction is correct. The square of the number is the product of *AC* and *CB* or $8 \times 2 = 16$.

Another factor besides two could have been used for segment *CB*. For example, if *CB* had been drawn one unit long, *AC* would have been measured as 16 units long. The square of the number would be the product of these two factors, or $16 \times 1 = 16$.

5-12 GRAPHICAL TRIGONOMETRY

Trigonometric functions can be found graphically by geometric construction and measurement with an engineers' scale. This system of construction is shown in Fig. 5-18, where an arc with a radius of 10 units is drawn at a convenient scale. The angle whose functions are desired is drawn accurately as shown. The table of values for this angle can be found by direct measurement on this diagram as illustrated.

For example, the sine of any angle is equal to the vertical leg divided by the hypotenuse, that is, Y/R in the small triangle. Since the radius of the arc, which is here the hypotenuse, was drawn as 10 units, the vertical distance, *BC*, can be scaled from the diagram as a decimal fraction. The cosine of the angle is the ratio of the horizontal leg, *X*, divided by the radius, 10, and

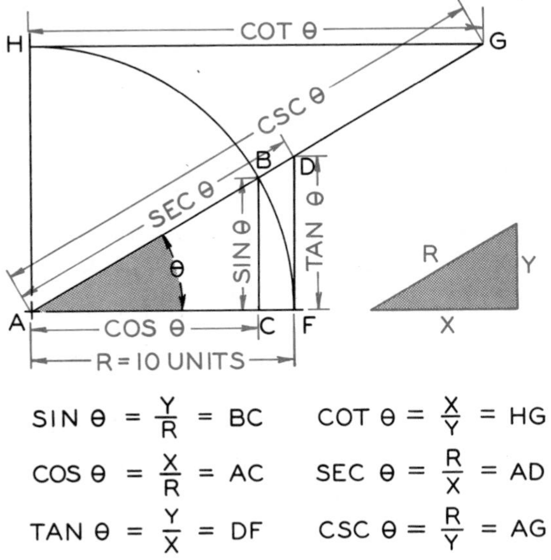

Fig. 5-18. Graphical determination of the fundamental trigonometric functions.

can be measured directly as line *AC*. The other functions can be found in a similar manner for this particular angle. For other angles, additional diagrams must be accurately drawn to afford precision of measurement.

These graphical functions can be used to verify other trigonometric identities by manipulation of relationships. For example, the tangent of the angle θ is equal to Y/X. Leg Y is equal to segment *BC* or to the sine of θ. Leg X is equal to segment *AC* or to the cosine of θ. Substitution of the trigonometric functions for legs X and Y gives the following relationship:

$$\frac{Y}{X} = \frac{\sin\theta}{\cos\theta} = \tan\theta,$$

with the reciprocal equal to the contangent of θ:

$$\frac{X}{Y} = \frac{\cos\theta}{\sin\theta} = \cot\theta.$$

Other fundamental identities are based on the Pythagorean theorem, which states that the sum of the squares of the sides is equal to the square of the hypotenuse. An example of this is the square of *BC* and *AC* to give the square of *AB*. Since these lengths represent trigonometric functions, the following substitutions can be made:

$$Y^2 + X^2 = R^2$$

or

$$\sin^2\theta + \cos^2\theta = 1.$$

Other Pythagorean relationships are

$$1 + \tan^2\theta = \sec^2\theta$$

and

$$1 + \cot^2\theta = \csc^2\theta.$$

These fundamental identities can be verified graphically by referring to Fig. 5-18. It is necessary that the construction be enlarged sufficiently to yield accurate measurements.

5-13 LETTERING

Lettering is a primary means of communicating engineering information and specifying methods of construction. In many cases, lettering may be more critical to a project than the drawings, since the drawing may consist of schematics with notes relating details and specifications. If lettering is poor, it may cause a misrepresentation of important information and failure in the design. Lettering must be both easy to execute and legible.

Many types of lettering devices are available for mechanical lettering. Also, specially-designed typewriters are sometimes used to type on large engineering drawings to ensure legibility. However, in spite of the many mechanical means available, most engineers develop a proficiency in freehand lettering for solving engineering problems, making general communication notes, and labeling design sketches. Lettering may take a variety of styles depending upon the standards of the industry or the individual's preference. General standards have

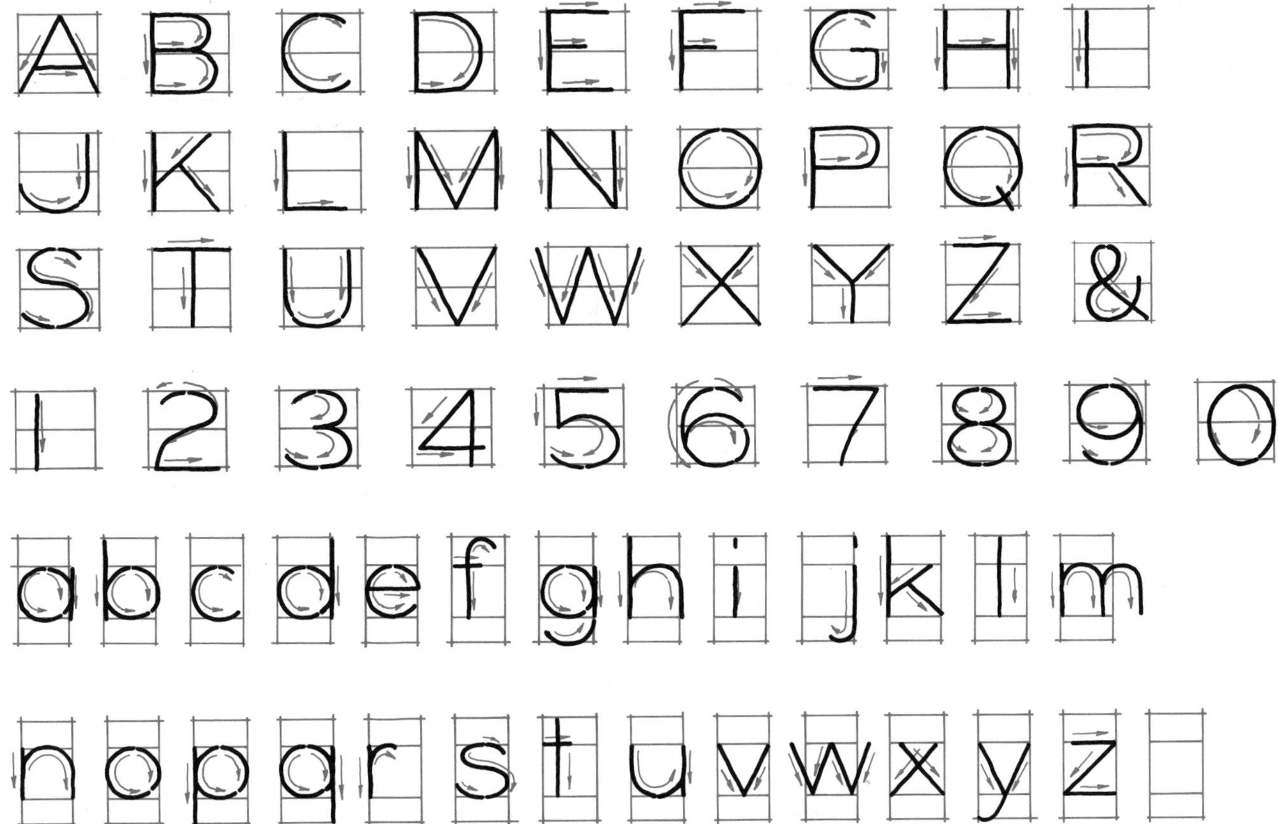

Fig. 5-19. Engineering single-stroke Gothic lettering: vertical upper- and lower-case letters with suggested strokes.

been established for the recommended letter forms as guides for uniformity of style. The most commonly accepted form of engineering lettering is single-stroke Gothic, vertical or inclined.

Capital and lower-case letters are illustrated in Fig. 5-19, with strokes suggested for their construction. Capital letters are drawn inside squares with a horizontal guideline at mid-height to give a visual guide in the construction of the letters. Capital letters are used almost entirely on most engineering drawings. The height of the letters is usually $\frac{1}{8}''$ on most drawings and guidelines are always used for uniformity. Strokes may vary with the individual, but those presented here will offer assistance to the beginner who is developing his technique.

The horizontal guidelines for the vertical, lower-case letters shown in Fig. 5-19 are based on four-unit vertical spacing. The body of the letters is two units high through the central portion of the guidelines, and one unit is left above and below for letters that extend above and/or below the body height. Lower-case letters are more often used in engineering notes and computations than on working drawings.

Both vertical letters and inclined letters are acceptable as standard forms of lettering. However, the same type of lettering should be used throughout the same drawing, rather than varying from one style to the next. The recommended angle of inclination for inclined lettering is 67.5°. The letter forms for both capital

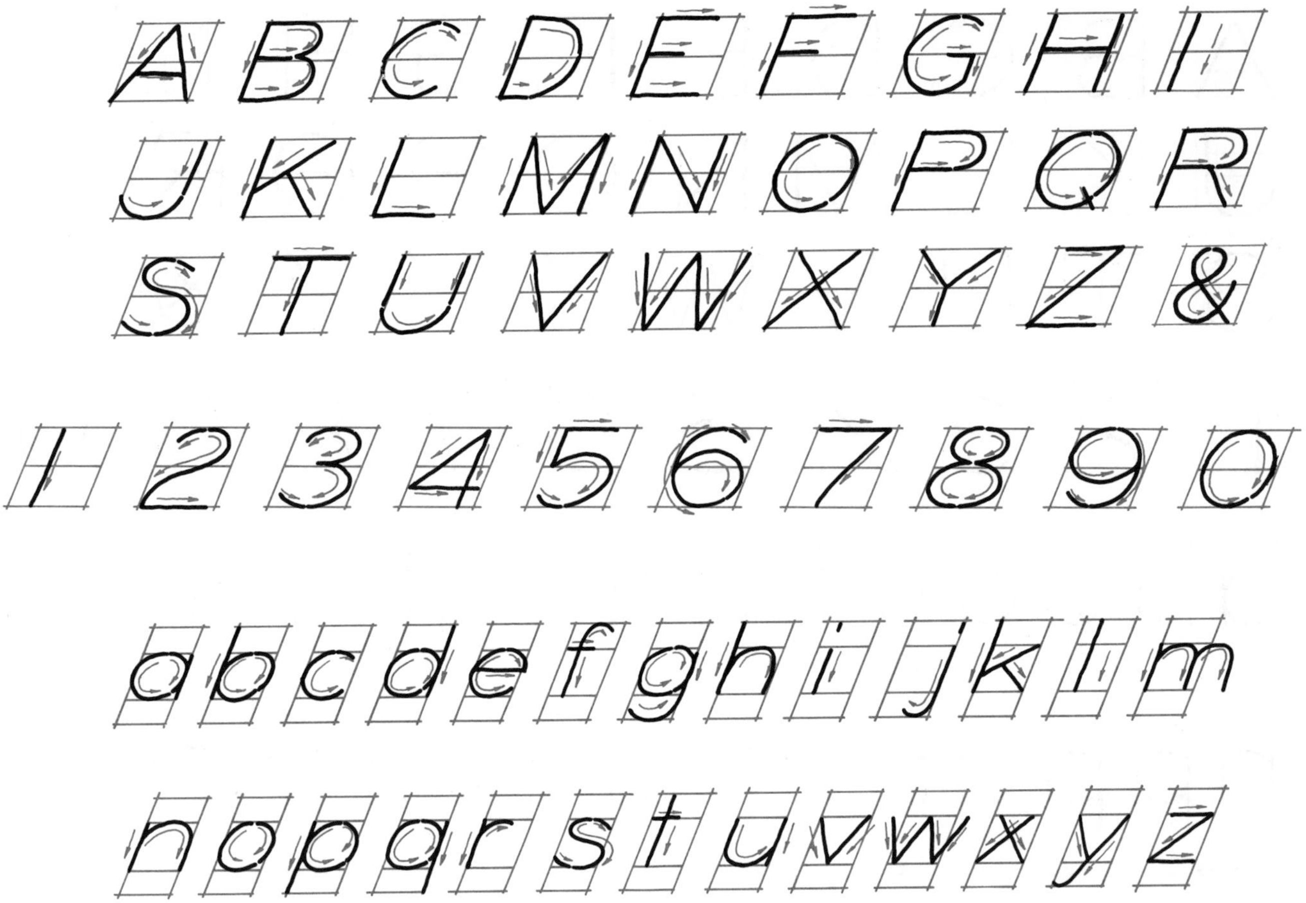

Fig. 5-20. Engineering single-stroke Gothic lettering: inclined upper- and lower-case letters with suggested strokes.

Fig. 5-21. Fractions are drawn twice as tall as whole numbers. The holes at the left are found on Braddock-Rowe lettering triangles. The numerals do not touch the crossbar of the fraction.

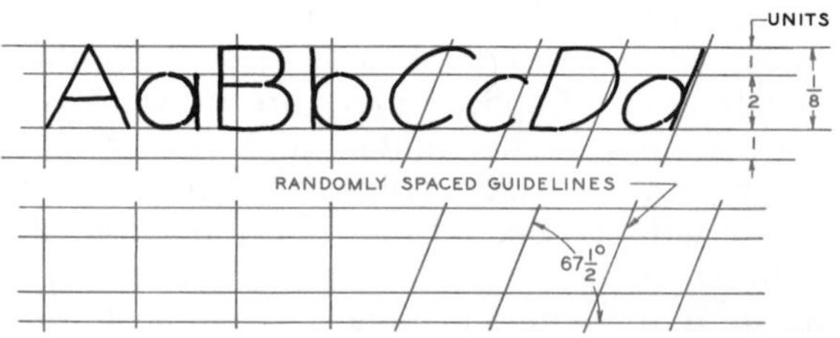

Fig. 5-22. The placement and use of guidelines for vertical and inclined letters. Vertical and inclined guidelines are randomly spaced as a visual guide.

and lower-case inclined letters are shown in Fig. 5-20. The strokes for making the letters are the same as those used in constructing vertical lettering.

Fractions for both vertical and inclined lettering are twice as tall as a single numeral (Fig. 5-21). If $\frac{1}{8}$-in. lettering is being used, as in the customary case, the fraction will be $\frac{1}{4}''$ tall with the crossbar placed at the center. The numerals used in the fraction are drawn to not touch the crossbar, so they are slightly less than $\frac{1}{8}''$ in height. It is very helpful to the improvement of lettering if randomly spaced vertical guidelines are drawn as visual guides for all lettering. Guidelines should be drawn very lightly with a 4H or 3H pencil so that they will not be noticeable. Guidelines should be used even though the lettering consists of a single letter or numeral.

A comparison of upper- and lower-case letters is given in Fig. 5-22, where both inclined and vertical styles are given. The body of lower-case letters is two-thirds the height of capital letters. Capital letters are commonly drawn to a height of $\frac{1}{8}''$ on most working drawings. This height gives adequate room and provides for ease of lettering. Larger lettering is sometimes used for special notes and titles that are used for emphasis. Vertical and inclined guidelines are used as visual guides for uniformity of lettering. No attempt is made to construct these guidelines to correspond to particular lines of letters; instead, they are merely drawn at random for convenience. Guidelines should be lightly drawn so that they do not detract from the finished lettering. The Braddock-Rowe triangle and the Ames lettering instrument are helpful in construction of uniform guidelines for lettering (see Appendix). The space between lines of lettering should be approximately the same as the height of the letter or a little less.

5-14 INTRODUCTION TO ORTHOGRAPHIC PROJECTION

The construction of orthographic views is the method whereby the draftsman prepares interpretable multiview drawings to represent a design. In this system, views of an object are projected perpendicularly onto projection planes with parallel projectors. The theory of this form of projection will be covered in greater detail in Chapter 7.

An important part of multiview drawing is the selection of pencils and line weights used to present the final engineering drawings. The following designations are used to identify the hardness of pencil leads; their uses are also given.

Designation	*Weight*	*Use*
7B	Soft	Sketching and artistic applications
6B	Soft	
5B	Soft	
4B	Soft	
3B	Soft	
2B	Soft	
B	Medium	Sketching
HB	Medium	Sketching
F	Medium	Object lines
H	Medium	Object lines
2H	Medium	Center lines
3H	Medium	Center lines
4H	Hard	For highly technical construction and accurate measurements
5H	Hard	
6H	Hard	
7H	Hard	
8H	Hard	
9H	Hard	

The medium-weight pencil grades are best suited for construction of engineering drawings that will be reproduced. Harder weights are too light to reproduce well, while the softer leads smear and give poor reproductions. The example engineering drawing shown in Fig. 5-23 gives the pencil weights recommended to achieve proper lines. The pencil weights will vary with the surface of the drawing material used. The use of standard line symbols serves to make an engineering drawing more readable and effective in communicating the idea presented.

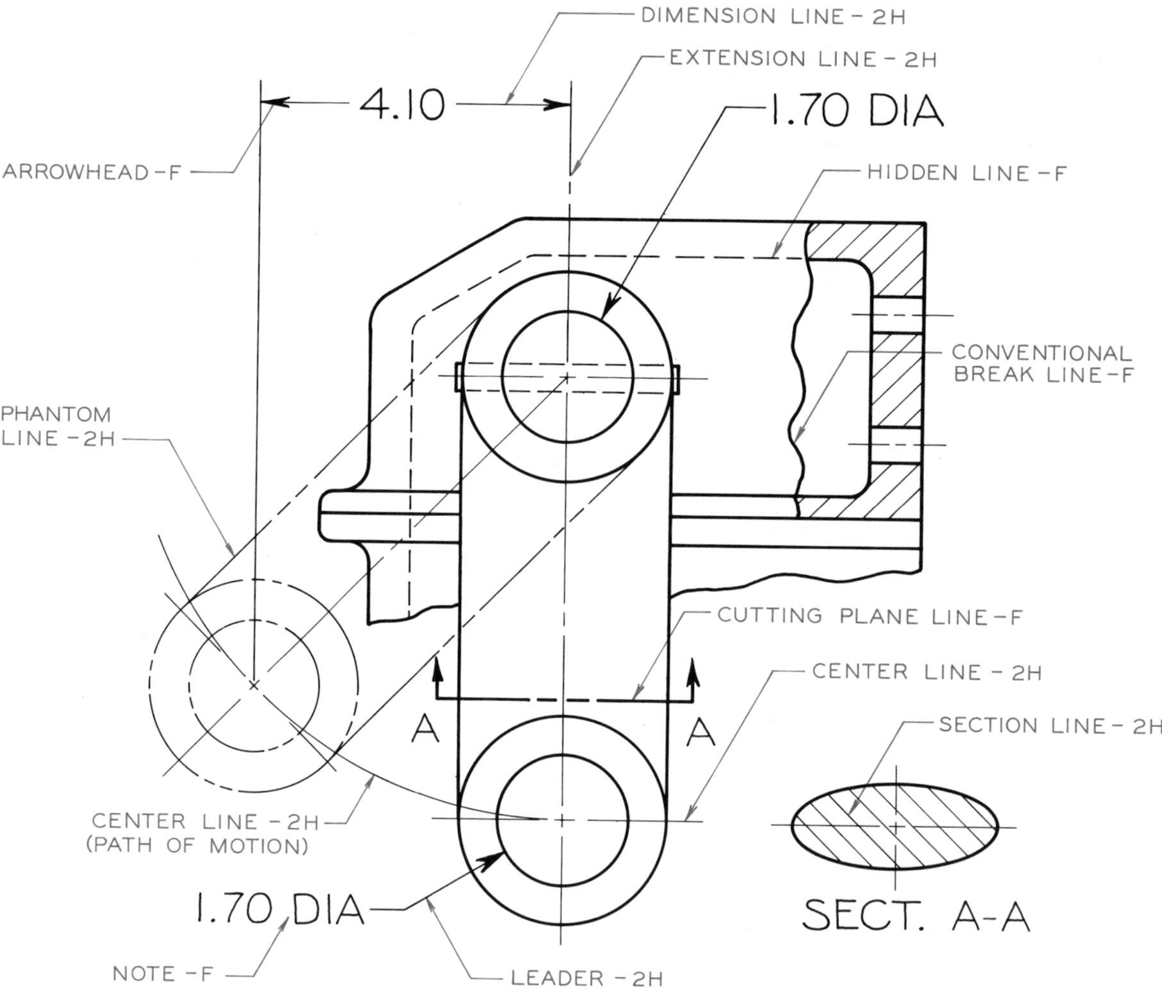

Fig. 5-23. Line weights recommended for engineering drawings, with the suggested pencil grades for each line.

5-15 THE SIX-VIEW DRAWING

The method of representing objects by a series of views drawn by the draftsman is called *orthographic projection*. Views of an object are projected perpendicularly onto projection planes with parallel projectors. The basic definition of orthographic projection is illustrated in Fig. 5-24.

Each of the projection planes is positioned to be perpendicular to the adjacent projection planes. This can be best understood by assuming that the object to be drawn is enclosed in a glass box, with the planes of the object parallel to the planes of the glass box (Fig. 5-25). The planes of the glass box represent the projection planes onto which the views will be projected with parallel projectors.

The imaginary glass box that encloses the object has six mutually perpendicular planes; hence, six principal views can be projected from any object by means of orthographic projection. The glass box is assumed to be opened into one plane (Fig. 5-26). The six views are drawn

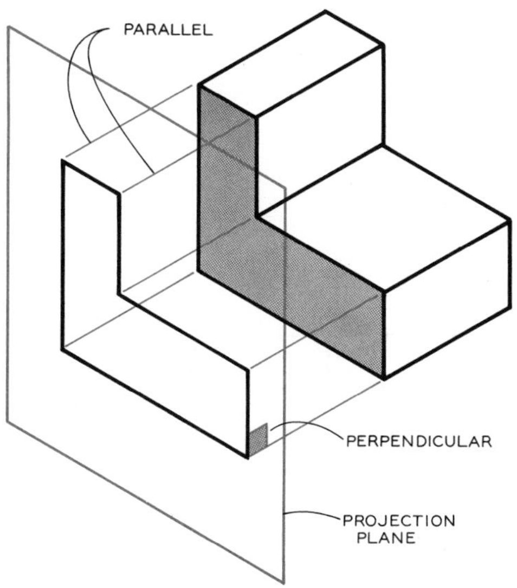

Fig. 5–24. Orthographic projection is defined as the projection of a view onto a projection plane with parallel projectors. The projectors are perpendicular to the projection plane.

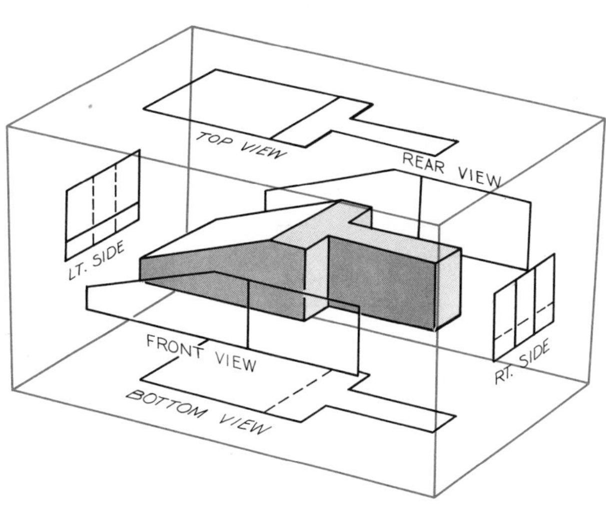

Fig. 5–25. Six principal views of an object can be drawn in orthographic projection. You can assume that the object is in a glass box with the views projected onto the six planes of projection.

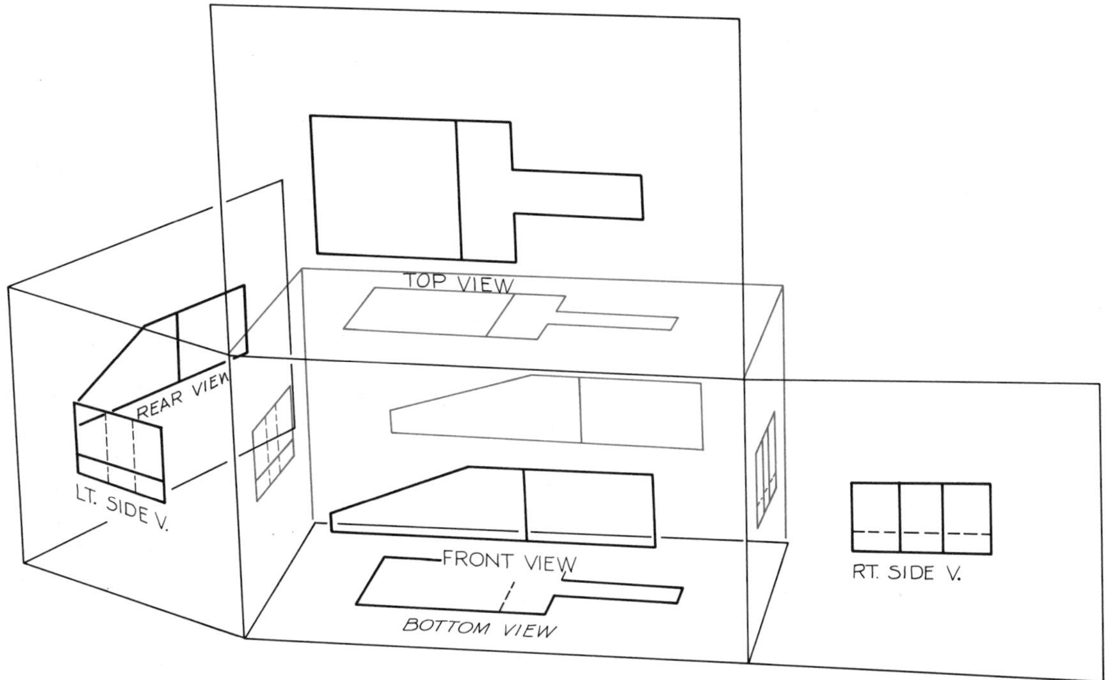

Fig. 5–26. The glass box can be opened into a common plane, the plane of the drawing paper.

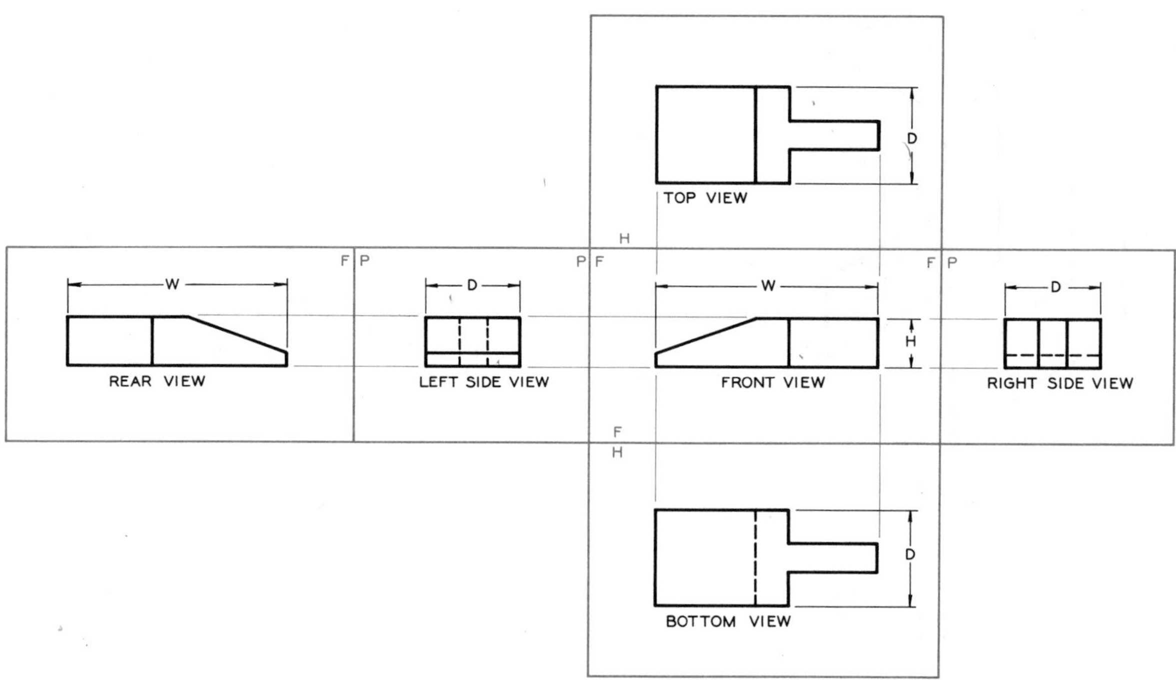

Fig. 5-27. Once the glass box is completely opened into a single plane, the six views are arranged as shown here to describe the object. Usually, the outlines of the glass planes are omitted. They are shown here to assist you in relating this figure to the previous figures.

in a logical sequence as shown in Fig. 5-27. The top view is placed over the front view, the bottom view under the front view, the right side view to the right of the front view, and the left side view to the left of the front view. The rear view is placed to the left of the left side view.

Each of these views could be seen by an observer who moved about the object to the six positions; the orthographic projection simply provides a composite of the six views in a conventional arrangement. Analysis of the composite makes it possible to visualize the object as a three-dimensional solid.

Note that the views are positioned so that four views can be projected horizontally in a row using the same height (*H*). The three vertically positioned views utilize the same width (*W*). This aids with the construction of the drawings of the views, since the dimensions can be projected from view to view. This procedure reduces the number of dimensions that must be measured during construction.

The principal dimensions are height (*H*), width (*W*), and depth (*D*). These dimensions will be represented by numerals on a finished working drawing. Note that a six-view drawing is dimensioned with two rows of dimensions to give the most orderly appearance and most readable arrangement (Fig. 5-27). Since the height dimension is common to four views, it can be dimensioned in only one view, the front view, and need not be repeated in the other views horizontally adjacent to the front view. Likewise, one width dimension serves the three vertically positioned views.

The three principal projection planes used in orthographic projection are the *horizontal*, the *frontal*, and the *profile*. Abbreviations *H*, *F*, and *P* are used on each side of the fold lines of Fig. 5-27 to label these projection planes.

It is very important that the six views of orthographic projection be positioned as shown in Fig. 5-27. Correctly drawn views that are not positioned in this arrangement cannot be interpreted as easily as when they are properly located. Also, they are more difficult to draw when arranged differently.

Some lines of an object will not be visible in a particular view; these lines are indicated with dashed lines called *hidden lines.* Showing lines as hidden lines may clarify details that might otherwise be overlooked.

The line weights for orthographic views should correspond to those in Fig. 5-23; the pencil grades listed there should be used. The most commonly used lines are shown in Fig. 5-28. When a drawing is made at a large scale, the weight of the lines is heavier than on a smaller drawing. The segments of a hidden line are longer in a large drawing than a small drawing. The dimensions given in Fig. 5-28 are average dimensions that can be used as a guide to construct orthographic views. The proper weight of drawing lines is essential to a readable drawing.

Six views are seldom required to describe an object. Usually, three or four views are adequate to identify its features.

5-16 THE THREE-VIEW DRAWING

The most commonly used orthographic arrangement is the three-view drawing composed of the front, top, and right side views. The reason is that three views are usually adequate to explain the shape of an object; in addition, the top, front, and right side views are so positioned that it is easy for the draftsman to lay them out.

The glass box theory introduced in Fig. 5-25 is used to illustrate the relationship between the three views of an object in Fig. 5-29. Objects that do not have an easily identifiable front view are positioned so that the front view is the most representative view, and the other views are projected from the front view. The three

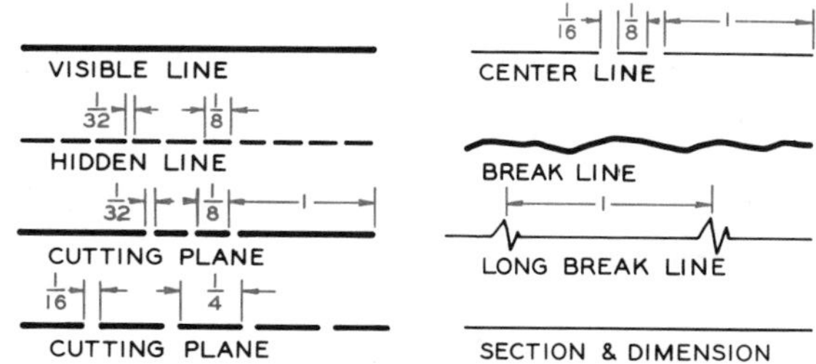

Fig. 5-28. A comparison of the line weights for lines that are used in engineering drawings. The dimensions should be approximated by eye when drawn.

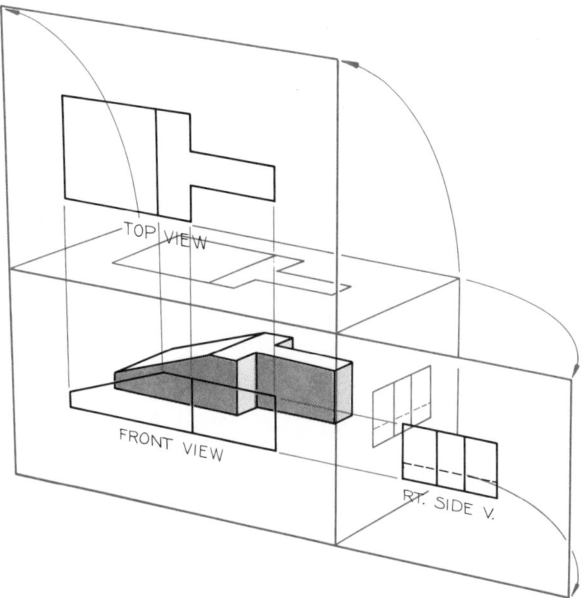

Fig. 5-29. Three-view drawings are commonly used for describing machine parts and other designs. The glass box is used to illustrate how the views are projected to their projection planes.

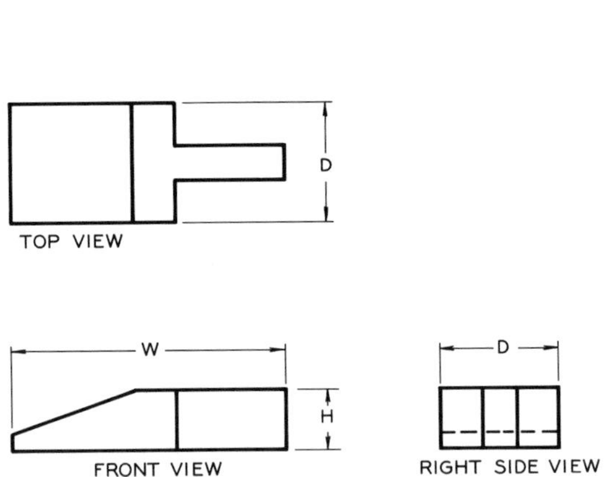

Fig. 5-30. The three orthographic views of the part that was illustrated in Fig. 5-29.

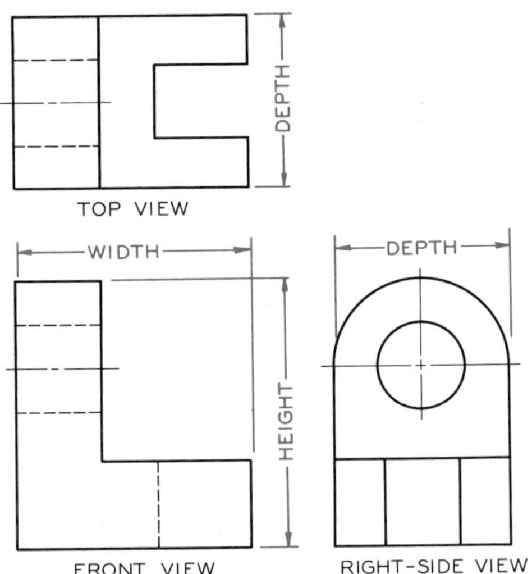

Fig. 5-32. The standard arrangement for a three-view orthographic drawing.

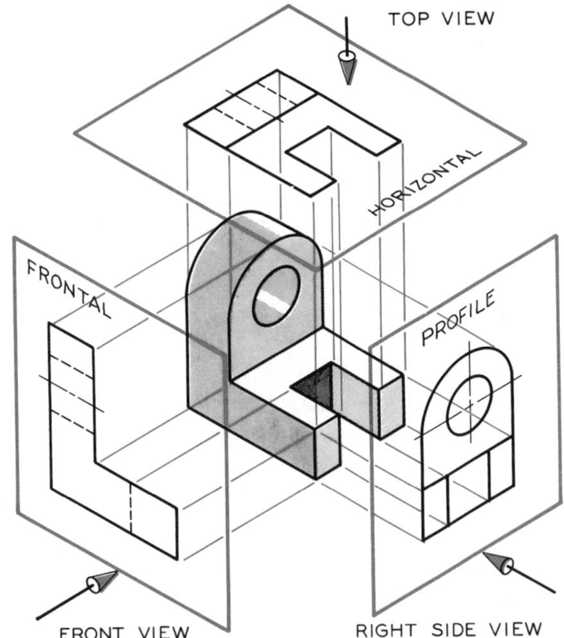

Fig. 5-31. Orthographic projection of three principal views onto the principal planes—horizontal, front, and profile.

orthographic views of the object in Fig. 5-29 are drawn as shown in Fig. 5-30.

Another example of a three-view drawing is shown in Fig. 5-31. The arrows represent the observer's lines of sight for viewing these three principal views. The resulting orthographic views are drawn in the arrangement shown in Fig. 5-32. Note that the most representative views with the fewest hidden lines have been selected. The left side view would have had more hidden lines than the right side view. If the views had been selected as shown in Fig. 5-33, the resulting right side view would have had hidden lines because of a poor choice of views.

It is not necessary that the three views always be the top, front, and right side views. It is only necessary that the three views selected be in the proper sequence so that they will be adjacent to each other. You may wish to use the front, top, and left side views in some cases.

Center lines are used in the three views of the object in Fig. 5-32 to call attention to the circular features of the object. The method of applying center lines to a drawing is illustrated in Fig. 5-34. Center lines are very thin lines with long and short dashes. In the circular view, the center lines are crossing at the exact center of the circle or arc. The crossing of the short dashes locates the center for drilling a hole or drawing the circular feature. Center lines should extend about $\frac{1}{8}''$ beyond the arc to which they apply in the circular view.

The rectangular view of the circular hole or feature cannot be interpreted as being cylindrical without a center line. Consequently, center lines are very helpful in clarifying a drawing. Center lines are secondary lines; that is, they are not absolutely necessary to a drawing. Therefore, they should be omitted if they confuse a drawing or if they coincide with a hidden or visible line (Fig. 5-34).

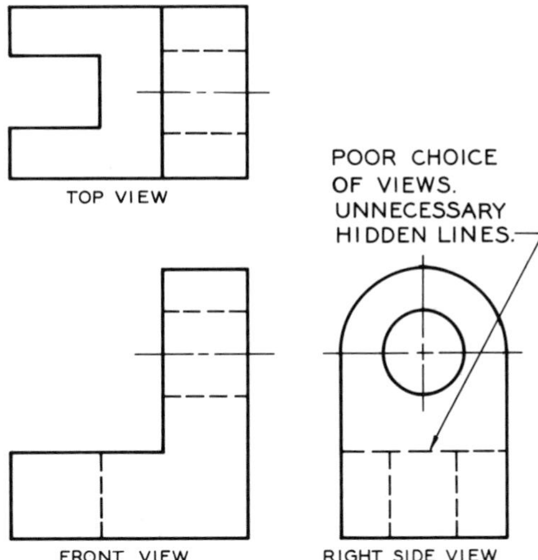

Fig. 5-33. When three views of an object are drawn, you should select the three best views with the fewest hidden lines. The selection of views here is not as good as the selection in Fig. 5-32.

5-17 THE THREE-VIEW SKETCH

The designer may sketch his preliminary ideas in the form of freehand orthographic sketches because this permits him to work more rapidly. Grid paper is very helpful for this purpose when instruments will not be used. Grid paper is also available commercially for pictorial sketches (Fig. 5-35). Orthographic sketches are usually drawn with a single pencil such as an F or HB. Freehand sketches are valuable for the communication and development of preliminary ideas during the ideation process.

Whether it is a sketch or an instrument drawing, the layout of a three-view drawing should be approached in much the same manner. The procedure is given in step form in Fig. 5-35. A pictorial sketch of a part is given, and we are required to construct three orthographic views. It is important that the proper proportions be maintained to give a realistic representation of the part in the three-view sketch. Since labels and principal dimensions will be given, space must be provided between the views for this information. The width, height, and depth are blocked in to indicate the general overall proportions of the part in step 1. Guidelines are drawn

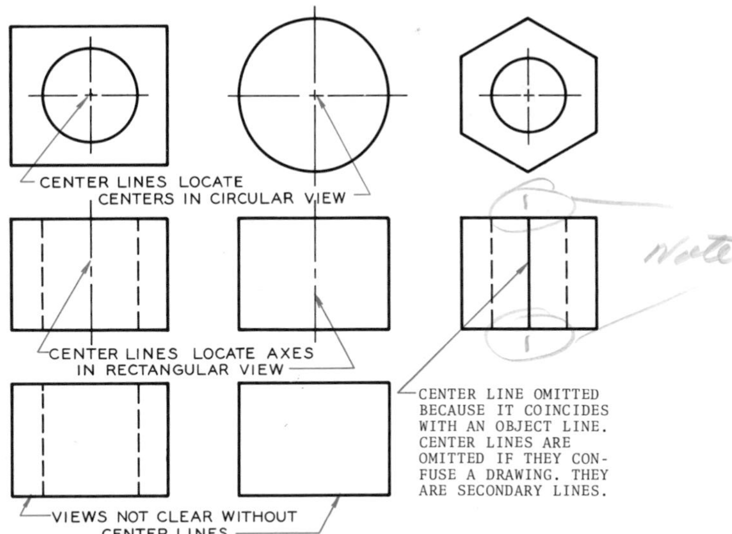

Fig. 5-34. Center lines are used to define cylindrical shapes, both external cylinders and interior holes.

FIGURE 5–35. LAYOUT OF A THREE-VIEW SKETCH

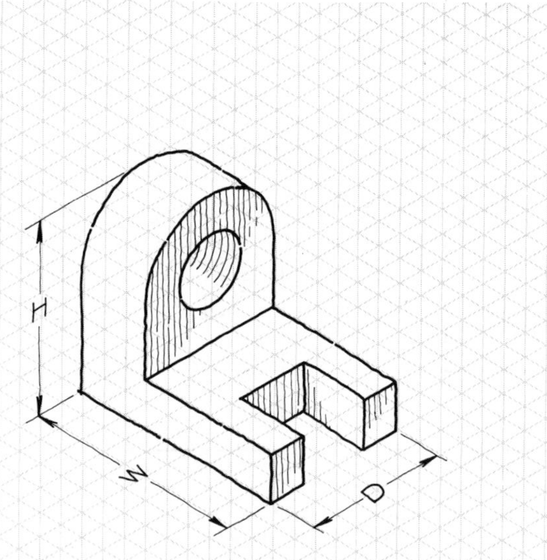

Given: A pictorial sketch of an object.
Required: Lay out a three-view sketch that will describe this object. Indicate general dimensions and label all views.
Reference: Article 5–17.

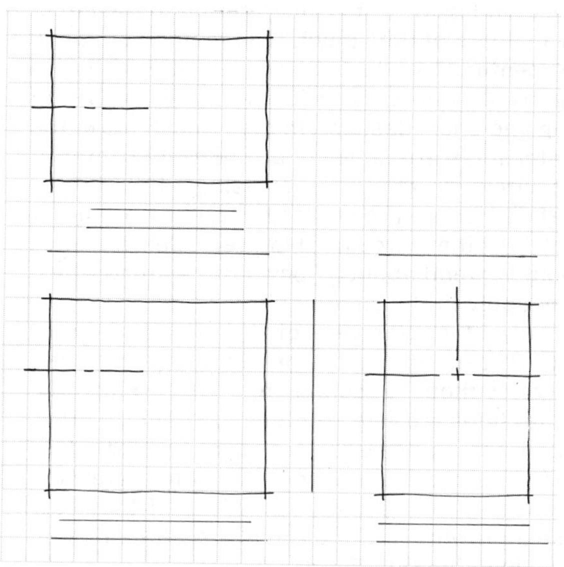

Step 1: Use the overall dimensions of the object to block in the general proportions of the part. Leave space between the views for labels and dimension lines. Project the depth of the top view to side views as shown. Guide lines for lettering should be made with a straight edge.

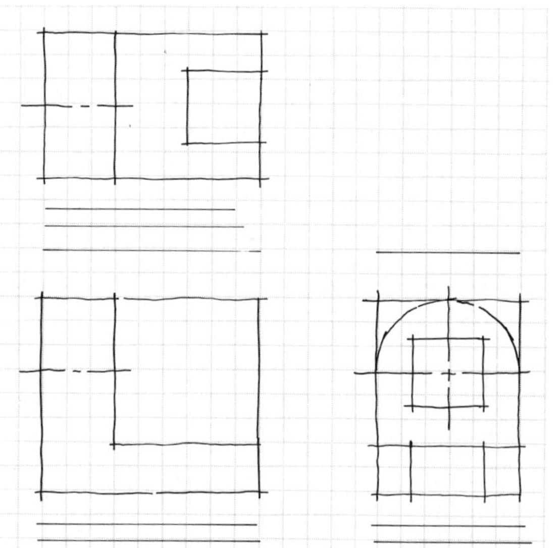

Step 2: Sketch in the remaining features, observing the proportions of the views. Project these lines to each view. Draw all construction lines lightly so that erasure will be unnecessary.

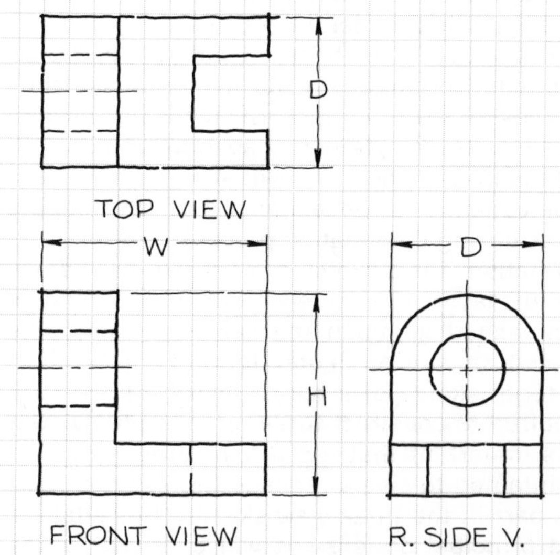

Step 3: Darken the lines with a medium-weight pencil (F or HB) to conform to the standard line weights. Add dimension lines, using *D*, *W*, and *H* to represent depth, width, and height. Label the views with $\frac{1}{8}''$ letters. Center lines aid in the interpretation of the views.

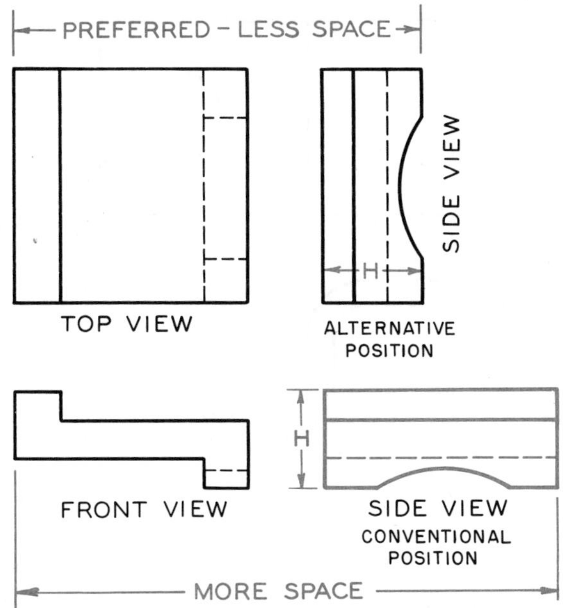

Fig. 5–36. Alternative position for the side view in orthographic drawing arrangement. (Courtesy of ANSI; Y14.3–1957.)

with a straightedge for the labels and dimensions. Note that the depth in the right side view can be transferred from the top view with your dividers.

Additional details are sketched in step 2. The notch is drawn in the top and projected to the front view. The circular shape in the side view is sketched using center lines and construction lines as guides for the arc. The lines are darkened to the appropriate quality in step 3 to complete the views. The views are labeled and dimensions of *W*, *D*, and *H* are indicated between the views as shown.

An alternative position for the location of the right side view in a three-view drawing is shown in Fig. 5–36. When the side view is projected directly from the top view, as shown, the sketch requires less width and makes better use of the available space. Whichever location is chosen, the right side view is drawn exactly the same, since the only difference is in the arrangement.

You have probably noticed that the depth dimension cannot be directly projected to the side views as width can be projected from the top to the front view. Three methods that can be used to transfer the depth dimension from the top view to the right side view are shown in Fig. 5–37. Any of these methods can be used,

FIGURE 5–37. TRANSFERRING DEPTH DIMENSIONS

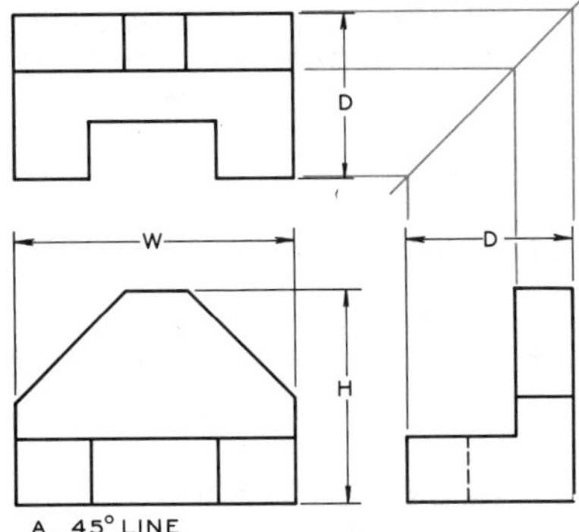

A. The depth dimension can be projected from the top view to the right side view by constructing a 45° line positioned as shown.

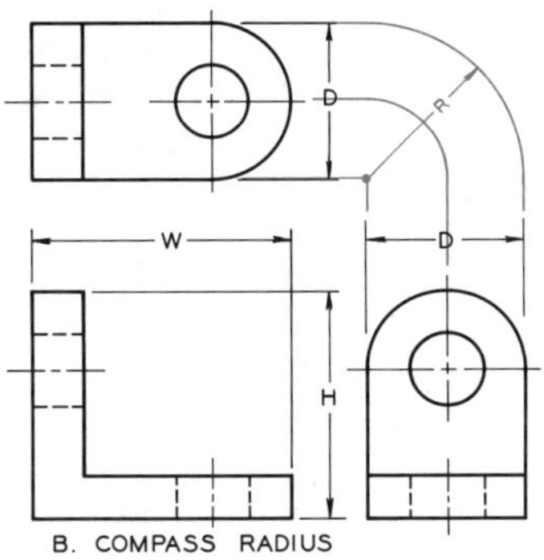

B. The depth dimension can be projected from the top view to the side view using a compass and a common center.

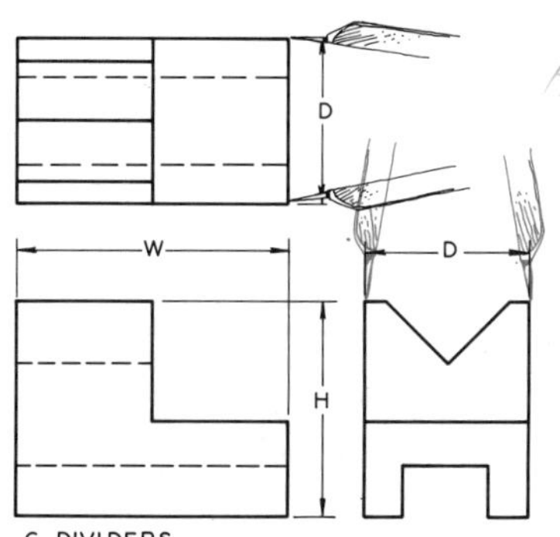

C. The depth dimension can be transferred from the top view to the side view using dividers or a scale.

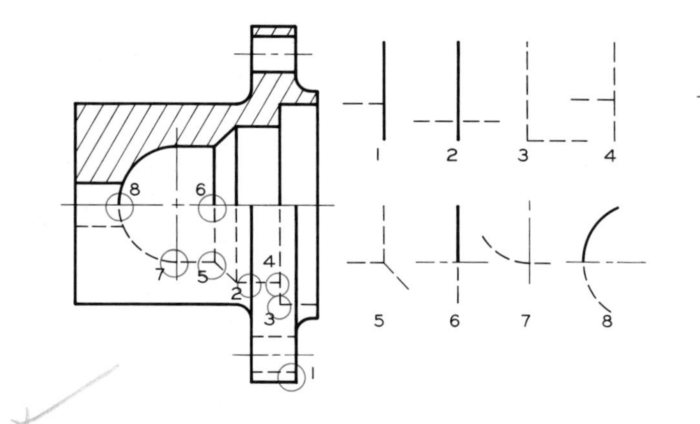

Fig. 5-38. Standards for the intersections of lines on engineering drawings.

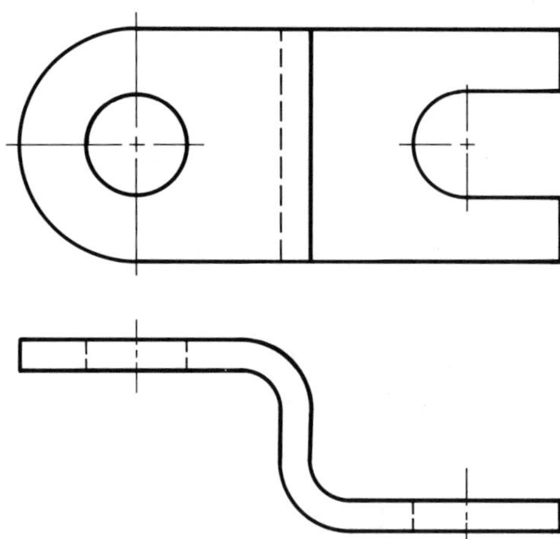

Fig. 5-41. An object requiring only two views to give its description.

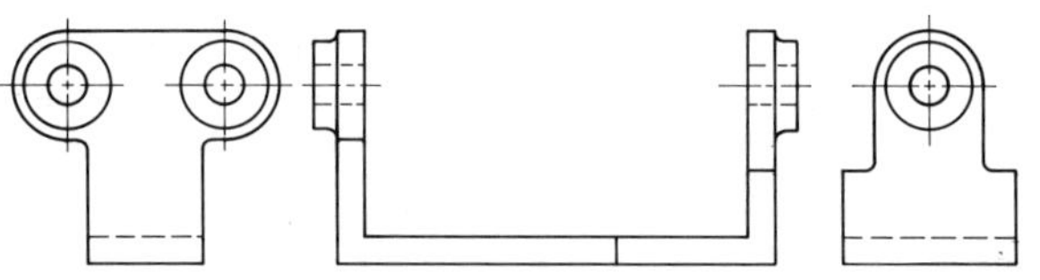

Fig. 5-39. An acceptable arrangement of views where unnecessary hidden lines are omitted.

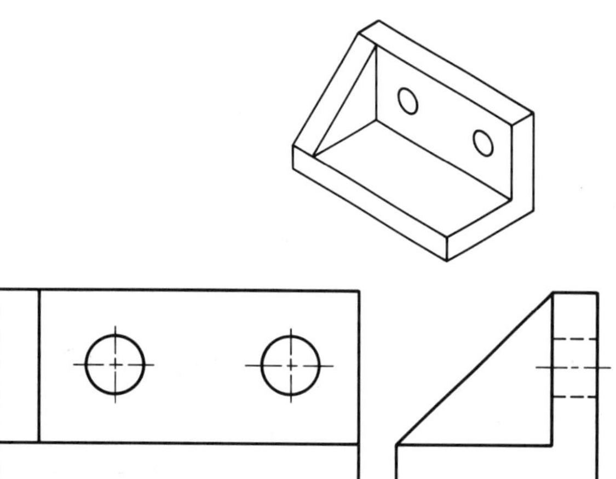

Fig. 5-40. An object requiring only two views to give its description.

but the method shown in C, where dividers are used, is preferred.

5-18 INTERSECTING LINE TECHNIQUES

Orthographic views are frequently composed of many intersections of hidden and visible lines as illustrated in Fig. 5-38. It is customary that standardized procedures be followed in joining these lines to give the best effect. Enlarged examples of the intersections are shown in the figure. These conventions for showing intersections, which are based on appearance and function, have become standard and should be used wherever possible.

5-19 TWO-VIEW DRAWINGS

Some drawings can be adequately explained in two views which depict the shape of an object or the information that is to be communicated in these views.

Hidden lines may be omitted in some cases to give a clearer description of an object. An example of this type of drawing is Fig. 5-39. Here, a front view and one side view could be used, but the hidden lines would confuse the

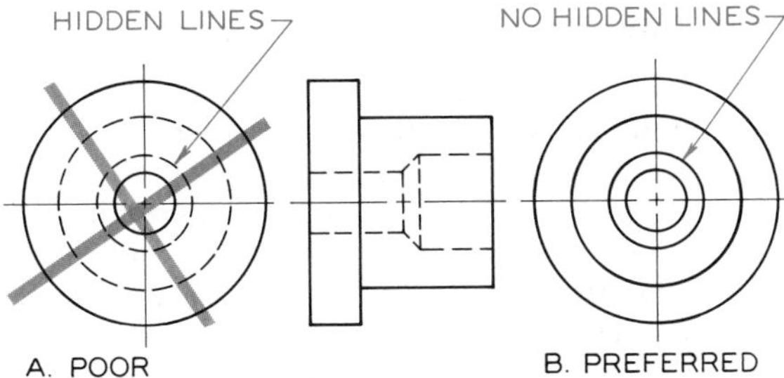

Fig. 5-42. Views should be chosen to avoid hidden lines when possible.

interpretation of a single side view. Instead, two side views are used, and the unnecessary hidden lines are omitted.

The object shown in Fig. 5-40 is adequately described in two views, making the third view unnecessary. Likewise, the front and top views of the part shown in Fig. 5-41 are sufficient to completely describe it. The elimination of unnecessary views reduces drawing time and effort.

When views are selected in a multiview drawing, it is better practice to select the views with the fewest hidden lines to give a better representation of the part. Such an example is Fig. 5-42, where the right side view is preferred over the left side view since it has fewer hidden lines.

Certain conventional practices are accepted where possible to conserve drawing time. Figure 5-43 is an example of a half-view that is adequate to describe the shape of the cylindrical part. When the half-view is used, the half that is drawn should be the one closer to the adjacent view. This arrangement gives a more direct relationship between the two views. The rear side of the half-view is bounded by a center line rather than the object line, thus indicating that the view is actually a conventional half-view. Another conventional practice for two-view drawings is illustrated in Fig. 5-44, where an inclined part is revolved into a horizontal position in the front view. This revolution permits a true projection in the top view that is more descriptive of the object than a conventional three-view drawing.

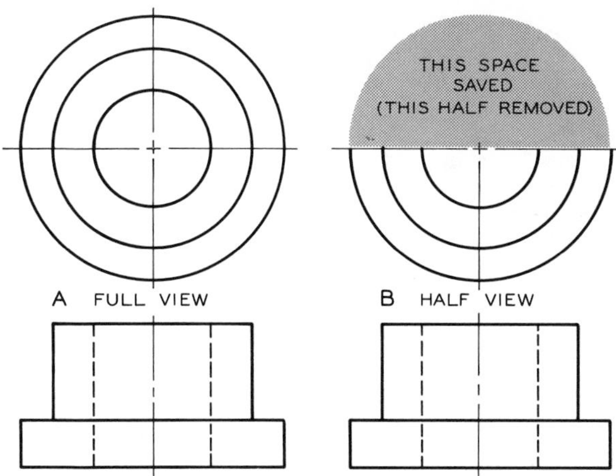

Fig. 5-43. Cylindrical and symmetrical shapes may be shown with half views to conserve space and drafting time. The half that is away from the adjacent view is the half that is omitted.

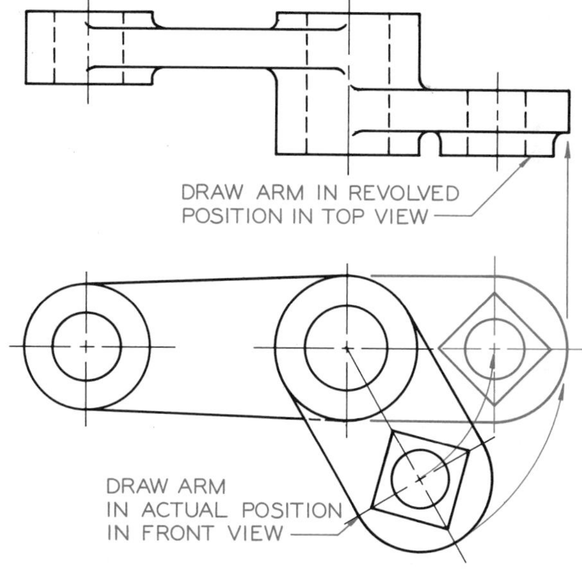

Fig. 5-44. It is conventional practice to draw the top view of a part of this type as if it were revolved in line with the horizontal member.

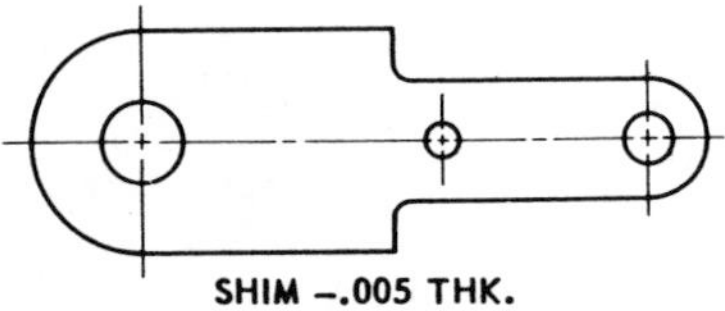

Fig. 5–45A. A part requiring only one view to adequately give its description. (Courtesy of ANSI; Y14.3–1957.)

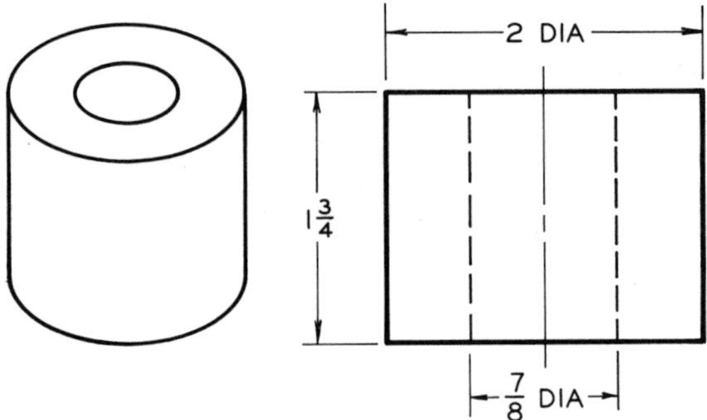

Fig. 5–45B. A cylinder can be described with one view. Note "DIA" is used to emphasize its circular characteristic.

5-20 SINGLE-VIEW DRAWINGS

Parts made of sheet metal or other materials of a constant thickness can be described with only one view and a note to indicate thickness. An example of this type of drawing is given in Fig. 5–45A. Other examples requiring only one view are nuts, bolts, and cylindrical shapes (Fig. 5–45B). The rectangular views are accompanied by notes which specify thicknesses or diameters.

5-21 CURVE PLOTTING

Not all drawings are composed of straight lines and planes. Often it is necessary to plot an irregular curve on a view of a drawing.

An example of curve plotting is shown in Fig. 5–46. The front and side views are complete but the top view is incomplete. In step 1, a series of points is projected from the front view to the side view and the points are numbered. In step 2, points 1, 2, and 3 are projected from the front and side views to locate corresponding points in the top view. In step 3, points 3, 4, and 5 are projected to the top view. The five points are then connected with the aid of an irregular curve to complete the drawing.

This same technique was used to find the elliptical view of the hole in the top view of Fig.

FIGURE 5–46. PLOTTING CURVED LINES

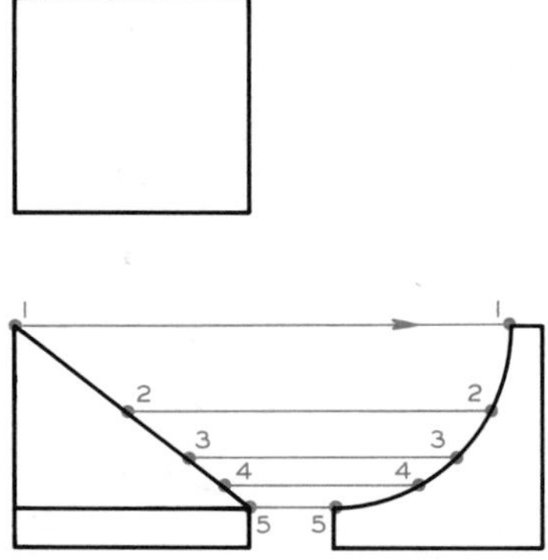

Step 1: To plot curved lines in orthographic projection, begin by locating and numbering points in two views.

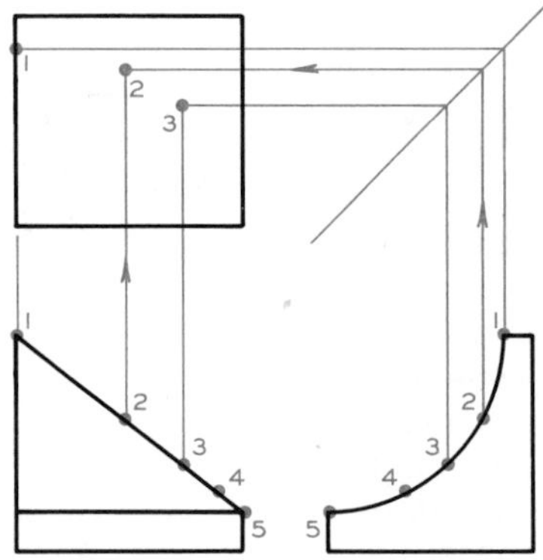

Step 2: The two views of each point are projected to the third view, where the projectors intersect to locate the points.

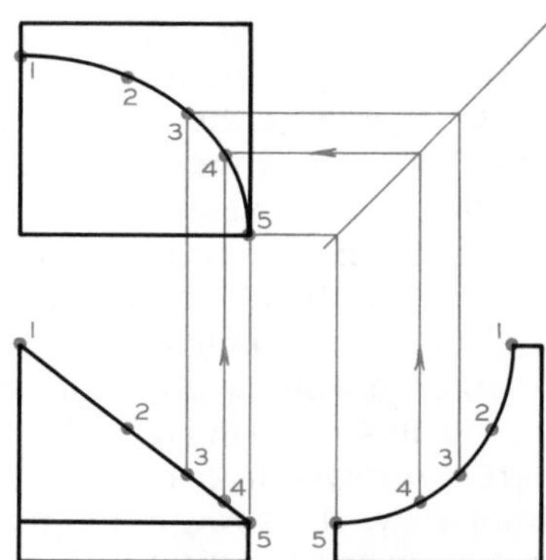

Step 3: All points are projected in this manner. The points are connected with the aid of an irregular curve.

5–47. Points are located in the given views and projected to the top view, where they are connected.

More accuracy is attained if the points are placed closer together.

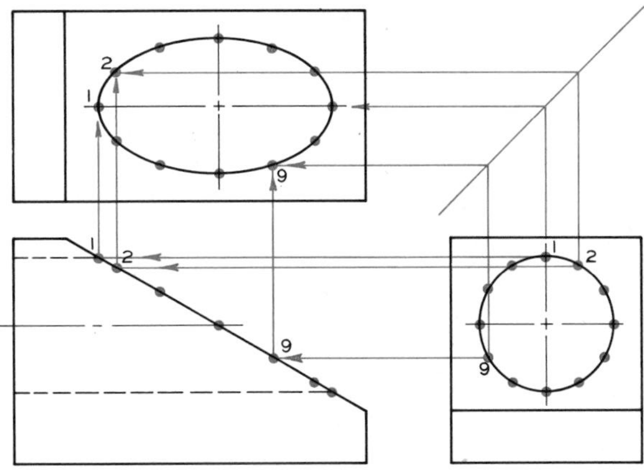

Fig. 5–47. The elliptical view of the hole in the top view was obtained by curve plotting.

5–22 CONVENTIONAL INTERSECTIONS

For the sake of improved clarity, it is sometimes necessary to utilize practices that may be violations of the strict rules of orthographic projection. The violation of rules to clarify a drawing is called *conventional practice*. Examples of conventional practice will be discussed in the following paragraphs.

In orthographic views, many of the lines of intersection between planes are obscured because the joints are rounded. The rounded corners, inside and outside, that are usually found on metal parts are illustrated in Fig. 5–48. A *round* is a rounded exterior corner; a *fillet* is a rounded interior corner. Fillets and rounds add strength to a part, are easy to produce, and make the part attractive.

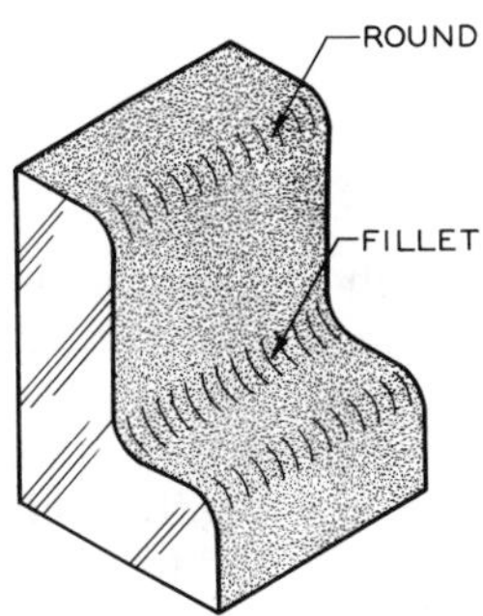

Fig. 5–48. Fillets and rounds.

Four examples of intersections are shown in Fig. 5–49 in which the front views are drawn both with and without fillets. Note that at the intersections between the features without fillets straight lines of intersection are drawn. Where there are fillets, the line of intersection

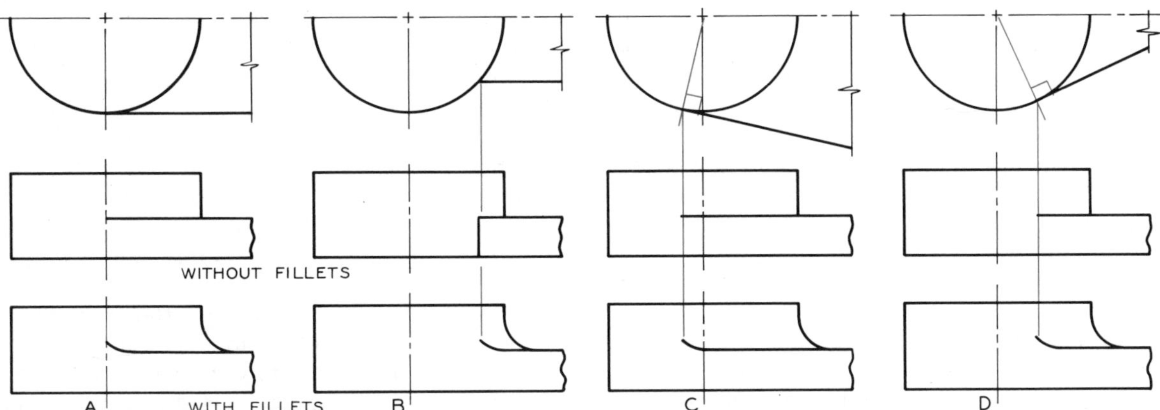

Fig. 5–49. Examples of intersections between parts of objects with and without fillets.

FIGURE 5-50. PLOTTING A RUNOUT

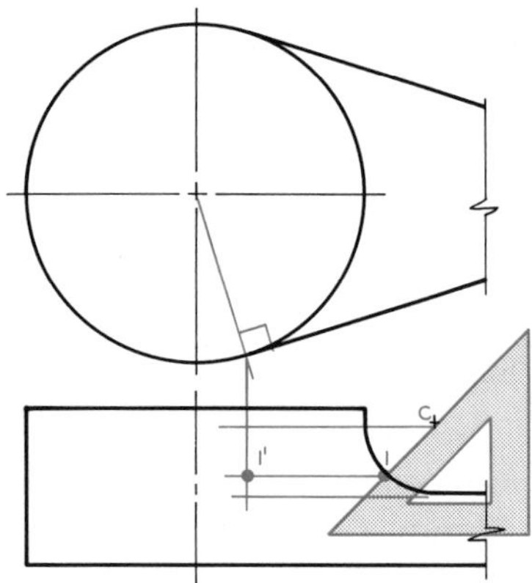

Step 1: The point of tangency between the circular part and the edge is found in the top view and projected to the front view. A 45° triangle is used to find point 1, which is projected to locate point 1′.

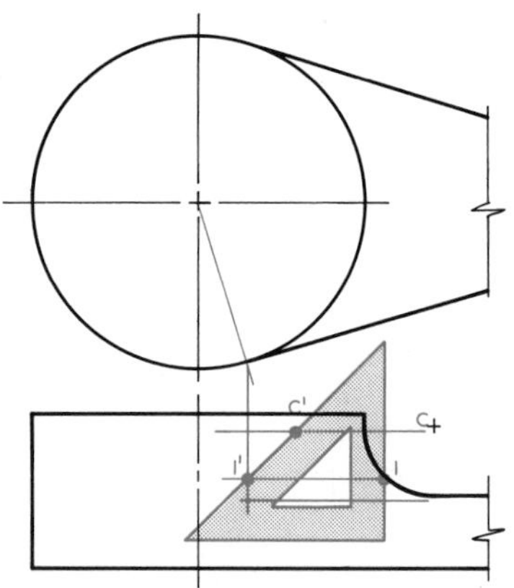

Step 2: A 45° triangle is used to locate point *C′*, which is on the horizontal projector from the center of the fillet, *C*.

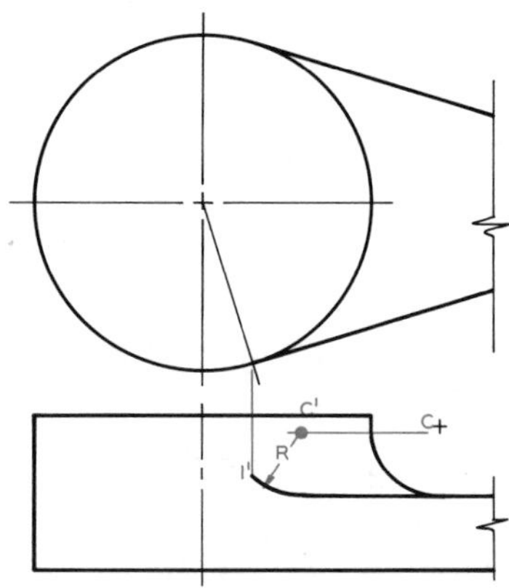

Step 3: The radius of the fillet is used to draw the runout with *C′* as the center. The runout arc is equal to one-eighth of a circle.

at the point of tangency in each problem ends with a curved line called a *runout*. The runout is drawn as illustrated in Fig. 5-50.

The runout is drawn with the same radius as the fillet. The length of the arc forming the runout is one-eighth of a total circle. A 45° triangle can be used to perform this construction as shown in Fig. 5-50.

The draftsman will find that most of the parts that are made in the foundry by casting have fillets and rounds on most corners. It is helpful if his drawings describe these features that might otherwise be overlooked. The part in Fig. 5-51A is designed to have fillets and rounds on each edge as illustrated in the pictorial sketch. The top and front views show how these fillets and their runouts are drawn. You may approximate these by eye instead of attempting the tedious process of plotting each point. A circle template can be used advantageously for drawing the runouts, thus saving drafting time.

You will note that the object shown in Fig. 5-51B varies somewhat from the example in A. In this case the rib has a rounded cross section, not just rounded corners. The runouts in this example are shown differently so that this feature can be recognized by looking at the top and front views.

Some parts are designed to have cylindrical or elliptical cross sections. Two examples are shown in Fig. 5-52 with fillets at the intersections. In part A, the horizontal member is elliptical in cross section and intersects the vertical cylinder. The line of intersection is approximated as shown with the aid of an irregular curve. In part B, both members are cylindrical. Since the intersection is filleted, there will be no sharp line of intersection. To approximate the intersection, only partial lines are drawn with an irregular curve as shown in the figure.

When cylinders intersect without fillets, the line of intersection will be a visible line, as shown in the examples in Fig. 5-53. When a relatively small cylinder intersects a larger cylinder, the line of intersection is conventionally shown as in part A, with no attempt made to plot the line of intersection. For intersecting cylinders of approximately the same size (part B), the line of intersection is drawn as an arc that passes through points 1, 2, and 3. The

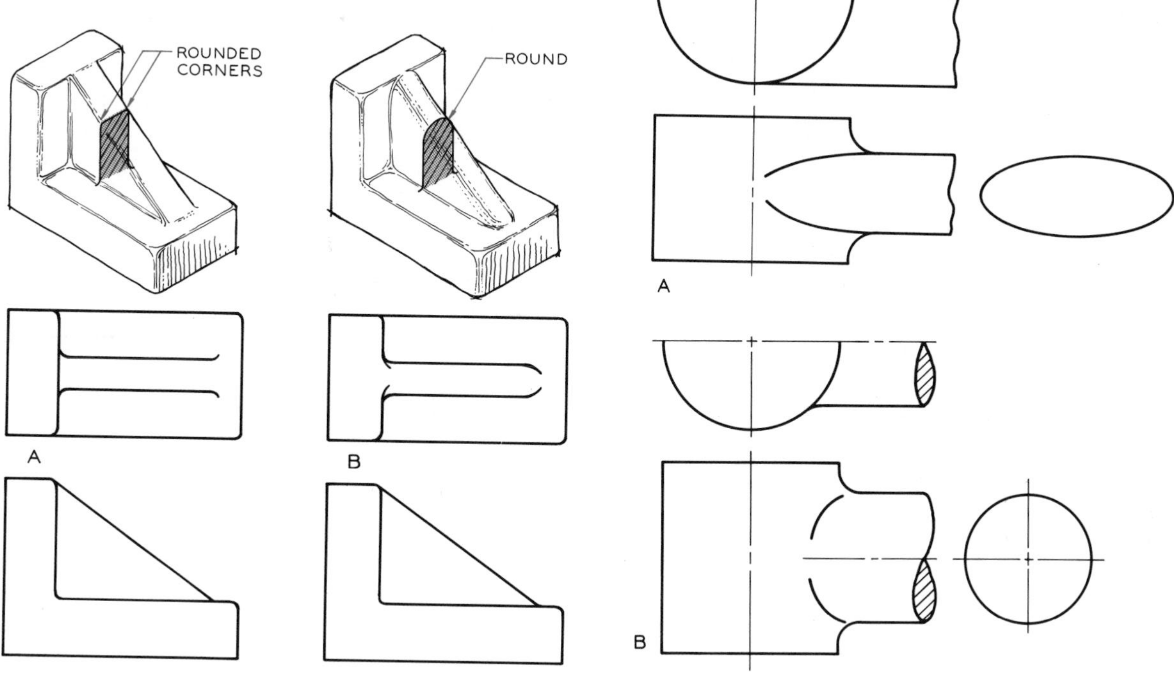

Fig. 5-51. Conventional intersections of ribs with rounded corner (A) and ribs with a completely rounded cross section (B).

Fig. 5-52. Conventional methods of representing intersections of elliptical and cylindrical shapes. These intersections are drawn by approximation.

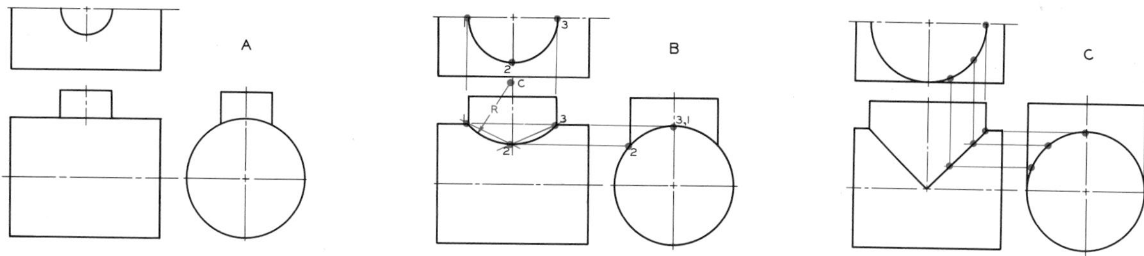

Fig. 5-53. Conventional intersections of cylindrical shapes.

center can be found by extending the perpendicular bisectors of chords 1–2 and 2–3 to their point of intersection. The intersection shown in part C is a true projection, since the cylinders have equal diameters and would actually intersect in this manner. Points are plotted to illustrate the method of finding the line of intersection.

Some conventional practices for illustrating the intersections of circular and rectangular

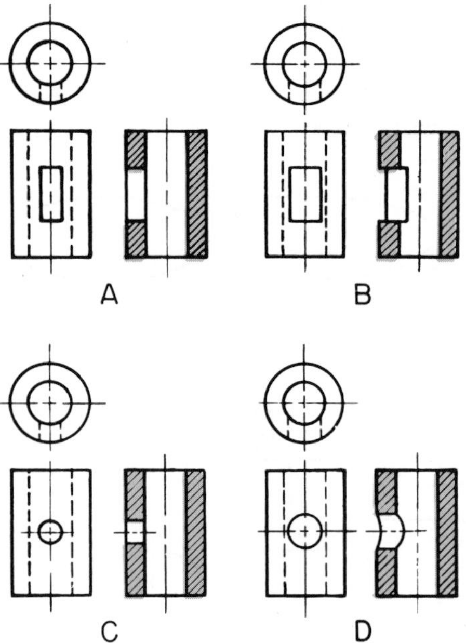

Fig. 5-54. Conventional intersections of holes in cylindrical shapes. The views with the crosshatching represent cross sections through the objects.

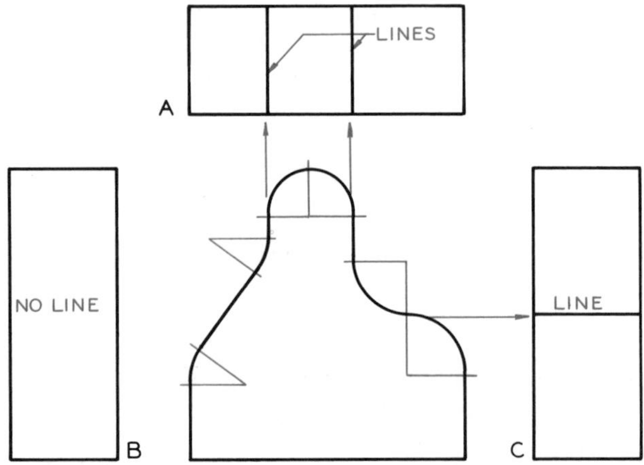

Fig. 5-55. Examples of the use of visible lines to complete a view.

holes in cylindrical shapes are shown in Fig. 5-54. Where the hole is narrow or small, as in parts A and C, the intersection is merely shown as a hole in the outer wall of the cylinder. A wider rectangular hole would be conventionally drawn as shown in part B. A medium-sized circular hole intersecting a cylinder would be constructed with circular arcs passing through the three points, as shown in part D. The construction of this example is similar to that of part B of Fig. 5-53.

The intersections discussed here are approximate intersections that are sufficient for most drafting applications; they involve a minimum expenditure of time. Exact intersections for larger parts and objects fabricated from sheet metal will be covered in Chapter 11. Accurate intersections must be plotted point by point.

5-23 CONVENTIONAL PRACTICES

As previously defined, a conventional practice is a method of preparing a drawing that has been found to be effective even though the method may deviate from rules in the strict sense. Many of the conventional practices are described in drafting standards, but some situations will require the draftsman to use his own judgment to prepare the most readable drawing.

An example of conventional practices is shown in Fig. 5-55. In general, when planes intersect with a large curve, the line of intersection between the planes is not visible to the eye and therefore no lines of intersection are shown in the view (part B). In part A, two lines are shown to represent the two vertical planes that appear as edges in the top view. The view in part C has a single line to represent the point where the two arcs of the object are tangent. This intersection forms a very thin horizontal plane that must be shown with a line.

A conventional practice for drawing parts with curved intersections is shown in Fig. 5-56. Since there are no sharp intersections at the corners of the object, by strict application of the rules the circular view would have no lines. The circular view would not be very descriptive if this rule were followed; consequently, conventional practices are followed instead. The imaginary corners of the object in the right side

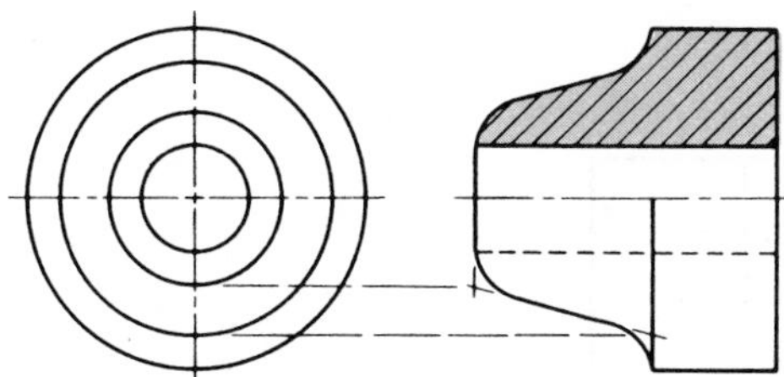

Fig. 5–56. Conventional projection of rounded and filleted corners in views and sections. (Courtesy of ANSI; Y14.2-1957.)

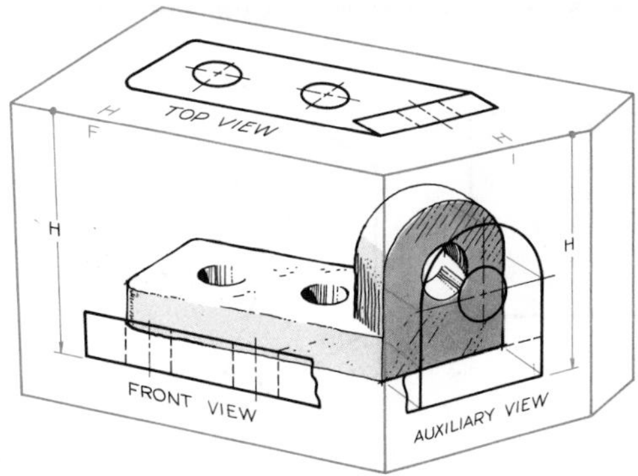

Fig. 5–57A. A pictorial showing the relationship of the projection planes used to find the true size of the inclined plane.

view are drawn as if they were not rounded, and these imaginary intersections are projected to the circular view where circles are drawn to represent these intersections. Thin extension lines are drawn on the right side view to locate the imaginary corners.

5–24 PRIMARY AUXILIARY VIEWS

Primary auxiliary views are forms of orthographic projections, since they are projected perpendicularly onto projection planes. They are described as auxiliary projections, since they are not in the principal positions but are inclined to a principal plane and appear as edges in principal views. An example of this is given pictorially in Fig. 5–57A. A surface is positioned so that it is inclined to the frontal plane and perpendicular to the horizontal plane, where it appears as an edge. The true size and shape of this surface can be found in a primary auxiliary projected from a primary view onto a plane positioned parallel to the inclined surface. This plane is called the auxiliary plane. The auxiliary plane is opened into the horizontal plane in Fig. 5–57B. The nomenclature used to letter the projection planes should be observed. At each fold line, letters are used to designate the intersection of the principal planes. The fold line between the frontal and horizontal planes is labeled H-F. The intersection between the holizontal plane and the auxiliary plane is lettered H-1. These designations can be seen in Fig. 5–57C, where the design is constructed in the orthographic, multiview arrangement.

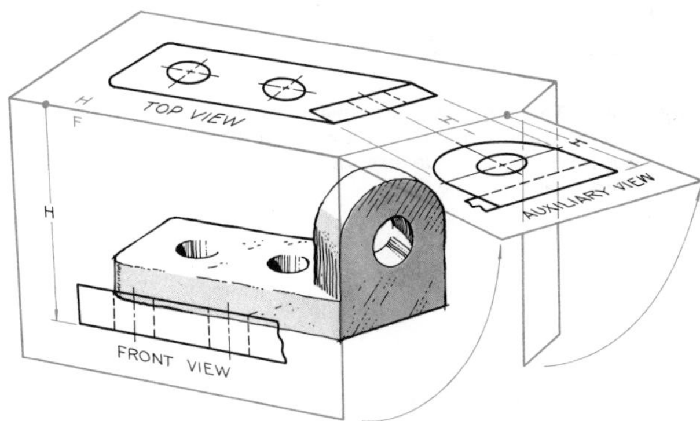

Fig. 5–57B. The projection planes are opened into a common plane to represent the plane of the drawing paper.

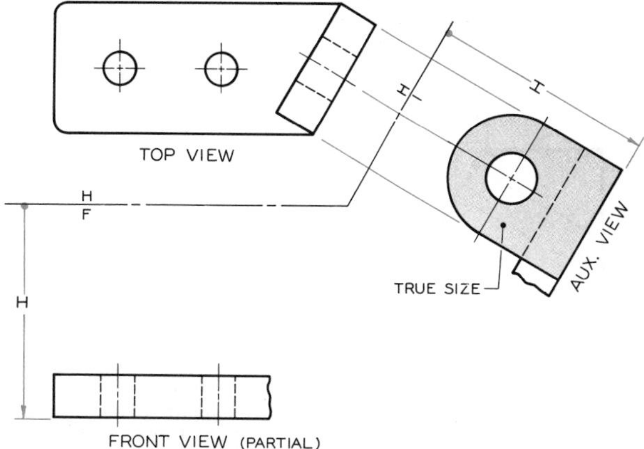

Fig. 5–57C. Construction of an auxiliary view of the object shown in Figs. 5–57A and 5–57B as it would appear on your drawing paper.

FIGURE 5–58. CONSTRUCTION OF A PRIMARY AUXILIARY VIEW

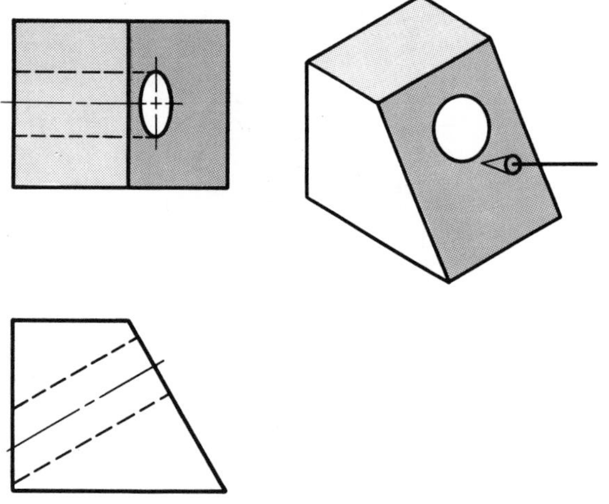

Given: The top and front views of a block with an inclined surface which appears as an edge in the front view.
Required: Find a true size view of the inclined surface.
References: Article 5–24.

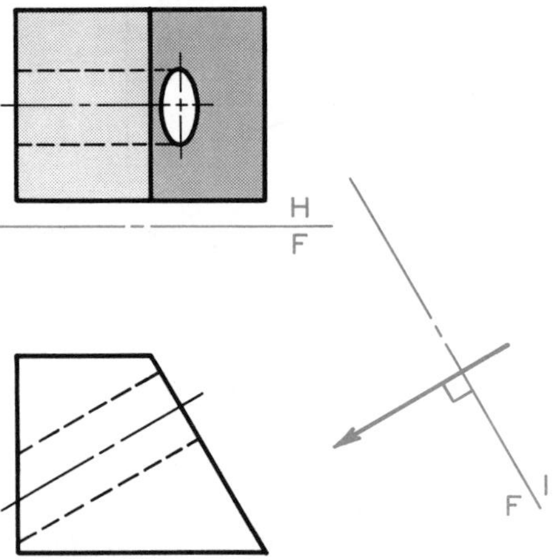

Step 1: Construct an HF reference plane conveniently between the top and front views that is perpendicular to the projectors between the views. Draw a line of sight perpendicular to the edge view of the inclined surface. Draw the edge view of the auxiliary plane perpendicular to the line of sight and parallel to the inclined surface.

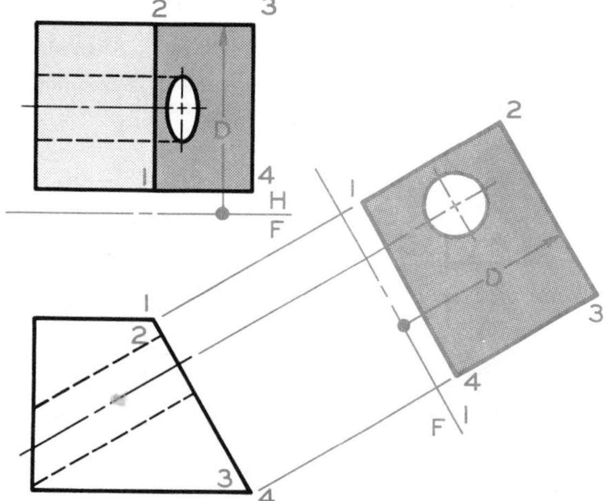

Step 2: Number points in the top and front views. Project the points perpendicularly from the inclined edge to the auxiliary plane. Transfer the dimensions from the HF plane to the auxiliary view, e.g., dimension *D*. Connect these points to give a true-size view of the surface.

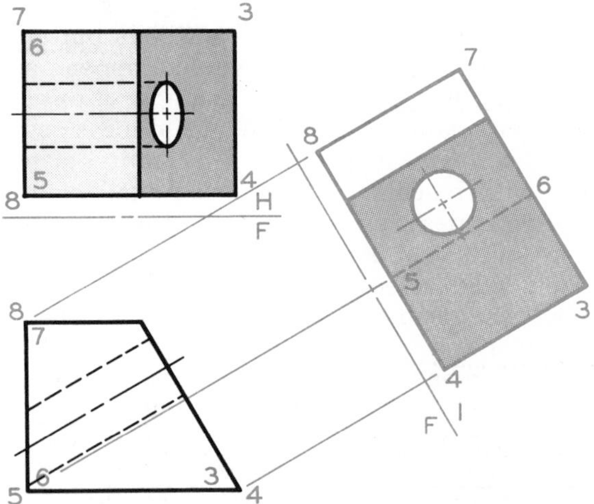

Step 3: Number the remaining points of the object in the top and front views and project them to the auxiliary view to complete the auxiliary view of the object. Line 5–6 will be a hidden line. Measure all dimensions perpendicularly to the reference planes used.

A reference plane, HF, is constructed between the two given views that will be used for constructing the auxiliary view. This reference plane will always be drawn perpendicular to the projections between the two adjacent views used. The edge view of the auxiliary plane, H1, is located parallel to the edge view of the inclined plane that is to be found true size in the auxiliary view. This plane also represents the edge view of the horizontal reference plane from which vertical measurements of height will be made by transferring these distances from the front view of the same horizontal reference plane, HF. By referring to the pictorial in Fig. 5-57A, we observe that the distance *H* from the horizontal plane, which is common to both the front and auxiliary views, is equal in both views. These measurements are transferred from the front view to the auxiliary view with dividers to locate significant points. This procedure will result in a completed auxiliary view in which the inclined surface appears true size.

The auxiliary view is drawn as a partial view, since the remainder of the object is adequately described in the top and front views. The front view is a partial view, also, since the inclined surface has circular holes that would appear as ellipses in this view. These are difficult to draw and impractical to dimension in an untrue view; consequently, this portion is broken away with conventional break lines as shown. The visualization of the total object requires a simultaneous analysis of all three views.

An example of constructing a primary auxiliary view projected from the front view of an object is shown in sequential steps in Fig. 5-58. These same steps will apply to any primary auxiliary view, regardless of the view from which the auxiliary view is projected.

An example of an object depicted by a right-side view and partial front and auxiliary views is given in Fig. 5-59. In this case, the reference plane used for construction of the auxiliary plane is drawn through the center of the inclined surface, since it is known to be symmetrical. It would be impossible to construct the auxiliary view from the two principal views without knowledge of the shape of the inclined surface, since the front view is partial. The foreshortened front view of the inclined surface would be necessary to provide points from which measurements could be made to construct an auxiliary view. Since a foreshortened view is confusing and difficult to construct, it is usually omitted as in this example.

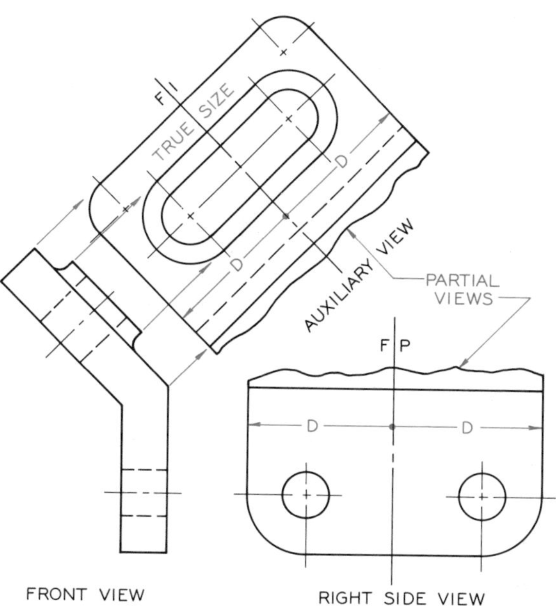

Fig. 5-59. Construction of partial auxiliary and principal views to depict an object.

An auxiliary view of an object projected from a front view is shown pictorially in Fig. 5-60A. The frontal plane is used as a reference plane and the depth dimension is the same in the auxiliary view as in the top and right side views. When drawn on the plane of the paper, the principal views and the auxiliary view will appear as shown in Fig. 5-60B.

The auxiliary view is a true-size view of the inclined plane that can be measured to locate the circular hole. The hole can be easily drawn, since it is a true circle in this view. The top and right side views are drawn as partial views.

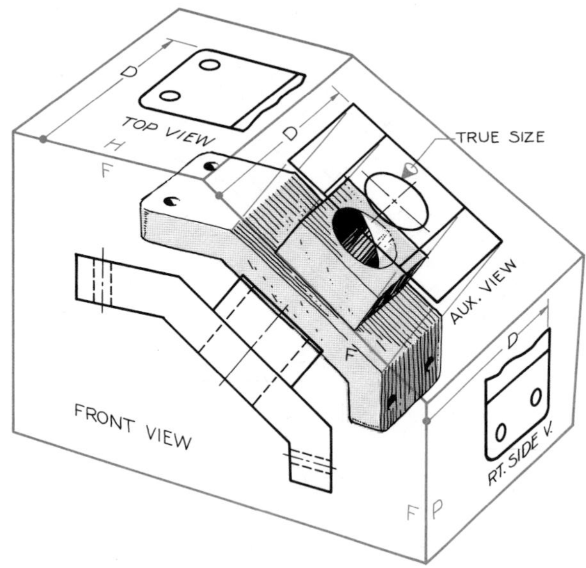

Fig. 5-60A. A pictorial showing the relationship of the projection planes used to find the true size of the inclined plane.

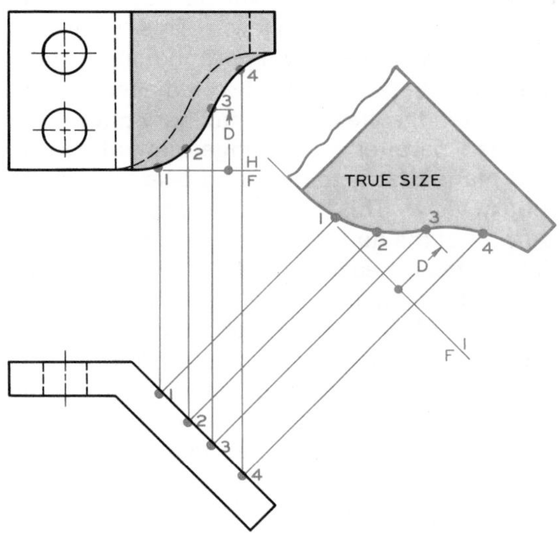

Fig. 5-61. Auxiliary view of an irregular curve.

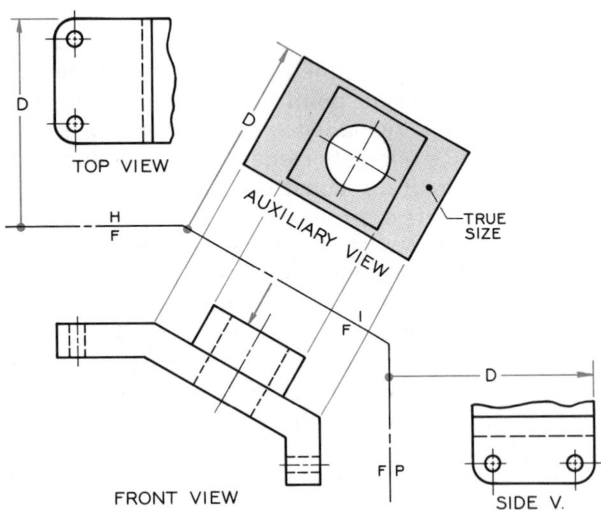

Fig. 5-60B. Construction of an auxiliary view of the object shown in Fig. 5-60A as it would appear on your drawing paper.

An auxiliary view of an object which has a curved edge is given in Fig. 5-61. The construction of the primary auxiliary view projected from the front view must be found by plotting a series of points which are located on the curved edge and projected to the auxiliary view. These points can be connected with an irregular curve to give the true shape of the inclined surface.

The problem illustrated in Fig. 5-62 is that of a plotted curve in an auxiliary view that was constructed by the same procedure used in Fig. 5-61. In this case the slanted surface appeared as an edge in the front view, making it possible to construct a true-size auxiliary view projected from the front view. Since the object is symmetrical, a reference plane is constructed through its center. Points are located on the edge view of the slanted surface and are projected to the side view. Each point on the front view is then projected to the auxiliary view and is located by transferring distances *A* and *B*

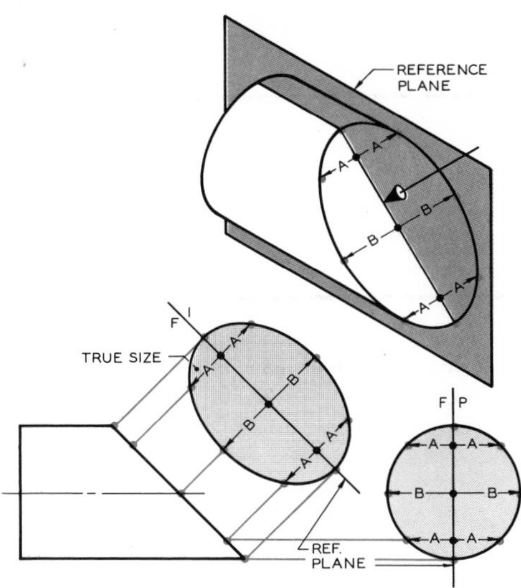

Fig. 5–62. Construction of an auxiliary view of an object requiring that a series of points be plotted. Since the object is symmetrical, the reference plane is positioned through its center.

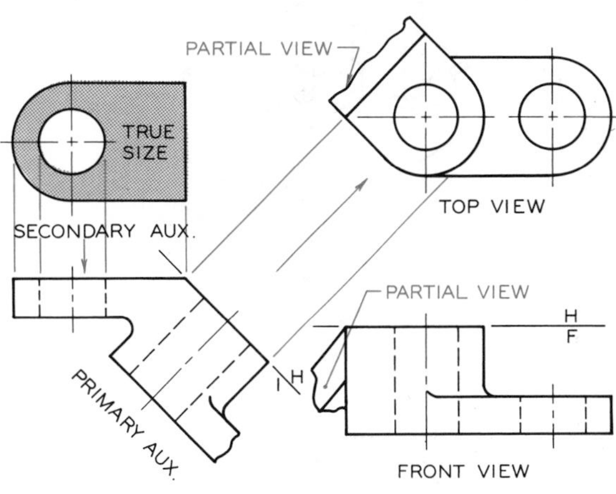

Fig. 5–63. An example of a secondary auxiliary view projected from a partial primary auxiliary view.

from the reference plane in the side view to the reference plane in the auxiliary view.

5–25 SECONDARY AUXILIARY VIEWS

When a surface is inclined to each of the principal planes and does not appear as an edge in any principal view, a secondary auxiliary view is necessary to find the true size of the surface. Figure 5–63 is an example of a secondary auxiliary view that is projected from a primary auxiliary view. Both these views are forms of orthographic projection, since they are projected perpendicularly onto projection planes with parallel projectors. Some hidden lines that are considered unimportant are omitted in the secondary view.

The theory of secondary auxiliary view projections is explained in greater detail in Chapter 9 in connection with the solution of spatial problems. Article 9–2 gives a step-by-step example of the construction of a secondary auxiliary view of solid objects. Other examples given throughout the chapter illustrate the principles of constructing successive auxiliary views of lines and planes in space.

5–26 SECTIONS

The conventional orthographic views may fail to clearly communicate the shape and details of a particular part because of numerous intersecting lines that tend to confuse the representation. This is especially true of internal parts that project as hidden lines. Such an example is the pictorial shown in Fig. 5–64A. Although this part is relatively simple, a complete understanding of its shape and its internal features requires close study of the given views. The top and front views of this part are given in Fig. 5–64B.

A conventional method of depicting parts of this type is the use of *sections*. A section is an

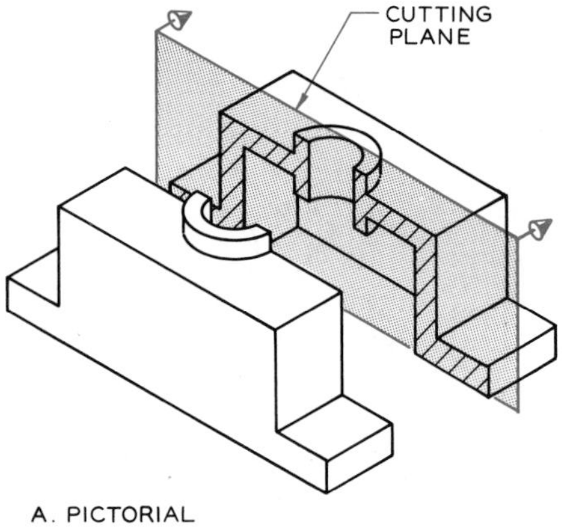

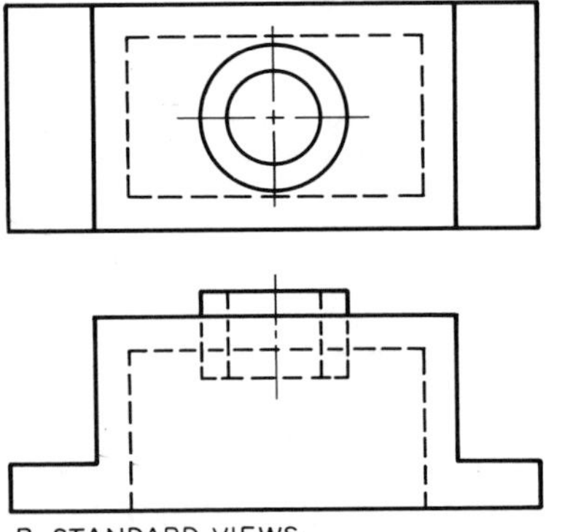

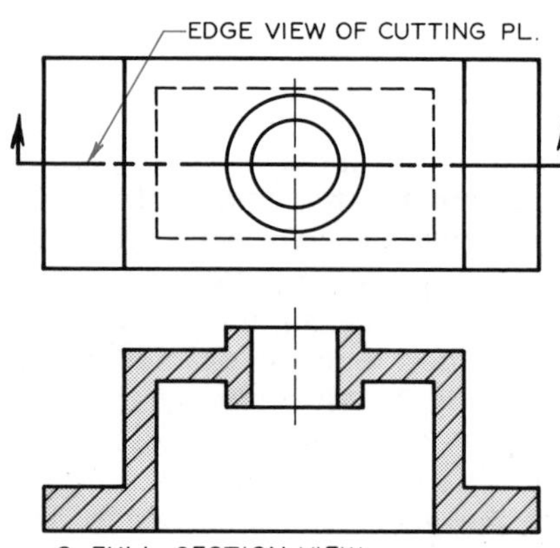

Fig. 5-64. A comparison of a regular view with a full section view of an object to show its internal as well as external features.

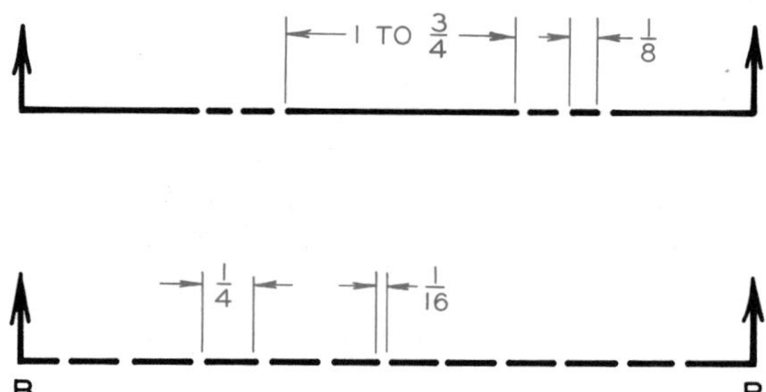

Fig. 5-65. Cutting-plane lines used in sections.

imaginary cutting plane that is used to show representative cross sections and thus give a better understanding of an object. A cutting plane passing through an object is shown pictorially in Fig. 5-64A. The arrows indicate the direction of the line of sight that will view the remaining half when the front portion has been removed. The sectioned view can be seen as it would be conveniently drawn in Fig. 5-64C. The portion cut by the cutting plane is crosshatched with section lines to depict the view as a section. This is a *full section,* since the cutting plane passes fully through it. The location of imaginary cutting planes is indicated in the top view by a heavy line broken by two short dashes at intervals; sight arrows are drawn perpendicular to it at each end. The cutting plane is shown only where it appears as an edge.

The sectioned view in Fig. 5-64C shows visible lines behind the cutting plane even though the cutting plane does not pass through them. These lines are shown to give a more complete description. Generally, hidden lines are omitted in sectioned views except when their inclusion is considered absolutely necessary for clarification.

The symbol for a cutting plane can be either of the two types shown in Fig. 5-65. These lines are heavy lines equal in weight to the visible lines of a drawing. Note that letters can be placed at the ends of a cutting plane to identify

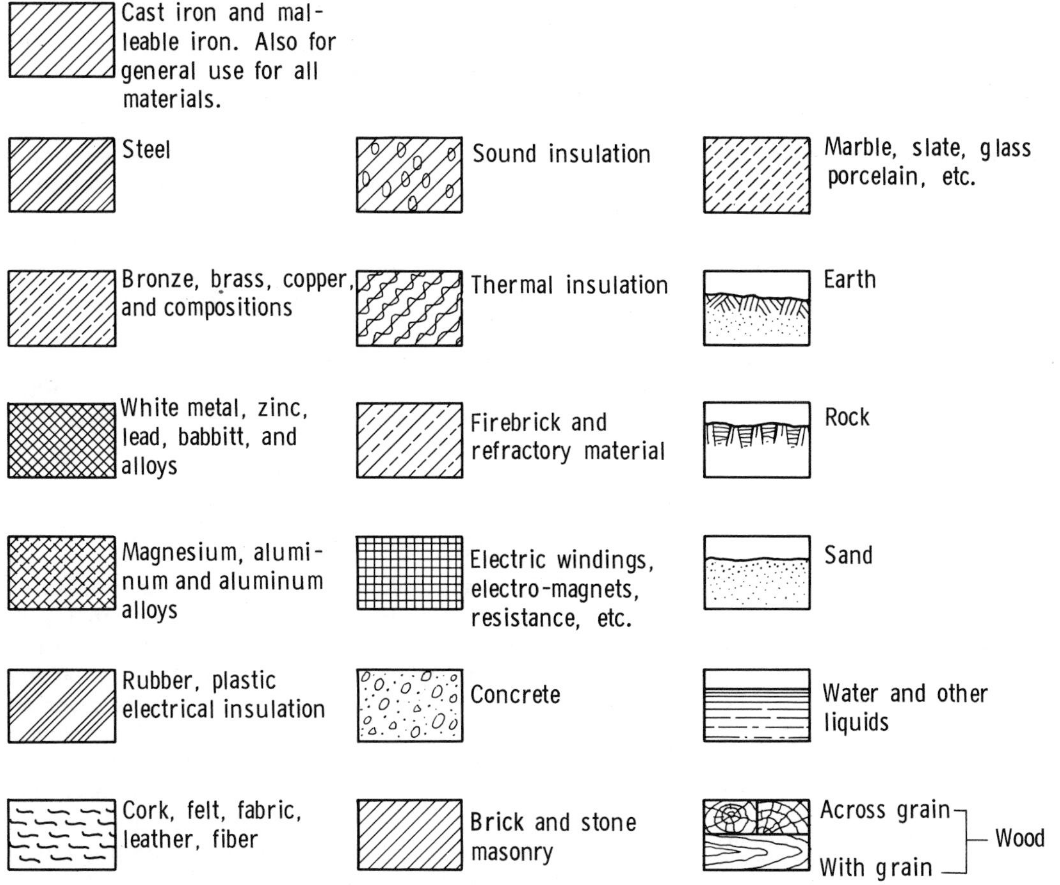

Fig. 5–66. Symbols for section-lining on assembly drawings. (Courtesy of ANSI; Y14.2-1957.)

the section that will be drawn elsewhere on the drawing and labeled as "section B-B."

5–27 SECTIONING SYMBOLS

Standard symbols that are used to distinguish between different materials in sections are shown in Fig. 5–66. These symbols are thin lines drawn with instruments and spaced by eye. On preliminary sketches, the symbols can be drawn freehand. Although the symbols can be used to indicate the general materials used in a section, it is good practice to include notes specifying the materials, to avoid misinterpretations.

The cast iron symbol of evenly spaced section lines can be used to represent any material if notes are added to identify the material. The cast iron symbol is usually drawn with a 2H pencil with the lines slanted at 45° or any other standard angle and spaced $\frac{1}{16}''$ apart. The spacing between the section lines will vary somewhat with the size of the part in that the smaller the part, the closer together the lines will be drawn.

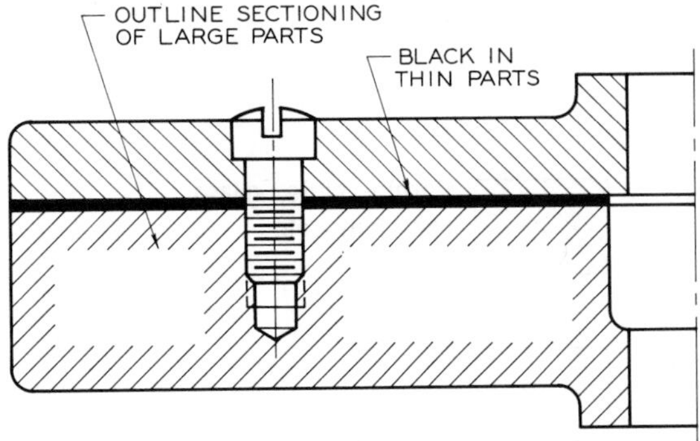

Fig. 5-67. Sectioning technique for large parts and thin parts.

Extremely thin parts, such as sheet metal parts, washers, or gaskets (Fig. 5-67) are sectioned by blacking the area in completely, rather than attempting to use section lines. Rather large parts are sectioned with an *outline section,* as shown in Fig. 5-67. Outline section-lining reduces time and effort that would be required to crosshatch the entire area.

Sectioned areas should be section-lined with line symbols that are neither parallel nor perpendicular to the outlines of the part. Lines parallel or perpendicular to the outlines may tend to distort the shape of the part and could possibly be confused as serrations or other machined treatments of the surface. This principle is illustrated in Fig. 5-68.

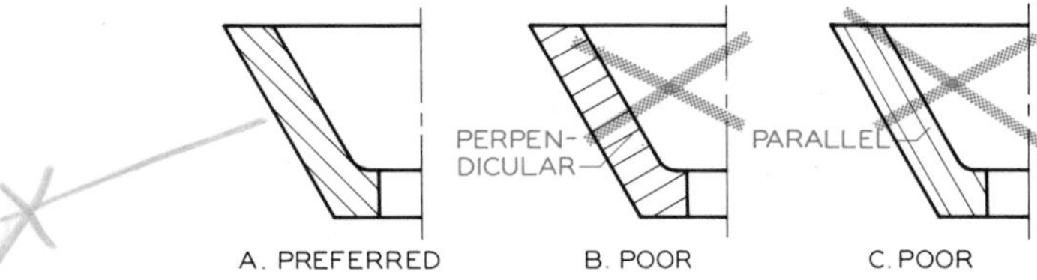

Fig. 5-68. Section lines should be drawn so that they are not parallel or perpendicular to the outlines of the part.

5-28 SECTIONING OF ASSEMBLIES

When assemblies of several parts are sectioned to give an understanding of the relationship of the parts, it is important that the section lines be drawn at varying angles to distinguish the parts. In the assembly of four parts given in Fig. 5-69B, note that, because of the choice of the direction of section lines, it can clearly be understood that the four areas represent separate parts.

Another example is the half section given in Fig. 5-69A. Not only are the section lines drawn at varying angles, but different material symbols are used to distinguish the materials. Note that all of each part in Fig. 5-69B is crosshatched at the same angle even though the section shows the part separated into different areas. A valve assembly is sectioned in Fig. 5-70 using different symbols to distinguish the various components of the assembly. The valve could not be so clearly described by a conventional view.

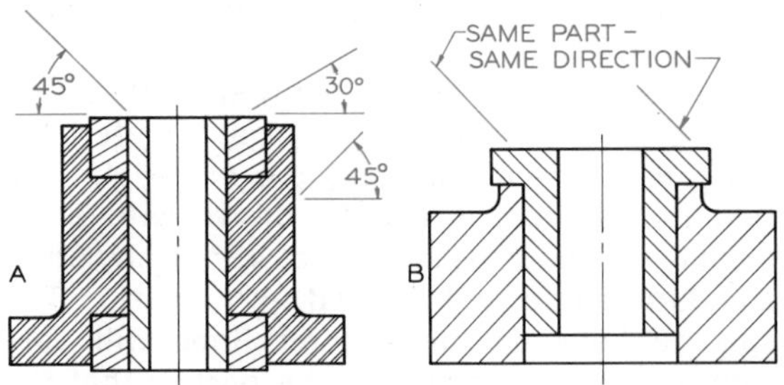

Fig. 5-69. Section lines of different parts in an assembly should be drawn at varying angles to distinguish the parts.

5-29 FULL SECTIONS

Full sections have previously been introduced in Fig. 5-63. A full section is a sectional view formed by passing a cutting plane fully through an object and removing half of it to give a view of its internal parts. Such an example is shown

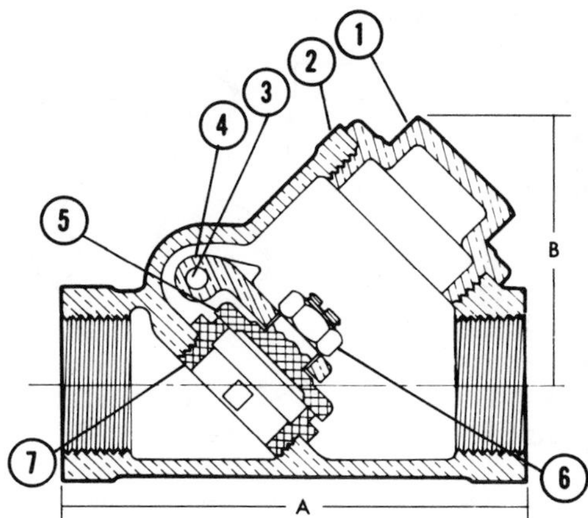

Fig. 5–70. Section lines are drawn in different directions in this check valve to distinguish the parts of the assembly. (Courtesy of Nibco Scott, Inc.)

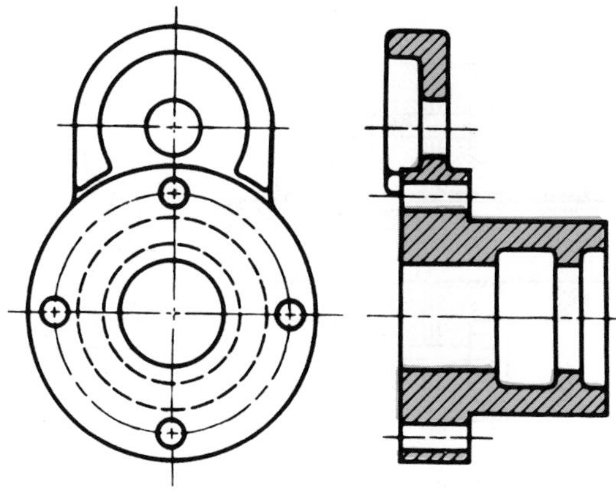

Fig. 5–71. A full section. (Courtesy of ANSI; Y14.2-1957.)

in Fig. 5–71. In this case, the cutting-plane line has been omitted in the front view, since it is obvious where the plane was passed through to result in the sectioned right view. This is a conventional practice that can be used to eliminate unnecessary construction.

A full section through a cylindrical part is shown pictorially in Fig. 5–72A, where the cutting plane has passed fully through the object, removing one half of it. A common mistake in constructing section views is the omission of visible lines behind the cutting plane (part B). For the view to be drawn correctly, the lines behind the cutting plane must be shown as in part C. Note that hidden lines are omitted, since they add nothing to the drawing's clarity.

FIGURE 5–72

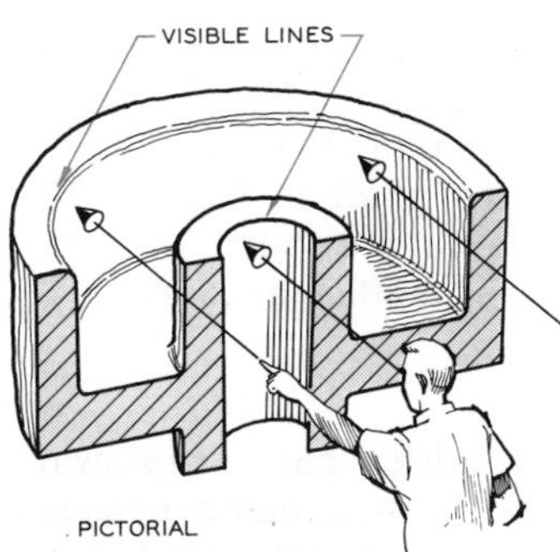

A. When a full section is taken through an object, you will see lines behind the sectioned area.

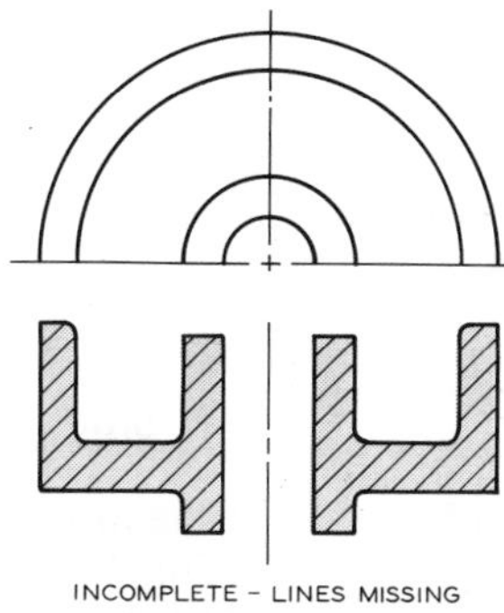

B. If only the sectioned area were shown, the view would be incomplete.

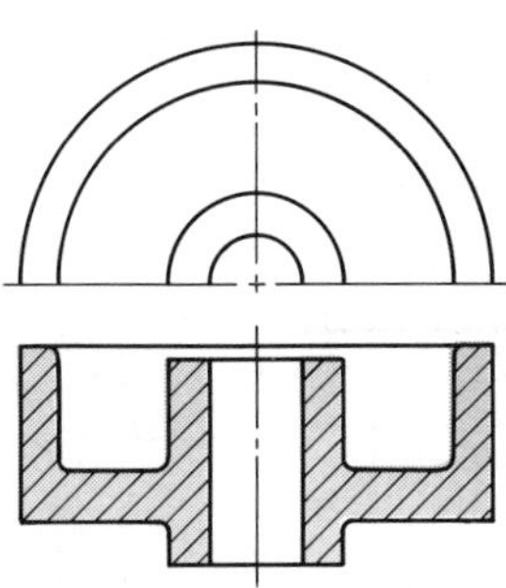

C. Visible lines behind the section must be shown also.

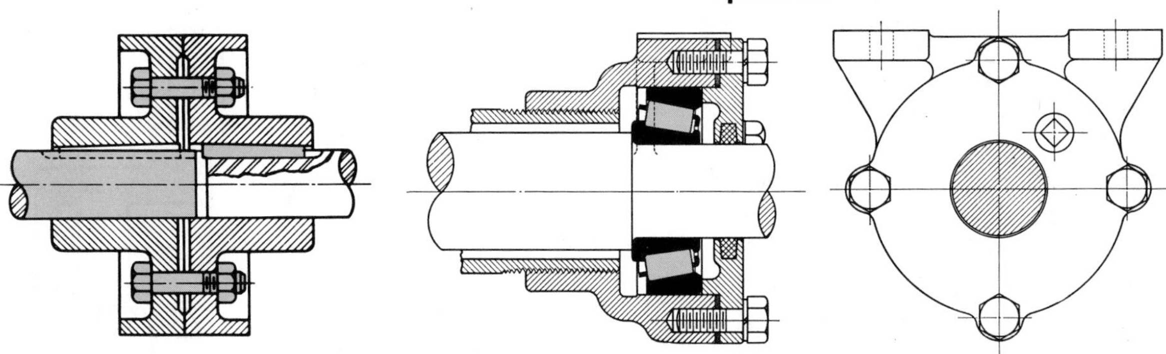

Fig. 5-73A. Parts not section-lined in an assembly—shafts, keys, bolts, and nuts. (Courtesy of ANSI; Y14.2-1957.)

Fig. 5-73B. An example of parts not section-lined in an assembly—shafts, bolts, and roller bearings. (Courtesy of the *Timken Engineering Journal.*)

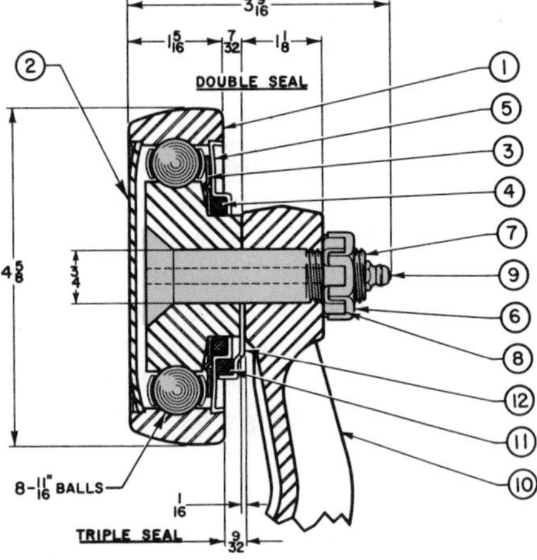

Fig. 5-73C. An example of parts not section-lined in an assembly—nuts, bolts, and ball bearings. (Courtesy of Mechanical Handling Systems, Inc.)

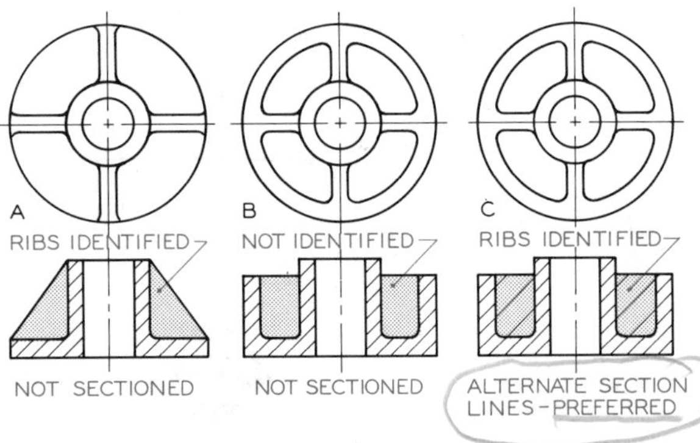

Fig. 5-74. Methods of depicting ribs in section.

5-30 PARTS NOT SECTIONED

More clarity may be obtained in sections if some of the more standard parts are not section-lined, even though the cutting plane passes through them. An example section is shown in Fig. 5-73A, where nuts, bolts, shafts, and keys are not section-lined. These parts have no internal features and the representation would not be improved if they were section-lined. Other parts not section-lined are ribs, spokes, webs, ball and roller bearings, rivets, pins, and similar standard parts. The section in Fig. 5-73B gives examples of shafts, bolts, washers, and roller bearings that are not section-lined, even though the cutting plane passes through them. Ball bearings and other standard components (Fig. 5-73C) are also not section-lined, thus providing a more readable section in this assembly.

When the cutting plane is passed perpendicular to the axis of shafts, bolts, rivets, and webs, the cut areas will be section-lined. For example, the right-side view of the shaft in Fig. 5-73B shows a section-lined view of the shaft. The cutting plane was passed perpendicular to its axis.

5-31 RIBS IN SECTION

Full sections through cylindrical parts are shown in Fig. 5-74, where the cutting plane passes through ribs that are used to add strength to the objects. The ribs in part A are not section-lined, since the cutting plane passes through the rib flatwise, and section-lining would give the impression that the section was a solid conical shape. This would be a misleading impression. If the cutting plane had been passed perpendicular to the rib, it would have been section-lined, since its true thickness would have been depicted.

An *alternative method* of section-lining ribs is shown in part C of Fig. 5-74. The rib is outlined with a solid line where it joins with the normally section-lined areas. Dashed lines could have been used instead of solid lines. Every other section line is extended through the rib to indicate that it has been cut by the cutting plane, but that it is a rib rather than a solid cylinder. The method shown in part B, where the rib is not section-lined at all, is also correct. However, in this particular example, the alternative method shown in part C is preferred, since it prevents the rib from being overlooked, as could be the case in part B.

When the cutting plane is passed perpendicular to the flatwise views of ribs, they are section-lined as shown in Fig. 5-75. The sectioned view gives a true impression of the relationship of the ribs and will not give a misrepresentation as it would when the plane is passed through the ribs in a flatwise direction.

5-32 HALF SECTIONS

A half section is a view that results from a cut by a cutting plane passing halfway through an object to remove a quarter of it. This is depicted pictorially in Fig. 5-76, where the cutting plane is shown in part B and the resulting sectional view in part C. The half section view is a half

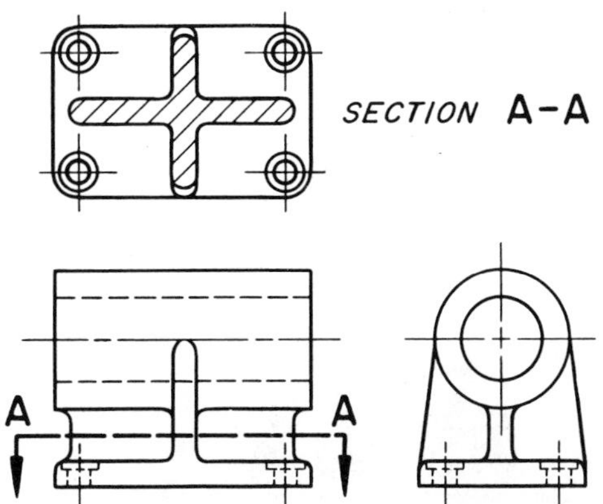

Fig. 5-75. Method of section-lining ribs when the cutting plane passes across the ribs. (Courtesy of General Motors Standards.)

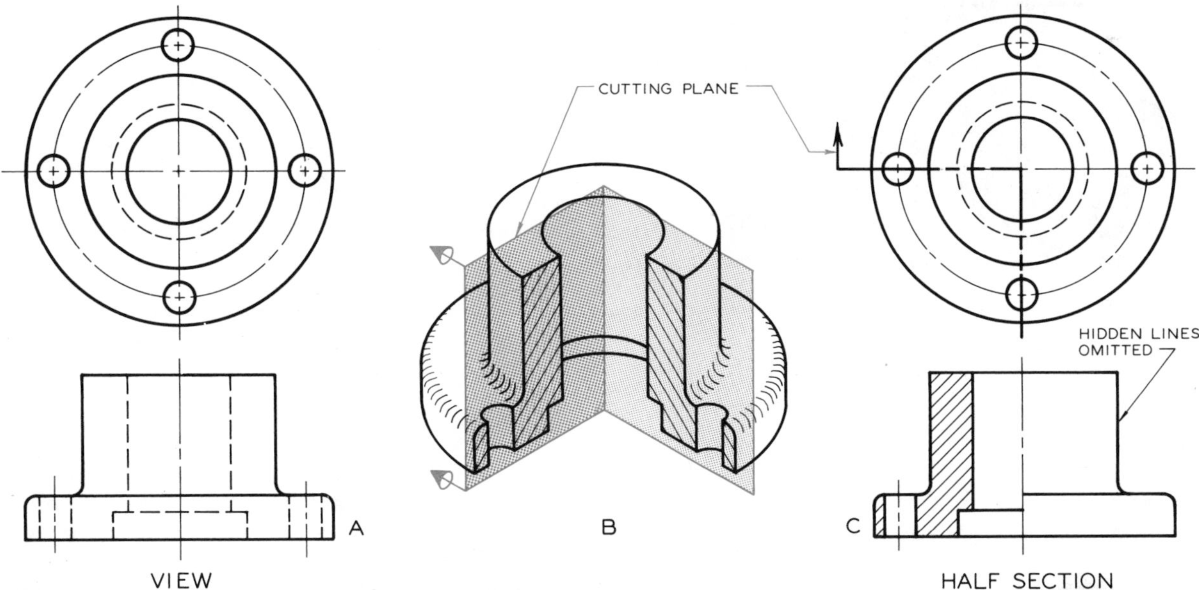

Fig. 5-76. A comparison between standard views and a half section of a part.

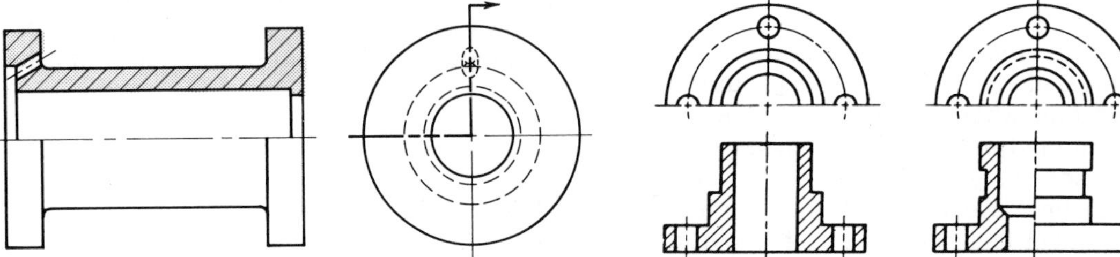

Fig. 5-77. A typical half section.

Fig. 5-78. A conventional use of half views in conjunction with sections to reduce construction. (Courtesy of ANSI; Y14.2-1957.)

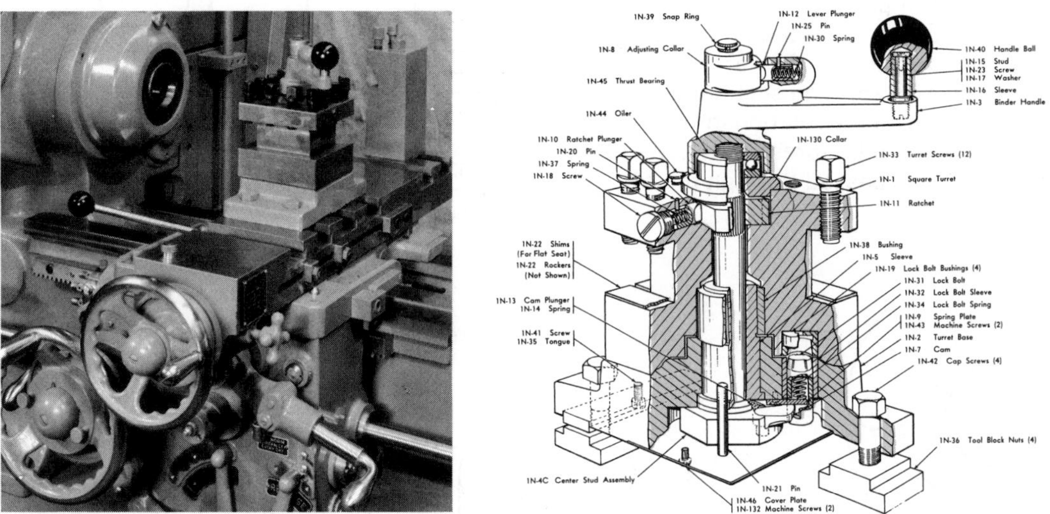

Fig. 5-79. A photograph and a pictorial half section of a square turret on a lathe. (Courtesy of Warner Swasey Company.)

view and a half section that gives a representation of both internal and external features.

The orthographic arrangement of the half section shown in Fig. 5-76B is compared in Fig. 5-76A with a standard front view. This standard view is confusing and difficult to interpret. The half section gives a much better impression of the object because unnecessary hidden

FIGURE 5-80

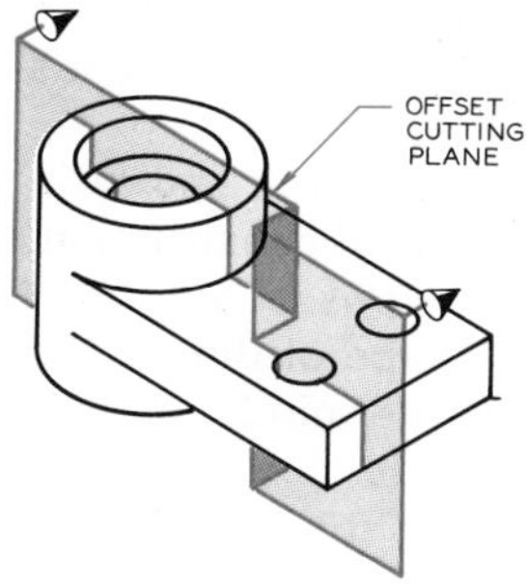

A. An offset section may be necessary to show all typical features.

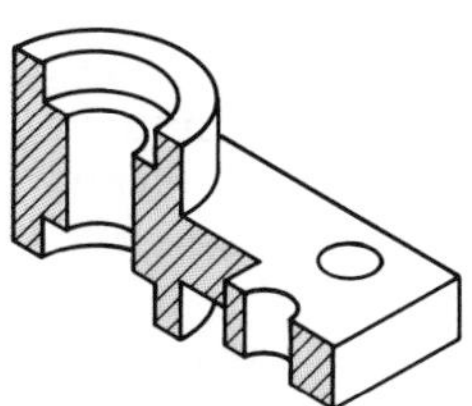

B. When the front portion is removed, the internal features can be seen.

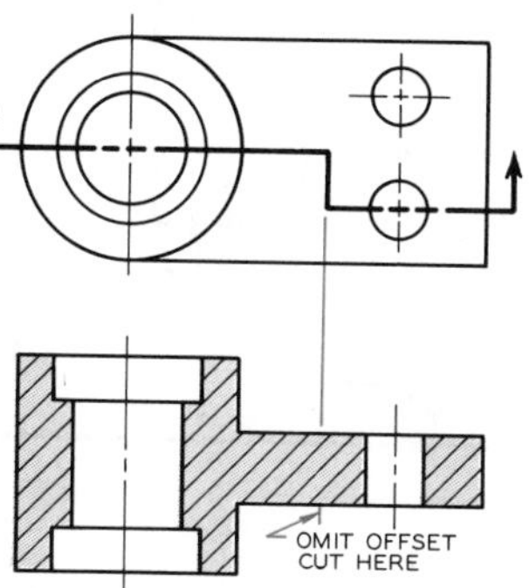

C. In an offset section, the offset cut is not shown; the section is shown as a smooth cut.

lines can be omitted, since the internal and external features are shown separately in the same view. The cut portion of the half section is section-lined to illustrate the cross sectioning of the part. Note that a center line is used in the sectioned view rather than a solid object line, since the removal of a quarter is imaginary and not an actual cut that would result in a solid line. The cutting-plane line in the front view could have been omitted, since it is obvious where the plane was positioned in the case of a symmetrical part of this type. A similar example, Fig. 5-77, of a half-section is shown without the cutting plane in the second view. Visible interior lines behind the cutting plane are shown in the half section, since these would be visible when looking inside if the part had actually been cut.

Section views can be conventionally arranged with half views, as shown in Fig. 5-78. When the views are sections, the top views are arranged so that the removed portions are adjacent to the sectioned views. Center lines are used along the line of departure in the top view rather than solid object lines, since the removed part is imaginary rather than a real break.

Pictorial sections are used to advantage for special applications where improved communication is desired. The pictorial half section in Fig. 5-79 adequately distinguishes the various parts of the turret assembly shown mounted on a lathe in the photograph. Pictorial sections are easier to read than orthographic sections; consequently, they are more often used in parts manuals and other literature prepared for the general public.

5-33 OFFSET SECTIONS

An *offset section* is a type of full section in which the cutting plane is offset to pass through important features that would be missed by the usual full section. An example is shown in Fig. 5-80, where the cutting plane is offset in order to pass through the large hole and the small hole. When the cut portion is removed and viewed in the direction of the line of sight, it appears as shown in part B. The conventional method of showing this offset section is given in part C. Note that the cut formed by the offset plane is not shown in the front view, since this is an imaginary cut.

Another example of an offset section is shown in Fig. 5-81. The same general principles apply here. Note that the broken cuts formed by the offset cutting plane are not shown in the offset section.

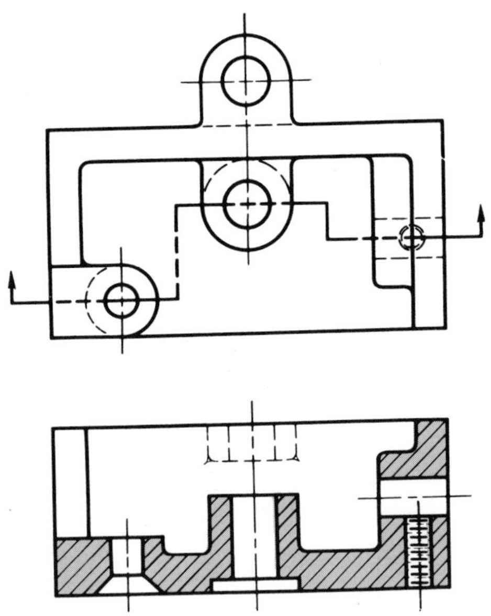

Fig. 5-81. An offset section. (Courtesy of ANSI; Y14.2-1957.)

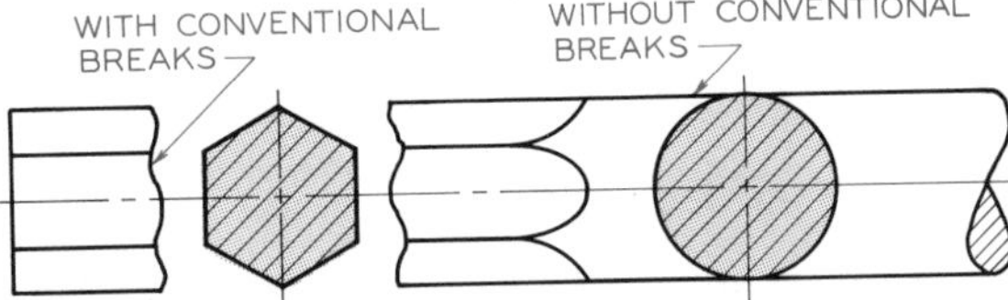

Fig. 5-82. Examples of revolved sections with and without conventional breaks.

5-34 REVOLVED SECTIONS

A revolved section is used to describe a cross section of a part to eliminate the need for an entire view. For example, revolved sections are shown to indicate cross sections of structural members in Fig. 5-82. The dimensions of these revolved sections could not have been drawn unless their dimensions were known or an additional view were given from which measurements could be made. Two approved methods of constructing revolved sections are given in the figure. The section can be revolved and superimposed on the view or it can be revolved into position with the view separated from the revolved section with conventional breaks, as shown in the section on the left.

An example of a *revolved section* is shown in Fig. 5-83 to illustrate the steps of construction. In step 1, the top and front views of an object are given. Because of the shape of the object, it would be difficult to show the middle area of the part in a conventional side view. By constructing a revolved section in the middle portion, you can clearly describe its shape. A cutting plane can be assumed to pass through the portion that is to be shown in a revolved section.

In step 2, this section is revolved in the top view and projected to the front view where the section can be drawn true size. The revolved section is drawn on top of the front view, but the object lines are not drawn through the section. Note that the bottom webs are perpendicular to the center web in this section; they are not parallel to the web in the front view. It is unnecessary to show the revolution in the top view because it is understood.

Conventional breaks could have been drawn on each side of the revolved section to separate it from the front view. An example of this is shown in Fig. 5-84B. This section could have been constructed on the front view without conventional breaks, as shown in part A. Either of these methods is correct for drawing revolved sections. The section in part C is revolved and *removed;* consequently it is called a *removed section*. Removed sections will be discussed in the following article.

5-35 REMOVED SECTIONS

A *removed section* can be described as a revolved section that has been removed from the view where it was revolved, as shown in part C of Fig. 5-84. This may be necessary where room does not permit revolution on the given view, as illustrated in Fig. 5-85A. In order to provide better clarity, the revolved section is removed from the view where it would normally appear (Fig. 5-85B).

FIGURE 5-83. A PICTORIAL OF A REVOLVED SECTION

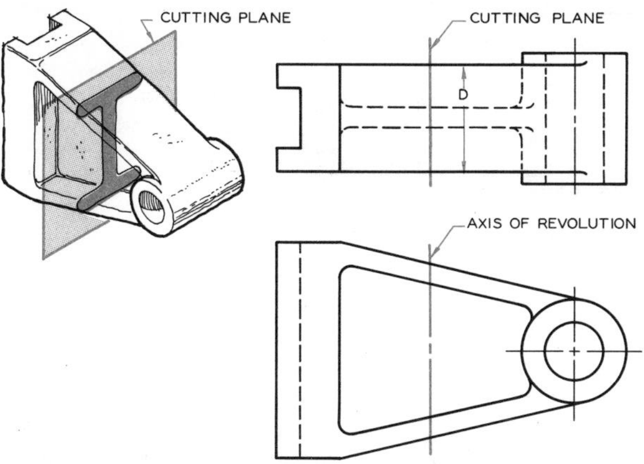

Step 1: An axis of revolution is shown in the front view. The cutting plane would appear in the top if drawn.

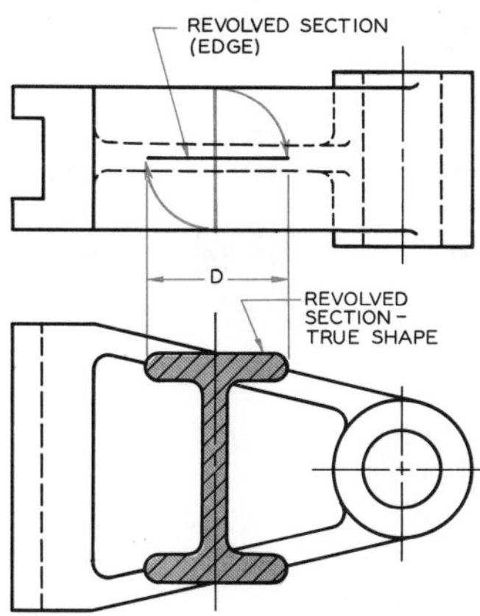

Step 2: The vertical section in the top view is revolved so that the section can be seen true size in the front view. Object lines do not pass through the revolved section.

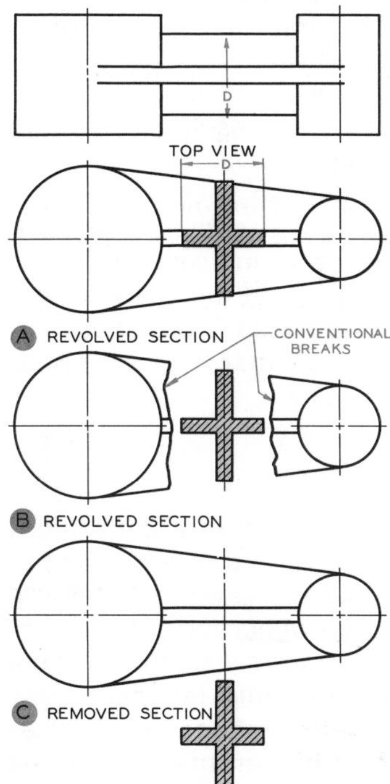

Fig. 5-84. Example of revolved and removed sections.

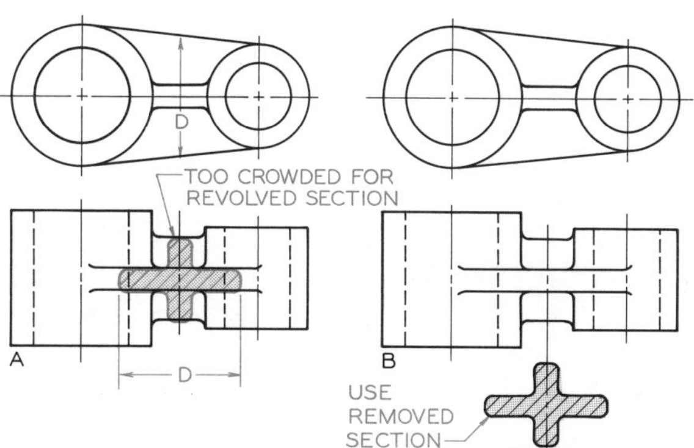

Fig. 5-85. Removed sections may be used where space does not permit the use of a revolved section.

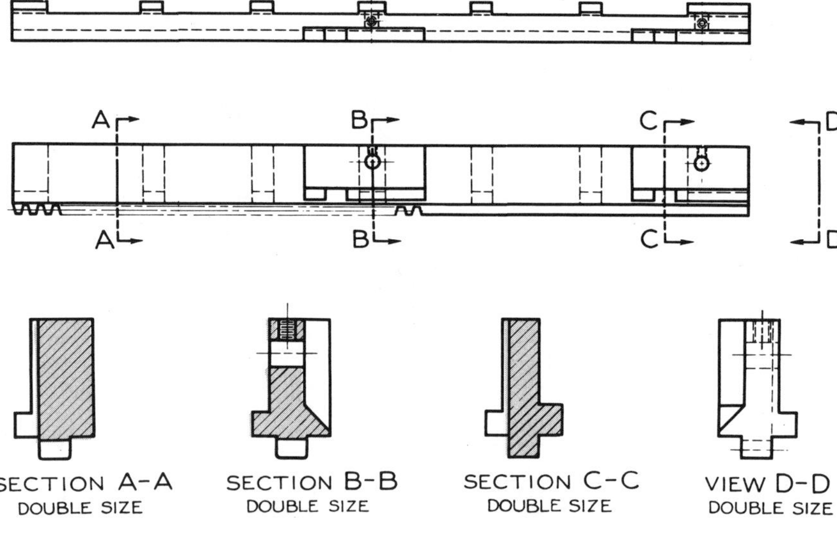

Fig. 5-86. Removed sections can be drawn larger than the view from which they were taken. (Courtesy of ANSI; Y14.2-1957.)

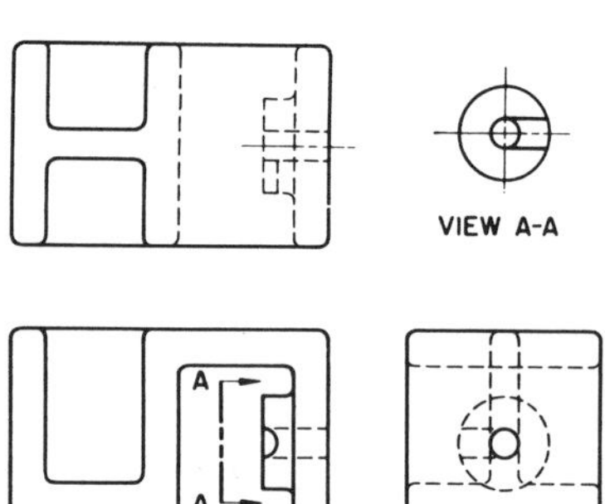

Fig. 5-87. A removed view. (Courtesy of ANSI; Y14.2-1957.)

Removed sections may also be drawn at a different scale, as shown in Fig. 5-86. The locations of the removed sections are indicated with cutting planes in the front view. The cutting planes are lettered to indicate where the double-size removed sections were taken from. The cutting plane lettered A-A results in section A-A, which may actually be on a separate sheet of a set of drawings. Section D-D is actually a right side view rather than a section. The scale of the removed sections is indicated on each view when it is different from the scale on the original views. The removed view shown in Fig. 5-87 describes a view that is inaccessible from the conventional view.

5-36 BROKEN-OUT SECTIONS

A broken-out section is used as a convenient method to show interior parts that would add to the understanding of a drawing without showing the entire view in section. A portion of the object (Fig. 5-88) is broken out to reveal details of the wall thickness that are helpful in interpreting the drawing. This broken-out section reduces the need for additional hidden lines, since the details can be adequately shown in the given views.

An industrial example of a broken-out section is shown in the right side view of Fig. 5-89. The

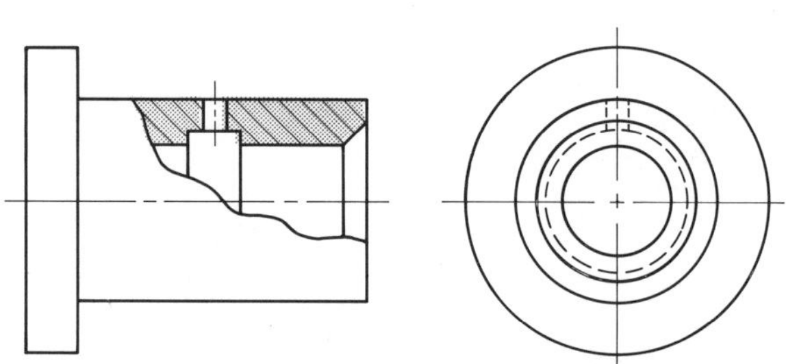

Fig. 5-88. A broken-out section. (Courtesy of ANSI; Y14.2-1957.)

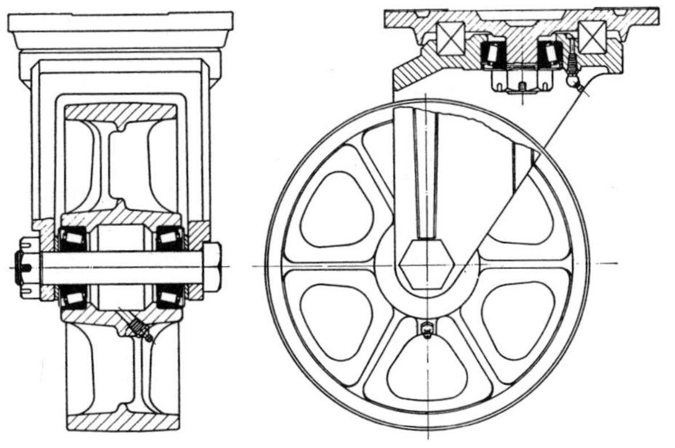

Fig. 5-89. A full section and a broken-out section used to illustrate a caster. (Courtesy of the *Timken Engineering Journal.*)

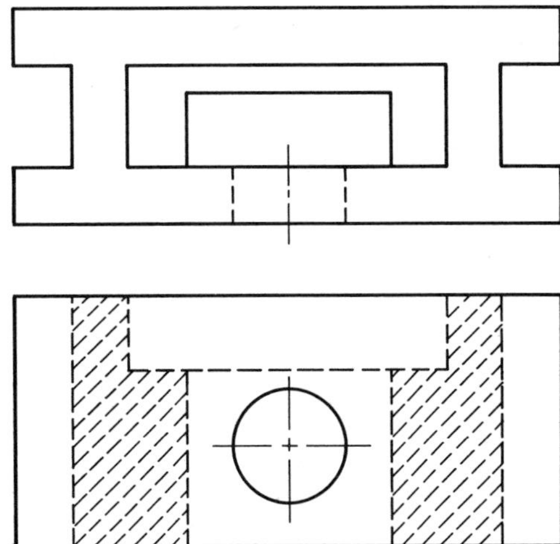

Fig. 5-90. A phantom section to give an "X-ray" view of an object.

assembly of the upper portion of this caster wheel can be seen in the broken-out section. The front view is a section taken through the wheel; no attempt is made to represent the upper assembly.

5-37 PHANTOM SECTIONS

A *phantom section* or ghost section is used occasionally to depict special parts that cannot be shown as well by other methods. This type of section is used when exterior as well as interior features must be shown. The part shown in Fig. 5-90 is represented in a phantom section that gives both the outside and inside features.

Note that the section lines are drawn as dashed lines to give an "X-ray" view of the part. This method of sectioning is not often used, but there are times when this technique can be effectively applied.

5-38 CONVENTIONAL BREAKS

The previous examples have made use of conventional breaks to indicate the removal of portions of the object for clarity. Some examples of this standard method for improving the representation of certain parts are illustrated in Fig. 5-91. In parts A and B of the figure, the

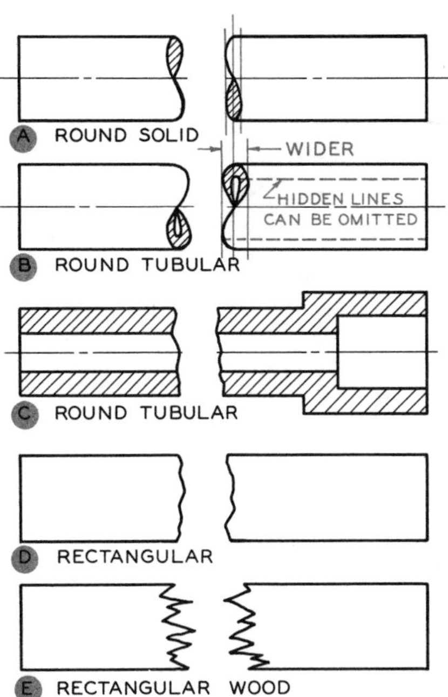

Fig. 5-91. Conventional breaks. (Courtesy of ANSI; Y14.2-1957.)

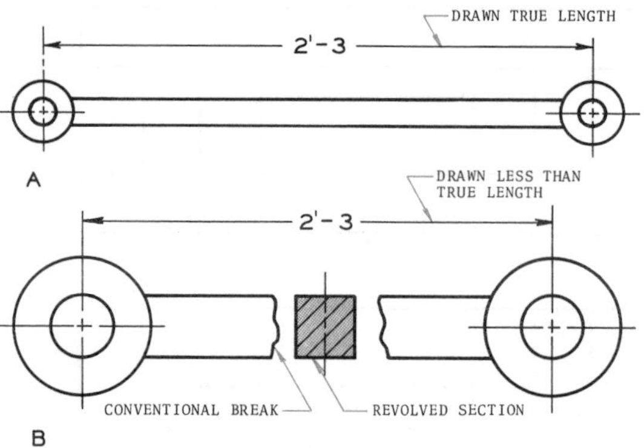

Fig. 5-92. Conventional breaks can be used to remove a portion of an object so that it can be drawn larger.

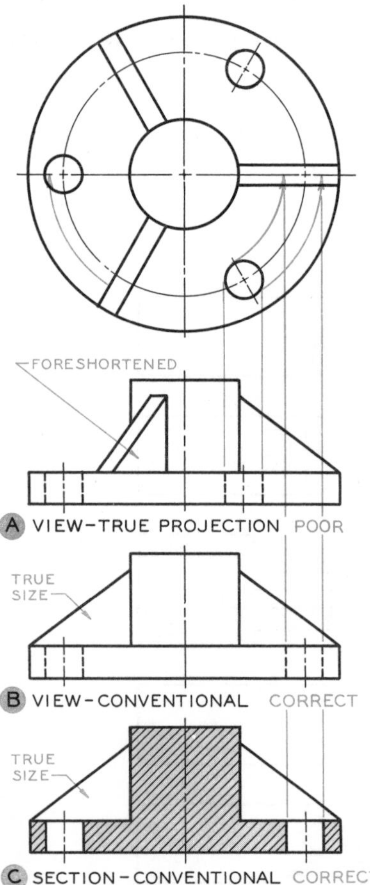

Fig. 5-93. Conventional method of representing ribs in views and sections.

conventional breaks are used to represent cylindrical objects. From these breaks it is possible to see by inspection that these parts are cylindrical. The cylindrical part in A is solid, while that in B is tubular. Guidelines are used for construction of the "figure 8" breaks, which are drawn freehand. Note that the widths of the tubular breaks are greater than those of the solid breaks.

A cylindrical part that has been sectioned, such as that shown in part C, will be broken with the same conventional break as that used to indicate a rectangular face of an object, as shown in part D. These breaks are used to represent metal, while the breaks shown in part E represent wood.

Conventional breaks are used to shorten a long piece that has a uniform cross section. This allows the part to be drawn in less space and at a larger scale with a portion broken out and removed (Fig. 5-92). The dimension placed on it will give its true length even though it cannot be scaled to this length on the drawing.

5-39 CONVENTIONAL REVOLUTIONS

To obtain improved clarity in engineering drawings, it is sometimes necessary to utilize conventional practices that may be violations of true projections. These conventional practices apply to both views and sections. An example of a conventional practice is shown in Fig. 5-93. The top view has three equally spaced ribs and holes. In the true projection of the front view shown in part A one rib is foreshortened, giving the impression that the object is not symmetrical. A direct projection of these holes gives the appearance that one of them is closer to the center of the cylindrical part than the other. Although this is a true projection, it is not as acceptable as the view shown in part B, where the rib has been revolved to show true size and the hole has been revolved to give its true radial distance from the center. The conventional view is easier to dimension and it gives a more representative impression of symmetry.

The same conventional practices apply to the construction of the sectioned view (part C) as were used in the view in part B. The part cut by

FIGURE 5-94

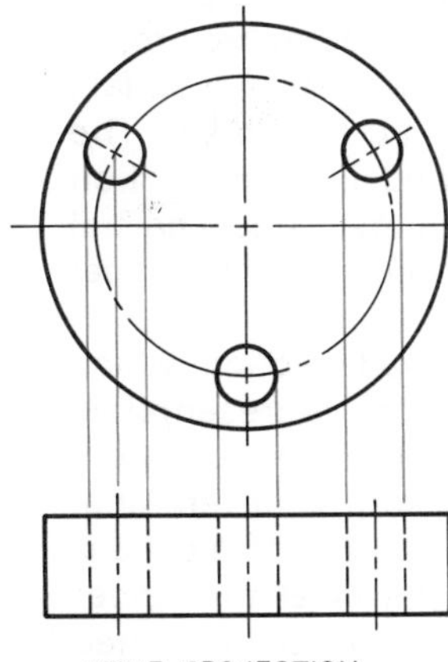

A. A true projection of the equally spaced holes does not give a good impression of the object. One hole appears to go through the center of the plane.

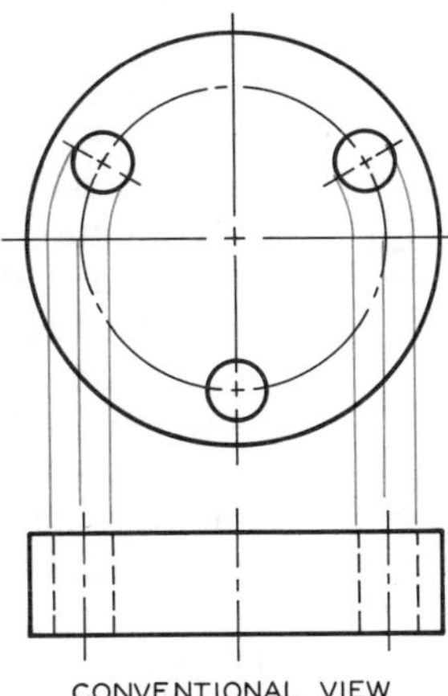

B. A conventional view is used to show the true radial distance of the holes from the center by revolution. The center hole is omitted.

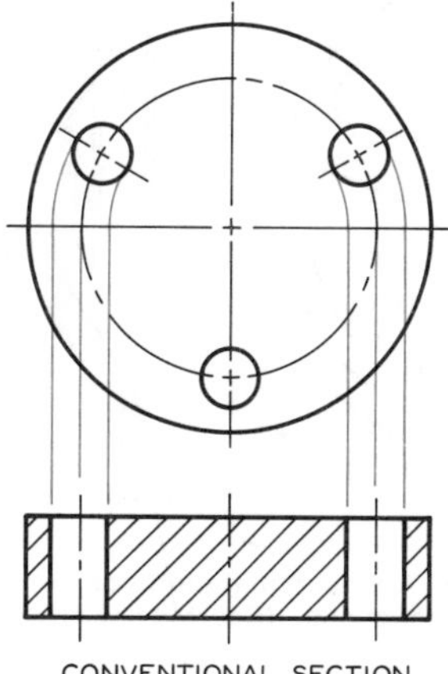

C. Conventional revolutions are used in sections also. Conventional views are often more representative of circular parts than are true projections.

the cutting plane is section-lined except for the ribs, which are not sectioned in the conventional practice.

The conventional practice for showing equally spaced holes in a circular plate is given in Fig. 5-94. In true projection (part A), the front view gives the impression that one hole passes through the center and that the holes are closer to the center than they really are. A better view is shown in part B, which is a conventional view rather than a true projection. The holes have been revolved to show their true distance from the center, and the hole appearing at the center has been omitted. The same procedure is used in sections, as shown in C.

It is conventional practice not to crosshatch spokes even though they have been cut by the cutting plane. The pulley in Fig. 5-95A has a solid web that should be crosshatched in the sectional view; however, the spokes in part B are not crosshatched to emphasize that they are spokes and not a solid web.

Symmetrically spaced spokes are conventionally handled as ribs, whether in a view or a

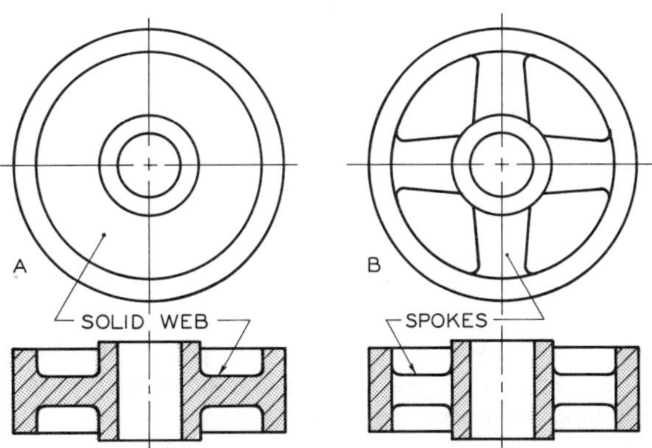

Fig. 5-95. Conventional practices of sectioning parts to distinguish between webs and spokes.

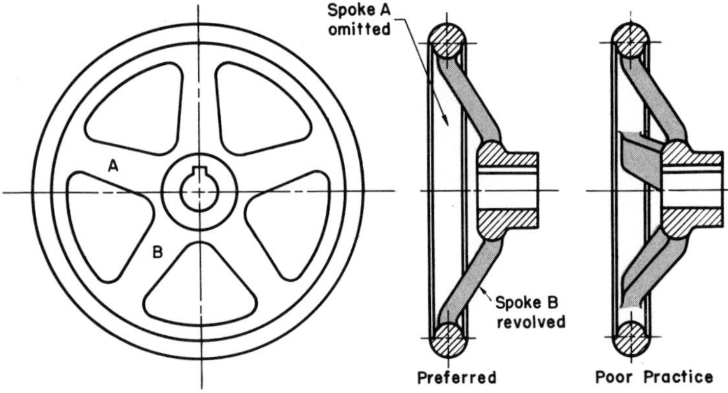

Fig. 5–96. Conventional methods of representing spokes in views and sections. (Courtesy of ANSI; Y14.2-1957.)

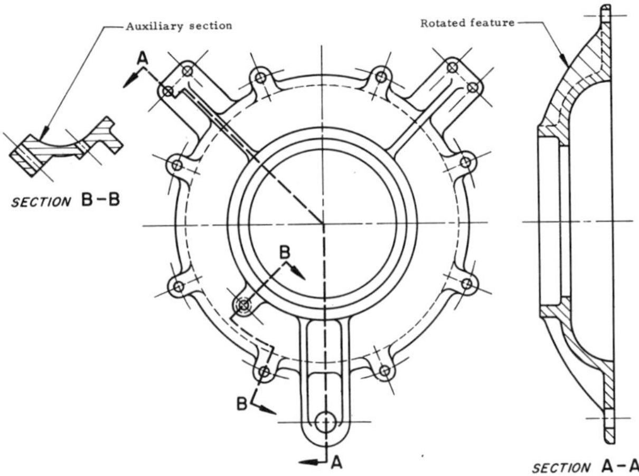

Fig. 5–97. Auxiliary sections used in combination with conventional revolutions to describe an object. (Courtesy of General Motors Standards.)

section. Figure 5–96 illustrates the preferred and poor practice methods of depicting spokes in a sectioned view. As is the case with ribs, spokes are not section-lined. Also, intermediate spokes are omitted to avoid confusion; two spokes are adequate to completely describe the hand wheel.

5–40 AUXILIARY SECTIONS

Auxiliary sections can be drawn to supplement the principal views used in orthographic projections, as shown in Fig. 5–97. An offset, auxiliary plane, B–B, is passed through the top view. The auxiliary section is a direct auxiliary projection made in the conventional manner. It is a partial view used to describe the object at one critical area for added clarity.

The side view is a revolved section which shows the side view in a more representative manner than would be shown by true projection. In addition to being revolved into a conventional position, the cutting plane, A–A, is offset to pass through one of the holes shown at the upper right of the top view. The ribs are section-lined in section A–A using conventional practices.

5–41 SKETCHING AND DESIGN

This chapter has been devoted to coverage of working-drawing standards that must be applied in the communication of ideas in the form of engineering drawings. Essentially all such drawings are executed with instruments in a precise manner to avoid misunderstanding. However, these same principles can be applied to freehand sketching, and valuable time can be saved by not making instrument drawings during the design stage.

Without the ability to prepare rapid freehand sketches, the designer could not function. Sketching is his means of communicating with others and with himself. It may sound strange to say that a person communicates with *himself*, but this is indeed true in the design process as discussed in Chapter 4.

The process of identifying good and bad aspects of an idea requires the designer to review each idea and sketch a modified solution. This procedure is almost impossible to perform without a pencil in hand; thus freehand sketching is a means of thinking and communicating with oneself. Every sketch that you make is an idea that has been saved, while fleeting ideas that are not sketched may be forgotten and lost.

Do not think of sketching as an artistic process, but as a disciplined method of presenting

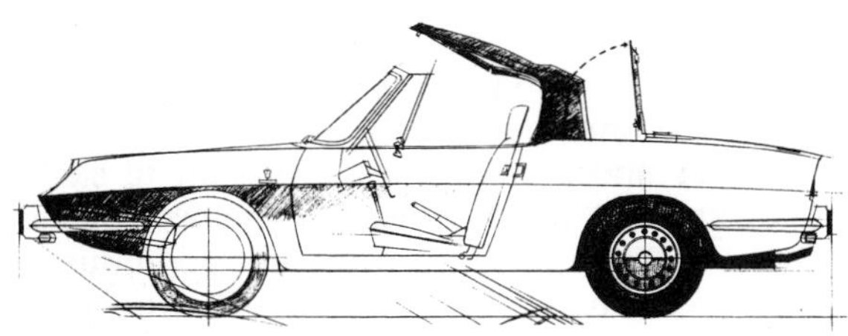

Fig. 5-98. Many design sketches will be drawn using principles of orthographic projection.

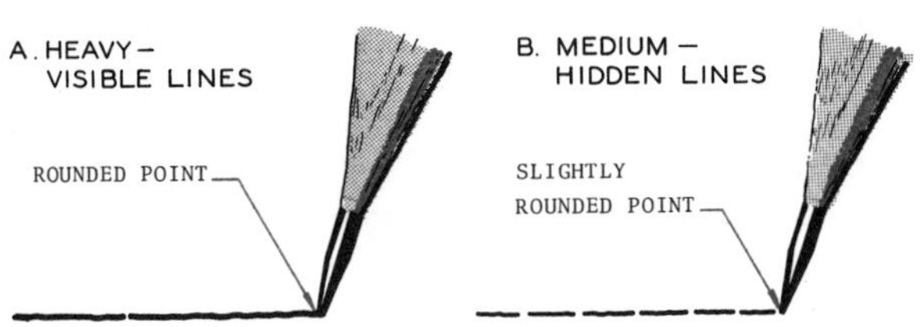

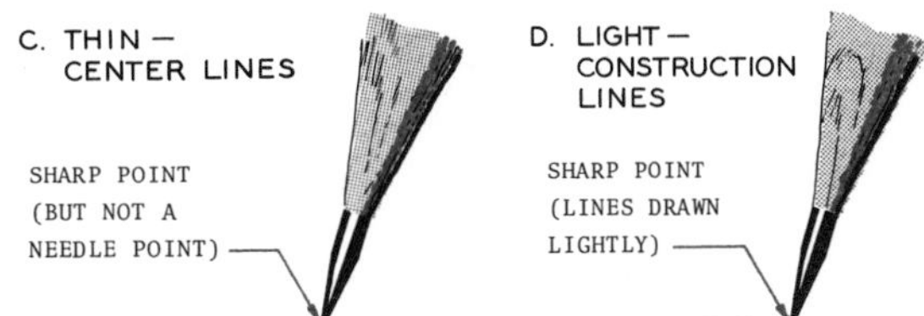

Fig. 5-99. The types of pencil points required to make the various types of lines used in freehand sketching. Practice sharpening your pencil to give these types of lines.

your ideas using the principles outlined in this chapter. It is important to develop speed. If you cannot sketch more rapidly than you can draw with instruments, you are defeating the purpose of freehand sketching. Practice making rapid sketches, but do not assume that fast sketches should be sloppy or difficult to read.

5-42 FREEHAND SKETCHING TECHNIQUES

The designer who is attempting to solve a technical problem may make a number of sketches using pictorials, diagrams, schematics, or any technique that will help him. Almost always, the designer will resort to orthographic projection principles for a major part of his work. The orthographic view of an automobile in Fig. 5-98 is an example of the application of this system of sketching. Consequently, for best results sketches should be drawn with adherence to the line weights suggested for orthographic views in Fig. 5-23.

A medium-grade pencil (B, HB, or F) will give good results for most sketches. It is suggested that the same pencil weight be used for all lines and that the sharpness of the point be altered to vary the weight of the line, as shown in Fig. 5-99. The two-view drawing in Fig. 5-100 illustrates the application of the various line weights to a sketch of this type.

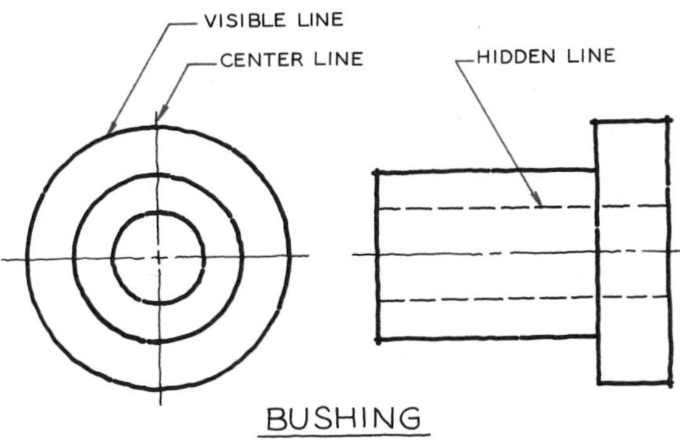

Fig. 5-100. The application of the standard line weights to an orthographic drawing.

Do not attempt to conceal the fact that your sketch was drawn freehand, since this type of drawing cannot duplicate the instrument technique and is not intended to do so. Develop a style of sketching that is effective but fast.

Figure 5-101 illustrates techniques of sketching intersecting lines at the corners of a drawing to make the sketch more effective. In general,

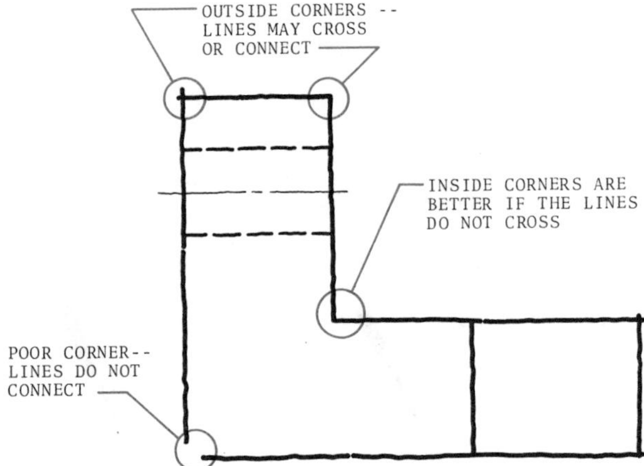

Fig. 5-101. Techniques of sketching intersecting lines to give the best effect.

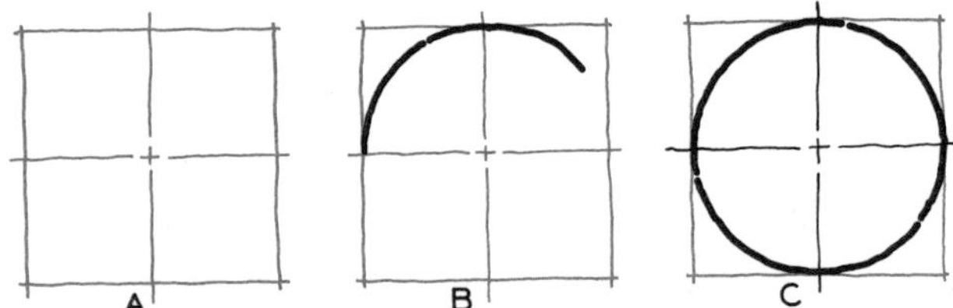

Fig. 5-102. The box method of sketching circles.

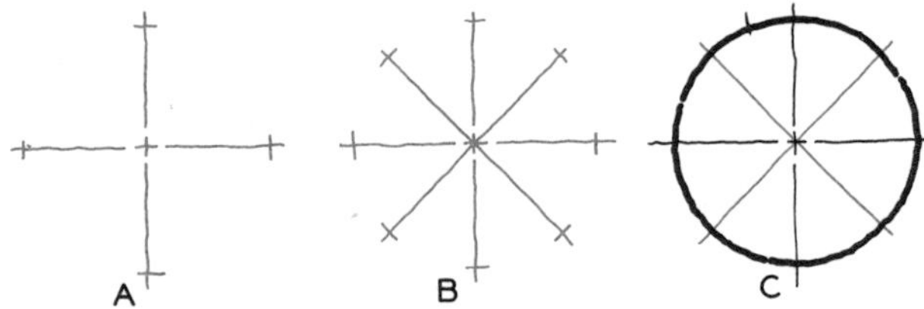

Fig. 5-103. The radius method of sketching circles.

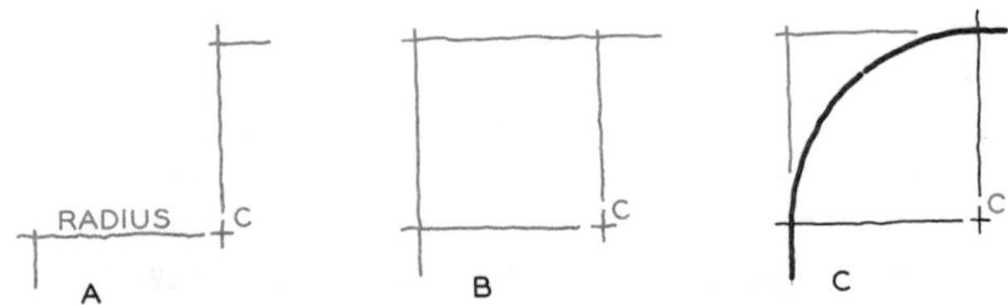

Fig. 5-104. A method of sketching arcs.

a corner should be distinctly defined with crossing lines or at least a continuous intersection where the lines butt together.

Circles and arcs are more difficult to sketch than straight lines; however, the use of construction lines will improve your technique. A method is illustrated in Fig. 5-102, where construction lines are used as a guide. The vertical and horizontal center lines are sketched (A) and a box is blocked in with construction lines. The distance across the square is the diameter of the circle to be sketched. The circle is drawn in segments (parts B and C) which are tangent to the box at the four points where the center lines cross.

Another method is illustrated in Fig. 5-103, where the center lines are drawn and the radius is measured from the center along each line (part A). Two 45° lines are drawn and the radius of the circle is measured along these lines (part B). The points located by this method are used as a guide in sketching the circle (part C). These same principles are used in sketching a portion of a circle, an arc, as shown in Fig. 5-104.

If the sketching of arcs requires more time than drawing them with instruments, then use your circle template or compass to draw them lightly, and darken the lines freehand to match your other freehand lines.

Since speed is the primary advantage of sketching rather than preparing instrument drawings, you should become familiar with the types of papers that will be helpful to you when sketching. Most of your sketches will be on $8\frac{1}{2}'' \times 11''$ sheets. Some papers have a grid printed on them that is very helpful (Fig. 5-105). It is preferable that the grid be printed in a light color so as not to be confused with the lines that are drawn on the sheet.

Since tracing paper is transparent enough to be seen through, a grid sheet can be placed under the sketching sheet and used as a guide. This removes the necessity of having a grid printed directly on the sketch sheet (Fig. 5-106).

Sketching is used more in the development of preliminary ideas than in the other steps of the design process. A review of Chapter 4 will give many examples of the use of sketching in the accumulation of ideas. This technique provides the designer with a rapid medium for generating and collecting many preliminary designs, but if his sketches are to be effective, he must understand the working-drawing standards covered in this chapter.

5–43 SUMMARY

The principles and fundamentals of engineering drawing covered in this chapter must necessarily be applied throughout the design process, whether the drawings are freehand sketches in the earlier stages or instrument drawings at the refinement or implementation stage of the design process. These fundamentals can be considered to be the language of the engineer that is used to communicate engineering ideas and designs. The draftsman must use these principles to prepare working drawings of the finished design that will be approved by the engineer and released for production.

The principles of geometric construction are mechanical methods of solving various aspects of engineering drawing problems. The proper use of scales and legible lettering practices must be observed in the preparation of drawings and sketches to provide effective communication. The fundamentals of orthographic, multiview drawings are the basis of most engineering drawing, except for drawings of the schematic or diagram variety. Auxiliary views are used to provide supplementary views in special cases where the principal views are not adequate. Chapters 7 and 8 give additional theory that relates to the understanding of orthographic projection and auxiliary views.

Sections and conventional practices provide designers and draftsmen with the means to better explain their ideas. Practical applications of sections will receive further discussion in the remaining chapters. These applications will be based on the principles introduced in this chapter.

Engineering drawing standards are employed to present and develop preliminary ideas, as described in Chapter 4. We shall also use these methods in the next chapter, Chapter 6, where we discuss the next step of the design process, refinement.

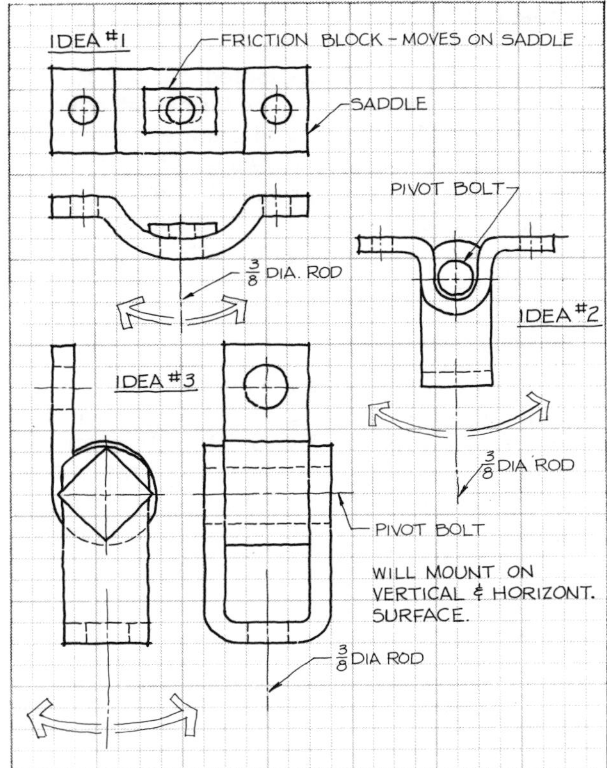

Fig. 5–105. Sketch pads with printed grids are available to assist the designer in sketching.

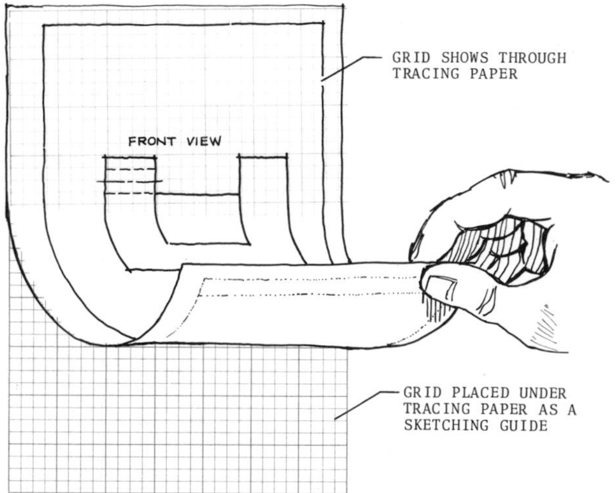

Fig. 5–106. A grid sheet can be used under a sheet of tracing paper as a guide for freehand sketching.

PROBLEMS

Problems should be presented on $8\frac{1}{2}'' \times 11''$ paper, grid or plain, using the format introduced in Article 1-19. Each grid square represents $\frac{1}{4}''$. All notes, sketches, drawings, and graphical work should be neatly prepared in keeping with good practices, as covered in this volume. Written matter should be legibly lettered using $\frac{1}{8}''$ guidelines.

Tangency Construction

1. (A through E) Using the radii indicated, construct arcs that are tangent to the lines and/or arcs that are given (Fig. 5-107). Indicate all points of tangency. (F) Find the points of tangency of a line drawn from point A to the given circle by geometric construction. Show all construction.

2. Make a drawing of the chain link in Fig. 5-108. Estimate the radii and dimensions. Show all construction.

3. Using the inside turning radius for an automobile, make a design layout of a one-car garage with a back-up space as shown in Fig. 5-109. Determine the dimensions of this space. Select an appropriate scale. Show all construction and points of tangency.

Use of Scales

4. Using your architects' and engineers' scales, lay out the lines in Fig. 5-110 according to the scales given. Letter the number of the problem, the length of the line, and the scale used as it appears in Fig. 5-110. Show each line as shown in the two examples.

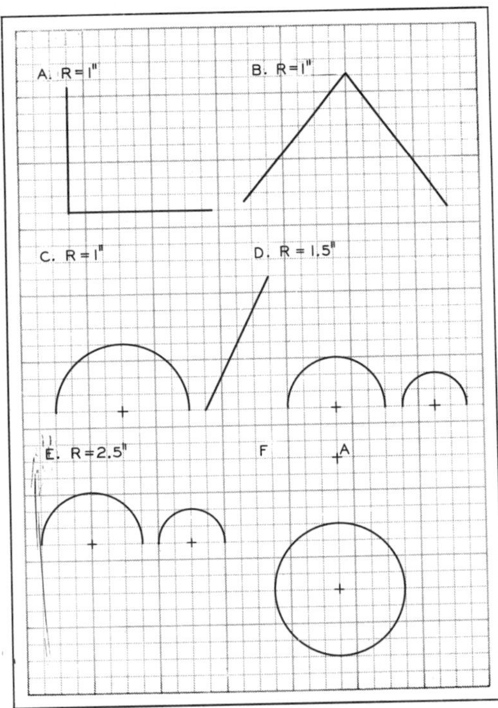

Fig. 5-107. Problem 1. Tangency problems.

Fig. 5-108. Problem 2. A link of a chain. (Courtesy of Link-Belt Company.)

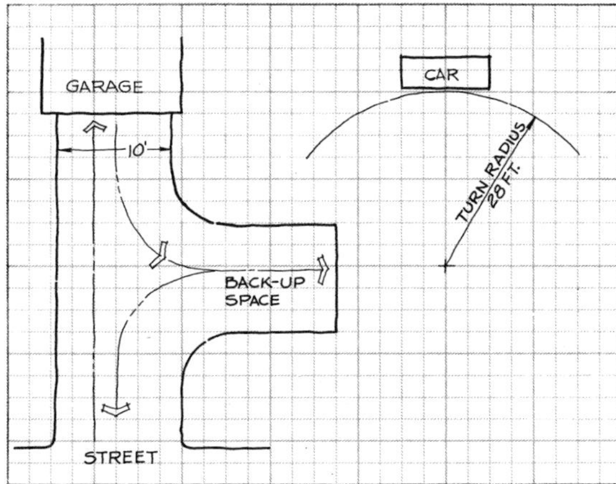

Fig. 5–109. Problem 3. Preliminary sketch of a driveway back-up system.

Graphical Mathematics

5. Use Fig. 5–111 for parts A through E. (A) Using the axes given, multiply 2.5 × 5.0 graphically. Show construction and label all work. (B) Using the axes given, multiply 3.0 × 4.0. Divide these axes, using the units indicated for determination of scale graduations. (C) Using the given axes, divide 18.0 × 3.0 graphically. Show all construction. (D) Using factors of 3 and 1, find the square root of 3. Three units are measured in the given portion of the problem. (E) Using the scale given, square 1.75 graphically. Show all construction.

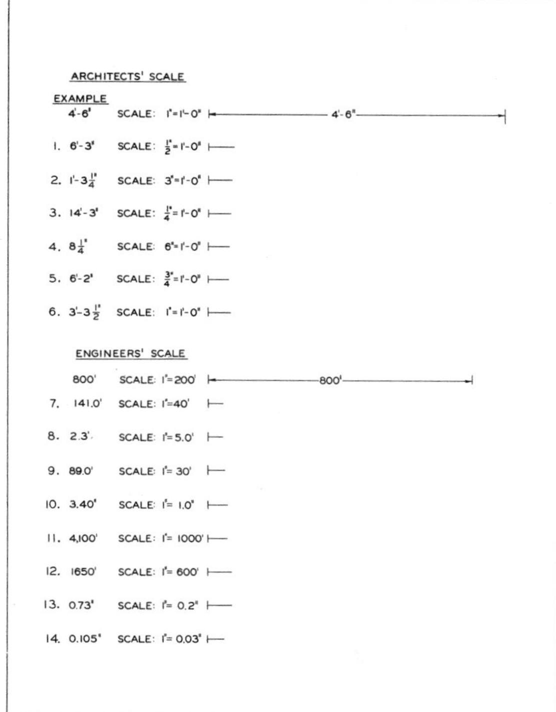

Fig. 5–110. Problem 4. Use of scales.

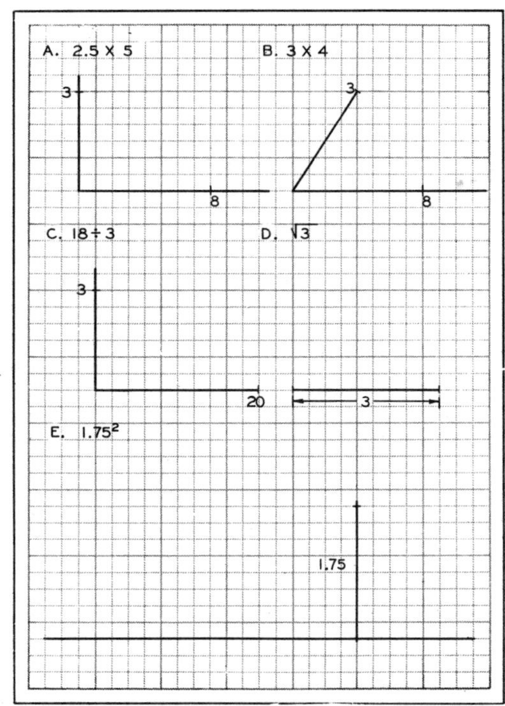

Fig. 5–111. Problem 5. Graphical mathematics problems.

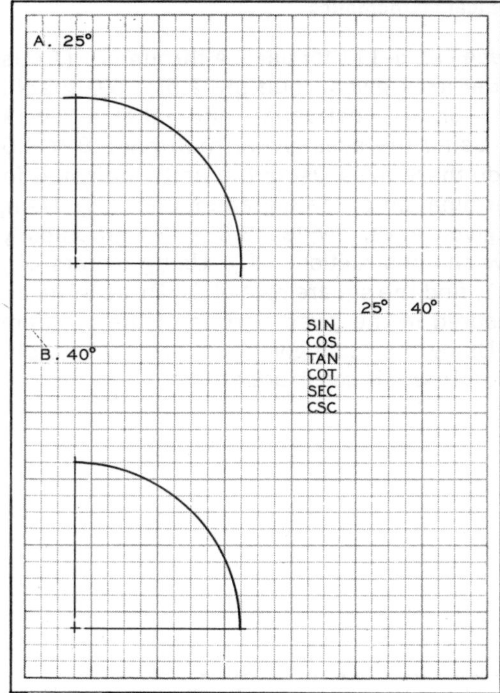

Fig. 5-112. Problem 6. Graphical trigonometric function problems.

6. (A) Using Fig. 5-112, find the trigonometric functions of 25° by graphical methods. Use the 40 scale of the engineers' scale. Complete the table of values and show all construction. (B) Find the trigonometric functions of 40° by graphical methods, using part B of the figure. Use the 40 scale of the engineers' scale. Complete the table of values and show all construction.

Orthographic Projection

7. Using instruments, lay out the given views of the objects shown in Figs. 5-113, 5-114, 5-115, and 5-116 as assigned. At least one view has missing lines that are to be completed in keeping with the rules of orthographic projection. Use the proper line weights.

8. Pictorials (Figs. 5-117, 5-118, and 5-119) are drawn on a pictorial grid where each grid is equal to $\frac{1}{2}''$ when drawn on $8\frac{1}{2}'' \times 11''$ paper. Either using instruments or by sketching, draw three views of the problems assigned, putting two problems on each sheet.

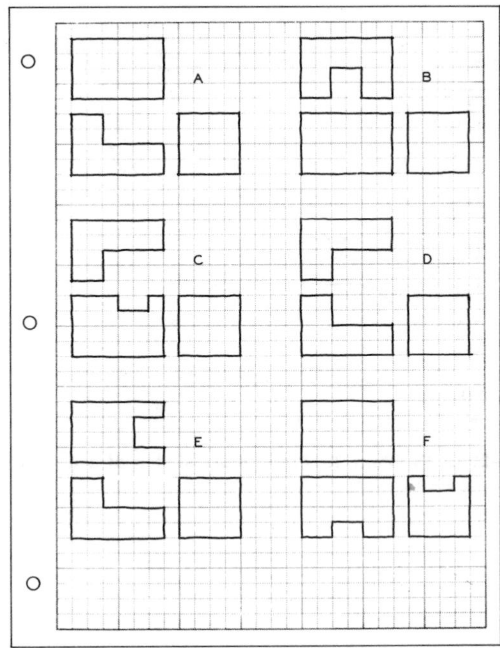

Fig. 5-113. Problem 7. Orthographic projection.

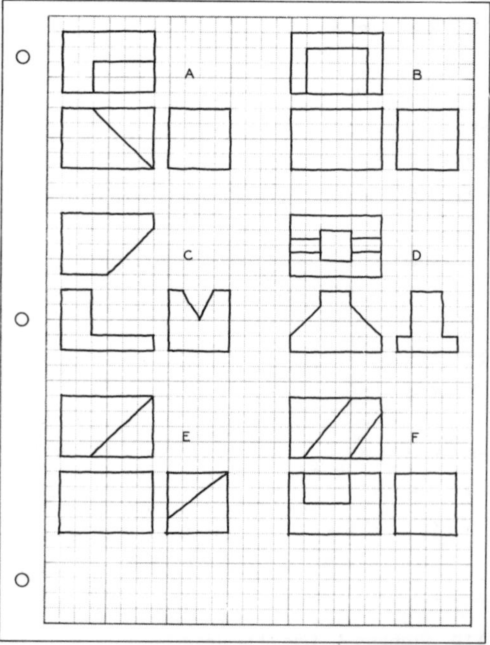

Fig. 5-114. Problem 7. Orthographic projection.

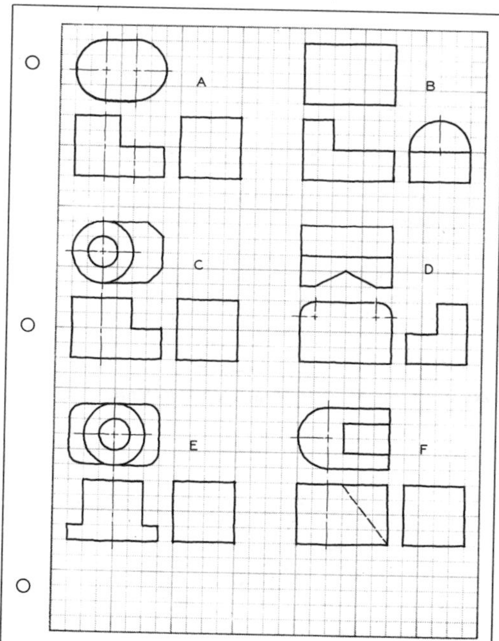

Fig. 5-115. Problem 7. Orthographic projection.

Fig. 5-117. Problem 8. Orthographic projection.

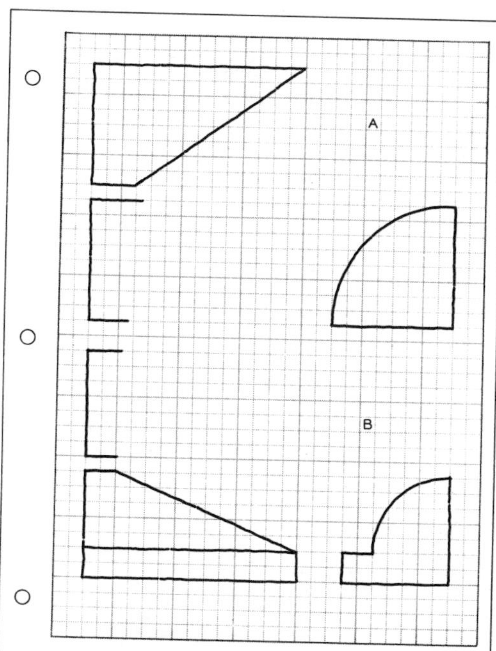

Fig. 5-116. Problem 7. Orthographic projection.

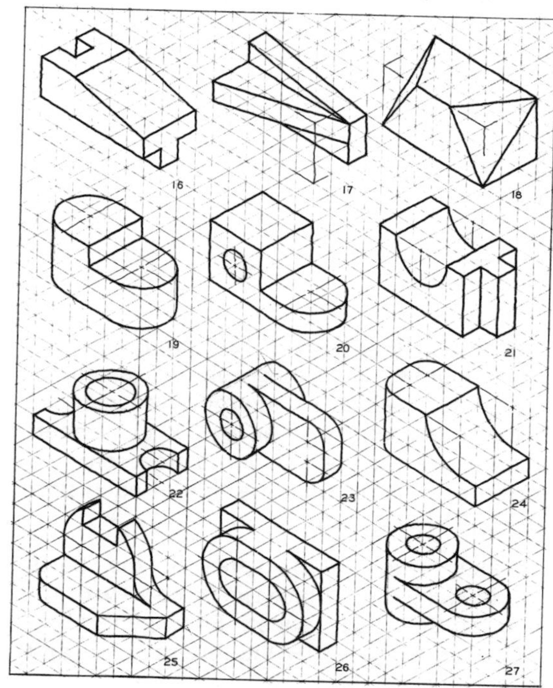

Fig. 5-118. Problem 8. Orthographic projection.

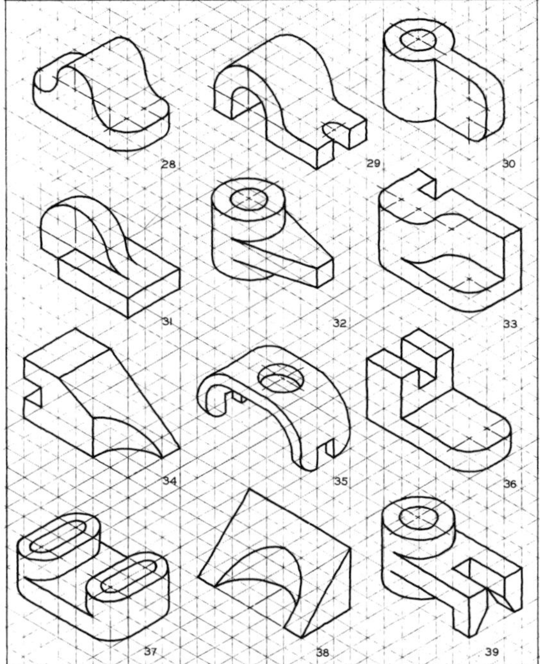

Fig. 5–119. Problem 8. Orthographic projection.

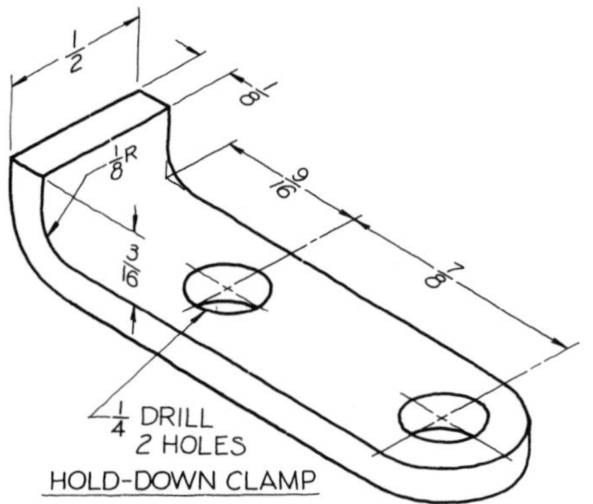

Fig. 5–120. Problem 9. Orthographic projection.

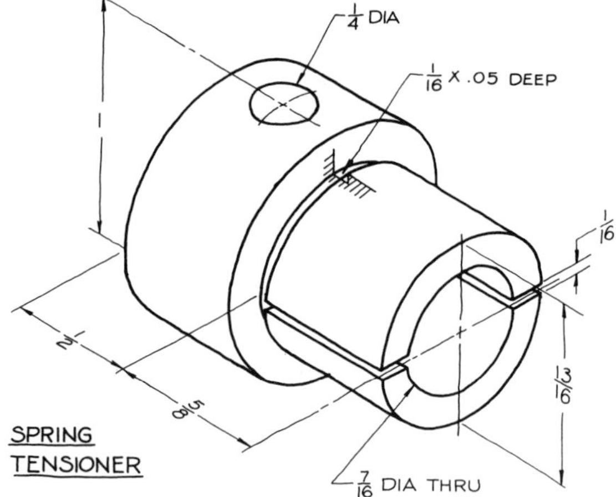

Fig. 5–121. Problem 9. Orthographic projection.

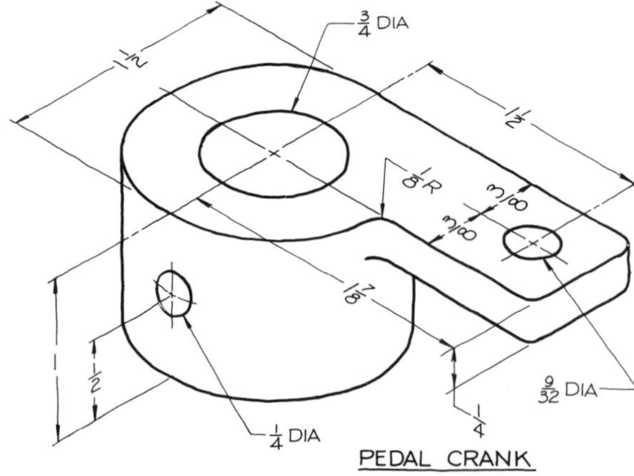

Fig. 5–122. Problem 9. Orthographic projection.

9. These problems (Figs. 5–120 through 5–125) are to be drawn as orthographic views using instruments. Select an appropriate scale so that the views will fit on an $8\frac{1}{2}'' \times 11''$ sheet. Use only the number of views necessary to describe each part. Give the title of each part on the completed sheet.

10. Make three-view sketches of the parts shown in Fig. 5–126. Place two three-view drawings on an $8\frac{1}{2}'' \times 11''$ sheet. Show general dimensions, designated by the letters *H*, *W*, and *D*, on each view.

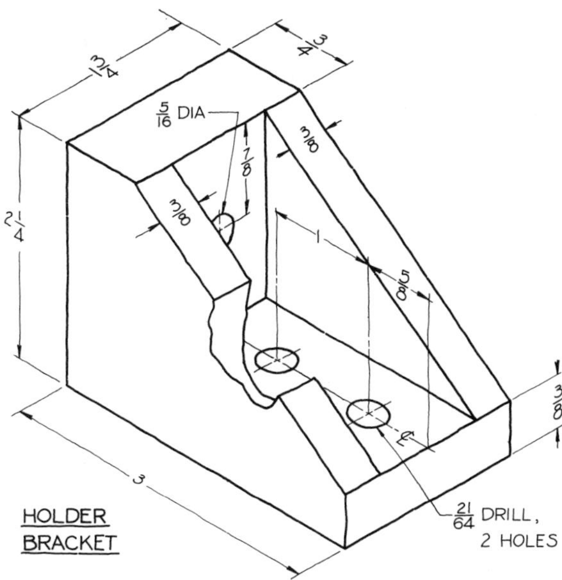

Fig. 5-123. Problem 9. Orthographic projection.

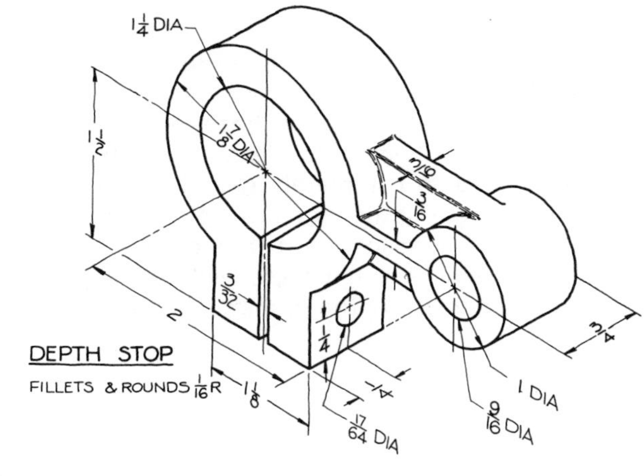

Fig. 5-125. Problem 9. Orthographic projection.

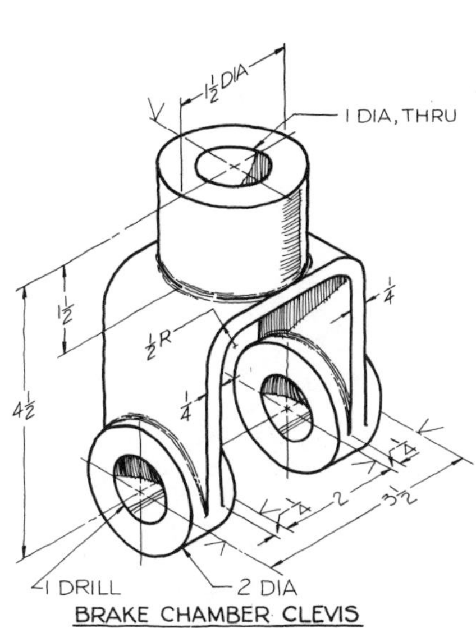

Fig. 5-124. Problem 9. Orthographic projection.

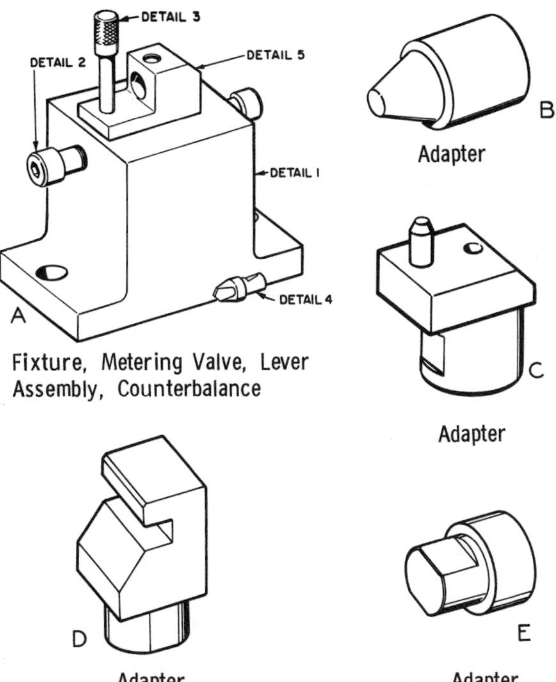

Fig. 5-126. Problem 10. Special maintenance tools. (Courtesy of Bendix Corporation.)

Auxiliary Views

11. Figures 5–127 through 5–136 are pictorials that are dimensioned. Using instruments on an $8\frac{1}{2}'' \times 11''$ sheet, draw these parts using the necessary orthographic views, including auxiliary views to completely describe the parts. Proper layout of the views to make good use of the available space is an important aspect of the problem. A rough sketch will be helpful to you in determining the proper arrangement.

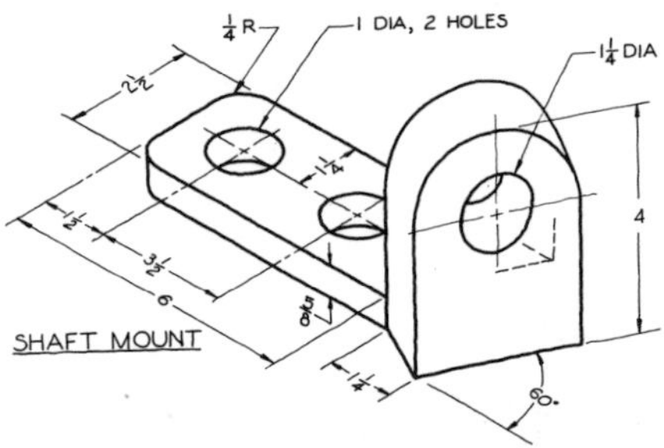

Fig. 5–127. Problem 11. Auxiliary views.

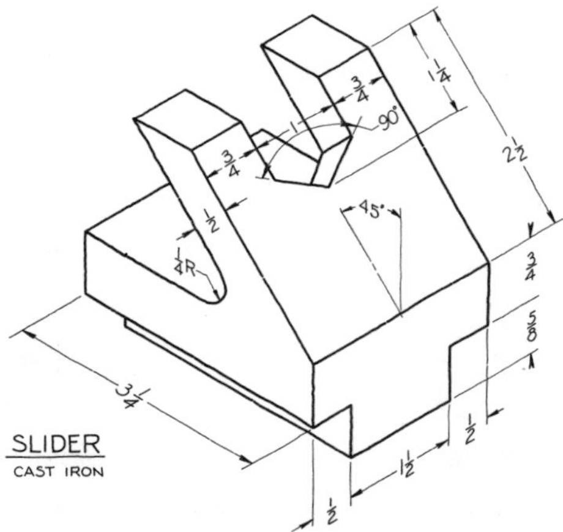

Fig. 5–128. Problem 11. Auxiliary views.

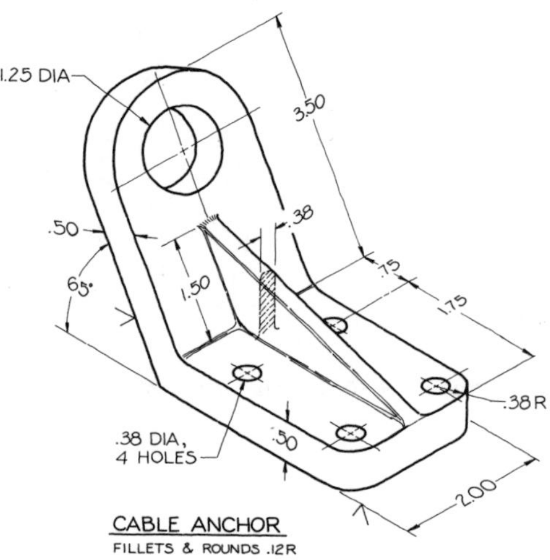

Fig. 5–129. Problem 11. Auxiliary views.

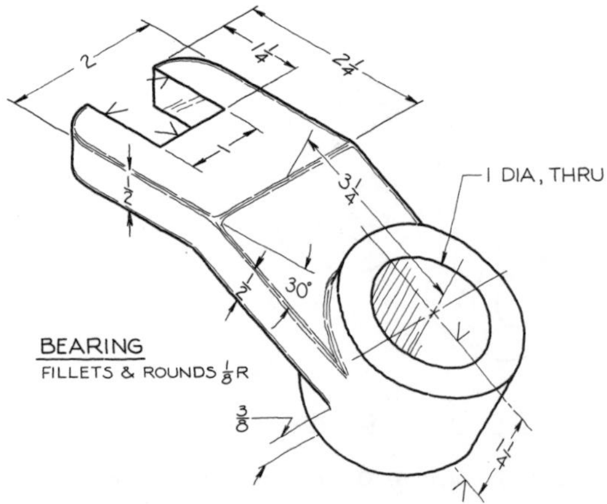

Fig. 5–130. Problem 11. Auxiliary views.

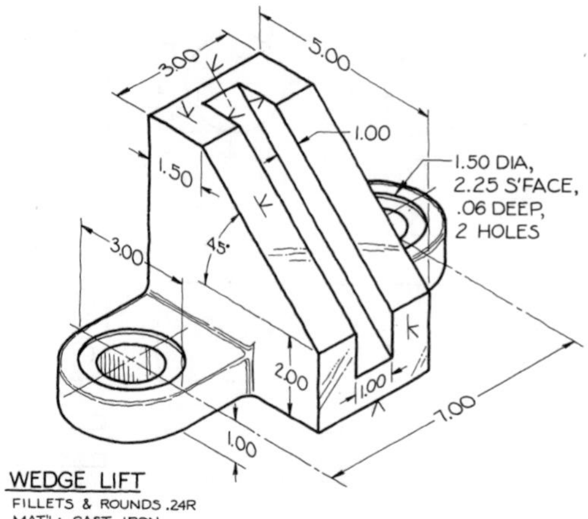

Fig. 5-131. Problem 11. Auxiliary views.

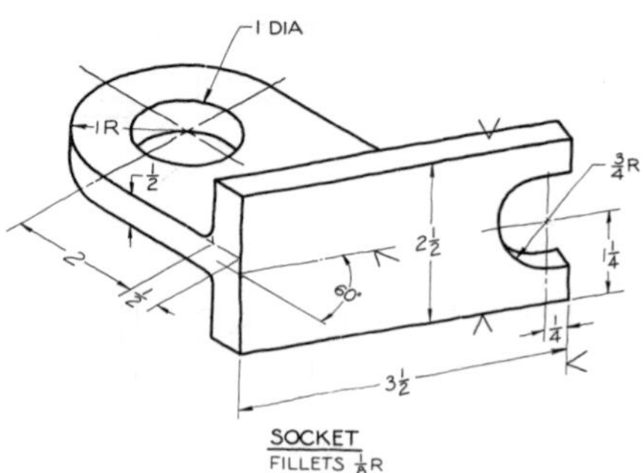

Fig. 5-132. Problem 11. Auxiliary views.

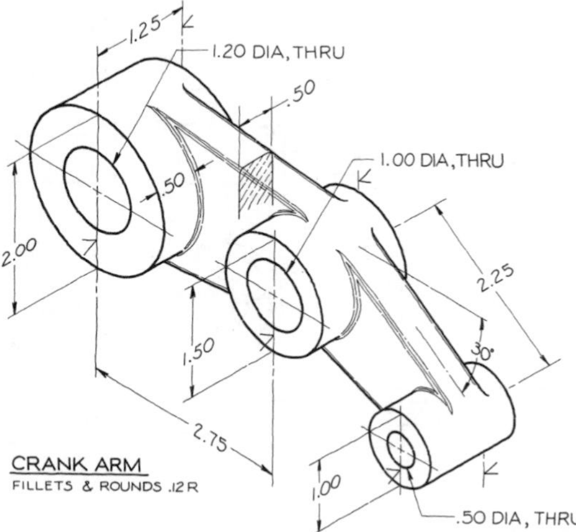

Fig. 5-133. Problem 11. Auxiliary views.

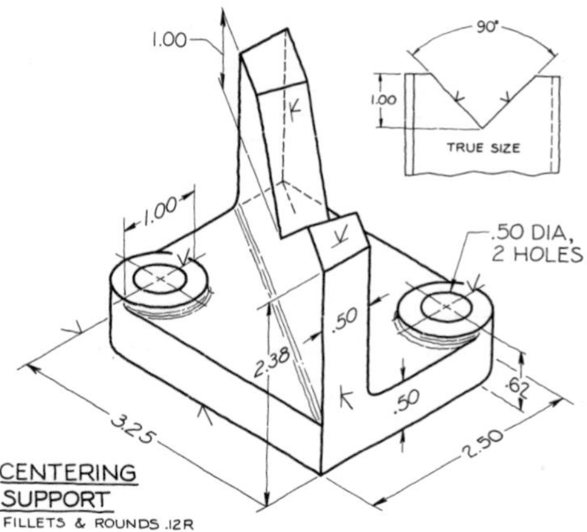

Fig. 5-134. Problem 11. Auxiliary views.

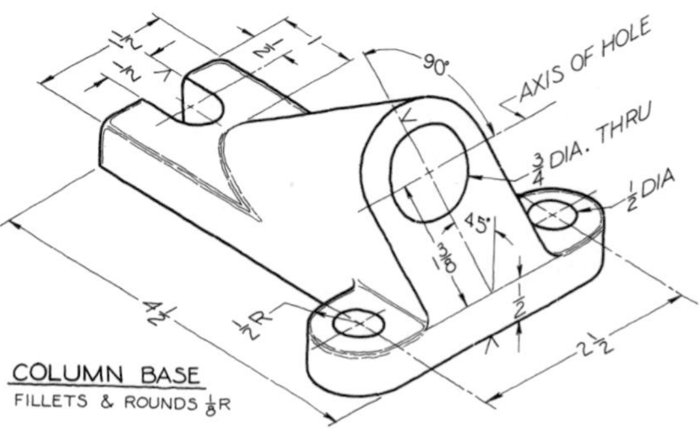

Fig. 5-135. Problem 11. Auxiliary views.

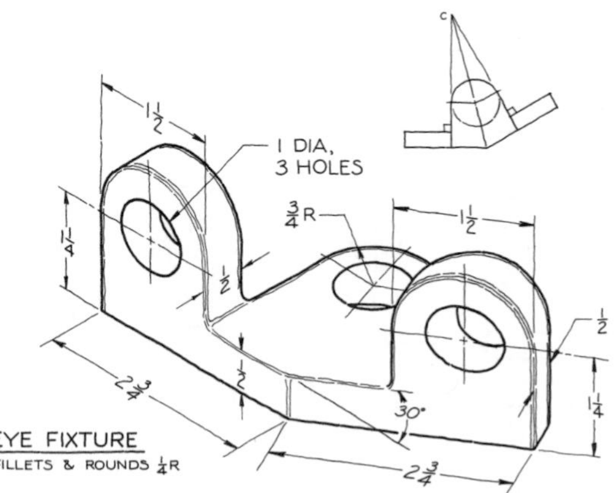

Fig. 5-136. Problem 11. Auxiliary views.

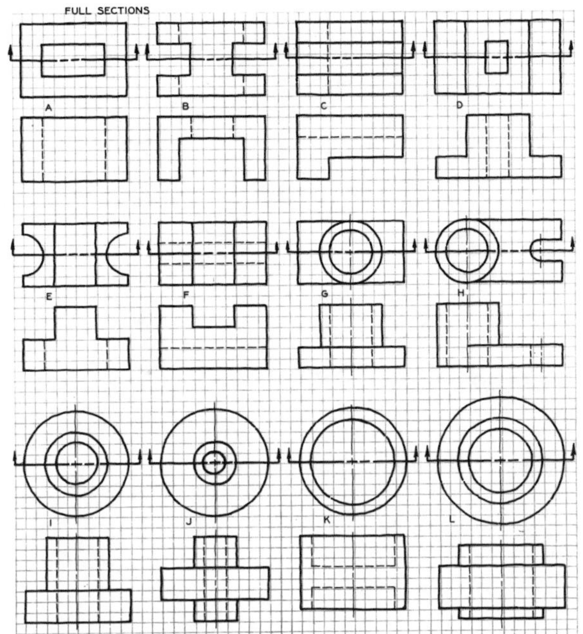

Fig. 5–137. Problem 12. Sections.

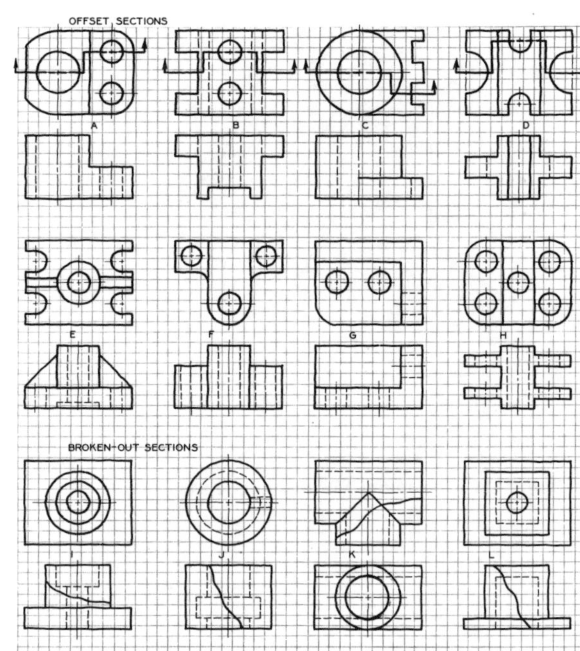

Fig. 5–139. Problem 12. Sections.

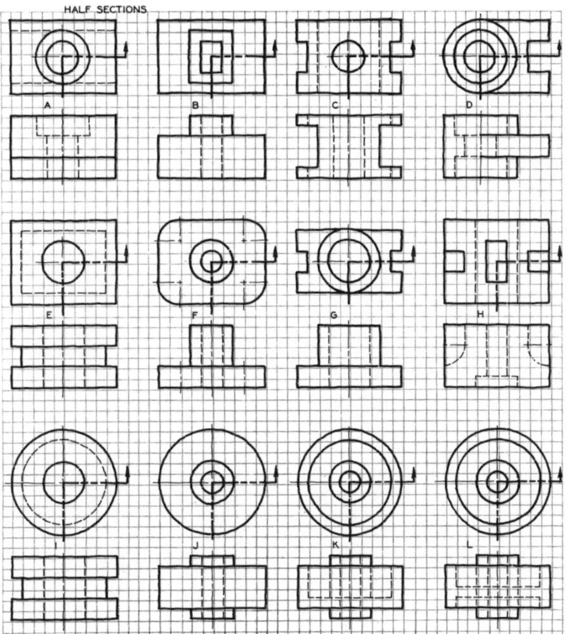

Fig. 5–138. Problem 12. Sections.

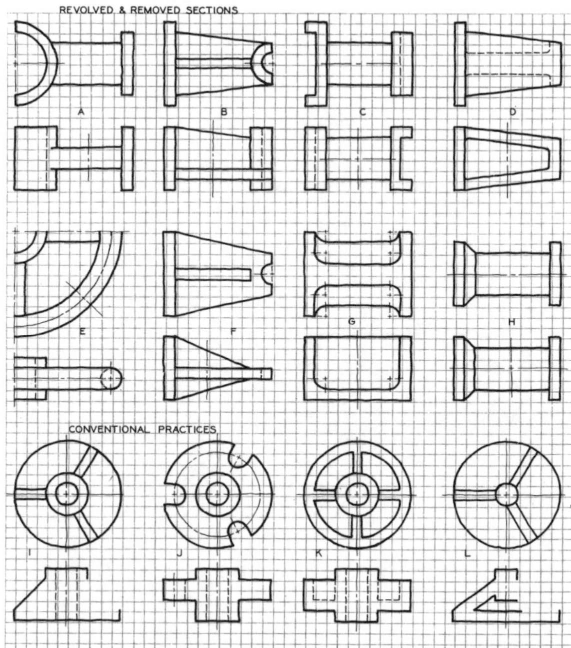

Fig. 5–140. Problem 12. Sections.

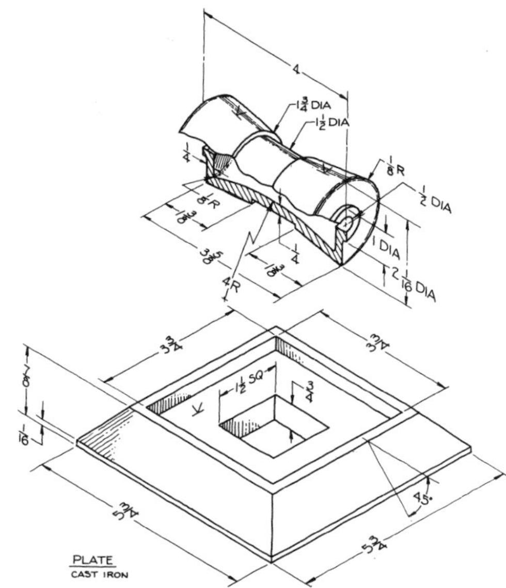

Fig. 5-141. Problem 13. (Courtesy of the Grinnel Company.)

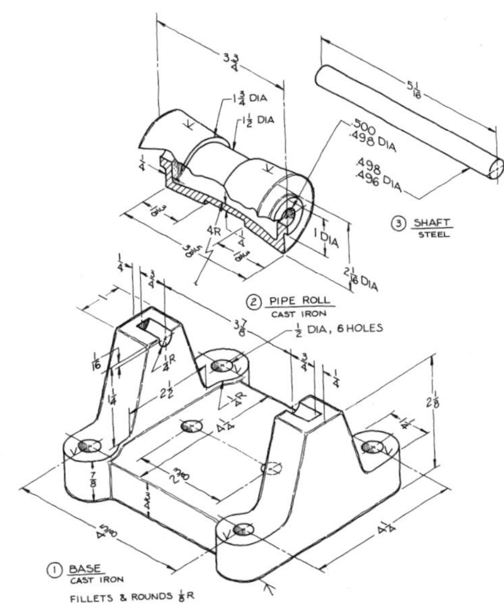

Fig. 5-142. Problem 13. (Courtesy of the Grinnel Company.)

Sections

12. Refer to Figs. 5-137 through 5-140 for sectioning problems that are to be drawn on $8\frac{1}{2}'' \times 11''$ paper with instruments. Each square of the grid represents $\frac{1}{4}''$. The drawings can be transferred to a grid paper of a similar type, or else the problems can be drawn on blank paper.

General Engineering Drawings

13. Refer to Figs. 5-141 through 5-143 for general engineering drawing problems that involve most of the principles of this chapter. Make either instrument or freehand orthographic drawings of each individual part of these assemblies. These views are to be drawn on

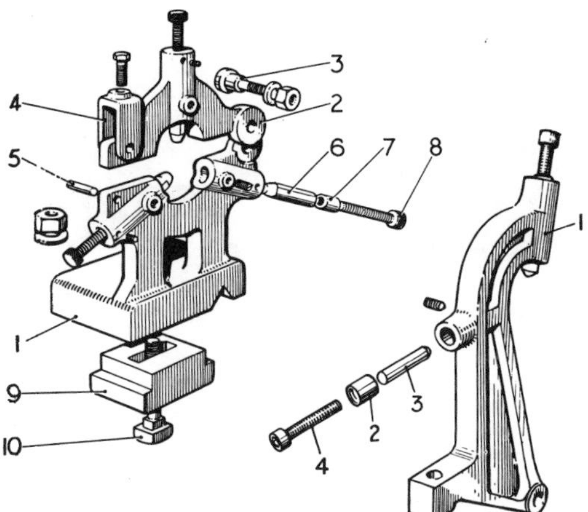

Fig. 5-143. Problem 13. Steadies. (Courtesy of Harrison and Sons Ltd.)

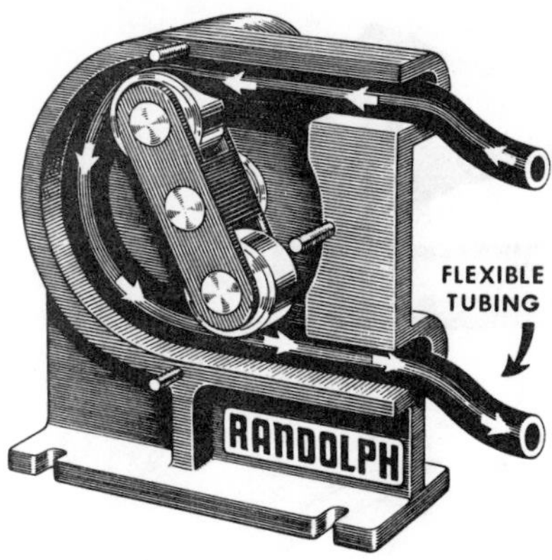

Fig. 5–144. Problem 14. Pumping device. (Courtesy of the Randolph Company.)

standard $8\frac{1}{2}'' \times 11''$ sheets with as many parts per sheet as possible. Each assembly will probably require several sheets.

14. Make either a freehand sketch or an instrument multiview drawing of each of the individual parts of the pumping device shown in Fig. 5–144. Estimate the dimensions of each part, basing them on a $\frac{3}{8}''$ outside diameter tube used for the liquid. Make drawings of the cover plate that is not shown. Use multiview drawings, sections, pictorials, or any other engineering drawing technique to illustrate each part as assigned by your instructor.

15. Make either freehand sketches or instrument multiview drawings of the parts assigned in Fig. 5–145. Estimate the general proportions of the parts. In each case drawings should be made of separate parts rather than of assemblies.

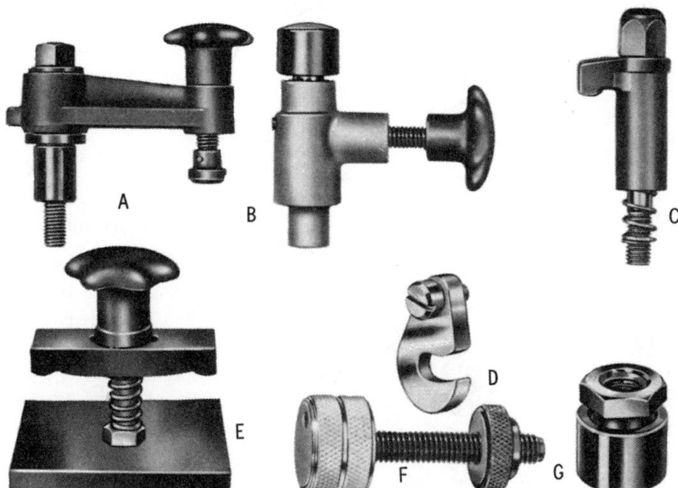

Fig. 5–145. Problem 15. Clamping devices. (Courtesy of Universal Engineering Company.)

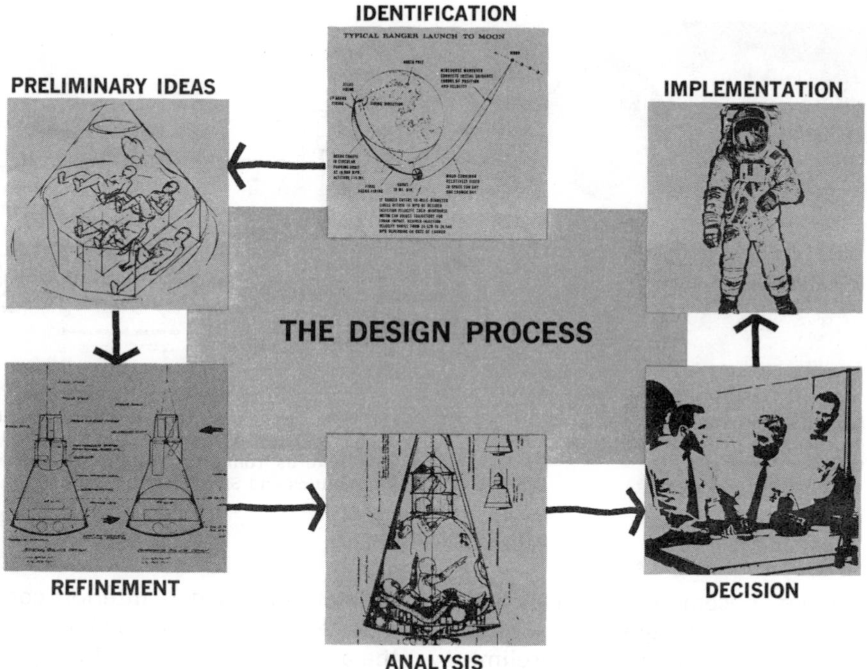

6 DESIGN REFINEMENT

6–1 GENERAL

Descriptive geometry is the graphical discipline that has the greatest application to the refinement step of the design process. The designer begins refinement only after he has accumulated a sufficient number of preliminary ideas in the form of sketches and notes. In design refinement it is necessary to make instrument drawings that are rendered to scale, to provide an accurate check on critical dimensions and measurements that were sketched during the early stages of the design process. When clearances or other measurements are critical, freehand sketches can be misleading. A scale drawing will give a true picture of the dimensions in question (Fig. 6–1).

Design refinement is the initial departure from the unrestricted freedom of creativity and imagination. Any design is subject to the limitations imposed by practicality of function and operation. Therefore, several better ideas must be selected and refined so that a comparison can be made during analysis and decision with regard to the final design solution to be implemented.

The designer must begin the analysis and decision functions to some extent during design refinement. He must select the preliminary ideas that have the most merit and are the most feasible in relation to the problem needs. Unless he makes a general analysis of the functional capabilities of the preliminary ideas, he will have to refine all of his designs, and this will require considerable time if he has drawn a number of preliminary ideas. Consequently, the designer needs to develop an ability to form opinions of preliminary ideas as they are con-

Fig. 6-1. The designer's first step in the refinement phase of his preliminary ideas is the preparation of scale drawings. (Courtesy of the Chrysler Corporation.)

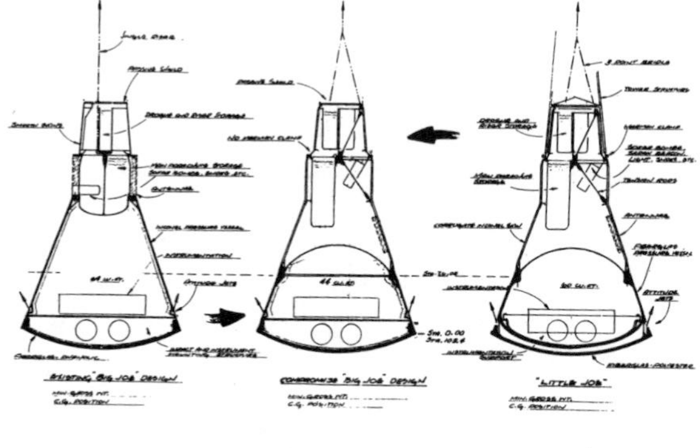

Fig. 6-2. These scale drawings were used to refine the final design of the "Big Joe" spacecraft and to incorporate desirable features from other systems. (Courtesy of the National Aeronautics and Space Administration.)

ceived—but without becoming negative and restricting his freedom of imagination. These opinions will help him in selecting the preliminary ideas that are most worthy of refinement for further evaluation.

6-2 DETERMINATION OF PHYSICAL PROPERTIES

The refinement stage of the design process is concerned primarily with the physical properties and general limitations that are evident prior to a formal analysis of a design. For example, scale drawings were made of three proposed configurations for the refinement of the "Big Joe" spacecraft (Fig. 6-2). These scale drawings evolved from many preliminary sketches and design features of experimental vehicles previously tested to determine the most desirable characteristics. Scale drawings of this type are helpful in developing the final shape and dimensions of a design. The functions and activities of the astronauts to be housed in the craft will have considerable influence on the size, volume, and general configuration of the capsule. Human engineering factors will be discussed in greater detail in Chapter 13. To determine the weight of the craft it is necessary to know the surface areas of the vehicle parts and the types of material used. Interior components and other equipment must be known also, as well as the approximate weight of the passengers. The volume of the craft must be determined to ensure that sufficient space is available for the accessory equipment required during flight.

The calculation of practically any given physical properties begins with basic geometric elements—points, lines, areas, volumes, and angles. The measurements of these elements are determined as a design is refined prior to the preparation of working drawings from which the object can be constructed. The refined design is not necessarily a working drawing, but it is a scale drawing from which a rather accurate appraisal can be made.

Design refinement may involve a three-dimensional problem requiring spatial analysis. It may also involve planning for the use of stock components, as in the portable stereo phonograph shown in Fig. 6-3 in its final form. After preliminary sketches were made of this product, scale drawings were prepared to assist in refining the details of construction to be as economical and efficient as possible. Stock materials were used to reduce the expense of special fabrication. As the problem was refined, a modular system of construction was developed that would be both attractive and economical

Fig. 6-3. The method of construction of a stereo portable phonograph was determined through the refinement of preliminary concepts. (Courtesy of Aluminum Corporation of America.)

Fig. 6-4. The assembled phonograph is shown here in its completed form with the dual purpose speakers detached for stereo listening. (Courtesy of Aluminum Corporation of America.)

(Fig. 6-4). After refinement of the structural system, a complete final working drawing was prepared to implement construction.

A problem of the spatial analysis variety is the gas processing system shown in Fig. 6-5. The general layout of the various units of the system can be drawn as a schematic diagram to indicate the sequence of the process. Refinement requires the determination of the sizes of the vessels, their volume, the land area required, and the fabrication details of the vessels and pipes. Since the vessels have a variety of shapes, and since the pipes and vessels intersect at different angles, the problem will require a three-dimensional analysis. The lengths of pipes must be found, vessels developed as patterns on flat metal stock, and intersections between pipes and surfaces determined.

Access to this information will enable the designer to formulate a final design with the necessary details for construction. Since stock components will be used as often as possible to reduce costs, the designer should revise his design during refinement to take advantage of available components. Pipe fittings are designed to join pipes at several standard angles, and a refinery system should be designed so that connections match these standard angles. This is possible with the application of descriptive geometry.

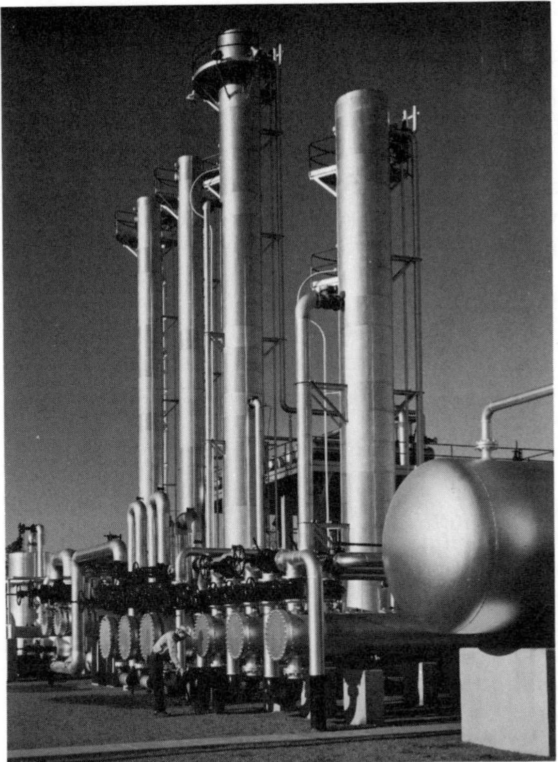

Fig. 6-5. This gas processing plant is an example of a system requiring considerable spatial analysis and the application of descriptive geometry principles. (Courtesy of Humble Oil and Refining Company.)

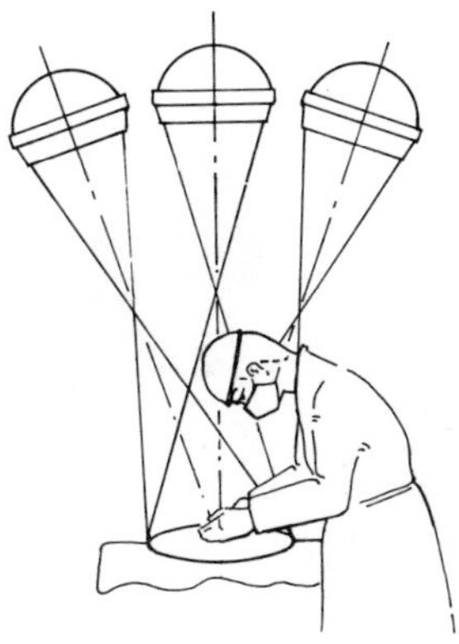

Fig. 6-6. A well-adapted surgical lamp emits light that passes around the surgeon's shoulders with the minimum of shadow. (Courtesy of Sybron Corporation.)

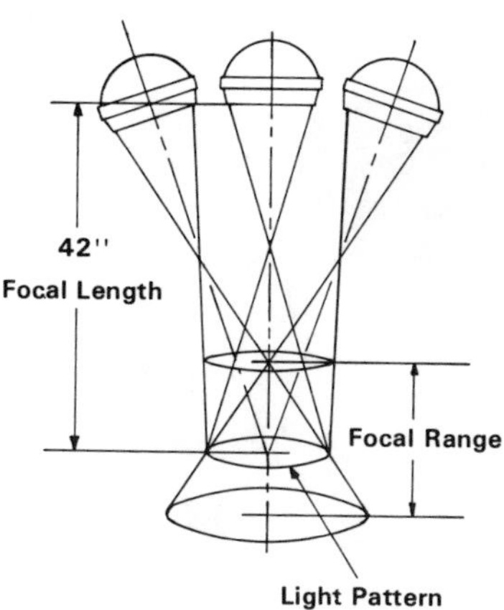

Fig. 6-7. The focal range of this surgical lamp is between 30'' and 60''. (Courtesy of Sybron Corporation.)

6-3 APPLICATION OF DESCRIPTIVE GEOMETRY

Descriptive geometry is the study of points, lines, and surfaces in three-dimensional space. This area of study has many applications to the refinement of a preliminary design and its analysis. Descriptive geometry can be applied to engineering problems that would be difficult to solve by other engineering methods.

An example of a problem requiring the use of descriptive geometry to determine geometric characteristics is a surgical light. The development of the light is a twofold problem, involving both the illumination and the geometry of the unit.

A major concern of the designer is the positioning of the light source so that maximum light falls on the work area with the minimum obstruction. A sketch of a well-adapted lamp is shown in Fig. 6-6. Note that the light emitted from specially designed reflectors converges to a small beam at shoulder level to minimize shadows cast by interference of the surgeon's shoulders, arms, and hands. The particular design that was developed, with a focal range between 30'' and 60'', is shown in Fig. 6-7.

Scale drawings of the design are drawn so that the geometry of the fixture can be studied in detail. Measurements, angles, areas, and other geometry can be determined from these drawings (Fig. 6-8).

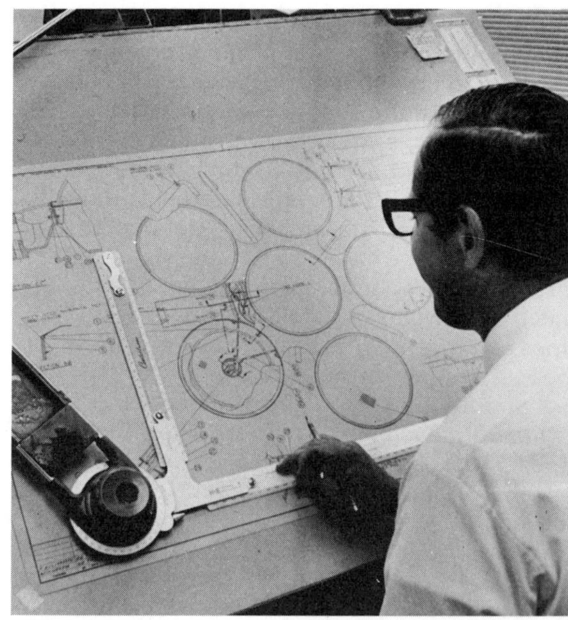

Fig. 6-8. The geometry of the surgical lamp can be studied through the use of scale drawings as a step toward refinement of preliminary ideas. (Courtesy of Sybron Corporation; photograph by Brad Bliss.)

Figure 6-9 is an example of a refinement drawing that shows critical dimensions. Eventually this geometry will be tested by construction of a working model to confirm the information found in the refinement drawings.

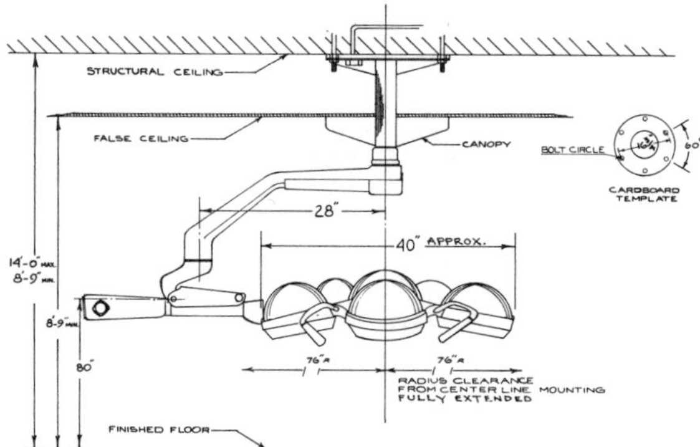

Fig. 6–9. The overall dimensions of the final design are shown in this refinement drawing. (Courtesy of Sybron Corporation.)

Fig. 6–10. This 10-ft-diameter underwater sphere could not have been designed without descriptive geometry methods. (Official photograph, U. S. Navy.)

Another example of a problem refined by descriptive geometry is a structural frame for the 10-ft-diameter underwater sphere (Fig. 6–10). Before working drawings could be made, the physical properties and dimensions of the spherical pentagons had to be determined through a series of auxiliary views. The determination of the angles between the members was necessary before the joints could be detailed to give the snug fit illustrated in Fig. 6–11. A further refinement was the development of the necessary jigs for holding the components during assembly (Fig. 6–12). The solution of this problem would be essentially impossible without the principles of descriptive geometry.

A layout drawing for refining an automotive design is shown in Fig. 6–13. Here the designer's task was to determine the limitations of the size of the fender opening so as to allow minimum clearance between the wheel and the fender. The wheel is turned to its maximum steering angles to locate lines of interference, which will determine the minimum opening of the front fender. The left side of the layout shows a section of the fender opening turn-under. Line X in the plan view shows the lowest part of the fender turn-under, which is the potential line of interference. The largest oversize tire is also shown. Section Z–Z is developed from the tire shape when it is in the position previously described. The shaded tire sections through line X indicate the conditions which determine the fender opening.

Fig. 6–11. The complex joints of the structural members were designed with the use of descriptive geometry. (Official photograph, U. S. Navy.)

Fig. 6–12. Jigs used to assemble the frame were designed through the use of descriptive geometry. (Official photograph, U. S. Navy.)

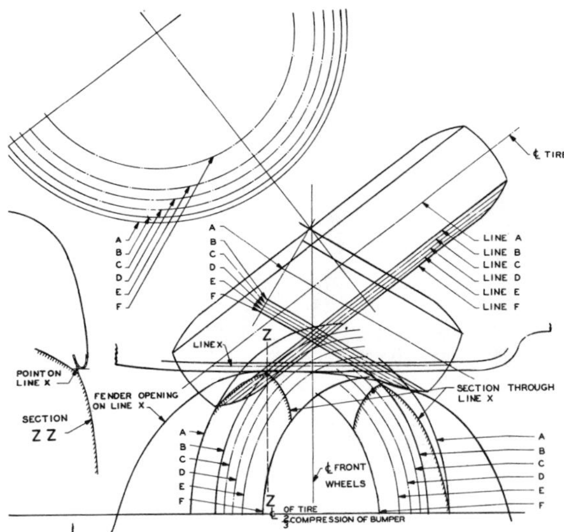

Fig. 6-13. The clearance between a fender and a tire is used to determine the fender opening of an automobile by the application of descriptive geometry and graphical methods. (Courtesy of Chrysler Corporation.)

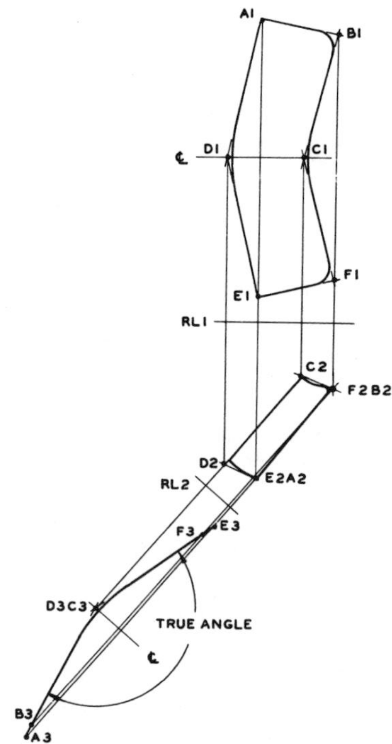

Fig. 6-14. The angle between the planes of a windshield can be determined by simplifying the problem to the fundamental planes involved. (Courtesy of Chrysler Corporation.)

6-4 PRESENTATION OF DESCRIPTIVE GEOMETRY

The succeeding six chapters are devoted to the introduction of those fundamentals of descriptive geometry that are most commonly applied to the refinement of design problems. Many examples of practical applications will be given in each chapter to illustrate uses of descriptive geometry for common design problems. The principles described can be applied to essentially all three-dimensional problems involving the relationships of points, lines, and surfaces; they thus give the designer access to a valuable problem-solving tool.

Problems have been reduced to the fundamental elements of points, lines, and surfaces for simplification of the basic principles. All actual engineering problems can be reduced to these elements and solved in the same manner as the example problems. Identification of the type of problems encountered is the initial step of problem solution. If the solution desired is the determination of the angle between two planes of a design, the problem can be resolved to the two planes in question and solved as the application of this principle. For example, the angle between two planes of an automobile windshield is found in Fig. 6-14 when two orthographic views have been obtained.

The succeeding chapters should be reviewed in detail, because the principles they present will be employed to a considerable extent to refine preliminary design solutions. Since the refinement phase of the design process provides the transition from a preliminary idea to the necessary specifications and information required for the preparation of working drawings, it is, in essence, the problem-solving portion of a design project. In this phase graphical methods are used extensively, with descriptive geometry being a primary tool for solving many problems that do not lend themselves to mathematical solutions.

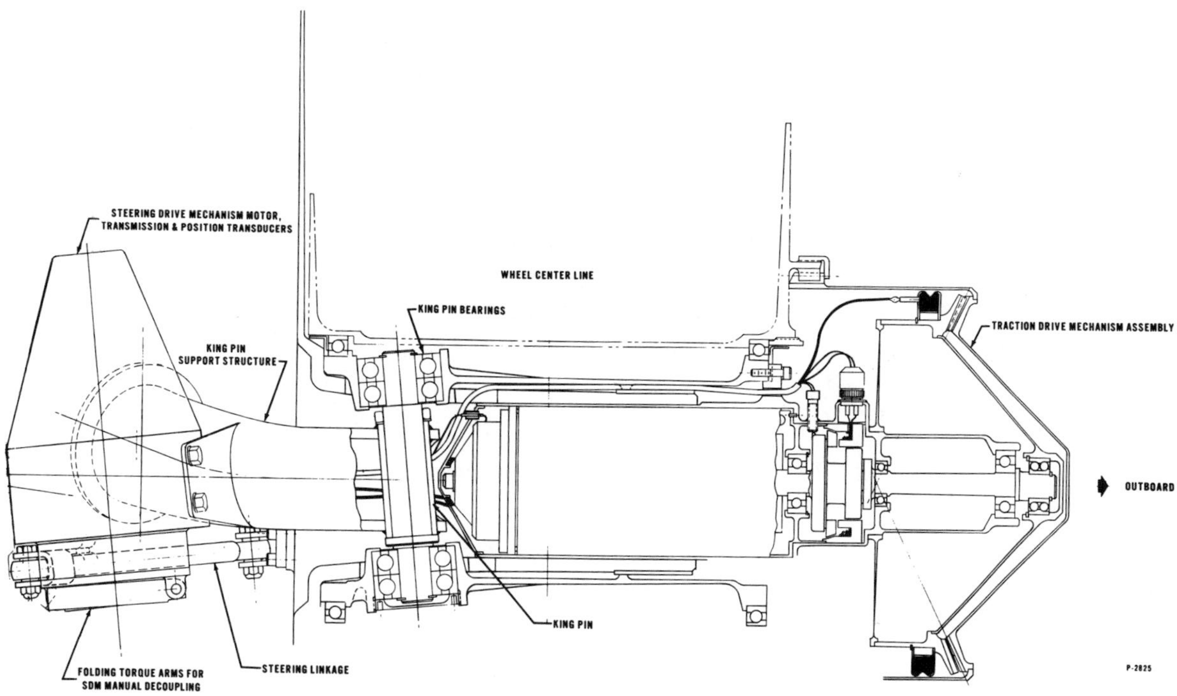

Fig. 6–15. A preliminary refinement drawing of a left front wheel for a vehicle designed to travel on the moon's surface. Dimensions and details of construction can be omitted on refinement drawings. (Courtesy of Bendix Corporation.)

6–5 REFINEMENT OF AN ENGINEERING DESIGN

An example design problem encountered in a research and development program was to develop a design for a Mobile Laboratory that would travel on the moon's surface. The vehicle was to provide a 14-day, 250-mile lunar operational range capability for two men. The Bendix Corporation was responsible for the four-wheel traction drive mechanism (TDM) and front-wheel steering drive mechanism (SDM) designs.

Many preliminary sketches were prepared to provide a selection of various possible solutions to this problem. These were evaluated to determine the most appropriate design for the project needs. Figure 6–15 shows the conceptual design layout of the left front wheel TDM and SDM incorporating DC series motors, two-ratio electric clutch systems and final stage hermetically sealed nutator transmission. The TDM units were designed to be mounted within each wheel axle. Although this drawing was drawn to scale, it is not a working drawing, since dimensions and sufficient information to construct the assembly are not given. This is merely a drawing used to refine the preliminary sketches. Note that several oblique angles are incorporated in the design, which will require solution by descriptive geometry.

A pictorial of the refined design introduced in Fig. 6–15 is shown in Fig. 6–16 to better describe the concept to the customer. It is easier to understand the relationships of the parts of the assembly in this partially sectioned pictorial. This final preliminary concept was accepted and the contract was awarded.

A follow-up contract was awarded for the design and fabrication of a mobility test article

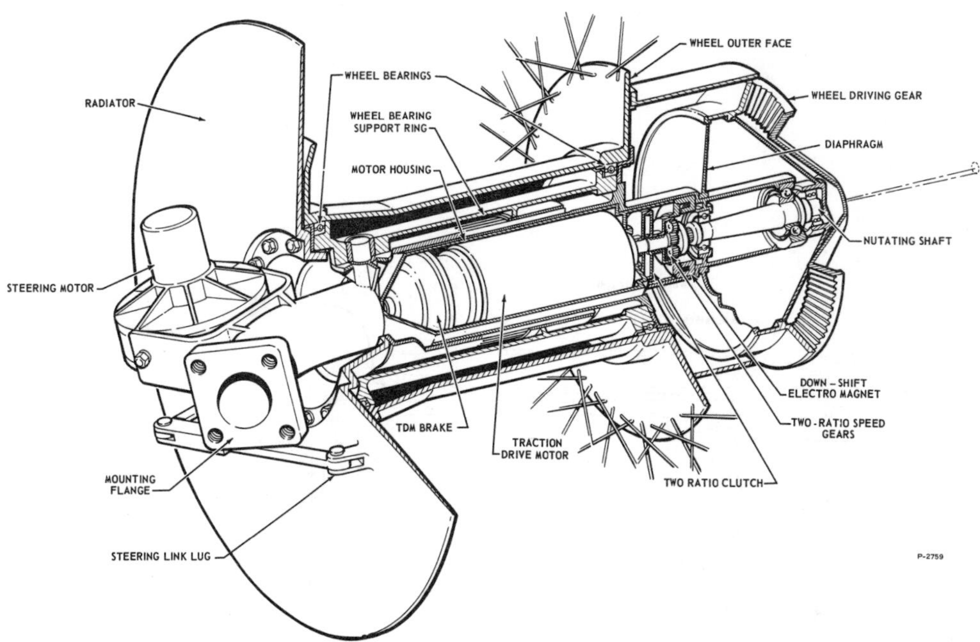

Fig. 6–16. A pictorial of the wheel assembly shown in Fig. 6–15, clarifying its assembly. (Courtesy of Bendix Corporation.)

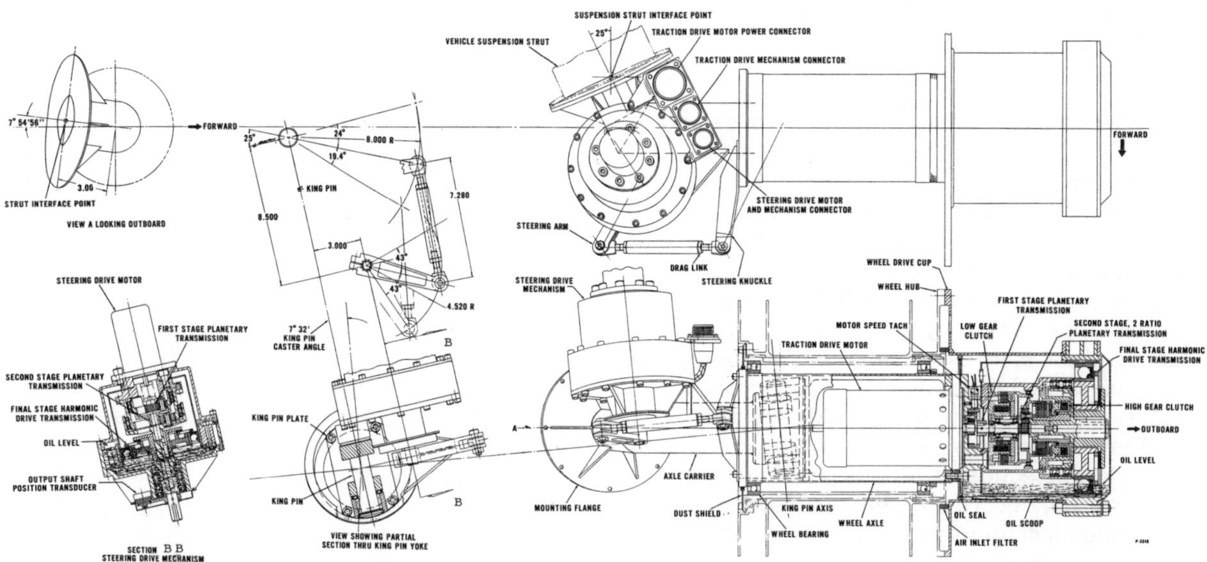

Fig. 6–17. The final refinement of the wheel mechanism is achieved through the application of descriptive geometry to determine physical properties of its linkage system. Additional auxiliary views were also used to finalize the design. Note that this assembly is more complicated than the initial refinement in Fig. 6–15. (Courtesy of Bendix Corporation.)

Fig. 6-18. A photograph of the completed, deliverable wheel assembly. (Courtesy of Bendix Corporation.)

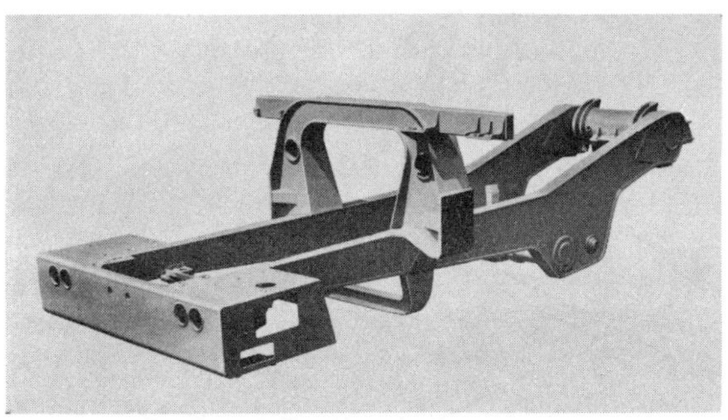

Fig. 6-19. Descriptive geometry principles were utilized in arriving at the final configuration of this heavy-duty truck frame. (Courtesy of LeTourneau-Westinghouse Company.)

(MTA) vehicle intended for earth-testing the MOLAB mobility system. The mobility test article TDM and SDM hardware was to provide the same mobility characteristics as the proposed MOLAB designs within a limited cost and delivery schedule. The final refinement of the design is shown in Fig. 6-17. This drawing shows the MTA hardware design for the left front wheel TDM and SDM systems. Two adjacent orthographic views were drawn to enable the designer to project auxiliary views using descriptive geometry so that the critical dimensions of the steering linkage could be determined. Descriptive geometry was also used to establish the position of the mounting flange so that it could be attached properly to the vehicle suspension strut. A comparison between this drawing and the initial refinement indicates the increased complexity of the completed design.

A photograph of the final deliverable hardware is shown in Fig. 6-18. This design problem is typical of those encountered in industry. Regardless of the degree of complexity of the design or the system employed, whether hydraulic, electronic, or mechanical, the final product must be designed to be assembled as a unit. This design of an assembly required the application of spatial relations and descriptive geometry principles to determine critical relationships.

Another problem of this type is the design of a frame for a heavy-duty truck (Fig. 6-19). This frame is composed of intersecting planes and surfaces that must be refined so that they may be analyzed for strength by the application of engineering principles. The true size of oblique surfaces must be found along with the angles between the intersecting planes and flanges. This information must be known before complete working drawings can be made. Again, descriptive geometry is the primary method used to obtain this information.

6-6 FORMAT OF DESIGN REFINEMENT

Problem identification work and preliminary ideas are accumulated on worksheets. These worksheets are $8\frac{1}{2}'' \times 11''$ and may be printed with a grid if desired. The designer's name, project title, date, and page number are placed at the top of each sheet for improved organization of work. In some cases, this same format and sheet size will be sufficient for the refinement work; however, it may be beneficial to work on a larger sheet that will give more space for the accurate construction and projections so necessary to this portion of the design process. The sheet size suggested, if a larger sheet is required, is an $11'' \times 15''$ sheet that will fold to an $8\frac{1}{2}'' \times 11''$ format so that it may be in-

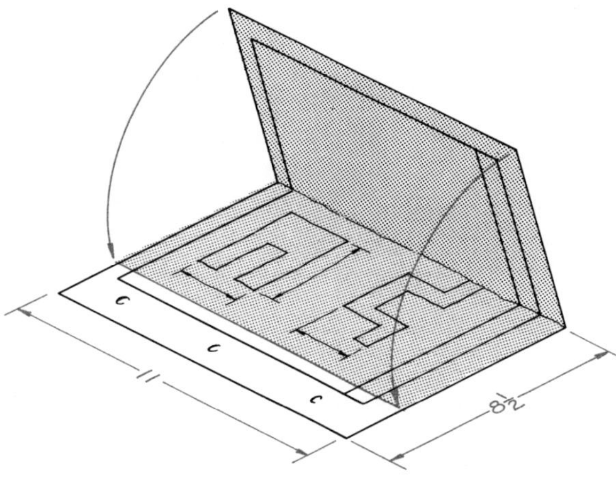

Fig. 6–20. When larger sheets are required, an oversize sheet of 11″ × 15″ is suggested for refinement drawings. This size can be folded to an $8\frac{1}{2}$″ × 11″ format for inclusion with the other design worksheets.

cluded with preliminary design materials for easy reference (Fig. 6–20). The same heading information should be included on the sheet to give a continuity to the sheets. Additional information may be given in the title block, as suggested in Chapter 19. Since the drawings must be drawn to scale using instruments it would probably be easier if unruled tracing paper were used rather than a paper with a printed grid. Reproductions can be made from tracings for checking and marking without damaging the original drawing.

The refinement drawings are not working drawings, but scale drawings used to solve isolated problems and to determine information essential to the preparation of working drawings. Dimensions need not be given on these drawings except where they would be of importance to the understanding of the drawing. Dimensions such as the overall size of an object and specific measurements found by descriptive geometry projections should be included.

Problem refinement should involve more than one preliminary idea unless one idea is greatly superior to the others. If several preliminary ideas are refined, it is more likely that the best design will be selected on a sound basis. Also, refining several designs may lead to a compromise design that would be a combination of the best features of several preliminary designs. The temptation to focus on a single solution should be resisted until the decision phase of the design process.

Although descriptive geometry has been emphasized as a primary tool of design refinement, other graphical methods are equally essential to the development of preliminary ideas. The engineering drawing principles reviewed in Chapter 5 must be used in refining standard details of construction and fabrication. All types of engineering drawing are used—pictorials, orthographic projection, sections, and conventional methods. In effect, the refinement process is the engineer's method of developing his ideas and communicating them to himself and to others. An analysis of detailed scale drawings of his preliminary concept provides him with the necessary data to begin the analysis of his design—the next step.

Drawings executed during the refinement process should employ the techniques and materials suggested in Chapter 5. Lettering and line work should be somewhat improved beyond that of the preliminary sketches. Properly executed drawings will be easier to read, will make better prints, and will be more accurate. However, these will not be finished working drawings, but merely refinements of the preliminary ideas. The final working drawings will be made after the analysis of the refined design.

6–7 PRODUCT DESIGN—REFINEMENT

To illustrate the method of refining a preliminary product design, the hunting seat design problem is used as an example. This problem is restated below:

Hunting Seat Problem. Many hunters, especially deer hunters, hunt from trees to obtain a better vantage point. Sitting in a tree for several hours can be uncomfortable and hazardous to the hunter, thus indicating a need for a hunting seat that could be used to improve this situation. Design a seat that would not only provide the hunter with comfort and safety while hunting

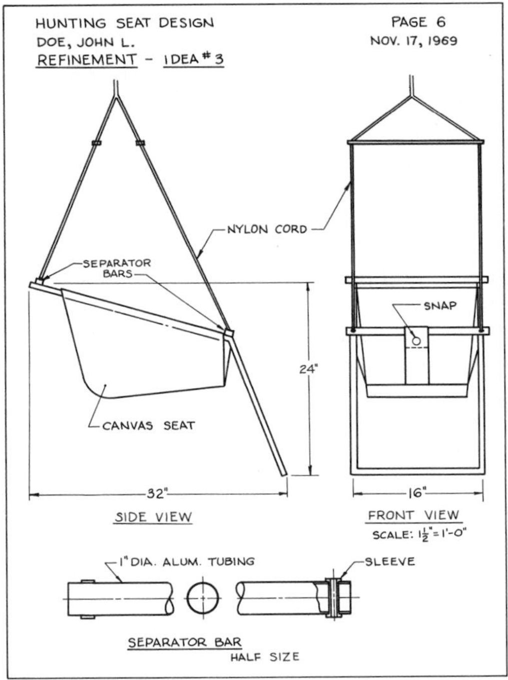

Fig. 6-21. A refinement drawing of idea #3 for a hunting seat previously developed in Fig. 4-25. Only general dimensions are given on the scale drawing.

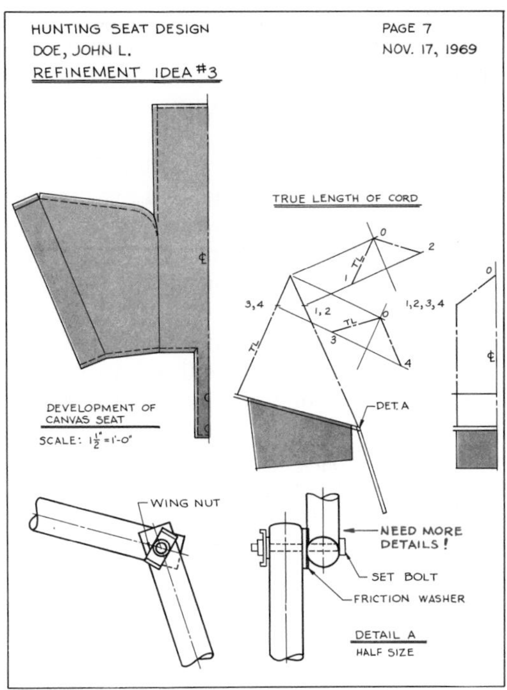

Fig. 6-22. The hunting seat design is refined through the use of descriptive geometry and working drawings. Many additional drawings of this type are required to completely refine a preliminary concept.

from a tree, but also meet the general requirements of economy and hunting limitations.

Preliminary ideas for this design are given in Article 4-9. Reference can be made to these sketches to review the concepts being developed. For this example of a refinement drawing, we have selected only one concept, rather than several as the case should be in an actual refinement situation. Principles of descriptive geometry and engineering drawing are used to refine the preliminary designs.

The first work sheet showing the refinement of idea #3 is illustrated in Fig. 6-21. A scale drawing of the seat is given in orthographic views. Structural components are blocked in, but no attempt has been made to give a detailed representation of each part since this would stifle the refinement process. Tubular parts, such as the separator bars, are blocked in as squares rather than drawn as circles because it is easier to draw them in this manner and the square representation will serve the same purpose at this stage. Some hidden lines are omitted. The important requirement of refinement drawings is that the drawings be made to scale to give a sense of proportion and to serve as a basis for determining angles, lengths, shapes, and other physical characteristics. Overall dimensions are given on the drawing to establish general sizes. Specific details are shown for the separator bar to indicate an idea for a sleeve through which the nylon cord will pass. A sleeve will prevent the cord from being cut by the edges of the tubular metal, as would happen if a hole were drilled through the bar without the sleeve.

Several other problems of refinement are solved in Fig. 6-22 by the application of descriptive geometry principles. The canvas seat is developed as an approximate pattern to indicate method of fabrication. Stitch lines are given to show specific details of assembly. This is a preliminary pattern that will be analyzed and developed to obtain the most functional design. The lengths of the nylon cords are found by descriptive geometry and from the two given orthographic views. A means of adjusting and securing the footrest is refined in a drawing of Detail A. A wing nut is used to tighten the tubular members against a friction washer so that the footrest can be locked in any position desired.

A note is given in colored pencil to indicate that additional details are required to clarify this joint. Also, a method of attaching the nylon cord near this junction is needed. Additional drawings of this type are necessary for the refinement of the design in greater detail. These drawings will permit the designer to communicate with himself and to formulate the necessary dimensions and configurations for the next step —analysis. These two example sheets do not represent a complete refinement, but are merely examples of the first drawings of the process, to illustrate the type of drawings required.

Note that color has been used on work-sheet page 7 (Fig. 6-22). In some cases, color can add emphasis to a drawing and improve the communication of ideas. However, the color should be added to the print of the drawing and not to the drawing itself. The reason for this is that reproduction systems reproduce color markings in the same color as inked lines, or not at all if a light color is used for marking. For example, both black inked lines and red emphasis markings on tracing paper would appear as blue lines in a print made by the diazo process. Colored pencils, felt-tip markers, colored ink, or transparent overlay sheets can be used to add color to a print after reproduction when required.

6-8 SYSTEMS DESIGN—REFINEMENT

The systems problem used in the previous chapters, the parking lot design, is refined in partial form to serve as a guide for this step. The problem is restated below.

Parking Lot Design. Select a building on your campus that is in need of an improved parking lot to accommodate the people who are housed in the building. This may be a dormitory, an office building, or a classroom building. Design a combination traffic and parking system that will be adequate for the requirements of the building's inhabitants. The solution of this problem must adhere to existing limitations, regulations, and policies of your campus so that the problem will be as realistic as possible.

The preliminary ideas in Figs. 4-23 and 4-24 are reviewed to determine the several that are most worthy of refinement and consideration as a possible solution. Idea #3 is selected as the first preliminary design to be refined. A scale drawing of the lot layout is shown in Fig. 6-23 to illustrate a refinement of the preliminary sketch. The layout is checked mathematically as well as graphically to assure that adequate space is available for the cars that will be assigned to the lot. The traffic flow is refined to be more appropriate for the needs of the lot. Sidewalks are shown to accommodate pedestrian traffic. A diazo print of the refined drawing can be shaded with color to indicate new paving for parking spaces and for access arteries. Dimensions are given from which square footage can be figured and analyzed for economy.

The entry and access routes at Detail A are drawn in Fig. 6-24 as an example of the more detailed refinement that will improve the analysis of the design in the next step. General dimensions are given to provide a comparison with accepted standards for a lot of this type. Radii of curb curvatures are also given in this detail, whereas the curbs were shown with square corners in Fig. 6-23. Other details of the layout will be drawn in this manner to permit a more detailed refinement of all aspects of the lot. Additional drawings are not shown in this series.

It is probable that the designer will refine several ideas by this same procedure rather than narrowing his solution to only one possibility. Refinement drawings are necessary to obtain a true understanding of the merits of the preliminary designs, which are given in sketch form and usually not drawn to scale. It is easy

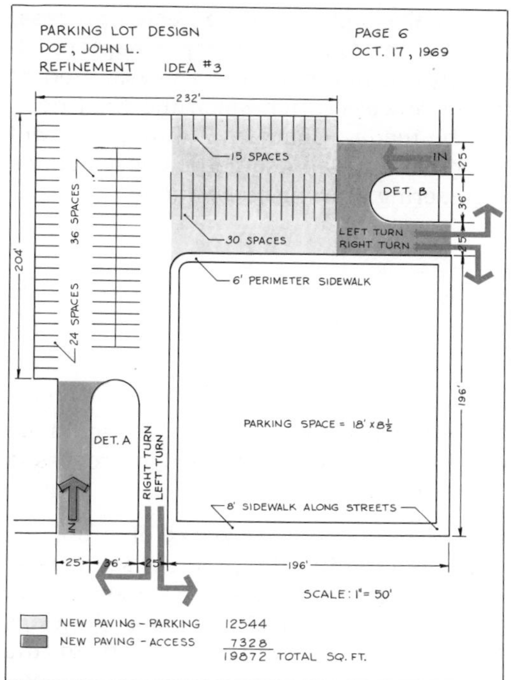

Fig. 6–23. A system—a parking lot design—is refined through this scale drawing, and the general traffic flow is indicated.

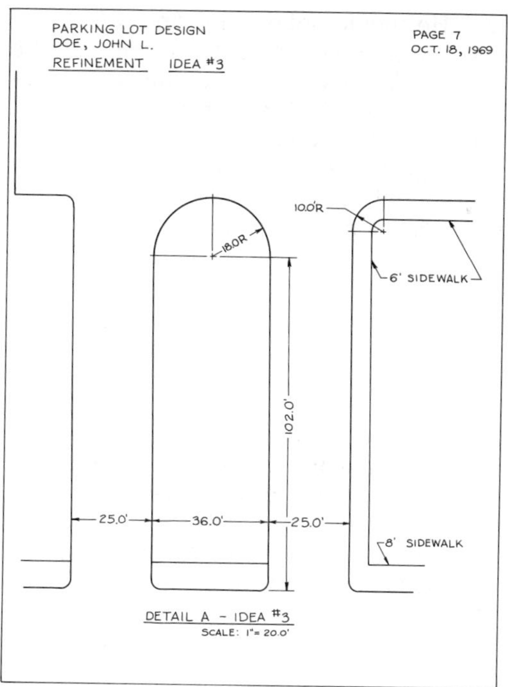

Fig. 6–24. The parking lot system is refined in greater detail by enlarging the various areas of its layout. At this stage, however, only general dimensions are given.

to exclude a more acceptable design whose features may not be apparent in sketch form unless refinement drawings are made and compared to other designs under consideration. This is as true for product design as for systems design. The analysis step of the design process will assist the designer further in selecting the most acceptable solution.

6–9 SUMMARY

Refinement is the process of developing several preliminary ideas into scale drawings to determine more of their physical characteristics, dimensions, angles, and other relationships that will affect their acceptance. Refinement drawings must be drawn accurately to scale so that graphical methods may be used to best advantage. These drawings may be a combination of schematics, diagrams, orthographic views, and pictorials to help the designer develop his preliminary concepts.

Descriptive geometry principles can be used to determine the physical properties important to the design refinement. Angles, lengths, shapes, and sizes can be found graphically by this method with less difficulty than is experienced when attempting to find this same information by mathematical methods. The solutions of problems of this type should be noted and dimensioned to provide an easy reference at a later date when the design is analyzed. Refinement drawings are added to the accumulation of worksheets and preliminary design work previously filed in the design binder or envelope.

Several ideas are refined to give the designer a broader selection of possibilities for the design solution. He should not develop and refine preliminary ideas that are obviously inferior, but he should refine as many ideas as he feels have desirable features. The refinement process will give him a better opportunity to study these designs in greater detail and, therefore, to be better prepared to support his final decision. The final decision should be postponed until after the analysis phase of the design process, which follows the refinement step. Chapters 13, 14, and 15 will introduce the analysis step of the design process, after which the final decision can be made. Chapters 7 through 12 will cover in greater detail geometric constructions and engineering drawing conventions.

PROBLEMS

Problems should be presented on $8\frac{1}{2}'' \times 11''$ paper, grid or plain, using the format introduced in Article 1–19. Each grid square represents $\frac{1}{4}''$. All notes, sketches, drawings, and graphical work should be neatly prepared in keeping with good practices as covered in this volume. Written matter should be legibly lettered using $\frac{1}{8}''$ guidelines.

1. When refining a design for a folding lawn chair, what physical properties would a designer need to determine? What physical properties would be needed for the following items: A TV-set base, a golf cart, a child's swing set, a portable typewriter, an earthen dam, a shortwave radio, a portable camping tent, a warehouse dolly used for moving heavy boxes?

2. Why should scale drawings be used in the refinement of a design rather than freehand sketches? Explain.

3. List five examples of problems that involve spatial relationships that could be solved by the application of descriptive geometry. Explain your answers.

4. Make a freehand sketch of two oblique planes that intersect. Indicate by notes and algebraic equations how you would determine the angle between these planes mathematically.

5. What is the difference between a working drawing and a refinement drawing? Explain your answer and give examples.

6. How many preliminary designs should be refined when this step of the design process is reached? Explain.

7. Prepare refinement drawings of problems that were identified in the problem sections at the end of Chapter 3, problems 6 through 9 and 12 through 16. Keep all of these drawings together as they accumulate throughout the design process. It may be necessary to postpone preparing these refinement drawings until you read some of the succeeding chapters and understand sufficient theory.

8. Make a list of other refinement drawings that would be necessary to better understand the parking lot problem covered in Article 6–8. Make freehand sketches of the types of drawings needed, with notes to explain your answers.

9. Make a list of refinement drawings that would be needed to develop the installation and design of a 100-ft radio antenna. Make rough sketches indicating the type of drawings needed with notes to explain their purposes.

10. Make a list of refinement drawings that would be needed to refine a preliminary design for a rear-view mirror that will attach to the outside of an automobile. Refer to Figs. 4–19 and 4–20.

11. Assuming that a refinement drawing has been made of the preliminary sketch of the clip shown in Fig. 5–105 (IDEA 1), explain the new information obtained from this drawing that would be of benefit to you in analyzing the design.

12. After a refinement drawing has been made and the design is found to be lacking in some respects, so that it is eliminated as a possible solution, what should be the designer's next step? Explain.

13. Would a pictorial be helpful as a refinement drawing? Explain your answer.

14. List several design projects that an engineer or technician in your particular field of engineering would probably be responsible for. Outline the type of refinement drawings that would be necessary in projects of this type.

15. For the hunting seat design covered in Article 6–7, what refinement drawings are necessary that were not given on the example work sheets? Make freehand sketches of the drawings needed, with notes to explain what they would reveal.

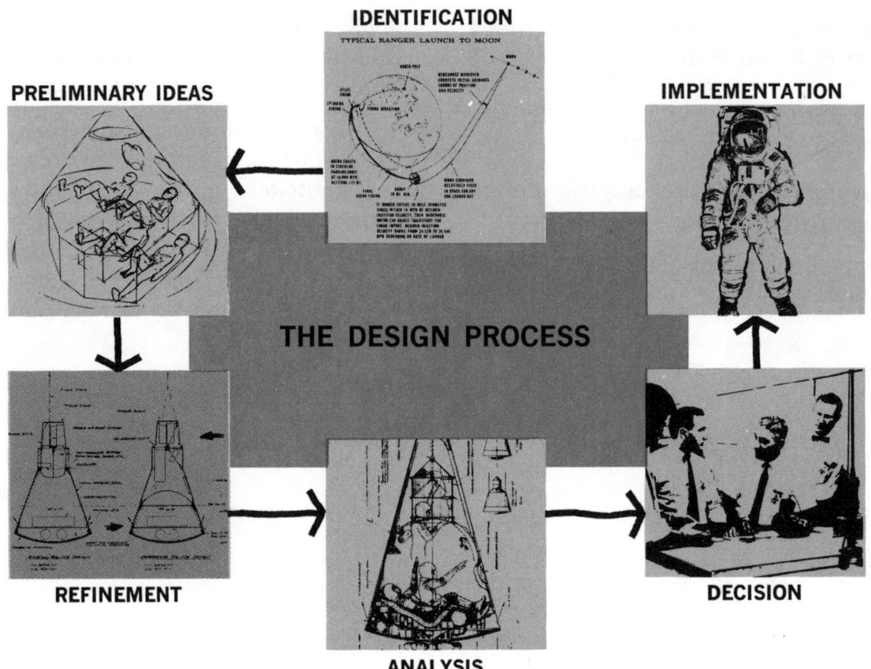

7 FUNDAMENTAL SPATIAL RELATIONSHIPS

7–1 ORTHOGRAPHIC PROJECTION

The preparation of engineering drawings that must be used by large numbers of people working on a common project in a variety of geographical locations requires a universal system of presentation. We touched briefly upon this universal system, *orthographic projection,* in Chapter 5, relating it to the standard practices and conventions of engineering drawing. We shall now take a more penetrating look at the underlying theory supporting this standardized form of presentation.

Orthographic projection may be defined as a method of representing three-dimensional objects through the use of views which are projected perpendicularly onto planes of projection with parallel projectors (Fig. 7–1). The three mutually perpendicular projection planes, called principal planes, are shown as they would be positioned in space in Fig. 7–2A. Part B of the figure shows the transformation of the three principal planes into one common plane (part C). This common plane is the sheet of paper on which the engineer, designer, or draftsman must represent a three-dimensional object that may vary in size from a small bolt to a large bridge girder. Since projection planes are infinite in size and therefore have no perimeters, there is no need to indicate the outlines of the projection box. However, the intersections of the planes, or fold lines, are usually drawn as shown in part C to aid in the solution of descriptive geometry problems. Note that the three principal planes—*horizontal, frontal,* and *profile*— are represented by means of the single letters H, F, and P placed on their respective sides of the fold lines. This system of notation will be used throughout this book.

Figure 7–2 illustrates the relationship between the three principal planes pictorially and orthographically. It should be noted that the *front view* is projected onto the *frontal* projection plane; the *side* view onto the *profile* projection plane; and the *top* view onto the *horizontal* projection plane. This system allows three-dimensional objects to be represented by means of related, two-dimensional views in a manner which will be developed in this chapter.

7–2 SIX PRINCIPAL VIEWS

Some objects cannot be fully represented through the three views mentioned in the first article, but require separate views projected from each side. The system of orthographic projection permits six principal views of a given object to be drawn. Figure 7–3A suggests how an imaginary box formed by the six principal planes is opened to form one common plane, as shown in part B of the figure. It should be observed that the top and bottom planes are both horizontal planes and are labeled with the letter H; the front and rear views are both frontal planes and are noted with the letter F,

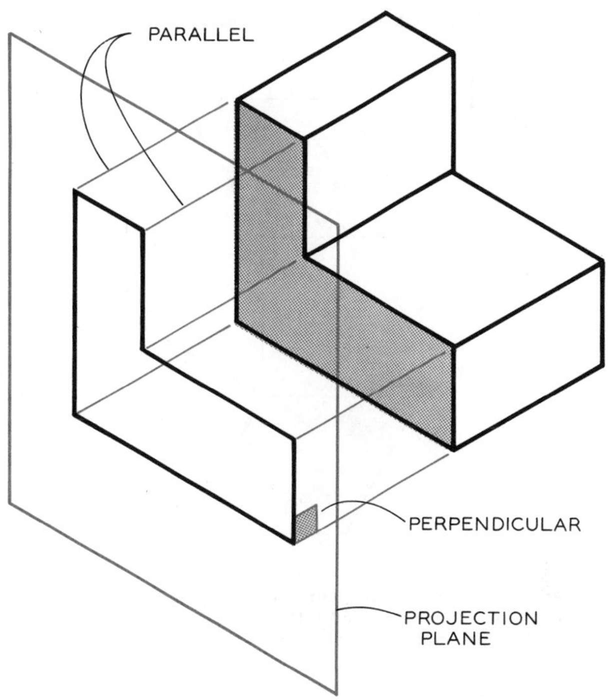

Fig. 7–1. Orthographic projection is defined as the projection of a view onto a projection plane with parallel projectors. The projectors are perpendicular to the projection plane.

FIGURE 7–2. THE PRINCIPAL PROJECTION PLANES

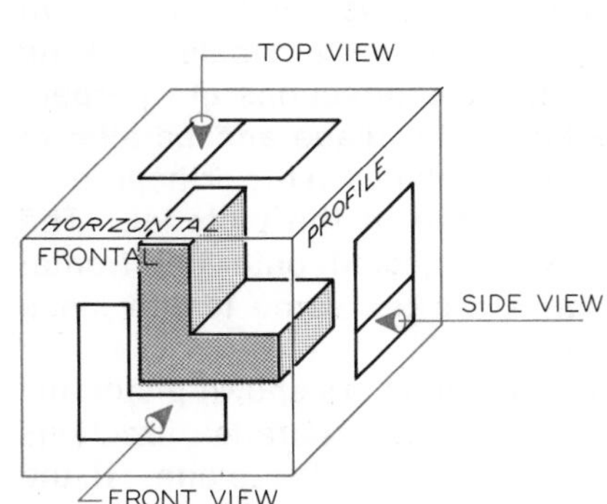

A. The three principal projection planes used in orthographic projection can be thought of as planes of a glass box.

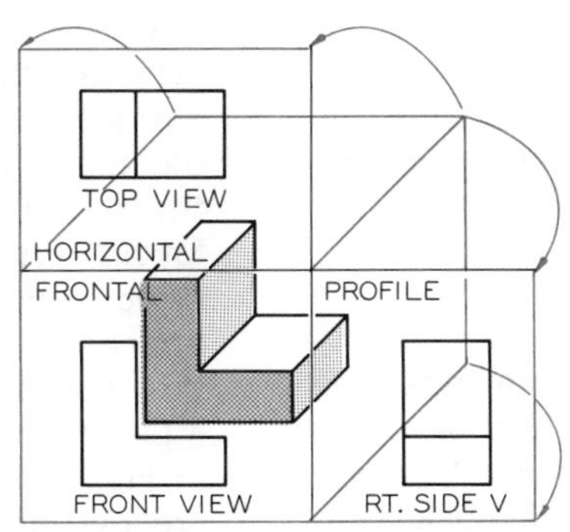

B. Views of an object are projected onto the projection planes, which are opened into the plane of the drawing surface.

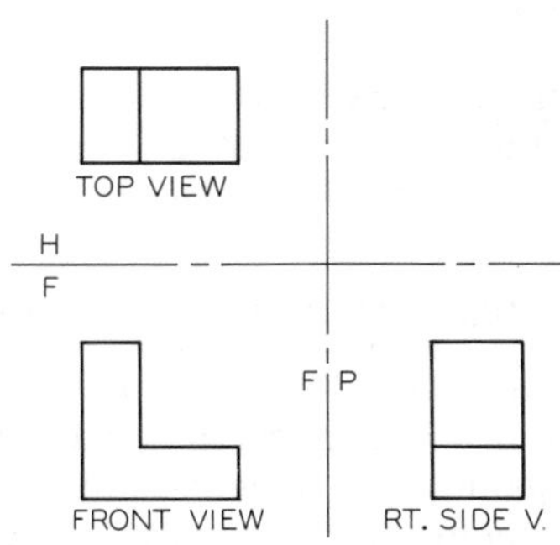

C. The outlines of the planes are omitted. The fold lines are drawn and labeled in this manner when descriptive geometry problems are solved.

FIGURE 7–3. SIX VIEWS OF AN OBJECT

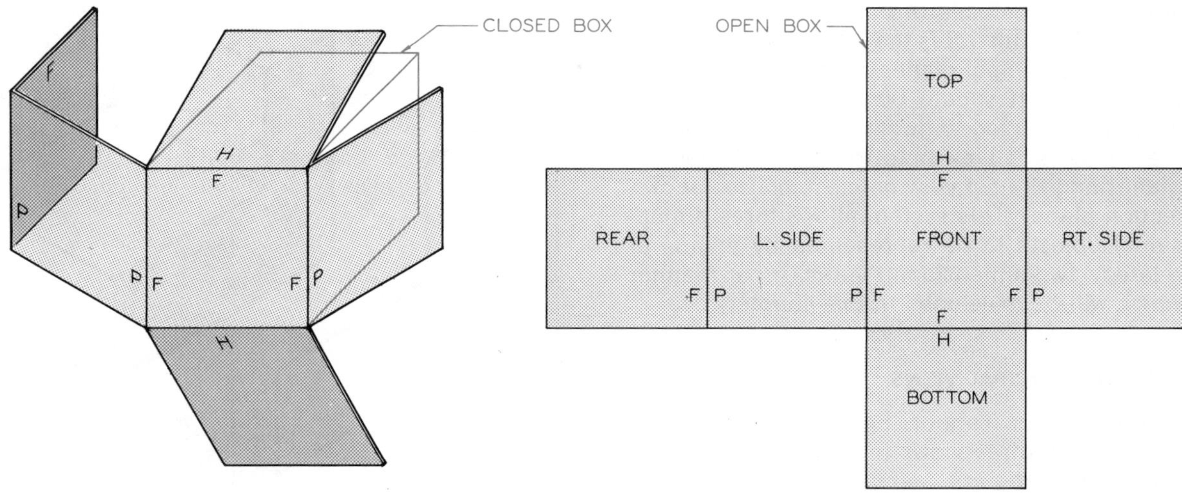

A. The six projection planes of the imaginary glass box can be opened into a single plane to give six principal views of an object.

B. This is the standard arrangement for a six-view drawing. Note how the fold lines are labeled using letters to represent the three principal planes, F, H, and P.

and the left and right side views are both profile planes and are labeled with the letter P.

Only rarely are all six principal projection planes required to describe an object. It is more usual that additional views other than principal views are required to describe certain details of an object. These views are projected onto planes called auxiliary planes, which are not parallel to the three principal planes. Succeeding chapters will develop this concept, while this chapter will be devoted to the review of principal projections.

7–3 DIRECTIONAL RELATIONSHIPS

Certain verbal terms are used to describe spatial relationships both in orthographic projection and in general discussion. The more commonly used terms are forward, back, left, right, up, and down. Combinations of these directions will allow an object to be generally located in space. A knowledge of the relationship of directional terms to orthographic projection is necessary for a thorough understanding of descriptive geometry principles.

The parallel directions of up and down are illustrated in Fig. 7–4A. These directions are perpendicular to the horizontal plane on which the top view is projected. Since the arrows which indicate up and down directions are vertical, they would appear as points on the horizontal plane if shown. Part B of the figure shows how the directional arrows would project in orthographic projection on a single drawing surface. Note that the directions are perpendicular to the horizontal plane and parallel to the frontal and profile planes in the orthographic layout, just as they are in the pictorial. The directional arrows projected onto the frontal and profile planes are the same length since they are vertical.

Left and right directions are shown pictorially in Fig. 7–5A. Both of these parallel directions are perpendicular to the profile plane. If the projection planes were revolved into the conventional position, the directions would project as shown in part B. The directional arrows are parallel to the horizontal plane and perpendicular to the profile plane. To locate a point that is to the right or left of a given point, we must use

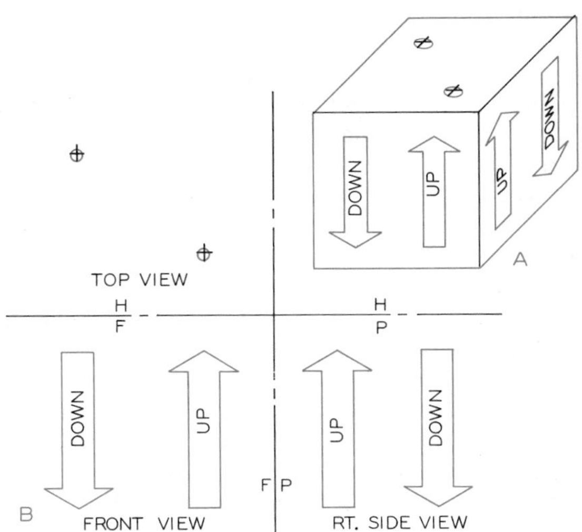

Fig. 7–4. The directions of up and down can be seen in the front and side views of orthographic drawings.

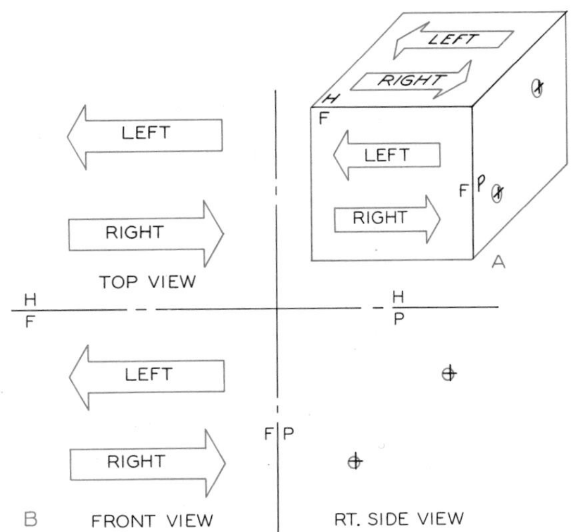

Fig. 7–5. The directions of left and right can be seen in the top and front views of orthographic drawings.

the front or top view, since the profile plane cannot reflect this difference in position.

Forward and backward directions are shown pictorially in Fig. 7–6A. The parallel directional arrows are parallel to the horizontal and profile planes. These relationships are also illustrated in the usual three-view arrangement for orthographic projection in part B. Location of a point in space with respect to forward or backward directions must be established in either the horizontal view or the profile view, since they cannot be established in the front view.

Any two of the three basic groups of directions will establish the location of a point on a principal plane. For example, a point located below the horizontal plane and to the left of the profile would be positioned on the frontal plane. The third basic direction, forward or back of the frontal plane, locates the point with respect to three-dimensional space.

7–4 ORTHOGRAPHIC PROJECTION OF A POINT

The point is the basic geometric element that is used to establish all other elements regardless of their degree of complication. A point is a

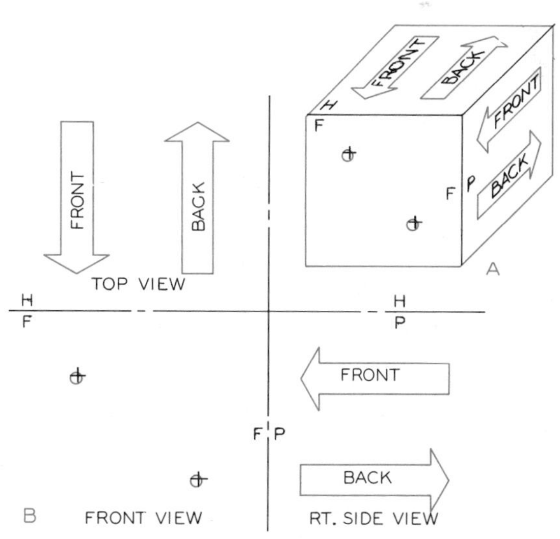

Fig. 7–6. The directions of forward and backward can be seen in the top and side views of orthographic drawings.

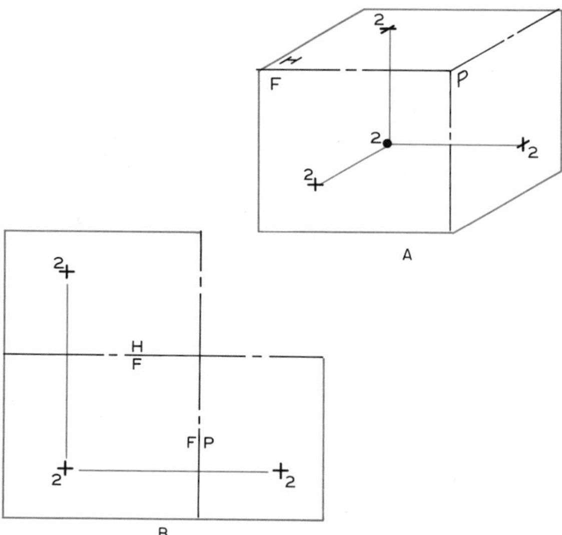

Fig. 7-7. Three views of a point projected onto the three principal planes: horizontal, frontal, and profile.

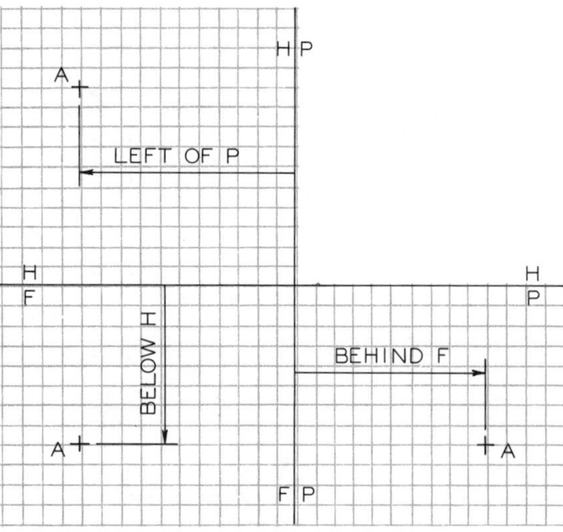

Fig. 7-8. Location of a point 8 units below the horizontal, 10 units back of the frontal, and 11 units to the left of the profile.

theoretical location in space and has no dimensions. However, a series of points can establish areas, volumes, and lengths, which are the basis of our physical world. An understanding of the orthographic projections of a point will enable the student to project essentially any geometric form onto an orthographic plane and thereby solve a multitude of graphical problems.

A point in space must be projected perpendicularly onto at least two principal planes to establish its true position. Figure 7-7A is a pictorial representation of a point projected onto each of the principal planes.

The three orthographic projections or views of point 2 are shown in Fig. 7-7B. The point is at the same distance below the horizontal projection plane in the front view as it is in the right side view, and it is located directly below the top view of point 2. Similarly, the top and side views of the point are at the same distance from the edge view of the frontal plane. These relationships are shown in pictorial form in Fig. 7-7A. Note that the projector lines between the three views of point 2 are perpendicular to the principal planes (fold lines) in both of these illustrations.

A point can be located easily from a verbal description which uses units of measurement taken from the fold lines. Assume that the following coordinates were given: (1) 11 units left of the profile plane, (2) 8 units below the horizontal plane, and (3) 10 units back of the frontal plane. The measurement of 11 units to the left can be established in the top and front views as shown in Fig. 7-8. This procedure locates a projector perpendicular to the H-F fold lines. The measurement of 8 units below the horizontal plane isolates the exact position of the frontal projection of point *A*. The right side view of point *A* will also lie on the projector 8 units below the horizontal plane. The third coordinate, 10 units back of the frontal plane, will complete the location of the top and side views of the point.

In the top or horizontal view, the frontal and profile planes appear as edges. In the frontal view the horizontal and profile planes appear as edges, and in the profile view the frontal and horizontal planes appear as edges. This rela-

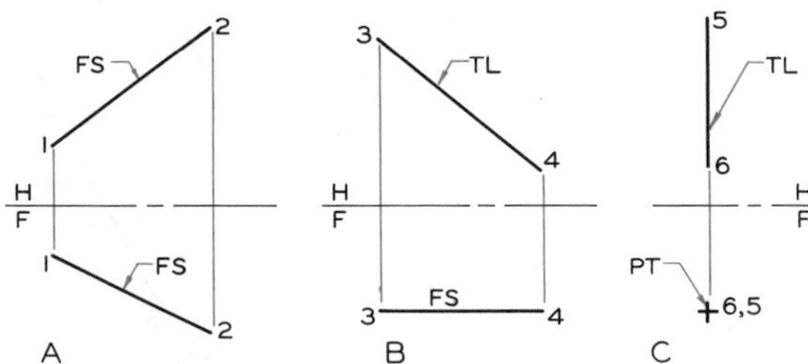

Fig. 7-9. A line in orthographic projection can appear as a point (PT), foreshortened (FS), or true length (TL).

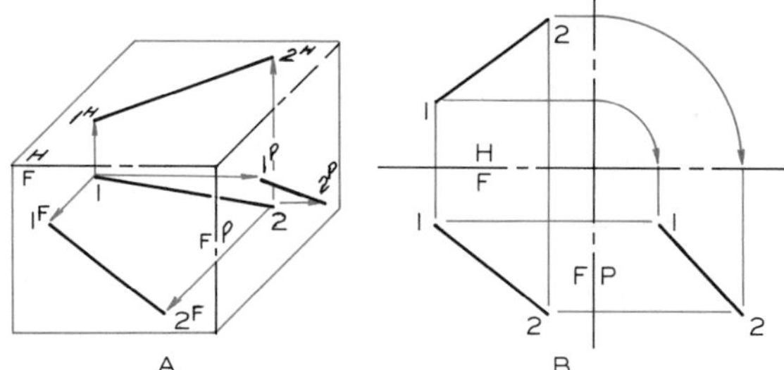

Fig. 7-10. Three orthographic views of an oblique line in space.

tionship permits two coordinates to be plotted in each view, since they are measured perpendicularly from planes that appear as edges. The edge view of the two other principal planes can be seen in each principal view.

7-5 LINES

A line is a straight path between two points in space. It can appear in three forms: (1) as a point, (2) as a line showing true length, or (3) as a foreshortened line (Fig. 7-9). Line 1-2 appears foreshortened in each view in Fig. 7-10. The line of sight is always perpendicular to a true-length line or, in other words, a true-length line is parallel to the plane on which it is projected. These relationships will be discussed further in the following examples.

Oblique Lines. An *oblique line* is a line that is neither perpendicular nor parallel to a principal projection plane, as shown in Fig. 7-10. When line 1-2 is projected onto the horizontal, frontal, and profile planes, it appears as represented in Fig. 7-10B. The process of projecting a line is identical to that used in projecting a point, as discussed in Article 7-4. The two endpoints must be established and then connected to represent the line. An oblique or foreshortened line is the general case of a line. It may have any direction or length provided that it is not parallel to a principal plane in any view. Each end of a line is usually lettered for easy reference and to lessen the possibility of error in projection.

Principal Lines. If a line is parallel to a principal plane, it is referred to as a *principal line*. There are three principal lines, (1) horizontal, (2) frontal, and (3) profile, since there are three principal planes to which they can be parallel. The principal lines are true length in the view where the principal plane with which they are parallel appears true size. For example, horizontal lines are true length in the top view, which is the view that shows the true size of the horizontal plane.

7-6 HORIZONTAL LINES

A *horizontal line* is parallel to the horizontal plane, as illustrated in Fig. 7-11A. A horizontal line may be shown in an infinite number of positions in the top view, provided that it is parallel to the horizontal plane in the frontal and profile projections, as shown in Fig. 7-11A. The observer's line of sight is perpendicular to the horizontal plane when he is viewing the top view, which is the one that gives a true-shape view of the plane. Therefore, the horizontal line is shown true length in the top view.

Note that observation of the top view of any given line cannot reveal whether the line is horizontal. This can be established only from the front and side views. A line is horizontal if the representation of the line in these views is parallel to the H-F fold line. A line projecting as a point in either of these views is also horizontal. A line appearing as a point in the front view is a

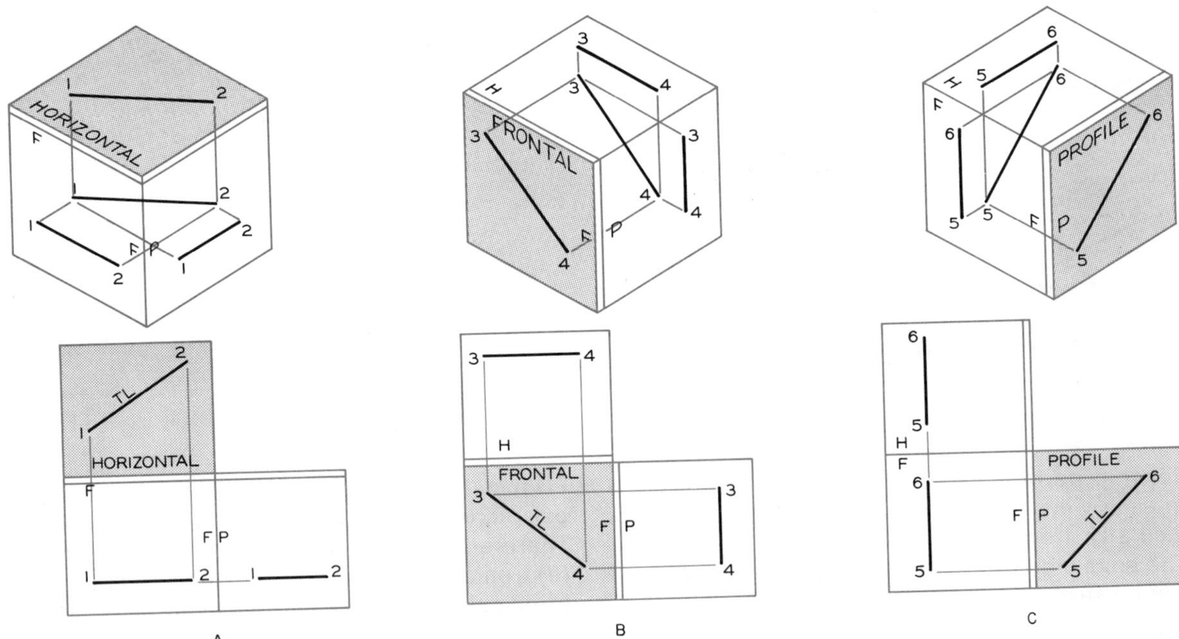

Fig. 7-11. Projections of the three principal lines: horizontal, frontal, and profile. Each of these is parallel to one of the principal planes and is true length when projected onto that plane.

combination horizontal and profile line, while a point view of a line in the profile view indicates a combination horizontal and frontal line.

7-7 FRONTAL LINES

Recall that the front view of an object is projected onto a principal plane called the frontal plane. A line parallel to this plane is a principal line, and is called a *frontal line*. The frontal plane appears true shape in the front view, since the observer's line of sight is perpendicular to it (Fig. 7-11B). His line of sight will also be perpendicular to any line parallel to the frontal plane. This line is projected as true length in the front view.

A frontal line is projected parallel to the frontal plane in both the top and side views, where the frontal plane appears as an edge. It is possible to see in the top and side views that line 3-4 is a frontal line, but in the front view it is not possible. A line that appeared as a point in the top view would be a combination frontal and profile line. A line projected as a point in the side view would be a combination horizontal and frontal line.

7-8 PROFILE LINES

The side view is projected onto the principal plane called the profile plane, which appears true shape in the side view. Line 5-6, which is parallel to the profile plane, is a principal line called a *profile line* (Fig. 7-11C). Since the profile plane is shown true shape in the side view, a profile line will be projected true length in the side view.

The relationship of three views of a profile line is shown in Fig. 7-11C. Line 5-6 is parallel to the profile plane in both of the views in which the profile plane appears as an edge, i.e., the top and front views. A line projecting as a point in the top view will be a combination profile and frontal line, while a line projecting as a point in the front view will be a combination profile and horizontal line.

7-9 LOCATION OF A POINT ON A LINE

A line is composed of an infinite number of points. The solution of descriptive geometry problems requires that the locations of specific points on lines and surfaces in space be determined. Figure 7-12 gives the top and front views of line 1-2. Since the endpoints of line 1-2 are located on projectors that are perpendicular to the fold lines, any point on the line can be found by applying the projection principles illustrated in the figure. For example, if point *O* is located on the line in the top view, the front view of the point may be found by projecting it perpendicular to the H-F fold line until *O* is found on the line in the front view.

Any point on the line can be found in the same manner. If the point is located at the midpoint of the line in any view, it will appear at the midpoint of the line in any other projection, although the line can vary in its projected length. Any other ratio of divisions of a line will remain constant in other views as well.

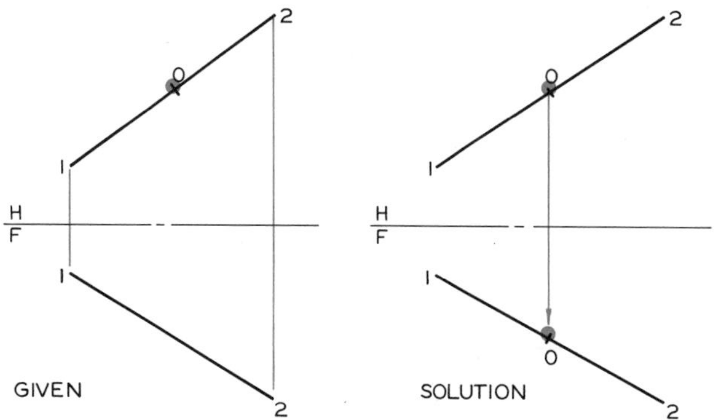

Fig. 7-12. A point on a line in the top view can be projected to the front view of the line.

7-10 NONINTERSECTING LINES

Lines may cross in many views, but crossing lines are not necessarily intersecting lines. Lines 3-4 and 5-6 cross in the top and front views in Fig. 7-13, although when the side view is inspected, it is obvious that these lines do not intersect.

A point of intersection is a common point that lies on both lines, and must therefore project to both lines in all views as did point *O* in Fig. 7-12. Even if the side view were not given in Fig. 7-13, it would be possible to determine whether the lines intersected by projecting the crossing point, *O*, to the front view. Since the lines do not cross at a common point along this projection line in the front view, it is apparent that point *O* is not common to both lines at a single point, and thus there is no point of intersection.

On the other hand, Fig. 7-14 illustrates two lines, 5-6 and 7-8, that do intersect at a common point, point *O*, which is the intersection of the projections from all views, as was the case in Fig. 7-12. It is necessary to have at least two views before it is possible to determine whether two crossing lines intersect.

adjacent } views
related }

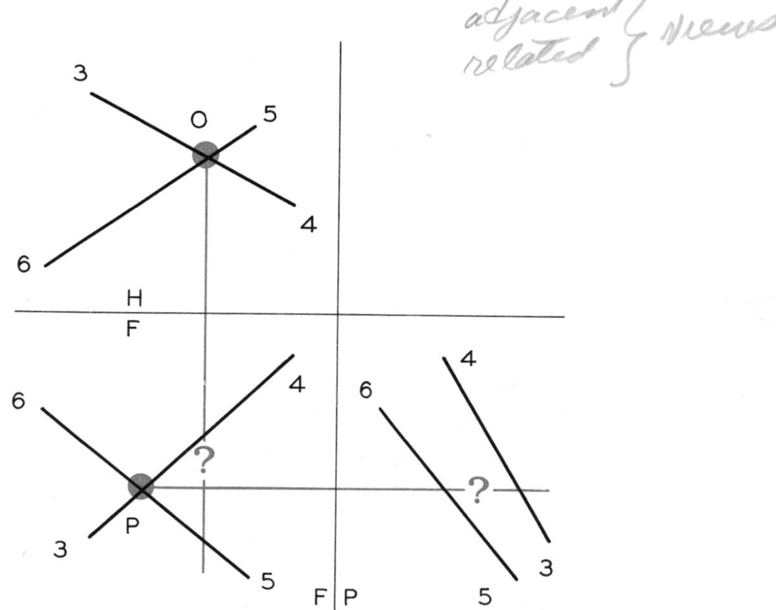

Fig. 7-13. Crossing lines do not intersect unless a projector from the point of intersection in one orthographic view passes through the point of intersection in the adjacent views. These lines do not intersect.

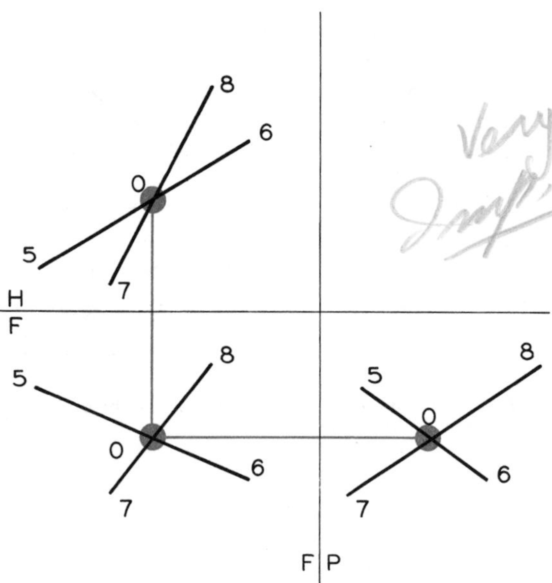

Fig. 7-14. These crossing lines actually intersect because point *O* is an orthographic projection of the point of intersection in the adjacent views.

7-11 VISIBILITY OF CROSSING LINES

Two lines, *AB* and *CD*, are shown crossing in the top and front views of Fig. 7-15. It is obvious that these lines do not intersect by application of principles outlined in Article 7-10. However, we want to determine which of the lines is visible in each view at the points of crossing.

The crossing point in the front view is projected to the top view in step 1. This projector intersects line *AB* before line *CD*, indicating that line *CD* is farther back. This establishes line *AB* as being visible in the front view, since the horizontal view depicts true distances from the frontal plane and since the line that is closest to the front view would therefore be the one that is visible.

FIGURE 7-15. VISIBILITY OF LINES

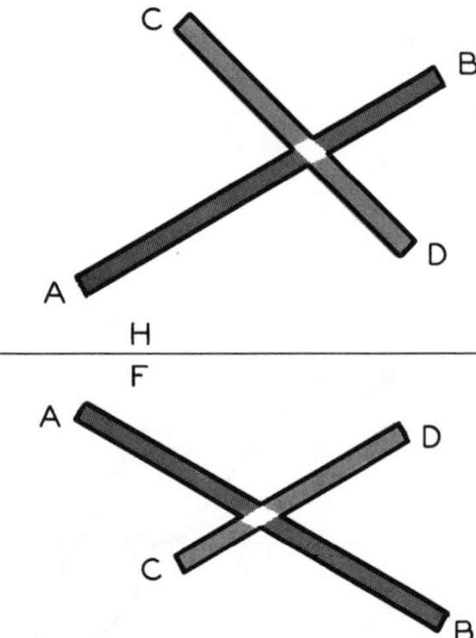

Given: The top and front views of lines *AB* and *CD*.
Required: Find the visibility of the lines in both views.

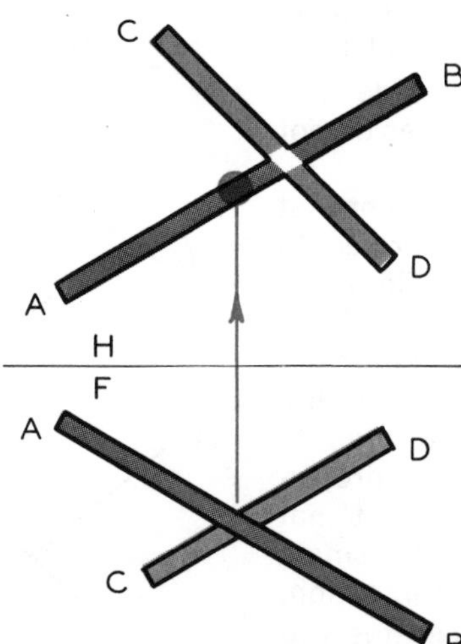

Step 1: Project the point of crossing from the front view to the top view. This projector encounters *AB* before *CD*; therefore, line *AB* is in front and is visible in the front view.

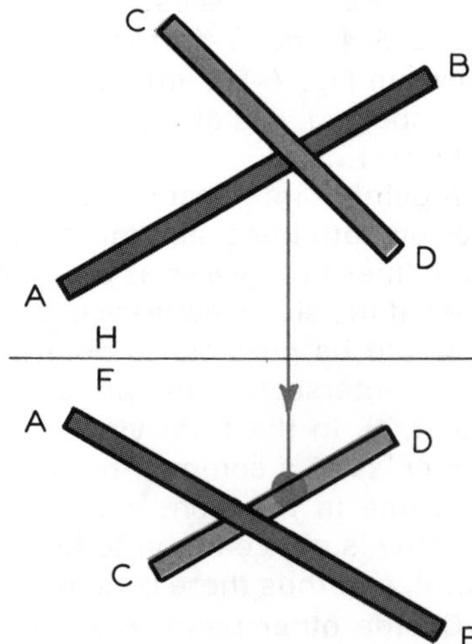

Step 2: Project the point of crossing from the top view to the front view. This projector encounters *CD* before *AB*; therefore, line *CD* is above *AB* and is visible in the top view.

The visibility of the top view is determined by projecting the crossing point from the top view to the front view shown in step 2 of Fig. 7-15. This projector intersects line *CD* first, establishing line *CD* as being higher than or above line *AB* and therefore visible in the top view.

Visibility in a given view cannot be established by that view only. It is necessary to determine visibility by inspecting the preceding view, as outlined in this example.

7-12 VISIBILITY OF A LINE AND A PLANE

The principle of visibility of intersecting lines applies to an intersecting line and plane in much the same manner as outlined in Article 7-11. The given part of Fig. 7-16 shows that plane 1-2-3 and line *AB* cross in the top and front views.

Line *AB* crosses two lines of the plane, lines 1-3 and 2-3, in the front view of step 1. To determine the visibility in the front view, we project these crossing points to the top view. In both cases, the projectors intersect the lines of the plane before they intersect line *AB*, which means that the plane is closer than the line in the front view. Therefore the portion of the line that crosses the plane in the front view is invisible and shown as a hidden line.

The visibility of the top view is found similarly by projecting the crossing points in the top view to the front view (step 2). These projectors intersect line *AB* before lines 1-3 and 2-3. Consequently, line *AB* is higher than the plane in the top view and is drawn as being visible.

These methods can be used to find visibility in essentially all orthographic problems. Auxiliary view methods will be discussed in succeeding chapters.

FIGURE 7-16. VISIBILITY OF A LINE AND A PLANE

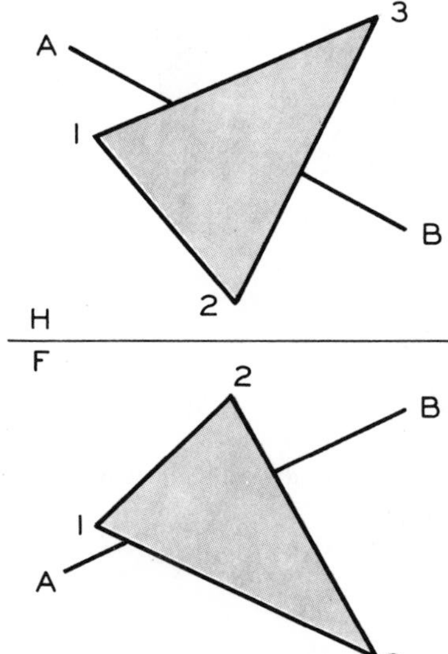

Given: The front and top views of plane 1-2-3 and line *AB*.
Required: Find the visibility of the plane and the line in both views.

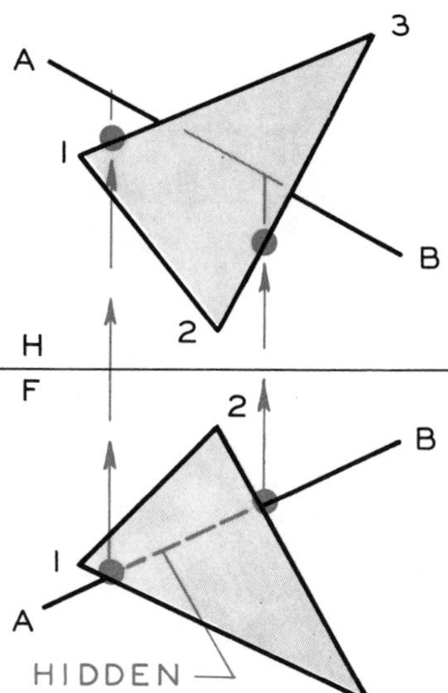

Step 1: Project the two points where *AB* crosses the outer sides of the plane in the front view to the top view. These projectors encounter lines of the plane (1-3 and 2-3) first; therefore, the plane is in front of the line, making the line invisible in the front view.

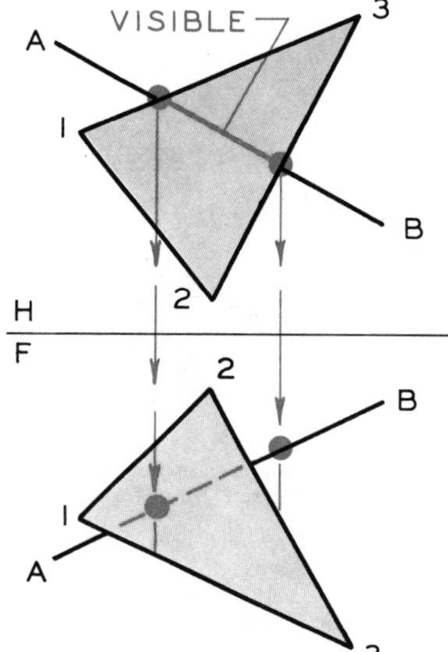

Step 2: Project the two points where *AB* crosses the outer sides of the plane in the top view to the front view. These projectors encounter line *AB* first; therefore, the line is higher than the plane, and the line is visible in the top view.

FIGURE 7-17. REPRESENTATIONS OF A PLANE

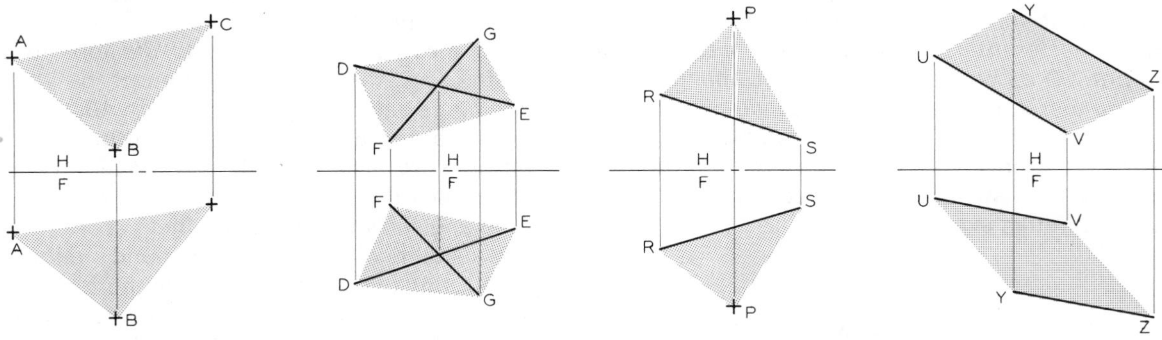

A. Three points not in a straight line.

B. Two intersecting lines.

C. A line and a point not on the line.

D. Two parallel lines.

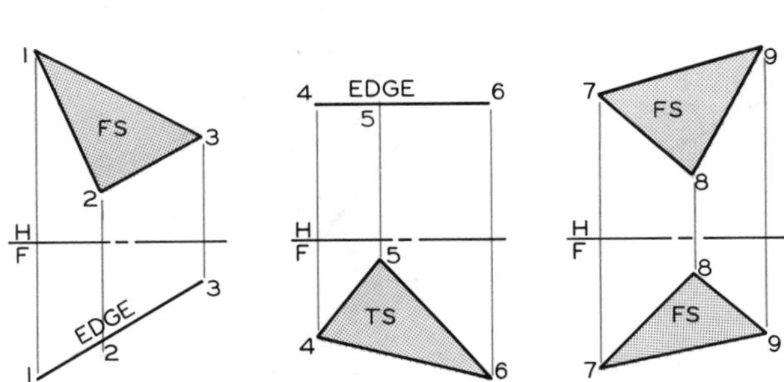

Fig. 7-18. A plane in orthographic projection can appear as an edge, true size (TS), or foreshortened (FS).

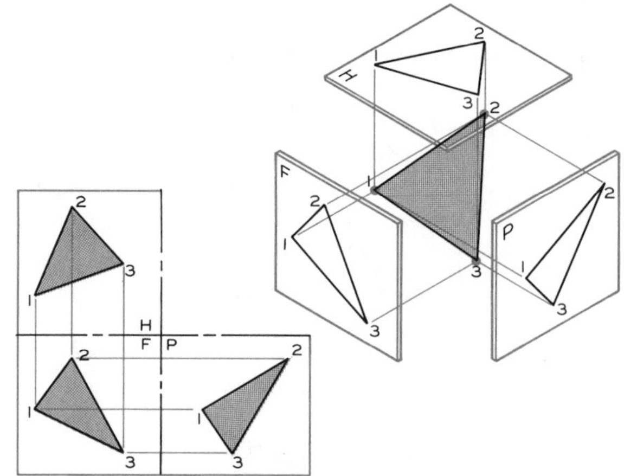

Fig. 7-19. The three projections of an oblique plane.

(not parallel to any principal plane)

7-13 PLANES

Whereas lines have only one dimension, length, planes have two dimensions that establish an area. Planes may be considered as infinite in certain problems. However, in most solutions segments of planes are used for convenience.

Four methods of representing planes are shown in Fig. 7-17. These are (A) three points not in a straight line, (B) two intersecting lines, (C) a point and a line, and (D) two parallel lines. The areas of the planes established by these

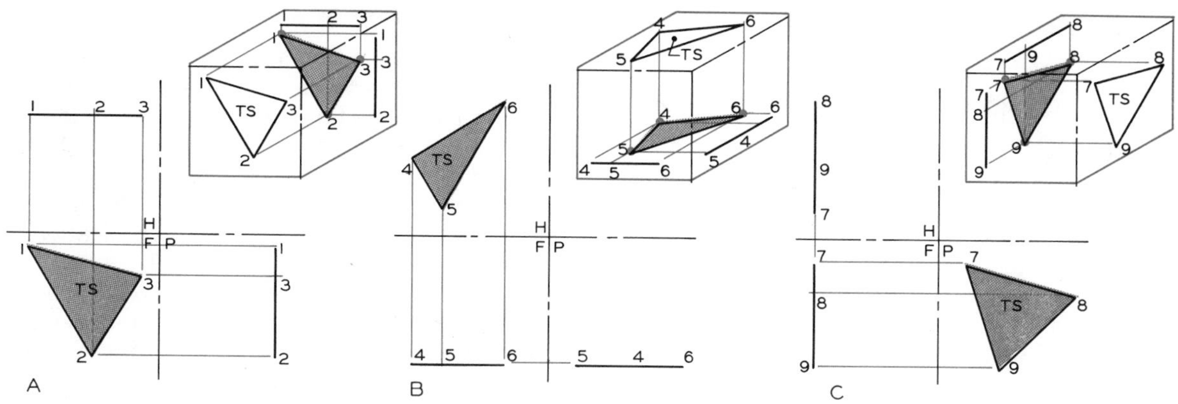

Fig. 7-20. Projections of the three principal planes: (A) frontal, (B) horizontal, and (C) profile. Each of these is parallel to one of the principal projection planes and appears true size on that plane.

methods need not be limited by the bounds of the points or lines used. The elements merely establish the necessary locations to orient the plane in space so it can be used in solving problems involving planes.

Planes may be projected in one of the following forms (Fig. 7-18): (A) as an edge, (B) as true size, or (C) foreshortened. Planes parallel to one of the three principal projection planes—horizontal, frontal, and profile—are principal planes that will appear true size in a principal view. Each of these and the exception, the oblique plane, are discussed below.

The Oblique Plane. An oblique plane is a plane that is not parallel to a principal projection plane in any view, as shown in Fig. 7-19. Its projections may appear as lines or as foreshortened areas which are smaller than its true size. Three orthographic views of plane 1-2-3 are shown in Fig. 7-19. This is the general case of a plane. Each of the vertex points is found in the same manner in each view as though it were an individual point.

The Frontal Plane. A frontal plane is parallel to the frontal projection plane, as shown pictorially in Fig. 7-20A. This principal plane appears true size in the front view and as an edge in the top and side views. The edge views of plane 1-2-3 are shown parallel to the frontal plane in Fig. 7-20A. There are an infinite number of shapes a frontal plane may have in the front view, but the top view and side views must be edges that are parallel to the frontal plane.

The Horizontal Plane. A horizontal plane is parallel to the horizontal projection plane, as shown in Fig. 7-20B. A horizontal plane is a principal plane and it appears true size in the top view. Three orthographic views of horizontal plane 4-5-6 are shown in Fig. 7-20B. If the plane appears as an edge in both the front and side views or if it appears as an edge in either the front or side view and is parallel to the H-F fold line in the same view, it is a horizontal plane. Observation of the top view of a plane is not sufficient to determine whether it is a horizontal plane.

The Profile Plane. The third principal plane is the profile plane, which is parallel to the profile projection plane (Fig. 7-20C). Plane 7-8-9 is true size in the profile view, or side view. Note that the plane appears as an edge in the top and front views and that these edges are parallel to the edge view of the profile plane.

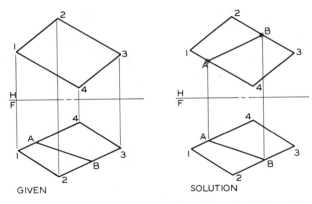

Fig. 7-21. To find the top view of line *AB* on the plane, points *A* and *B* are projected to lines 1-4 and 2-3 respectively.

7-14 PROJECTION OF A LINE ON A PLANE

Plane 1-2-3-4 is given in Fig. 7-21 with line *AB* drawn on the plane in the front view. We are required to locate line *AB* on the plane in the top view. Point *A* lies on line 1-4, while point *B* lies on line 2-3; thus it is possible to find these points in the top view by projecting them as shown in the solution. This is an application of the principle covered in Article 7-9.

The connection of points *A* and *B* will establish the line on plane 1-2-3-4 in the top view. This principle will have application in more advanced descriptive geometry problems, which we shall discuss in succeeding articles and chapters.

7-15 LOCATION OF A POINT ON A PLANE

Many problems require that points be located on a plane in several views. Plane *ABC* (Fig.

FIGURE 7-22. PROJECTION OF A POINT ON A PLANE

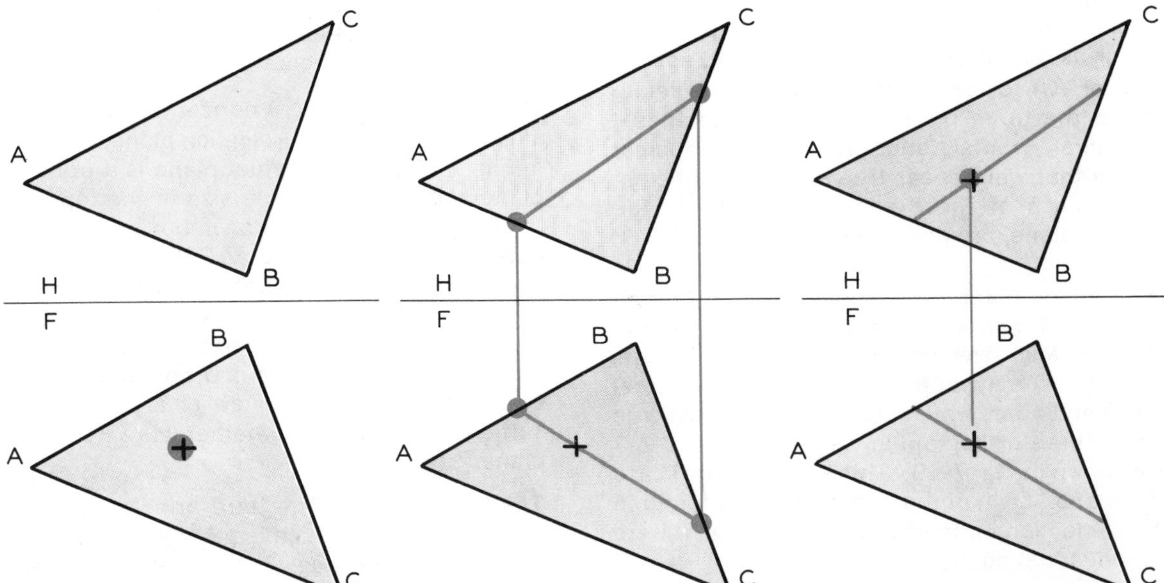

Given: The top and front views of a plane and a point on the front view. **Required:** Find the top view of the point on the plane.

Step 1: Draw a line through the point in the front view and project the line to the top view.

Step 2: To locate the point, project the point from the front view to the line in the top view.

7-22) has a point indicated on its surface in the front view. We desire to locate the top view of this point as well. A line is drawn in any direction other than vertical through the point in the given view (step 1). The points where this line intersects the edges of the plane in the front view are projected to these same respective lines in the top view. The point can be located by projecting from the front view to this line in the top view (step 2). Review Article 7-9 for a stronger understanding of this principle.

7-16 PRINCIPAL LINES ON A PLANE

Principal lines—horizontal, frontal, and profile—may be found in any view of a plane by application of the previously discussed principles. Principal lines are essential to the system of successive auxiliary views, which will be studied in later chapters.

Two horizontal lines are shown on plane 1-2-3 in Fig. 7-23A. These were found by constructing lines on plane 1-2-3 that are parallel to the horizontal projection plane. The top views are found by projecting to the plane in the top view. These lines lie on the plane and are true length in the top view since they are horizontal.

Frontal lines which are parallel to the frontal projection plane are located in the top view of Fig. 7-23B. The front view of the lines is found by projection. Frontal lines are true length in the front view.

Profile lines must be located in the front or top view and projected to the side view, as shown in Fig. 7-23C. Profile lines are true length in the side views.

It should be observed that principal lines on any view of an oblique plane are parallel. For example, many profile lines could have been drawn in Fig. 7-23C, but all would have been parallel and would have appeared true length in the side views.

7-17 PARALLELISM

In the solution of spatial problems it is often necessary to know whether lines or planes are parallel. This information can be determined by orthographic projection.

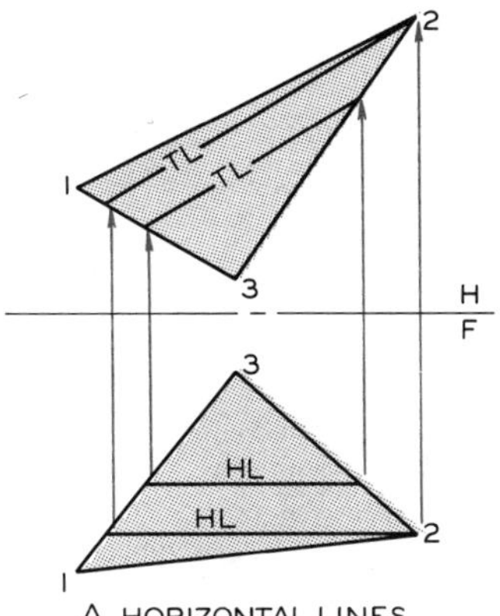

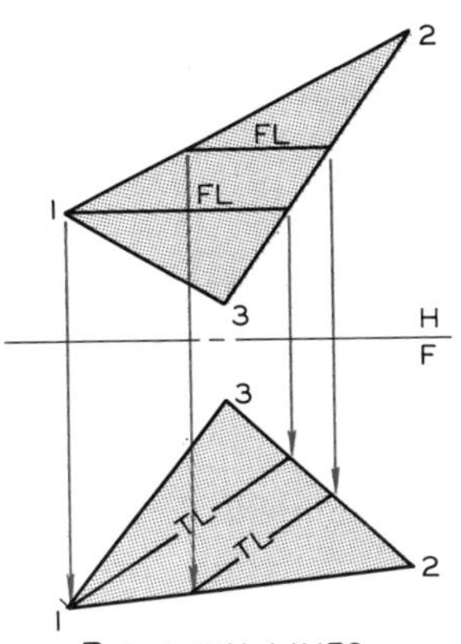

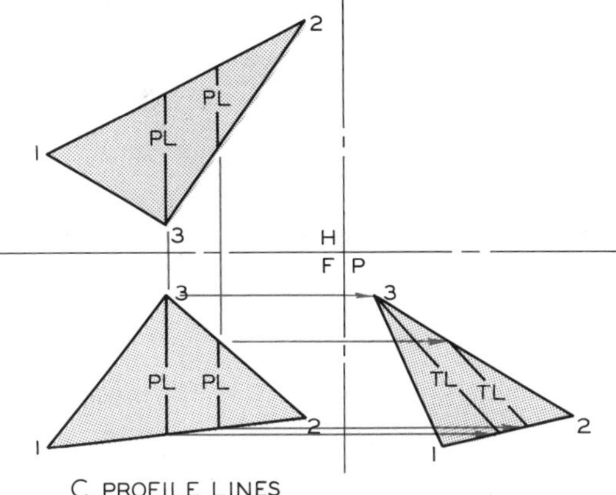

Fig. 7-23. Construction of the principal lines—horizontal, frontal, and profile—on a given plane.

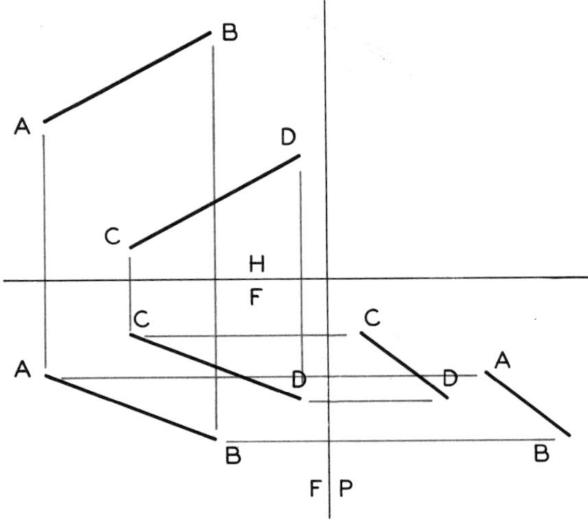

Fig. 7–24. When two lines are parallel, they will project as parallel in all orthographic views.

Two lines that are parallel will be projected parallel in all views, except in the view where both lines appear as points. Lines *AB* and *CD* in Fig. 7–24 appear oblique in three views, but they are also parallel in each; therefore the lines are parallel in space.

When only one view of two lines is available, it cannot be assumed that the lines are parallel even though they are projected as parallel in this view. More than one view is necessary to determine whether two lines are parallel.

Figure 7–25 illustrates how this principle may be applied to a problem. Given is line 3–4 and point *O*. We are required to construct a line equal in length and parallel to 3–4, with its midpoint at *O*. Since the midpoint of a line will be the midpoint of any projection of that line, the top view of the line is drawn through point *O* with its midpoint as shown in step 1. The projection of this line is the same length as the projection of line 3–4. The front view of the line is drawn parallel to the front projection of line 3–4 in step 2. The ends of the line are established by projecting from the top view. The frontal

FIGURE 7–25. CONSTRUCTION OF A LINE PARALLEL TO A LINE

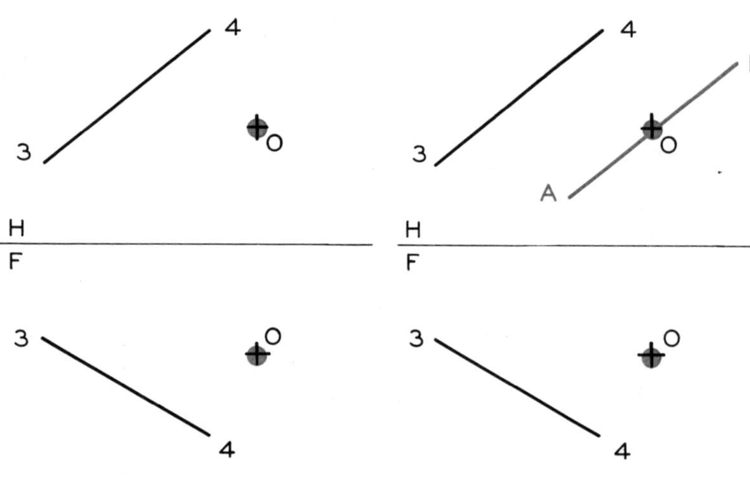

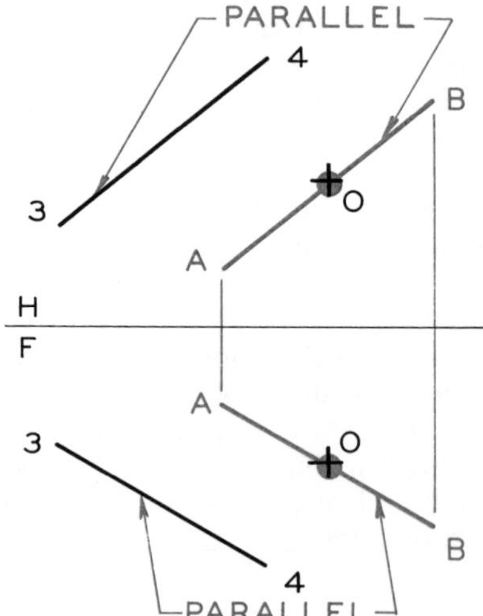

Given: The top and front views of line 3–4 and point *O*.
Required: Construct a line with its midpoint at *O* that is parallel to line 3–4.

Step 1: Draw line *AB* parallel to the top view of line 3–4 with its midpoint at *O*.

Step 2: Draw the front view of line *AB* parallel to the front view of line 3–4, which is an orthographic projection of the top view.

projections of the two lines are also equal in length, and the resulting line is parallel to the given line 3–4.

7-18 PARALLELISM OF PLANES

Two planes are parallel when intersecting lines in one plane are parallel to intersecting lines in the other, as shown pictorially in Fig. 7–26. Orthographic projections of parallel planes are shown in Fig. 7–27. Note that the same two sets of lines are parallel in the top view of part A as in the front view. These lines happen to be exterior lines of the planes concerned, but this does not have to be the case. The planes could be dissimilar in shape as shown in the example in part B. Plane 7–8–9 and plane *ABCD* were found to be parallel by drawing parallel lines on each plane in one view and projecting them to the other. If these lines are parallel in this view also, then the planes are parallel. When two planes appear as parallel edges in one view, such as in part C, they are parallel in space.

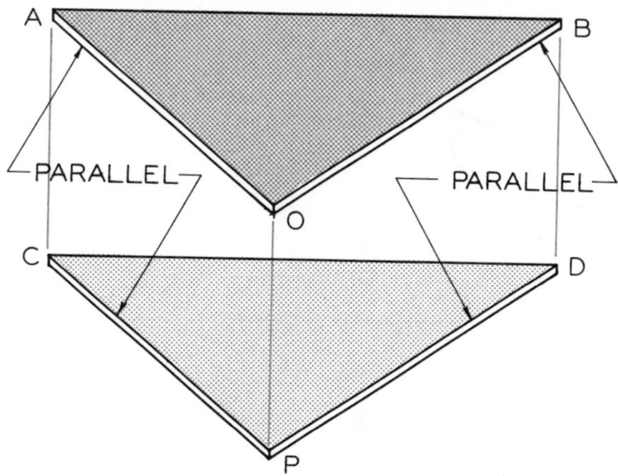

Fig. 7–26. Two planes are parallel when two intersecting lines in one plane are parallel to two lines in the other plane.

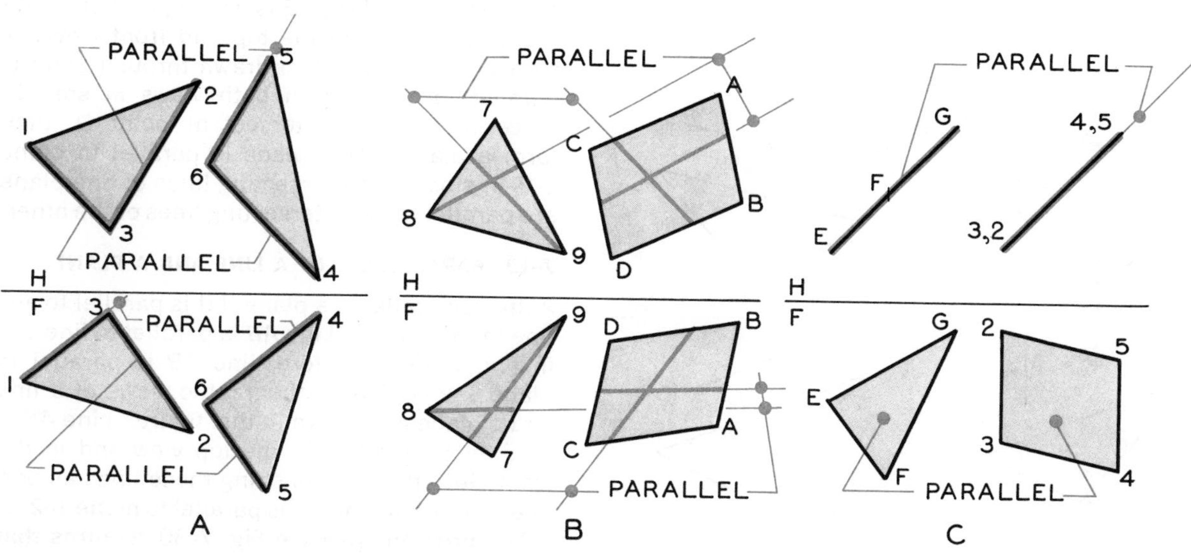

Fig. 7–27. Examples of planes that are parallel.

FIGURE 7-28. CONSTRUCTION OF A PLANE THROUGH A POINT PARALLEL TO A PLANE

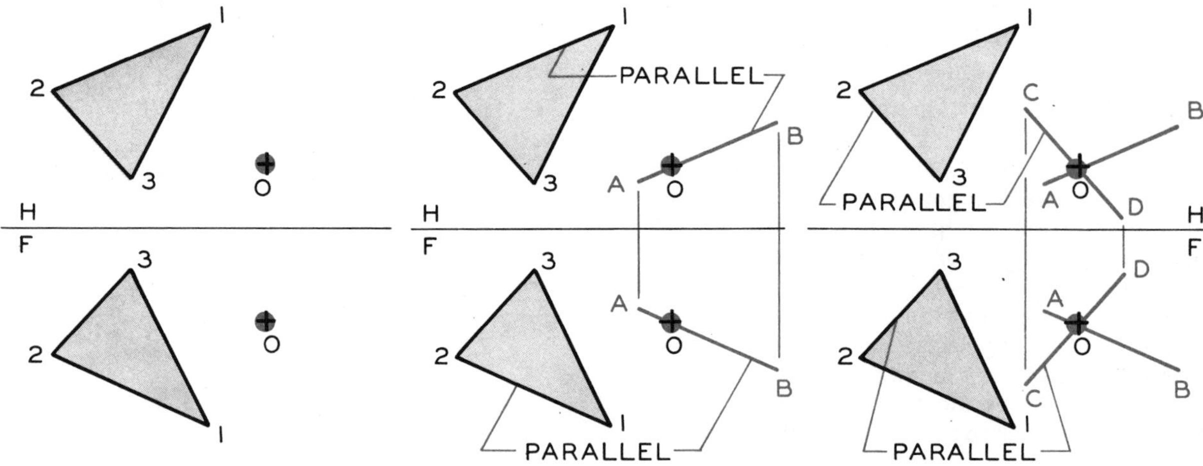

Given: The top and front views of plane 1–2–3 and point *O*.
Required: Construct a plane through point *O* parallel to plane 1–2–3.

Step 1: Draw line *AB* parallel to line 1–2 in both views.

Step 2: Draw line *CD* parallel to line 2–3 in both views. Plane *ABCD* is parallel to plane 1–2–3.

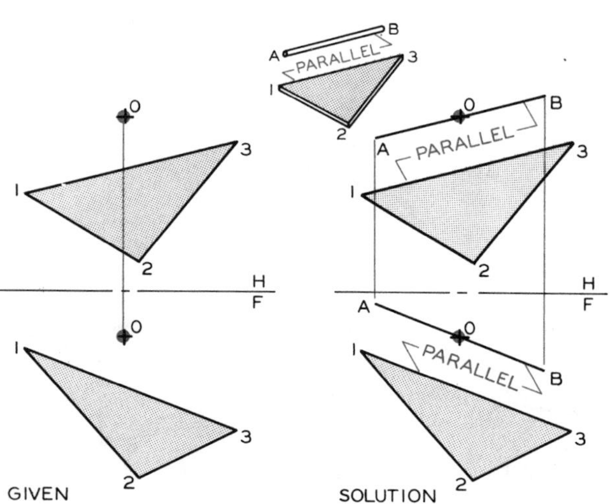

Fig. 7–29. Construction of a line through point *O* parallel to plane 1–2–3. Line *AB* is drawn parallel to line 1–3 in the front and top views.

The problem in Fig. 7–28 requires that a plane be constructed through point *O* parallel to plane 1–2–3. Line *AB* is drawn parallel to line 1–2 of the plane in the top and front views in step 1. Line *CD* is then drawn through point *O* parallel to line 2–3 in both views in step 2. Since these lines intersect at point *O*, they form a plane. This plane is parallel to plane 1–2–3, since two intersecting lines of one plane are parallel to two intersecting lines of the other.

7-19 PARALLELISM OF A LINE AND A PLANE

A line is parallel to a plane if it is parallel to any line in that plane. Line *AB* is parallel to line 1–3 in Fig. 7–29; therefore, line *AB* is parallel to plane 1–2–3. Two orthographic views of a line and a plane are shown in this figure. Line *AB* is parallel to line 1–3 in the top view and in the front view, thus establishing these lines as parallel; therefore line *AB* is parallel to plane 1–2–3.

The problem given in Fig. 7–30 requires that a line drawn through point *O* be parallel to the plane formed by the two intersecting lines, 1–2

FIGURE 7-30. CONSTRUCTION OF A LINE PARALLEL TO A PLANE

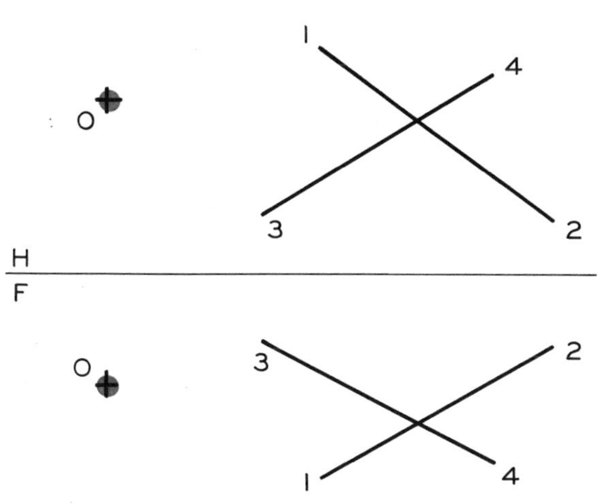

Given: The top and front views of point *O* and plane 1–2–3–4.
Required: Draw the two views of a line through point *O* that is parallel to the plane.

Solution: Line *AB* is drawn parallel to one of the lines in the plane, line 1–2 in this case, in both views. The line could have been drawn parallel to any line in the plane.

and 3–4. The line is constructed in step 1 through point *O* and parallel to line 1–2 in both views. This line is parallel to the plane, since it is parallel to a line in the plane. This line could have also been drawn parallel to line 3–4.

7-20 PERPENDICULARITY OF LINES

The engineer will design many mechanisms that are composed of perpendiculars, whether they are lines or planes. It is therefore necessary that perpendicularity be understood sufficiently in order that it may be recognized or drawn when it occurs.

Figure 7-31 illustrates pictorially and orthographically the basic rules of perpendicularity. *Two perpendicular lines will be projected as perpendicular in any view where one or both are true length.* A line may be revolved around another line in an infinite number of positions and still be perpendicular to the other line, the axis.

In the orthographic view, the lines *OA* and *OB* are projected such that they are perpendicular to the true-length axis. The axis and

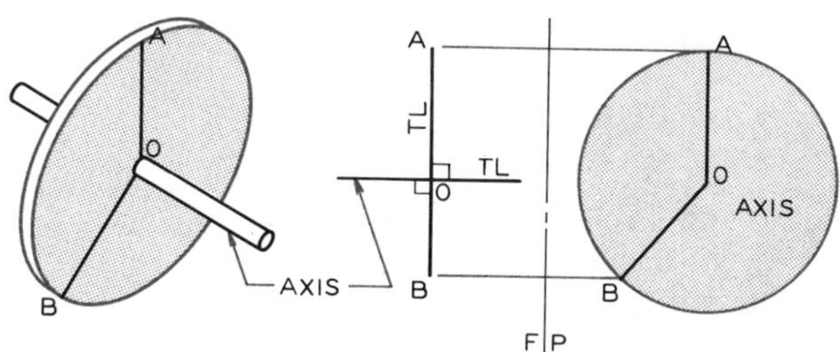

Fig. 7-31. Perpendicular lines will be projected as perpendicular in a view where one or both of the lines appear true length.

FIGURE 7-32. CONSTRUCTION OF A LINE PERPENDICULAR TO A PRINCIPAL LINE

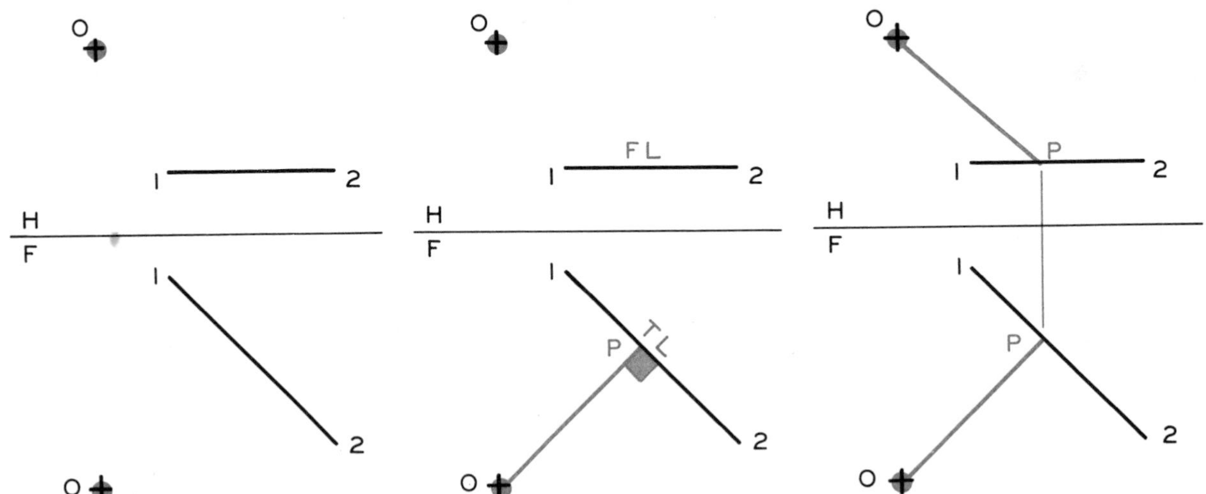

Given: The top and front views of principal line 1–2 and point *O*. **Required:** Construct a line from point *O* perpendicular to line 1–2.

Step 1: Draw a line perpendicular to the true-length line 1–2 in the front view.

Step 2: Locate point *P* on line 1–2 in the top view and connect this point with point *O*.

line *OA* are both true length, but line *OB* is not true length. However, line *OB* is projected as perpendicular to the axis because the axis is true length, thereby satisfying the previously stated rule.

When two lines are perpendicular, but neither is true length, they will not project with a true 90° angle. The plane of the 90° angle will appear foreshortened and distorted.

7-21 A LINE PERPENDICULAR TO A PRINCIPAL LINE

Given in Fig. 7–32 are frontal line 1–2 and point *O*. Construct the top and front views of a line through point *O* that intersects line 1–2 and is perpendicular to it.

Line 1–2 is a principal line, a frontal line, and is consequently true length in the front view. By applying the rule of perpendicularity from Article 7–20, it is possible to construct line *OP* in the front view perpendicular to the true-length line. Since point *P* lies on the line, it may be found in the top view by projecting above its front view to line 1–2, as shown in step 2. These lines do not appear as perpendicular in the top view since neither are true length in this view.

7-22 A LINE PERPENDICULAR TO AN OBLIQUE LINE

The top and front views of an oblique line, 3–4 are given in Fig. 7–33. We are required to construct a line through the midpoint of line 3–4 that would be perpendicular to it.

It is necessary that a true-length line be constructed before a perpendicular can be found. Thus in step 1 a horizontal line, *OP*, is drawn through the midpoint of the front view of line 3–4 to some convenient length. Line *OP* will be

FIGURE 7-33. CONSTRUCTION OF A LINE PERPENDICULAR TO AN OBLIQUE LINE

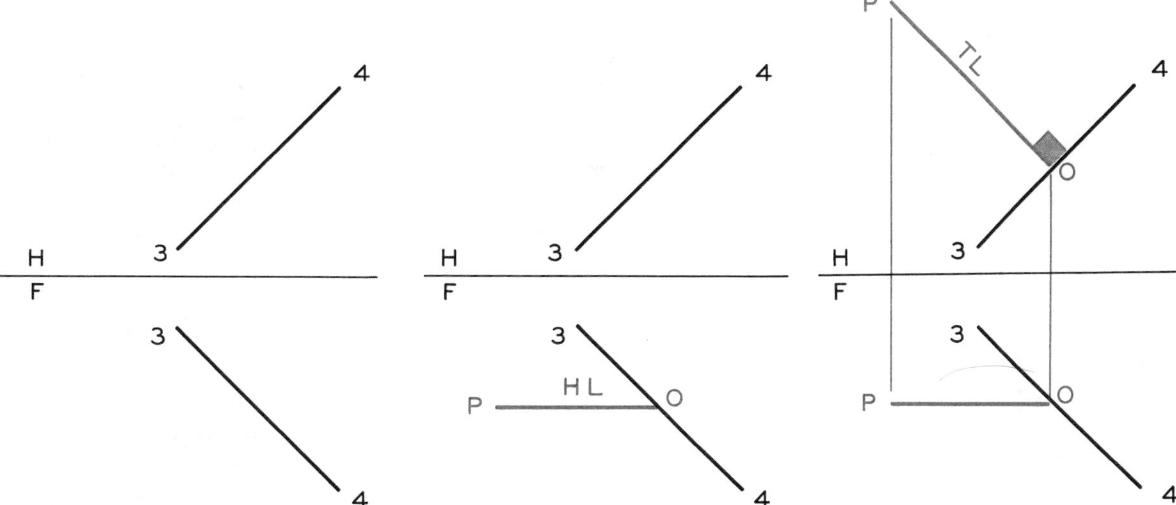

Given: The top and front views of an oblique line 3–4.
Required: Construct a line from the midpoint of the oblique line 3–4 that is perpendicular to it.

Step 1: Construct a horizontal line from the midpoint of the front view of line 3–4.

Step 2: Project point *O* to the top view of the line and draw line *OP* (which is true length in the top view) perpendicular to line 3–4.

projected true length in the top view since it is horizontal. It may be drawn in any direction and still be true length; therefore, it is constructed perpendicular to line 3-4 through point *O*. The top view of point *P* is found by projecting from the front view (step 2). These two lines are perpendicular because they are perpendicular in the view where one of them is true length.

7-23 PERPENDICULARITY INVOLVING PLANES

A plane or a line can be constructed perpendicular to another plane by applying the principles of the previous articles. A line is perpendicular to a plane if it is perpendicular to two intersecting lines on that plane, as illustrated in Fig. 7-34A.

Also, a plane is perpendicular to another plane if a line in one plane is perpendicular to the other plane. This is illustrated in Fig. 7-34B.

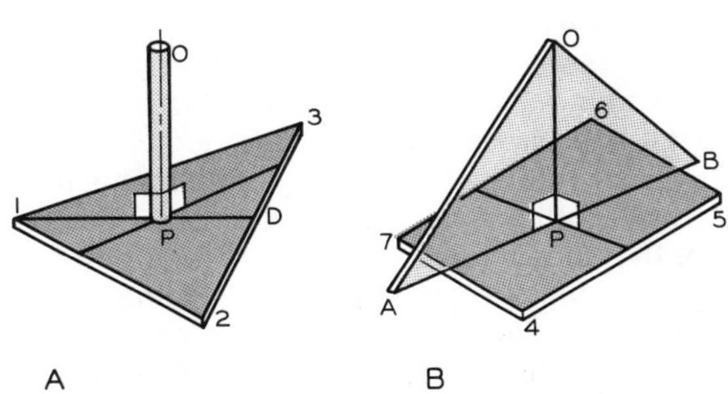

Fig. 7-34. (A) A line is perpendicular to a plane if it is perpendicular to two intersecting lines on the plane. (B) A plane is perpendicular to another plane if the plane contains a line that is perpendicular to the other plane.

FIGURE 7–35. CONSTRUCTION OF A LINE PERPENDICULAR TO A PLANE

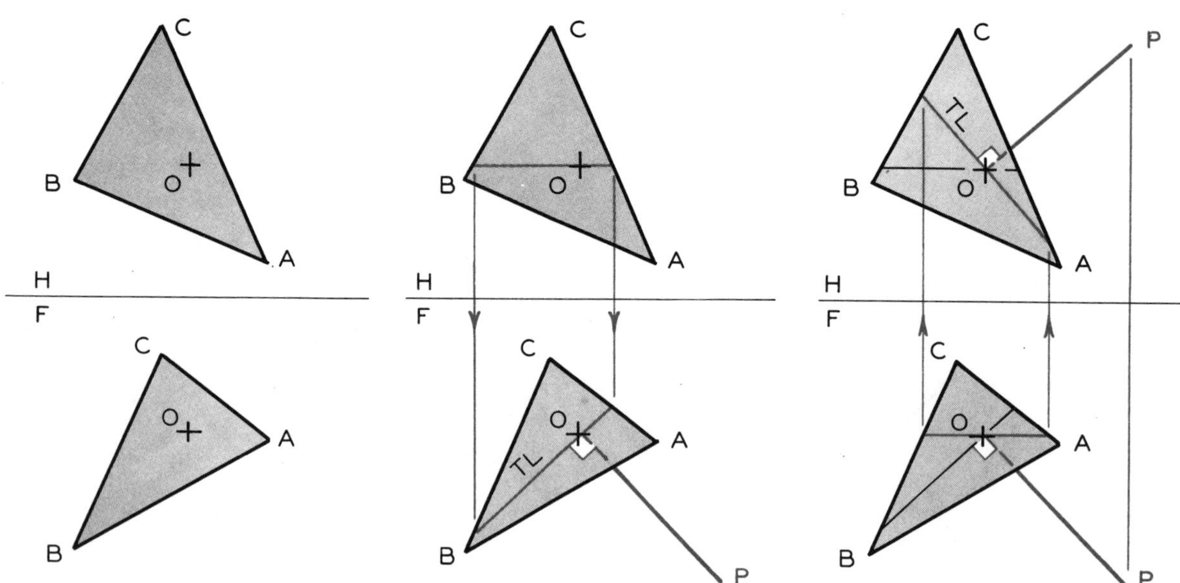

Given: The top and front views of plane *ABC* and point *O* on the plane. **Required:** Construct a line from point *O* that is perpendicular to plane *ABC*.

Step 1: Construct a frontal line through point *O* in the top view to find a true-length view of the line in the front view. Construct a perpendicular to this line.

Step 2: Construct a true-length horizontal line in the top view and draw a perpendicular to this line.

7–24 A LINE PERPENDICULAR TO A PLANE

Plane *ABC* is given in Fig. 7–35 with point *O* located on the plane. We are required to construct a perpendicular to the plane through point *O*. It is possible to find a true-length line on any view of a plane by constructing a principal line, as covered previously. A true-length line is found in the front view by constructing a frontal line through point *O* in the top view and projecting it to the front view (step 1). This line is true length and is a line on the plane, consequently, line *OP* can be drawn through point *O* perpendicular to the frontal line. If line *OP* is to be perpendicular to another line as well, we can draw a horizontal line on the plane in the front view (step 2) and project it to the top view, where it appears true length. The top view of *OP* is constructed perpendicular to this line to establish the top view of line *OP*.

This line is perpendicular to the plane because it is perpendicular to two intersecting lines on the plane. This relationship is apparent where lines on the plane are shown true length.

7–25 A PLANE PERPENDICULAR TO AN OBLIQUE LINE

Line 1–2 and point *O* are given in Fig. 7–36. We are required to construct a plane through point *O* that will be perpendicular to line 1–2.

A plane may be established through point *O* by drawing two intersecting lines that intersect at point *O*. These lines will be true length if they are principal lines, which will permit perpendicularity to be established. Frontal line *AB* is drawn through point *O* in the top view and projected to the front view, where it is true length (step 1). It is drawn perpendicular to line 1–2,

FIGURE 7–36. CONSTRUCTION OF A PLANE THROUGH A POINT PERPENDICULAR TO AN OBLIQUE LINE

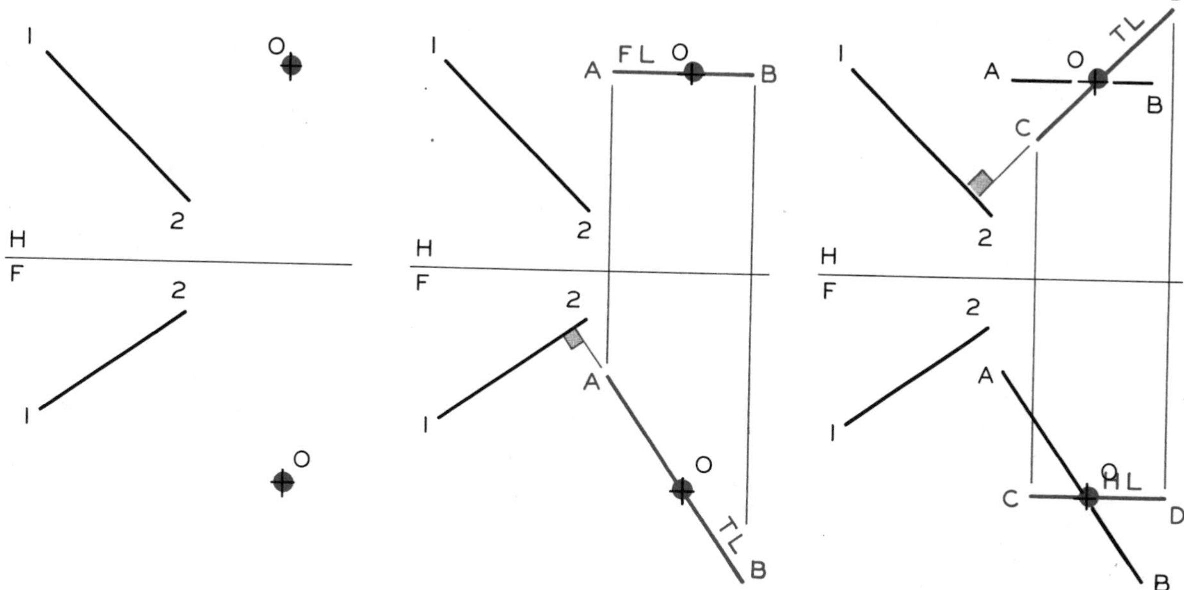

Given: The top and front views of an oblique line 1–2 and point *O*.
Required: Construct a plane through point *O* that is perpendicular to oblique line 1–2.

Step 1: Draw frontal line *AB* in the top view and perpendicular to the front view of line 1–2. Line *AB* is true length in the front view.

Step 2: Draw horizontal line *CD* in the front view and perpendicular to the top view of line 1–2. Line *CD* is true length in the top view. Plane *ABCD* is perpendicular to line 1–2.

which gives one line in the plane perpendicular to line 1–2.

A second line, *CD*, is drawn as a horizontal line (step 2) in the front view and it is projected to the top view, where it will be true length and perpendicular to line 1–2. Line 1–2 is perpendicular to two intersecting lines in the plane, and we have now constructed a plane perpendicular to the given line.

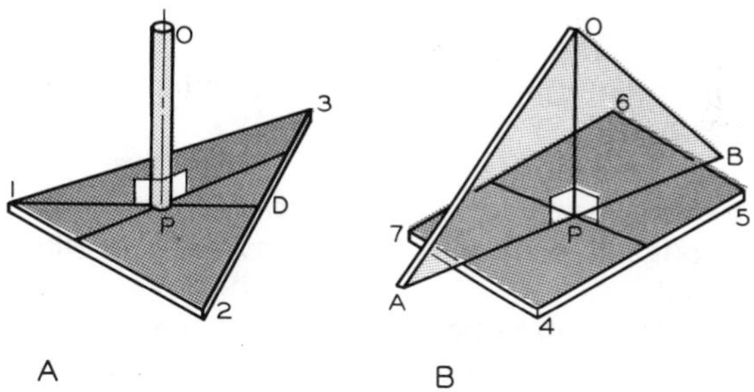

Fig. 7–37. (A) A line is perpendicular to a plane if it is perpendicular to two intersecting lines on the plane. (B) A plane is perpendicular to another plane if the plane contains a line that is perpendicular to the other plane.

7–26 PERPENDICULARITY OF PLANES

Planes may be perpendicular to other planes in many technological problems. The rule for determining perpendicularity of planes is a combination of the previously covered principles of perpendicularity.

A plane is perpendicular to another plane if a line in one plane is perpendicular to the other plane. This is illustrated in Fig. 7–37B, where plane *OAB* is perpendicular to plane 4–5–6–7, because if line *OP* is perpendicular to two intersecting lines on a plane, then it is perpendicular

FIGURE 7–38. CONSTRUCTION OF A PLANE THROUGH A LINE PERPENDICULAR TO A PLANE

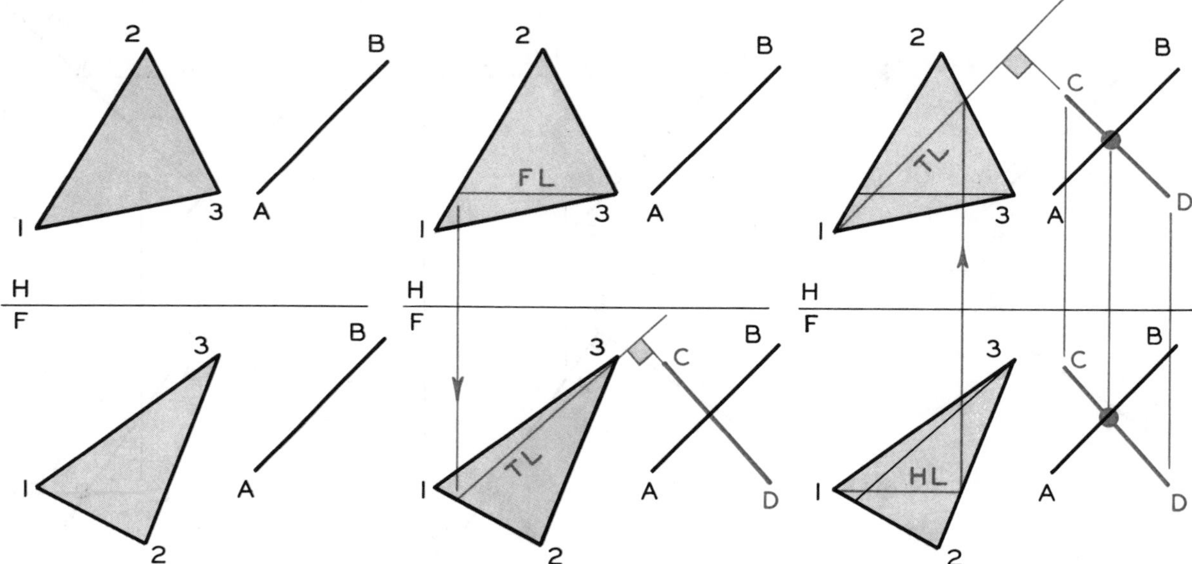

Given: The top and front views of plane 1–2–3 and line *AB*.
Required: Construct two views of a plane that passes through line *AB* and is perpendicular to the given plane.

Step 1: A frontal line is drawn in the top view and found true length in the front view. Line *CD* is drawn through any point on *AB* to be perpendicular to the true-length line.

Step 2: A horizontal line is drawn on the plane and is found true length in the top view. Line *CD* is drawn through the point of intersection on line *AB* to be perpendicular to the true-length line in the top view.

to the plane. It can be seen from these principles that plane *OAB* is perpendicular to plane 4–5–6–7.

A plane and a line are given in Fig. 7–38. We are required to construct a plane passing through line *AB* that is perpendicular to plane 1–2–3.

A plane can be passed through a line if the line lies in the plane that is constructed; therefore, an infinite number of planes can be established through line *AB* by intersecting it with another line. Two intersecting lines form a plane. If the line drawn to intersect line *AB* were drawn perpendicular to plane 1–2–3, the plane formed would be perpendicular to plane 1–2–3.

A true-length line is found in the front view of plane 1–2–3 in step 1 by constructing a frontal line in the top view and projecting it to the front view. Line *CD* is drawn through a convenient point on line *AB* perpendicular to the extension of the true-length line in the front view. A horizontal line is constructed in the front view of step 2, and projected to the top view, where it is true length. The top-view projection of line *CD* is drawn perpendicular to this true-length line which goes through the top view of the point on line *CD*.

Line *CD* has been constructed perpendicular to two intersecting lines on the plane and is known to be perpendicular to the plane. Since the line *CD* intersects line *AB*, it forms a plane containing a line parallel to plane 1–2–3, which results in two perpendicular planes. These two planes do not actually intersect as they are represented in this illustration; however, they are perpendicular and would intersect at a 90° angle if both were extended to their line of intersection.

7-27 SUMMARY

The principles of orthographic projection covered in this chapter are fundamentals that will be applied in the development of spatial problems involving descriptive geometry principles in succeeding chapters. A review of the basic elements—the point, line, and plane—and their relationship to each other in space is the basis of the solution of all graphical and descriptive geometry problems.

It is important that a solid understanding be gained of the principal projection planes in this chapter before continuing further. Principal lines and principal planes are related to the projection planes to which they are parallel. The principal planes are: (1) horizontal, (2) frontal, and (3) profile. Similarly, principal planes and principal lines are identified by these three terms. Principal lines are true length in the view where they are parallel to the projection plane being viewed; principal planes are true size in this view also.

Relationships such as parallelism and perpendicularity are common in essentially all engineering problems. The designer can prepare more accurate and efficient plans if he understands these projections.

The succeeding chapters will discuss the principles of projection as they relate to the auxiliary-view method of problem solution. The projection of auxiliary views is possible through a thorough understanding of the basic projection principles covered here. Frequent reference should be made to this chapter when necessary, to review projection principles that are used in other solutions.

PROBLEMS

General: The problems for this chapter can be constructed and solved on eight $8\frac{1}{2}'' \times 11''$ sheets as illustrated by the accompanying figures. Given that each grid represents $\frac{1}{4}''$, lay out and solve the problems on grid or plain paper. All reference planes and points should be labeled in all cases, using $\frac{1}{8}''$ letters and guidelines.

1. Use Fig. 7–39 for all parts of this problem. (A) Draw the missing view of point *A*. Locate point *B* from point *A* 3 units forward, 2 units to the right, and 2 units below. Show this in three views. (B) Find the missing view of point *C*. With respect to point *C*, locate in three views point *D* that is 4 units forward, 2 units to the right, and 3 units above. (C) Draw three views of line *EF*. Point *F* is 4 units in front, 5 units to the right, and 3 units below point *E*. (D) Draw three views of line *GH*. Point *H* is 4 units behind, 3 units below, and 5 units to the right of point *G*. (E) Line *IJ* is a horizontal line 3 units below the horizontal plane. Draw the line in all views and label its true-length view. (F) Line *KL* is a frontal

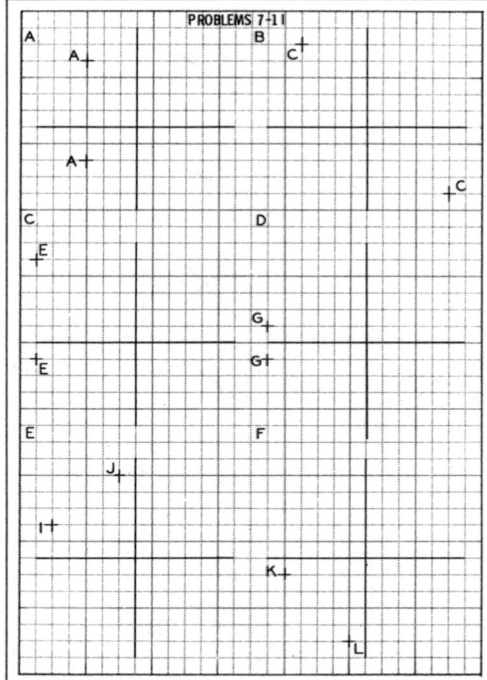

Fig. 7–39. Projections of a point.

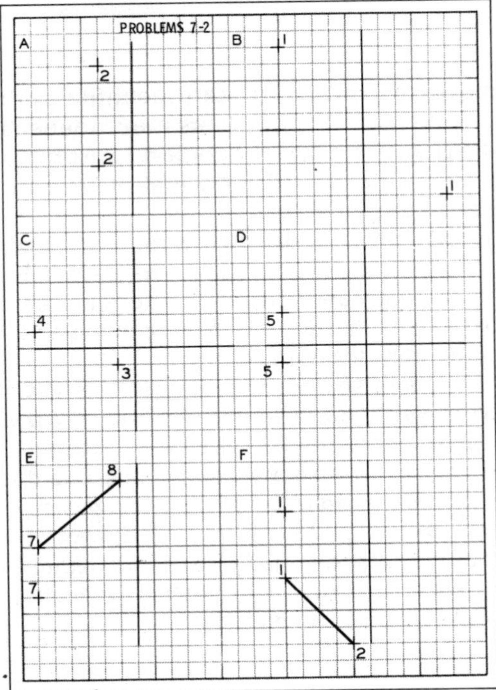

Fig. 7–40. Projections of principal lines.

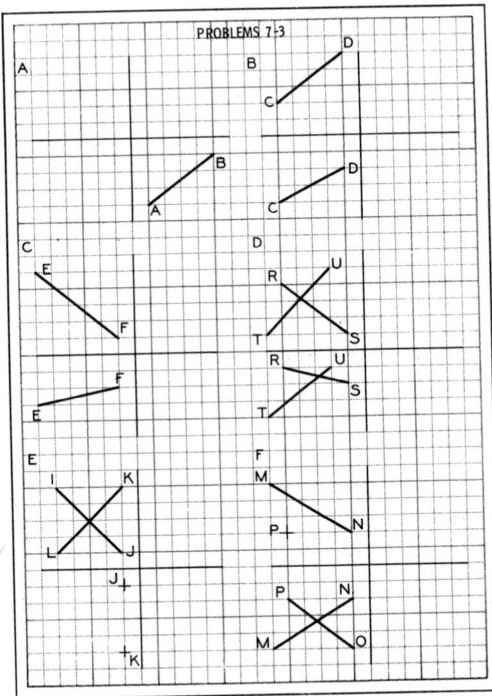

Fig. 7–41. Spatial relationships of lines.

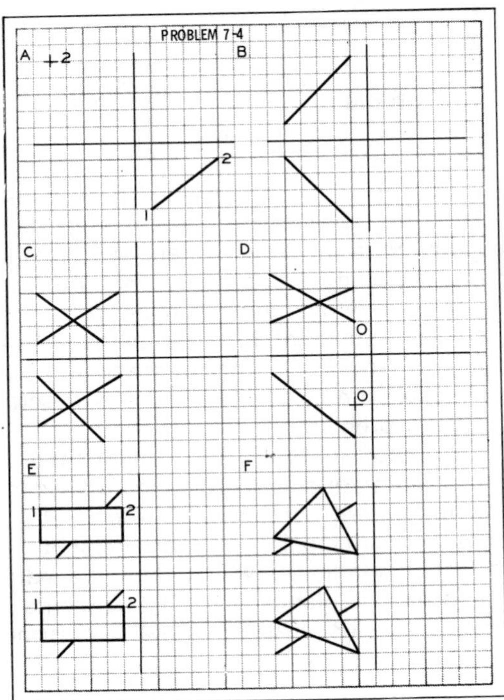

Fig. 7–42. Intersecting lines and visibility.

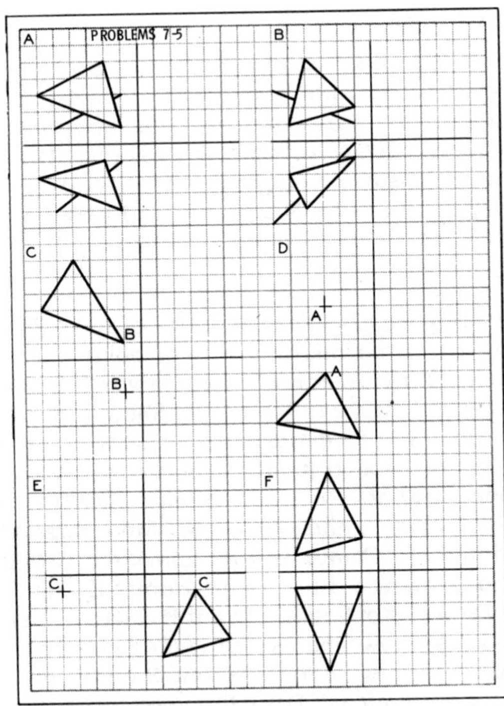

Fig. 7–43. Relationships of lines and planes.

line 4 units behind the frontal plane. Draw three views of the line and label its true-length view.

2. Use Fig. 7–40 for all parts of the problem. (A) Draw three views of line 1–2 with point 1 located 4 units to the left, 2 units below, and 3 units in front of point 2. (B) Draw three views of line 1–2 given that point 2 is located 4 units to the right, 2 units above, and 4 units in front of point 1. (C) Draw three views of frontal line 3–4 with point 4 located 3 units below point 3. Label its true-length view. (D) Draw three views of horizontal line 5–6 with point 6 located 4 units to the right and 3 units behind point 5. Label its true-length view. (E) Draw three views of horizontal line 7–8. Label its true-length view. (F) Draw three views of frontal line 1–2 and label its true-length view.

3. Use Fig. 7–41 for all parts of this problem. (A) Draw three views of profile line AB and label its true-length view. (B) Locate the midpoint of line *CD* in three views. (C) Divide line *EF* into three equal parts and show the divisions in three views. (D) Draw the side view of the two lines in part D. Determine whether they intersect. (E) Construct three views of the lines *KL* and *IJ* so that they will be intersecting lines. (F) Construct line *PO* in three views such that it will intersect line *MN*.

4. Use Fig. 7–42 for all parts of the problem. (A) Draw three views of profile line 1–2. Draw three views of a line 1″ long that intersects 1–2 at its midpoint and appears as a point in the profile view. (B) Draw three views of a line $\frac{1}{2}$″ long that intersects the given line at its midpoint and appears as a point in the front view. (C) Draw the side view of the given lines and determine whether they are intersecting lines. (D) Construct line *OP* that passes under the given line and does not intersect it. (E) Draw three views of the line and the plane and indicate visibility. (F) Draw three views of the line and the plane and indicate visibility.

5. Use Fig. 7–43 for all parts of this problem. (A) Draw three views of the line and the plane and indicate visibility. (B) Draw three views of the line and the plane and indicate visibility.

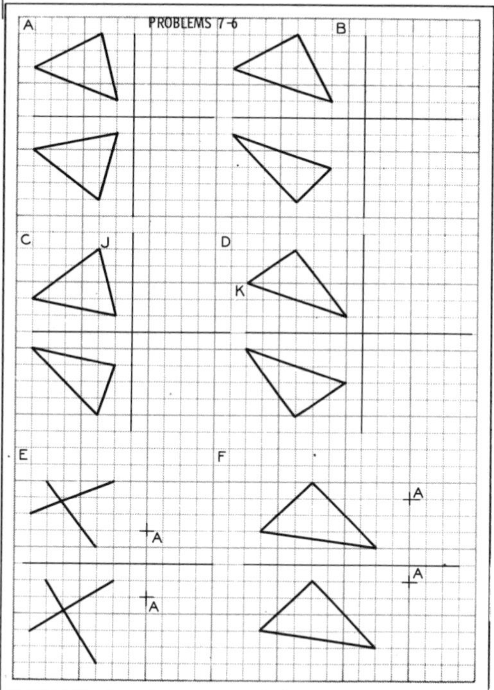

Fig. 7–44. Principal planes and spatial relationships.

(C) Construct three views of the horizontal plane and label its true-size view. (D) Construct three views of the frontal plane and label its true-size view. (E) Construct three views of the profile plane and label its true-size view. (F) Draw three equally spaced frontal lines on the plane in three views. Draw the side view.

6. Use Fig. 7–44 for all parts of this problem. (A) Draw two equally spaced horizontal lines on the plane and show them in three views. (B) Draw three equally spaced profile lines on the plane and show them in three views. (C) Construct line *JP* which lies on a plane that slopes upward to the left. Show the line and the plane in the side view also. (D) Construct line *KR* in a plane that slopes downward and backward. Show the line and the plane in the side view also.

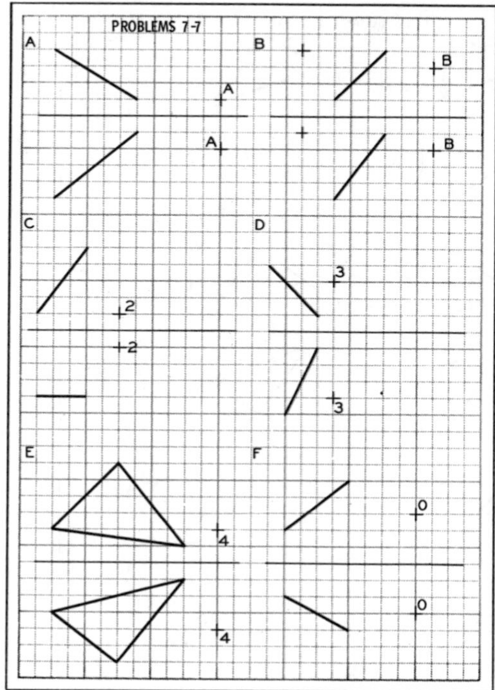

Fig. 7–45. Perpendicularity problems.

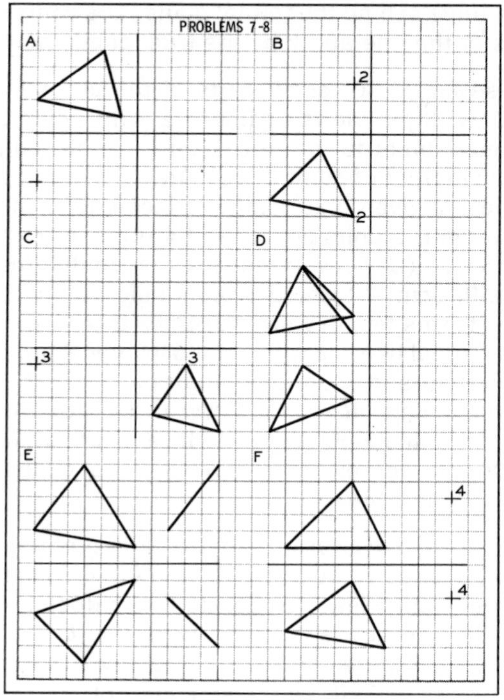

Fig. 7–46. Perpendicularity problems.

(E) Construct a line through point *A* that is parallel to the plane. (F) Construct a line through point *A* that is parallel to the plane.

7. Use Fig. 7–45 for all parts of this problem. (A) Construct a line through point *A* that is parallel to the line and equal in length. (B) Construct a line through point *B* that is parallel to the plane formed by the line and point. (C) Construct a line from point 2 that is perpendicular to the line at its midpoint. (D) Construct a line from point 3 in the front view that will be perpendicular to the front view of the line. Show this line in three views. Is it perpendicular to the line? (E) Construct a line from point 4 that will be perpendicular to the plane. (F) Construct a plane through point *O* that will be perpendicular to the line.

8. Use Fig. 7–46 for all parts of this problem. (A) Draw three views of the horizontal plane. Construct a line $\frac{1}{2}''$ long perpendicular to it and show the plane and the line in three views. (B) Draw three views of a line $\frac{1}{2}''$ long that is perpendicular to and intersecting the frontal plane on its back side. Show the line and the plane in three views. (C) Construct three views of a line $\frac{1}{2}''$ long that is perpendicular to and intersecting the profile plane on its right side. Show the line and the plane in three views. (D) Construct three views of the plane and line with the line lying on the plane as shown in part D of the figure. (E) Construct a plane through the line that is perpendicular to the plane given in part E of the figure. (F) Construct a plane through point 4 that is perpendicular to the plane given in part F of the figure.

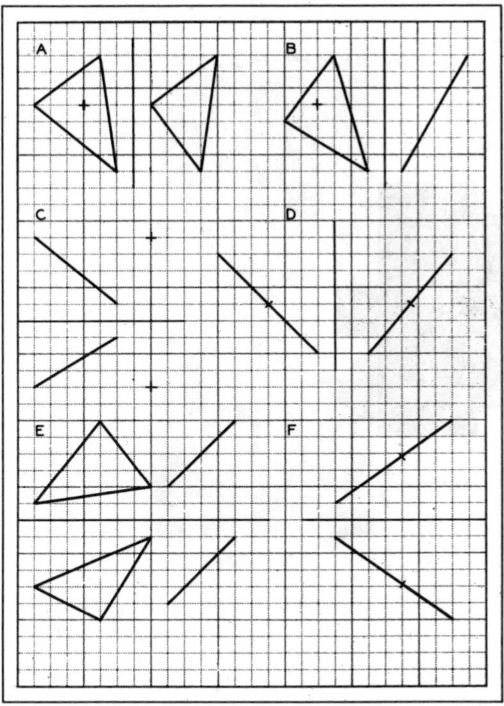

Fig. 7–47. Combination problems.

9. Use Fig. 7–47 for all parts of this problem. (A) Construct a plane that passes through the point on the plane and is perpendicular to the plane. (B) Construct a plane that passes through the point on the plane and is perpendicular to the plane. (C) Construct a plane through the point that is perpendicular to the line. (D) Construct a line from the point on a line that is perpendicular to the line on the upward side. (E) Construct a plane through the line that is perpendicular to the plane. (F) Construct a plane that passes through the point on the line and is perpendicular to the line.

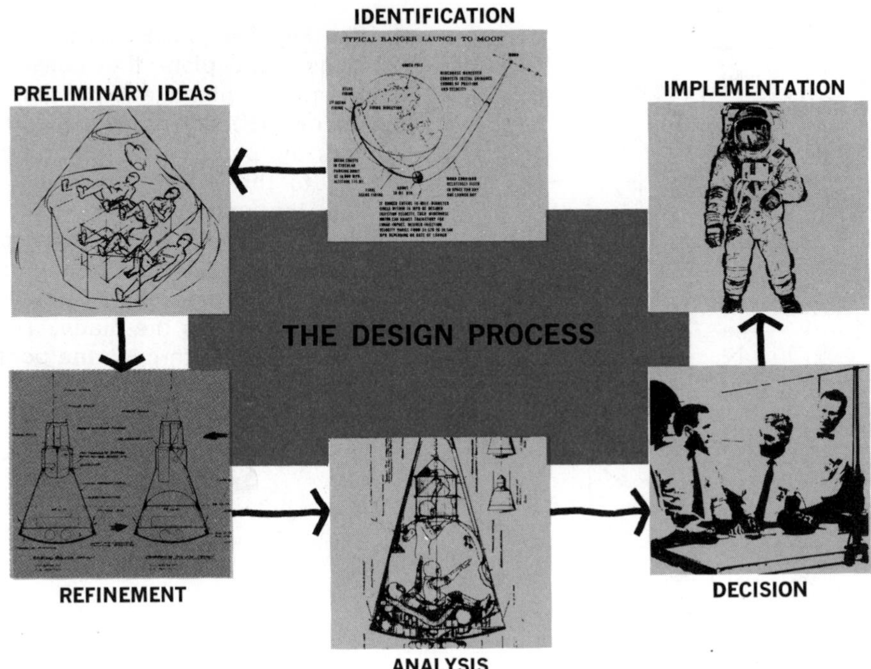

8 PRIMARY AUXILIARY VIEWS

8-1 INTRODUCTION

Chapter 7 reviewed principles of orthographic projection as applied to the principal views of points, lines, and planes in space. Although orthographic projection in principal views offers solutions to many spatial problems, auxiliary projections are necessary to analyze many designs for critical information that would be difficult to obtain by other means. Distances, lengths, angles, sizes, and areas must be determined during the refinement of preliminary designs to permit analysis in the next phase of the design process.

An example of a simple design problem appears in Fig. 8–1, which shows an exhaust pipe designed for installation in an automobile. It was necessary to determine the bend angles of the pipe and its length while providing the necessary clearance with other interior components. Design of the support brackets required that angular measurements, distances, and similar information be found by descriptive geometry methods prior to the preparation of the finished specifications. It should be easy to visualize problems of a greater complexity that would require considerably more refinement of dimensional properties of this type, but on more advanced levels.

Primary auxiliary views are necessary to determine spatial information pertaining to a design that cannot be found in the principal views. A *primary auxiliary view* is a view projected onto a projection plane that is perpendicular to only one of the principal planes. (If a projection plane is perpendicular to two principal planes,

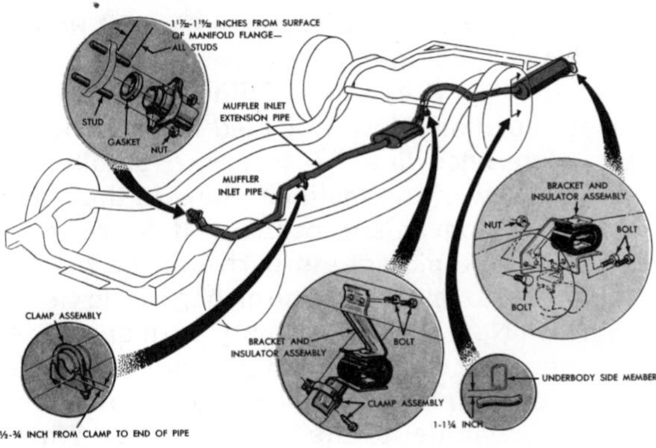

Fig. 8-1. The exhaust system of this automobile is an example of a spatial problem requiring the application of primary auxiliary views for solution. (Courtesy of Ford Motor Company.)

Fig. 8-2. The structural frame of the Mariner spacecraft illustrates many spatial relationships that must be determined during its design. (Courtesy of the National Aeronautics and Space Administration.)

it is a principal plane rather than an auxiliary view.) A primary auxiliary view is projected from one of the principal views—the top, front, or side views.

The Mariner spacecraft shown in Fig. 8-2 illustrates a number of applications of primary auxiliary views and secondary auxiliary views, which will be covered in the chapter that follows. The dimensions of each structural member must be found prior to the analysis of the frame for strength. Similarly, the dimensions of the members must be known to compute the weight of the vehicle, which is a critical aspect of space travel. The angles between the members must be obtained in order that the connecting joints may be designed. Knowledge of the angles between planes is necessary for fabrication of this system and for the determination of the true size of the planes formed by structural members. Graphical methods and descriptive geometry form the practical approach to solving realistic technological problems of the types shown in Figs. 8-1 and 8-2. Every effort should be made by the student to develop an understanding of these principles, since such understanding will enable him to recognize problems that can be solved graphically when this method is superior to mathematical methods.

Fig. 8-3. The inclined display panel of the Videx receiver is an example of a plane that must be found true size by a primary auxiliary view. (Courtesy of ITT Industrial Laboratories.)

8-2 TRUE SIZE OF INCLINED SURFACES

A plane that appears as an oblique edge in a principal view may be found true size in a primary auxiliary view. Such a plane will appear foreshortened in adjacent principal views from which the oblique edge view is projected. The inclined plane of the Videx unit in Fig. 8-3 will appear as an edge in one principal view and foreshortened in the other two. Since the plane does appear as an edge in one of the principal views, the true size of the plane can be found by a primary auxiliary view.

Primary auxiliary views are projected from any of the three principal views—the horizontal, frontal, or profile. A view projected from a horizontal view will require a horizontal reference plane, one projected from a front view will require a frontal reference plane, and one projected from a side view will require a profile reference plane. The procedure will be covered in the following explanation.

True Size of an Inclined Surface—Frontal Reference Plane. A plane that appears as an edge in front view (Fig. 8-4) can be found true size in a primary auxiliary view projected from the front view. Reference line F-1 is drawn parallel to the edge view of the inclined plane in the front view at any convenient location. It is drawn to conform to the pictorial in part A of the figure, in this case, to relate with the orthographic views in part B. Note that the primary auxiliary plane is perpendicular to the frontal plane and that the line of sight is perpendicular to the auxiliary plane and parallel to the frontal plane. When an observer views the object in the direction indicated by the line of sight, he will see the frontal projection plane as an edge, and consequently, he will see measurements perpendicular to the frontal plane true length. These dimensions are those of the depth, represented here by *D*, which is perpendicular to the edge view of the frontal plane in the top and side views (part B).

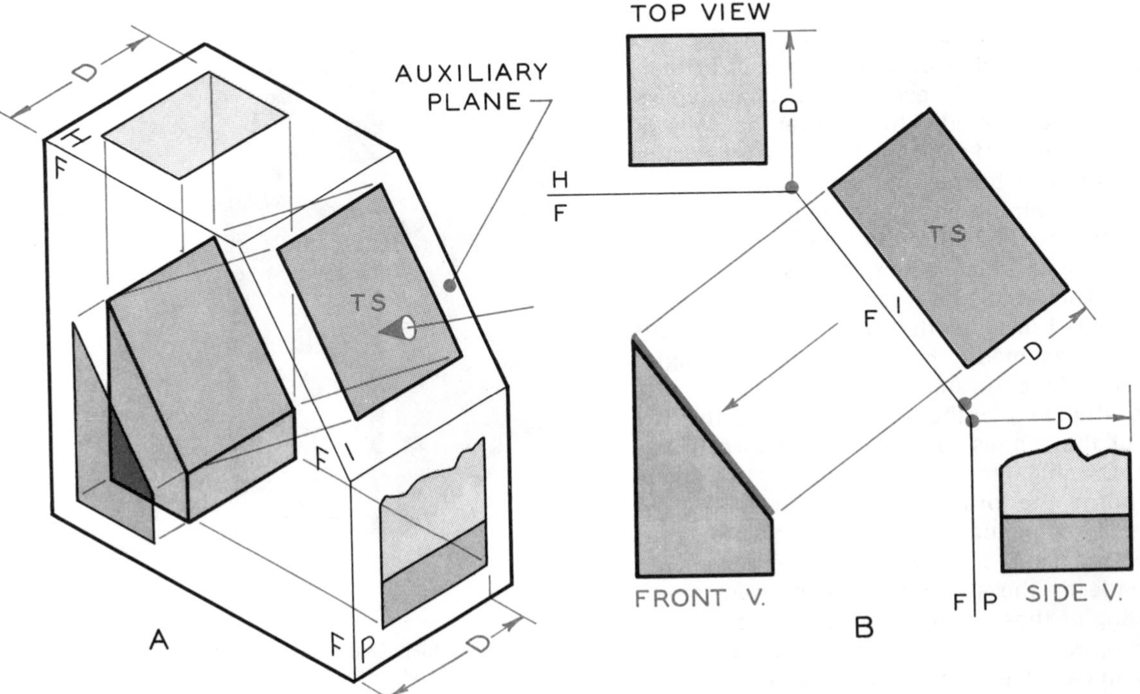

Fig. 8-4. True size of an inclined surface—frontal reference line.

The inclined plane is projected from the front view perpendicular to the F–1 line. Depth *D* is measured in the top or side views and transferred to the auxiliary view with dividers. Each of the four corners of the surface is found in this manner and then all four corners are connected with one another to give the true size of the inclined plane.

True Size of an Inclined Surface—Horizontal Reference Plane. The inclined plane in Fig. 8–5A is inclined to the frontal and profile planes and is perpendicular to the horizontal plane. It will appear true size when projected onto an auxiliary plane which is parallel to the inclined plane and perpendicular to the horizontal plane.

Reference line H–1 is drawn parallel to the edge view of the inclined plane in part B of the figure. When the line of sight is perpendicular to an auxiliary plane projected from the horizontal (top) view, the horizontal plane will appear as an edge, and the height dimension *H* will appear true length. Each corner of the inclined plane is projected perpendicularly to the auxiliary plane and located by transferring the *H* distance from the front view to the auxiliary view with dividers. The four corner points are connected to give the true-size view of the inclined plane.

Since a plane can be represented by two intersecting lines, the true length of a curved pipe segment (Fig. 8–6), as well as its radius of curvature, can be found by application of a primary auxiliary view projected from the horizontal view. The plane of this curved section of pipe will appear as an edge in the top view. A primary auxiliary plane can be constructed parallel to the edge view of the plane of the curved pipe and perpendicular to the horizontal projection plane. The resulting auxiliary view locates the endpoints of the pipe, from which the curve can be designed to fulfill the requirements of this connection.

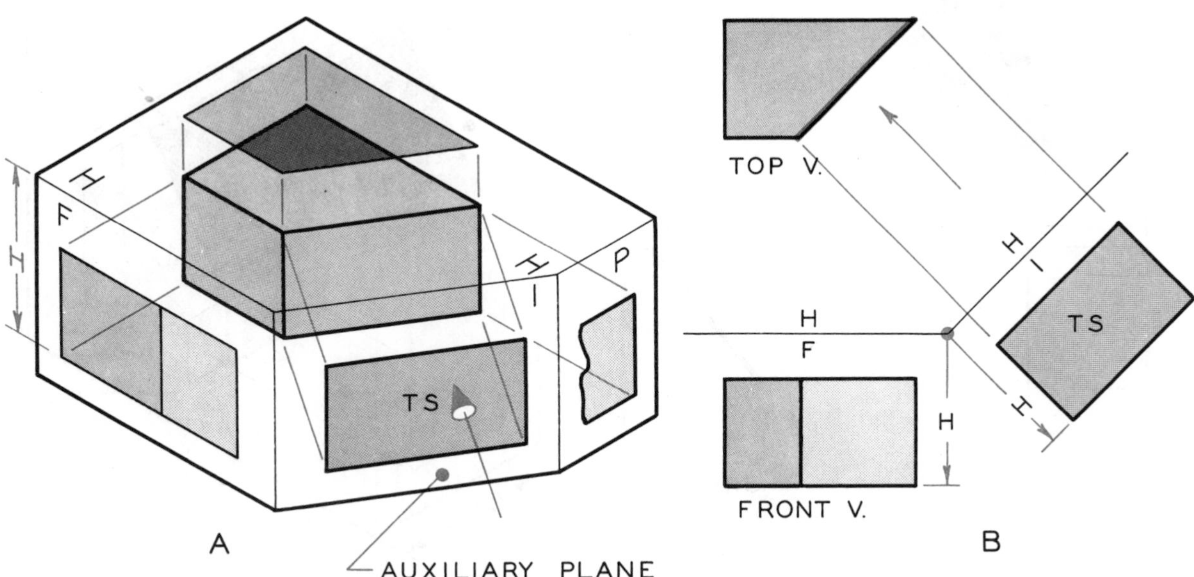

Fig. 8–5. True size of an inclined surface—horizontal reference line.

Fig. 8-6. The lengths of the curved pipe segments can be found by auxiliary views during its design. The pipes here are part of a pneumatic conveying system at Phillips Chemical Company. (Courtesy of General American Transportation Corporation.)

Fig. 8-8. The bed of this Model 45 Haulpak truck was designed through the use of auxiliary views to determine sizes of oblique planes. (Courtesy of LeTourneau-Westinghouse Company.)

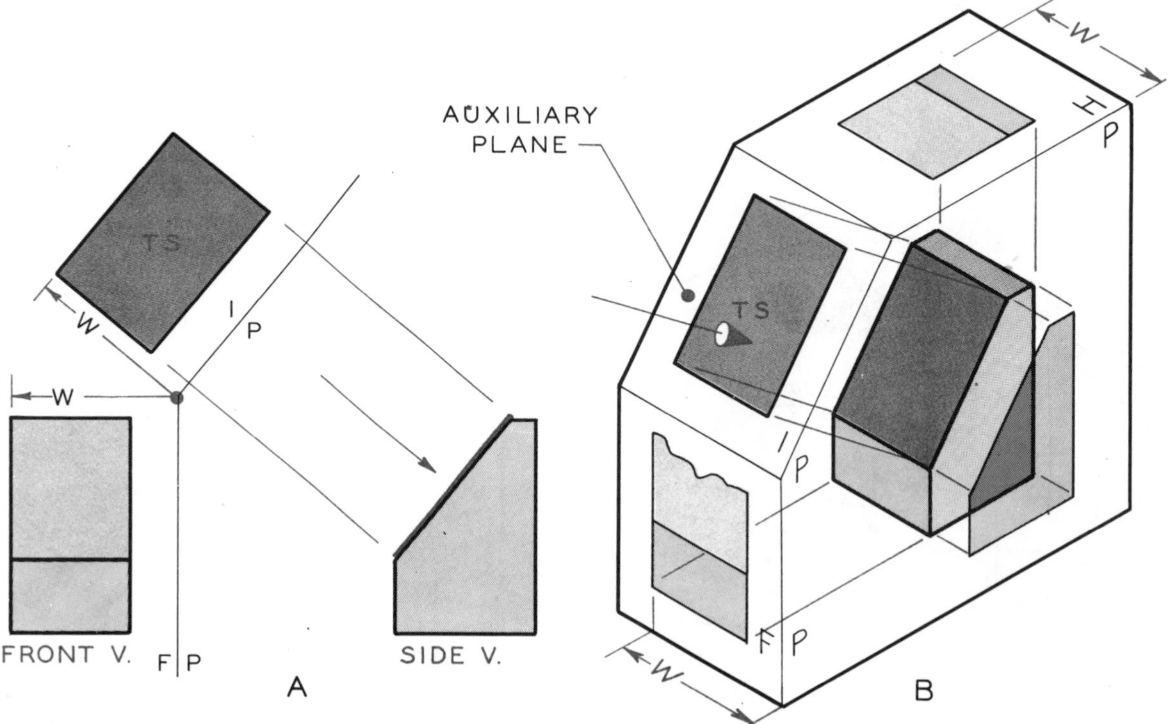

Fig. 8-7. True size of an inclined surface—profile reference line.

True Size of an Inclined Surface—Profile Reference Plane. The inclined plane in Fig. 8–7 appears as an edge in the side view, which means it is inclined to the horizontal and frontal planes and perpendicular to the profile plane. Auxiliary line P–1 is drawn parallel to the edge view of the inclined surface in the side view at some convenient location. An observer whose line of sight is perpendicular to the auxiliary plane will see the profile plane as an edge. Consequently, dimensions of width *W* will appear true length in the auxiliary view. The observer also sees the profile plane as an edge when he views the front view, so the width *W* dimensions are true length in this view. Therefore each measurement of *W* can be transferred from the front view to the auxiliary view to establish the corners of the inclined surface. The corners are connected to give the true-size view of the inclined surface.

The truck bed shown in Fig. 8–8 is composed of oblique planes that can be found true size by auxiliary views. Any two adjacent orthographic views of these planes can be used to find each plane true size by following the previously covered principles. It is necessary only for the planes to appear as edges in a principal view.

8–3 PRIMARY AUXILIARY VIEW OF A POINT

Point 3 is shown pictorially in Fig. 8–9A, where it is projected onto the horizontal, frontal, and auxiliary planes. Note that the auxiliary plane is perpendicular to the horizontal plane; consequently, the observer will see the horizontal plane as an edge when his line of sight is perpendicular to the auxiliary plane. Distances that are perpendicular to the horizontal plane will appear true length when the horizontal plane appears as an edge. Therefore point 3 can be located in the auxiliary view by measuring its distance, *H*, from the horizontal plane in the front view and transferring this distance to the auxiliary plane, where the horizontal plane appears as an edge also.

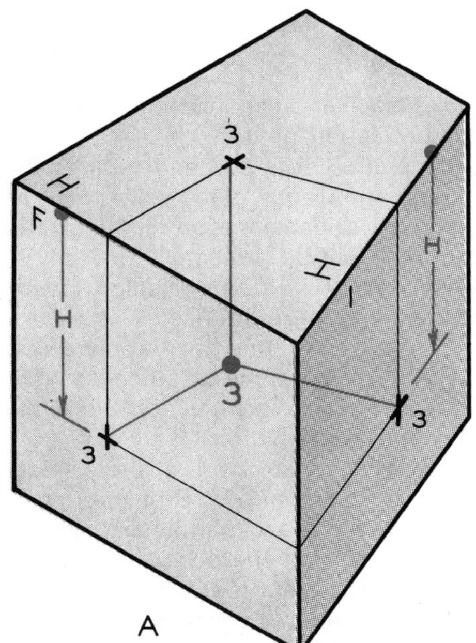

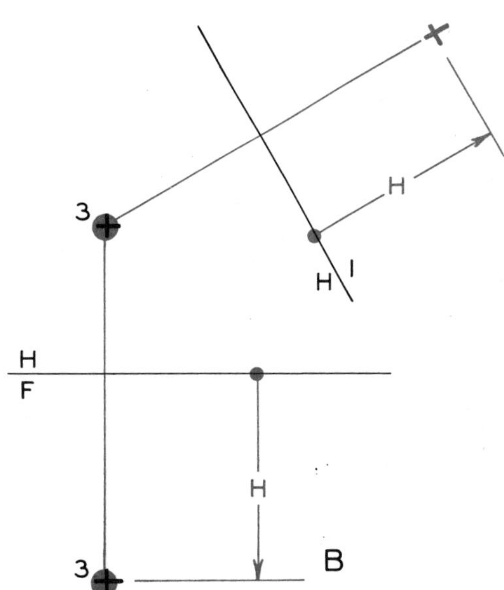

Fig. 8–9. Primary auxiliary view of a point shown pictorially and orthographically.

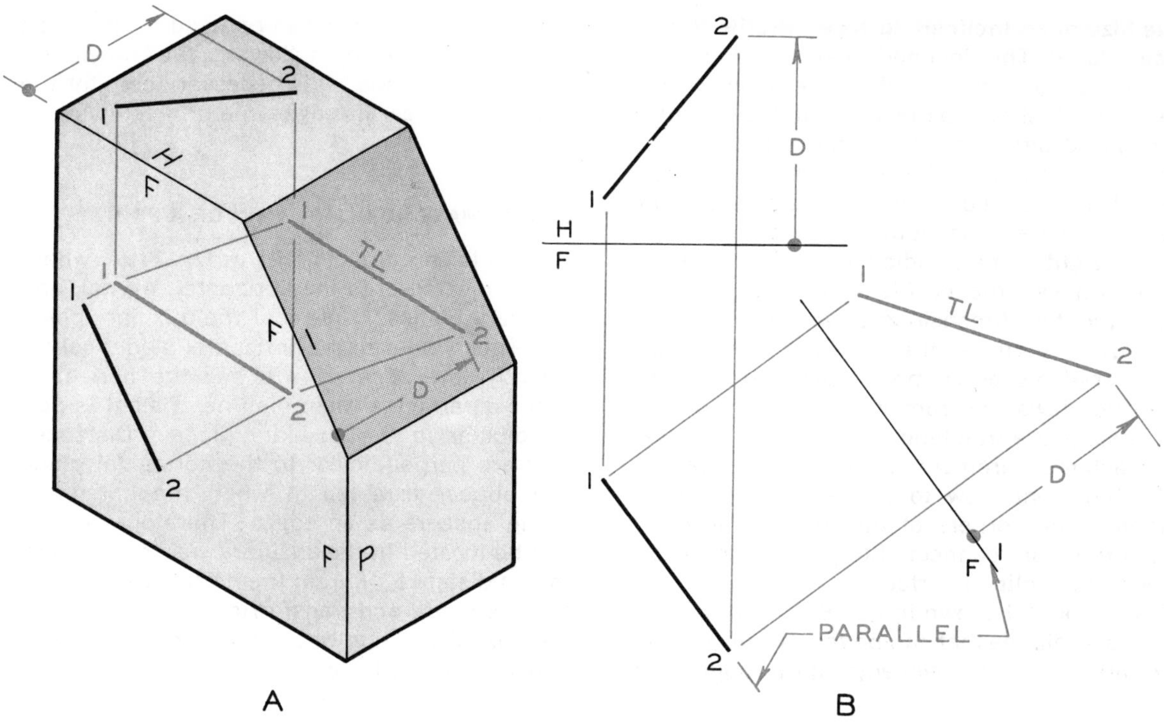

Fig. 8-10. Primary auxiliary view of a line.

The orthographic construction of the primary auxiliary view is illustrated in part B of the figure. It should be observed that there are an infinite number of positions for the auxiliary plane projected from the top view, but in every case point 3 would lie at the distance *H* from the horizontal plane. Similarly, an auxiliary view could have been projected from the front view through the use of an auxiliary plane that was perpendicular to the frontal plane, as introduced in Article 8-2. An auxiliary view of a point in space, such as that in this example, is of little value to the refinement or analysis of a preliminary design; however, it is a basic principle of projection that must be applied in all auxiliary view construction.

8-4 PRIMARY AUXILIARY VIEW OF A LINE

The projections of line 1-2 are shown pictorially in Fig. 8-10A. The line is projected onto the horizontal, frontal, and auxiliary planes with the primary auxiliary plane constructed parallel to the frontal projection of line 1-2. When the observer's line of sight is perpendicular to the auxiliary plane, the frontal plane will appear as an edge, and all dimensions perpendicular to the frontal plane will be projected true length. Depth dimension *D* is perpendicular to the frontal plane and is therefore used as the measurement to construct the auxiliary view of line 1-2. Point 2 is the same distance from the frontal plane in the auxiliary view as it is in the horizontal projection (top view).

The orthographic construction of the primary auxiliary view is shown in part B of the figure. The auxiliary plane is drawn parallel to the front view of line 1-2 so that the observer's line of sight will be perpendicular to the line when it is perpendicular to the auxiliary plane. A line is projected true length in the view where the observer's line of sight is perpendicular to the line—in this case, the auxiliary view. We can measure the line's true length in this view.

FIGURE 8–11. TRUE LENGTH OF A LINE

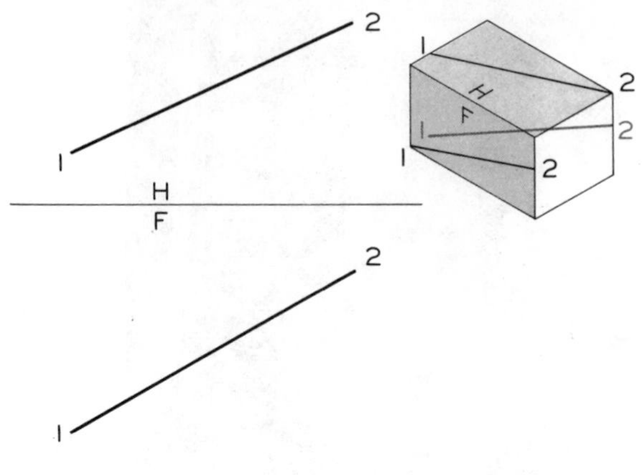

Given: The top and front views of line 1–2.
Required: Find the true length view of line 1–2 by the auxiliary-view method.
References: Article 5–22 and 8–4.

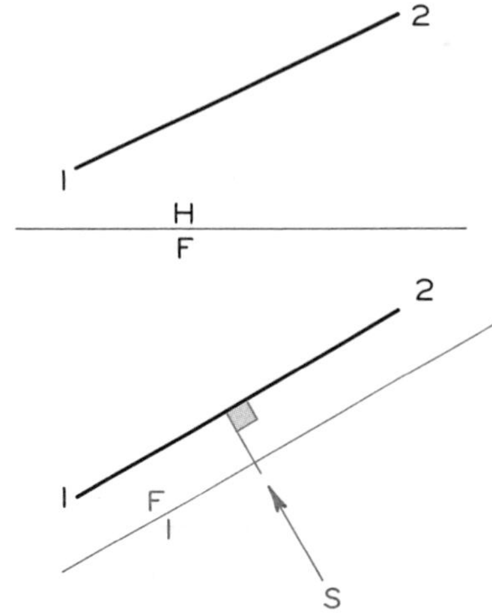

Step 1: A line will appear true length when viewed in a perpendicular direction. Therefore we shall establish a line of sight perpendicular to the front view of 1–2 and draw reference line F–1 parallel to line 1–2 and perpendicular to the line of sight. Label the reference line F–1 since it is perpendicular to the frontal plane.

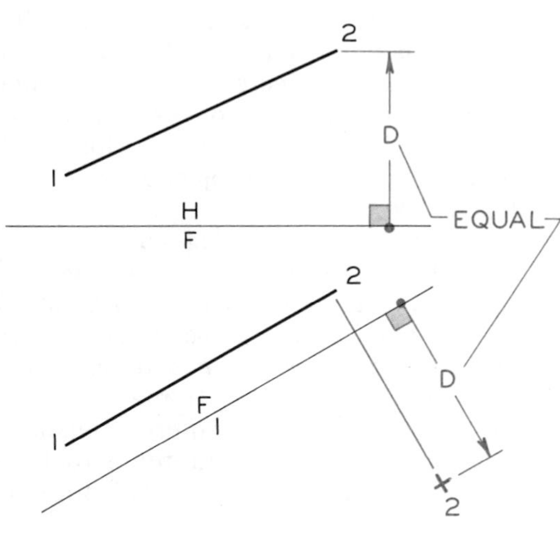

Step 2: We shall use the frontal plane as a reference plane for measurements since the auxiliary view is projected from the front view. Point 2 is distance *D* from the frontal plane in the top view. Measure this distance, which is perpendicular to the F–1 line, in the auxiliary view along the projector from the front view of point 2.

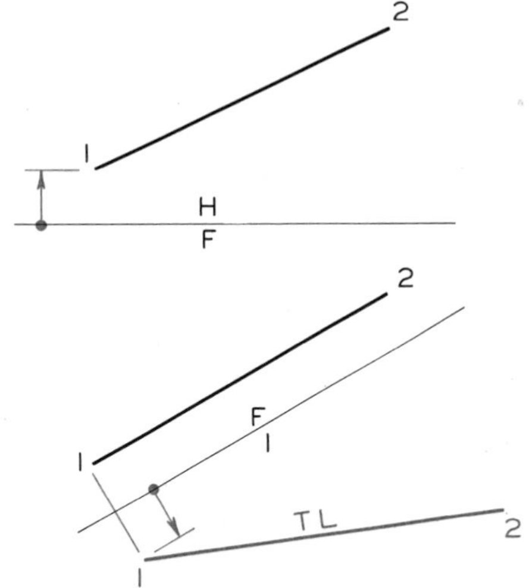

Step 3: Locate point 1 in the auxiliary view in the same manner as we did point 2. Connect points 1 and 2 to establish the true-length view of line 1–2. We could also find the true length of line 1–2 by projecting from the top view and using an H–1 reference line.

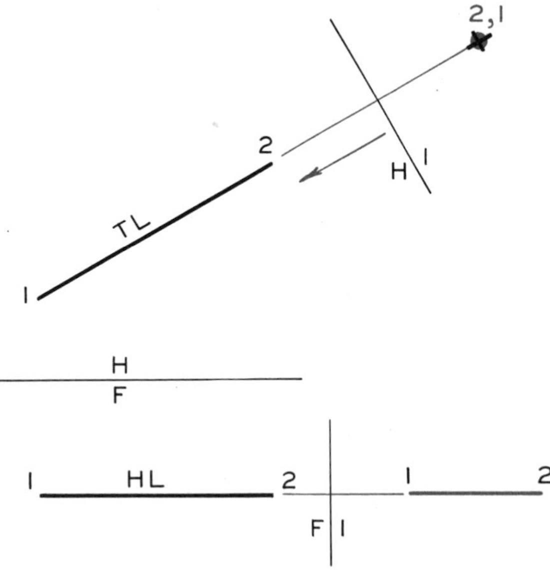

Fig 8–12. A primary auxiliary view which is projected parallel to a true-length line gives a point view of the line.

Fig. 8–13. The diagonal structural members of the Saturn 1–B launch vehicle could have been designed by using primary auxiliary views to determine their true lengths. (Courtesy of National Aeronautics and Space Administration.)

Figure 8–11 separates the sequential steps required to find the true length of an oblique line. It is beneficial to letter all reference planes using the notation suggested in the example illustrations. The reference line drawn between the principal plane and the primary auxiliary plane is a line representing the line of intersection between the primary and auxiliary planes, as shown in Fig. 8–10. A primary view projected from a front view has a reference line labeled F–1, from the horizontal view, H–1, and from the profile view, P–1. The true length of a line can be found by projecting from any of these views.

The point view of a line can be found in a primary auxiliary view when the line is true length in a principal view. Line 1–2 in Fig. 8–12 is horizontal in the front view, which makes the top view true length. When auxiliary line H–1 is drawn perpendicular to the direction of the top view of line 1–2, the resulting auxiliary view will project as a point view of line 1–2. In order that the point view may be obtained, a line must appear true length in the view from which the auxiliary view is projected. Note that the auxiliary view, which is projected from the frontal projection of line 1–2, does not result in a point view of the line, but instead gives a foreshortened view. This particular projection is actually a right-side view.

The true length of the diagonal structural members of the Saturn 1–B launch vehicle (Fig. 8–13) can be found by primary auxiliary views with a high degree of accuracy. These structural members would not appear true length in principal views. Numerous other examples of oblique lines requiring auxiliary view solution can be seen in the structural framework in the background of this illustration.

8–5 TRUE LENGTH BY ANALYTICAL GEOMETRY

The analytical approach to determining the true length of a line is illustrated in Fig. 8–14, where line 3–4 appears true length in the front view.

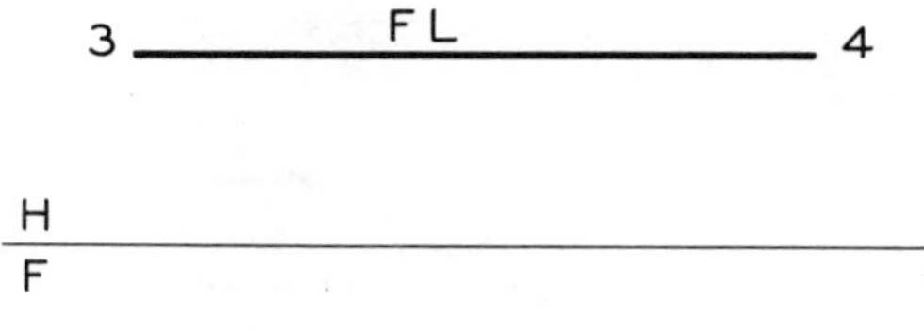

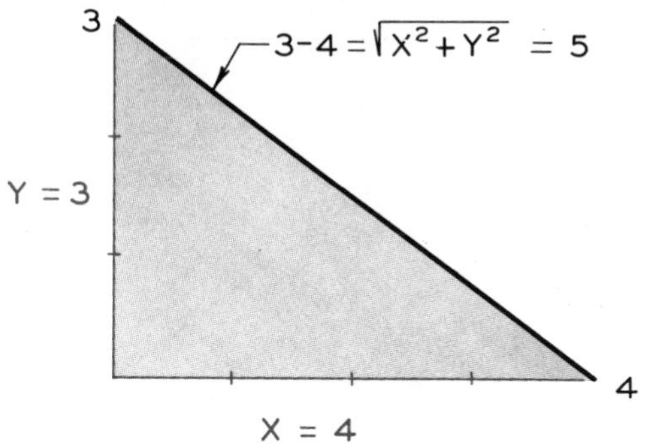

Fig. 8-14. The true length of a frontal line can be found analytically by the Pythagorean theorem.

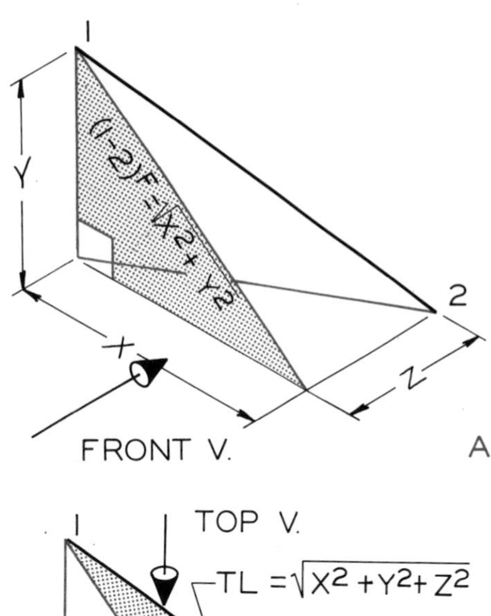

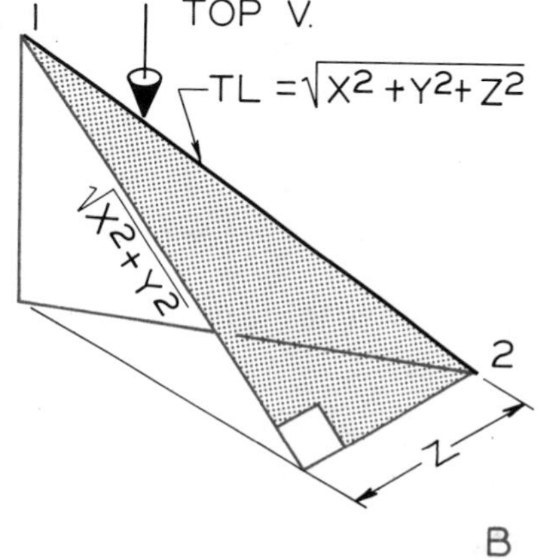

Fig. 8-15. The *X*-, *Y*-, and *Z*-coordinates used for finding the true length of an oblique line.

The line can be measured graphically for its true length or else its true length can be found by application of the Pythagorean theorem. The Pythagorean theorem states that the hypotenuse of a right triangle is equal to the square root of the sum of the squares of the other two sides. Line 3–4 is found to be 5 units long by application of this principle when the horizontal distance between the ends of the line is 4 units and the vertical distance is 3 units.

An oblique line that does not project true length in the principal views requires the manipulation of three coordinates—*X*, *Y*, and *Z*. Such a line is shown pictorially in Fig. 8–15. Note that the *X*- and *Y*-coordinates are projected true length in the front view while the *Z*-coordinate is true length in the top view. Two views are needed to determine the true length of an oblique line by analytical methods, just as two views were needed to find a graphical solution.

The steps for determining the true length of line 1–2 using the analytical method are illustrated in Fig. 8–16.

Step 1. Right triangles are constructed with line 1–2 as the hypotenuse in the top and front views. The coordinates, or legs of the right triangles, are drawn parallel and perpendicular to the H–F reference line.

Step 2. The true length of the frontal projection of line 1–2 is found by application of the Pythagorean theorem as though the line were true length in the front view. The frontal projection of line 1–2 is found to be 5 units in length by substituting the units of 3 and 4 as the *X*- and *Y*-coordinates. The resulting length can be

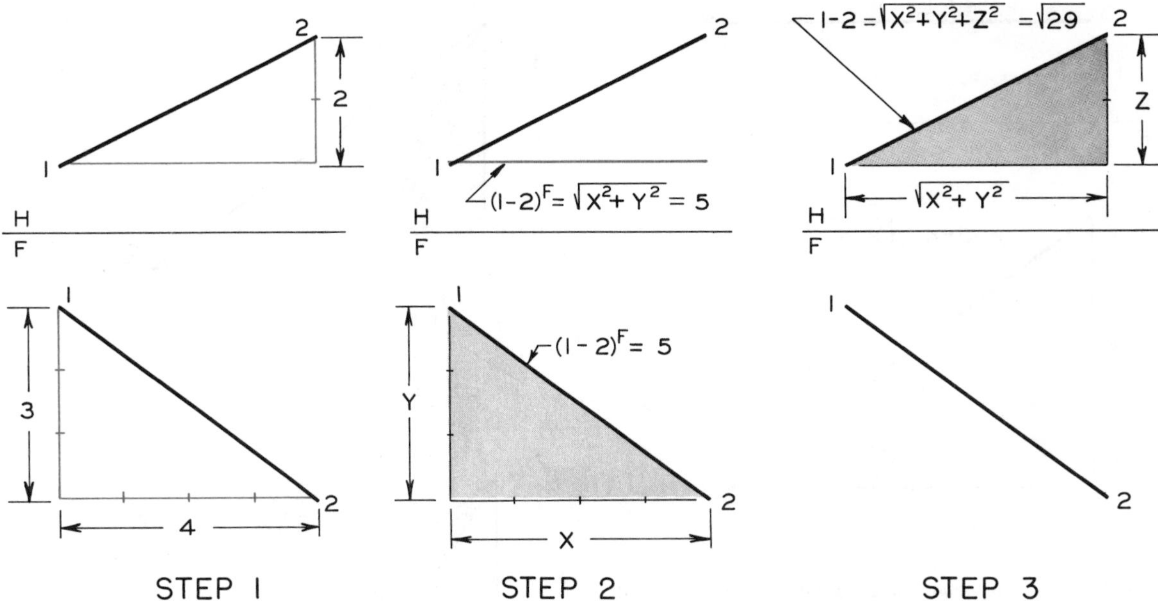

Fig. 8–16. The analytical method of finding the true length of an oblique line.

visualized by referring to the pictorial of the line in Fig. 8–15.

Step 3. The true length of the line can be found by combining the true length of the frontal projection with the true length of the *Z*-coordinate in the top view. The total equation of line 1–2 becomes

$$1\text{–}2 = \sqrt{X^2 + Y^2 + Z^2} = \sqrt{29}.$$

It can be seen by comparison that the analytical methods for determination of the true length of a line are very similar to the primary auxiliary method, where the projection of a line is used as the basis for an additional view in which the missing coordinate appears true length. For example, an auxiliary view projected from the front view of line 1–2 would result in a combination of coordinates where both the frontal projection of line 1–2 and the *Z*-coordinate appear

FIGURE 8–17. TRUE-LENGTH DIAGRAM

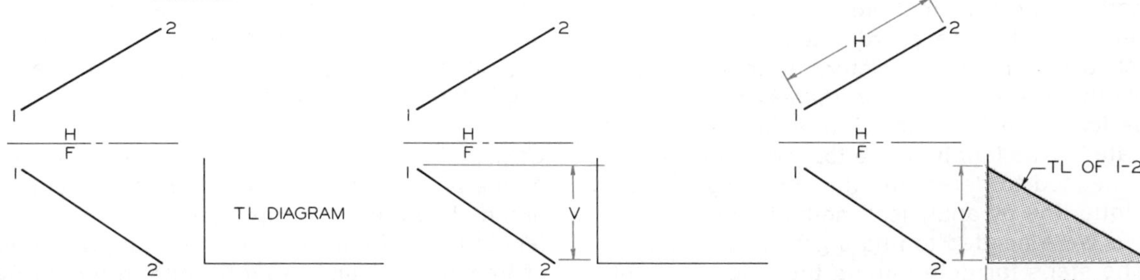

Given: Two views of line 1–2. **Required:** Find 1–2 true length in the TL diagram.

Step 1: The vertical distance between the ends of line 1–2 is transferred to the vertical leg of the TL diagram.

Step 2: The horizontal distance between the ends of line 1–2 is transferred from the top view to the other leg of the TL diagram. The true length is found by connecting these points.

true length, thus giving the true length of line 1–2. Both systems of spatial analysis should be used in combination to promote accuracy and to provide a means for a more thorough analysis.

8–6 TRUE LENGTH BY A TRUE-LENGTH DIAGRAM

The true length of line 1–2, or any oblique line, can be found by a true-length diagram such as that illustrated in Fig. 8–17. This is not an auxiliary view method, but a knowledge of primary auxiliary views is necessary to understand this method.

Step 1. The top and front views of line 1–2 are given. The vertical distance between the ends of the front view is projected to form one leg of a right triangle that will be the true-length diagram. This diagram can be constructed equally well from either view.

Step 2. The projected length of line 1–2 in the top view is transferred to the true-length diagram to represent the horizontal leg of the triangle. The hypotenuse of this right triangle is the true length of the line.

The true-length diagram method does not give a direction for the line, but merely its true length. In general, a true-length diagram can be projected from any two adjacent views, with one measurement being the distance measured between the two endpoints in a direction perpendicular to the reference plane between the two views. The other measurement is the projected length of the line in the other adjacent view.

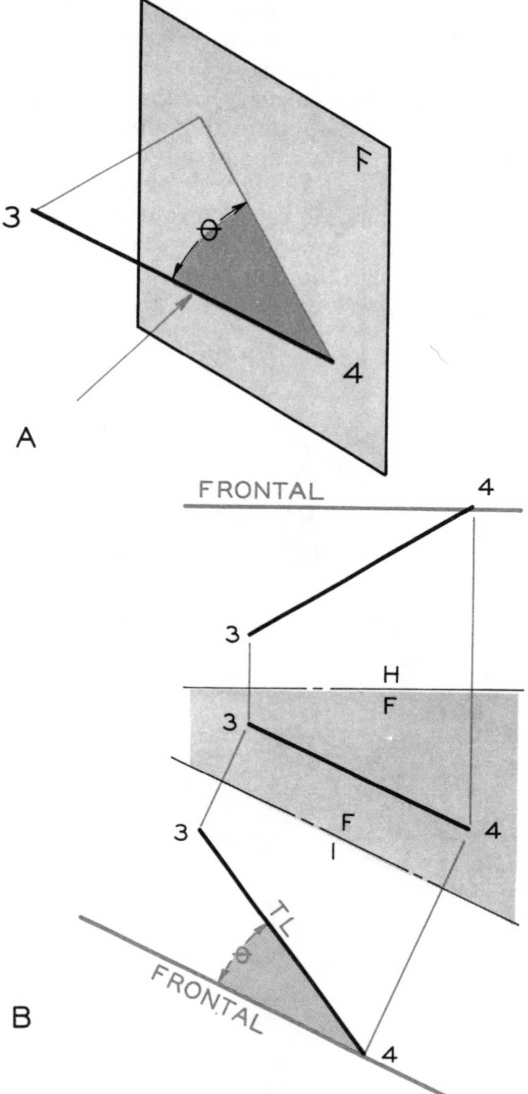

Fig. 8–18. Determining the angle made by a line with the frontal plane.

8–7 ANGLE BETWEEN A LINE AND PRINCIPAL PLANES

When a primary auxiliary view is drawn, an edge view of a principal plane will appear in the resulting auxiliary view. When the auxiliary view is projected from the front view, the frontal plane will appear as an edge; when it is projected from the horizontal view, the horizontal plane will appear as an edge; and when it is projected from the profile view, the profile plane will appear as an edge. The true angle between a principal plane and a line can be found in the view where the principal plane in question appears as an edge and the line is true length.

Angle with the Frontal Plane. Figure 8–18 illustrates a technique for determining the angle between line 3–4 and the frontal plane. The line of sight in part A is parallel to the frontal plane and perpendicular to line 3–4 and is the view required to obtain the true angle, θ, between the line and the frontal plane. The orthographic construction of the auxiliary view is shown in part B, where the auxiliary view is projected from the front view. Note that the reference plane is located through point 4 in the top view, rather than between the two views as a folding line, as is usually the case. A reference plane can be located in any position in the top view, including through the line itself, provided that it is a frontal reference plane. Due to space limitations on drawing layouts, the plane is usually drawn near the existing top view to conserve space in the auxiliary view. Point 3 in the top view is in front of the frontal reference plane and is located in front of the frontal plane in the auxiliary view as well.

Angle with the Horizontal Plane. Figure 8-19A pictorially illustrates the angle between the horizontal plane and line 1-2. In a projection from the top view of line 1-2, the horizontal

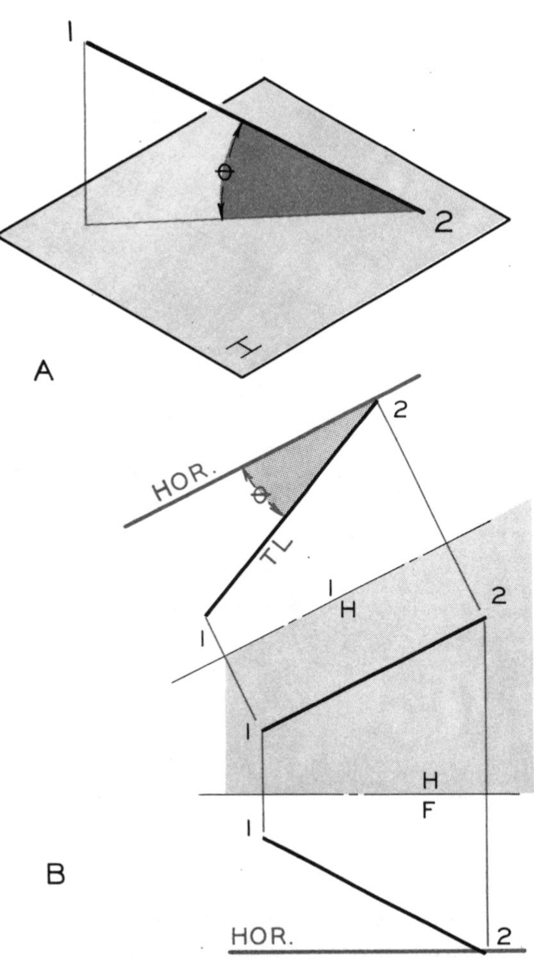

Fig. 8-19. Determining the angle made by a line with the horizontal plane.

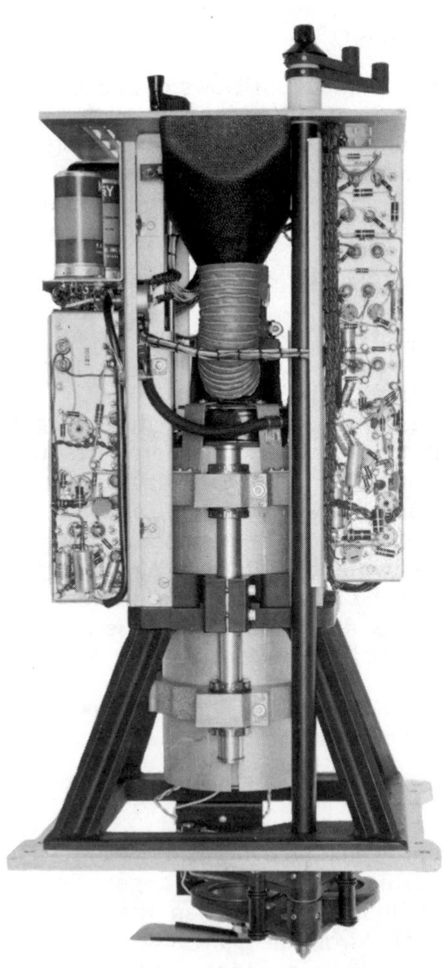

Fig. 8-20. The angle of the diagonal base supports with the horizontal base of the image orthicon camera could have been determined by an auxiliary view. (Courtesy of ITT Industrial Laboratories.)

plane will appear as an edge in the auxiliary view and the line will appear true length, as shown in part B of the figure. The true angle, θ, cannot be measured in the front view, where the horizontal plane appears as an edge, because line 1–2 is not true length in this view.

The structural mount used to attach the image orthicon camera (Fig. 8–20) to a telescope is an example of the need to determine the angle between a line and a principal plane. In this case, the line represents the diagonal base supports, while the horizontal plane is the plane of the base. This angle must be known to fabricate the design.

Angle with the Profile Plane. Figure 8–21A pictorially illustrates the angle between the profile plane and line 5–6. This angle can be determined by projecting from the profile view (part B). The profile plane appears true size in the profile view, and will therefore appear as an edge in the auxiliary view that is perpendicular to it, as in this example. The true size of the angle is found in the primary auxiliary view, where line 5–6 is true length and the profile plane appears as an edge.

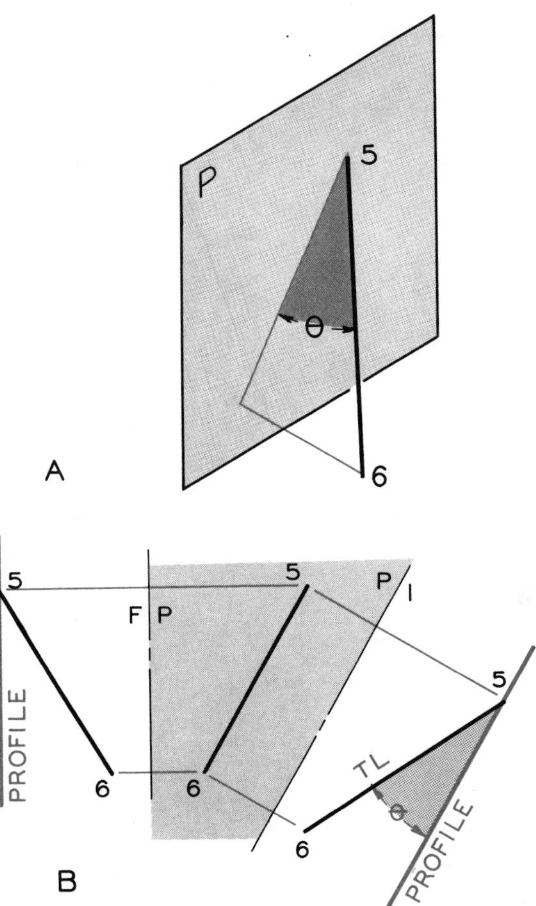

Fig. 8–21. Determining the angle made by a line with the profile plane.

8–8 SLOPE OF A LINE

Many engineering problems require that the slope of a line be determined and specified. Slope is the angle a line makes with the horizontal plane. It may be specified in angular degrees or as a percent grade.

Angular Slope. Line 1–2 in Fig. 8–22 is found true length in a primary auxiliary view projected from the top view. This gives the line true length and the horizontal plane as an edge where the slope can be measured as 30°. The true-length auxiliary must be projected from the top view to find the horizontal plane as an edge.

Percent Grade. The percent grade of a line is the ratio of its horizontal (run) to its vertical (rise) from one end to the other. Two methods of finding the percent grade of a line are shown in Fig. 8–23. These are special cases, since the lines are true length in the front view where the horizontal plane will automatically appear as an edge.

In part A, the vertical rise is divided by the horizontal run to give a percent grade of −58%. It is given a minus sign since it slopes downhill from *A* to *B*. If the direction had been specified from *B* to *A*, the percent grade would have been positive (+). Note that the percent grade is actually the *tangent* of θ, but it is converted to a percent by multiplying by 100.

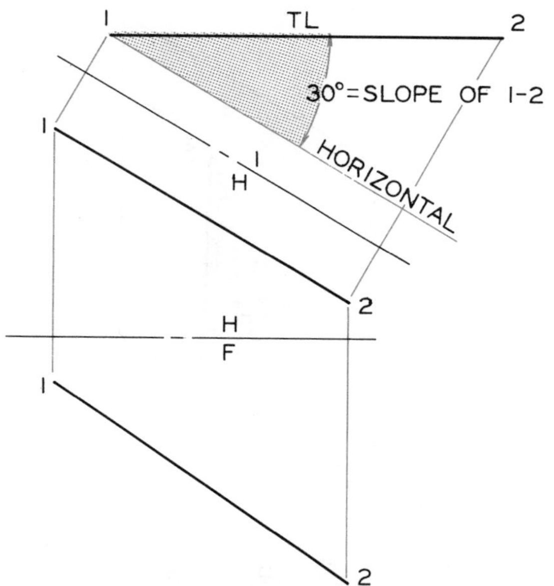

Fig. 8-22. The slope of a line can be found in a view where the line appears true length and the horizontal plane appears as an edge. The angle between them can be measured in an auxiliary view projected from the top view.

In part B, the percent grade of the line from *C* to *D* is found by using a graphical technique that eliminates the mathematics used in part A. An engineers' scale is used to measure 10 units along the horizontal and a vertical distance perpendicular to the 10 units. The vertical distance can be measured and the percent grade found by moving the decimal point one place to the right. Since the line is specified from *C* to *D*, it is given a positive grade of +58% because it slopes uphill.

Percent Grade of an Oblique Line. Oblique line 3–4 is shown pictorially in Fig. 8–24A. Since it is not true length in the front view, it must be found true length in an auxiliary view projected from the top view so that the angle between the horizontal and the true length can be found (part B). Using your engineer's scale, find the grade by laying off 10 units along the horizontal and then measure the vertical distance perpendicularly from the end of this measurement. Scale this line to find a 50% grade. From 3 to 4 the grade is positive (+); from 4 to 3, negative (−).

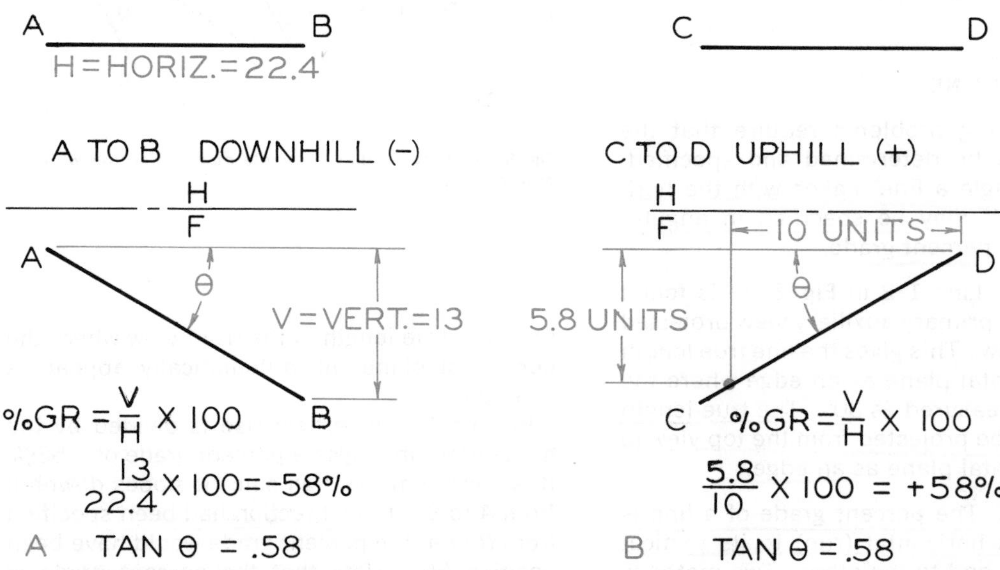

Fig. 8-23. The percent grade of a line is the vertical rise divided by the horizontal run, converted to a percent. Percent grade can be found also by converting the tangent of the slope angle to a percent.

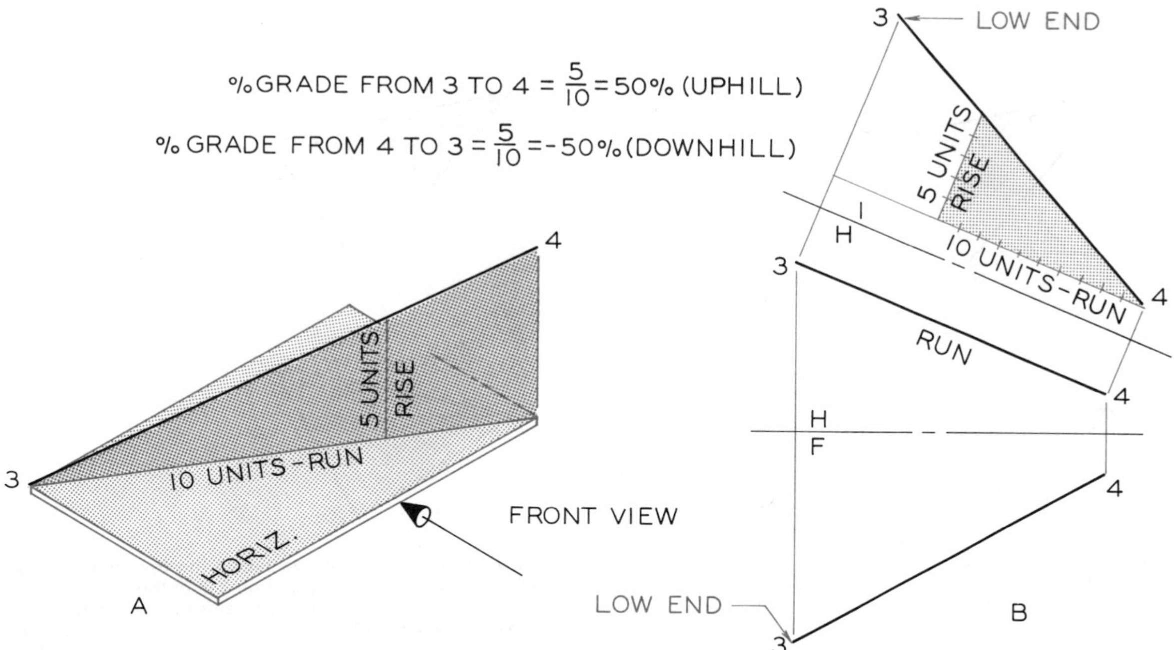

Fig. 8–24. The percent grade of an oblique line.

Fig. 8–25. The slope a pipe line is to follow at various intervals must be established during its design. (Courtesy of Trunkline Gas Transmission Company.)

All gravity-flow drainage systems must be analyzed to determine the slopes and percent grades within the system. In the pipeline in Fig. 8–25, for example, the slope was calculated from field data to determine the length and operational effectiveness of the pipeline.

8–9 EDGE VIEW OF A PLANE

The edge view of a plane can be found in any primary auxiliary view by applying previously covered principles. A plane will appear as an edge in any view where any line on the plane appears as a point.

This construction is illustrated in Fig. 8–26 by a sequence of steps. A true-length line can be constructed on any plane by drawing the line parallel to one of the principal planes and projecting it to the adjacent view, as shown in step 1, where a horizontal line is drawn. Since line 1–*O* is true length in the top view, its point view may be found as shown in Fig. 8–12. The remainder of the plane will appear as an edge

FIGURE 8-26. EDGE VIEW OF A PLANE

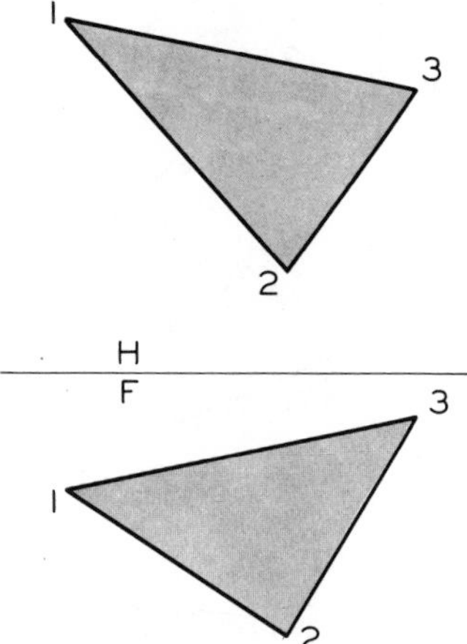

Given: The top and front views of plane 1-2-3.
Required: Find the edge view of plane 1-2-3.
References: Articles 8-4 and 8-9.

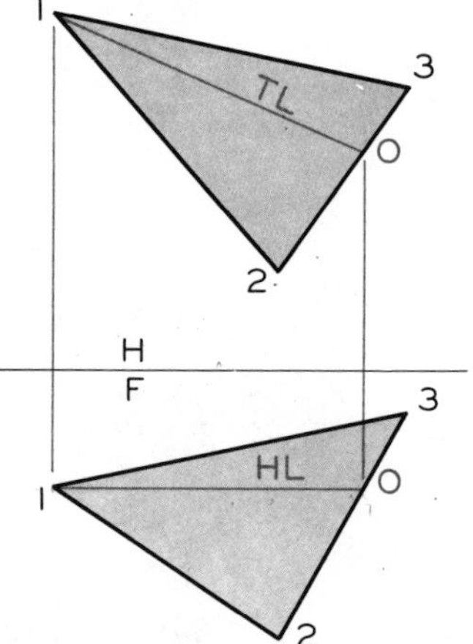

Step 1: Draw horizontal line 1-*O* in the front view of plane 1-2-3, and project point *O* to line 2-3 in the top view. Line 1-*O* is true length in the top view, since the horizontal plane appears true size in the top view and line 1-*O* is parallel to the horizontal. *Note:* Any horizontal line other than line 1-*O* could have been drawn in the front view.

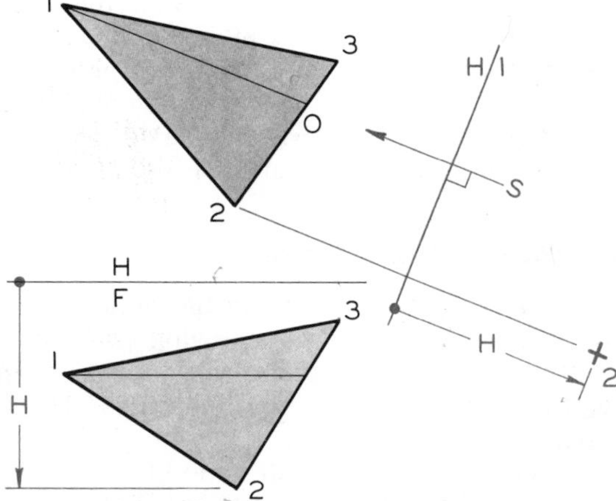

Step 2: A plane will project as an edge in the view where a line on the plane projects as a point. Line 1-*O* will appear as a point if the line of sight is established parallel to the true-length view of 1-*O*. Draw the H-1 reference line perpendicular to 1-*O*. Locate point 2 by projecting parallel to the line of sight and transferring the *H*-distance from the front to the auxiliary view.

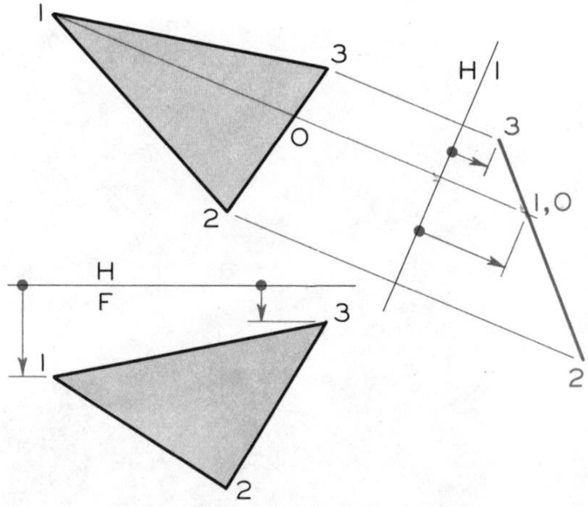

Step 3: Determine points 1 and 3 in the same manner by projecting them parallel to the true-length line 1-*O* (which is perpendicular to the H-1 reference line). Find the location of each point from the H-1 line by transferring the *H*-distance from the H-F line in the front view to the auxiliary view, as in step 2.

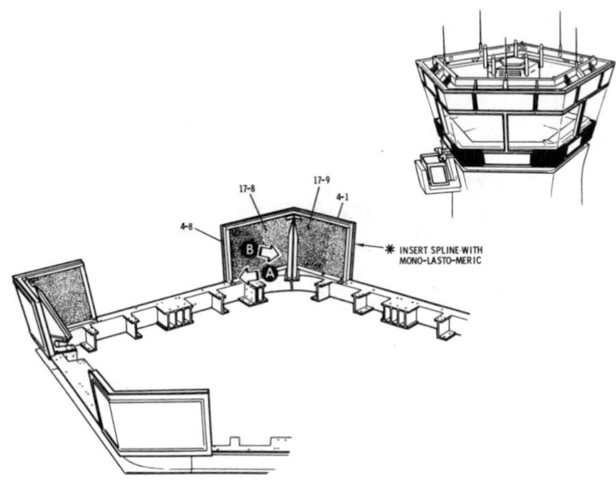

Fig. 8-27A. The angles between the corner planes of this control tower had to be determined in order to design a connecting bracket. (Courtesy of the Federal Aviation Agency.)

Fig. 8-27C. The angles between planes of the basic structure of this Comsat satellite were determined prior to the design of a system for fabricating the joints. (Courtesy of TRW Systems.)

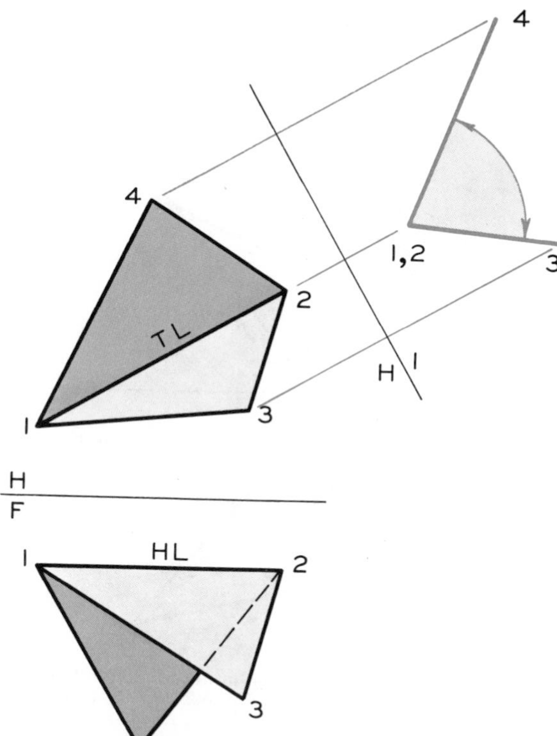

Fig. 8-27B. The determination of the angle between two planes.

in this view. This is a basic projection that affords the designer a method for solving advanced problems such as those covered in following chapters.

8-10 ANGLE BETWEEN TWO PLANES

It is often necessary for the angle between two planes, which is called a *dihedral angle,* to be found in order for a design to be refined. Perhaps a connecting bracket must be designed to assemble planes in a desired position based on the angle between them, as in Fig. 8-27A, where the angular planes of a control tower must be joined with an acceptable bracket. In another case, the planes might represent strata of ore under the ground.

The angle between two planes can be measured in the view where their line of intersection appears as a point.

The angle between planes 1-2-3 and 1-2-4 in Fig. 8-27B can be found in a primary auxiliary view, since the line of intersection, 1-2, is true length in the top view. Auxiliary line H-1 is drawn so that it is perpendicular to the direction of the top view of 1-2. A view is projected to the auxiliary plane where the point view of line 1-2

FIGURE 8-28. PIERCING POINT OF A LINE ON A PLANE—PROJECTION METHOD

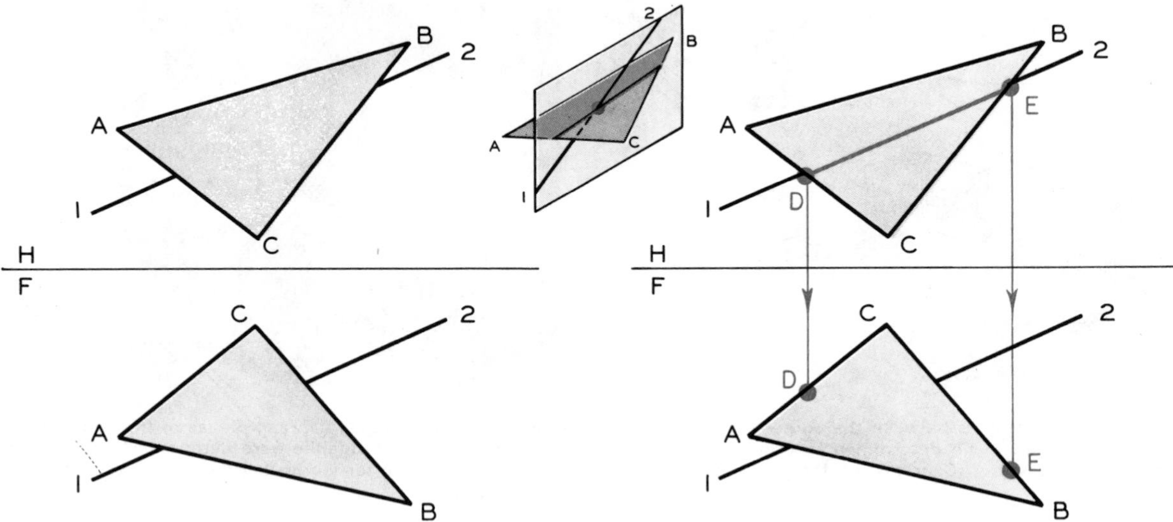

Given: The top and front views of plane *ABC* and line 1–2.
Required: Determine the piercing point of line 1–2 on the plane and the visibility of both views by the projection method.
References: Articles 7–12 and 8–11.

Step 1: Assume that a vertical cutting plane is passed through the top view of line 1–2. The plane intersects *AC* and *BC* at points *D* and *E*. Project points *D* and *E* to the front view.

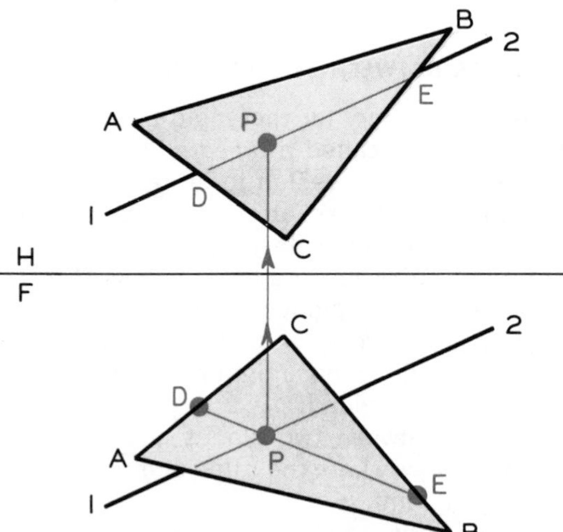

Step 2: Line *DE* represents the trace of the line of intersection between the imaginary vertical cutting plane and plane *ABC*. Any line that lies in the cutting plane and intersects plane *ABC* will intersect along line *DE*. Line 1–2 lies in the plane, therefore it intersects *ABC* at point *P* in the front view. Project point *P* to the top view.

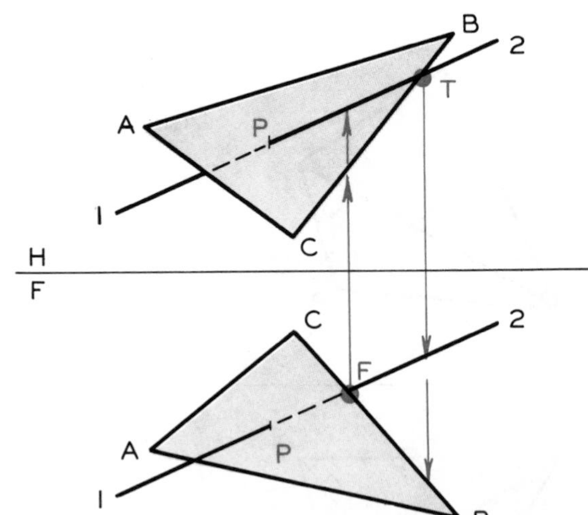

Step 3: The visibility of line 1–2 in the front view is determined by analyzing point *F* where *P*–2 and *BC* cross. By projecting this point to the top view, we see that *BC* is in front of *P*–2; therefore *BC* is visible in the front view. The top-view visibility is determined by analyzing point *T* in the same manner; we find that *P*–2 is higher than *BC* in the front view and is therefore visible in the top view.

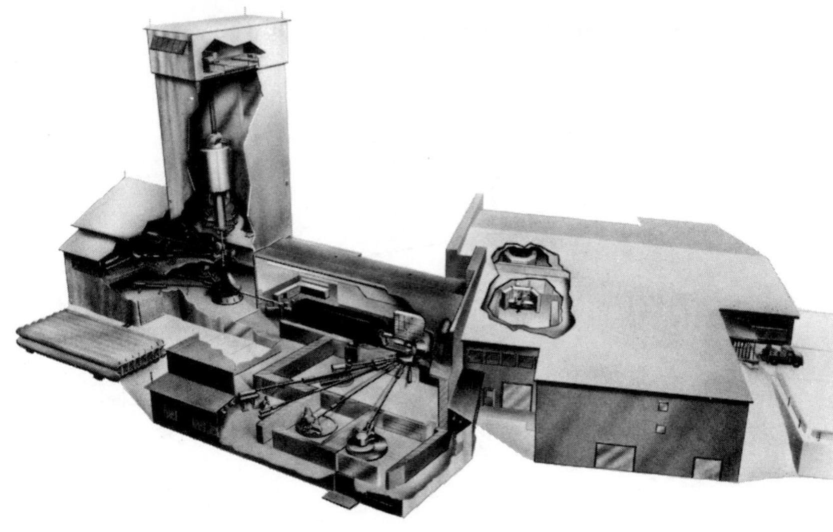

Fig. 8–29. The piercing points of the appendages of the tandem accelerator facility could have been determined by projection methods. (Courtesy Los Alamos Scientific Laboratory.)

is found. The edge views of both planes are found in this view since line 1–2 is a line common to both planes. The dihedral angle is measured in this view.

The satellite pictured in Fig. 8–27C illustrates intersecting planes for which the determination of the dihedral angles was required. These angles affect the inner structural members and the methods of connecting the planes.

8–11 PIERCING POINT OF A LINE ON A PLANE BY PROJECTION

The location of a point where a line intersects a plane is necessary to the design of many engineering projects. The line may represent a structural member that must be attached to an oblique plane, or a cable that must have clearance through a plane of an enclosure.

Figure 8–28 gives the sequential steps necessary for the determination of the piercing point of a line passing through a plane by the application of projection principles similar to those covered in Chapter 7. The visibility of the line can be found by the application of the principles covered in Article 7–12. If a line intersects a plane it will be visible on one side of the piercing point and hidden on the other side.

The appendages of the tandem accelerator facility are shown piercing the protective walls in Fig. 8–29. These piercing points can be found graphically by the procedure given in Fig. 8–28.

8–12 PIERCING POINT OF A LINE WITH A PLANE BY AUXILIARY VIEW

An alternative method for finding the piercing point of a line intersecting a plane is the auxiliary view method illustrated in Fig. 8–30. The edge view of the plane is found by projecting from either view into the primary auxiliary view. The piercing point is found to be the point where the line and edge view of the plane intersect. Piercing point P is found in the principal views by projecting from the auxiliary view back to line AB in the top view and then to the front view. The front view of point P will also lie on line AB. However, in many cases it is helpful to check the location for greater accuracy by transferring the distance, H, from the auxiliary view to the front view. This is especially necessary when the front view of the piercing line approaches being a vertical line. Visibility is easily determined in the view from which the primary auxiliary was projected. The portion of the line on the upper side of the plane in the primary

FIGURE 8–30. PIERCING POINT OF A LINE THROUGH A PLANE—AUXILIARY METHOD

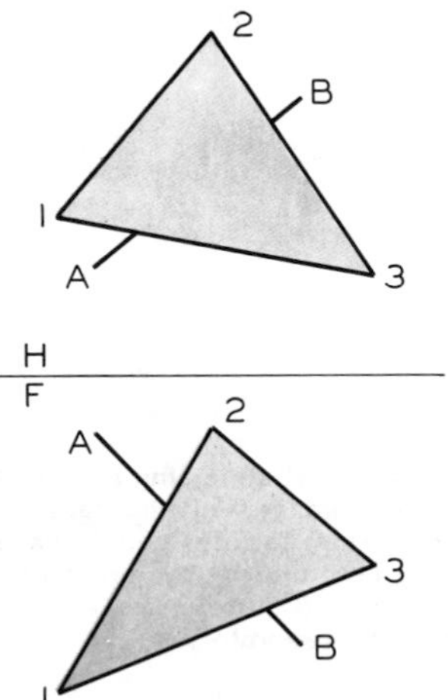

Given: The top and front views of plane 1–2–3 and line *AB*. **Required:** Find the piercing point of line *AB* on plane 1–2–3 and the visibility in both views by the auxiliary-view method. **Reference:** Article 8–12.

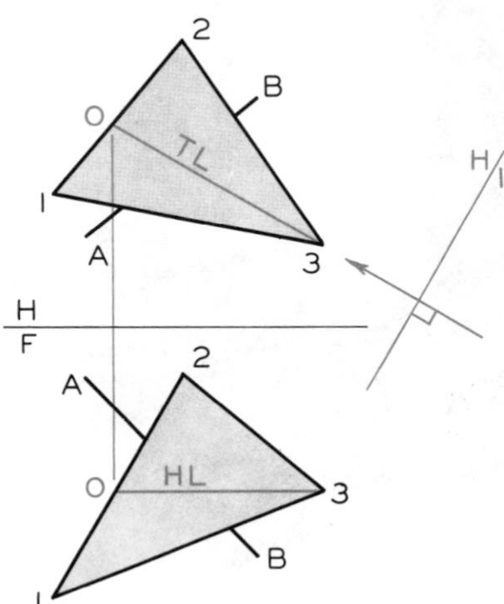

Step 1: Draw horizontal line, *O*–3 in the front view and project it to the top view. Line *O*–3 projects true length in the top view. Establish the line of sight for the primary auxiliary view parallel to *O*–3 in the top view. Reference line H–1 is drawn perpendicular to the line of sight and *O*–3.

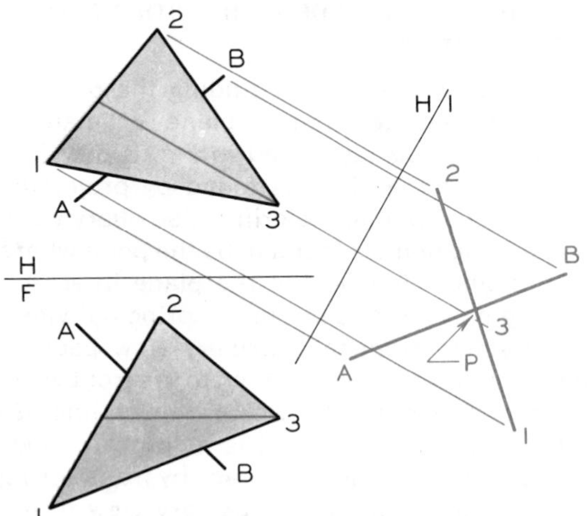

Step 2: Find the edge view of plane 1–2–3 by finding the point view of line *O*–3. Project line *AB* also. Point *P* in the auxiliary view is the piercing point of line *AB* on plane 1–2–3.

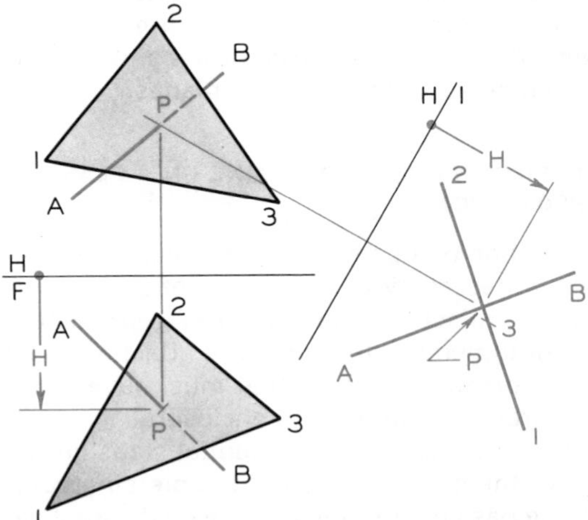

Step 3: Point *P* is projected to the top and front views in sequence. The front view of *P* can be checked by transferring distance *H* from the auxiliary view to the front view. Point *A* is closer to the H–1 line in the auxiliary view, therefore, line *AP* is higher than the plane and visible in the top view. Visibility in the front view is found by the method used in Fig. 8–28.

auxiliary is visible in the principal view—line *AP* in this case.

The piercing point between the steering column and the inclined firewall of the truck shown in Fig. 8–31 can be found by applying this principle of descriptive geometry. The accurate location of this point is necessary to the function of the steering linkage.

8–13 A LINE PERPENDICULAR TO A PLANE

Economy of design dictates that materials be reduced to a minimum. If a structural member were to be attached to an oblique plane, it would be more economical if the member were designed to be perpendicular to the plane, thus giving the shortest distance and requiring the minimum of materials.

Figure 8–32 is an example requiring that the shortest distance from a point to a plane be found. The edge view of the plane is found by an auxiliary view. The shortest distance (perpendicular distance) will be shown true length in this view when drawn from point *O* perpendicular to the edge view of the plane. The piercing point is projected to the top view to intersect with a line drawn from point *O* parallel to the H–1 reference line. Line *O–P* must be parallel to the H–1 line in the top view, since it is true length in the auxiliary view. Line *O–P* is also perpendicular to the true-length lines in the top view, since perpendicular lines will project as perpendicular when one or both of two perpendiculars are true length, as covered in Article 7–20. Line *O–P* is perpendicular to all lines in the plane; consequently, it is perpendicular to the true-length lines in the top view. The front view of the piercing point and its visibility is found in the manner outlined in Article 8–12.

A problem involving this principle is shown in Fig. 8–33. The solar panels are attached to the satellite in such a manner that they can rotate to take full advantage of the available solar energy. The orientation of the solar panels with respect to the perpendicular rays of the sun is an application of the principles covered in Fig. 8–32.

Fig. 8–31. The piercing point between the steering column and the firewall could be designed using descriptive geometry principles. (Courtesy of LeTourneau-Westinghouse Company.)

8–14 INTERSECTION BETWEEN PLANES BY PROJECTION

The line of intersection between two intersecting planes can be found by applying the principles covered in Article 8–11. The line of intersection is found by locating by projection on one plane the piercing points of two lines in the other plane. This procedure is shown by steps in Fig. 8–34. It can be determined by observation that lines 1–2, 2–3, and *AB* do not pierce either of the planes, since they fall outside of the planes in the given views. Therefore, lines *AB* and *BC* are selected to be lines which have a probability of intersecting plane 1–2–3. Line *AC* is analyzed as though it were a single line rather than a line on a plane. A vertical cutting plane is passed through the line in the top view, as in Fig. 8–28. The piercing point *P* is found and projected to both views, and line *BC* is analyzed in the same manner for piercing point *T*. *Note:* It is necessary to work with one plane, instead of finding the piercing point of one line of a plane and then skipping to a line on the other plane. The solution should be approached in a systematic fashion.

If the piercing points of two lines on a plane are found, then all lines in the plane that pierce

FIGURE 8-32. LINE PERPENDICULAR TO A PLANE

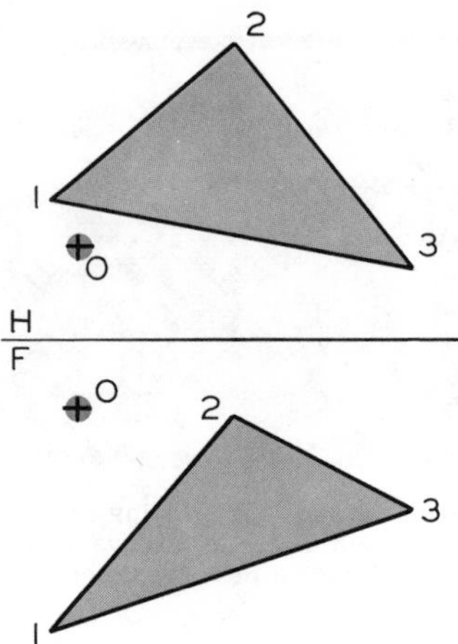

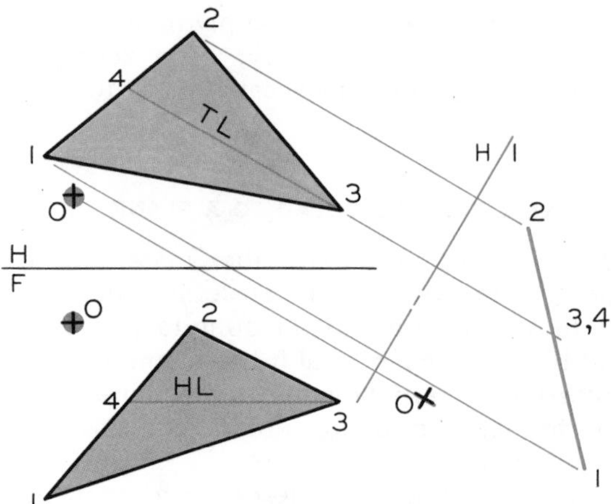

Given: Plane 1–2–3 and point *O* in two views.
Required: Find the shortest distance from point *O* to the plane 1–2–3 and show it in all views.
References: Articles 7–20 and 8–13.

Step 1: Draw horizontal line 3–4 in the front view of the plane 1–2–3. This line will be projected true length in the top view. Plane 1–2–3 will be projected as an edge in the auxiliary view where 3–4 appears as a point. Project point *O* to this view also.

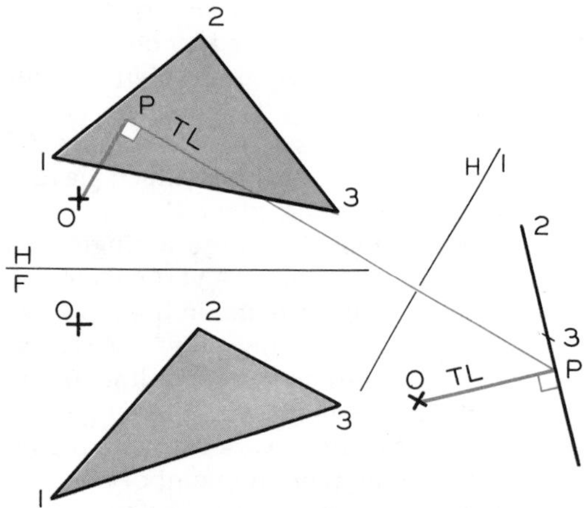

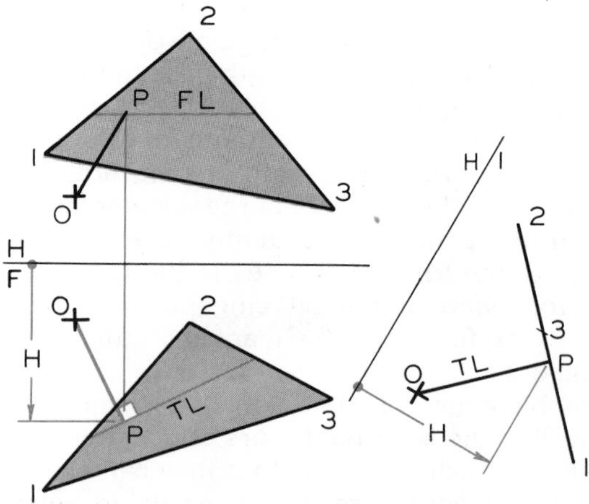

Step 2: Line *O–P* is drawn perpendicular to the edge view of plane 1–2–3, since the shortest distance is perpendicular to the plane. Because line *O–P* is true length in the auxiliary view, the top view of the line must be parallel to the H–1 reference line. It is also perpendicular to the direction of a true-length line in the top view.

Step 3: The front view of line *O–P* is found by projecting point *P* to the front and locating it *H* distance from the H–F reference line by transferring the *H* distance from the auxiliary view. Line *O–P* is visible in all views. Line *O–P* is also perpendicular to a true-length frontal line in the front view.

the other plane must intersect along a line connecting the two piercing points. Points P and T are connected to form the line of intersection. The visibility is determined by analyzing the points where the lines of each cross. Visibility analysis is covered in Article 7-12.

Fig. 8-33. The solar panels of this satellite are designed to remain perpendicular to the sun's rays to take full advantage of its solar energy. (Courtesy of Ryan Aeronautics, Incorporated.)

8-15 INTERSECTION BETWEEN PLANES—AUXILIARY VIEW METHOD

An alternative method of finding the line of intersection between two intersecting planes is the auxiliary view method, illustrated in Fig. 8-35. An edge view of either of the planes is found in step 1 by a primary auxiliary view, with the other plane appearing foreshortened. Piercing points L and M are projected from the auxiliary view to their respective lines, 5-6 and 4-6, in the top view of step 2. The visibility of plane 4-5-6 in the top view is apparent in step 3 by inspection of the auxiliary view, where sight line S_1 has an unobstructed view of the 4-5-L-M portion of the plane. Plane 4-5-L-M is visible in the front view, since sight line S_2 has an unobstructed view of the top view of this portion of the plane.

8-16 COMPASS BEARINGS OF A LINE

In civil engineering and geological applications, lines are often drawn from verbal information and field notes. Lines may also represent paths of motion in navigation, where verbal instructions are given by voice from a remote source. A commonly accepted method of locating a line verbally is by using the points of a compass.

Figure 8-36 gives the compass bearings of four lines. Note that the bearings begin with the north or south direction in all cases. The bearing of a line 30° to the west of north is given as North 30° West or N 30° W. A line making 60° with the south point of a compass is given as South 60° East or S 60° E. Since a compass can be read only when held horizontally, the bearings of a line can be determined in the horizontal (top) view only. A bearing is a horizontal direction.

Figure 8-37 is an example of an azimuth, which is measured from the north point of a compass in a clockwise direction. Azimuth readings are used to avoid the confusion that might be caused by reference to the four points of a compass. An azimuth of 120° is the direction making 120° with north. This is the same bearing as S 60° E shown in Fig. 8-36. The azimuth of 210° is equivalent to S 30° W. A topography crew (Fig. 8-38) must take many bearings to survey an area.

Although bearings and azimuths are horizontal directions, these terms are often used to specify the construction of a drainage system or the design of a piping system whose pipes are inclined with the horizontal plane. In these cases, the bearings usually refer to the direction of the line with respect to the lower end, if not specified. Figure 8-39 illustrates that lines 0-2, 0-1, and 0-3 each have a bearing of N 45° E, since the lines lie in a common vertical plane with point 0 being the low end of the line.

FIGURE 8-34. INTERSECTION OF PLANES BY PROJECTION

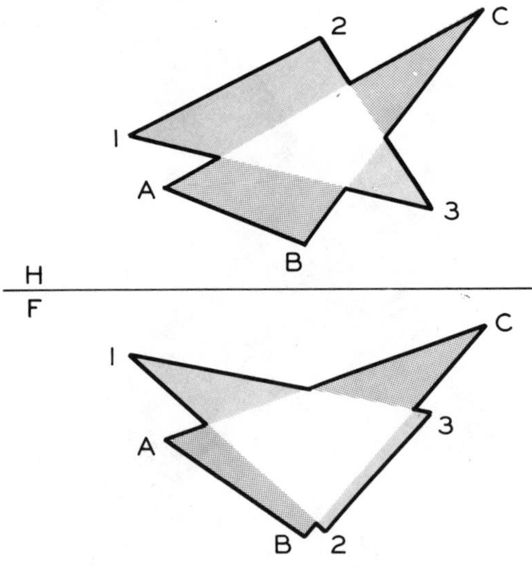

Given: The top and front views of planes 1-2-3 and *ABC*.
Required: Find the line of intersection between the planes and determine visibility in both views by projection.
References: Articles 8-11 and 8-14.

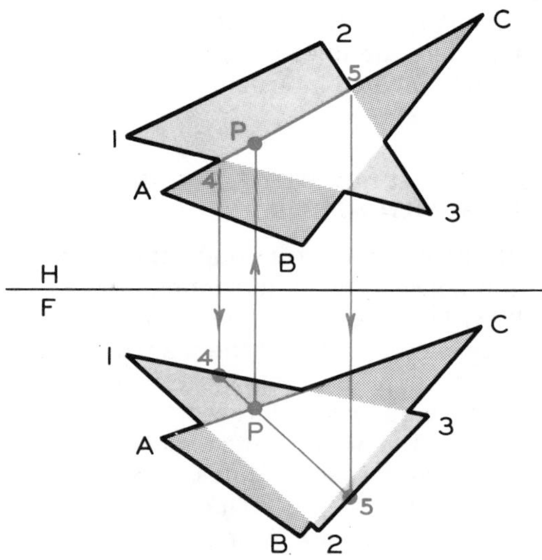

Step 1: Pass a vertical cutting plane through line *AC* in the top view to establish points 4 and 5. Project points 4 and 5 to lines 1-3 and 2-3 in the front view. Line *AC* pierces plane 1-2-3 where it crosses 4-5. Project point *P* to *AC* in the top view.

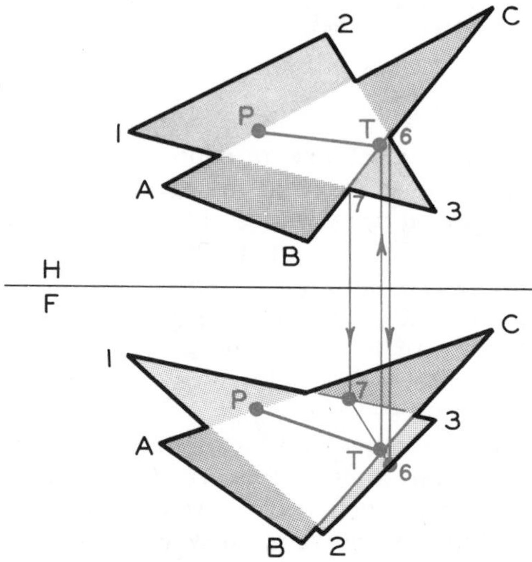

Step 2: Pass a vertical cutting plane through line *BC* in the top view to establish points 6 and 7. Project line 6-7 to the front view. Point *T* is the piercing point of line *BC* in plane 1-2-3. Line *PT* is the line of intersection between the planes. The piercing points of *AC* and *BC* are found as though they were independent lines rather than lines of a plane.

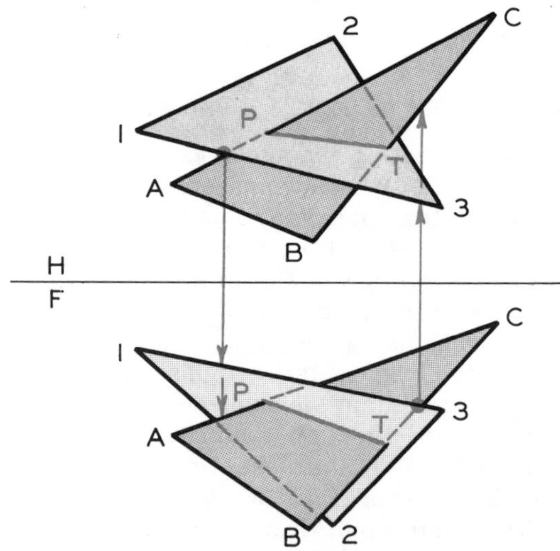

Step 3: Analyze the intersection of *AP* and 1-3 in the top view for visibility by projecting to the front view, where 1-3 is found to be higher and, consequently, visible in the top view. Line *PC* is also visible in the top view; therefore, *PCT* is visible. Frontal visibility is found by the analysis of the intersection of *CT* and 1-3, where 1-3 is in front and visible.

FIGURE 8–35. INTERSECTION OF TWO PLANES BY AUXILIARY VIEW

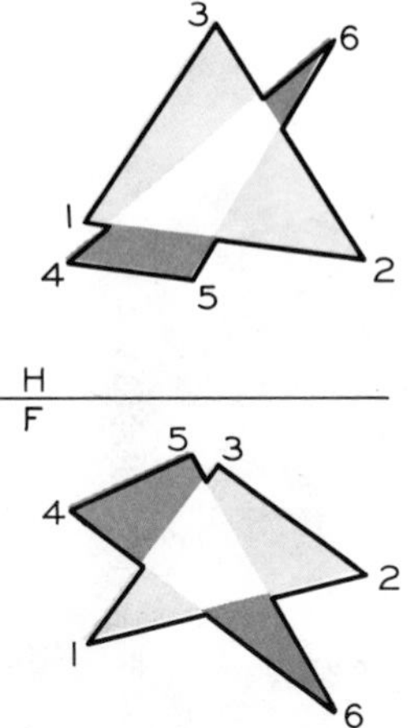

Given: The top and front views of planes 1–2–3 and 4–5–6.
Required: Find the line of intersection between the planes and determine the visibility in both views by the auxiliary view method.
References: Articles 7–12, 8–12, and 8–15.

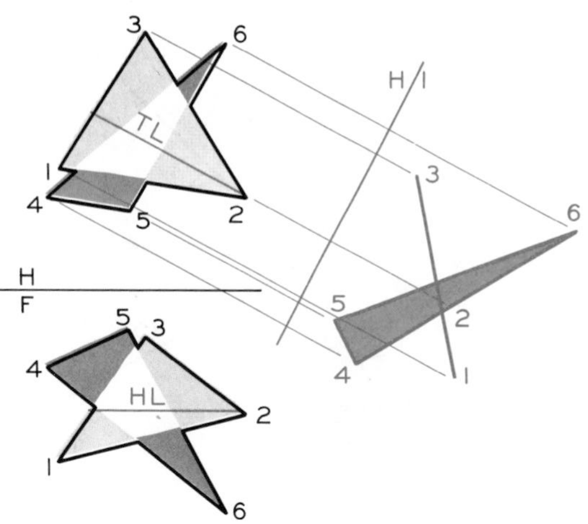

Step 1: Draw a horizontal line in plane 1–2–3 and project it to the top view where the line is true length. Find the edge view of plane 1–2–3 by finding the point view of the true-length line. Project plane 4–5–6 to the auxiliary view also.

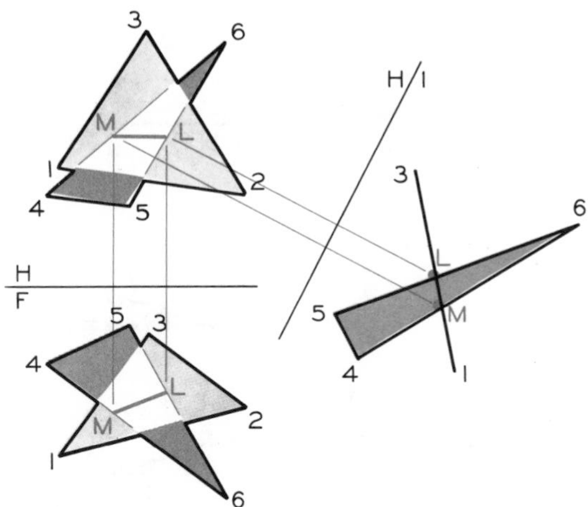

Step 2: Points L and M in the auxiliary view are the points of intersection of lines 5–6 and 4–6. These points are projected to the top and front views to give the line of intersection, LM.

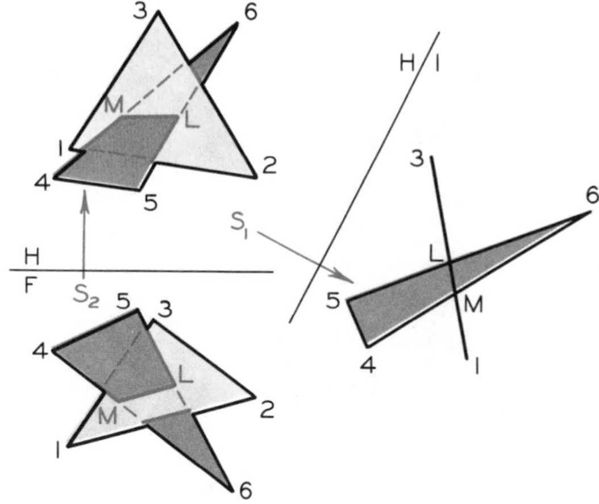

Step 3: Visibility in the top view is found by viewing the auxiliary view in the direction of S_1, where plane 4–5–L–M is seen to be above plane 1–2–3 and is visible in the top view. Frontal visibility is found by viewing the top view in the direction of S_2, where 4–5 is in front of 1–3 and is therefore visible in the front view.

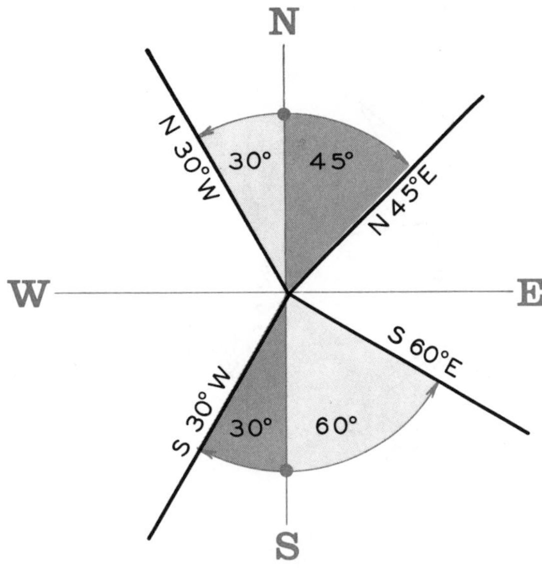

Fig. 8-36. Compass bearings of four lines.

Fig. 8-38 A topography crew must use many bearings to record an irrigation area. (Courtesy of the Bureau of Reclamation.)

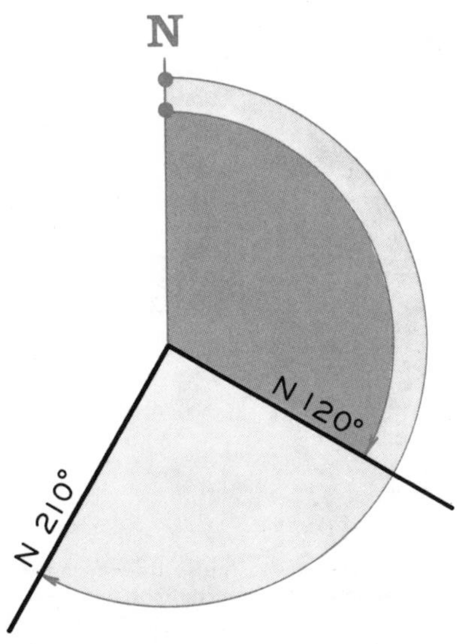

Fig. 8-37. Azimuth bearings of lines.

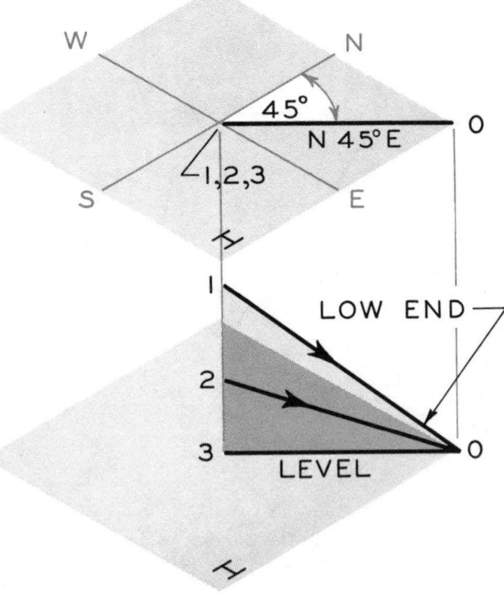

Fig. 8-39. The compass bearing of a line is in the direction of its low end.

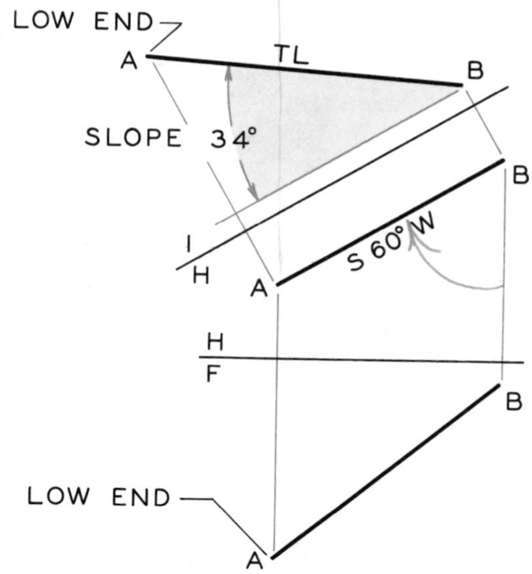

Fig. 8–40. Determining the slope and bearing of line by an auxiliary view.

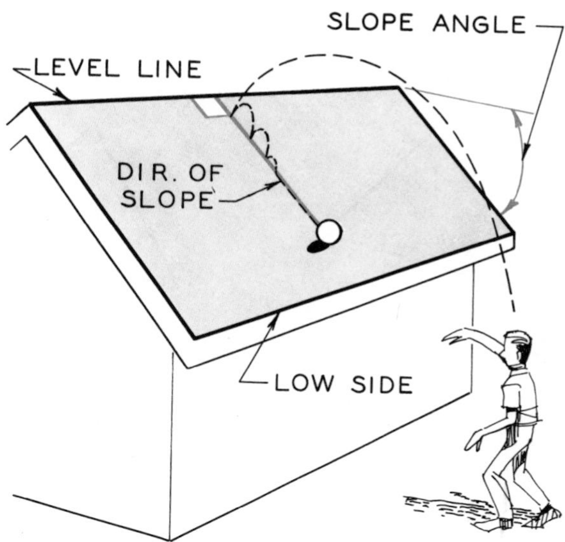

Fig. 8–41. The slope and direction of a slope of a plane.

Line 0–3 is a horizontal line that appears true length in the top view. Lines 0–1 and 0–2 are not completely described by bearing only, because they are not horizontal lines. These lines can be described verbally by including their slopes. The slope of a line bearing S 60° W in Fig. 8–40 is found by projecting an auxiliary view from the top view in order that the horizontal plane may be seen as an edge. Slope (the angle a line makes with the horizontal) is in this case found to be 34°. Had the low end been point *B*, the bearing of line *AB* would have been N 60° E instead.

To accurately establish a line in space, it is sufficient to locate a single point in the top and front views and list the bearing and slope specifications of the line through the point. This method is often used in written specifications of construction contracts.

8–17 SLOPE OF A PLANE

Planes can be established in space by verbal specification of the *slope* and the *direction of slope* of the plane, as defined below.

Slope. The slope of a plane is the angle it makes with the horizontal plane.

Direction of slope. The direction of slope is the compass bearing of a line which is perpendicular to a true-length line in the top view of a plane taken toward its low side. This is the direction in which a ball would roll on the plane.

These terms are illustrated pictorially in Fig. 8–41. Note that the true angle of the slope is seen when it is viewed parallel to the ridge of the roof (the line of intersection). Since the ridge line is horizontal, a ball will roll perpendicular to it thereby establishing the direction of slope, which is given as a compass bearing.

Figure 8–42 gives the steps involved in determining the slope and direction of slope of the oblique plane 1–2–3.

Step 1. A horizontal line is drawn in the front view of plane 1–2–3 and projected to the top view where it is a true-length level line. The direction of slope is the compass bearing of a line perpendicular to the level line in the top view. The arrow head is placed on the low side toward line 1–3 to indicate the downward direction of slope.

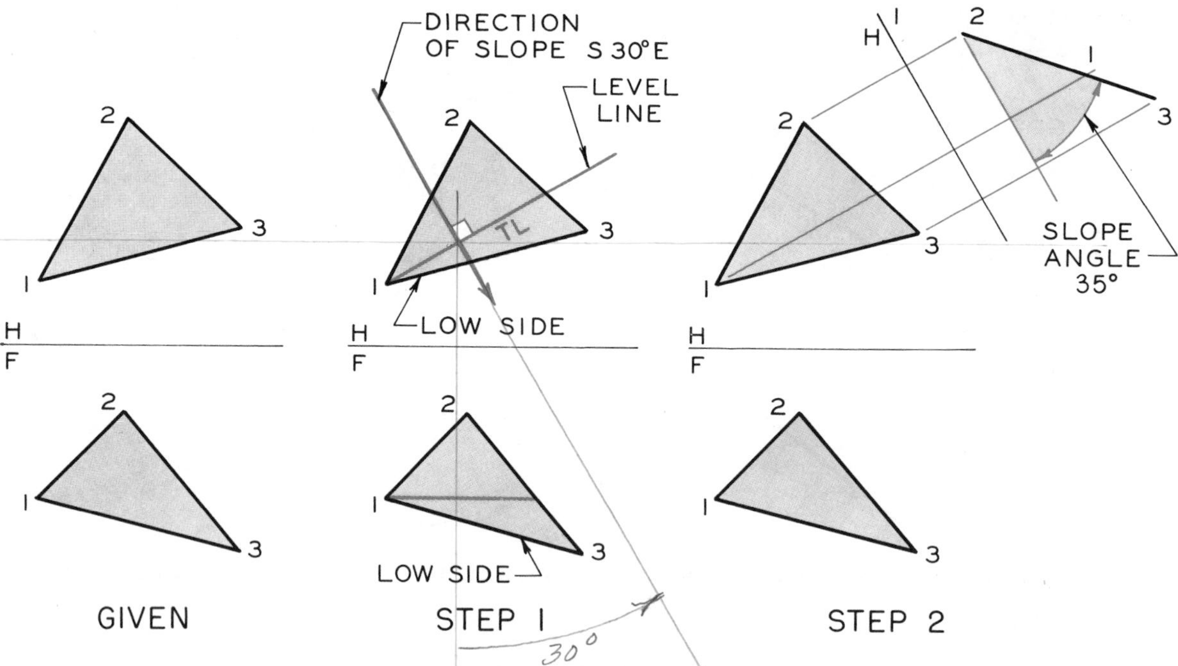

Fig. 8–42. The determination of slope and direction of slope of a plane.

Fig. 8–43. The slopes of inclined surfaces of a dam are constructed from written specifications. (Courtesy of Kaiser Engineers.)

Step 2. The slope angle is found by measuring the angle between the edge view of the plane and the horizontal reference plane in the primary auxiliary view. Following verbal specifications, we can locate plane 1–2–3 in space as a plane passing through point 1 with a slope of 35° and a slope direction of S 30° E. This information is not sufficient to determine the limits of the plane, but merely establishes an infinite plane of which plane 1–2–3 is a part. The slope of the dam in Fig. 8–43 is an example of a plane that can be established verbally in written specifications by the engineer.

8–18 STRIKE AND DIP OF A PLANE

Strike and *dip* are terms used in geological engineering and mining to refer to strata of ore under the surface of the earth. It is important in these applications to locate the orientation of the strata by verbal terms that are somewhat similar to *slope* and *direction of slope.*

FIGURE 8–44. STRIKE AND DIP OF A PLANE

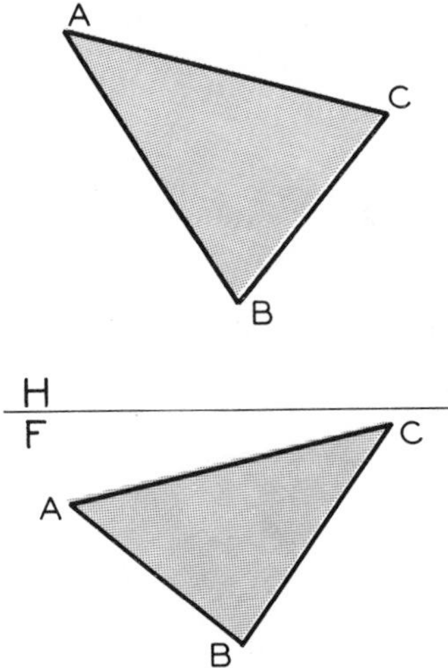

Given: The top and front views of plane *ABC*.
Required: The strike and dip of plane *ABC*.
Reference: Article 8–18.

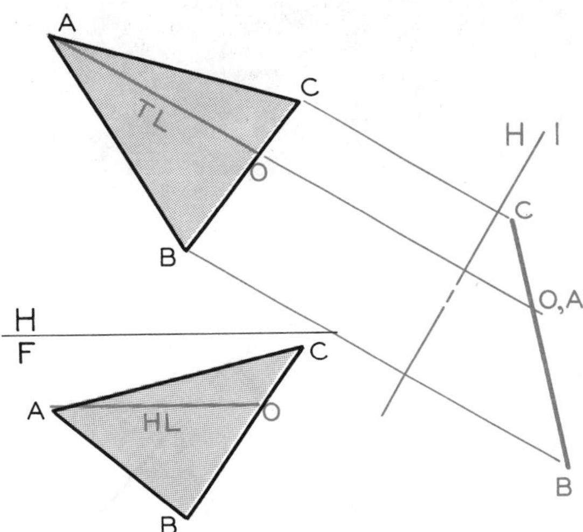

Step 1: Draw a horizontal line, *AO*, in the front view of plane *ABC*. This line will project true length in the top view. Project plane *ABC* as an edge in the auxiliary view where *AO* appears as a point. Project only from the top view in order to find the edge view of the horizontal plane.

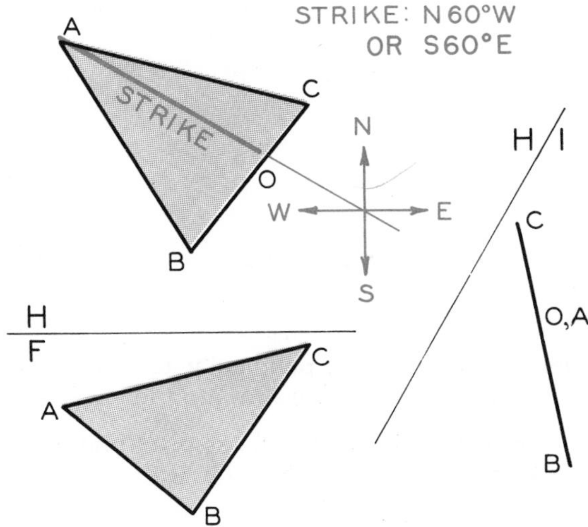

Step 2: The strike of a plane is the compass direction of a horizontal line in the plane. Line *AO* is the strike of *ABC* since it is a horizontal line. Its compass direction is measured in the top view as either N 60° W or S 60° E. The line has no slope, therefore either compass direction is correct.

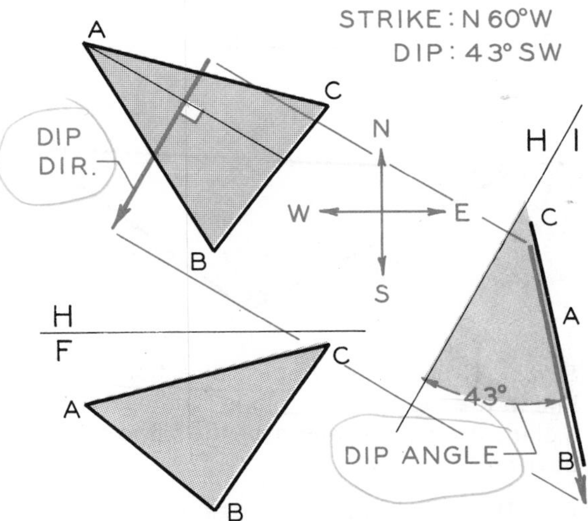

Step 3: The dip of a plane is its angle with the horizontal plane plus its general compass direction. This angle can be measured in the auxiliary view. The dip direction is perpendicular to the strike line in the top view. The dip of *ABC* is 43° SW. The strike and dip establishes the plane.

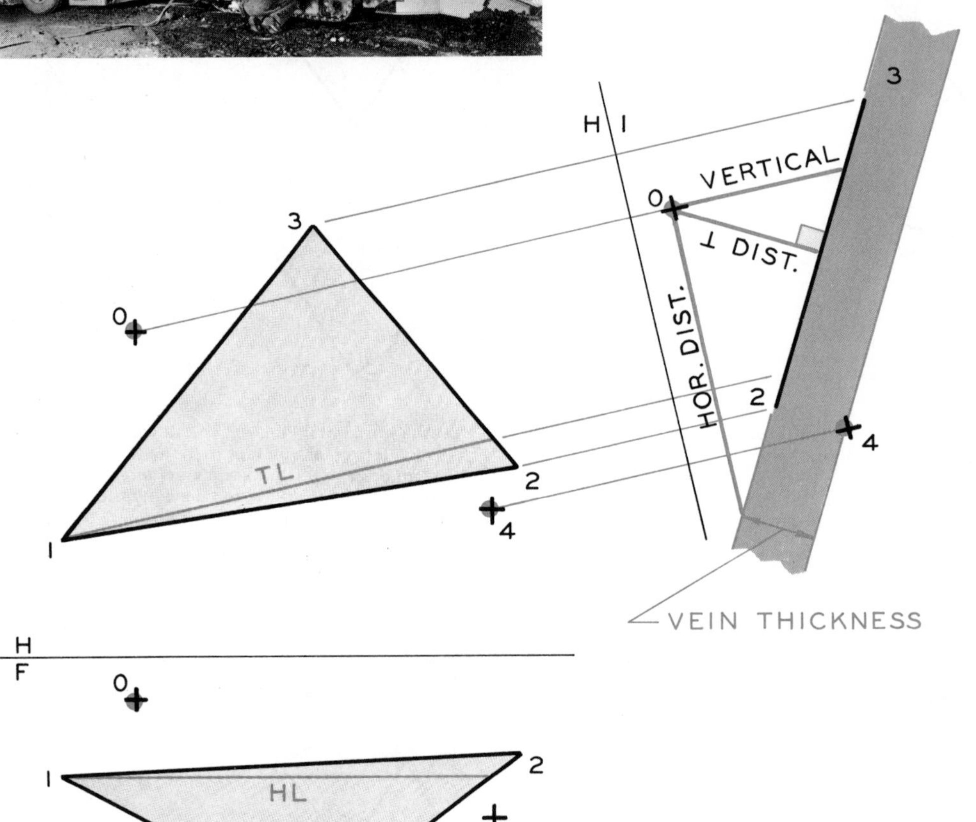

Fig. 8-45. Descriptive geometry principles have many applications to mining problems. (Courtesy of Joy Manufacturing Corporation.)

Fig. 8-46. Distances from a point to a vein of ore.

Strike. Strike is the compass direction of a level line in the top view of a plane. All level lines in a plane are parallel and have the same compass bearing.

Dip. Dip is the angle the edge view of a plane makes with the horizontal plane plus its general compass direction, such as NW or SW. The dip angle is found in the primary auxiliary view that is projected from the top view, and its general direction is measured in the top view. Dip direction is measured perpendicular to a level line in a plane in the top view toward the low inside.

Figure 8-44 illustrates the steps of finding the strike and dip of a given plane *ABC*.

8-19 DISTANCES FROM A POINT TO AN ORE VEIN

In the mining operation shown in Fig. 8-45 coal is being removed from its vein. Descriptive geometry principles can be used to find the most economical distances from a point on the surface of the earth to a productive vein of ore.

Three points are located on the top plane of a stratum of ore which lies under the surface of the earth (Fig. 8–46). Point *O* is a point on the surface from which tunnels will be drilled to the vein of ore for mining purposes. Point 4 is a point on the lower plane of the stratum of the vein. We are required to determine the lengths of the following tunnels: (1) the shortest distance to the ore, (2) the vertical distance to the ore, and (3) the shortest horizontal distance to the ore. The edge view of the ore vein is found by projecting from the top view. The lower plane is drawn parallel to the upper plane through point 4. The vertical distance is perpendicular to horizontal plane H–1, and the horizontal tunnel is parallel to the H–1 plane. The shortest tunnel is perpendicular to the plane. The vein thickness can be approximated by measurement in the auxiliary view. The strike and dip of the plane can be found by referring to the principles covered in Article 8–18.

Fig. 8–47. The position of a stratum of oil-bearing sand with respect to the ocean floor would influence the location of offshore exploration. (Courtesy of Humble Oil and Refining Company.)

8–20 INTERSECTION BETWEEN TWO PLANES—CUTTING PLANE METHOD

The intersection between strata or planes is important to the exploration for minerals, which are usually contained in strata that approximate planes. For example, if a stratum of oil-bearing sand were located beneath the surface, it would be significant to approximate the general location of the intersection of the stratum with the ocean floor if it were continuous to a point of intersection. This information would influence the location of offshore explorations such as that shown in Fig. 8–47.

Planes 1–2–3 and 4–5–6 are segments of infinite planes in Fig. 8–48. We are required to find the line of intersection between them. Cutting planes are passed through either view at any angle and projected to the adjacent view. The two points where the lines formed by the cutting plane intersect in the top view establish the direction of the line of intersection. The compass direction of this line can be used to describe its orientation in space. The front view of the line of intersection is found by projecting the points from the top view to their respective planes in the front view.

8–21 INTERSECTION BETWEEN MINERAL VEINS—AUXILIARY METHOD

The locations of two mineral veins are given in a combination of verbal information and graphical representation in Fig. 8–49. We are required to locate the line of intersection, assuming that the two planes are continuous to a line of intersection.

The strike and dip of planes *C* and *D* are given in each view. Since the strike lines are true-length level lines in the top view, the edge view of the planes can be found in the view where the strike appears as a point. The plane can be drawn by the application of the dip angles given in specifications. Horizontal datum planes, H–F and H′–F′, are used to find lines on each plane that will intersect when projected from the auxiliary views to the top views. Points *A* and *B* are connected to determine the line of

FIGURE 8-48. INTERSECTION OF TWO INFINITE PLANES BY THE CUTTING-PLANE METHOD

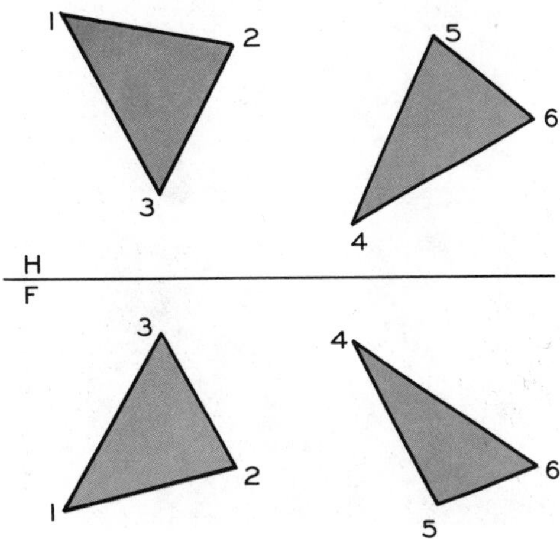

Given: The top and front views of two planes, 1–2–3 and 4–5–6.
Required: Find the line of intersection between these planes by projection given that they are infinite in size.
Reference: Article 8–20.

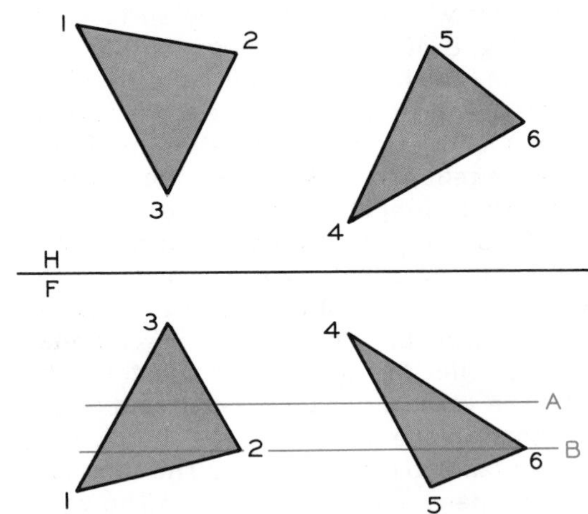

Step 1: Construct two cutting planes, *A* and *B*, in the front view. They are drawn parallel and horizontal in this case for convenience only. They could have been constructed in any direction and nonparallel.

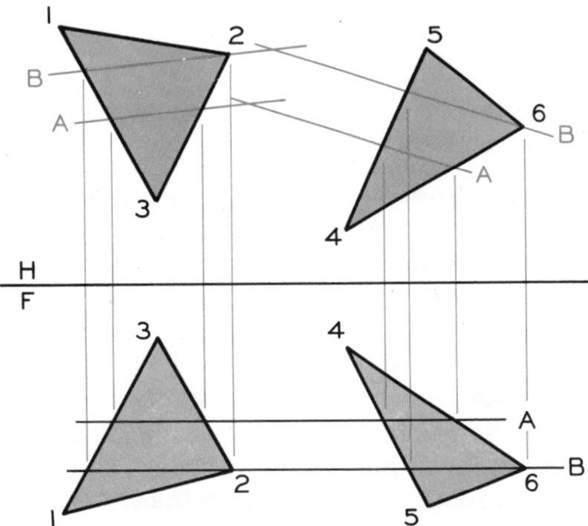

Step 2: The lines of intersection between the cutting planes and the given planes are projected to the top view. These lines are extended to cross their respective projections. Care should be taken to assure that the lines determined by the *B* cutting plane intersect and that those determined by the *A* cutting plane intersect.

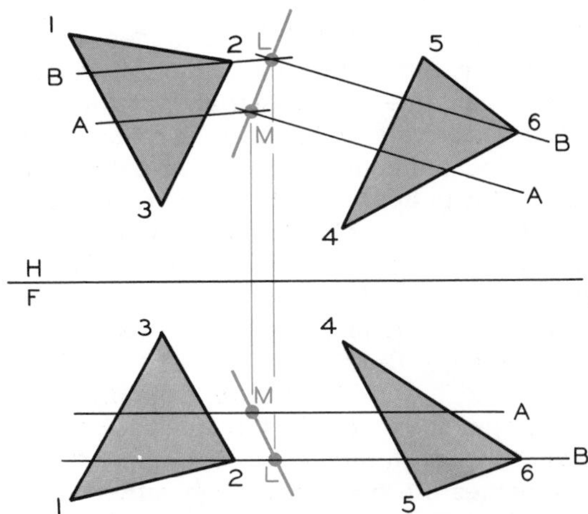

Step 3: Points *L* and *M* in the top view are the points where lines in a common horizontal plane intersect to form a line of intersection. Point *L* is projected to the front view of plane *B* and point *M* to front view of plane *A*. The line of intersection is *LM*.

FIGURE 8–49. INTERSECTION BETWEEN ORE VEINS BY AUXILIARY VIEW

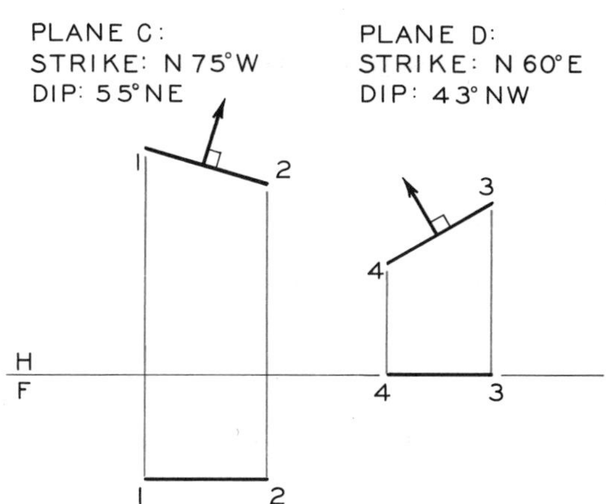

Given: The strike and dip of two ore veins, plane *C* and plane *D*.
Required: Find the line of intersection between the ore veins, assuming that each is continuous.
Reference: Article 8–21.

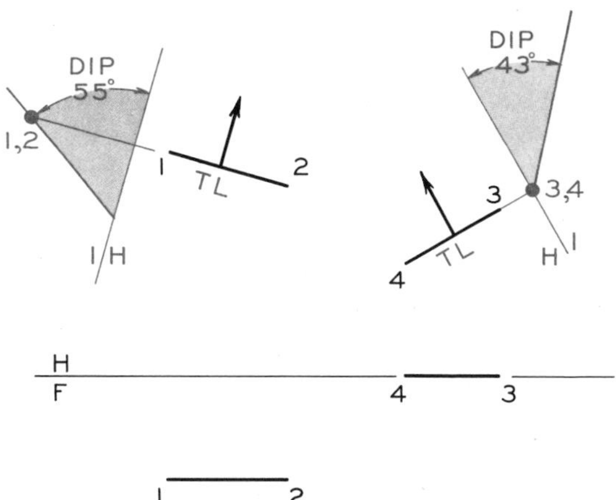

Step 1: Lines 1–2 and 3–4 are strike lines and are true length in the horizontal view. The point view of each strike line is found by an auxiliary view, using a common reference plane. The edge view of the ore veins can be found by constructing the dip angles with the H–1 line through the point views. The low side is the side of the dip arrow.

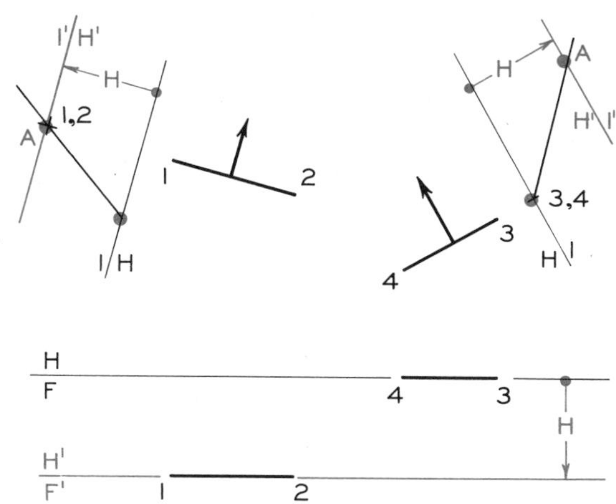

Step 2: A supplementary horizontal plane, H′–F′, is constructed at a convenient location in the front view. This plane is shown in both auxiliary views located *H* distance from the H–1 reference line. The H′–1′ plane cuts through each ore vein edge in the auxiliary views.

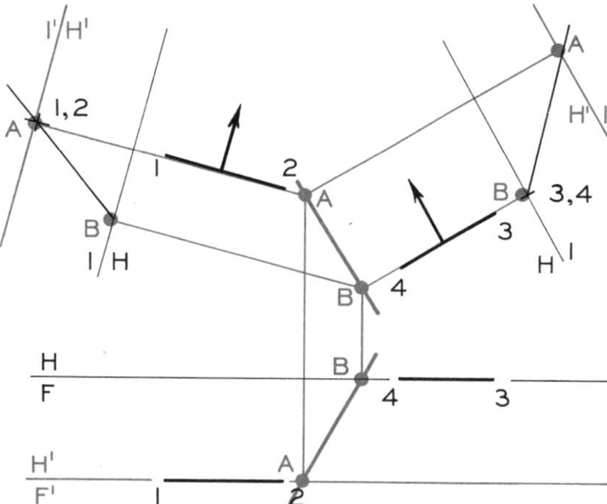

Step 3: Points *A*, which were established on each auxiliary view by the H′–1′ plane, are projected to the top view, and they intersect at point *A*. Points *B* on *H*–1 plane are projected to their intersection in the top view at point *B*. Points *A* and *B* are projected to their respective planes in the front view. Line *AB* is the line of intersection between the two planes.

8-50

Fig. 8-50. Core samples are helpful in determining information about the orientation of a mineral vein under the ground. (Courtesy of Humble Oil and Refining Company.)

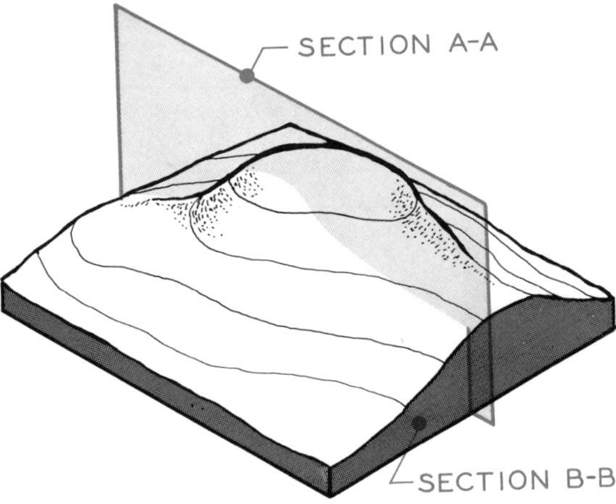

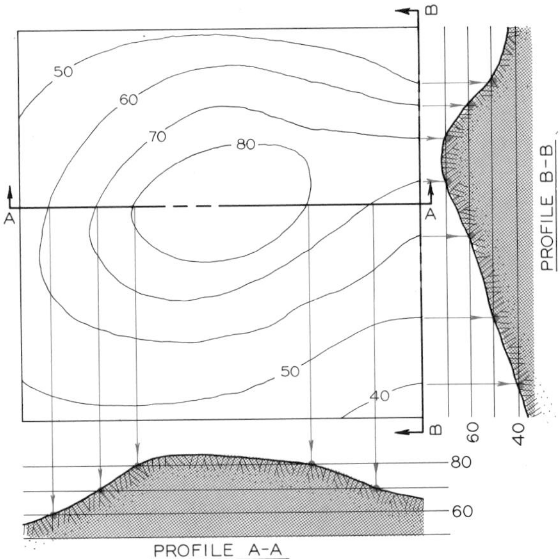

8-51

Fig. 8-51. A contour map and profiles.

intersection between the two planes in the top view. These points are projected to the front view, where line *AB* is found.

Core samples taken from well sites are helpful in establishing information about the orientation of a mineral vein under the ground (Fig. 8-50). This information is used in the evaluation of the prospects for additional exploration in the immediate area.

8-22 CONTOUR MAPS AND PROFILES

Since the surface of the earth is rarely uniform or level, some system is required that will be acceptable for representing irregularities graphically in a drawing. A contour map is a widely accepted method employed by engineers to represent irregular shapes and surfaces of the earth. A pictorial view and a conventional map view of a contour map are shown in Fig. 8-51. The following definitions should be understood prior to further discussion:

Contour lines. Contour lines are lines that represent constant elevations from a common horizontal datum plane, such as sea level. Contour lines can be thought of as the intersection of horizontal planes with the surface of the earth. These horizontal planes are usually equally spaced in a vertical direction. The interval of spacing in Fig. 8-51 is 10′.

Contour maps. A contour map represents the irregularities on the surface of the earth with a network of contour lines, as shown in Fig. 8-51. Contour lines do not cross each other on a contour map. The closer the contour lines are to each other in the contour map, the steeper the terrain.

Fig. 8–52A. Contours apply to irregular-shaped designs as well as the earth's surface. The method of developing templates for an irregular surface such as the body of this experimental vehicle is called lofting. (Courtesy of the Goodyear Corporation.)

Fig. 8–52B. Geologists study the surface of the earth by viewing separate photographs which give a three-dimensional view of the terrain. (Courtesy of Humble Oil and Refining Company.)

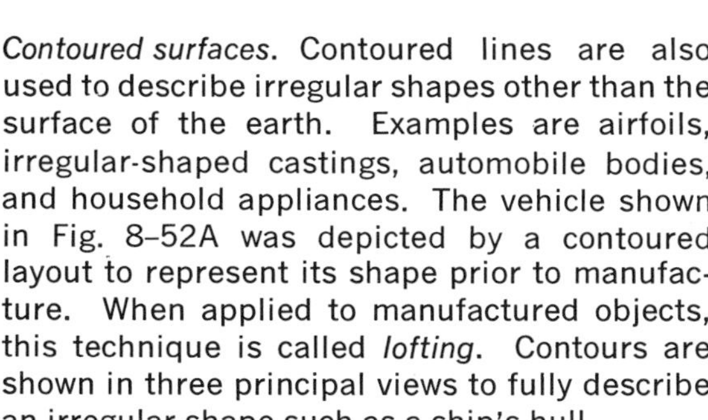

Contoured surfaces. Contoured lines are also used to describe irregular shapes other than the surface of the earth. Examples are airfoils, irregular-shaped castings, automobile bodies, and household appliances. The vehicle shown in Fig. 8–52A was depicted by a contoured layout to represent its shape prior to manufacture. When applied to manufactured objects, this technique is called *lofting*. Contours are shown in three principal views to fully describe an irregular shape such as a ship's hull.

Profile. A profile is a vertical section through the surface of the earth which describes the contour of the earth's surface at any desired location. Two profiles are shown in Fig. 8–51. When applied to topography, a vertical section is called a profile regardless of the direction in which the view is projected. Contour lines appear as the edge views of equally spaced horizontal planes in the profiles. The true representation of a profile is drawn such that the vertical scale is equal to the scale of the contour map; however, this scale may be increased to emphasize changes in elevation that would not otherwise be apparent.

Geologists study irregularities on the surface of the earth through a three-dimensional viewer or stereoscope (Fig. 8–52B). Each of the two photographs viewed through the stereoscope must be made with a separate camera lens which is calibrated to match the lens of the viewer. This three-dimensional analysis, which is called photogrammetry, can be used to study the contour of the surface and to determine contour lines.

An understanding of these definitions and their applications enables the designer to solve a variety of problems dealing with structures on the surface of the earth and the irregular shapes of some manufactured products.

8–23 PLAN PROFILES

A plan profile is a combination drawing that includes a plan with contours and a vertical section called a profile. A plan profile is used to show a drainage system underground from manhole 1 to manhole 3 in Figs. 8–53A and 8–53B.

The profile section is drawn with an exaggerated vertical scale to emphasize the variations in the surface of the earth and the grade of the

FIGURE 8–53A. PLAN PROFILE

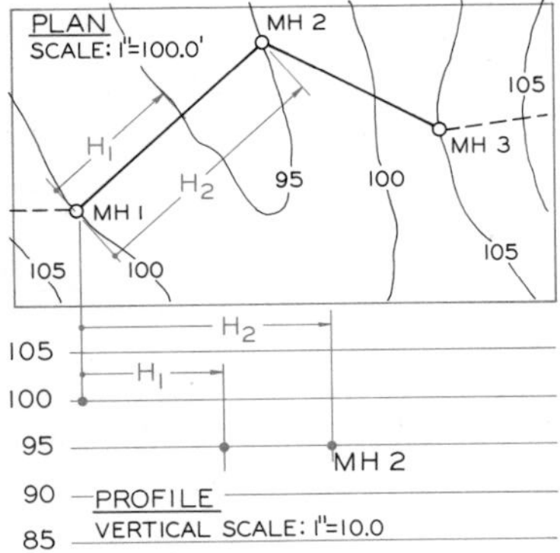

Given: The plan profile shown.
Required: Find the profile of the earth over the underground drainage system.
Step 1: Distances H_1 and H_2 from manhole 1 are transferred to their respective elevations in the profile. This is not an orthographic projection.

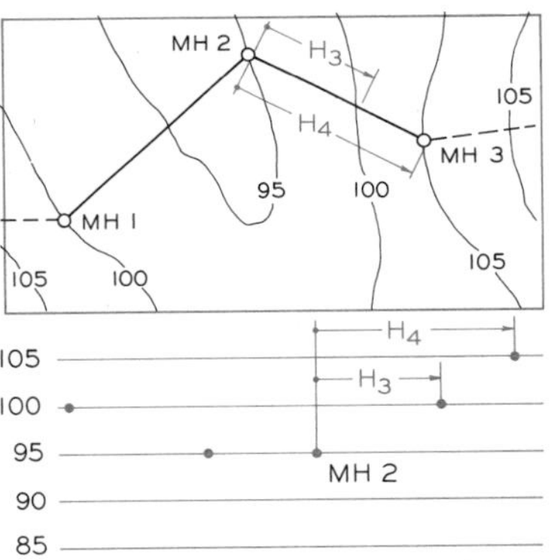

Step 2: Distances H_3 and H_4 are measured from manhole 2 in the plan and are transferred to their respective elevations in the profile. These points represent elevations of points on the earth above the pipe.

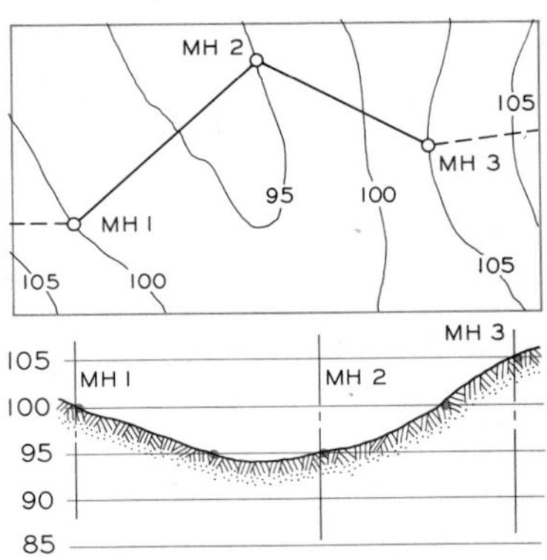

Step 3: The five points are connected with a freehand line and the drawing is crosshatched using the symbol given in Chapter 5 to represent the earth's surface. Center lines are drawn to show the locations of the three manholes that will be located in Fig. 8–53B.

FIGURE 8–53B. PLAN PROFILE, MANHOLE LOCATION

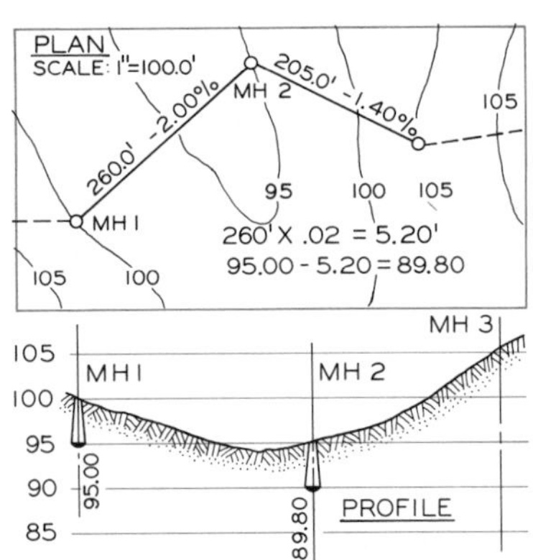

Given: The plan profile and pipe specifications for a drainage system.
Required: Locate the manholes and give their elevations.
Step 1: The horizontal distances from the manholes and the percent grade of flow lines of the pipes are given on the plan. The elevation of the bottom of manhole 2 is calculated by subtracting from the given elevation of manhole 1.

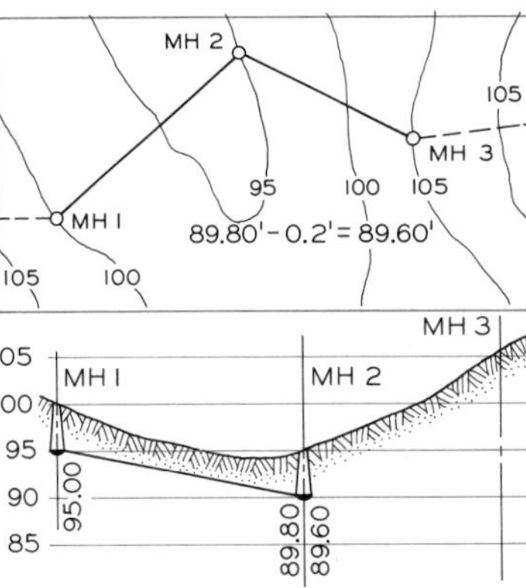

Step 2: The lower side of manhole 2 is .20′ lower than the inlet side to compensate for loss of head (pressure) due to the turn in the pipeline. The lower side is found to be 89.60 and is labeled.

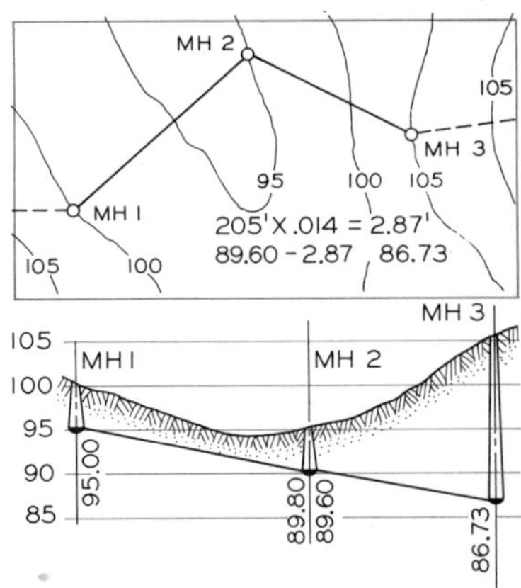

Step 3: The elevation of manhole 3 is calculated to be 86.73 since the grade is 1.40% from manhole 2 to manhole 3. The flow line of the pipeline is drawn from manhole to manhole and the elevations are labeled. This profile shows the relationship of the pipe to the surface above it.

Fig. 8–54. This mountain road was constructed by cutting and filling volumes of the irregular hillside. (Courtesy of the Colorado Department of Highways.)

pipe. Although the vertical scale is usually exaggerated, it need not be; it could be drawn using the same scale as is used in the plan.

Manhole 1 is projected to the profile section, but the other points are not orthographic projections (Fig. 8–53A). Distances H_1 and H_2 are transferred to the profile with dividers so that the horizontal distances will be true length in this view. The points where the contour lines cross the pipe in the top view are transferred to their respective elevations in the profile. All these points are connected to give the profile of the earth over the underground pipe and the location of the manhole center lines.

It is easy to calculate the vertical drop from one end to the other of a pipe, since the slope is given in percent grade (Fig. 8–53B). The vertical drop from manhole 1 to manhole 2 is found to be 5.20′ by multiplying the horizontal distance of 260.00′ by −2.00% grade. This drop is subtracted from the depth of manhole 1 to find the elevation of manhole 2 to be 89.80′.

Since the pipes intersect at manhole 2 at an angle, the flow of the drainage is disrupted at the turn; consequently a drop of .20′ is given from the inlet to the outlet across the floor of the manhole to compensate for the loss of pressure (head) through the manhole. The elevations on both sides of the manhole are specified as shown in step 2 of Fig. 8–53B. This system of calculation is used successively from manhole to manhole.

The true lengths of the pipes cannot be measured graphically in the profile section when the vertical scale is different from the horizontal scale. True length can be found by trigonometry.

The profile makes it possible to illustrate the relationship of the top of the earth to the underground pipe. Also, the contractor can estimate the expense of excavation to lay the pipe.

8–24 CUT AND FILL OF A LEVEL ROADWAY

A level roadway routed through irregular terrain, such as the one pictured in Fig. 8–54, must cut through existing embankments in many locations. Also, volumes of fill must be provided to support the road at low points. It is more economical in most cases if the amount of fill is about equal to the cut volume in order that the earth removed by the cut can be transferred to the low area and used as fill. This problem lends itself to graphical solution by application of primary auxiliary views.

FIGURE 8–55. CUT AND FILL OF A LEVEL ROADWAY

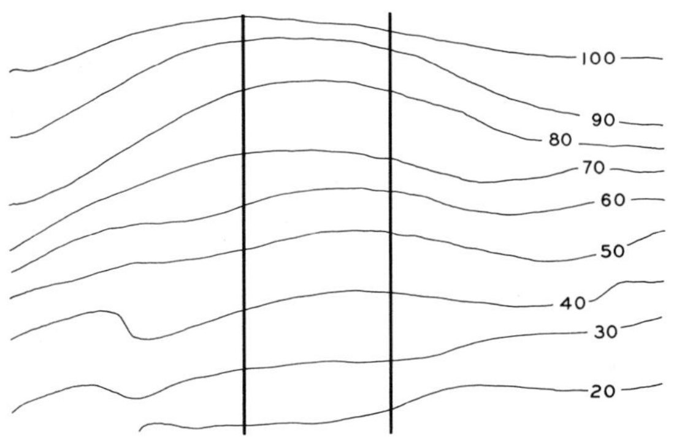

Given: A contour map with a level roadway given at an elevation of 60′.
Required: Find the top view given that the roadway is to have a 45° fill angle and a 30° cut angle.
Reference: Article 8–24.

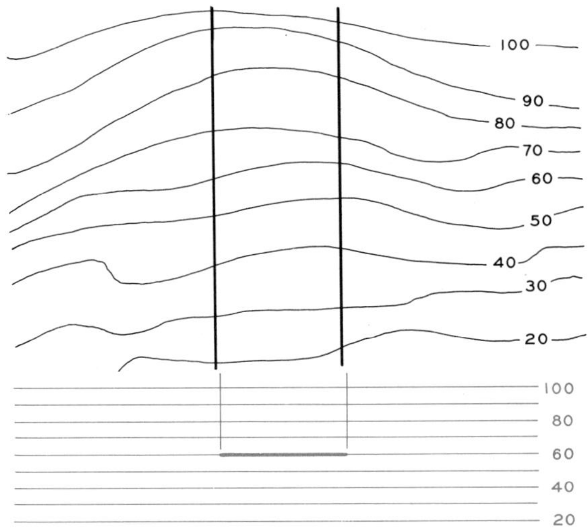

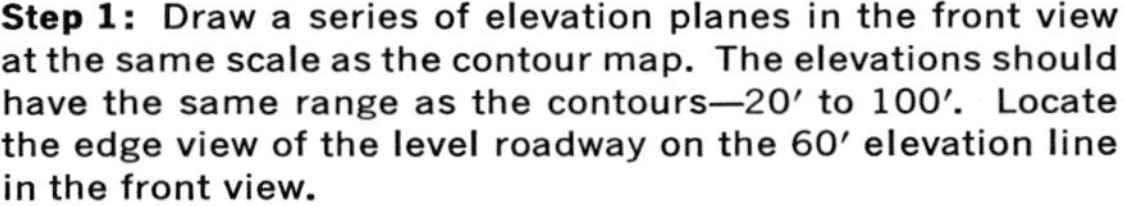

Step 1: Draw a series of elevation planes in the front view at the same scale as the contour map. The elevations should have the same range as the contours—20′ to 100′. Locate the edge view of the level roadway on the 60′ elevation line in the front view.

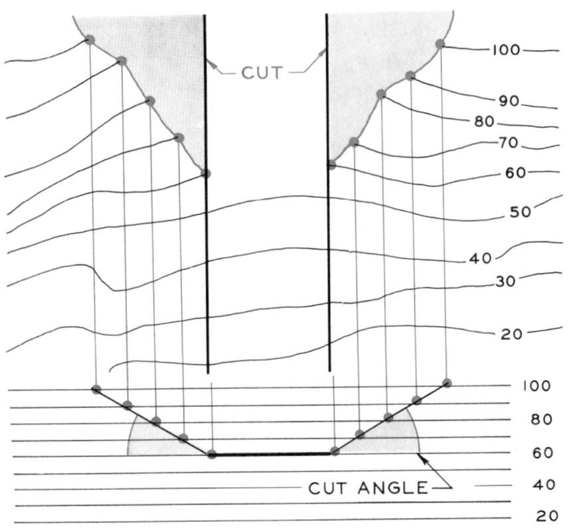

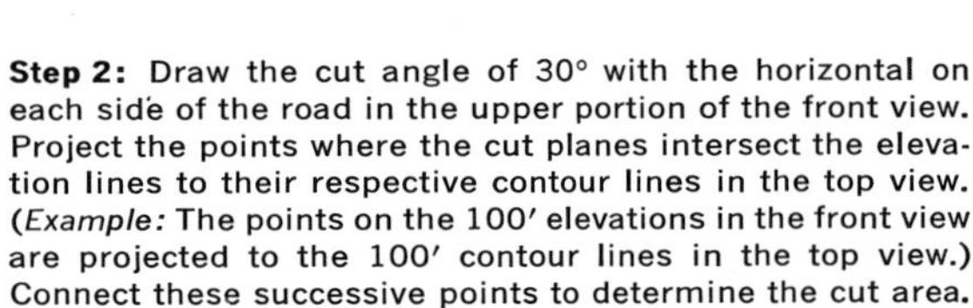

Step 2: Draw the cut angle of 30° with the horizontal on each side of the road in the upper portion of the front view. Project the points where the cut planes intersect the elevation lines to their respective contour lines in the top view. (*Example:* The points on the 100′ elevations in the front view are projected to the 100′ contour lines in the top view.) Connect these successive points to determine the cut area.

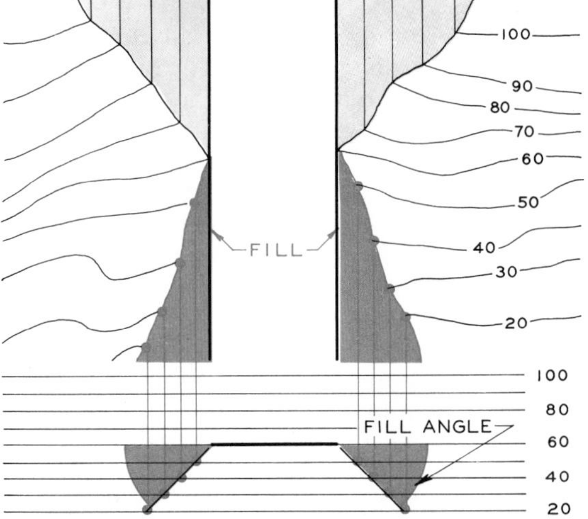

Step 3: The fill angles of 45° are drawn on each side of the roadway in the lower portion of the front view. The points on the plane of the fill are projected to the top view in the same manner that was used for the cut planes. The fill area is indicated by connecting the points. Note that the contour lines have been changed in the cut-and-fill areas to indicate the new contour of the land following construction.

The steps for solution of a cut-and-fill problem are given in Fig. 8–55. A contour map, the route of the level roadway to be constructed, and the angles of cut and fill are given. The contour lines located in the front view of step 1 are spaced 10′ apart, using the same scale that was used on the contour map. The profile of the contour lines shows the same lines as those given in the top view in the 20′ to 100′ elevation range. The roadway will project as an edge in the front view on the 60′ elevation line, the given level of the road.

The angle of cut is drawn on the upper side of the roadway, toward the higher elevations, by measuring the angle of cut with the horizontal plane on each side of the road. The fill angle is on the low side, or toward the contour lines of the smaller elevations. The top views of these planes are found in steps 2 and 3 by projecting points that lie on the cut-and-fill planes at each elevation line in the front view to their respective contour lines in the top view. These points are connected in sequence between each successive pair of contour lines. The resulting line represents the line of intersection between the cut-and-fill planes and the surface of the earth.

The volume of earth involved in each area can be approximated by passing a series of vertical cutting planes through the top view to determine several profiles where the cut-and-fill planes will project as edges in the front view. The areas of cut and fill can be averaged in these views and multiplied by the linear distance in the top view to give the volume of cut and fill. This principle is illustrated in Article 8–25, where a sloping roadway is analyzed.

The cut-and-fill areas found in the map view should be crosshatched or shaded by some method to indicate the solution. The shading or cross-hatching used to represent the cut should be different from that used to indicate the fill area, and each symbol should be identified on the drawing. Crosshatching or shading used on an engineering drawing should be neatly presented to be as attractive as possible and to make the drawing more readable. Use sufficient notes and labels to fully explain the construction and the solution so that the drawing can be interpreted at a later date.

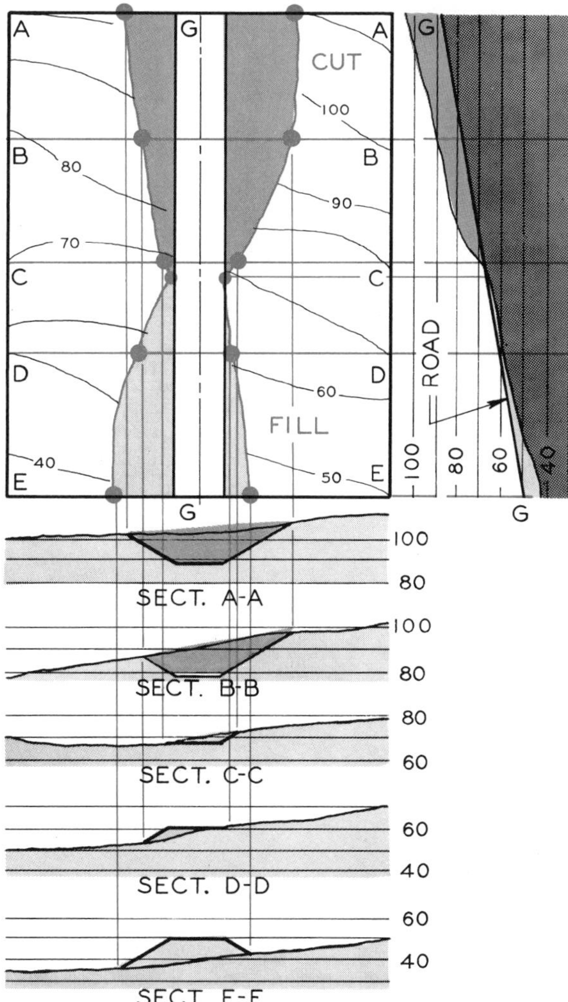

Fig. 8–56. Determining the cut and fill of a roadway on a grade.

8–25 CUT AND FILL OF A ROADWAY ON A GRADE

A highway cannot always be level; in many cases it will be constructed on a grade through irregular terrain. The problem given in Fig. 8–56 is an example of a road which required cut and fill during its construction on a grade. The following steps explain how the completed contour map view can be found and how an estimate can be made of the earth that must be cut and filled.

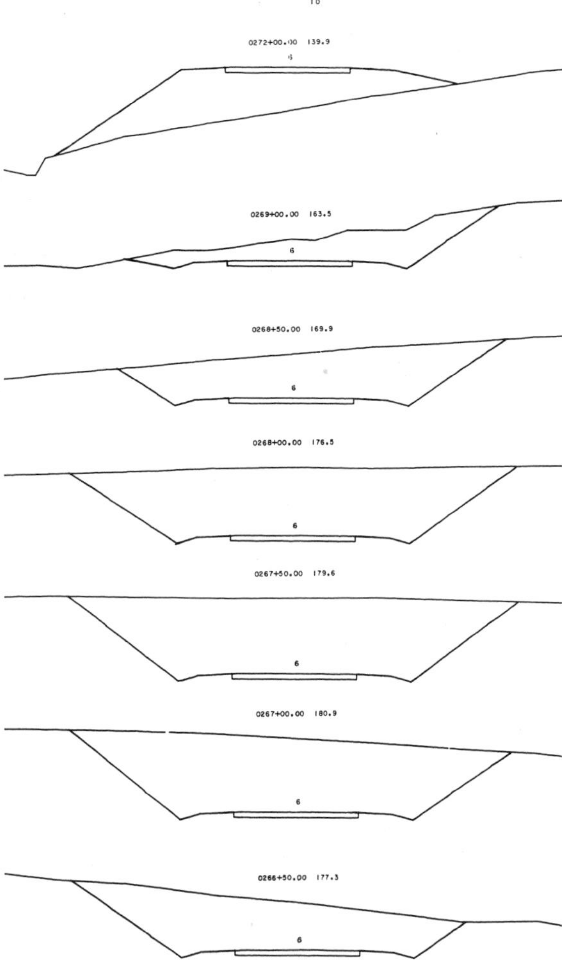

Fig. 8–57. The cut and fill areas of this roadway were plotted by a computer. Note that station points are given as 0268 + 50.00, for example. This is the equivalent to 26,850 ft. from the origin of measurement. This is the civil engineers' technique of locating measurements by locating stations at 100-ft intervals. Intermediate measurements are measured from the nearest 100-ft station. (Courtesy of EAI.)

Step 1. A profile section, G–G, is taken through the center of the highway in order to show the true length and grade of the highway and its relationship to the terrain. The highway is constructed through a given point at the grade specified in this view. It can be seen in profile G–G that a portion of the highway is beneath the terrain, therefore requiring that a cut be made to route the road at the specified grade. Fill is necessary where the level of the highway is above the earth's surface.

Step 2. The top view of the cut and fill areas can be approximated by constructing a series of vertical sections through the map view (top view of the terrain). These cutting planes, A–A, B–B, C–C, D–D, and E–E, are drawn perpendicular to the center line of the highway. The sections cut by these planes appear as profiles in the front view.

Step 3. Each of the sections formed by the cutting planes is drawn as a profile in the front view by constructing horizontal elevation planes in these views to correspond to the contour lines in the map view. The contour planes appear as horizontal elevation planes in these sections, and the angles of cut and fill appear as edges at the location of the cutting plane.

Step 4. Each of the profiles corresponding to the cutting planes is found by projecting to the profile section the intersection of the cutting plane with each contour line in the top view. For example, Section B–B is drawn by projecting points on the 80′, 90′, and 100′ elevation contours to the profile to find the surface of the earth. The elevation of the highway at this section can be found in the profile by transferring the highway elevation found in profile G–G to profile B–B. The angles of cut and fill are constructed in each profile section by measuring their angle with the horizontal plane.

Step 5. The top view of the area of cut and fill is found by projecting the extreme points where the cut planes pierce the surface of the earth in each profile to the top view of the cutting plane used to form the profile. When these points are connected, they establish the limits of the cut and fill, as labeled in the map view.

The spacing of the cutting planes in the top view must be determined by the designer's judgment, and is based on the characteristics of the terrain. The closer the sections are to each other, the more accurate the succeeding constructions and estimations of the volume of cut and fill will be. Note that the volume of fill can be determined by averaging the fill areas in profiles C–C, D–D, E–E, and multiplying this average cross section by the length of the road in the top view from section C–C to section E–E.

An example solution to this type of problem as plotted by a computer is shown in Fig. 8–57. A series of cross sections are plotted to indicate cut and fill from field data that were fed into a system similar to the one shown in Fig. 8–58. A basic knowledge of the graphical process must be understood to permit the drawings to be interpreted or programmed.

Fig. 8–58. Field data are transcribed into the language of a computer prior to plotting. (Courtesy of IBM.)

8–26 GRAPHICAL DESIGN OF A DAM

A dam is located on the contour map shown in Fig. 8–59. The angle on each side of the dam and its radius of curvature from center point *C* are given. The top of the dam is to be level to provide a roadway on the surface. The top view of the dam is to be drawn, and the level of the water is to be indicated in this view.

Step 1. The top view of the dam is constructed by drawing concentric arcs with point *C* as the center, using the given radii of curvature.

Step 2. A radial line is drawn at a convenient direction to serve as the top view of a vertical section that will be used to find a section through the dam, as shown. The crest of the dam is established at the specified level of 70′, and the elevation planes shown in this view are equally spaced parallel planes drawn at the same scale as the contour map. The slope of the dam is established on each side to conform to given specifications.

Step 3. Points are located where each elevation plane intersects the slopes of the dam in the auxiliary profile view. These points are projected to the radial line drawn through point *C* in the top view. For example, Point 2 lies on the 50′ elevation plane in the auxiliary profile. It is projected to the radial line in the top view where it is revolved using line *C*–2 as a radius until it intersects the 50′ contour line in the top view at two points. These points represent the points on the surface of the earth where the downhill slope of the dam intersects the surface of the earth. The remaining points are projected in this manner.

Step 4. If the dam has a freeboard of 5′ above the waterlevel to the crest, the elevation of the water will be 65′. The area of the water can be found in the top view by using the 65′ contour line as the limits of the water.

The volume of the water can be approximated as follows: Construct a series of vertical sections through the water in the top view and determine the average area for all the sections. Multiply this average cross section by the length of the water from the dam to its farthest-back point. This method is very similar to the method suggested in the preceding article for estimating volumes of cut and fill.

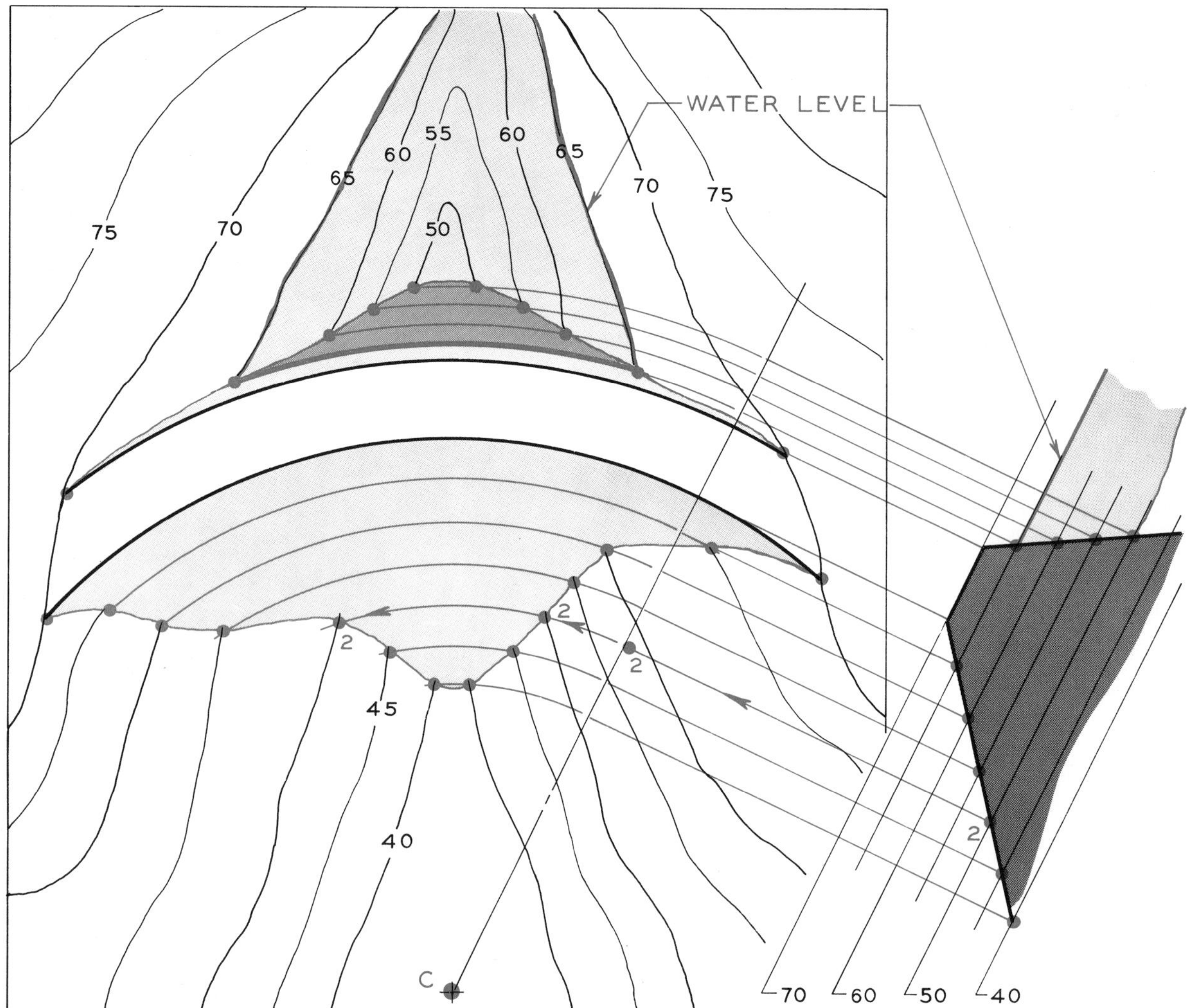

Fig. 8-59. Graphical design of a dam.

An application of these principles can easily be related to the Hoover Dam (Fig. 8-60), which was built for water control and power generation during the period from 1931 to 1935. Lake Mead, which is formed by this dam, originally had a capacity of 32,471,000 acre feet, the entire two-year flow of the Colorado River, making it the largest reservoir in the world. The dimensions of the dam are shown in Fig. 8-61 in a pictorial schematic of the generating system and spillways. The location and design of these systems involved many applications of graphics and descriptive geometry.

The top view of the dam and a view of a section taken through the center of the dam are shown in Fig. 8-62, which is closely related to the example given in Fig. 8-59. The top view of the dam is built in the shape of an arch to take

8–60

Fig. 8–60. An aerial view of Hoover Dam and Lake Mead, which were built during the period 1931 to 1935. (Courtesy of the Bureau of Reclamation, Department of Interior.)

Fig. 8–61. A schematic of the spillway system of Hoover Dam illustrates many spatial problems that could be solved graphically. (Courtesy of the Bureau of Reclamation, Department of Interior.)

Fig. 8–62. The top view and a sectional view of Hoover Dam. (Courtesy of the Bureau of Reclamation, Department of Interior.)

Fig. 8–63. The Colorado River begins backing up to form Lake Mead in 1935. (Courtesy of the Bureau of Reclamation, Department of Interior.)

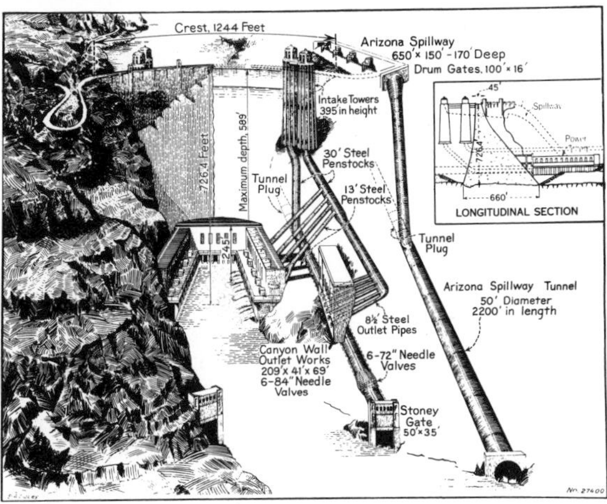

8–61

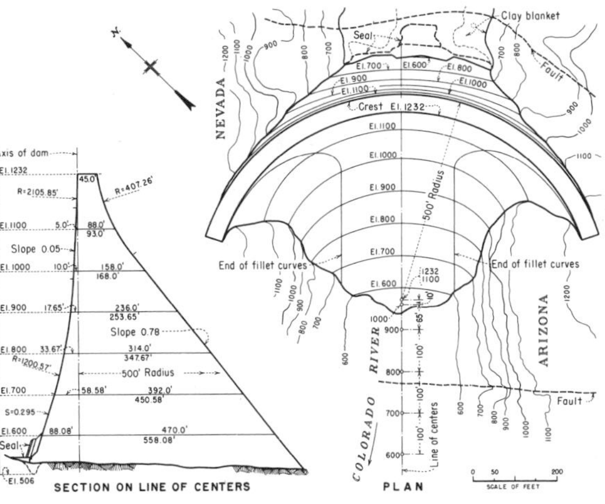

8–62

8–63

advantage of the compressive strength of concrete. The section shows that the dam is progressively thicker as the depth of the water increases. This thickness is necessary to withstand the increased pressure at lower depths.

The Colorado River is shown in Fig. 8–63 as it begins backing up behind Hoover Dam in 1935, under control for the first time in the river's history. The water is shown approaching the upstream cofferdam which was used to divert the river around the damsite through four tunnels. The 726′ high structure required a total of 3,250,000 cu yd of concrete during its construction. Hoover Dam remains as one of engineering's wonders of the world, and Lake Mead is the world's largest man-made reservoir.

Fig. 8-64. Open mines are located on sites where ore veins outcrop to the surface of the earth. (Courtesy of LeTourneau-Westinghouse Company.)

8-27 OUTCROP OF AN ORE VEIN

Strata of ore or rock formations usually approximate planes of a somewhat uniform thickness. This assumption is employed in analyzing known data concerning the orientation of ore veins that are underground and are consequently difficult to study. A vein of ore may be inclined to the surface to the earth and may actually outcrop on its surface in some cases. Outcrops on the surface of the earth can permit open surface mining operations at the minimum of expense (Fig. 8-64). If the vein does not intersect the surface of the earth, its theoretical location of outcrop will serve as a site for further exploration.

Figure 8-65 is an example of a problem in which an inclined ore vein is analyzed graphically to determine its area of outcrop, assuming that the plane is continuous to the surface of the earth. The locations of sample drillings, *A*, *B*, and *C*, are shown in the contour map and their elevations are plotted on the surface of the upper plane of the ore vein in the front view. Point *D* is a point on the lower plane of the stratum. The edge view of plane *ABC* is found by auxiliary view, where the elevation planes are used as datum planes in step 1. The lower plane of the vein is drawn parallel to the upper vein through point *D* to indicate the thickness of the vein. Points on the upper plane where the edge view intersects the elevation planes are projected to their respective contour lines in the contour map, as shown in step 2. These points are connected from contour line to contour line, resulting in the line of intersection between the upper plane of the vein and the surface of the earth. The lower plane is also projected to the top view in the same manner in step 3 to find its line of outcrop. The space between these lines is crosshatched to indicate the area where the plane would outcrop through the surface of the earth provided that the ore vein were continuous in this direction.

8-28 SUMMARY

The primary auxiliary view, which is projected from one of the principal views, has many applications similar to those covered in this chapter. Practically all engineering problems consist of a series of points, lines, and planes that represent most components of a design or project. Only a portion of the many applications of these principles have been covered in this chapter.

An understanding of the construction of auxiliary views of points, lines, and planes will enable the designer to solve many practical problems graphically when analytical solutions are impractical. Other applications of primary auxiliary views will become apparent when the principles are thoroughly understood.

Major emphasis has been placed on the theoretical concepts and principles throughout this chapter, as is the case in most chapters of this volume. However, the appearance of all drawings should be carefully considered for clarity; the drawings should clearly communicate ideas and specifications. A drawing presented with the minimum of notes and explanation may be

FIGURE 8-65. ORE VEIN OUTCROP

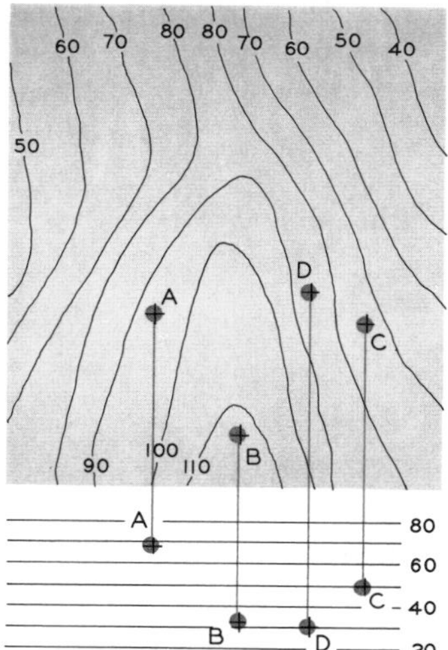

Given: Two views of points *ABC* on the upper plane of a stratum of ore and point *D* on the lower plane. The top view is a contour map and the front view is a series of elevation planes.
Required: Find the area where the vein outcrops on the surface, assuming that the vein is continuous.
Reference: Article 8-27.

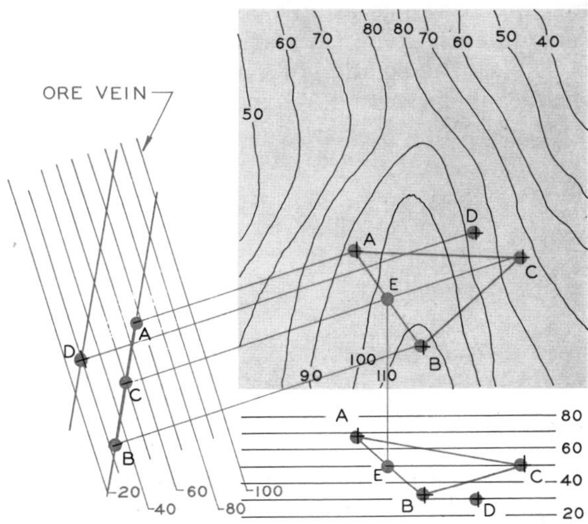

Step 1: Connect points *ABC* to form a plane in each view. Find the edge view of plane *ABC* by projecting from the top view. Locate point *D* in the auxiliary view. Construct the lower surface of the vein parallel to the upper plane in the auxiliary view with the same position as in the front view.

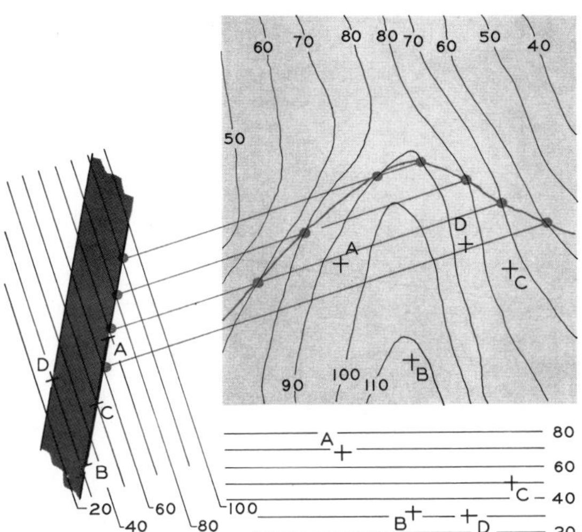

Step 2: Project the points where the upper plane of the vein crosses the elevation lines in the auxiliary view to their respective contours in the top view. For example, the point on the upper plane crossing the 90′ elevation line is projected to the 90′ contour line in the top view. Connect all points between contours in the top view.

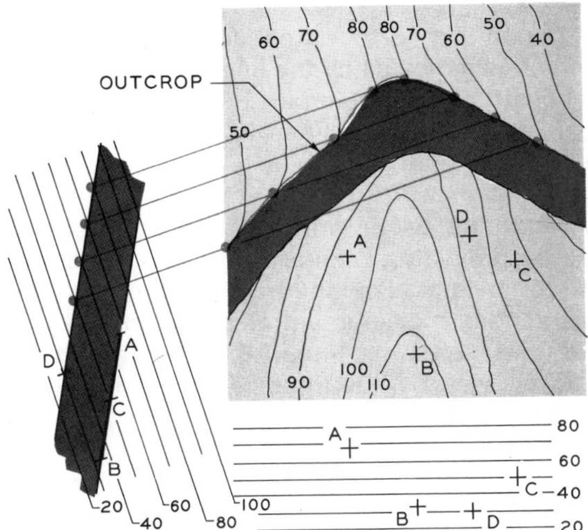

Step 3: Project the points where the lower plane crosses the elevation lines to the top view in the same manner as the upper plane. Connect these points with a line. The area between the two lines in the top view is the area where the stratum would outcrop on the surface if the plane were continuous.

very costly if insufficient information is given. The designer himself may be unable to interpret his own drawings after a few days unless he records each step of his solution as clearly as possible. The solution of a problem by the correct graphical procedures is insufficient unless the results, measurements, angles, and other findings are presented in an understandable form. The student can realize the importance of this if he attempts to interpret a problem unfamiliar to him that has been solved by a classmate.

PROBLEMS

General: The problems for this chapter can be constructed and solved on $8\frac{1}{2}'' \times 11''$ sheets, with instruments as illustrated by the accompanying figures. Each grid represents $\frac{1}{4}''$. Reference planes and points should be labeled in all cases using $\frac{1}{8}''$ letters with guidelines.

1. (A through D) In Fig. 8–66 find the true-size views of the inclined planes. Label all points and construction.

2. (A) In Fig. 8–67A find auxiliary views of point 2 as indicated by the lines of sight. Label all construction. (B) In part B of the figure find auxiliary views of the lines 1–2 as indicated by the lines of sight.

3. (A) In Fig. 8–68A find the true length of the line by projecting auxiliary views from the top and front views. Find the true length of the line by true-length diagrams projected from the top and front views. (B) In part B of the figure find auxiliary views of the lines as indicated by the lines of sight.

4. Use Fig. 8–69 for all parts of this problem. (A) Find the angle the line makes with the horizontal plane. (B) Find the angle the line makes with the frontal reference plane. (C) Find the angle between the line and the profile reference plane. (D) Find the slope of the line in the given top and front views.

5. Find the slope angle, tangent of the slope angle, and the percent grade of the four lines shown in Fig. 8–70. Determine the direction of the slope from the smaller numbered end to the larger numbered end of each line.

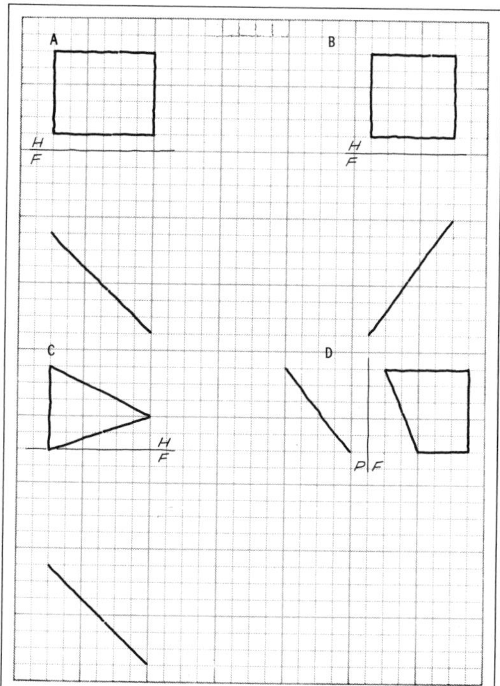

Fig. 8–66. Edge view of inclined planes.

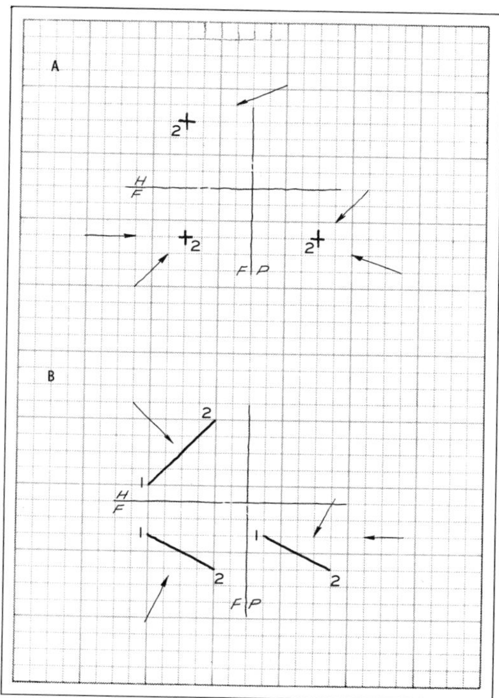

Fig. 8–67. Primary auxiliary views of a point and line.

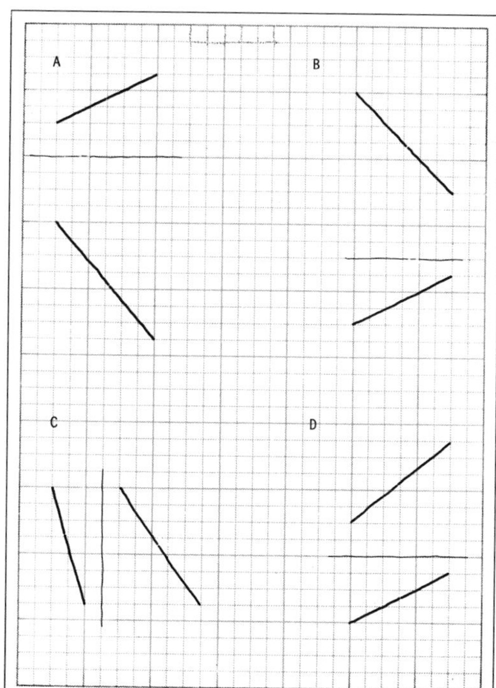

Fig. 8–69. Angle made by a line with principal planes.

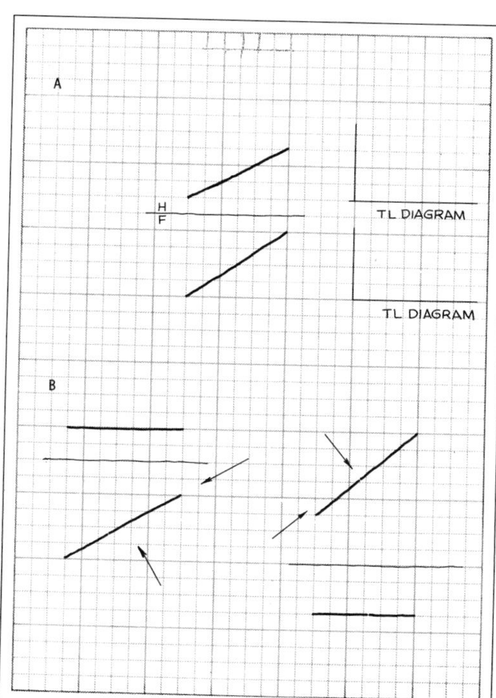

Fig. 8–68. True length of a line by auxiliary view and by true-length diagram.

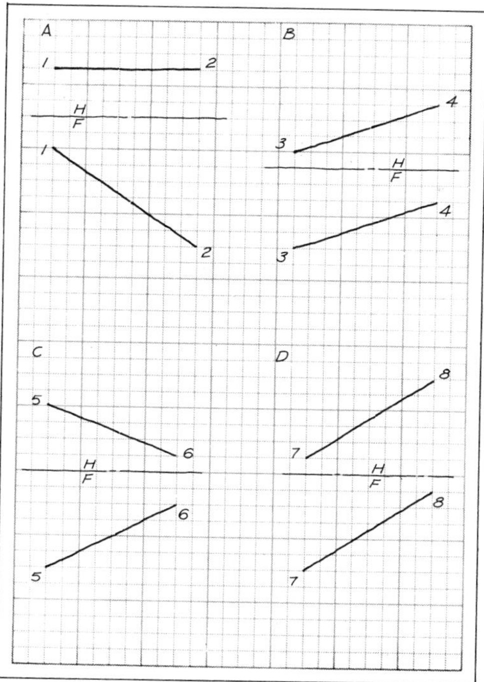

Fig. 8–70. Slope and percent grades of lines.

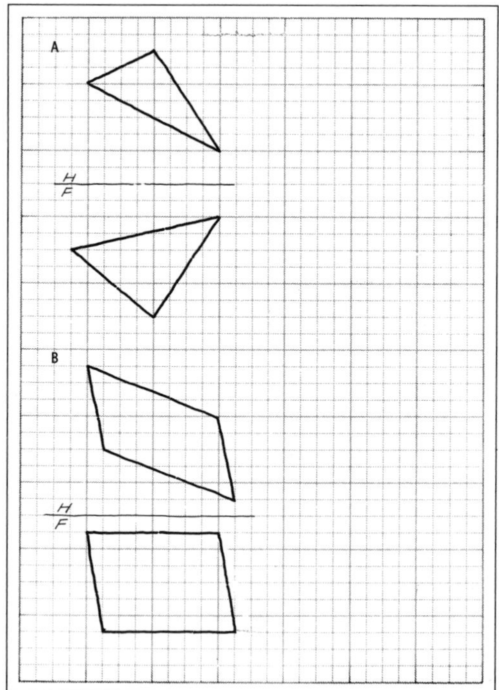

Fig. 8–71. Edge view of planes.

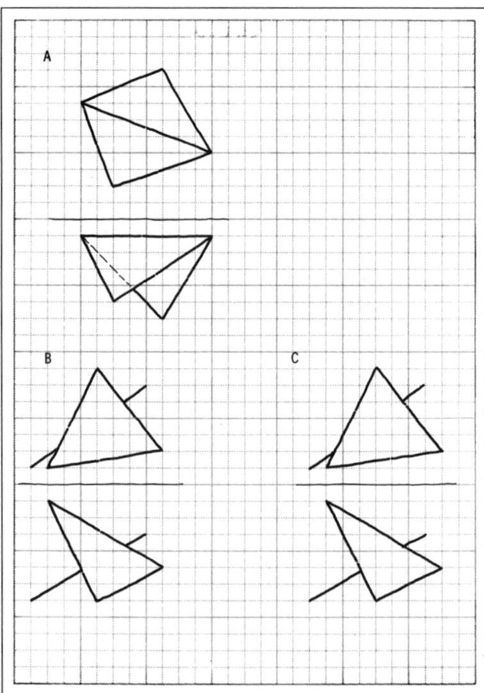

Fig. 8–72. Angle between planes and intersection of a line and plane.

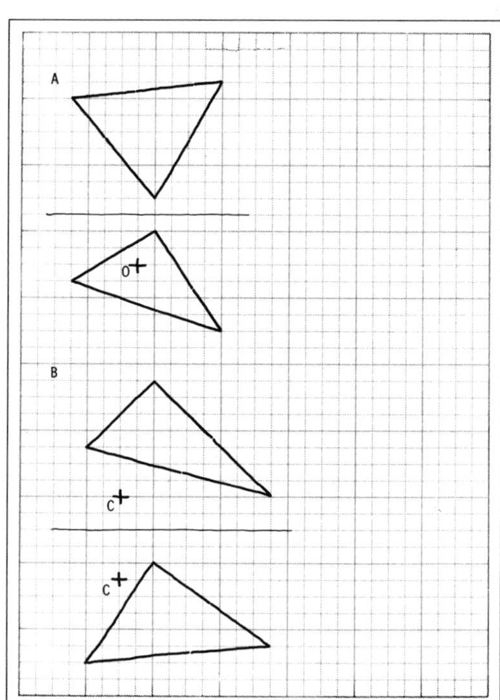

Fig. 8–73. Line perpendicular to a plane.

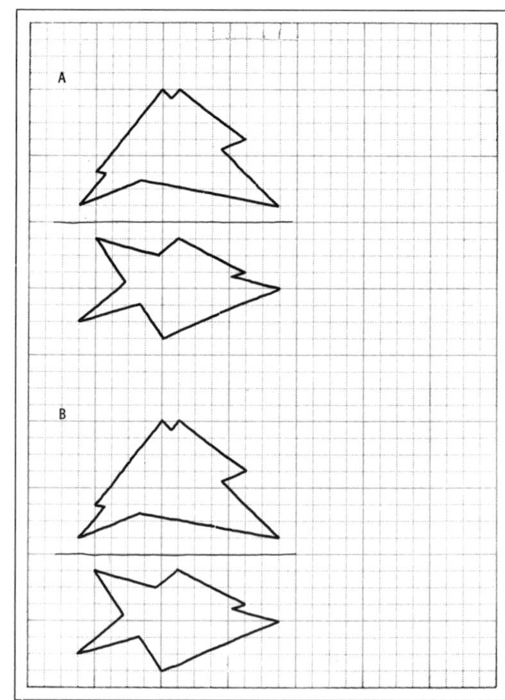

Fig. 8–74. Intersection between planes by projection and auxiliary views.

6. (A and B) In Fig. 8–71 find the edge views of the two planes.

7. Use Fig. 8–72 for all parts of this problem. (A) Find the angle between the two intersecting planes. (B) Find the piercing point and determine the visibility of the plane and line by projection methods. (C) Find the piercing point and determine the visibility of the plane and line by the auxiliary view method.

8. (A) In Fig. 8–73A construct a line $\frac{1}{2}''$ long on the upper side of the plane through point *O* on the plane. (B) In part B of the figure construct a line from point *C* that will be perpendicular to the plane. Indicate the piercing point and visibility.

9. (A) In Fig. 8–74A determine the line of intersection and the visibility between the two planes by projection. (B) In part B of the figure find the line of intersection and the visibility of the two planes by the auxiliary-view method.

10. Use Fig. 8–75 for all parts of this problem. (A and B) Find the slope and direction of slope of each of the planes. Indicate all measurements. (C and D) Find the strike and dip of each of the planes in parts A and B on a separate sheet of paper.

11. The plane represents the location of points on the upper plane of a stratum of ore under the ground. Point 2 is a point on top of the surface; point 1 is a point on the bottom plane of the stratum of ore. Find the shortest distance, the shortest horizontal distance, and the shortest vertical distance from point 2. What is the thickness of the stratum? Use Fig. 8–76.

12. In Fig. 8–77A find the line of intersection between the two planes by cutting planes, assuming that the two are continuous planes.

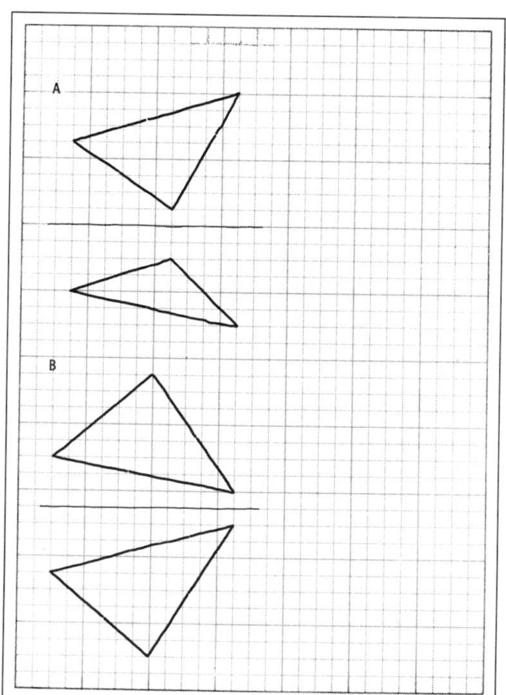

Fig. 8–75. Slope, strike, and dip of a plane.

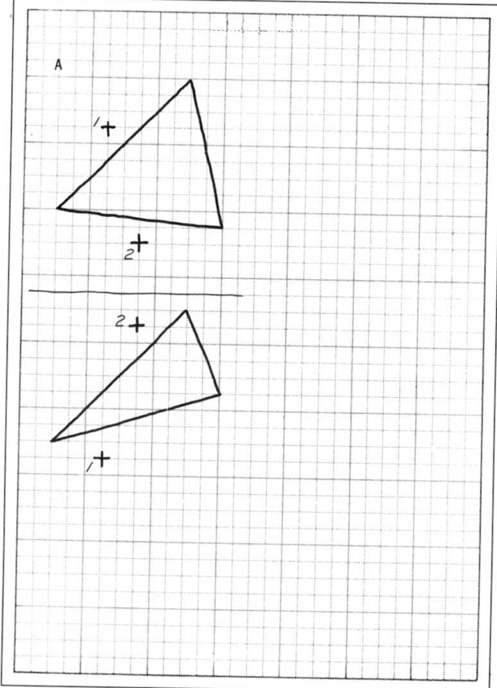

Fig. 8–76. Distance to an ore vein.

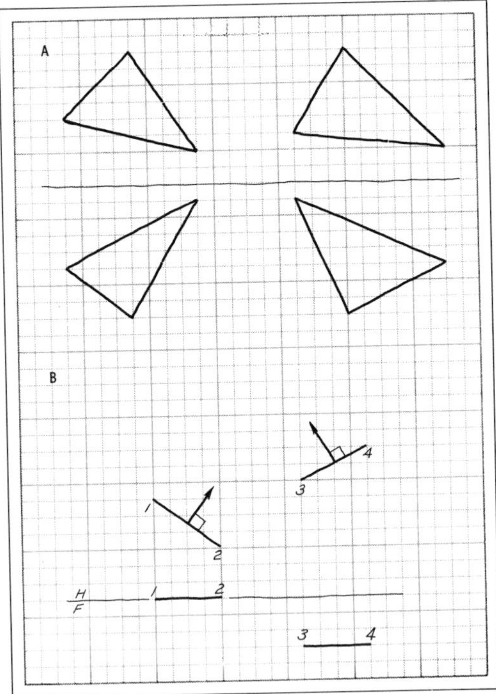

Fig. 8–77. Intersections between planes.

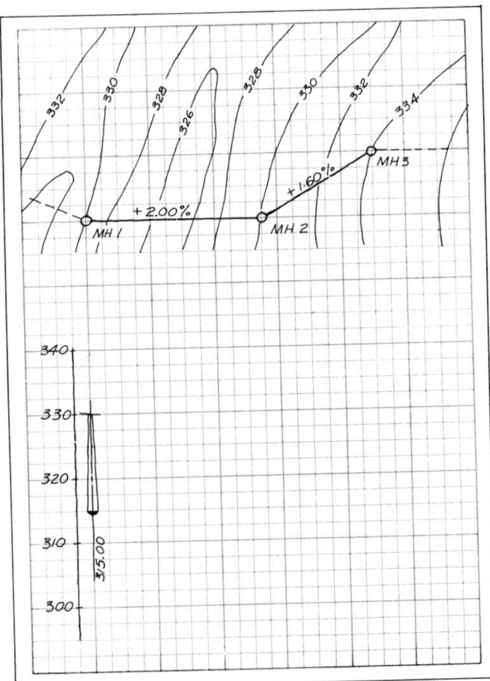

Fig. 8–78. A plan-profile problem.

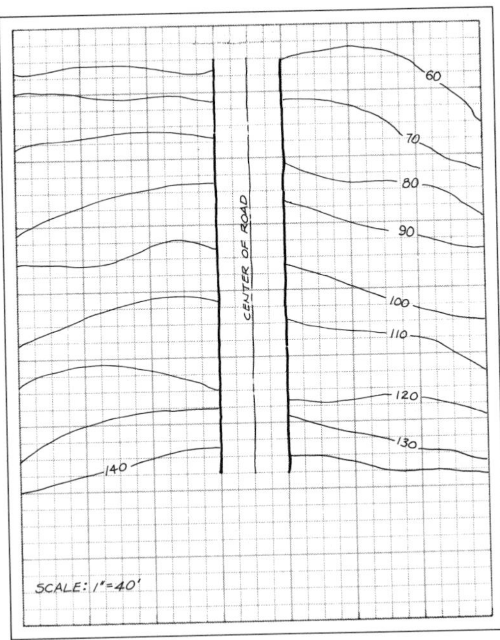

Fig. 8–79. Cut and fill of a level roadway.

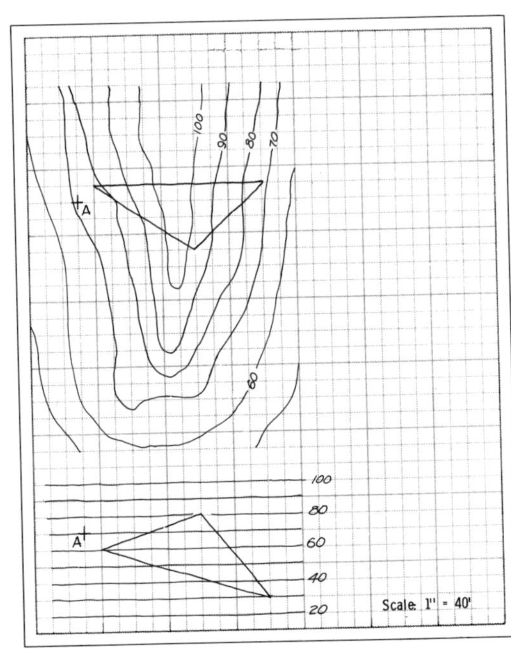

Fig. 8–80. Outcrop of an ore vein.

In part B of the figure two strike lines of an ore vein are given—1–2 and 3–4. The plane with strike 1–2 dips 30° northeast, and the plane with strike 3–4 dips 45° northwest. Find the line of intersection between the two views in both views.

13. A drainage system is to be laid from manhole 1 to manhole 3 using the specifications given in Fig. 8–78. Complete the plan-profile drawing beginning with manhole 1, using the vertical scale of 1″ = 10′. Allow a drop of .20′ across each manhole to compensate for loss of head. The scale of the plan view is 1″ = 100′. Refer to Article 8–23.

14. (A) In Fig. 8–79 the level road has an elevation of 100′. Find the cut and fill in the top view given that the cut angle is 30° with the horizontal and the fill angle is 35° with the horizontal. Label all construction. (B) Assume that the roadway is sloping at a 10-percent grade with its low end toward the bottom of the sheet. Determine the cut and fill areas for this situation, using the same angles as in the previous problem. Use a separate sheet. Estimate the amount of earth to be cut and filled.

15. In Fig. 8–80 the plane represents two views of the top plane of a stratum of ore under the ground. Point *A* is in the bottom plane of the stratum of ore. Find the area of outcrop where the stratum pierces through the surface of the earth in the top view. Scale: 1″ = 40′.

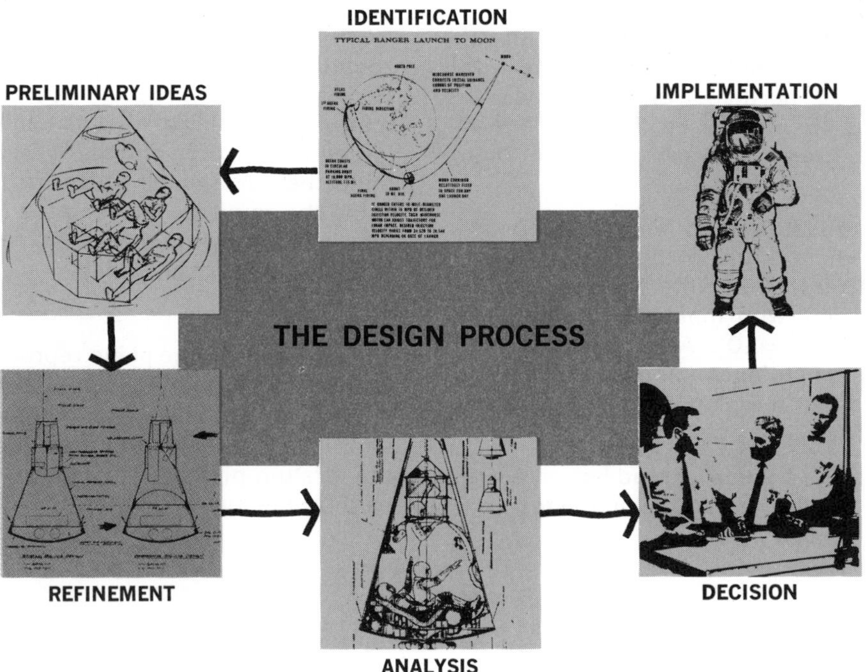

9 SUCCESSIVE AUXILIARY VIEWS

9-1 INTRODUCTION

Many industrial problems cannot be solved by primary auxiliary views, but instead they require that secondary auxiliary projections be made before the desired information can be obtained. The designer is concerned with much the same type of design information as that covered in Chapter 8, namely, physical dimensions and shapes. For example, a basic requirement of a design involving intersecting planes of irregular shapes is the true shape and size of the planes (Fig. 9-1). A design cannot be detailed with the complete specifications necessary for construction unless all details of fabrication have been determined; these details include true shapes of planes, angles between planes, distances from points to lines, and angles between lines and planes. An example of a typical project that required the solution of many descriptive geometry problems is a structural frame for a 65-ton truck (Fig. 9-2). Prior to its fabrication, drawings and specifications were prepared to describe completely each component of this system through the application of graphic principles. It should be rather obvious from observation of the problems covered in this chapter that many of the solutions that are obtained graphically would be quite complicated if attempted from an analytical approach or through the application of mathematical principles. The best method for solving complicated spatial problems is a mixture of graphical and analytical procedures which combines the ad-

Fig. 9–1. The many facets of the U.S. pavilion dome at Expo 67 provide an example of the interrelationships between lines, points, and planes that require spatial analysis. (Courtesy of Rohm and Haas Company.)

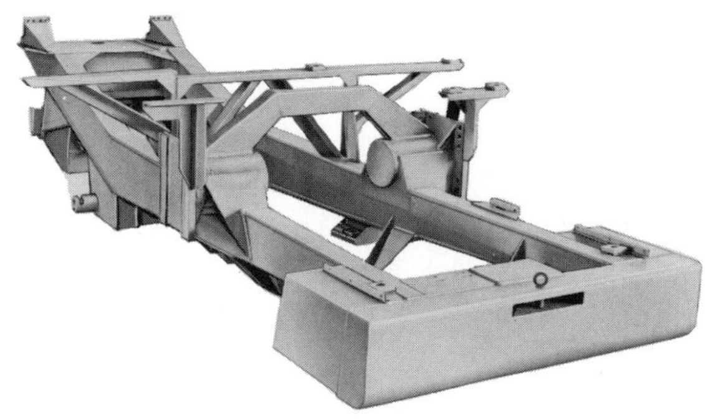

Fig. 9–2. This frame for a 65-ton Haulpak truck illustrates the many design problems that require the application of descriptive geometry. (Courtesy of LeTourneau-Westinghouse Company.)

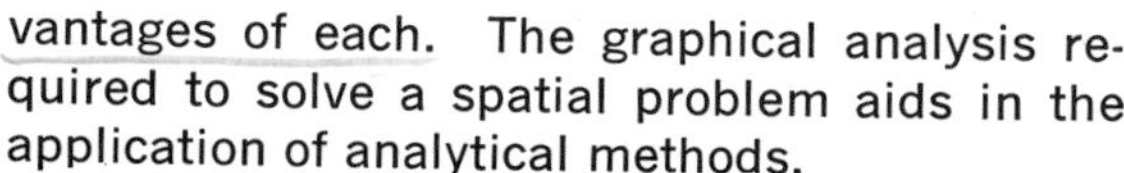

vantages of each. The graphical analysis required to solve a spatial problem aids in the application of analytical methods.

Primary auxiliary views are supplementary views projected from primary orthographic views—the horizontal, frontal, or profile views. A *secondary* auxiliary view is a view projected from a primary auxiliary view. The reference line between the principal plane and the auxiliary view is labeled F–1, H–1 or P–1, but the reference line between a primary auxiliary view and a secondary auxiliary view is labeled 1–2, regardless of the primary view from which it is projected (Fig. 9–3). A *successive auxiliary view* is a view projected from a *secondary* auxiliary view or from another successive auxiliary view. In other words, an infinite sequence of auxiliary views can be produced by continuing to project successively from auxiliary view to auxiliary view.

Auxiliary views have the same relationship between their adjacent views as the principal views have with each other. A secondary auxiliary plane is perpendicular to the primary auxiliary plane, and the plane of a successive auxiliary view projected from a secondary auxiliary view is perpendicular to the secondary auxiliary plane. It should be remembered that all sequential auxiliary planes are perpendicular to the preceding plane from which the projection was made.

9–2 SECONDARY AUXILIARY VIEW OF A SOLID

It is easier to understand spatial relationships of abstract lines and planes in space if a familiar three-dimensional solid is used to introduce the principles of projection. A simple rectangular prism is therefore used to introduce secondary auxiliary-view construction in Fig. 9–3.

A line of sight is arbitrarily chosen in the top and front views. Since we are required to view the prism in the direction of the line of sight, we must construct a view in which the line of sight will appear as a point. In step 1, a primary auxiliary view is drawn to find the true length of the line of sight; the object is also projected to this view. The secondary auxiliary plane, 1–2, is located perpendicular to the true-length line of sight in step 2. The two edge views of the prism are projected to the secondary auxiliary view as independent planes to simplify the formation of the solid and the determination of visibility.

It can be seen in step 3 that plane 1–2–3–4 is a visible plane in the secondary auxiliary view; that is, the line of sight from the secondary auxiliary view gives an unobstructed view of the

FIGURE 9–3. SECONDARY AUXILIARY VIEW OF A SOLID

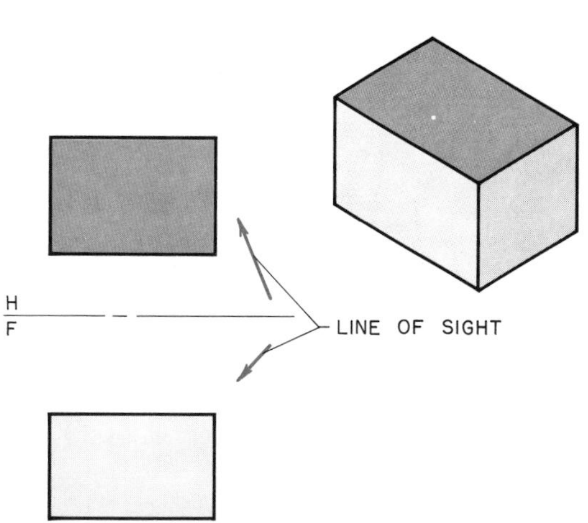

Given: The top and front views of a solid and a line of sight.
Required: Find the view of the solid indicated by the line of sight.
References: Articles 8–4 and 9–2.

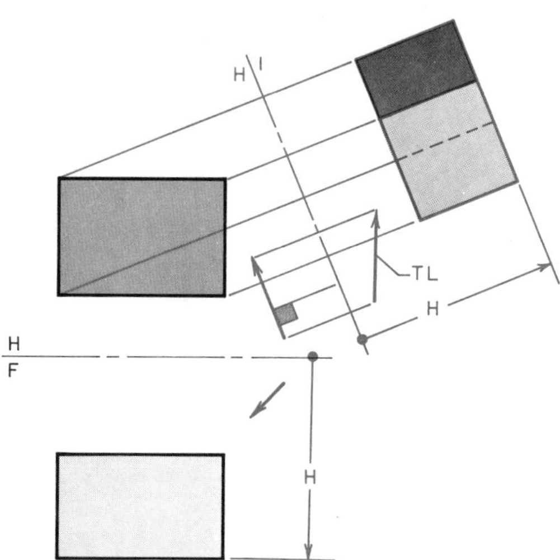

Step 1: Project a primary auxiliary view from one of the given views so that it is perpendicular to the line of sight. The primary auxiliary will give the true length of the line of sight since it is viewed perpendicularly. Project the solid to this view in the same manner. Transfer dimension *H* from the front view to establish points in the primary auxiliary view.

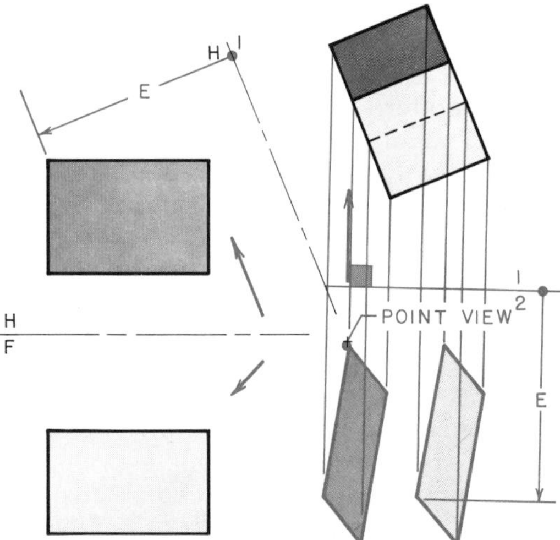

Step 2: Since the line of sight is true length in the primary auxiliary, a point view of the line can be found in a secondary projection plane, which is drawn perpendicular to the line. This will give the required view of the object. Project the upper and lower planes to the secondary auxiliary by transferring all dimensions from the H–1 line in the manner of measurement *E*.

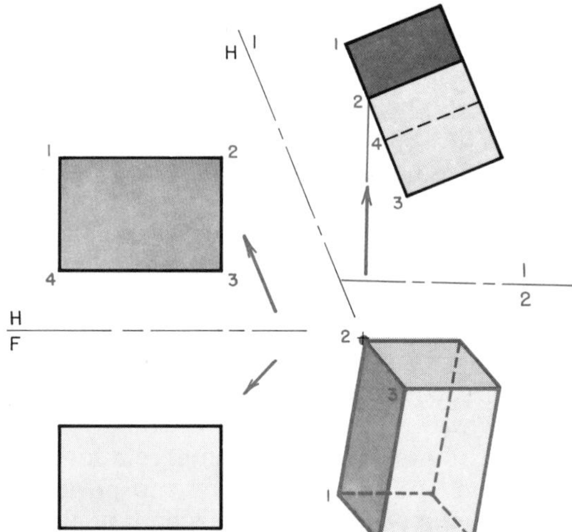

Step 3: Complete the object by connecting the respective corners with the missing lines. Plane 1–2–3–4 will appear visible in the secondary auxiliary view since the line of sight gives an unobstructed view of the plane in the primary auxiliary view. Any line crossing this plane must be behind it and therefore is hidden, as shown above. The outlines of a solid are always visible.

FIGURE 9–4. POINT VIEW OF A LINE

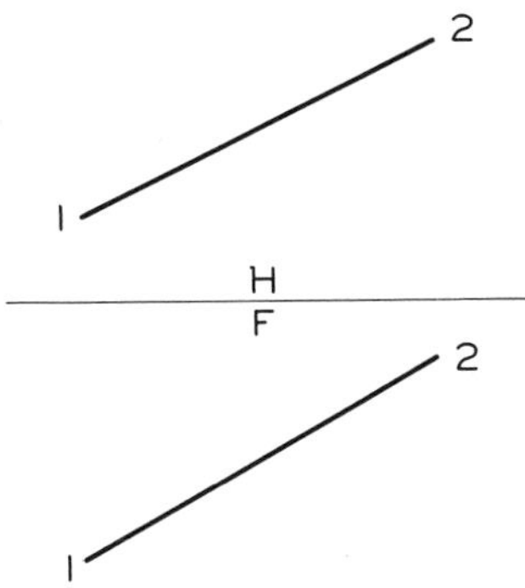

Given: The top and front views of oblique line 1–2.
Required: Find the point view of the line by a secondary auxiliary view.
References: Articles 8–4 and 9–3.

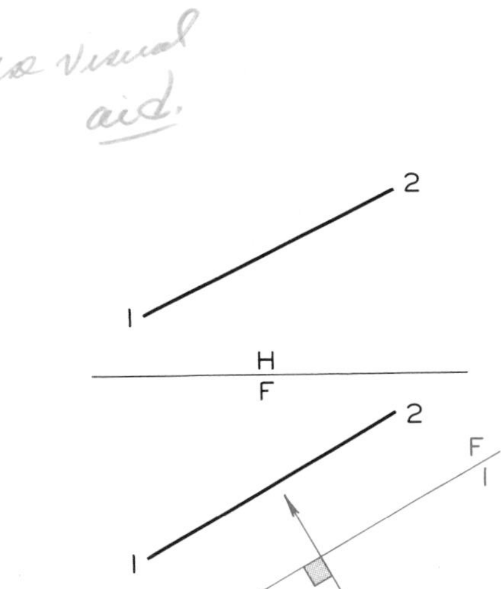

Step 1: Project an auxiliary view from one of the principal views. In this case, the reference line is established parallel to the front view of line 1–2. The projectors will be parallel to the given line of sight, which is perpendicular to the F–1 line. The primary auxiliary view could have also been projected from the horizontal view.

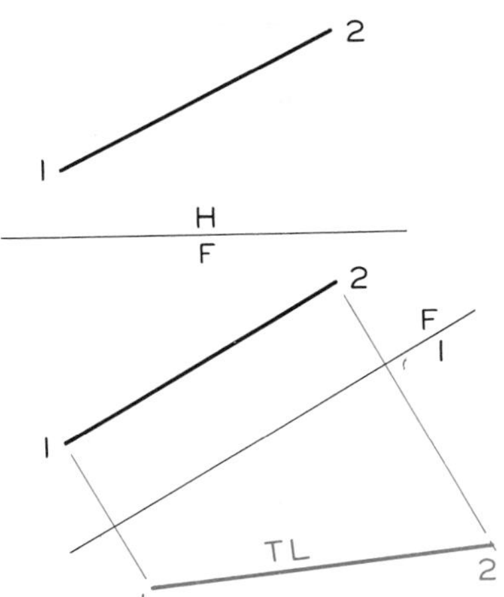

Step 2: Find the primary auxiliary view by projecting as specified in step 1. Line 1–2 is true length in this view, since the line is parallel to the reference plane in the preceding view. This construction is illustrated in Fig. 8-11.

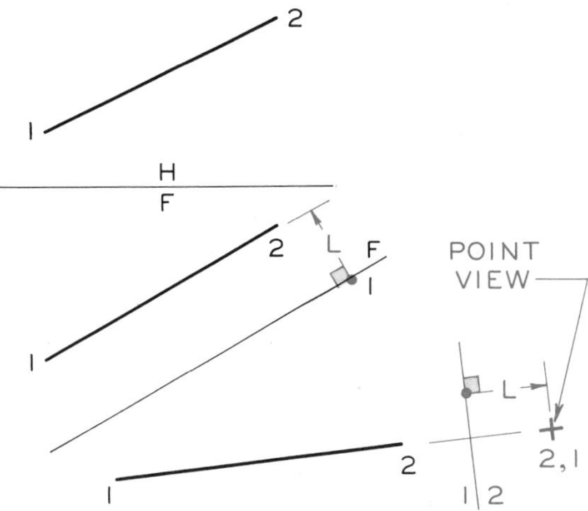

Step 3: Draw a secondary line, 1–2, perpendicular to the true-length view of line 1–2. Transfer measurement *L*, which is taken from the F–1 line to the front view of the line, to the secondary auxiliary view to find the point view. Measurement *L* will appear true length in these positions, since it is perpendicular to the primary auxiliary plane, which appears as an edge in the front and secondary auxiliary views.

plane in the primary auxiliary view. Since plane 1–2–3–4 is visible in the secondary auxiliary view, all lines crossing the plane must be behind it and consequently are hidden. All outlines of a solid are visible. The respective points of each of the two similar planes are connected in the secondary auxiliary view with solid and dashed lines to indicate visibility.

9–3 POINT VIEW OF A LINE

The principle involved in the determination of the point view of a line is a basic one that must be utilized to solve many problems in spatial geometry. The preceding problem has provided an introduction to this principle in relationship to a familiar solid object. Figure 9–4 reviews the steps involved in finding the point view of line 1–2 in its isolated form. The true length of the line must be found before its point view can be found in a secondary auxiliary view. The secondary auxiliary plane is constructed perpendicular to the true-length view of line 1–2 in step 3 and projectors are drawn parallel to line 1–2. The secondary auxiliary plane is perpendicular to the primary auxiliary plane, as is the frontal plane; consequently, a dimension perpendicular to the primary auxiliary plane will project true length in the front and secondary auxiliary views, as shown in step 3.

When two adjacent views are given, the point view of a line can be found by projecting a secondary auxiliary view from either view. For example, we could have found the true length of line 1–2 in Fig. 9–4 by projecting it from the top view, and then developing a secondary auxiliary view from this projected view. Similarly, the primary auxiliary could have been projected from the profile view.

9–4 ANGLE BETWEEN TWO PLANES

Nearly all designs involve the intersection of planes at many unusual angles that must be specified in detail by the designer before fabrication. These angles must be known so that a means for connecting the two planes may be devised, or perhaps so that a form may be designed for casting the design in concrete,

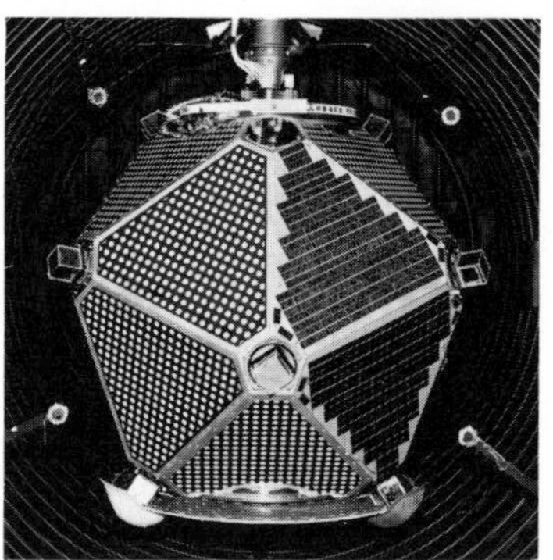

Fig. 9–5. A nuclear detection satellite is composed of planes and angles that can be determined with successive auxiliary views. (Courtesy of TRW Space Technology Laboratories.)

metal, or even glass. The nuclear detection satellite shown in Fig. 9–5 is an example of an assembly for which angles need to be determined. The dihedral angles between the planes of the exterior surface are very critical. These angles must be formed within a high degree of tolerance to permit a highly accurate joint, which is a necessity for the successful function of the satellite in outer space.

Two planes, 1–2–3 and 1–2–4, are joined by an oblique line of intersection, 1–2, in Fig. 9–6. Since this line of intersection does not appear true length in either view, we must develop a secondary auxiliary view to solve the problem. The true angle between two planes can be measured in the view in which the line of intersection appears as a point and both planes project as edges. The true length of the line of intersection is found in step 1, and the line is found as a point in step 2 by applying the procedures outlined in Fig. 9–4. The true angle is measured in step 3, where the plane of the angle, which is perpendicular to the line of intersection, appears true size. This sequence of auxiliary views could have also been projected from the front view.

9–5 TRUE SIZE OF A PLANE

Most products and engineering designs contain many oblique surfaces and planes whose true size must be found in order that appropriate

FIGURE 9–6. ANGLE BETWEEN TWO OBLIQUE PLANES

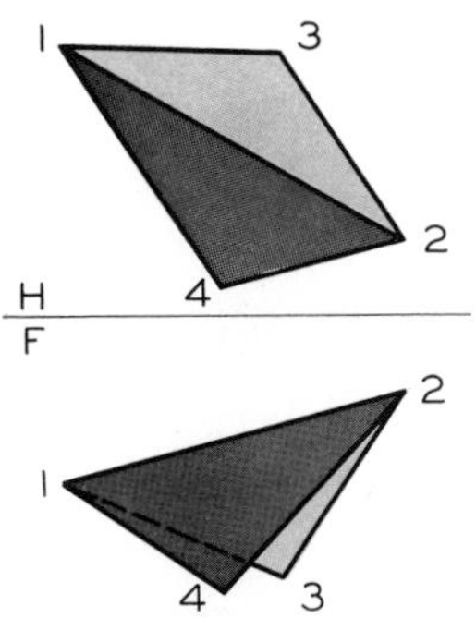

Given: The top and front views of two intersecting planes.
Required: The angle between the two planes.
References: Articles 8–10 and 9–4.

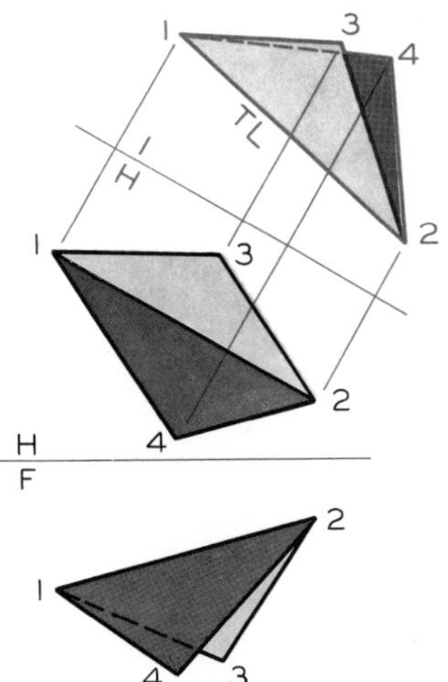

Step 1: The angle between two planes can be seen in a view where the line of intersection appears as a point. Project a primary auxiliary view perpendicularly from a principal view of the line of intersection. In this case, a view is projected from the top view. Line 1–2 will appear true length in the primary auxiliary view.

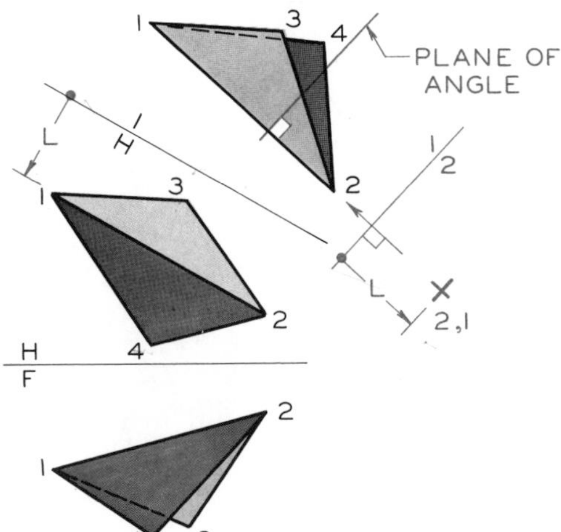

Step 2: The point view of the line of intersection 1–2 is found in the secondary auxiliary view. Locate this view by transferring measurement *L* from the edge view of the primary projection plane as indicated. The plane of the angle appears as an edge perpendicular to the true-length view of the line of intersection in the primary auxiliary.

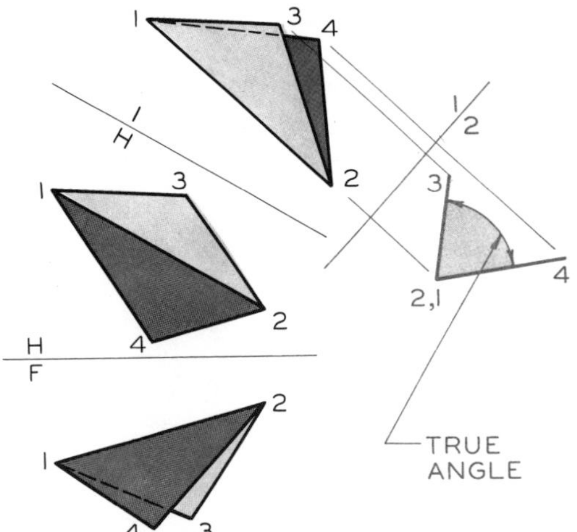

Step 3: The edge views of the planes are completed in the secondary auxiliary view by locating points 3 and 4 in the same manner as in step 2. The angle between the planes can be measured in this view since the line of intersection appears as a point and the planes appear as edges.

FIGURE 9-7. TRUE SIZE OF A PLANE

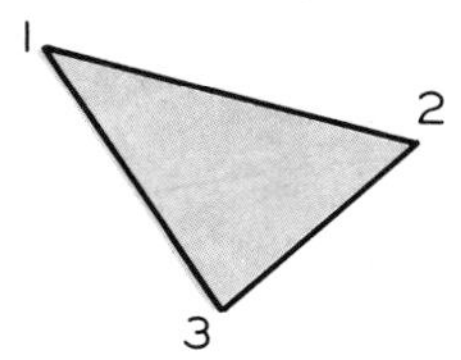

H
F

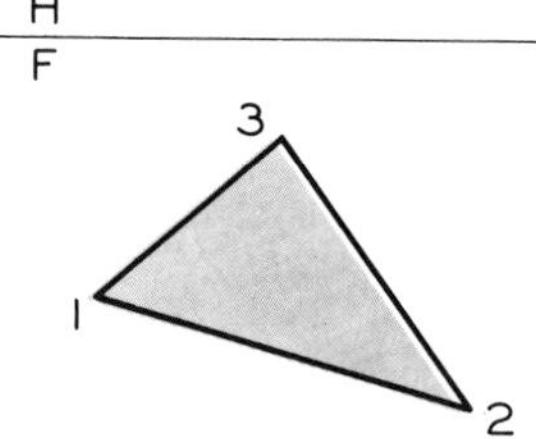

Given: The top and front views of a plane.
Required: Find the true size of the plane.
References: Articles 8-4 and 9-5.

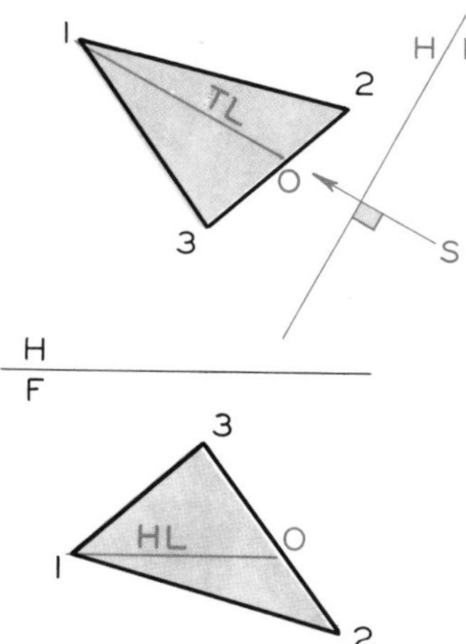

Step 1: Draw horizontal line 1-0 in the front view of plane 1-2-3 and project it to the top view, where the line appears true length. Project a primary auxiliary view from the top view parallel to the direction of line 1-0. The H-1 reference line is perpendicular to 1-0 and the line of sight.

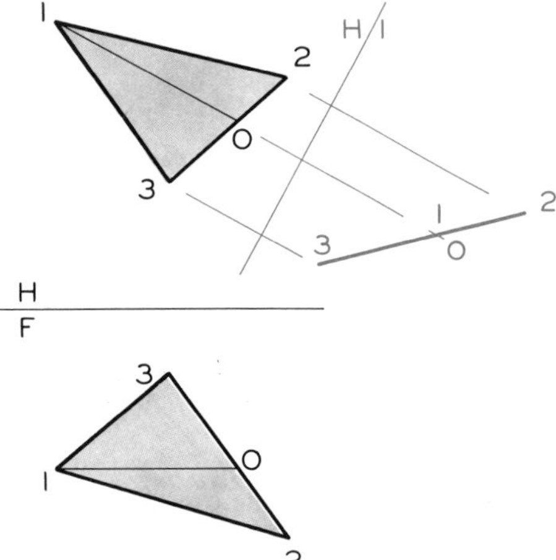

Step 2: The point view of line 1-0 is found in the primary auxiliary view. Project points 2 and 3 to this view where the plane will appear as an edge.

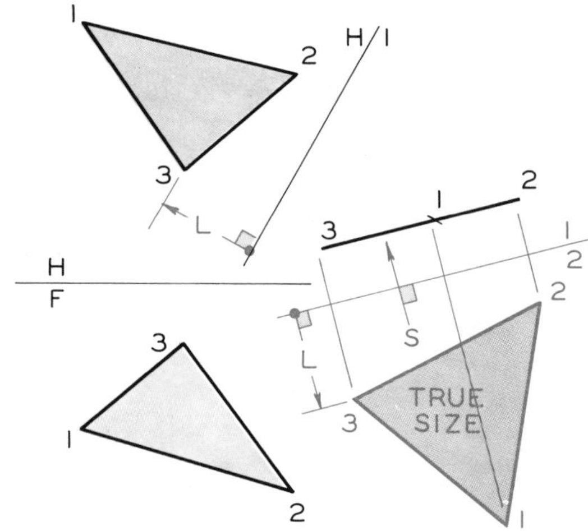

Step 3: A secondary auxiliary view of line 1-2 is drawn parallel to the edge view of plane 1-2-3. The line of sight is drawn perpendicular to the 1-2 line. The true-size view of the plane is found by locating each point with measurements taken perpendicularly from the edge view of the primary auxiliary plane, as indicated.

working drawings may be prepared for the construction of the finished design. The nuclear detection satellite in Fig. 9–5 illustrates an assembly in which there is a need for finding the true size and shape of each of the oblique surface planes. These surfaces are precisely assembled to close tolerances. The determination of the true size of a plane is a fundamental procedure that is applied to many subsequent spatial problems.

The true size of plane 1–2–3 is found in sequential steps in Fig. 9–7. The edge view of the plane is found in step 1 by a primary auxiliary view. The secondary auxiliary reference line, 1–2, is constructed parallel to the edge view of plane 1–2–3. The true size of the plane is found in the secondary auxiliary view by projecting perpendicular to the 1–2 line and transferring the measurements from the H–1 line in the top view to the secondary auxiliary view, as shown in step 3.

It should be noted at this point that the representation of a plane, as defined in descriptive geometry, can take a variety of forms, including two intersecting lines, two parallel lines, three points, or a line and a point. This allows many applications of the principle for finding the true size of a plane. For instance, Fig. 9–8 illustrates the fuel system for a gas turbine engine; the tubing for the system must be bent to fit the contours of the engine properly. The determination of the lengths of tubing and the angular bends is an application of the principle for finding the true size of a plane. A problem similar to this is shown in Fig. 9–9, where the top and front views of points on the center line of a fuel line are given. The true angle, 1–2–3, can be found in the view where plane 1–2–3 appears true size. The primary auxiliary view is found by projecting in a direction parallel to line 1–2 in

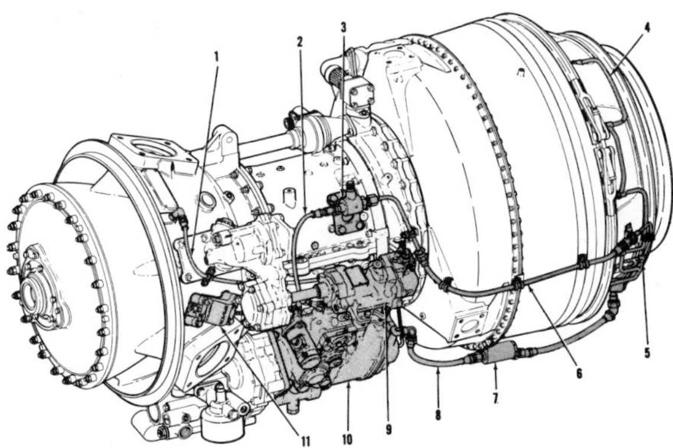

Fig. 9–8. The determination of the bends in a fuel line is an application of the principle of finding the angle between two lines. (Courtesy of Avco Lycoming.)

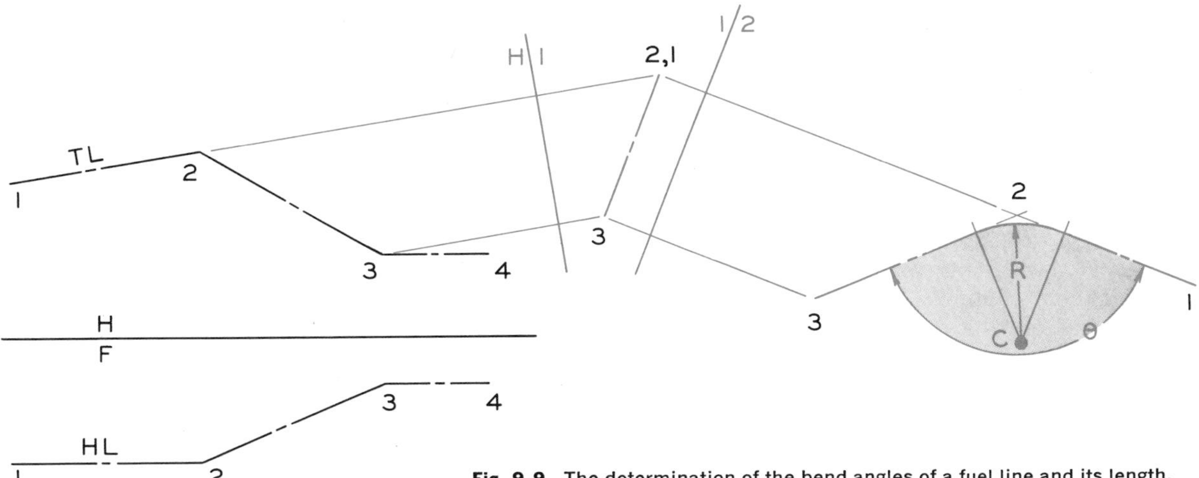

Fig. 9–9. The determination of the bend angles of a fuel line and its length.

Fig. 9-10. The base of the Unisphere ®, symbol of the New York World's Fair, is shown under construction. This is an application of the principle of finding the angle between two lines. (Courtesy of U.S. Steel Corporation.)

Fig. 9-12. The elliptical paths of satellites are shown in the partially completed Unisphere ®. (Courtesy of U.S. Steel Corporation.)

Fig. 9-11. A detailed pictorial of the XV-5A aircraft illustrates many applications of ellipse construction. (Courtesy of Ryan Aeronautical Company.)

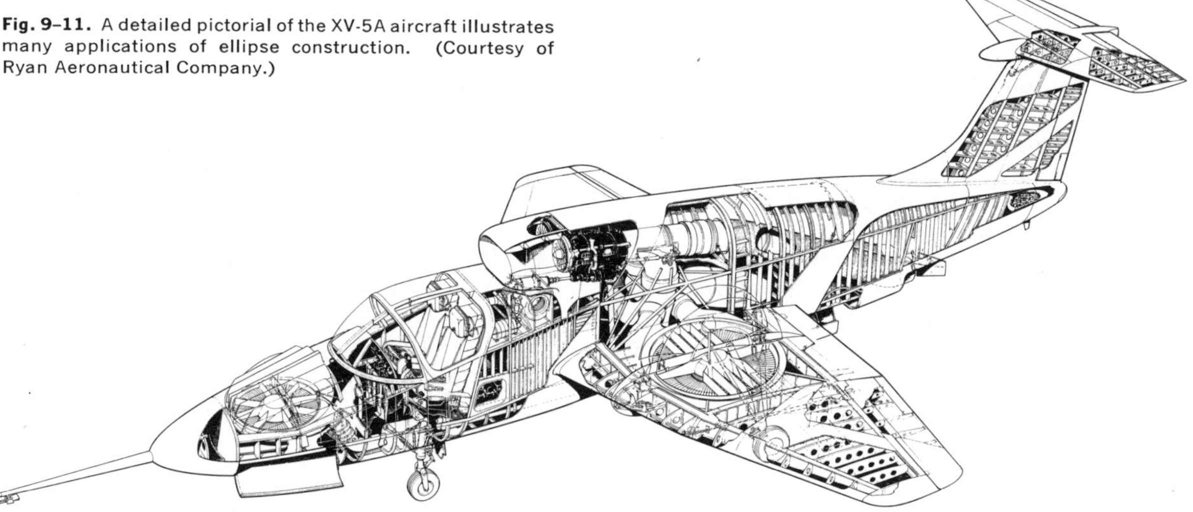

the top view, which is true length, to find the edge view of the plane. A secondary auxiliary view projected perpendicular to the edge view gives the plane true size, where both lines are true length and the angle between them is true size. A given bend radius can be used to construct the curvature arc at point 2 with point C as the center. The straight lengths can be scaled directly, while the arc distance can be found mathematically by application of the formula for finding the circumference of a circle. The solution to this problem would be quite complex if it had to be solved entirely by mathematical methods.

Another application of the angle between two lines is illustrated in Fig. 9-10, which shows a connecting joint designed to support the structural members of the 1965 New York World's Fair Unisphere ®. It was necessary to construct a view in which the angle between the chordal member and the support element appeared true size. It was also necessary to find the angles between the intersecting planes at this point of support so that the details could be prepared for fabrication and erection. A structural project of this type is designed to be erected on the site with a minimum of modification of the structural forms.

Covered in E 6 TD

9-6 ELLIPTICAL VIEWS OF A CIRCLE

Circular and cylindrical shapes are commonly used in most designs. Many uses of these are illustrated in Fig. 9-11, the pictorial of the aircraft, where the circular features appear as ellipses rather than circles. The orbital paths of satellites will project as ellipses in most views, whether in actual space or as depicted symbolically in Fig. 9-12, which shows the Unisphere® in the final stages of its construction. Circles appear true size and shape when the observer's line of sight is perpendicular to the plane of the circle. However, there are many instances when the line of sight is oblique to the plane of the circle; in the resulting foreshortened views the circles will appear as ellipses. The representation of circular features requires an understanding of the principles of ellipse construction.

The following definitions are given to explain terminology associated with ellipses. Refer to Fig. 9-13.

Ellipse. A view of a circle in which the line of sight is oblique to the plane of the circle.

Major Diameter. The greatest possible diameter that can be measured across an ellipse. By definition, a diameter passes through the center of the ellipse. The major diameter is always true length in any view of a circle.

Minor Diameter. The shortest possible diameter that can be measured across an ellipse. This diameter is perpendicular to the major diameter at its midpoint in all views.

Ellipse Angle. The angle between the line of sight and the edge view of the plane of the circle, usually found in a primary auxiliary view.

Cylindrical Axis. In a right circular cylinder, an imaginary line connecting the centers of all right sections and perpendicular to them.

Ellipse Template. A template composed of a series of various sizes of ellipses, used for drawing the ellipses when the major and minor diameters are known. Ellipse guides are graduated in 5° intervals (ellipse angles) in most cases. A set of ellipse guides is illustrated in Fig. 9-14.

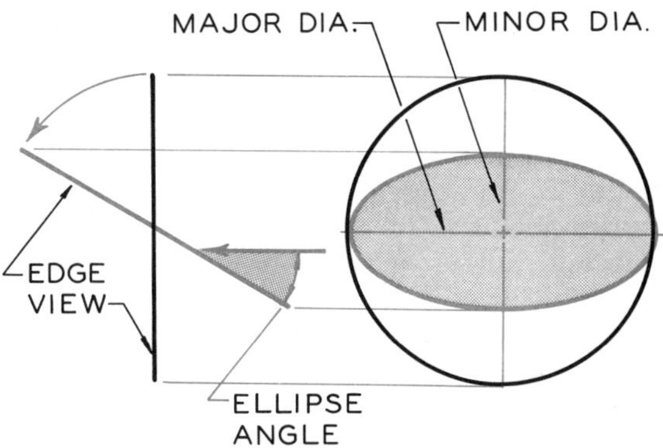

Fig. 9-13. The relationship of an ellipse to a circle and the selection of ellipse templates.

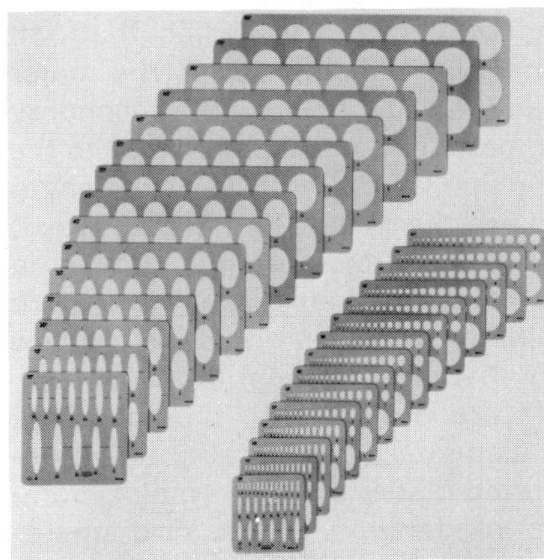

Fig. 9-14. Typical ellipse templates used for ellipse representation. (Courtesy of The A. Lietz Co.)

Fig. 9-15. It can be seen by inspection of tire molds that circles appear as ellipses when viewed obliquely. (Courtesy of ALCOA.)

An example of an elliptical view of a circular shape can be seen in Fig. 9–15, where the line of sight is oblique to the circular plane of the tire mold. Note that the major diameter is true length in any view and the minor diameter is perpendicular to it, as indicated, whether the object is viewed in actuality or depicted in a drawing.

Suppose that we are required to construct a circle passing through points 1, 2, and 3 as shown in all views in Fig. 9–16. The true size of plane 1–2–3 must be found in order to construct the circle in true shape. The circle is found in step 1 by locating the center, where the three perpendicular bisectors of each line of the plane intersect, and by selecting a radius that will pass through each point. In step 2, the major and minor diameters are drawn in the secondary auxiliary view parallel and perpendicular to the 1–2 reference line. Both will be true length in this view since the plane is true size. Next, the diameters of the circle are projected to the edge view in the primary auxiliary view, where the major diameter coincides with the edge view and the minor diameter is equal to zero. Then the diameters are projected to the top view, where major diameter *CD* is parallel to a true-length line on the plane, since the major diameter is always true length. The major-diameter length is found by transferring the measurements from the secondary auxiliary view, as shown in step 2. The minor diameter is drawn perpendicular to the major diameter through point *O*. Its length is found by projecting points *A* and *B* from the edge view. These diameters will be used to position the ellipse template that will be used to draw the ellipse in the top view. The ellipse template angle is found in the primary auxiliary view by measuring the angle between the line of sight and the edge view of the plane. The ellipse size is selected from the ellipse template such that it will be as nearly equal to the major diameter as possible. The ellipse can be drawn by aligning the cross markings on the template with the major and minor diameters.

The construction of the ellipse in the front view is found in much the same manner as in step 2; however, the true-size view is unnecessary since the center of the circle has been found in step 1. Point *O* is projected to the front view of plane 1–2–3. The edge view of the plane is found by projecting from the front view, where the ellipse guide angle can be found as shown in step 3. Note that the edge view of the plane is extended on each side of point *O* in order for the diameter to appear true length in this view. The major diameter is drawn true length in the front view through point *O* parallel to a true-length line in the plane. The minor diameter is perpendicular to the major diameter and its length is found by projecting its extreme points from the edge view of the circle. The ellipse template can be used to construct the completed elliptical view as well as to find the top view.

There are several methods of constructing ellipses graphically without the use of an ellipse template; however, these methods are tedious and require considerable time. The ellipse template affords the designer the most practical method of constructing ellipses. Today's technology demands that time be used as economically as possible, thereby emphasizing methods that will expedite all phases of the engineering process.

Right circular cylinders are closely related to ellipses in that they are composed of a series of circles that may project as ellipses in conventional views. The construction of cylinders that appear foreshortened requires that the procedures outlined in Fig. 9–16 be followed, with the addition of one step. This additional step is the construction of the axis of the cylinder. The right sectional ends of a cylinder will be perpendicular to the axis of a cylinder, as shown in Fig. 9–17B. It is rather obvious even to the untrained eye that the ends of the cylinder in part A of the figure are not perpendicular to the cylindrical axis. When a line is perpendicular to a plane, it is perpendicular to all of the lines in that plane intersecting at the piercing point. Such a line will project as perpendicular to any true-length line in a perpendicular plane; consequently, the axis of a right cylinder will always be perpendicular to the major diameter

FIGURE 9–16. ELLIPTICAL VIEWS OF A CIRCLE

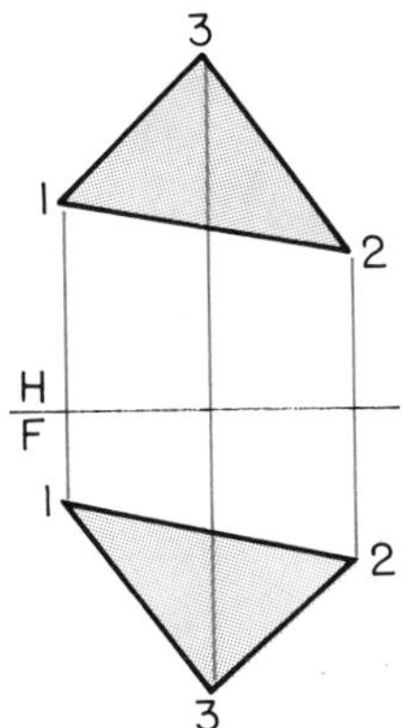

Given: The top and front views of plane 1–2–3.
Required: Construct a circle that will pass through each vertex of the plane. Show the circle in all views.
References: Articles 9–5 and 9–6.

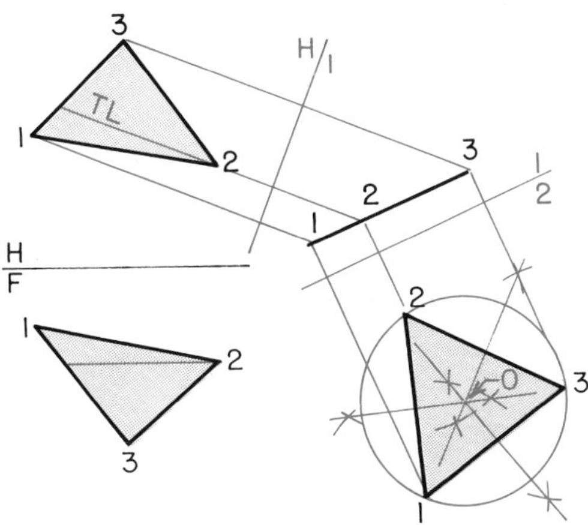

Step 1: Determine the true size of plane 1–2–3 in the manner illustrated in Article 9–5. Draw a circle through the vertexes in the true-size view. The center of the circle, *O*, is found at the intersection of the perpendicular bisectors of each of the triangle's sides.

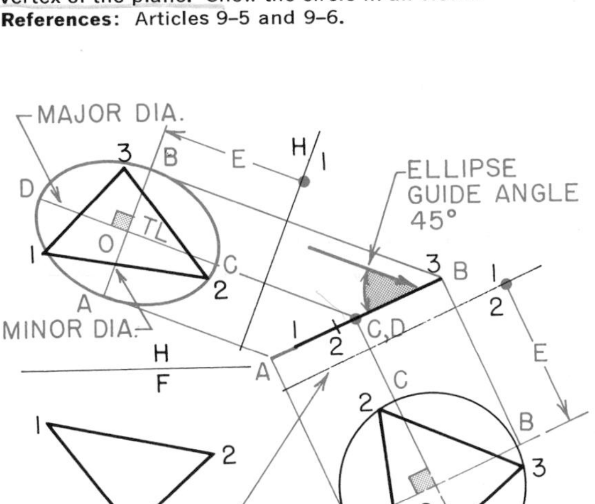

Step 2: Draw the diameters, *AB* and *CD*, parallel and perpendicular to the 1–2 line, respectively, in the secondary auxiliary view. Project these lines to the primary auxiliary and top views, where they will represent the major and minor diameters of an ellipse. Select the ellipse template for drawing the top view by measuring the angle between the line of sight and the edge view of the plane.

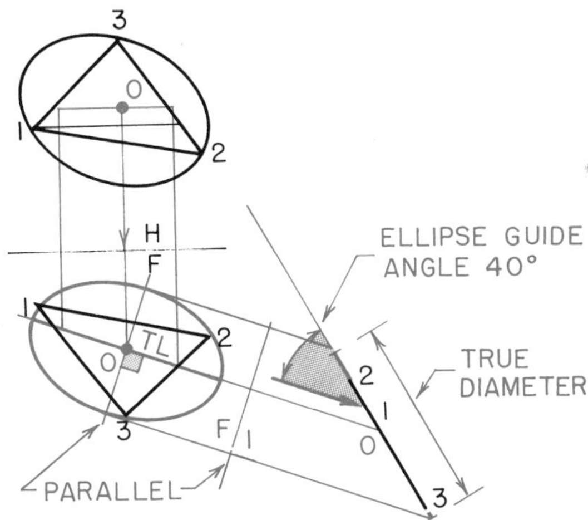

Step 3: Determine the particular ellipse template for drawing the ellipse in the front view by locating the edge view of the plane in an auxiliary view which is projected from the front view. The ellipse angle is measured in the auxiliary view as shown. Note that the major diameter is true length and that it is parallel to a true-length line on the plane in the front view. The minor diameter is perpendicular to it.

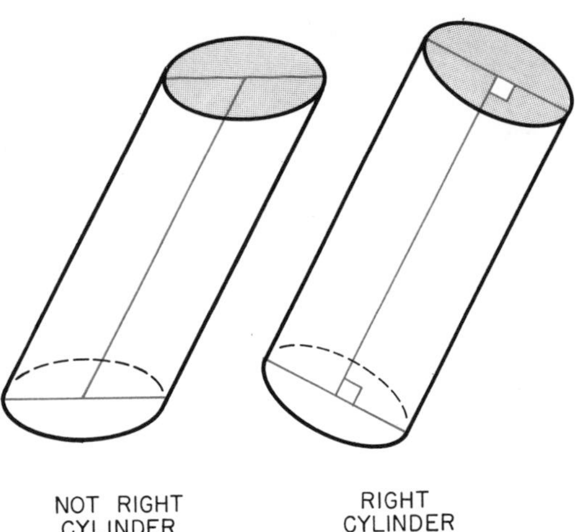

Fig. 9–17. The axis of a right cylinder is perpendicular to the major diameter of its right section.

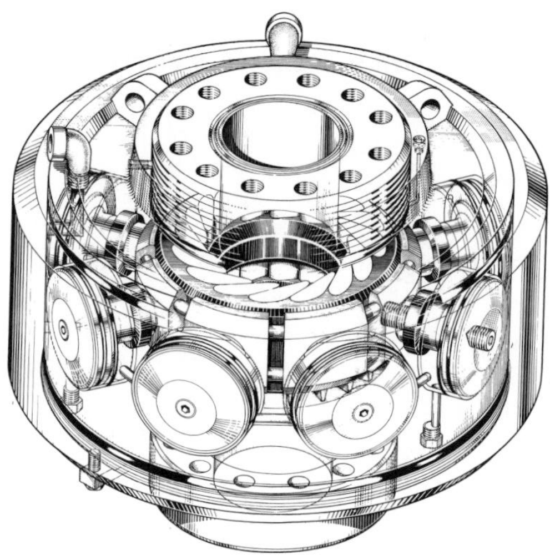

Fig. 9–18. This diaphanous view of a blowout preventer was drawn using an ellipse template to illustrate the circular features. (Courtesy of Cameron Iron Works, Inc., and L. G. Whitfield.)

of the elliptical right section in a foreshortened view. This is illustrated in Fig. 9–17B. An example of the application of this principle is shown in Fig. 9–18, a pictorial of a blowout preventer. Note that there are elliptical holes and features in the internal portion of the device; the drawing of these required the application of the previously covered principles.

9–7 SHORTEST DISTANCE FROM A POINT TO A LINE

The shortest distance from a given point to a line must be known in order to make the most economical use of material, whether it is pipe, structural members, or power conductors. The steps required to find this shortest distance are given in Fig. 9–19.

The true length of the line is found in step 1 and its point view is found in step 2. The perpendicular distance from the point to the line can be seen true length in the view in which the line appears as a point. This line is projected to the primary auxiliary view, where it will be perpendicular to the line that is true length. Since line 3–0 is true length in the secondary auxiliary view, it must be parallel to the 1–2 reference plane in the preceding view, as shown in step 3. Line 3–0 is projected back to the other views in sequence.

The shortest distance from a point to a line can also be found by an alternative method covered in Article 9–5. The true size of plane 1–2–3 can be found where the perpendicular distance can be drawn perpendicular to line 1–2 and measured true length in the same view.

It can be seen in Fig. 9–20 that in industry the determining of the shortest distances from points to lines is a frequent necessity to conserve expensive materials and labor.

9–8 SHORTEST DISTANCE BETWEEN SKEWED LINES—LINE METHOD

The determination of the shortest clearance between two lines is applicable to a number of industrial situations encountered by the engineer and technician. The high-voltage power lines shown in Fig. 9–21 must have a minimum clearance, which is specified by regulations. The design of the support towers will be affected by this specified clearance, as will the safety factors related to the clearance.

FIGURE 9–19. SHORTEST DISTANCE FROM A POINT TO A LINE

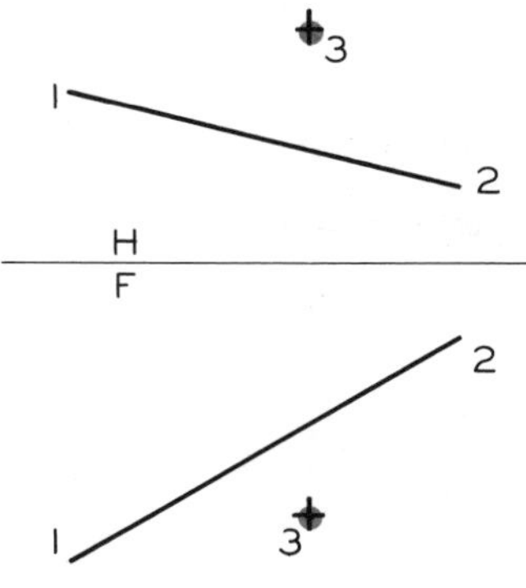

Given: The top and front views of line 1–2 and point 3.
Required: Find the shortest distance from point 3 to line 1–2 and show it in all views.
References: Articles 9–3 and 9–7.

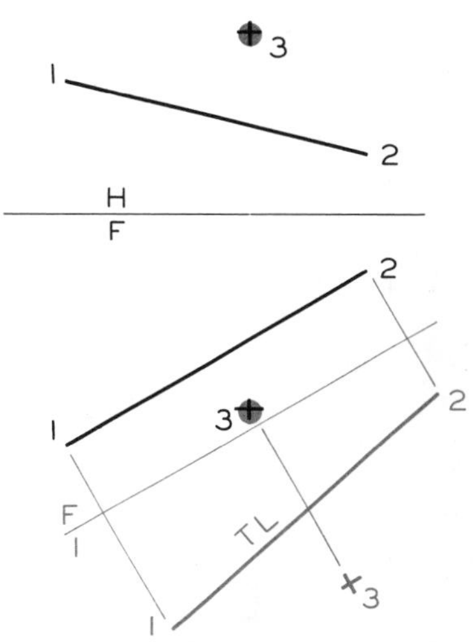

Step 1: Find the true length of line 1–2 by projecting a primary auxiliary view from the front view. Draw the reference line, F–1, parallel to the front view of line 1–2 and make all projections perpendicular to the F–1 line. Project point 3 to this view also.

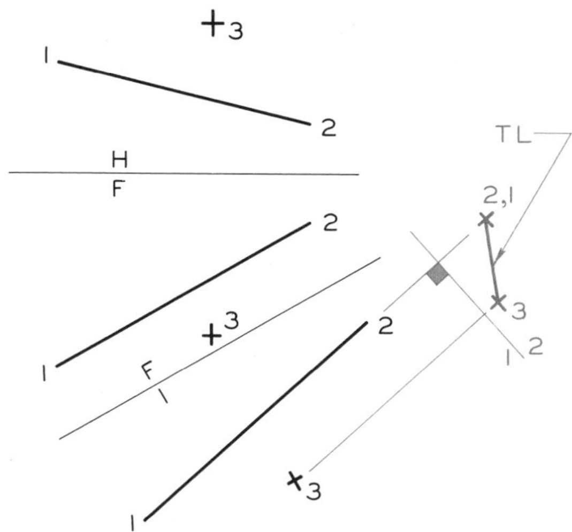

Step 2: Draw a secondary reference line, 1–2, perpendicular to line 1–2, in order to find the point view of line 1–2. The perpendicular distance from point 3 to line 1–2 can be seen true length in this view.

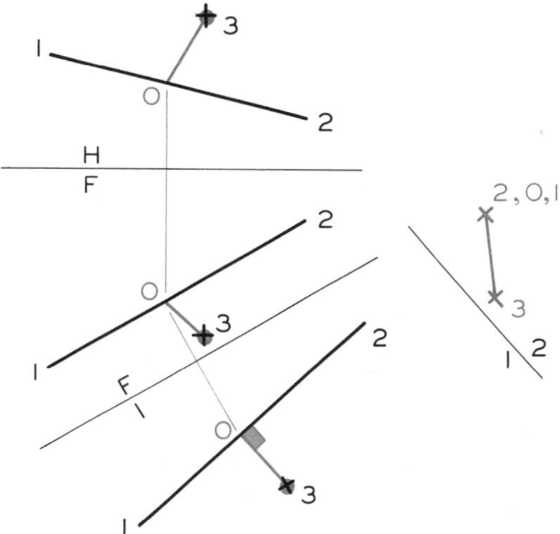

Step 3: Since line 3–O is true length in the secondary auxiliary view, it must be parallel to the 1–2 line in the primary auxiliary view and perpendicular to line 1–2. When one or both perpendicular lines are true length, they will project as perpendicular. Determine the front and top views of line 3–O by projecting from the primary auxiliary view in sequence.

Fig. 9-20. This top structure of a blast furnace involves applications of finding a shortest distance from a point to a line. (Courtesy of Jones & Laughlin Steel Corporation.)

Fig. 9-21. The shortest distance between two crossing high-voltage power lines can be found by descriptive geometry theory. (Courtesy of the Tennessee Valley Authority.)

Two methods—the line method and the plane method—are used to find the shortest distance between two lines. The line method is presented in Fig. 9-22 in sequential steps. Since the shortest distance between two lines will be a line perpendicular to both, the line will appear true length in the secondary auxiliary view, where line 3-4 projects as a point. To establish point *P*, line *OP* is projected to the primary auxiliary view, where it is drawn perpendicular to line 3-4, which is true length in this view. Points *O* and *P* are projected to the front and top views to represent the shortest distance between the two lines.

9-9 SHORTEST DISTANCE BETWEEN SKEWED LINES—PLANE METHOD

The problem covered in Article 9-8 can be solved by the application of the plane method, as illustrated in Fig. 9-23. We shall use the projection principles discussed in Chapter 7 to construct in the top and front views of a plane that is parallel to line 1-2. A line is constructed through a point (point 4 in this case) parallel to line 1-2 in both views. Two intersecting lines, 4-0 and 3-4, form a plane. A number of planes could be constructed in this manner, but all would lie on a common infinite plane. When an edge view of the plane is found in a primary auxiliary view, the two lines will be projected as parallel, as shown in step 1. The plane has served its purpose when the auxiliary view is found and can be ignored in the remaining steps of the solution.

The shortest distance between the two lines will be projected as perpendicular to each of the lines in the primary auxiliary view, where the lines are parallel (step 2). Although a number of lines can be drawn apparently perpendicular to the lines, only one will be truly perpendicular —the one that appears true length in the primary auxiliary view. This line will appear as a point in the secondary auxiliary view, which is projected perpendicularly from the primary auxiliary view, as shown in step 3. Both lines, 1-2 and 3-4, appear true length in this view; consequently, the shortest distance between them is

FIGURE 9-22. SHORTEST DISTANCE BETWEEN SKEWED LINES—LINE METHOD

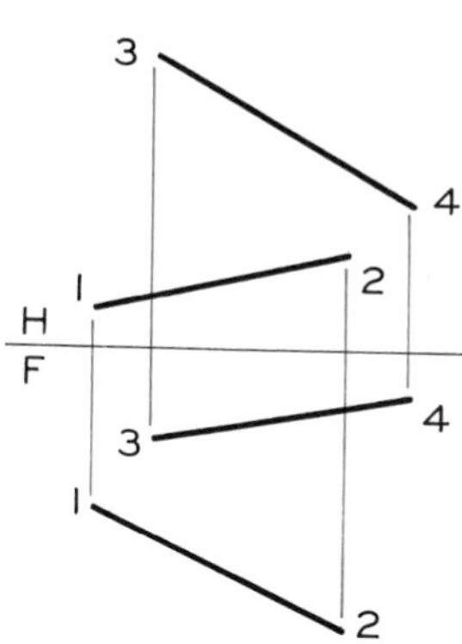

Given: The front and top views of lines 1-2 and 3-4.
Required: Find the shortest distance between the two lines by the line method and show it in all views.
References: Articles 9-3 and 9-8.

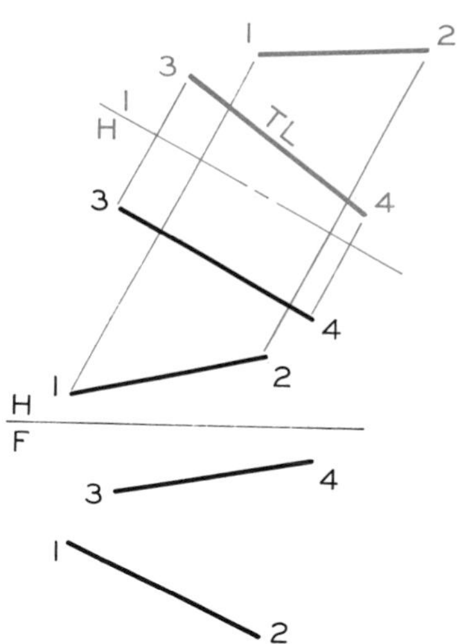

Step 1: Find line 3-4 true length in a primary auxiliary view projected from the horizontal view. Project line 1-2 to this view also. The primary auxiliary view could have been projected from the front view equally well.

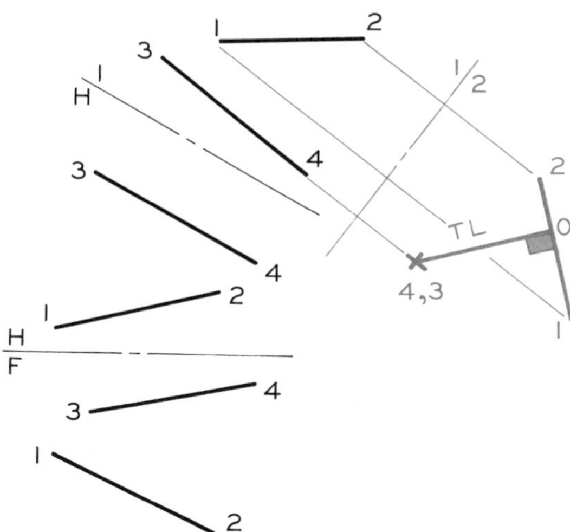

Step 2: Draw a secondary auxiliary view to find line 3-4 as a point. The shortest distance between the two lines is a line perpendicular to both. This line will appear true length in the secondary auxiliary view, where it is drawn perpendicular to line 1-2.

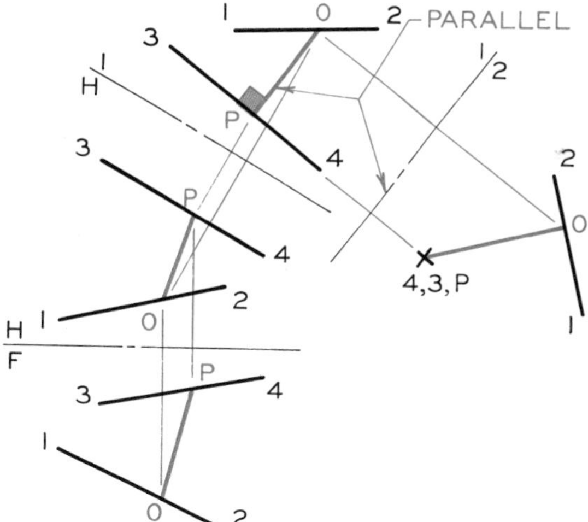

Step 3: Locate *O* in the primary auxiliary view by projection. Locate point *P* on line 3-4 by constructing line *O-P* through point *O* perpendicular to line 3-4. These points are projected back to the top and front views to represent the line. Note that line *O-P* is parallel to the 1-2 reference line in the primary auxiliary view since it is true length in the secondary view.

FIGURE 9–23. SHORTEST DISTANCE BETWEEN SKEWED LINES—PLANE METHOD

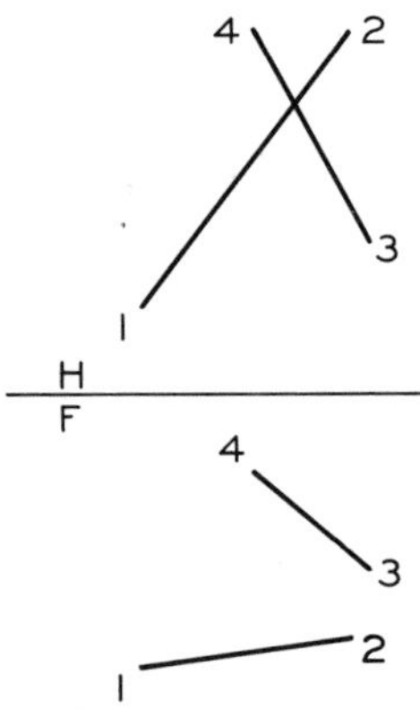

Given: The top and front views of line 1–2 and 3–4.
Required: Find the shortest distance between the two lines by the plane method. Show this distance in all views.
References: Articles 7–19 and 9–9.

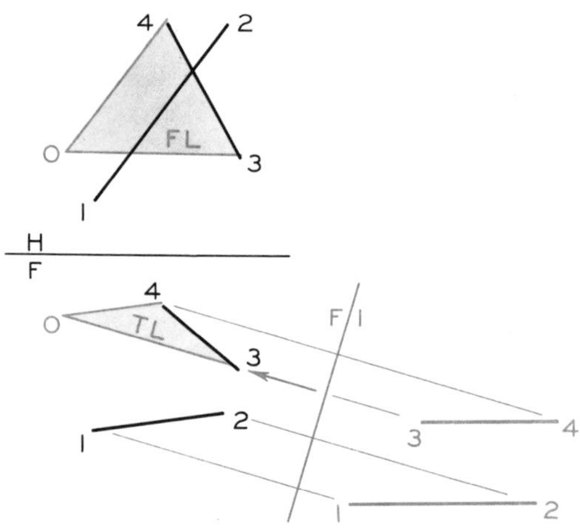

Step 1: Construct a plane through line 3–4 that is parallel to line 1–2. Line 4–0 is drawn parallel to line 1–2 in both views. Since plane 3–4–0 contains a line parallel to line 1–2, the plane is parallel to the line. Both lines project parallel in an auxiliary view where plane 3–4–0 projects as an edge.

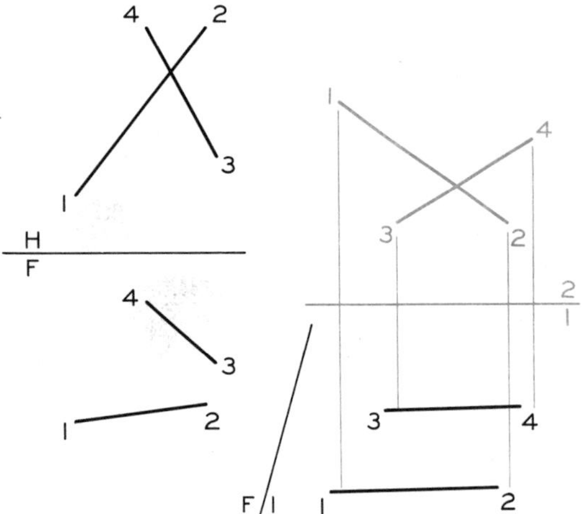

Step 2: The shortest distance will appear true length in the primary auxiliary view, where it will be perpendicular to both lines. Draw a secondary auxiliary view by projecting perpendicularly from the lines in the primary auxiliary view. Lines 1–2 and 3–4 cross in this view.

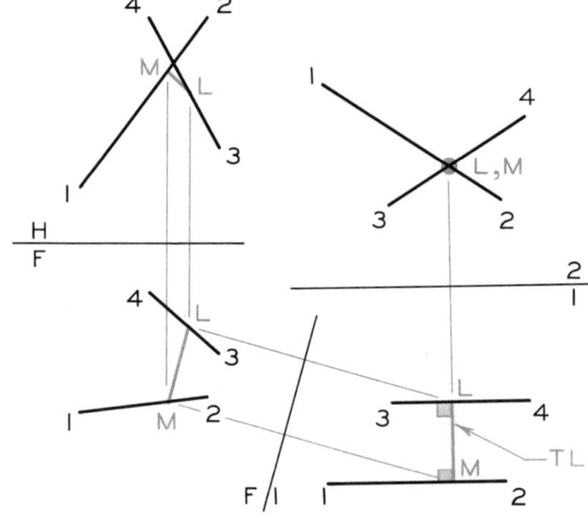

Step 3: The crossing point of lines 1–2 and 3–4 establishes the point view of the perpendicular distance, *LM*, between the lines. This distance is projected to the primary auxiliary view, where it is true length. The line is found in the front and top views by projecting points *L* and *M* to their respective lines in these views.

at the point of crossing, where line *LM* projects as a point. The true-length view of line *LM* is found in the primary auxiliary view. The line is projected to the two principal views to complete the requirements of the problem.

This method of solving for the shortest distance between two lines is the general case that can be used in the solution of problems covered in Articles 9–10 and 9–11. Complicated traffic systems, such as that shown in Fig. 9–24, must be analyzed to determine the clearances between the center lines of the crossing highways. Also, the vertical clearances are critical to the design of the overpasses. Vertical distances between skewed lines appear true length in the front view directly beneath the point where the two lines cross in the top view.

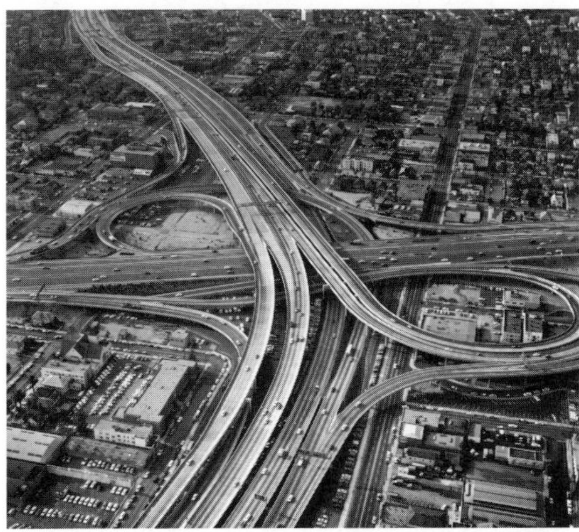

Fig. 9–24. The interchange of Harbor and Santa Monica Freeways in downtown Los Angeles illustrates a variety of skewed line applications. (Courtesy of the California Division of Highways.)

9–10 SHORTEST LEVEL DISTANCE BETWEEN TWO SKEWED LINES

The shortest level, or horizontal, distance between two lines is found by using the plane method in the initial steps, as illustrated in Article 9–9. A plane is constructed through one of the lines to be parallel to the other given line in step 1, Fig. 9–25. An edge view of the plane is projected from the *top view* in order that the horizontal reference line may appear as an edge in the primary auxiliary view, where the level distance can be drawn parallel to the horizontal plane. This problem *cannot* be solved by projecting from the front view, because in that case the frontal plane, rather than the horizontal plane, will appear as an edge. The direction of the shortest level line will appear true length in step 2 and parallel to the H–1 reference line. Only the *shortest* level line will appear true length in this view. A secondary auxiliary view is required to locate its position. The point view of line *LM* is found in the secondary auxiliary view and is projected to the primary auxiliary view, where it appears true length. As a check on the accuracy of the construction, line *LM* should appear level in the front view.

An application of this problem is the connection of two roadways with a level tunnel (Fig. 9–26). This principle is also used to connect mining shafts with tunnels which must remain level, but which also must be as short as possible for reasons of economy.

Fig. 9–26. Construction of a three-mile tunnel to be used for a rapid transit system in the Berkeley Hills area of San Francisco. (Courtesy of Kaiser Engineers.)

FIGURE 9-25. SHORTEST LEVEL DISTANCE BETWEEN SKEWED LINES

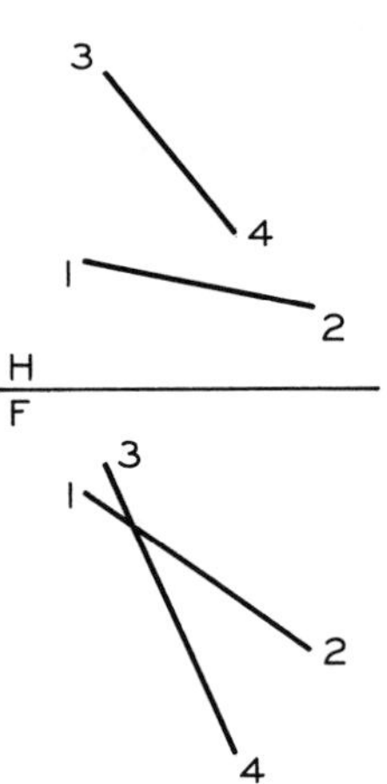

Given: The top and front views of lines 1–2 and 3–4.
Required: Find the shortest level distance between the lines and project it to all views.
References: Articles 7–19, 9–9 and 9–10.

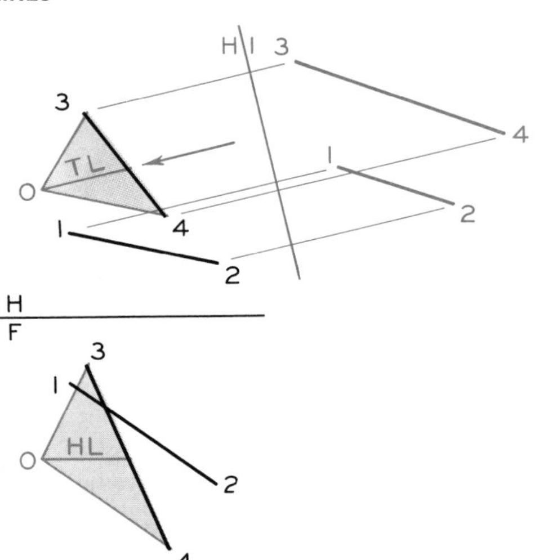

Step 1: Construct plane 3-4-0 parallel to line 1-2 by drawing line 4-0 parallel to line 1-2 in the top and front views. Plane 3-4-0 is found as an edge in the primary auxiliary view where the lines are projected as parallel. *Note:* The primary auxiliary *must* be projected from the *top view* to find the horizontal plane as an edge.

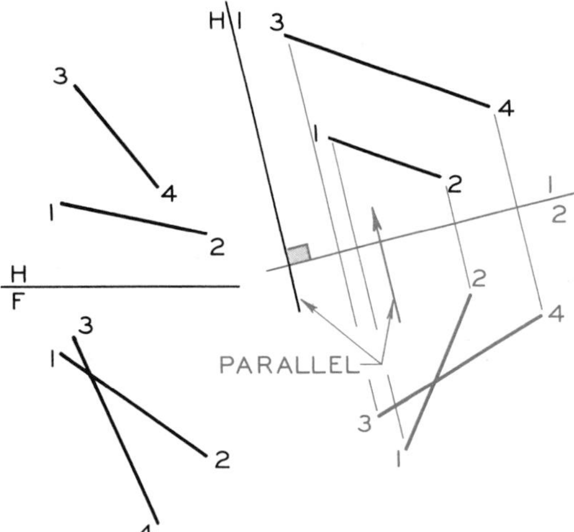

Step 2: An infinite number of horizontal (level) lines can be drawn parallel to H-1, between the lines in the primary auxiliary view, but only the shortest level line will project true length in the primary auxiliary view. Draw the secondary auxiliary plane, 1-2, perpendicular to the H-1 line, and project lines 1-2 and 3-4 to this view.

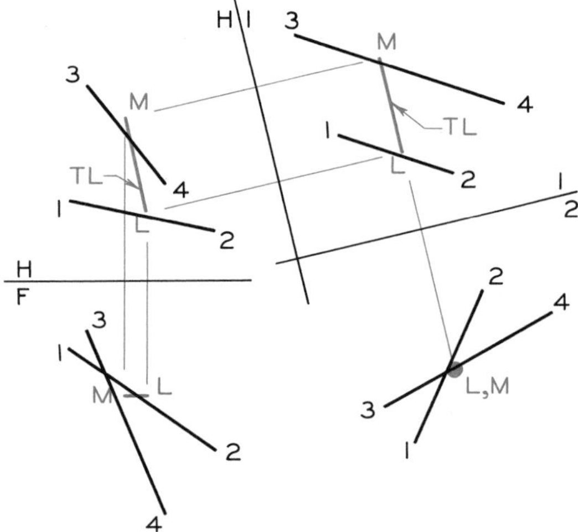

Step 3: The point where lines 1-2 and 3-4 cross in the secondary auxiliary view establishes the point view of line *LM* that will appear true length in the primary auxiliary view. Project line *LM* to the top view and front views. Line *LM* is parallel to the H-plane in the front view, which verifies that it is a level line.

FIGURE 9-27. GRADE DISTANCE BETWEEN SKEWED LINES

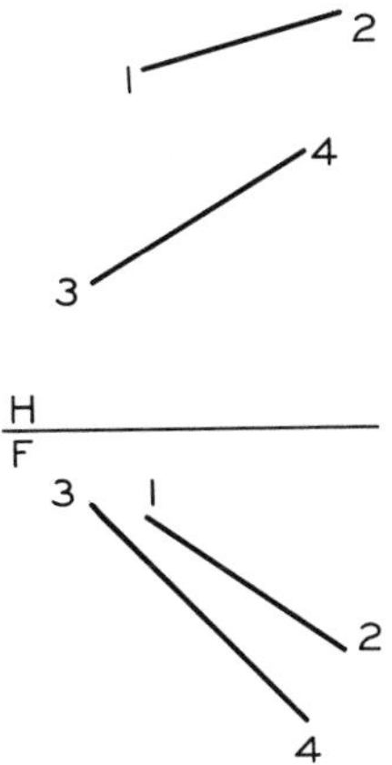

Given: The top and front views of lines 1–2 and 3–4.
Required: Find the shortest line having a 50 percent grade between the two lines.
References: Articles 7–19 and 9–11.

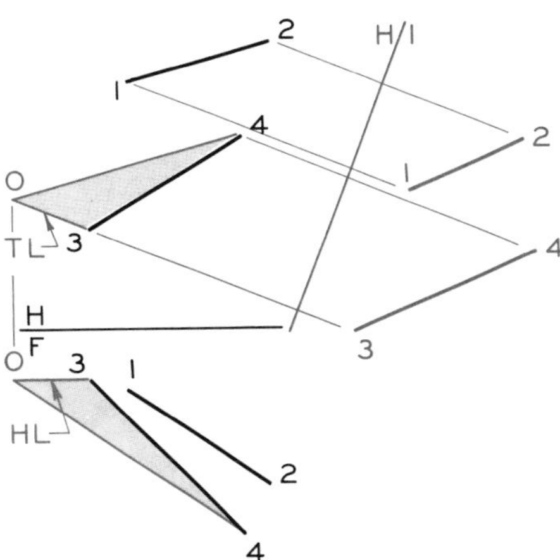

Step 1: Draw 3-4-0 parallel to line 1–2 by drawing line 4–0 parallel to line 1–2 in both views. The edge view of the plane is found where both lines project as parallel. *Note:* The primary auxiliary *must* be projected from the *top* view in order that the horizontal plane may appear as an edge in the primary auxiliary view.

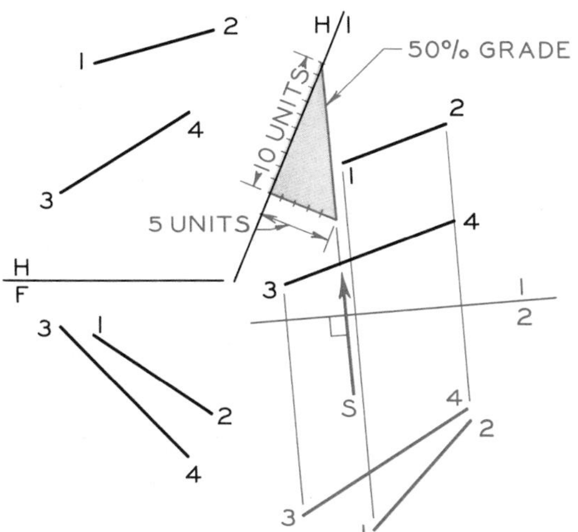

Step 2: Construct a 50-percent grade line with respect to the edge view of the H-1 line in the primary auxiliary view. Draw this line as nearly perpendicular to the lines as possible for the shortest connector. Project a secondary auxiliary parallel to the direction of the grade line. The shortest grade distance will appear true length in the primary auxiliary view.

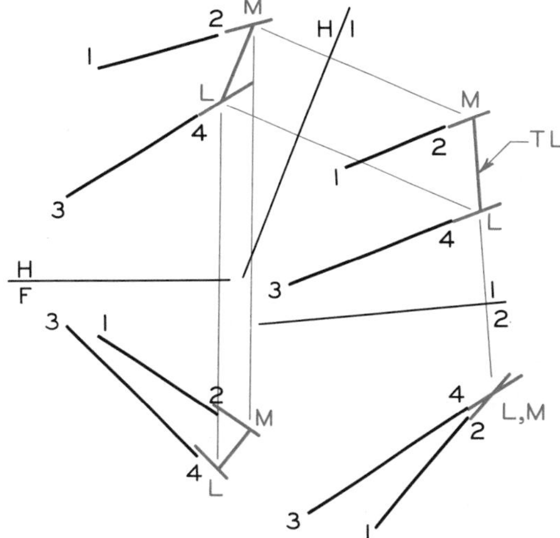

Step 3: Extend the lines in the secondary view to establish their point of intersection, where the point view of *LM* is located. *LM* will appear true length at a 50% grade in the primary auxiliary. Line *LM* is projected back to the top and front views. Lines 1–2 and 3–4 must be extended in each view.

9–11 SHORTEST GRADE DISTANCE BETWEEN SKEWED LINES

The plane method introduced in Article 9–9 must be employed in solving for the shortest grade line between two skewed lines. It can be seen from this series of problems that the plane method is a general approach to solving all skewed-line problems, whereas the line method is applicable only to the perpendicular distance between two skewed lines.

The lines are projected as parallel in the primary auxiliary view by finding the edge view of a plane constructed parallel to one of the lines through the other, as shown in step 1 of Fig. 9–27. This primary auxiliary view must be projected from the *top view* in order for the horizontal plane to appear as an edge, from which the percent grade of a line can be drawn. Recall that grade is the ratio of the vertical rise to the horizontal run of a line, expressed as a percentage. These components can be used to establish the specified grade in the primary auxiliary view, as shown in step 2. The grade could be drawn in two directions with respect to the H–1 reference line. However, the shortest grade between two lines will be the line drawn in the direction that is most nearly perpendicular to the lines. This direction can be determined by visual inspection in the primary auxiliary view. The secondary auxiliary line, 1–2, is drawn perpendicular to the grade line that has been constructed, and the view is projected parallel to the direction of the grade line. The lines in this example do not cross in the secondary auxiliary view. Since lines 1–2 and 3–4 are only segments of longer, continuous lines, they can be extended to their point of intersection, as shown in step 3. This locates the point view of the shortest line that can be drawn at a 50-percent grade. This line, *LM*, can be projected back to the horizontal and frontal views, as illustrated.

Figure 9–28 illustrates a multitude of pipes that had to be designed to conform to grade specifications in order for the system to function under design conditions. Figure 9–29 shows a complex traffic interchange where highways connect with intermediate arteries on a grade. Drainage problems and sewer systems must also be critically analyzed with respect to grade distances between drainage channels and culverts.

Fig. 9–28. Clearances between interrelated pipes must be evaluated to reduce cost of materials and installation. (Courtesy of Standard Oil Corporation of New Jersey.)

Fig. 9–29. Highways often present skewed line problems requiring graphical solutions. (Courtesy of the California Division of Highways.)

FIGURE 9–30. A LINE THROUGH A POINT WITH A GIVEN ANGLE TO A LINE

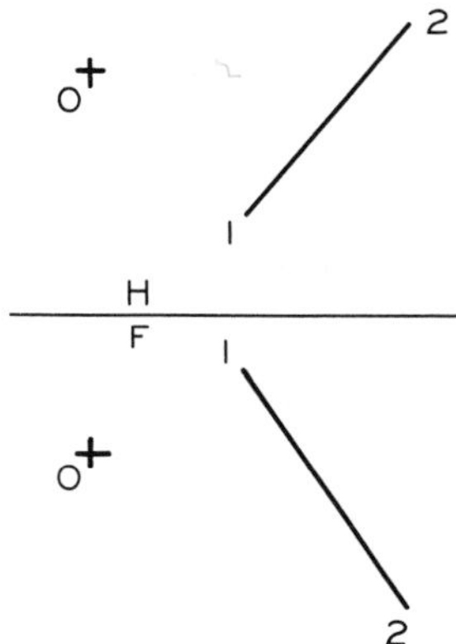

Given: The top and front views of line 1–2 and point *O*.
Required: Construct a line sloping downward from point *O* that will make an angle of 45° with line 1–2.
References: Articles 9–5 and 9–12.

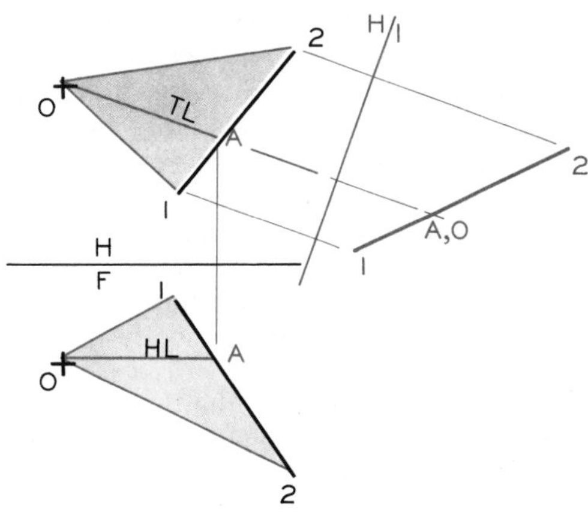

Step 1: Connect point *O* to each end of the line to form plane 1–2–*O* in both views. Draw a horizontal line in the front view of the plane and project it to the top view, where it is true length. Determine the edge view of the plane by finding the point view of line *OA*.

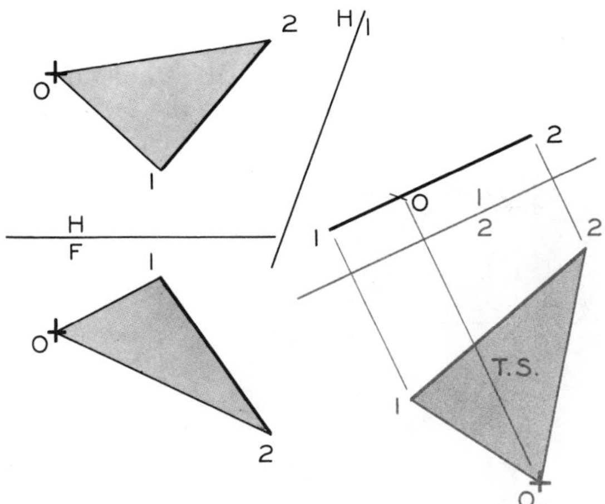

Step 2: Determine the true size of plane 1–2–*O* by perpendicularly projecting an auxiliary view from the edge view of the plane in the primary auxiliary view. The plane need not be drawn in the secondary auxiliary view since it will not be used further.

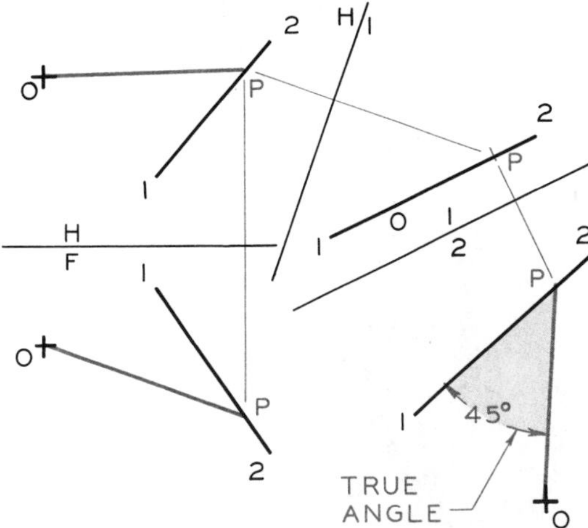

Step 3: Line *OP* can be constructed at the specified angle of 45° with line 1–2 in the secondary auxiliary view toward the low end, since point *O* and line 1–2 lie in the same plane. Project point *P* back to the primary auxiliary, top, and front views, and connect it with point *O*. This problem could have also been solved by projecting from the front view.

9–12 A LINE THROUGH A POINT AT A GIVEN ANGLE TO A LINE

Seldom is it necessary to design all of the components of a single system. In fact, to reduce expense and delay it is customary to utilize as many standard, commercially available parts as possible. Standard connectors are available for joining pipes, structural beams, and other engineering forms encountered in industrial projects. Of course, the standard connectors have been designed for only the most commonly used angles, since it would be economically impossible to provide connectors that varied from 0° to 90° at 1° intervals. Consequently, it is important to know how to design connections corresponding to a given common angle.

The example problem in Fig. 9–30 illustrates the procedure for constructing a line from a given point to another line such that a standard 45° angle will be formed between the lines. This procedure could be utilized practically to design a connection that would allow a standard connector to be used. Symbols for piping drawings as well as the dimensions for standard connections are given in the appendix.

This problem specifies that the line from point *O* slope downward to the line 1–2. Observation of the front view tells you that the point of intersection will be located closer to point 2 than to point 1, since point 2 is the low end of the line. Line *OP* is drawn from point *O* to intersect line 1–2 at 45°, the standard angle, in step 3. Line *OP* is projected back to the given views in sequence.

Designing for standard connectors is common practice in the complex chemical and petroleum industry, as illustrated in Fig. 9–31. The details of construction of a refinery or processing plant are so complicated that often three-dimensional models are used to assist in the solution of the design problems (Fig. 9–32).

9–13 ANGLE BETWEEN A LINE AND A PLANE—PLANE METHOD

Although standard connectors and hardware components should be considered for connecting structural members to a plane, there will be cases where a particular nonstandard angle is unavoidable, so the designer must be able to determine the angle between a line and a plane to design the special connector. This principle has many applications; for instance, in space vehicles the angle of the observer's line of sight to the plane of the instrument panel must fall within the operational limitations previously determined. In addition to a line of sight, a line may also represent a center line of a pipe, a structural member, a power line, or many other components.

These problems are solved by establishing a segment of the plane in question and the line in two views, as given in Fig. 9–33. The plane is

Fig. 9–31. The design of a processing plant such as this involves problems which lend themselves to solution by successive auxiliary views. (Courtesy of Standard Oil Corporation of New Jersey.)

Fig. 9–32. In complicated systems, clearances and optimum distances are often checked by analysis of three-dimensional models. (Courtesy of Esso Research of New Jersey.)

FIGURE 9-33. ANGLE BETWEEN A LINE AND A PLANE—PLANE METHOD

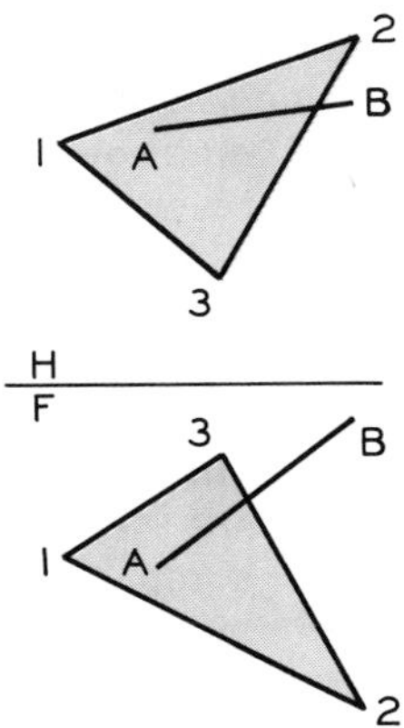

Given: The top and front views of plane 1-2-3 and line *AB*.
Required: Find the angle between the line and plane and determine its visibility in all views.
References: Articles 9-5 and 9-13.

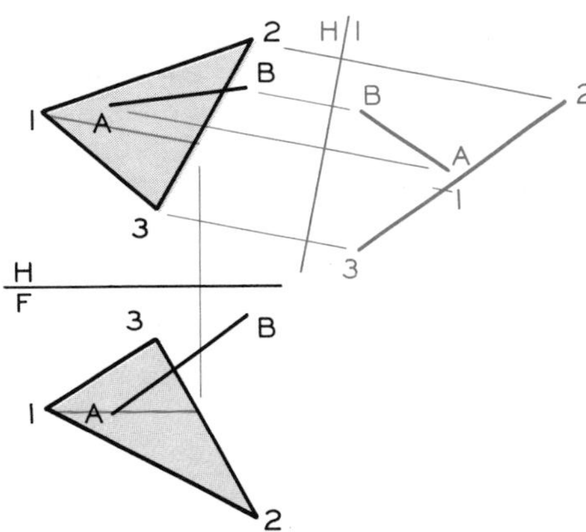

Step 1: Determine the edge view of plane 1-2-3 by projecting from either the front or top view. Find the edge view by projecting from the top view in this example; project line *AB* also. The angle cannot be measured in this view since the line is not true length.

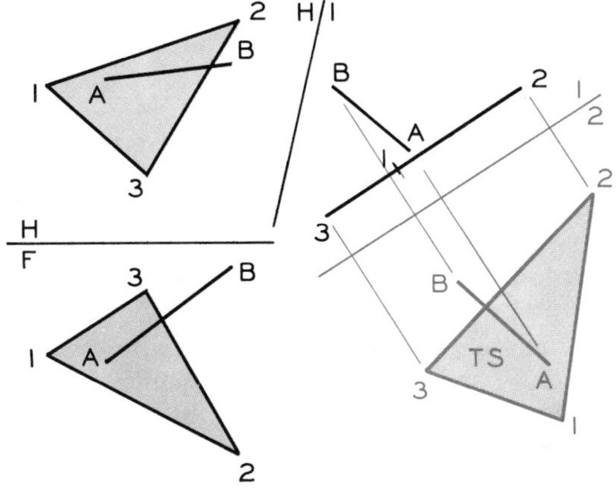

Step 2: Determine the true size of plane 1-2-3 in a secondary auxiliary view projected perpendicularly from the edge view of the plane. Line *AB* is not true length in this view. Draw line *AB* lightly since visibility must be determined.

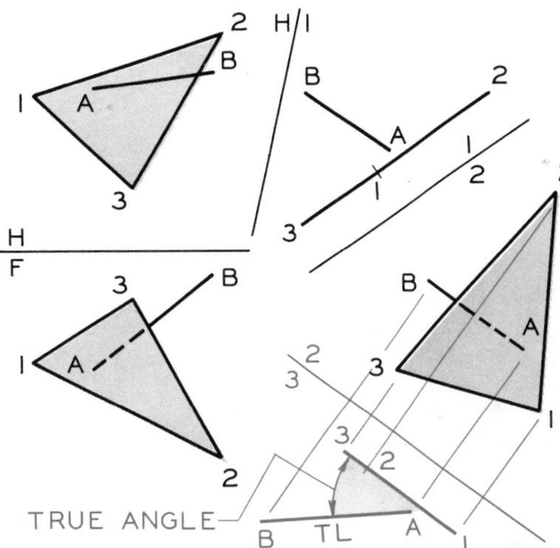

Step 3: A view projected in any direction from a true-size view of a plane will result in an edge view of the plane. Since line *AB* must be true length at the same time, project a third auxiliary view perpendicularly from line *AB*. The line appears true length and the plane appears as an edge, thus satisfying the conditions for measuring the angle between them. Visibility is shown in all views.

found as an edge in the primary auxiliary view in step 1, and true size in step 2. Since the plane is true shape in this view, any auxiliary view projected from it will result in an edge view of the plane. The third auxiliary view plane, 2-3, is drawn parallel to line *AB* in step 3 in order to find the true length of line *AB* and an edge view of the plane. The true angle between a line and a plane can be measured in the view where the plane appears as an edge and the line appears true length. This condition exists in step 3; therefore, the true angle can be measured in the third auxiliary view.

An application of this principle can be seen in Fig. 9-34 in the Hydra 5 sea-test vehicle. A series of tripods have been constructed at intervals along the body of the vehicle. Finding the angle which one leg of each tripod forms with the other two is the same as finding the angle between a line and a plane, since two intersecting lines form a plane. This information was necessary to design the tripods. Similarly, the angles between the guy rods and the plane of the cylindrical collar at the left end were required for design of the bracing connectors.

Fig. 9-34. The Hydra 5 sea-test vehicle required application of the principle for finding the angle between a line and plane by successive auxiliary views. (Courtesy of Pacific Missile Range, Naval Missile Center.)

9-14 ANGLE BETWEEN A LINE AND A PLANE—LINE METHOD

An alternative method for finding the angle between a line and a plane is the line method illustrated in Fig. 9-35. The true length of line *AB* is found in step 1 and the point view of the line is found in step 2. Any view of a line projected from its point view will show the true length of the line. A line is constructed on the plane in the primary auxiliary view that is parallel to the 1-2 reference line. This line is projected to the plane in the secondary auxiliary view, where it appears true length on plane 1-2-3. Since line *AB* appears as a point in the secondary auxiliary view, any view projected from it will result in a true-length view of the line. Therefore the edge view of the plane can be found in the third auxiliary view by projecting a point view of the true-length line on the plane (step 3). The line appears true length and the plane appears as an edge, making possible the measurement in the final view. The point of intersection is located in each view and the visibility is determined.

9-15 SUMMARY

Successive auxiliary views can be used to great advantage to refine preliminary designs and to determine information that is needed for design finalization and analysis. Many of the solutions illustrated would be virtually impossible without using the principles of descriptive geometry and graphical methods. The engineer and technician should have command of these methods in order to recognize problems that lend themselves to graphical solutions but which would be difficult to solve by other methods.

It should be remembered that auxiliary views are merely orthographic projections that have the same relationship to each other as do principal views. Fundamentals of orthographic projection can be reviewed in Chapter 7. A thorough understanding of these basic principles is a prerequisite to the solution of problems by successive auxiliary views, since each construction step must be analyzed for spatial relationships before the next view is projected.

FIGURE 9–35. ANGLE BETWEEN A LINE AND A PLANE—LINE METHOD

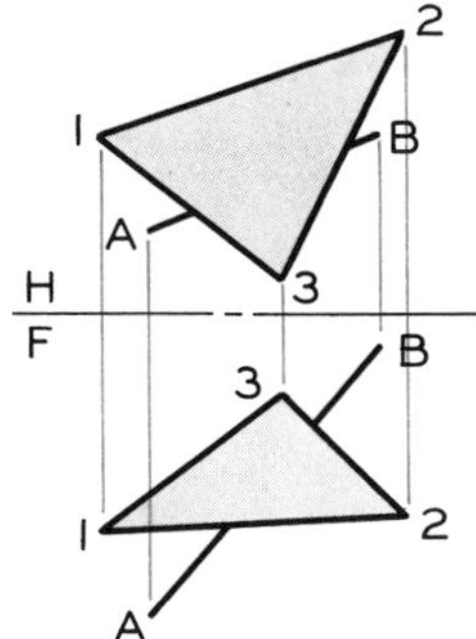

Given: The top and front views of plane 1–2–3 and line *AB*.
Required: Find the angle between line *AB* and plane 1–2–3 by the line method.
References: Articles 9–13 and 9–14.

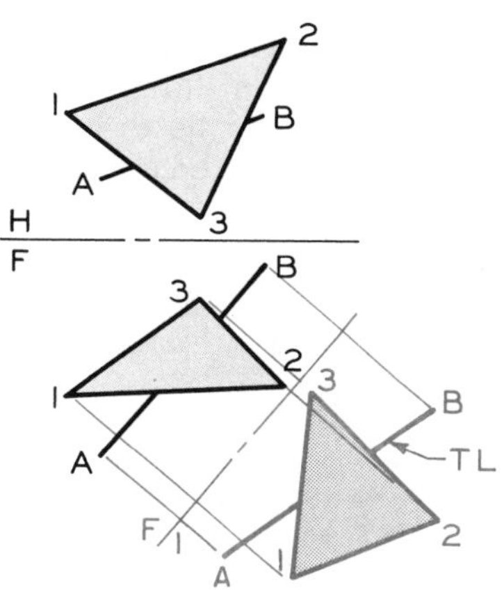

Step 1: Determine the true length of line *AB* in a primary auxiliary view by projecting from either principal view. Plane 1–2–3 is projected also; however, it does not appear true size in this view except in a special case.

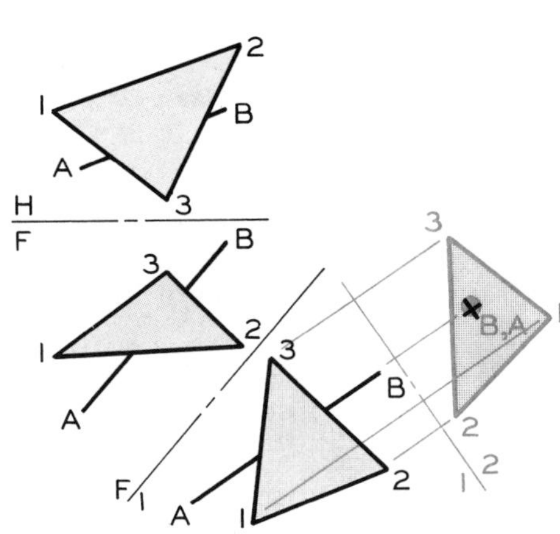

Step 2: Construct the point view of line *AB* in the secondary auxiliary view. Plane 1–2–3 does not appear true size in this view unless the line is perpendicular to the plane. The point view of the line in this view is also the piercing point on the plane.

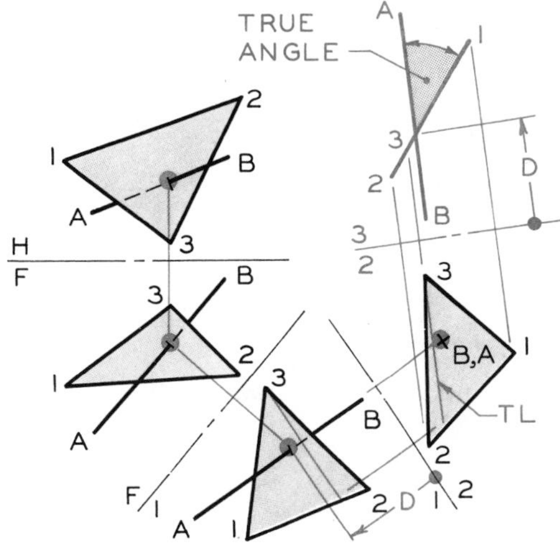

Step 3: Construct a true-length line on plane 1–2–3 in the secondary auxiliary view, from which the edge view of the plane can be found in the third auxiliary view. Line *AB* will be true length in this view, since it appeared as a point in the secondary auxiliary view. Measure the angle in the third auxiliary view and determine the piercing point and visibility in the previous views.

PROBLEMS

Lay out the following problems on graph paper with a $\frac{1}{4}''$ grid. The method of locating the starting points on each problem is illustrated in Fig. 9–36. These problems can be drawn on blank paper with a scale if preferred. Refer to Article 1–19.

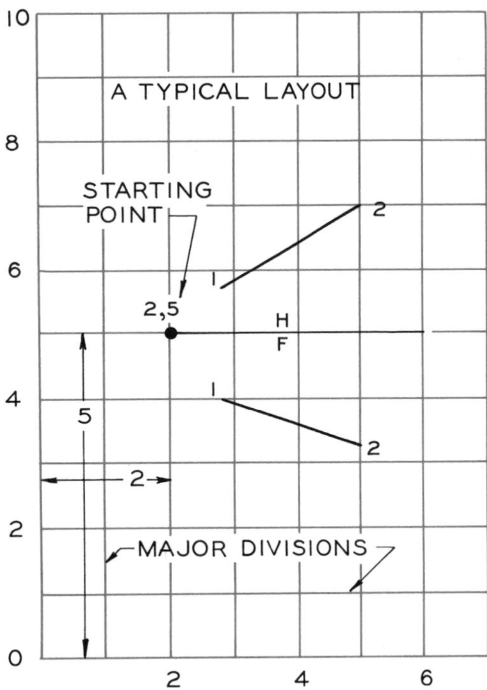

Figure 9–36

Point View of a Line

1 and 2. Find the point views of the lines in Fig. 9–37.

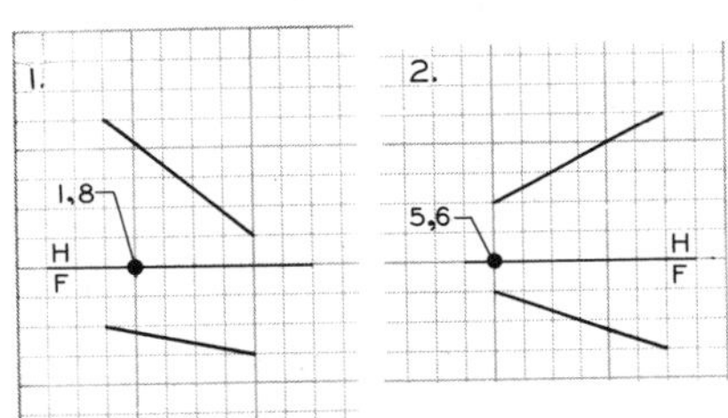

Figure 9–37

Angle between Two Planes

3 and 4. Find the angle between the intersecting planes shown in Fig. 9–38.

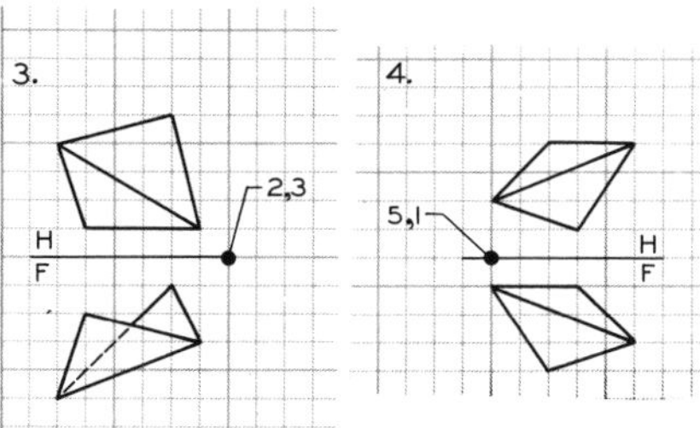

Figure 9–38

True Size of a Plane

5. Find the true size of the plane in Fig. 9–39.

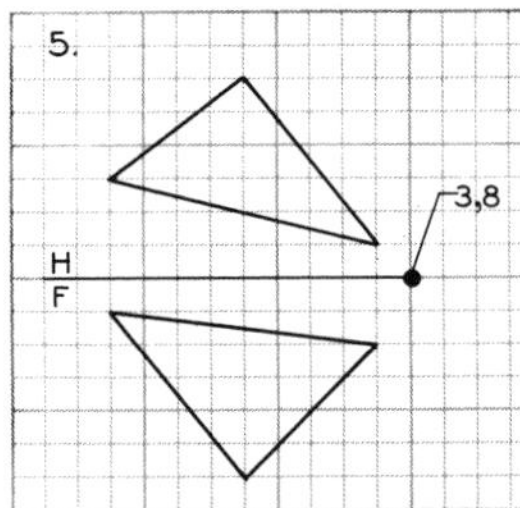

Figure 9–39

6. Find the bend angle at point 2 in Fig. 9–40. Find the length of pipe from point 1 to point 3, including the arc distance, given that the radius of bend is 3′ with the center line of the pipe. Scale: $\frac{1}{4}'' = 1'\text{-}0''$.

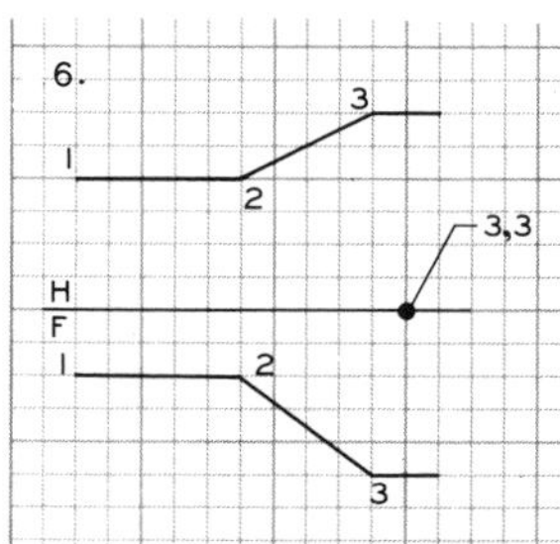

Figure 9–40

Elliptical View of a Circle

7. Points 1, 2, and 3 in Fig. 9–41 are points on the earth which are located vertically beneath a great-circle path of an orbiting satellite. Plot the path of the satellite in all views.

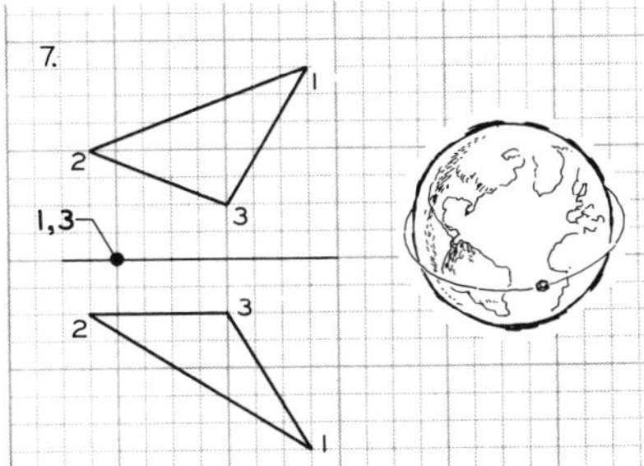

Figure 9–41

8. Line 1–2 in Fig. 9–42 represents the center line of a right cylinder in which each circular end is perpendicular to the axis. Show the cylinder in all views with a 1″ diameter.

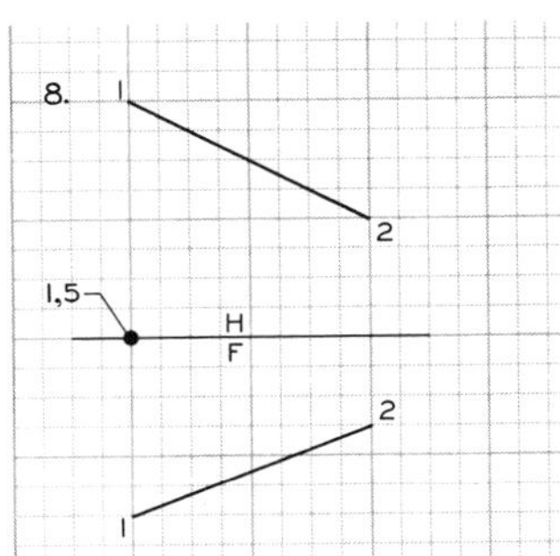

Figure 9–42

Shortest Distance from a Point to a Line

9. A pipe is to be connected with a standard 90° tee to the pipe represented by line 3–4 in Fig. 9–43. Find the shortest distance from point *O* to line 3–4, where the tee will be inserted.

10. Find the shortest distance from point *P* to line 5–6 in Fig. 9–43. Show it in all views.

Skewed Lines

11. The two skewed lines in Fig. 9–44 represent nearly straight segments of two high-voltage power lines that cross on irregular terrain. Determine the clearance between the lines by the line method. Scale: $\frac{1}{8}'' = 1'\text{-}0''$.

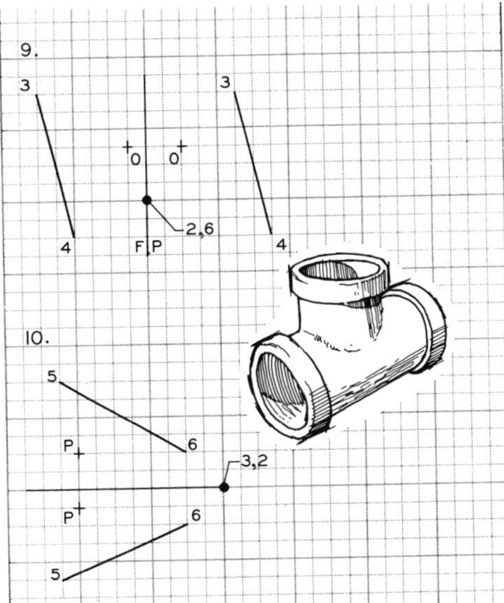

Figure 9–43

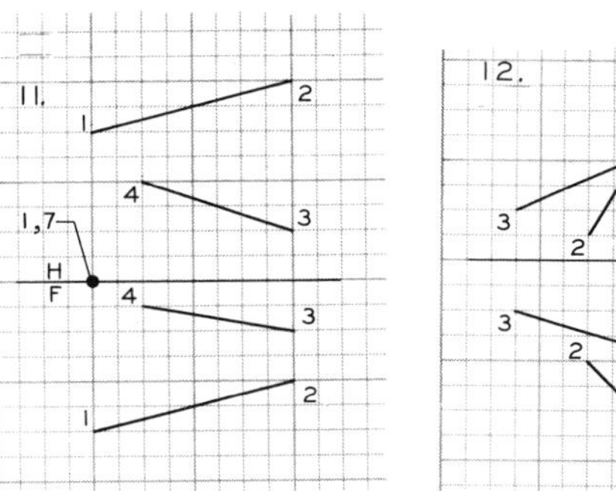

Figure 9–44

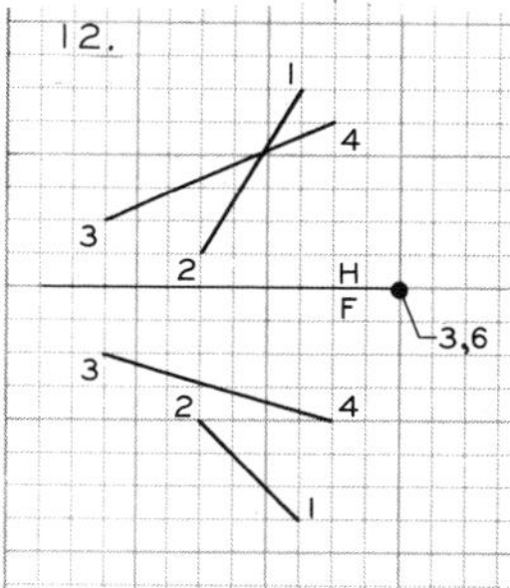

Figure 9–45

12. On one page, find the shortest distance between the skewed lines in Fig. 9–45 by the plane method.

13. On a separate page, solve problem 12 by the line method.

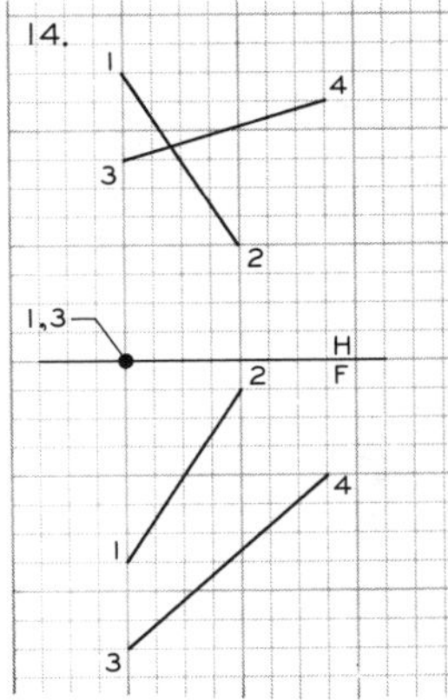

Figure 9–46

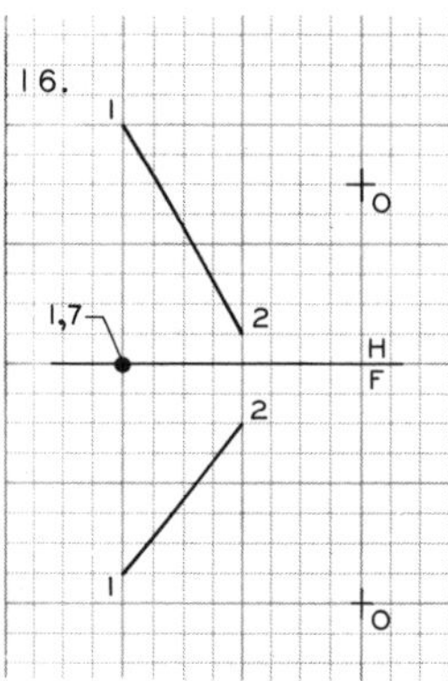

Figure 9–47

14. Find the shortest horizontal distance between the two skewed lines in Fig. 9–46 and show it in all views.

15. Find the shortest 50 percent grade distance between the lines given in problem 14 on a separate sheet.

Angle from a Point to a Line

16. In Fig. 9–47, find the shortest distance from point O to line 1–2 that will intersect at 60°, thus allowing standard connecting hardware to be used. Lay out and solve this problem on a separate sheet.

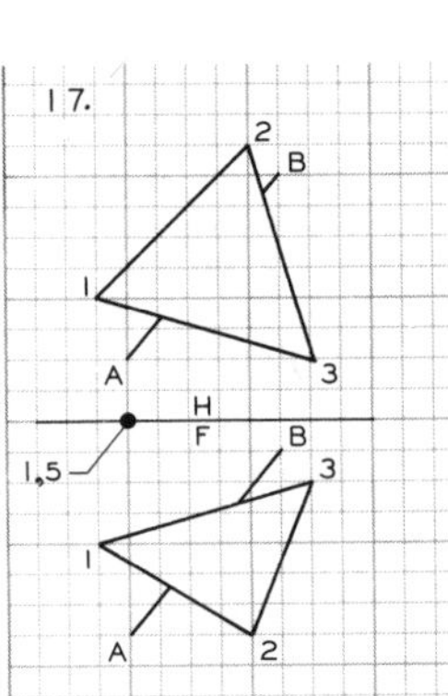

Figure 9–48

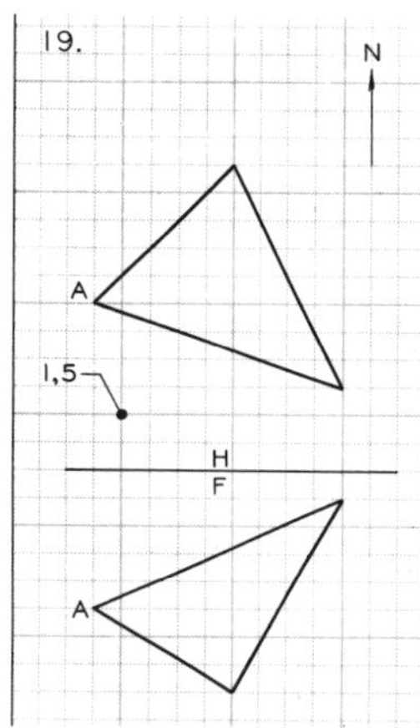

Figure 9–49

Angle between a Line and a Plane

17. Find the angle between the plane and the line in Fig. 9–48 by the plane method and show visibility in all views.

18. On a separate sheet, find the angle between the plane and the line given in problem 17, using the line method. Show visibility in all views.

Combination problem

19. In Fig. 9–49, a line that is 2.3″ long is to be constructed through point A that will have a bearing of N 66° E and slope upward from point A with a 20° slope. Draw this line in all views. Find the angle between this line and the plane.

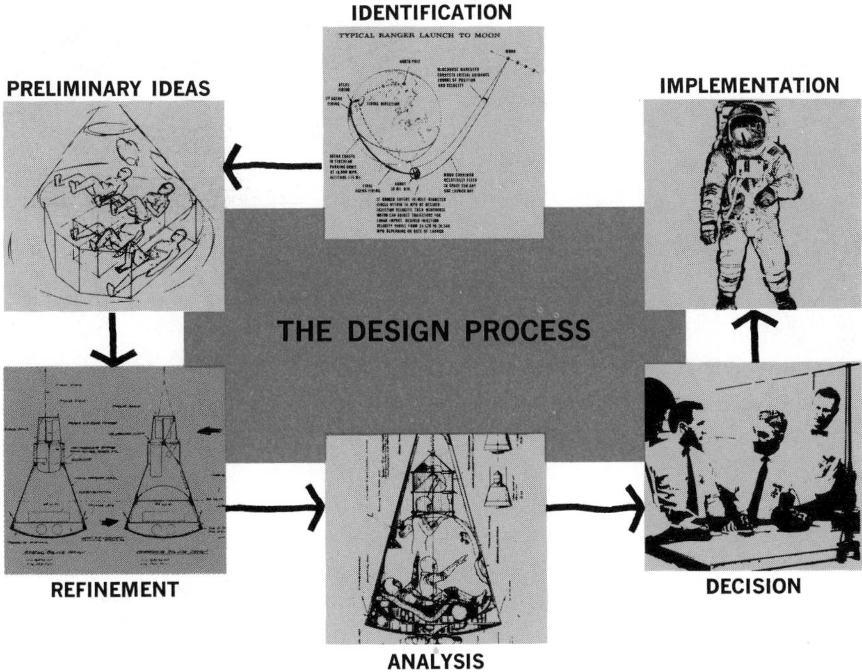

10 REVOLUTION

10–1 INTRODUCTION

The F-111, the world's first variable-geometry aircraft, is shown in Fig. 10–1 in a sequence of photographs which illustrate the full range of positions of its wings during flight. The wings are shown revolved from a 16° spread at takeoff to a fully swept 72.5° they assume for supersonic speed.

This plane will be able to do everything the military services want—take off from or land on a relatively rough, unimproved forward-area airfield or a naval carrier deck; cruise long distances or "loiter" for extended periods; dash to the attack at more than twice the speed of sound; fly supersonically at high altitudes or fly "hugging the deck"; have transoceanic range; be able, with aerial refueling, to be ferried anywhere in the world within one day.

The development of an aircraft of this type involved many hours of testing, planning, and design. The wing system of the plane is an example of an application of revolution to the design of an aircraft that permits variable positions during flight.

Revolution is another method of solving problems that could also, in most cases, be solved by auxiliary views. It is sometimes more advantageous to use the revolution method than the auxiliary view method, which was covered in Chapters 8 and 9. An understanding of revolution will reinforce an understanding of auxiliary view principles, which is necessary for the solution of spatial problems. Many engineering

Fig. 10–1. The F-111, the world's first variable-geometry aircraft designed as an operational plane, involves principles of revolution in the design of its wings. (Courtesy of General Dynamics Corporation.)

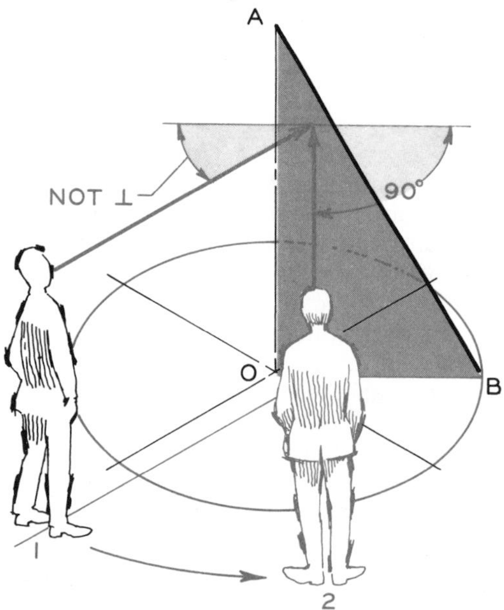

Fig. 10–2. The observer in the conventional front-view position will not see the true length of line *AB*, whereas the line will appear true length when viewed from position 2.

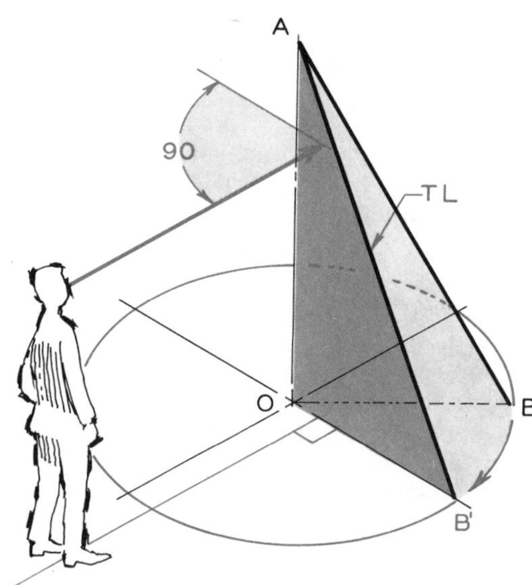

Fig. 10–3. The observer will see line *AB* true length in the front view when it has been revolved in the horizontal plane until the line becomes frontal line *AB'*.

designs utilize rotating or revolving mechanisms that must be analyzed for critical information by means of the principles of revolution.

The basic relationship between the projection method and revolution is shown in Fig. 10–2, where the observer, located at point 1, is viewing line *AB* from the front. Note that line *AB* is drawn as though it were an element of a cone, with line *AO* as the axis of the cone. The observer at point 1 will not see the true length of the line since his line of sight is not perpendicular to plane *ABO* in which line *AB* lies. The observer can change his position by moving to point 2, and, looking perpendicularly at plane *ABO*, he then sees line *AB* true length. This illustrates the auxiliary view method, as covered in Chapter 8. The observer moves his position to obtain the desired view, while the object being viewed remains stationary.

The true-length view of the line could be found by the observer located at position 1 in Fig. 10–2 if the line were revolved while he remained stationary. To demonstrate this principle, we revolve line *AB* in Fig. 10–3 into plane *AOB′*, which is perpendicular to the observer's line of sight. An observer whose line of sight is perpendicular to the axis of a cone will always see a triangular section of the cone in true size and shape. In this case, the observer is standing at the conventional front view position and he is viewing an oblique line that does not appear true length in the front view. Then point *B* is revolved into the true-size frontal plane, *AOB′*. The observer has not moved, but the line has been revolved into a plane perpendicular to his line of sight. In the auxiliary view method the observer changes positions, whereas in the revolution method the line is revolved to a new position while the observer remains stationary.

Fig. 10–4. The true length of the structural members of Saturn S-IVB could be found by revolution during the refinement process. (Courtesy of National Aeronautics and Space Administration.)

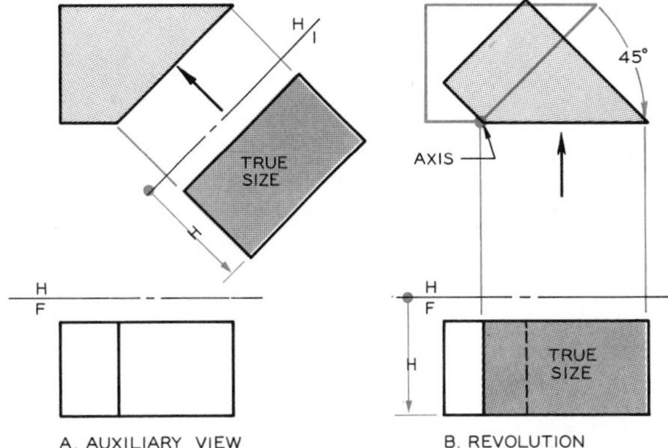

Fig. 10–5. A comparison of the auxiliary view with revolution to find the true size of a plane as it would appear on your drawing paper.

10–2 TRUE LENGTH OF A LINE IN THE FRONT VIEW BY REVOLUTION

The Saturn S-IVB, shown in Fig. 10–4, has a conical configuration composed of intersecting structural members. The lengths of these and the angles they make with the circular planes at each end can be determined by applying revolution principles as well as by applying auxiliary views. The procedure for this is developed in the following explanation.

A simple object (Fig. 10–5) is used to introduce the principles required to find a plane

FIGURE 10–6. TRUE LENGTH IN THE FRONT VIEW

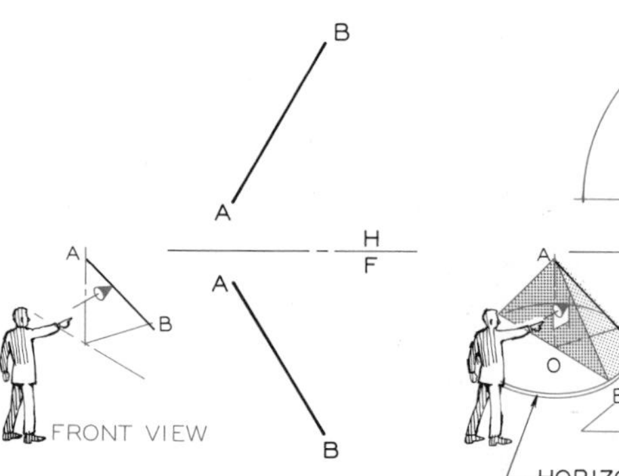

Given: The top and front views of line *AB*.
Required: Find the true-length view of line *AB* in the front view by revolution.

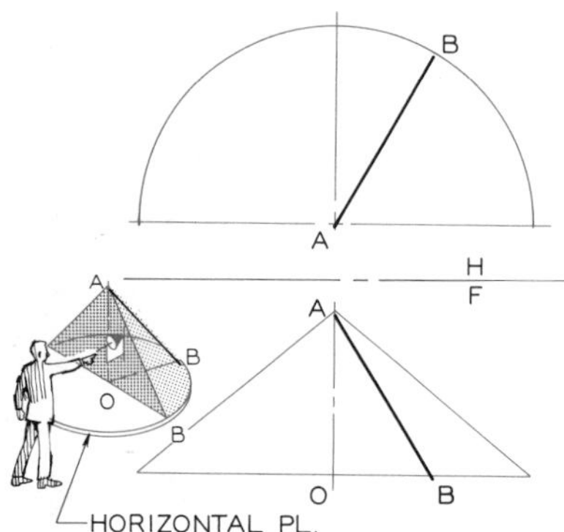

Step 1: The top view of *AB* is used as a radius to draw the base of a cone with point *A* as the apex. The front view of the cone is drawn with a horizontal base through point *B*. Line *AO* is the axis of the cone.

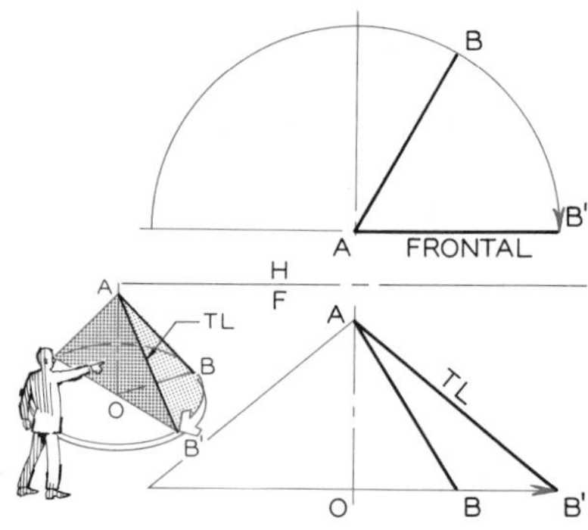

Step 2: The top view of line *AB* is revolved to be parallel to the frontal plane, *AB′*. When projected to the front view, frontal line *AB′* is the outside element of the cone and is true length.

true size by revolution. The slanted surface that appears as an edge in the top view can be found true size by a primary auxiliary view or by a single revolution. Your position as an observer must be changed so that your line of sight is perpendicular to the slanted surface in the auxiliary view in A. However, it is possible to find this surface true size using the same line of sight used for finding the front view of the object and by revolving the object. Since the axis of the revolution is vertical, it appears as a point in the top view. The top view is revolved until the slanted surface is parallel to the frontal plane; the slanted surface is then projected to the front view. The height dimensions are shown to complete the true-size view.

In Fig. 10–3 the observer is positioned in the conventional front-view location where he is viewing oblique line *AB*. His line of sight is not perpendicular to plane *ABO*, in which line *AB* lies; consequently, the true length of line *AB* will not be seen in the front view. Therefore we revolve line *AB* as an element of a cone, with point *B* traveling in a horizontal plane and point *A* remaining stationary at the apex of the imaginary cone. Line *AB′* will now appear true length, since it is revolved into the frontal plane, which is perpendicular to the observer's line of sight. We have rotated the line to show its true length in the front view by revolving it parallel to the horizontal plane, which appears as an edge in the front view.

The true length of a similar line, *AB*, is found in the front view by revolving it parallel to the horizontal plane in Fig. 10–6. The top and front views of an oblique line, *AB*, are given. Point *A* is used as the apex of a cone, and the half view of the top view of the cone is drawn in step 1, using line *AB* as a radius. The front view of the cone is projected from the top view. The top view of line *AB* is revolved into the frontal plane of the cone and its projection found in the front view in step 2. Since line *AB′* has been revolved into the frontal plane, its true length is found in the front view where it is an extreme element of the cone. Point *B* traveled in the horizontal plane, so the vertical height between points *A* and *B* was not changed. Consequently, the front view of point *B′* is found by projecting horizontally from the front view of point *B* to the projector from the top view of point *B′*.

10–3 TRUE LENGTH OF A LINE IN THE HORIZONTAL VIEW BY REVOLUTION

The handle for operating the speed control on the lathe shown in Fig. 10–7 allows the operator to apply the principle of revolution of a line about an axis. The handle has been positioned to take into account the human factors involved in the operation of the lathe and the position of the operator.

A slanted surface that appears as an edge in the front view can be found true size by a primary auxiliary view or by a single revolution. This comparison is shown in Fig. 10–8. When revolution is used, you need not change your position, but the same line of sight can be used that gives the top view.

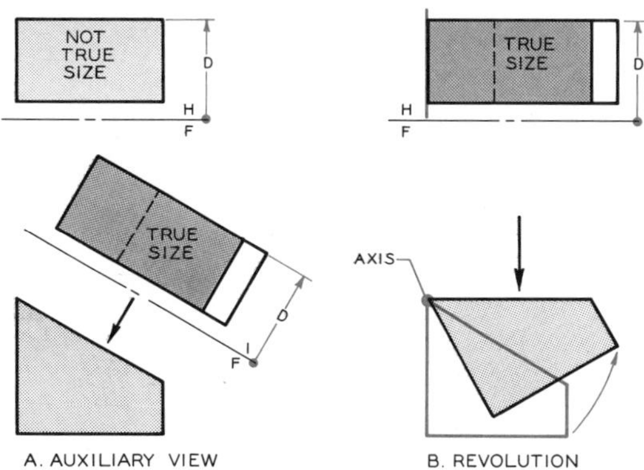

Fig. 10–8. Determination of the true size of a surface that appears as an edge in the front view by an auxiliary view and by revolution.

An axis is located in the front view as a point, and is a true-length line in the top view. The front view is revolved about the axis until the slanted surface is a horizontal edge in the front view; from this it is possible to project a true-size view in the top view. As in the auxiliary view, the depth dimension (*D*) does not change.

These principles are applied to find a line true length by revolution. The orthographic views of line *CD* are given in Fig. 10–9. The front view of line *CD* is used as a radius to draw the front view of the cone that is obtained when point *D* is revolved parallel to a frontal plane (step 1). The triangular view of the cone is constructed in the top view by projection, as shown in step 1. Line *CD* is revolved in the front view to position *CD′*, where it is horizontal (step 2). It becomes the extreme, outside element of the cone in the top view, where it appears true length. Note that points *D* and *D′* are in the same frontal plane in the top view. Point *D′* is found by projecting parallel to the H–F reference line until it intersects the projector from the front view.

Fig. 10–7. The spindle speed lever on the lathe was designed through the use of principles of revolution and with consideration of human factors. (Courtesy of Jones and Lamson Corporation.)

FIGURE 10-9. TRUE LENGTH OF A LINE IN THE TOP VIEW

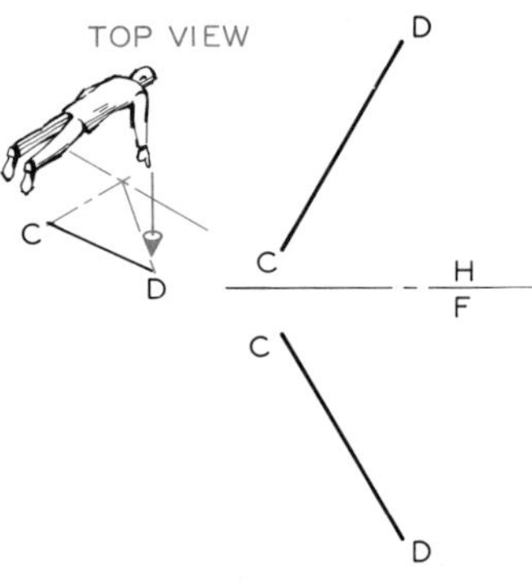

Given: The top and front views of line *CD*.
Required: Find the true-length view of line *CD* in the front view by revolution.

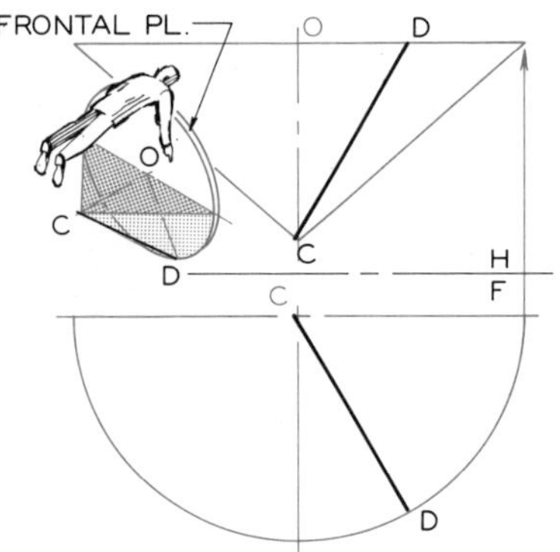

Step 1: The front view of *CD* is used as a radius to draw the base of a cone with point *C* as the apex. The top view of the cone is drawn with the base shown as a frontal plane. The axis, *CO*, is perpendicular to the frontal base.

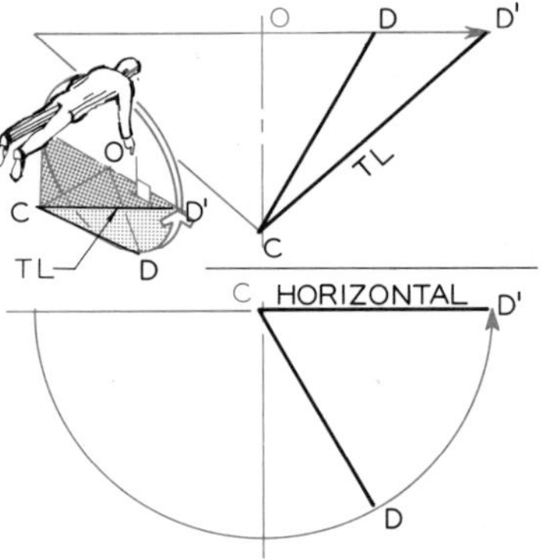

Step 2: The front view of line *CD* is revolved into position *CD′* where it is horizontal. When projected to the top view, *CD′* is the outside element of the cone and is true length.

Figure 10-10 shows a crucible that revolves about an axis, pouring aluminum to form ingots. As viewed in the photograph, the center line of the spout will revolve about its axis parallel to the frontal projection plane. The design of this crucible and its operating system was analyzed through the use of the principles of revolution to establish its limits of operation.

Fig. 10-10. The crucible used to pour 700-pound ingots of aluminum was designed to revolve about an axis to the position required for efficient flow of metal. (Courtesy of ALCOA.)

10-4 TRUE LENGTH OF A LINE IN THE PROFILE VIEW BY REVOLUTION

The observer viewing line *EF* from the conventional right-side view position will see the line foreshortened, since his line of sight is not perpendicular to plane *EFO*, as shown in Fig. 10-11. When line *EF* is revolved about the edge view of the frontal plane (Fig. 10-12) until it is parallel to the profile plane, the observer will see the true length of the line from his conventional profile-view vantage point.

The orthographic projections and revolutions of line *EF* are given in Fig. 10-13. In order for the line to be true length in the side view, it is revolved in the front view as though it were an element of a cone (step 1). The circular view of the cone is projected to the side view, where

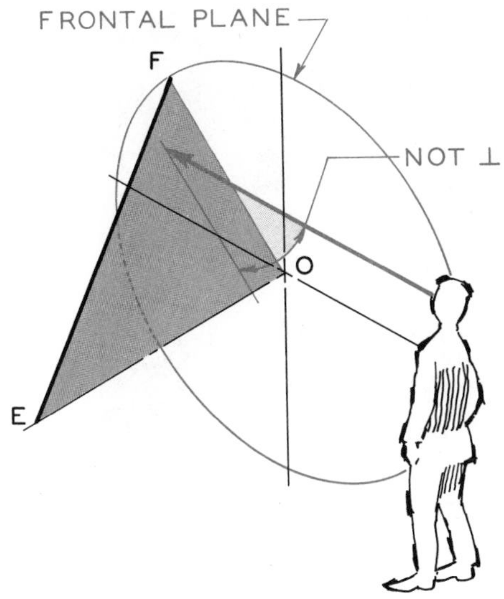

Fig. 10-11. The observer will not see the true length of line *EF* in the profile view, since his line of sight is not perpendicular to plane *EFO*.

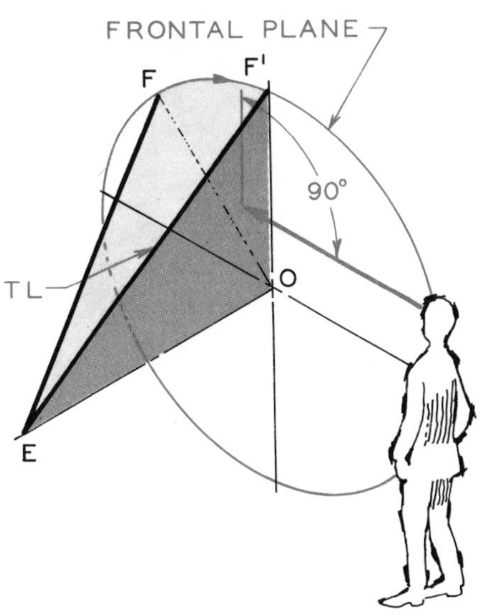

Fig. 10-12. The observer will see the true length of line *EF* when it has been revolved until it is in position *EF′*, parallel to the profile plane.

FIGURE 10-13. TRUE LENGTH OF A LINE IN THE SIDE VIEW

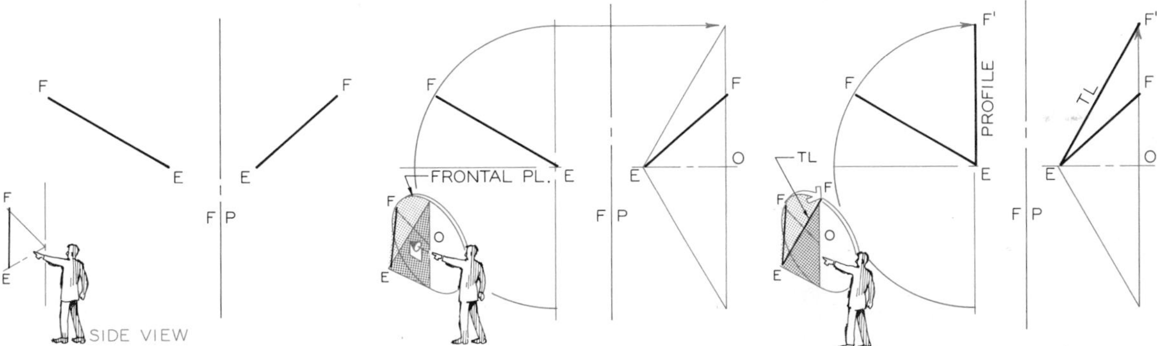

Given: The front and side views of line *EF*.
Required: Find the true-length view of *EF* in the profile view by revolution.

Step 1: The front view of *EF* is used as radius to draw the circular view of the base of a cone. The side view of the cone is drawn with a base through point *F* that is a frontal edge.

Step 2: Line *EF* in the front view is revolved to position *EF′* where it is a profile line. Line *EF′* in the profile view is true length, since it is a profile line and the outside element of the cone.

its triangular shape is seen. In step 2, point *F* is revolved to *F′* in the front view and projected to the side view, where the line represents the extreme element of the cone and is true length, since it is a profile line in this position.

It should be noted that the true length of any line can be found by revolution in either view when two adjacent views are given. The true length of line *EF* could have been found in the front view of Fig. 10-13 by revolving the line into

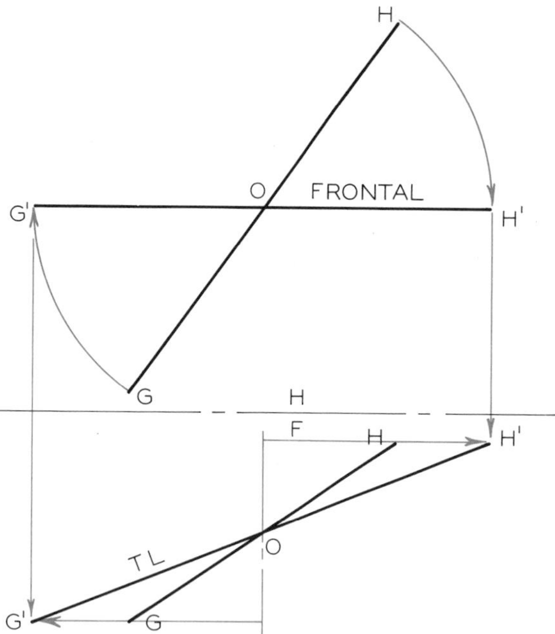

Fig. 10–14. The axis of revolution used to find the true-length view of a line can be placed anywhere on the line to be revolved. In this case a vertical axis was placed through point *O* of line *GH*.

Fig. 10–16. Two smelting components were designed to revolve into a position that will permit hot metal to be charged into a basic oxygen furnace. (Courtesy of Jones and Laughlin Steel Corporation.)

Fig. 10–15. The portable well work-over equipment and the pump are examples of mechanisms that were designed to revolve about an axis into a variety of positions. (Courtesy of Humble Oil and Refining Company.)

a position that was parallel to the frontal plane instead of the profile plane. The examples previously covered revolve each line about one of its given ends, because this is a simple way of introducing the principles of revolution. However, the line could be revolved about any point on its length equally as well (Fig. 10–14).

The portable well work-over equipment and the pump shown in Fig. 10–15 illustrate revolutions about an axis. The design of each was analyzed by revolution principles to refine and develop operational functions.

10–5 ANGLES BETWEEN A LINE AND PRINCIPAL PLANES BY REVOLUTION

The process of pouring hot metal into the tilted basic oxygen furnace in Fig. 10–16 illustrates the revolution of a line to make a specified angle with a principal plane. The furnace is tilted to a required angle with this imaginary plane in order to best receive the charge of hot metal.

It should be remembered that the angle between a line and a plane will appear true size in the view where the plane is an edge and the line is true length. In all principal views, two principal planes appear as edges. Consequently,

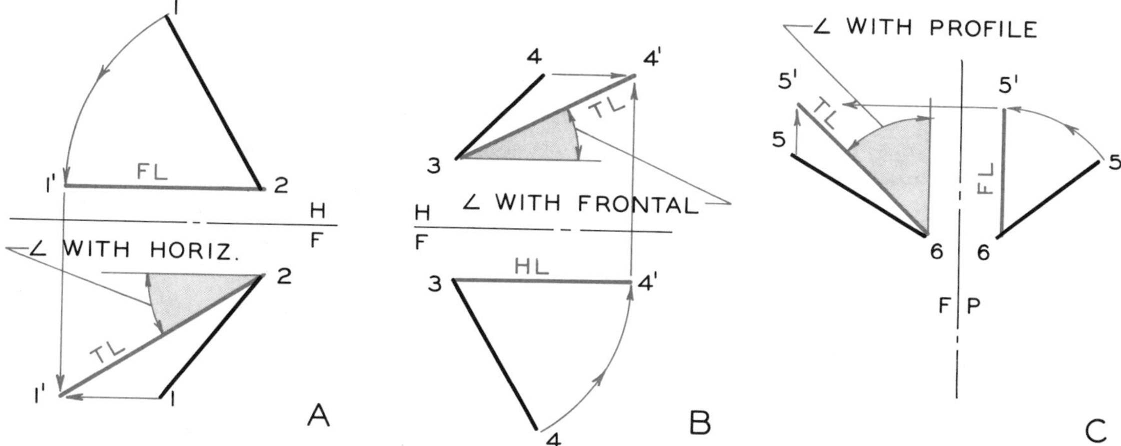

Fig. 10–17. Determining angles between lines and principal planes.

when a line appears true length in a principal view, the angle between the line and at least one principal plane can be measured.

A line may be revolved to find its true length in any principal view, as illustrated in Fig. 10–17. Since the horizontal plane appears as an edge in the front view, the true angle between the horizontal plane and an oblique line, 1–2, can be found by constructing the true length of the line in the front view by revolution, as shown in part A. The frontal plane projects as an edge in the top view (part B). The angle between line 3–4 and the frontal plane can be found in the top view by revolving point 4 to a horizontal position in the front view and then projecting to find the true length of 3–4 in the top view, as shown in part B.

The angle between line 5–6 and the profile plane can be found in the front view, where the profile plane is a vertical edge (part C). Line 5–6 is revolved in the side view until it becomes a frontal line and is projected to the front view. The true length of the line is found in the front view by projecting point 5 parallel to the edge view of the profile plane until it intersects with the projector from point 5′ in the profile view. The angle line 5′–6 makes with the profile plane can be measured in the front view.

Fig. 10–18. The 45-ton Haulpak truck was designed to permit the bed to revolve about an axis, as required for functional operation. (Courtesy of LeTourneau-Westinghouse Corporation.)

10–6 TRUE SIZE OF A PLANE BY REVOLUTION

A plane can be revolved about an axis until it becomes true size in much the same manner as a truck bed is revolved about an axis (Fig. 10–18). This principle of revolving a plane is closely related to the revolution of a line when the plane being revolved appears as an edge.

FIGURE 10-19. TRUE SIZE OF A PLANE BY REVOLUTION

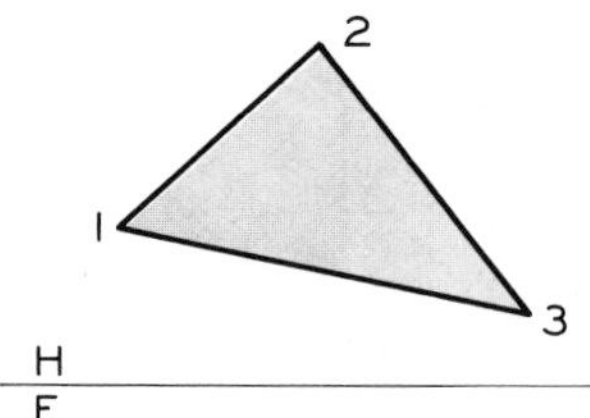

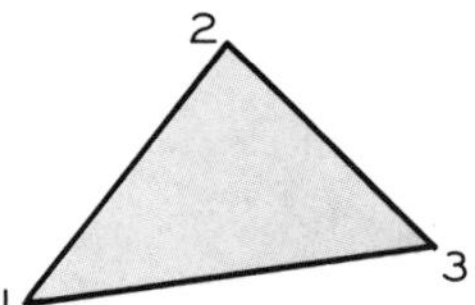

Given: The top and front views of plane 1–2–3
Required: Find the true size of the plane by revolution
References: Articles 8–9 and 10–6.

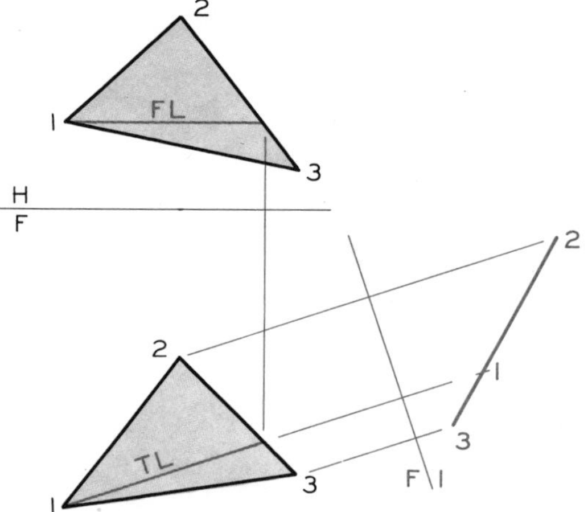

Step 1: Construct a true-length line in the front view of plane 1–2–3. Since the plane will appear as an edge in a view where the true-length line projects as a point, project a primary auxiliary view of the plane from the front view. The edge view could have been projected from the top view as well.

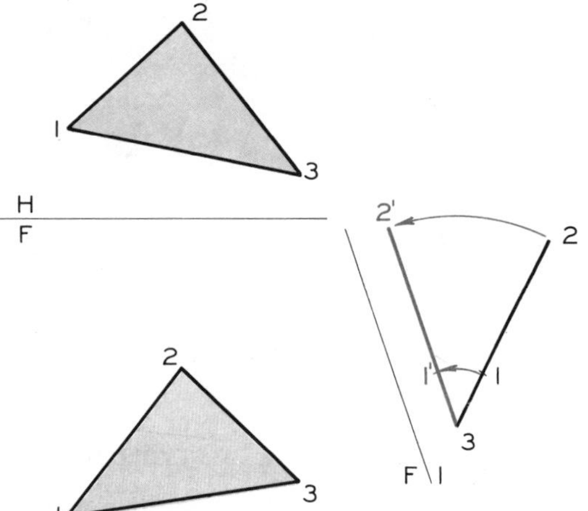

Step 2: Revolve the edge view of the plane about an axis through point 3 until the plane is parallel to the F–1 line. The plane, 1′–2′–3, will be a true-size projection when projected to the front view since it has revolved into a plane which is parallel to the frontal projection plane.

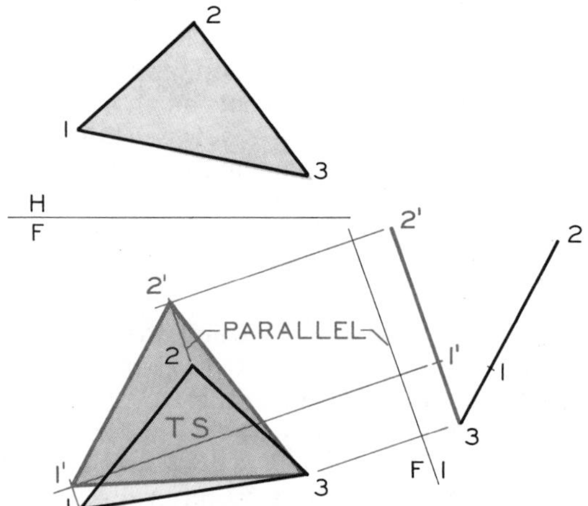

Step 3: Project points 1′ and 2′ from their revolved positions to the front view. Locate points 1′ and 2′ in the front view by extending projectors from the original points 1 and 2 parallel to the F–1 line, because the plane was revolved to a position parallel to the auxiliary plane in Step 2.

FIGURE 10–20. EDGE VIEW OF A PLANE BY REVOLUTION

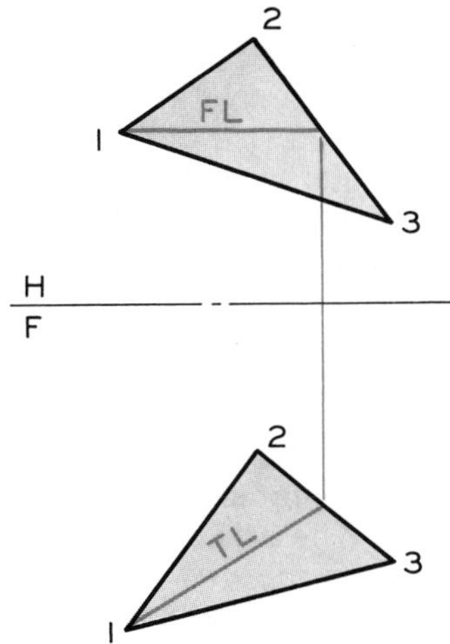

Step 1: It is required that we find the edge view of plane 1–2–3. A frontal line is found true length on the front view of the plane.

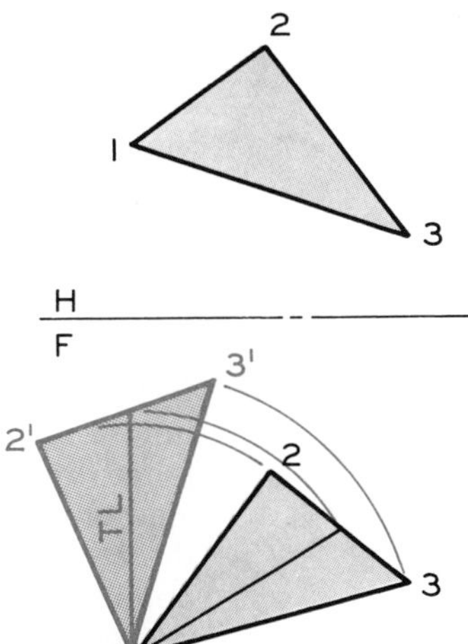

Step 2: The front view of the plane is revolved until the true-length line is vertical.

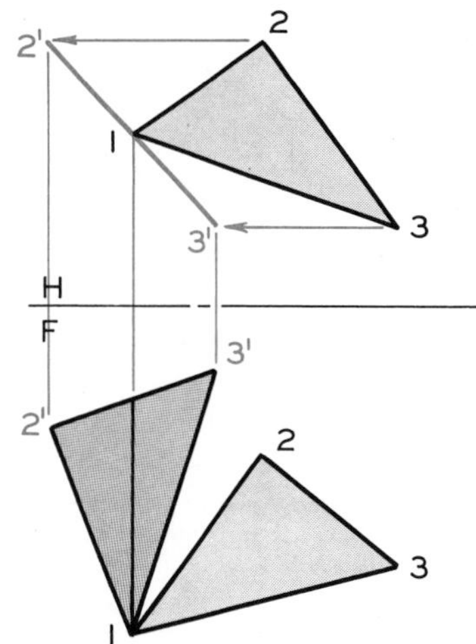

Step 3: Since the true-length line is vertical, it will appear as a point in the top view and the plane will appear as an edge, 1–2′–3′.

The steps required to find the true size of a plane by revolution are presented in Fig. 10–19 through a combination of auxiliary-view and revolution methods. The plane is found as an edge in the primary auxiliary view by locating the point view of a line on the plane (step 1). Because the edge view is oblique to the F-1 line in this projection, it has to be revolved in the primary auxiliary view until it is parallel to the F-1 line in step 2. Any point could have been selected for the axis of revolution. Since the plane was revolved parallel to the auxiliary plane, the true size of the plane is obtained by projecting the original points in the front view parallel to the F-1 line to intersect the projectors from 1′ and 2′. These form the true-size plane 1′–2′–3 in the front view. The true size of the plane could have also been found by projecting the edge view from the top view and revolving the plane in this auxiliary view.

10–7 EDGE VIEW OF A PLANE BY REVOLUTION

The edge view of a plane can also be found by revolution without using auxiliary views as was done in Fig. 10–19. The revolution method is illustrated in Fig. 10–20. In this case, plane 1-2-3 is given in the top and front views in part A, where a frontal line is drawn on the plane in the top view and projected to the front view. This line appears true length in the front view. The plane is revolved until the true-length line becomes vertical in the front view (part B). The true-length line will project as a point in the top view. The edge view of the plane is found in part C by projecting original points, 2 and 3, in the top view parallel to the H–F reference line to intersect the projectors from the revolved points, 2′ and 3′, in the front view. This can be done because the plane was revolved parallel to the frontal plane.

FIGURE 10-21. TRUE SIZE BY DOUBLE REVOLUTION

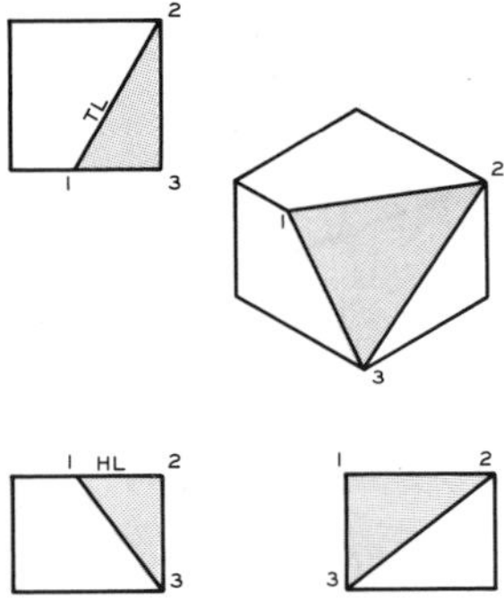

Given: Three views of a block with an oblique plane across one corner. It is required to find the plane true size by revolution.

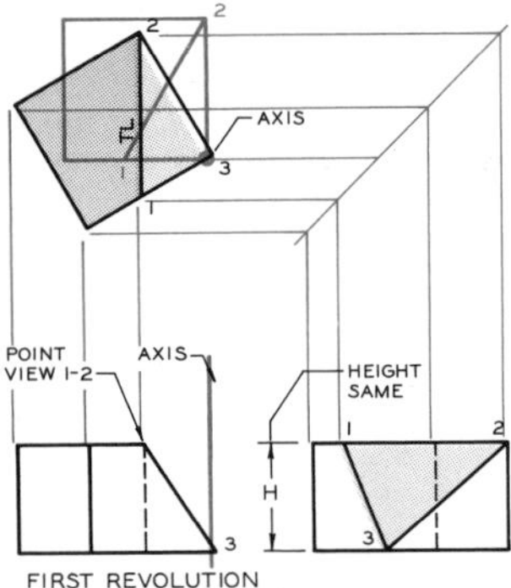

Step 1: Since line 1–2 is horizontal in the front view, it is true length in the top view. The top view is revolved into a position where line 1–2 can be seen as a point in the front view.

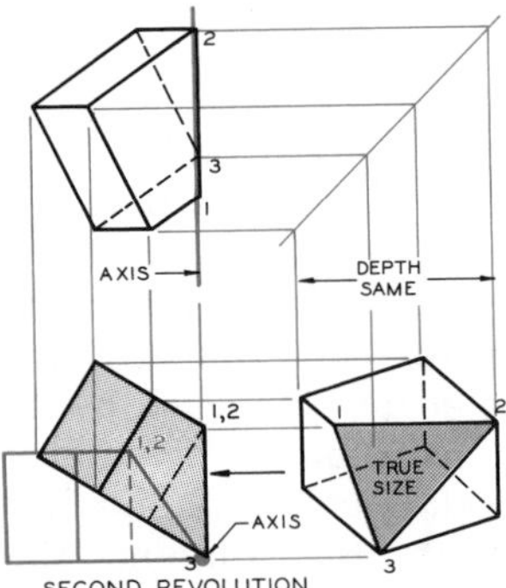

Step 2: Since plane 1–2–3 was found as an edge in step 1, this plane can be revolved into a vertical position in the front view, so that it will appear true size in the side view. The depth dimension does not change, since it is parallel to the axis of revolution.

A second revolution, sometimes called a *double revolution,* can be made to revolve the edge view of the plane in the top view until it is parallel to the edge view of the frontal plane. Since frontal planes are true size in the front view, we can obtain the true size of the plane through a procedure similar to that covered in the sequential steps of Fig. 10–20. This last step is illustrated in Fig. 10–21, where a different problem is solved by double revolution.

It is required to find the true size of plane 1–2–3 of the block in Fig. 10–21 by double revolution. In step 1, line 1–2 (which appears true length in the top view) is revolved in the top view until it is parallel to the projectors between the top and front views. The axis of revolution appears as a point in the top view and as a vertical axis in the front view. The height does not change.

Now that plane 1–2–3 appears as an edge in the front view, this view can be revolved until the edge view is vertical. This will give a true-size view of the plane in the side view. The depth will remain the same, since this dimension is parallel to the axis that appears as a point in the front view. The entire object is found in this view by projecting dimensions from the top and front views.

10-8 ANGLE BETWEEN TWO PLANES BY REVOLUTION

The line of intersection of the two intersecting planes given in Fig. 10–22 is true length in the top view. The plane of the angle between the two planes will appear as an edge, in this view, since it is perpendicular to the true-length line of intersection. Points 1, 2, and 3 in the plane of the angle are projected to the front view where the plane of the angle appears foreshortened (step 1). The true size of this plane can be found in the front view by revolving the edge view of the plane in the top view until it becomes a frontal plane (step 2). Points 1′, 2′, and 3 are then projected from the top view to the front view and located in the same horizontal planes as the original points in the foreshortened view. Angle 1′–2′–3 appears true size in the front view.

FIGURE 10–22. ANGLE BETWEEN TWO PLANES

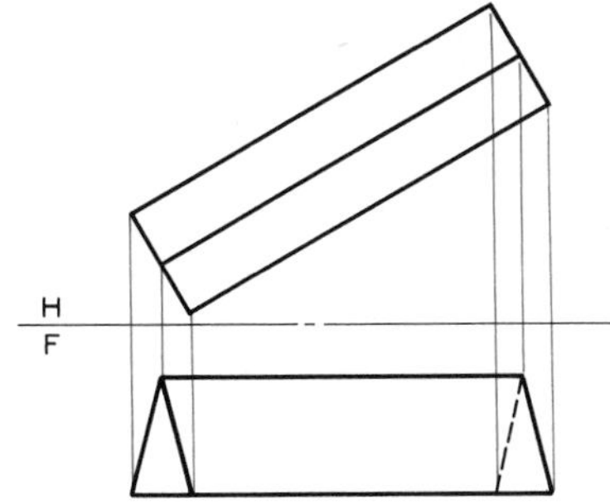

Given: The top and front views of two intersecting planes.
Required: Find the angle between the planes by revolution.

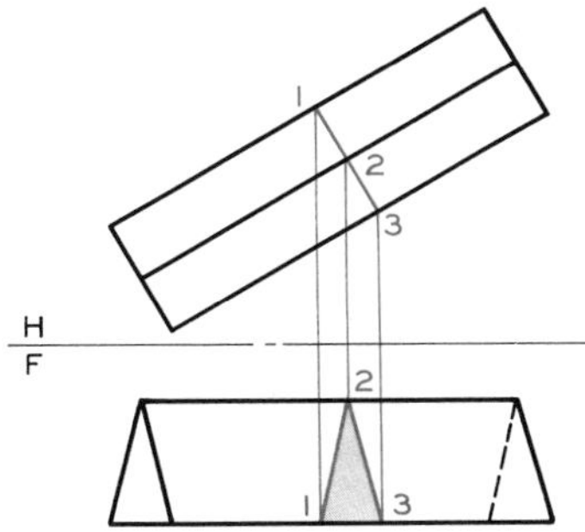

Step 1: A right section is drawn perpendicular to the true-length line of intersection between the planes in the top view and is projected to the front view. The section is not true size in the front view.

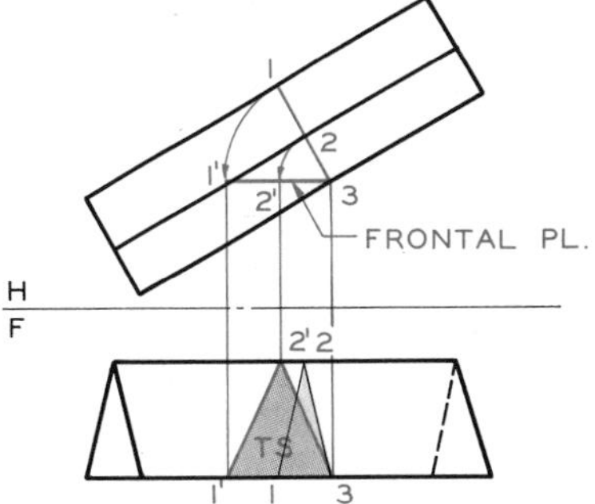

Step 2: The edge view of the right section is revolved to position 1′–2′–3 in the top view to be parallel to the frontal plane. This section is projected to the front view, where it is true size since it is a frontal plane.

Often the line of intersection between two intersecting lines will not project as true length in a principal view. Such is the case in Fig. 10–23, which shows an engine mount frame of a helicopter. The angle between these planes must be determined to design the joints and to analyze the clearances within the frame.

In the top and front views of two intersecting planes in part A of Fig. 10–24, the line of intersection does not appear true length in either view. The true length of the line of intersection is found in a primary auxiliary view which is projected perpendicularly from the line of intersection in the top view. The plane of the angle between the two planes projects as an edge that is perpendicular to the true-length view of the line of intersection (step 1). Plane 1–2–3 is projected as a foreshortened plane in the top view. The edge view of plane 1–2–3 is therefore revolved about the axis, 3–1, in the primary auxiliary view until it is parallel to the H–1 line (step 2). It is then projected back to the top view. Angle 1–2′–3 appears true size in the top view when point 2′ has been located by projecting from point 2 parallel to the H–1 line.

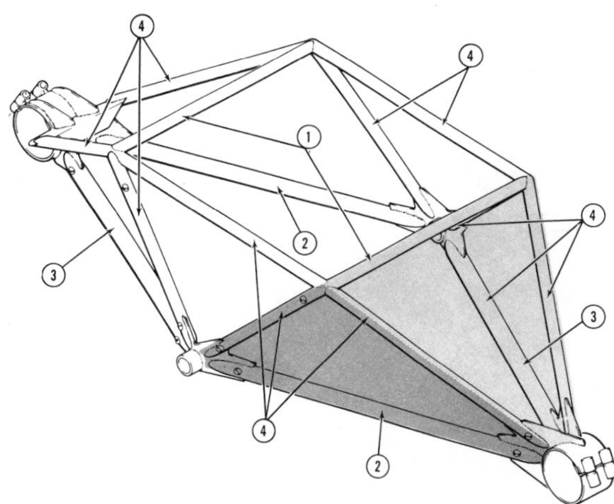

Fig. 10–23. The angular measurements between the two planes of the helicopter engine mount can be determined by revolution principles. (Courtesy of Bell Helicopter Corporation.)

FIGURE 10-24. ANGLE BETWEEN OBLIQUE PLANES

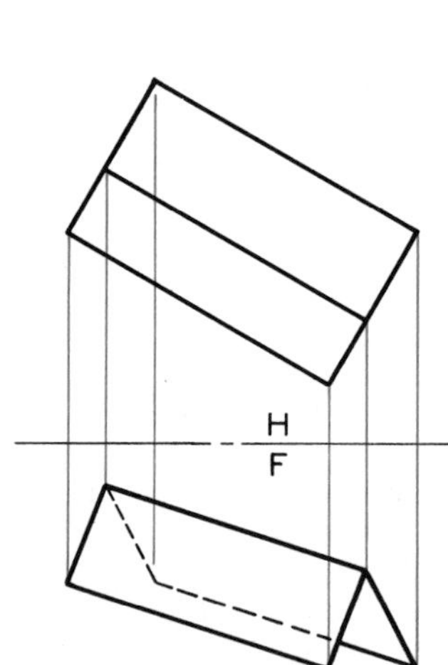

Given: The top and front views of two intersecting planes.
Required: Find the angle between the two planes.

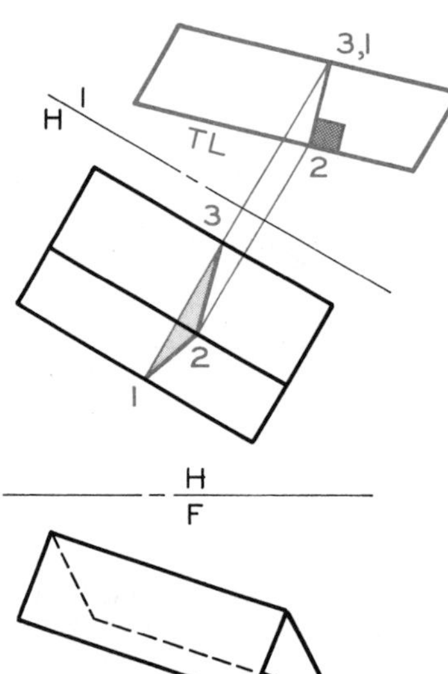

Step 1: A true-length view of the line of intersection is found in an auxiliary view projected from the top view. The right section is constructed perpendicular to the true length of the line of intersection and is projected to the top view.

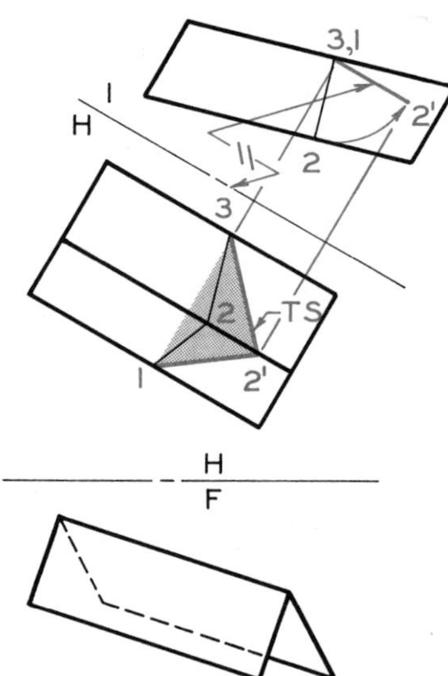

Step 2: The edge view of the right section is revolved to be parallel to the H-1 reference line so the plane will appear true size in the top view after being revolved. The angle between the planes can be found by measuring angle 1-2′-3.

Fig. 10-25. The hand cranks on the mass-production machine were designed to permit adequate clearance when they are revolved about their axes. (Courtesy of Ex-Cell-O Corporation.)

10-9 REVOLUTION OF A POINT ABOUT AN OBLIQUE AXIS

Handwheels and hand cranks are mechanical means of adjusting all types of machines from common household appliances to mass-production equipment such as the machine shown in Fig. 10-25. Note that the hand cranks are positioned to be accessible to the operator while having sufficient clearance with the other components of the machine. Principles of revolution were applied to these hand adjustments in the early stages of their design. The same principles can be applied to the location of a power line with respect to another by revolving a point on one wire about the axis of the other to determine the required minimum clearance.

The revolution of a point about a line is illustrated in Fig. 10-26. The top and front views of axis 1-2 and point *O*, the point to be revolved, are given. We are to revolve point *O* into its highest position to determine its location in the given

FIGURE 10–26. REVOLUTION OF A POINT ABOUT AN AXIS

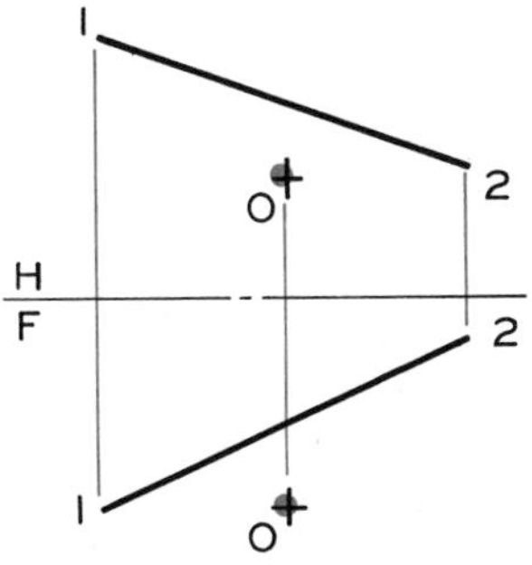

Given: The top and front views of axis 1–2 and point *O*.
Required: Revolve point *O* about the axis, locate its highest position, and show it in all views.
References: Articles 7–3, 9–3, 9–6, and 10–9.

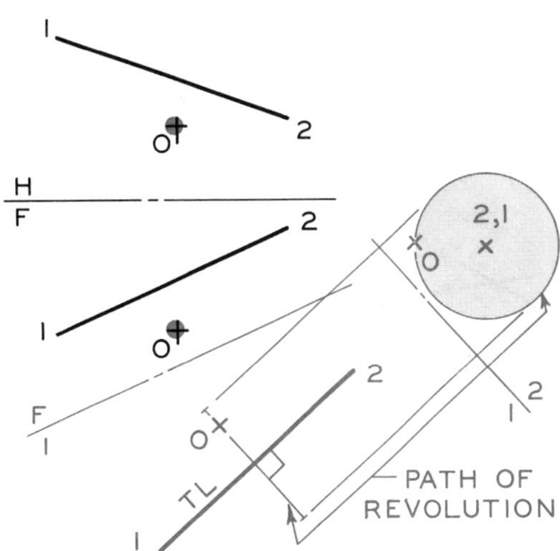

Step 1: Locate the true length of axis 1–2 in a primary auxiliary view, and construct its point view in the secondary auxiliary view. Project point *O* to these views also. Using as a radius the distance from the point view of axis 1–2 to point *O*, construct the circular path of revolution in the secondary auxiliary view. The path of revolution appears as an edge in primary auxiliary view.

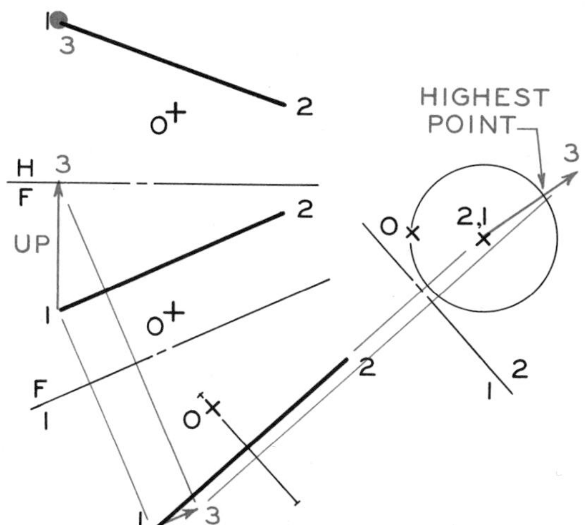

Step 2: Determine the highest point by constructing line 1–3 upward in the front view and projecting it as a point in the top view. This line is then projected back through the primary auxiliary view to the secondary auxiliary view. The point where this directional arrow crosses the circular path locates the highest point of the path of point *O*.

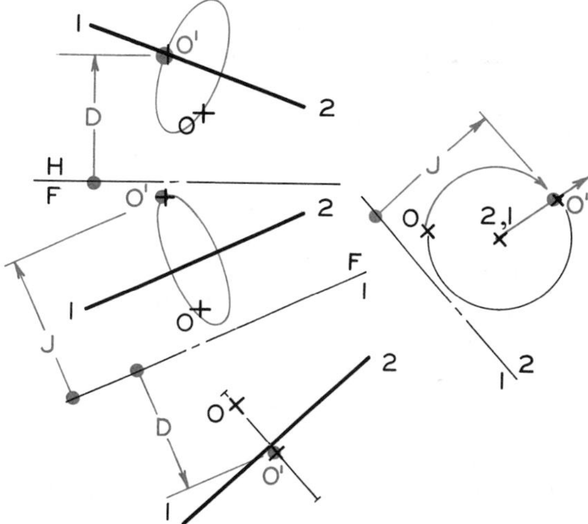

Step 3: Point *O′* is projected from its circular view back through the successive views. Note that the highest point, *O′*, lies on line 1–2 in the top view, which verifies that it is in its highest position. This problem could have been solved by projecting from the top view as well. The circular path appears elliptical in the front and top views.

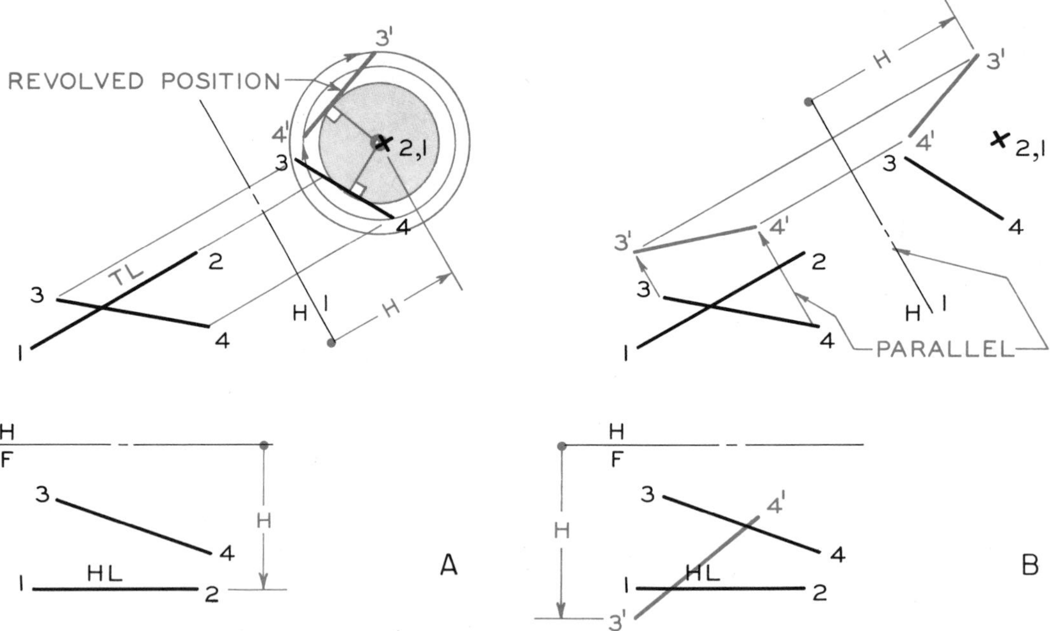

Fig. 10-27. Determining the revolution of a line about an axis.

views and its relationship to adjacent components. The circular path of revolution of point *O* about line 1-2 can be seen in the view where line 1-2 appears as a point (step 1). The highest position of point *O* is found in step 2 by constructing line 1-3 in an upward direction in the two given views. This directional line is then projected back to the secondary auxiliary view where the highest point is located on the circular path. Point *O'*, the highest point on the path, is found in each view by projecting to the primary auxiliary view, the front view, and the top view (step 3). The measurements from the reference planes are used to establish accurately these views of the point. Note that the circular path of the point projects as an edge which is perpendicular to axis 1-2 in the primary auxiliary view. Projection principles in Chapter 7 covering the directions of forward, backward, up and down, and left and right should be reviewed if necessary, since those principles are used in locating the positions of a point that is revolved about a given axis.

The elliptical paths of point *O* can be constructed in principal views by application of the principles covered in Article 9-6. The ellipse guide angle for the front view is the angle formed by the line of sight from the front view and the edge view of the circular path of revolution. The ellipse angle for the top view must be found by an auxiliary view projected from the top view in which the axis appears true length and the circular path appears as a perpendicular edge. The angle formed by the line of sight from the top view and the edge view of this circular path establishes the ellipse angle that will be used in selecting the proper ellipse template for drawing the ellipse in the top view.

The point could have been located in any specified position, such as its highest, lowest, or most forward position, by constructing a line of the required direction in the principal views and projecting it into all views. The point would be located in the circular view indicated by the position of the directional line constructed in the principal views.

10–10 REVOLUTION OF A LINE ABOUT AN AXIS

A line can be revolved about another line, as shown in Fig. 10–27, if the line to be used as an axis is found as a point. The point view of line 1–2 is obtained in part A of the figure in the primary auxiliary view, since the top view of line 1–2 is true length. A circle is drawn tangent to line 3–4 with its center at the axis, 1–2. Each end of line 3–4 is revolved the specified number of degrees and drawn in its new position as shown in part A. The top view of line 3′–4′ is found by projecting parallel to the H–1 line from the original points of 3 and 4 in the top view, as shown in part B. These projectors will intersect the projectors from the primary auxiliary view. The front view is obtained by projecting from the top view and transferring the height dimensions from the primary auxiliary view, as shown in part A.

A closely related application of this principle is the revolution of a plane about an axis to form a geometric shell or solid. An example of a shell is the tracking antenna in Fig. 10–28. This parabolic shell is formed by the theoretical revolution of a parabola about its axis of symmetry.

The orientation of a spacecraft by command signals from the earth is an application of the theory of revolution; the craft is revolved about an axis to a specified position. In Fig. 10–29, the Ranger spacecraft is revolved to position its cameras to obtain medium resolution pictures of the moon's surface and to determine the presence of radioactive elements. The photograph of the landing area of the Ranger, shown in Fig. 10–30, was taken through a telescope in

10–28

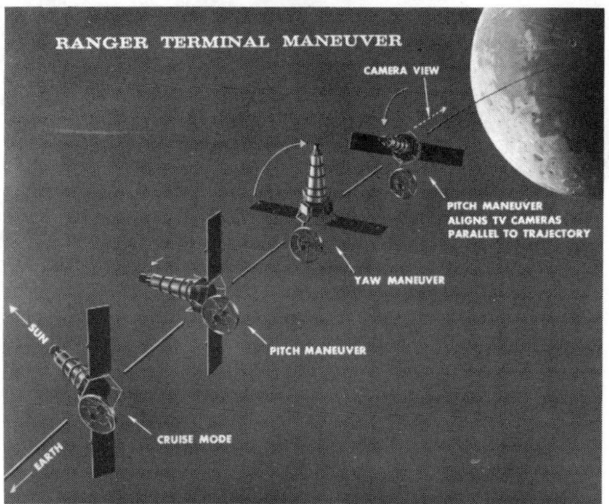

10–29

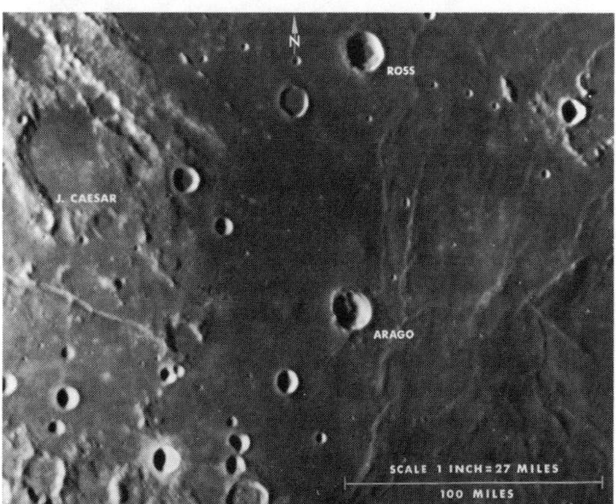

10–30

Fig. 10–28. This 60-ft diameter antenna is used for precision tracking of communication satellites. Its shell is formed by the revolution of a parabola about its axis of symmetry. (Courtesy of Ryan Aeronautical Company.)

Fig. 10–29. The Ranger spacecraft is revolved about three axes to position its cameras for photographing the moon. (Courtesy of National Aeronautics and Space Administration.)

Fig. 10–30. This photograph, taken through a telescope in September 1919, is a view of the expected landing area of Ranger. (Courtesy of the Jet Propulsion Laboratory, California Institute of Technology.)

Fig. 10-31. The cradle of this orthicon camera was designed to permit revolution to any position for tracking space vehicles and astronomical bodies. (Courtesy of ITT Industrial Laboratories.)

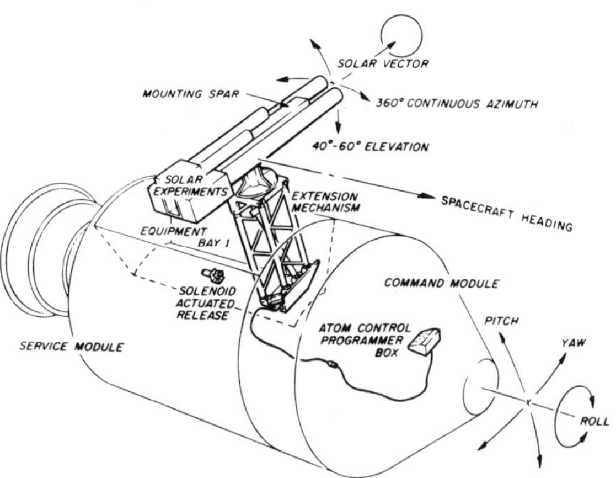

Fig. 10-33. The Apollo command service module was designed to permit the automatic revolution of a telescope to keep it directed toward the sun as the vehicle travels through space. (Courtesy of the National Aeronautics and Space Administration.)

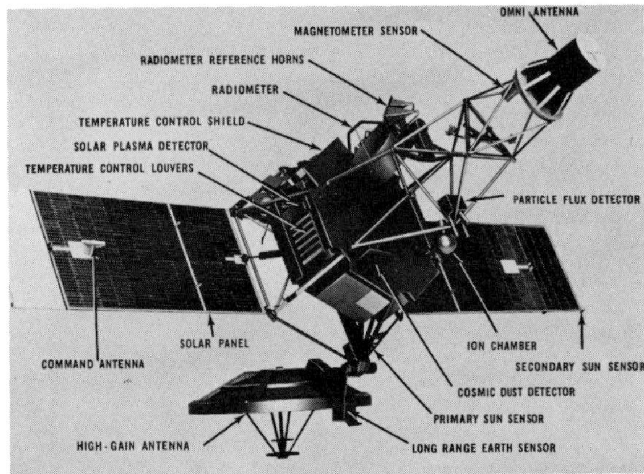

Fig. 10-32. Mariner 2 was man's first successful voyager through space that scanned Venus. (Courtesy of National Aeronautics and Space Administration.)

September 1919. Thanks to successful flights by Ranger and other spacecraft, we now have much clearer photos of the moon's surface. The path of Ranger was controlled by commands that revolved it about its three axes with maneuvers of pitch, yaw, and roll. Note that the antenna in Fig. 10-29 is designed to maintain a constant position for reception of command signals from earth even though the spacecraft revolves in space. Principles of revolution are also applied to the design of cameras used to track space vehicles (Fig. 10-31).

The contributions to spacecraft technology by the Ranger project were instrumental in the development of the Mariner 2 spacecraft shown in Fig. 10-32. Mariner 2 was man's first successful voyager through space; its mission was

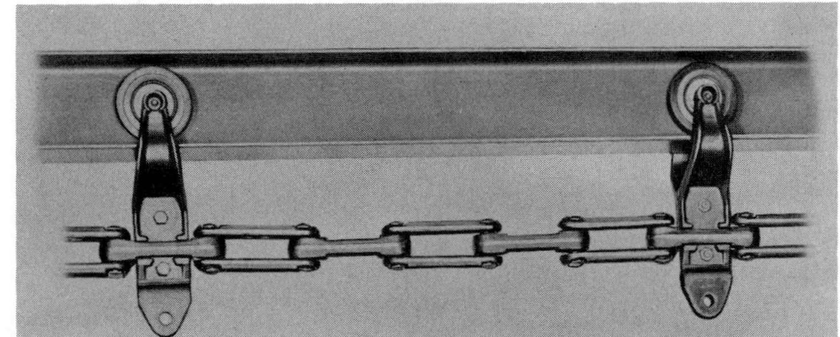

Fig. 10–34. The overhead track of this conveyor system must be designed in such a manner that the track web is positioned in a vertical plane at all times. (Courtesy of Mechanical Handling Systems, Inc.)

to scan Venus and gather information on the temperature and composition of its cloud cover.

An artist's drawing of the atom system in the Apollo command service module is shown in Fig. 10–33. The maneuvers of pitch, roll, and yaw are illustrated with respect to the path of the spacecraft. Pitch is the up-and-down revolution with respect to the spacecraft heading, while yaw is the left-or-right rotation, and roll is the revolution of the spacecraft along the path of its heading. The commands given to a module will be for revolutions about these three axes, whether the commands come from the earth by radio waves or from the astronauts aboard. The telescopes are mounted on a spar that will extend outside the service module on a two-axis gimbal that can automatically correct for the yaw or the pitch of the spacecraft. This system will be used for observing the sun through telescopes.

It is our understanding of the revolution of geometric shapes in space that enables us to control the revolutions of a spacecraft in flight. These principles are very similar to the revolution of a point about a line, as discussed in Article 10–9, and the revolution of a line about an axis, as covered in this article.

10–11 REVOLUTION OF A RIGHT PRISM ABOUT AN AXIS

The handling of materials in mass-production plants is a complex engineering problem that requires considerable skill and engineering experience. Many plants employ automatic

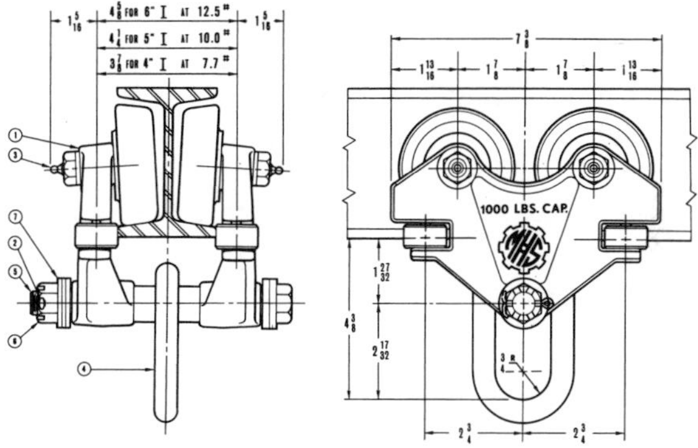

Fig. 10–35. A detail view of a trolley that will utilize a track like that shown in Fig. 10–34. (Courtesy of Mechanical Handling Systems, Inc.)

tow lines located overhead or under the floor to transport parts and materials through the manufacturing process. An example of a portion of an overhead system is shown in Fig. 10–34. The track is an I-beam and the trolleys are designed to roll on its lower flange, as shown in Fig. 10–35. The tracks are designed to be suspended from the structural beams of the plant's interior structure. It is obvious that the trolley system will work effectively only when the track's right section is positioned so that the interior web of the beam is positioned in a vertical plane and the lower flange is positioned horizontally. If the web were not vertical, the trolley would bind and not roll properly. Consequently, it is necessary to design a method for suspending the track in

FIGURE 10-36. REVOLUTION OF A RIGHT PRISM ABOUT ITS AXIS

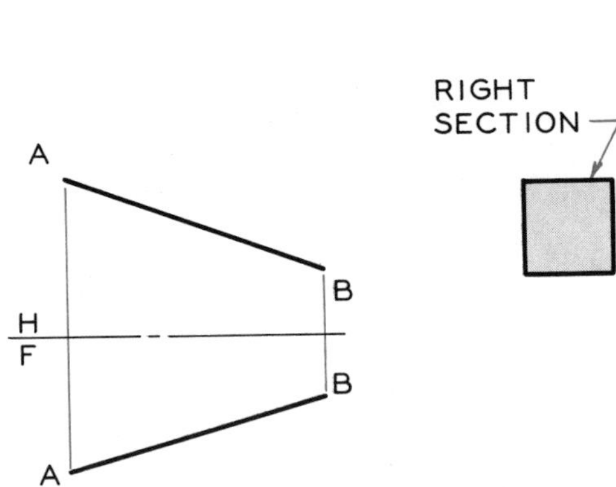

Given: The top and front views of line *AB*, the center line of a prism.
Required: Revolve the given right section about the axis to establish the prism with two surfaces in the vertical plane. Show the prism in all views.
References: Articles 7-3, 9-3, 10-9, and 10-11.

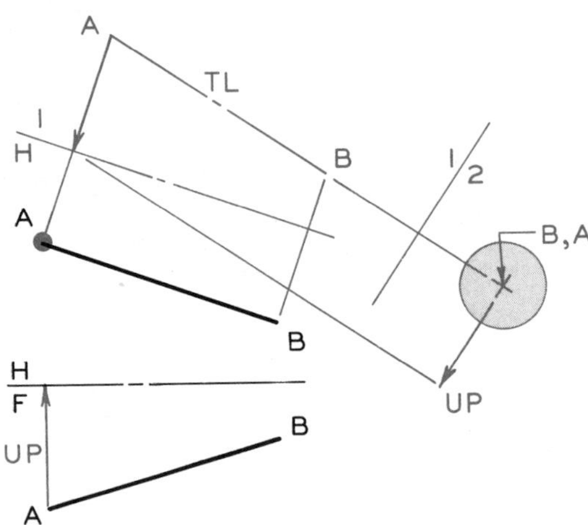

Step 1: Locate the point view of center line *AB* in the secondary auxiliary view by drawing a circle about the axis with a diameter equal to one side of the square right section. Draw a vertical arrow in the front and top views and project it to the secondary auxiliary view to indicate the direction of vertical in this view.

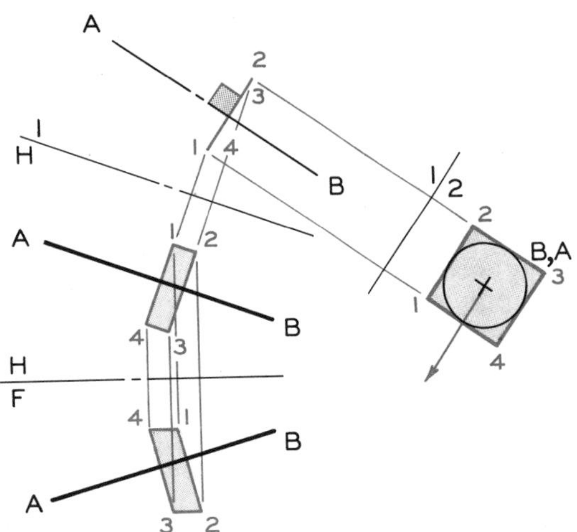

Step 2: Draw the right section, 1-2-3-4, in the secondary auxiliary with two sides parallel to the vertical directional arrow. Project this section back to the successive views by transferring measurements with dividers. The edge view of the section could have been located in any position along center line *AB* in the primary auxiliary view, so long as it was perpendicular to the center line.

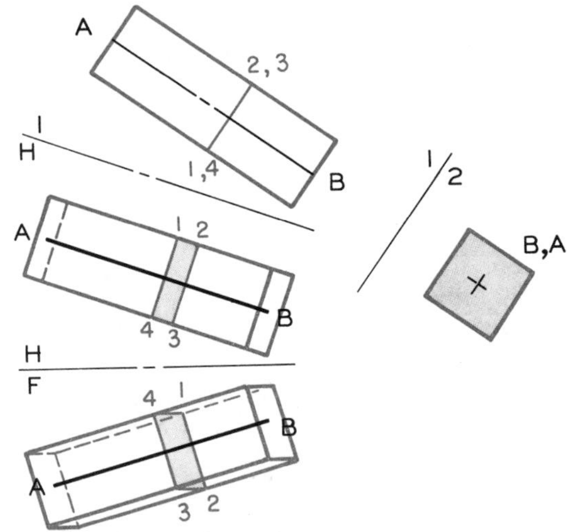

Step 3: Draw the lateral edges of the prism through the corners of the right section so that they are parallel to the center line in all views. Terminate the ends of the prism in the primary auxiliary where they appear as edges that are perpendicular to the center line. Project the corner points of the ends to the top and front views to establish the ends in these views.

Fig. 10-37. Each of the chutes for transporting iron ore in this installation was designed so that two edges of its right section are vertical and the other two are horizontal. These designs were developed by applying the principle of revolving a prism about its axis. (Courtesy of Kaiser Steel Corporation.)

such a way that the web is positioned in a vertical plane.

A problem of this type is illustrated in Fig. 10-36, in which a prism with a square right section is revolved about its axis until two of its planes are vertical. This prism could represent the I-beam mentioned above; for simplicity, the details of each flange are not drawn. The center line is found as a point in a secondary auxiliary view in step 1. The direction of vertical is found in this view by projecting a vertical directional arrow in the front view to the secondary auxiliary view. In step 2, the square right section is positioned about the point view of the center line so that two sides are parallel to the directional arrow. The sides of the prism are found by drawing the lateral sides parallel to the center line through the corner points of the right section in all views. The length of the prism is drawn from specifications in the primary auxiliary view; the ends will be perpendicular to the center line (step 3). They are found in the top and front views by projection.

These principles apply to structural members, hallways, and conveyor belts which, to function properly, must be designed so that their surfaces are positioned with respect to certain planes. A chute connecting two planes through which material will be conveyed must have two sides of its right section in the vertical plane and the other two sides in the horizontal plane (Fig. 10-37). The revolution of a prismatic shape about its axis to a desired position is a necessary step in the design of the connections at all chute supports and the openings at the ends of the chutes where they join other structures.

10-12 ANGLE BETWEEN A LINE AND A PLANE BY REVOLUTION

A third way of finding the angle between a line and a plane is by revolution, as shown in Fig. 10-38. This problem was solved by auxiliary view methods in Articles 9-13 and 9-14.

The true size of the plane is found in a secondary auxiliary view in step 1 of Fig. 10-38. The

FIGURE 10-38. ANGLE BETWEEN A LINE AND A PLANE BY REVOLUTION

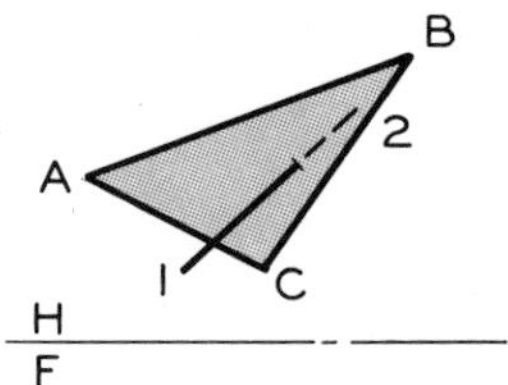

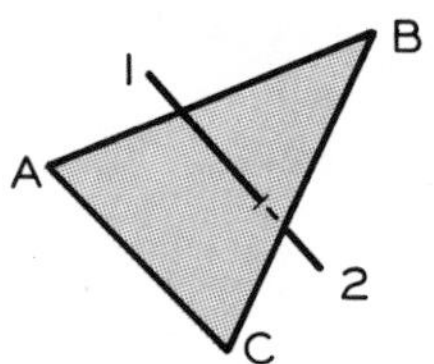

Given: The top and front views of plane *ABC* and line 1-2.
Required: Find the angle between the line and plane by revolution.
References: Articles 9-13, 9-14, and 10-12.

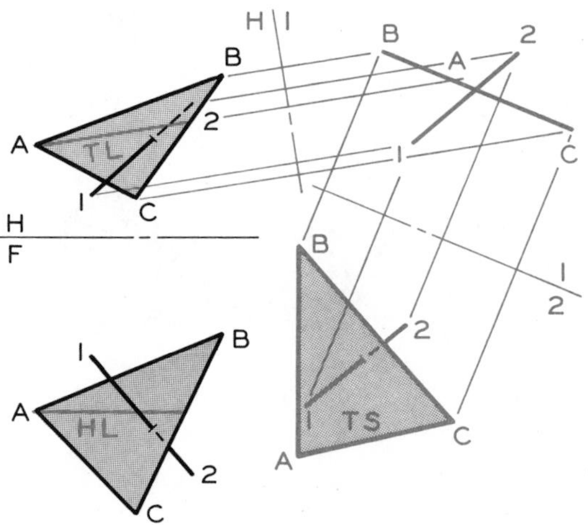

Step 1: Construct plane *ABC* as an edge in a primary auxiliary view, which can be projected from either view. Determine the true size of the plane in secondary auxiliary view, and project line 1-2 to each view.

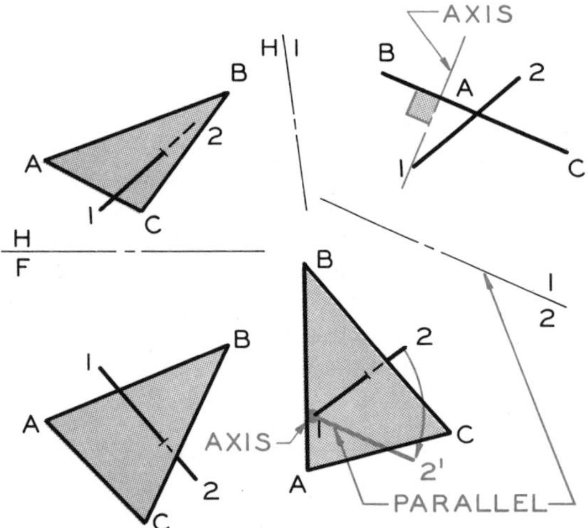

Step 2: Revolve the secondary auxiliary view of the line until it is parallel to the 1-2 reference line. The axis of revolution appears as a point through point 1 in the secondary auxiliary view. The axis appears true length and is perpendicular to the 1-2 line and plane *ABC* in the primary auxiliary.

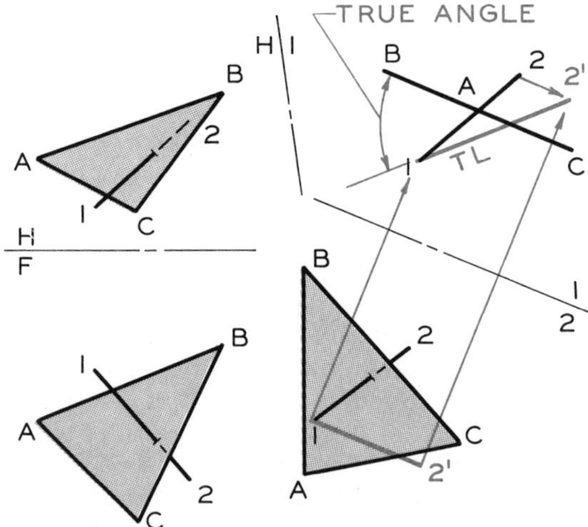

Step 3: Point 2′ is projected to the primary auxiliary where the true length of line 1-2′ is found by projecting the primary auxiliary view of point 2 parallel to the 1-2 line as shown. Since the plane appears as an edge and the line appears true length in this view, the true angle between the line and the plane can be measured.

Fig. 10–39. Angles between the structural members and planes of the spacecraft can be determined by revolution. (Courtesy of the National Aeronautics and Space Administration.)

Fig. 10–40. The cradle of these image orthicon cameras was designed to permit revolution to any position for tracking space vehicles and astronomical bodies. (Courtesy of ITT Industrial Laboratories.)

line is revolved in the secondary auxiliary view until it is parallel to the 1–2 reference line (step 2). Line 1–2′ will project true length in the primary auxiliary view because it was parallel to the edge view of the primary auxiliary line. Point 2′ is found by projecting point 2 parallel to the 1–2 line in the primary auxiliary view, as shown in step 3. Since the line appears true length and the plane appears as an edge, the true angle between the line and plane can be measured in this view.

The spacecraft shown in Fig. 10–39 is an example of planes formed by intersecting lines that connect with other lines. These angles must be determined during the refinement stages of developing the final design. Revolution principles can be used to good advantage in many cases for finding these angles once the preliminary configuration has been drawn.

10–13 A LINE AT SPECIFIED ANGLES WITH TWO PRINCIPAL PLANES

The facet-eye camera shown in Fig. 10–40 can be revolved about three axes, giving it full mobility and flexibility for viewing any point in the sky. These television cameras are used for tracking satellites and bodies in space, and they receive excellent contrast even under poor visibility conditions. The design of the camera's cradle involves applications of revolution about several axes. These cameras can be positioned to make a required angle with the two adjacent principal planes. For instance, the direction of the cameras could be positioned to make an angle of 44° with the horizontal and 35° with the frontal plane. This example is illustrated in Fig. 10–41.

In step 1 of Fig. 10–41, cone *A* is drawn to contain all the lines making an angle of 35° with the frontal plane. These lines are the elements on the surface of the cone. Cone *A* will be triangular in the top view and circular in the front view. Cone *B* is drawn in step 2 to contain elements which make an angle of 44° with the horizontal plane. The elements are drawn equal in length to element *E* of the previously drawn cone *A*. The two cones will intersect with common elements, since the elements of each cone are equal in length. Two lines, 0–1 and 0–2, satisfy the requirements of the problem. If the requirements had specified that the line slope to the right or left, then only one of the lines would have satisfied the requirements.

These principles can also be applied to determining the intersections between piping systems that must be joined with standard connectors which are cast in standard angles.

FIGURE 10-41. A LINE AT SPECIFIED ANGLES TO TWO PRINCIPAL PLANES

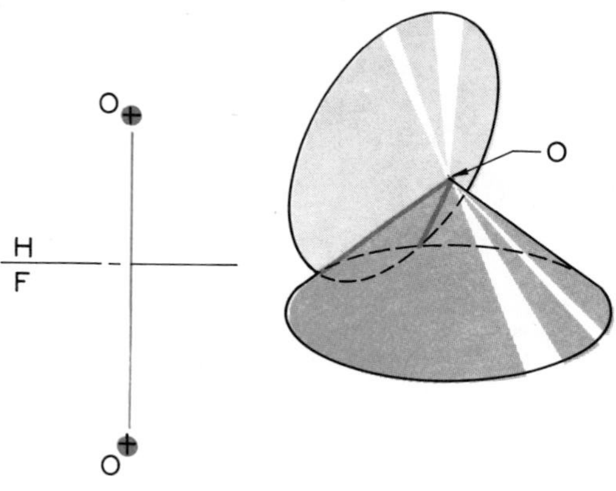

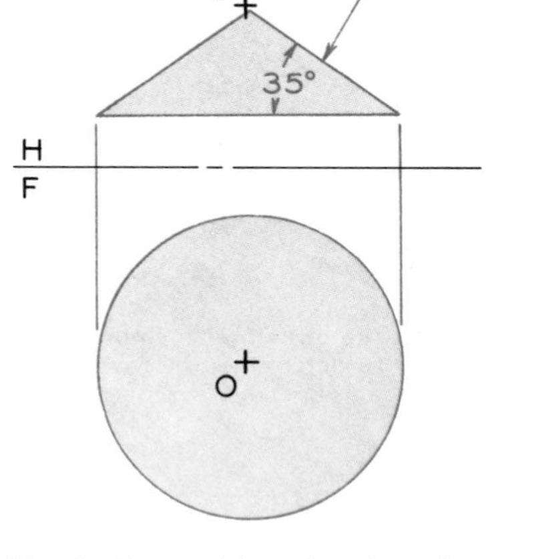

Given: The top and front views of point *O*.
Required: Construct a line through point *O* that will make angles of 35° with the frontal plane and 44° with the horizontal plane, sloping forward and downward.
Reference: Article 10-13.

Step 1: Draw a triangular view of a cone in the top view such that the extreme elements make an angle of 35° with the edge view of the frontal plane. Construct the circular view of the cone in the front view, using *O* as the apex. All elements of this cone make an angle of 35° with the frontal plane.

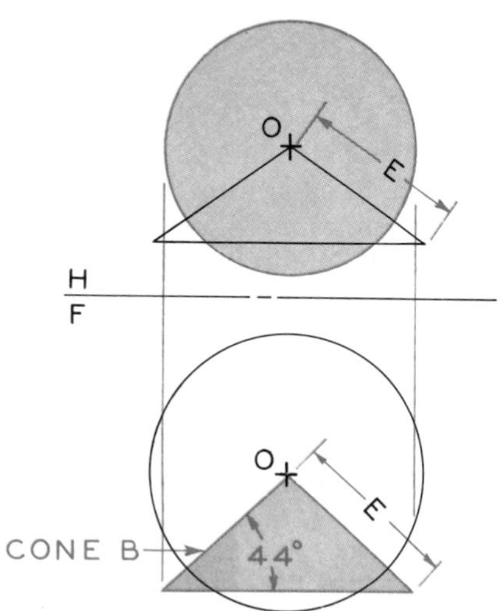

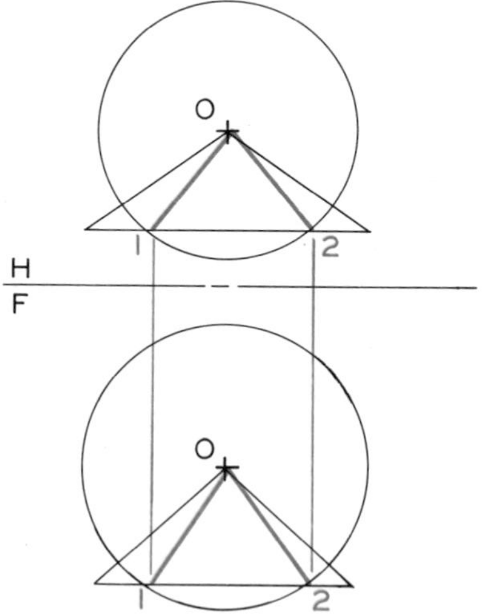

Step 2: Draw a triangular view of a cone in the front view such that the elements make an angle of 44° with the edge view of the horizontal plane. Draw the elements of this cone equal in length to element *E* of cone *A*. All elements of cone *B* make an angle of 44° with the horizontal plane.

Step 3: Since the elements of cones *A* and *B* are equal in length, there will be two common elements that lie on the surface of each cone, elements 0-1 and 0-2. Locate points 1 and 2 at the point where the bases of the cone intersect in both views. Either of these lines will satisfy the problem requirements.

10-14 SUMMARY

Principles of revolution are closely related to principles of auxiliary-view projections. In revolution, the observer maintains his position to view principal views in the conventional direction while the object is revolved into the desired position to give the required view. The auxiliary view method of projection moves the observer's position about the stationary object so that the object is viewed from auxiliary positions.

In many instances, the principles of revolution can be used to supplement those of auxiliary views, allowing the designer to find the true sizes and shapes of geometric figures with greater ease than would be possible with auxiliary views alone. Spatial problems should always be analyzed to determine the most appropriate method of solution available. Once the preliminary designs have been scaled and drawn in preliminary form, the configurations can be refined through the application of revolution principles and auxiliary views. Angles, true lengths, true sizes, and other physical properties must be found to permit further analysis of the final design, as will be discussed in the succeeding chapters.

PROBLEMS

General

The problems for this chapter should be constructed and solved on $8\frac{1}{2}'' \times 11''$ sheets, as illustrated by the accompanying figures, in accordance with the practices outlined in Article 1-19. Each grid represents $\frac{1}{4}''$. All reference planes and points should be labeled using $\frac{1}{8}''$ letters with guidelines.

1. Use Fig. 10-42 for all parts of this problem. (A) Find the true length of the line in the front view by revolution. Indicate the angle this line makes with the horizontal plane. (B) Find the true length of the line in the front view by revolution. Indicate the angle this line makes with the horizontal plane. (C) Find the true length of the line in the horizontal view by revolution. Indicate the angle this line makes with the frontal plane. (D) Find the true length of the line in the horizontal view by revolution. Indicate the angle this line makes with the frontal plane.

2. Use Fig. 10-43 for all parts of this problem. (A) Find the true length of the line in the profile view by revolution. Indicate the angle this line makes with the frontal plane. (B) Find the true length of the line in the profile view by revolution. Indicate the angle this line makes with the frontal plane. (C) Find the true size of the plane by a primary auxiliary view and a single revolution.

3. (A) In Fig. 10-44A find the edge view of the plane by revolution. (B) Find the true size of the plane by double revolution in part B of the figure.

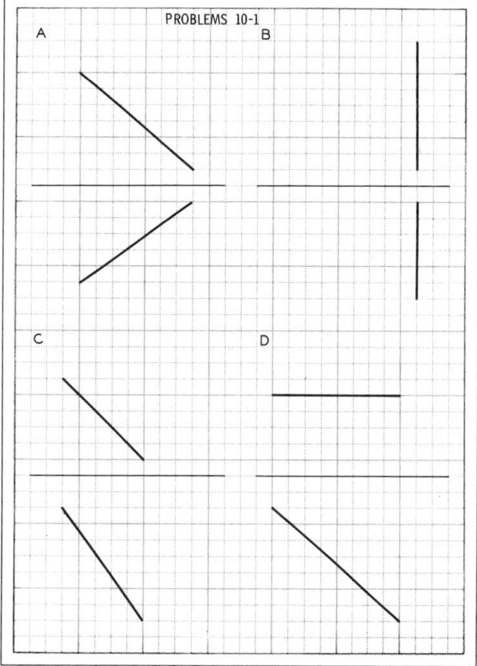

Fig. 10-42. Revolution of lines.

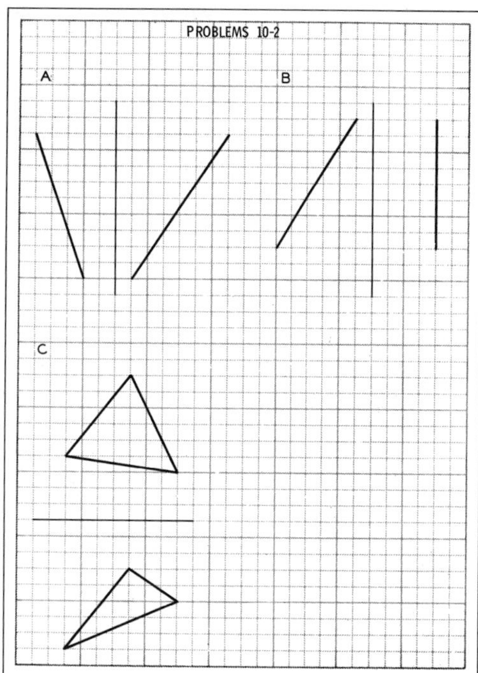

Fig. 10–43. Revolution of lines and planes.

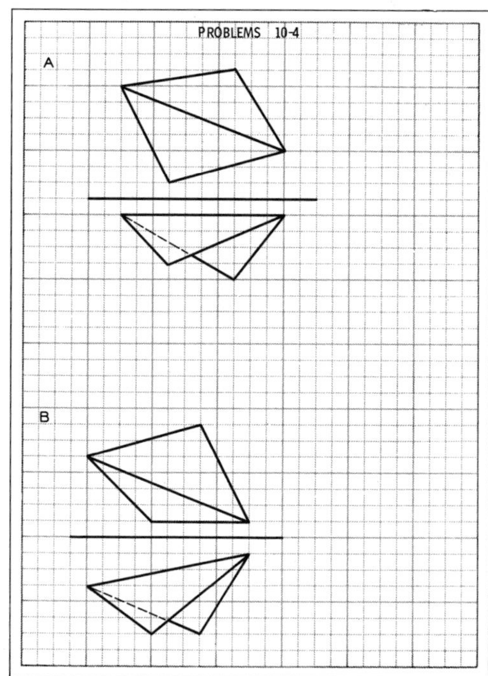

Fig. 10–45. Determining the angle between planes by revolution.

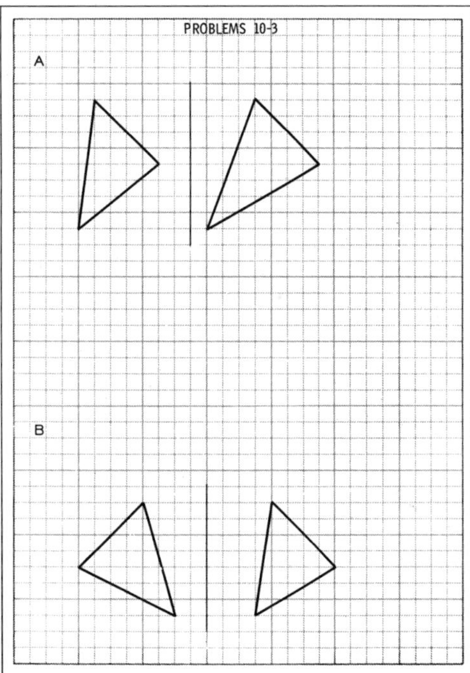

Fig. 10–44. Revolution of a plane.

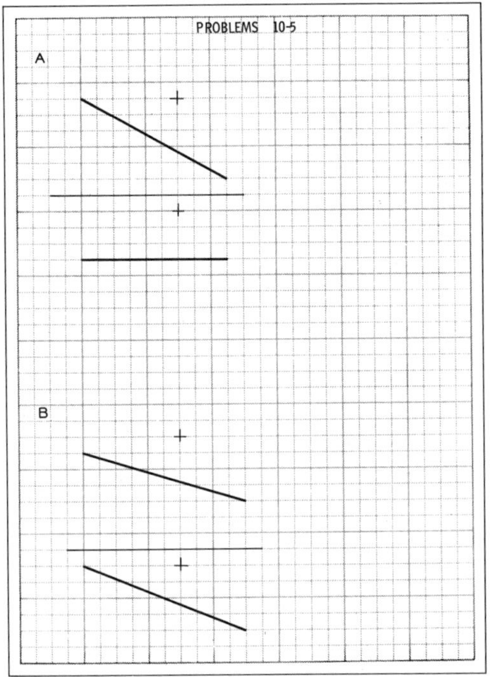

Fig. 10–46. Revolution of a point about a line.

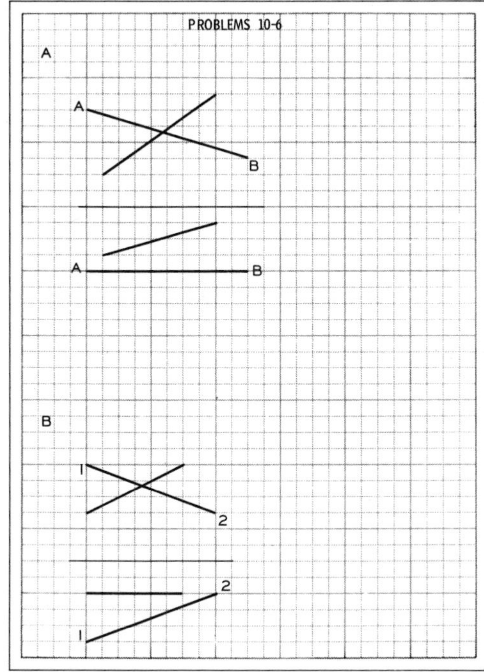

Fig. 10–47. Revolution of a line about an axis.

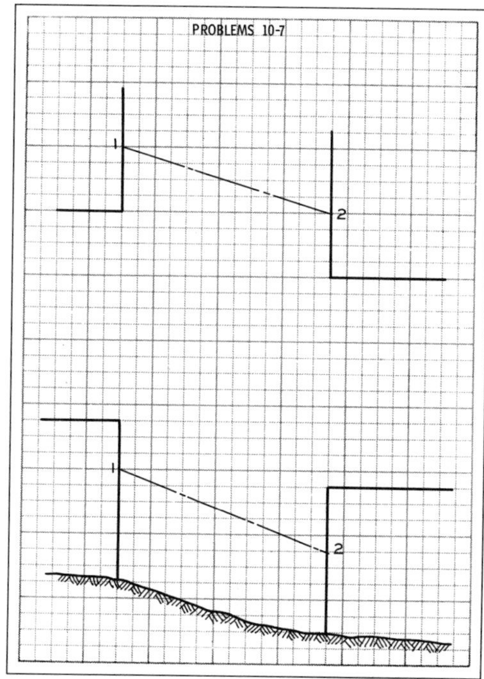

Fig. 10–48. Revolution of a prism about an axis.

4. (A) In Fig. 10–45A find the angle between the two intersecting planes by revolution. (B) Find the angle between the intersecting planes in part B of the figure by revolution.

5. (A) In Fig. 10–46A revolve the point about the line and locate its highest and lowest positions. (B) Revolve the point about the oblique line in part B of the figure. Locate its highest and most forward positions. Indicate it in all views.

6. (A) In Fig. 10–47A revolve the line about the axis *AB* 90° in a clockwise direction. Show the revolution in all views. (B) Revolve the line about axis 1–2 90° in a counterclockwise direction in part B of the figure. Show the revolution in all views.

7. Line 1–2 in Fig. 10–48 is the center line of a conveyer chute, such as that shown in Fig. 10–49, which has a 10-ft-square cross section.

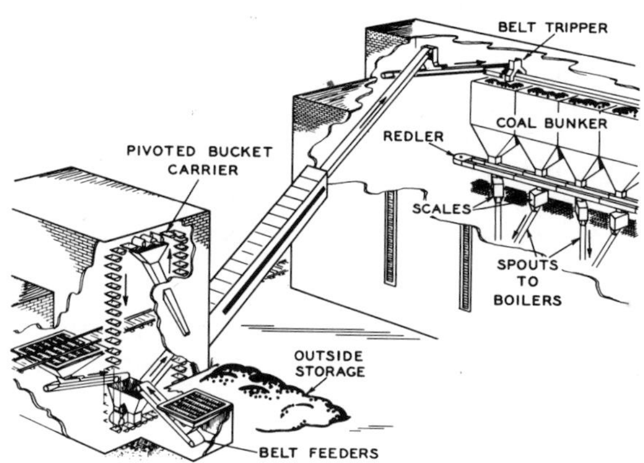

Fig. 10–49. An example of a coal chute between two buildings which is similar to that represented by Fig. 10–48. (Courtesy of Stephens-Adamson Manufacturing Company.)

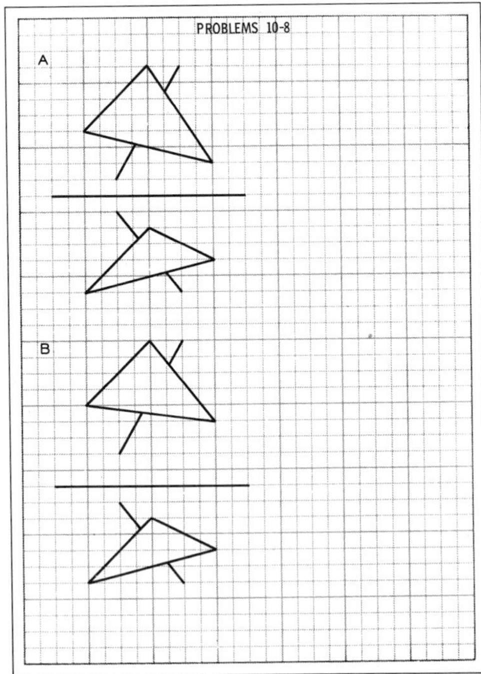

Fig. 10–50. Determining angle between a line and a plane by revolution and by auxiliary view.

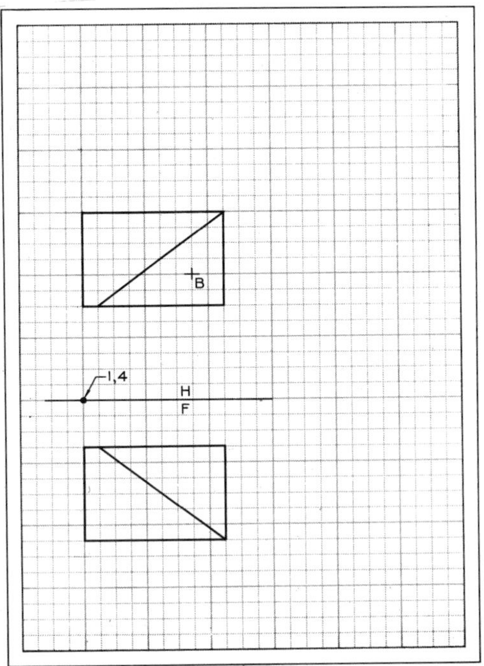

Fig. 10–51. Fixture block.

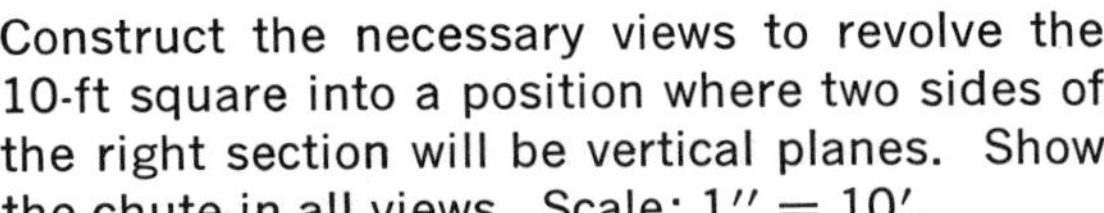

Construct the necessary views to revolve the 10-ft square into a position where two sides of the right section will be vertical planes. Show the chute in all views. Scale: 1″ = 10′.

8. In Fig. 10–50A find the angle between the line and plane by two auxiliary views and one revolution. Show all construction. (B) Find the angle between the line and plane in part B of the figure by the auxiliary-view method. Compare the solutions obtained in both parts.

9. Locate two views of a point $3\frac{1}{2}''$ apart on an $8\frac{1}{2}'' \times 11''$ sheet. Using a conical element of 2″, find the direction of a line that slopes forward and makes an angle of 30° with the frontal plane and slopes downward and makes an angle of 50° with the horizontal plane. Show all construction.

10. A fixture block (Fig. 10–51) must have a hole drilled perpendicular to the inclined surface with its center at point *B*, which lies on the plane. Using principles of revolution, determine the angles of revolution necessary to position the block under a vertically mounted drill for drilling. This information will be needed to design a jig for holding the block during this operation. Show the new positions of the block after revolution in all views.

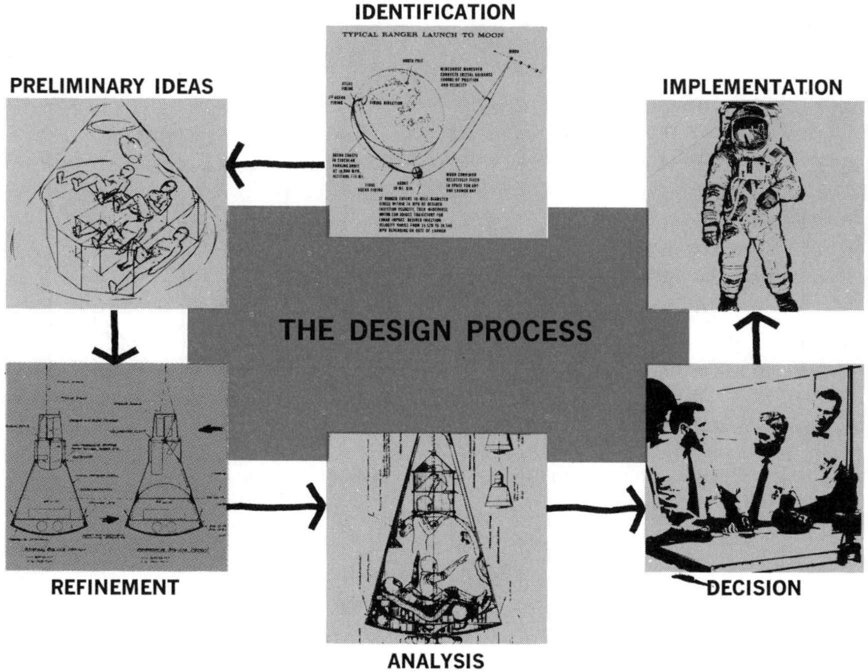

11 INTERSECTIONS

11-1 INTRODUCTION

Practically every product or engineering project designed is composed of planes, lines, or solids that intersect, often at unusual angles. The simple attachment of a rear-view mirror on the exterior body of an automobile is an intersection problem that must be solved prior to production. Massive concrete structures often involve the intersection of geometric forms with each other. The engineer must understand the principles of intersections in order to present his designs and to supervise the construction of the concrete forms into which the concrete will be poured.

The design of the dashboard of an automobile requires the solution of many intersection problems. The forms that intersect vary from lines to contoured shapes. All intersections must be developed graphically in the early stages of the design refinement, since the intersections will influence the final configuration and appearance of the instrument panel and the included accessories.

Many of the principles of intersection covered in this chapter are of a conventional nature and involve planes and regular geometric shapes. An understanding of the principles given will be sufficient for practically any problem encountered, since all intersection applications will involve variations of fundamental examples. As often as possible in our discussion, we shall include industrial examples to illustrate applications of the principles being covered.

It is advantageous to letter the significant points and lines that are used in the solution of intersection problems, as shown in the examples that follow. It is unnecessary to letter each and every point, but key points should be labeled to

FIGURE 11-1. INTERSECTION OF A LINE AND A PLANE

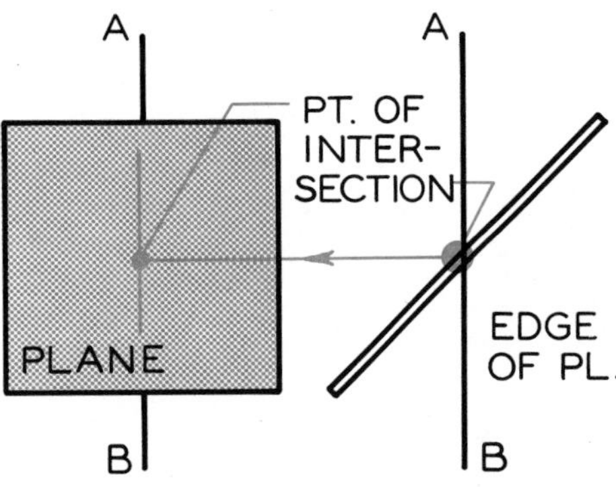

Step 1: The point of intersection can be found in the view where the plane appears as an edge, the side view in this example.

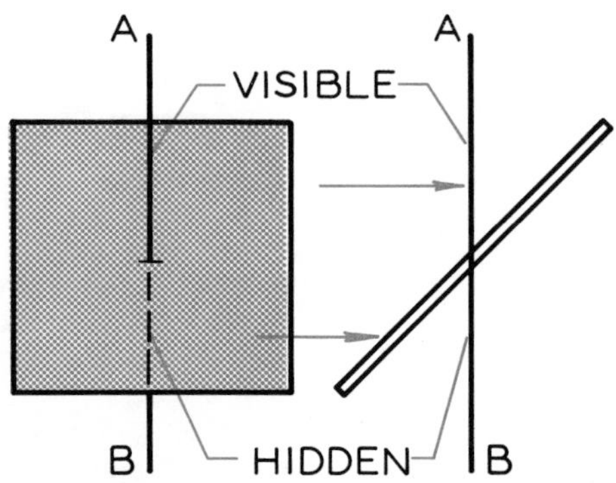

Step 2: Visibility in the front view is determined by looking from the front view to the right side view.

FIGURE 11-2. INTERSECTION BETWEEN PLANES

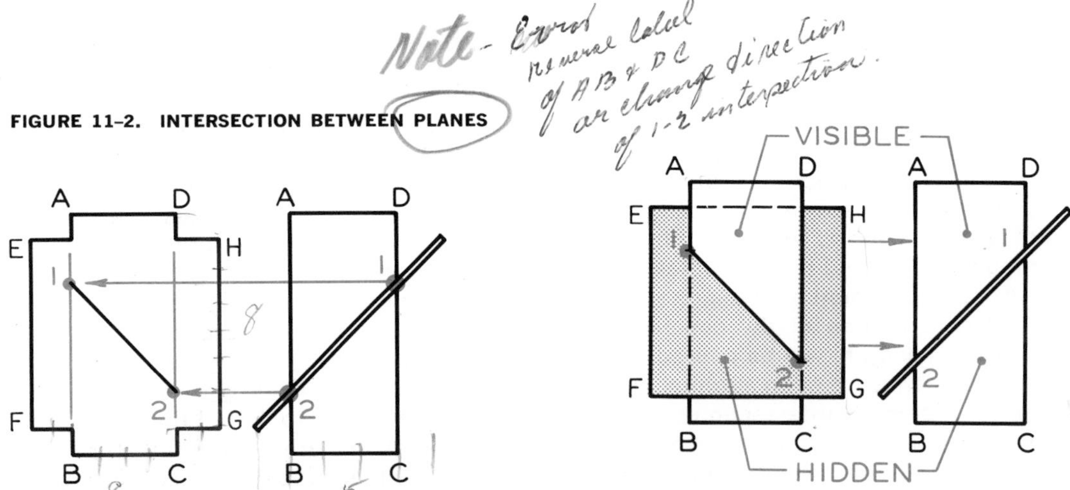

Step 1: The points where plane *EFGH* intersects lines *AB* and *DC* are found in the view where the plane appears as an edge. These points are projected to the front view.

Step 2: Line 1–2 is the line of intersection. Visibility is determined by looking from the front view to the right side view.

clarify construction and projection. Guidelines and constructions should be drawn very lightly to avoid the need for erasure upon completion of the problems.

11–2 INTERSECTIONS OF LINES AND PLANES

The basic step of finding an intersection between geometric shapes is the determination of the intersection between a line and a plane. This is illustrated in Fig. 11–1, where the plane is inclined at a 45° angle and the intersecting line is *AB*. This is a special case, since the plane appears as an edge in the side view, where the point of intersection can be found and projected to the front view. Visibility is found in step 2.

If you can understand the simple principle of this problem, it will be easy for you to solve more complex problems, since all shapes are composed of lines. This principle is used in Fig. 11–2 to find the line of intersection between two planes. Since plane *EFGH* appears as an edge in the side view, points of intersection 1 and 2 can be found and projected to the front view. The problem is completed by determining visibility in step 2. Note that the problem was solved by finding the points of intersection (piercing points) of lines *AB* and *DC*.

The same principle is used to find the intersection of a plane and a prism in Fig. 11–3, where the plane appears as an edge. A prism is composed of planes, which are in turn composed of lines; hence, it is possible for the principle introduced in Fig. 11–1 to be used again. The points of intersection are found for each line and are connected; visibility is determined to complete the solution.

A general case of intersection between a plane and a prism is shown in Fig. 11–4. The vertical corners of the prism project true length in the front view and the plane appears foreshortened in both views. Imaginary cutting planes are passed vertically through the planes of the prism in the top view to find piercing points of the corners of these planes in the front view. The points are connected and the visibility is determined to complete the solution.

FIGURE 11–3. INTERSECTION OF A PLANE AND A PRISM

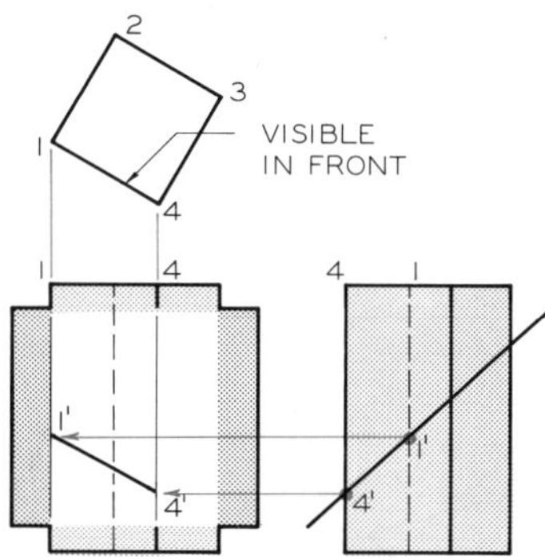

Step 1: Vertical corners 1 and 4 intersect the edge view of the plane in the side view at 1′ and 4′. These points are projected to the front view and are connected with a visible line.

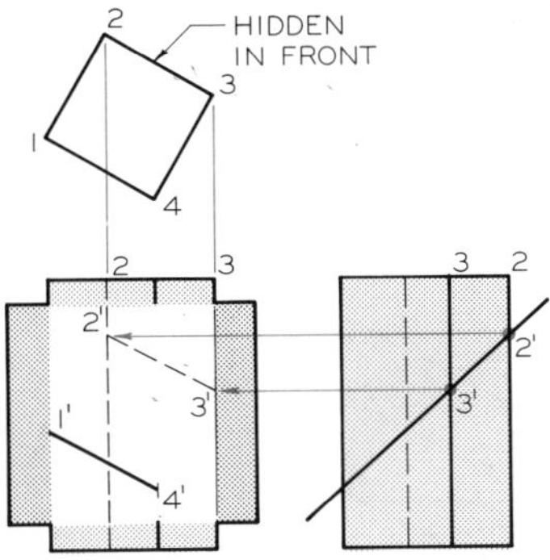

Step 2: Vertical corners 2 and 3 intersect the edge of the inclined plane at 2′ and 3′ in the side view. These points are connected in the front view with a hidden line. Inspection of the top view tells us that this line is hidden.

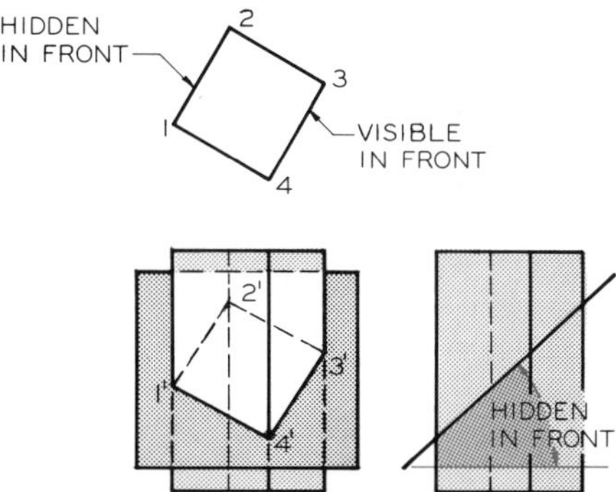

Step 3: Lines 1′–2′ and 3′–4′ are drawn as hidden and visible lines respectively. Visibility is determined by inspection of the top and side views and by projection to the front view.

FIGURE 11-4. INTERSECTION OF AN OBLIQUE PLANE AND A PRISM

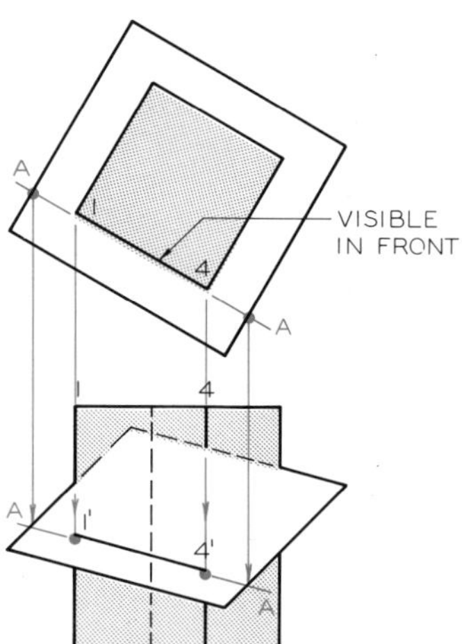

Step 1: Vertical cutting plane A–A is passed through the vertical plane, 1–4, in the top view and is projected to the front view. Piercing points 1′ and 4′ are found in this view.

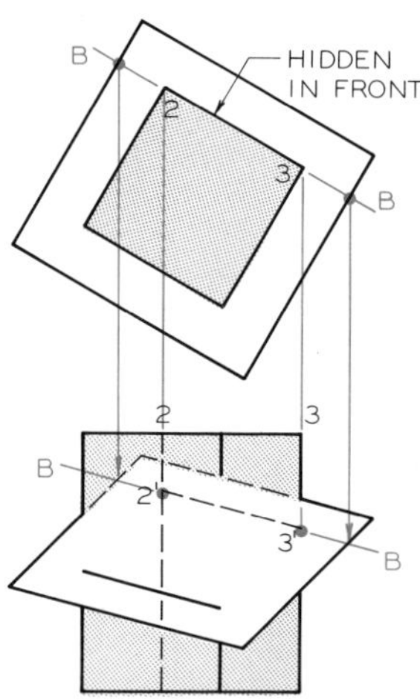

Step 2: Vertical plane B–B is passed through the top view of plane 2–3 and is projected to the front view where piercing points 2′ and 3′ are found. Line 2′–3′ is a hidden line.

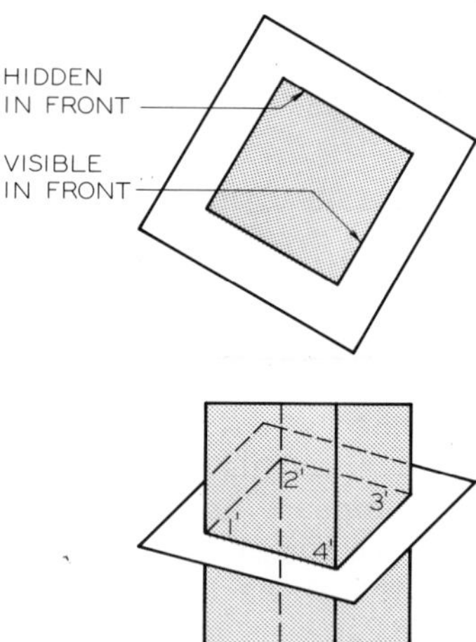

Step 3: The line of intersection is completed by connecting the four points in the front view. Visibility in the front view is found by inspection of the top view.

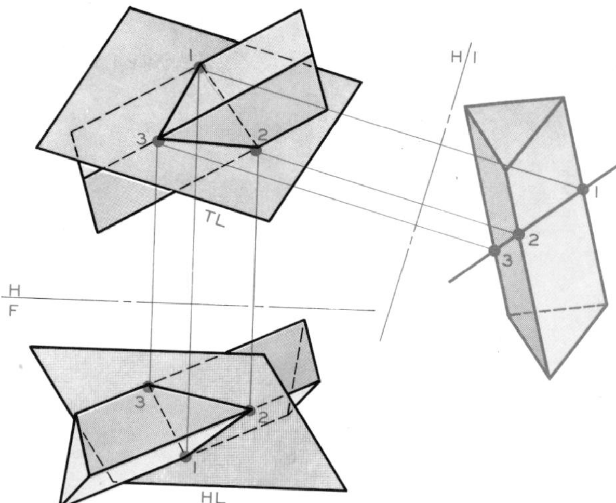

Fig. 11-5. Intersection of an oblique plane and an oblique prism.

The general case of the intersection between an oblique plane and an oblique prism is shown in Fig. 11-5. Since both the plane and the prism are oblique in the given views, neither the plane nor any of the planes of the prism appears as an edge. This problem can be solved in the same manner as the example in Fig. 11-3, if a view can be found where the plane projects as an edge. This view can be found in a primary auxiliary view by taking the point view of a line on the plane by projection from either view. The lateral edges of the prism do not appear true length in the auxiliary view, but this does not complicate the problem. In the figure, points 1, 2, and 3 are located in the auxiliary view where the corner edges of the prism intersect the plane. These points are projected to the top and front views as shown. Visibility is determined in both views by inspection. Principles of visibility can be reviewed in Article 7-12.

11-3 INTERSECTION BETWEEN PRISMS

The intersection between two prisms can be found by applying the principles that were used to find the intersection between a single plane and a prism in the preceding article. Prisms are composed of planes; consequently, it is possible to work with each plane individually until all lines of intersection are found. An example is solved by steps in Fig. 11-6.

FIGURE 11-6. INTERSECTION BETWEEN TWO PRISMS

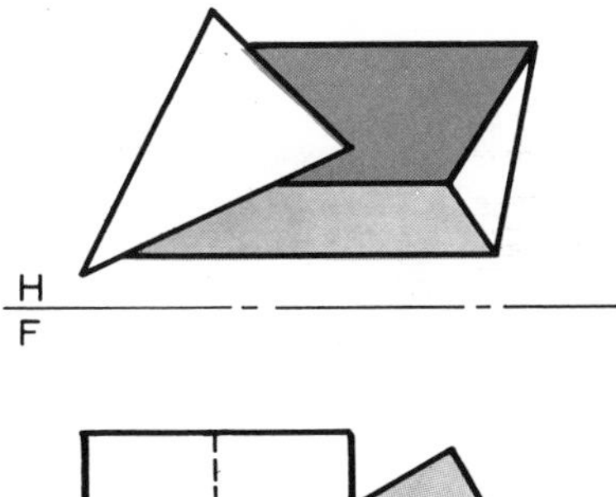

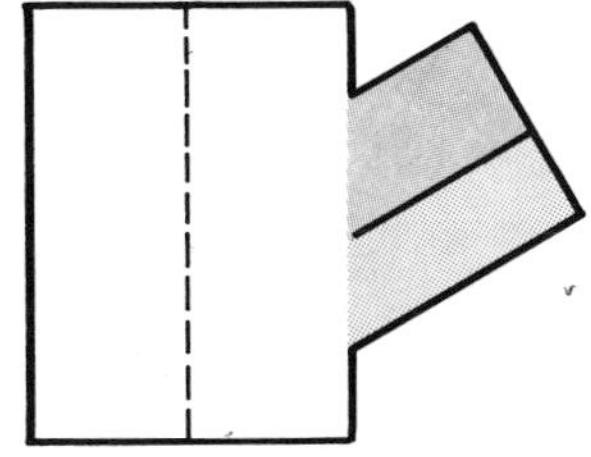

Given: The top and front views of two prisms.
Required: The line of intersection between the two prisms in both views with visibility indicated.
References: Articles 11-2 and 11-3.

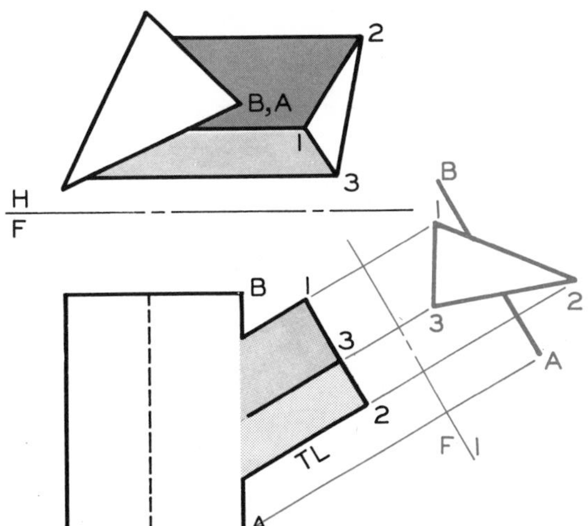

Step 1: Construct the end view of the inclined prism by projecting an auxiliary view from the front view. Show only line *AB*, the corner line of the vertical prism, in the auxiliary view because this is the only critical line. Letter the points.

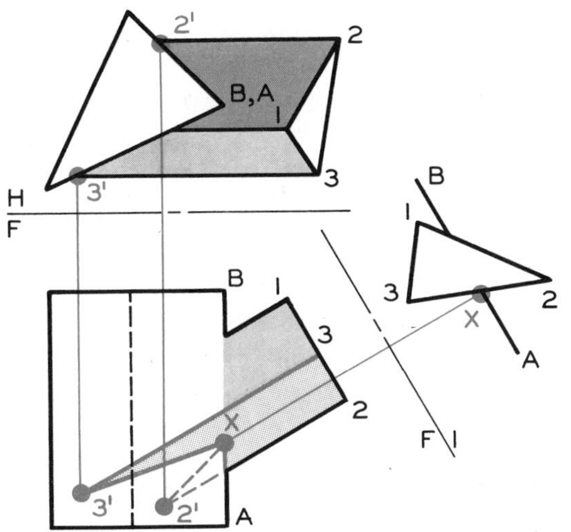

Step 2: Locate the piercing points of lines 2-2′ and 3-3′ in the top view and project them to the front view to the extension of the corner lines. It is rather obvious that a line connecting points 2′ and 3′ will not be a straight line, but will bend around the corner line *AB*. The point where this line intersects the corner is found to be point *X* in the primary auxiliary. Project it back to the front view.

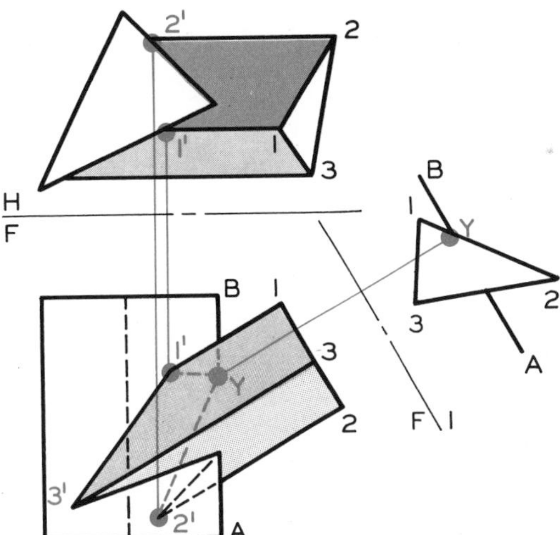

Step 3: It can be seen in the primary auxiliary view that line 1′-2′ bends around corner line *AB* at point *Y*. Draw line 1′-Y-2′ in the front view. This line is found to be invisible in the front view by inspection of the primary auxiliary view. Draw line 1′-3′ as a visible straight line; it does not bend around a corner.

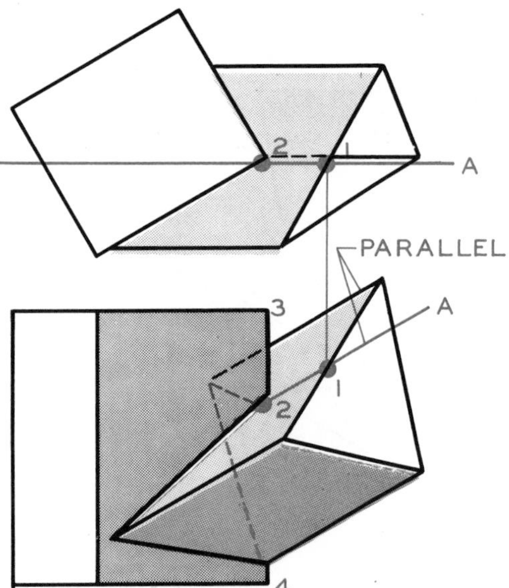

Fig. 11-7. Intersection between prisms by projection.

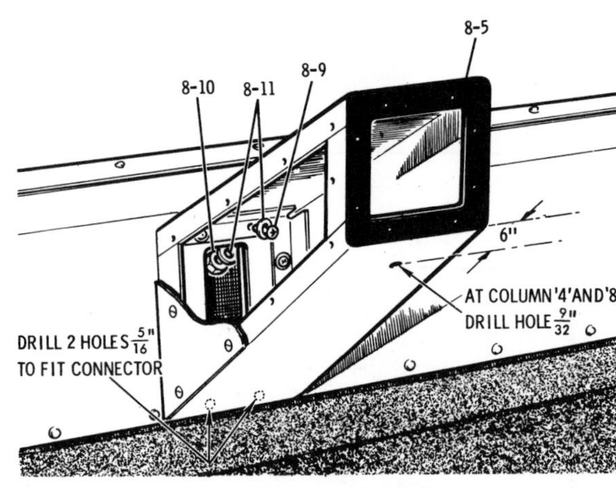

Fig. 11-8. This conduit connector was designed through the use of the principles of intersection of a plane and a prism. (Courtesy of Federal Aviation Agency.)

The top and front views of two intersecting prisms are given, and we are required to find their lines of intersection. The surfaces of one prism appear as edges in the top view, which makes it possible to see where the corner edges of the other prism intersect. It is necessary to draw an auxiliary view (step 1) in order to find the relationship between line *AB* and the end view of the prism, since two of the lines of intersection must bend around this corner line. The points of intersection, 3′ and 2′, are found in the top view in step 2, and then are projected to the front view. Point *X*, the point where line 2′–3′ bends around line *AB*, is found in the auxiliary view and projected to the front view. Line 2′–*X*–3′ is completed in the front view and visibility is indicated. The remaining lines of intersection are found, as explained in step 3, by repeating this procedure.

An alternative method of finding the line of intersection between two prisms is illustrated in Fig. 11-7. Vertical cutting plane *A* is passed through the point view of corner line 3-4 in the top view, and points 1 and 2 are established on the second prism. Since the cutting plane is parallel to the corner edges of the upper surface of the oblique prism, line 1-2 will be drawn parallel to these sides in the front view, where it is found to intersect line 3-4 at point 2. Point 2 is the point where the line of intersection bends around corner line 3-4. The other piercing points are found in the manner described in Fig. 11-6.

The conduit connector shown in Fig. 11-8 is an example of the intersection of planes and prisms. This connector is designed to intersect an oblique wall at an angle.

11-4 INTERSECTION OF A PLANE AND A CYLINDER

The catalytic cracking unit shown in Fig. 11-9 illustrates many intersections of cylindrical shapes with geometric forms. Cylinders are fundamental shapes that are used extensively in processing plants of this type and have many engineering applications in all other industries as well.

Fig. 11-9. Many intersections of cylinders and planes can be seen in this refinery. (Courtesy of Humble Oil and Refining Company.)

A special case of a plane intersecting a cylinder is shown in Fig. 11-10. The plane appears as an edge in the side view.

The line of intersection is found by passing vertical cutting planes through the vertical cylinder in the top view to establish elements on it and their points of intersection. These points can be located in the side view, where the plane appears as an edge, by the principle introduced in Fig. 11-1.

FIGURE 11-10. INTERSECTION BETWEEN A CYLINDER AND A PLANE

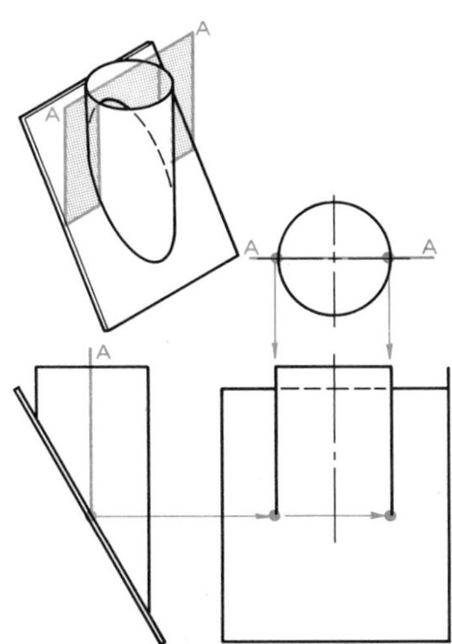

Step 1: A vertical cutting plane, A-A, is passed through the cylinder parallel to its axis to find two points of intersection.

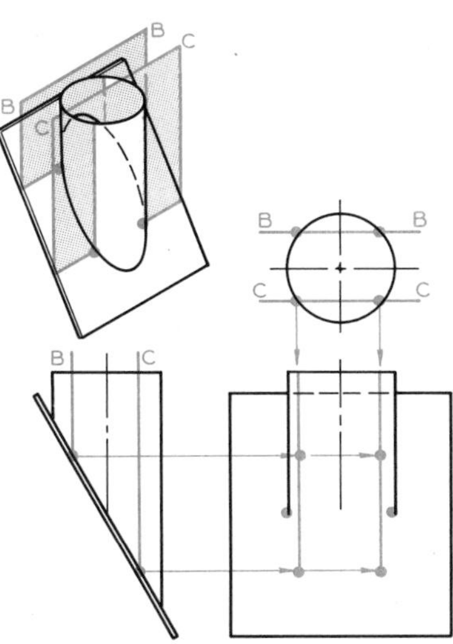

Step 2: Two more cutting planes, B-B and C-C, are used to find four additional points in the top and the left side views; these points are projected to the front view.

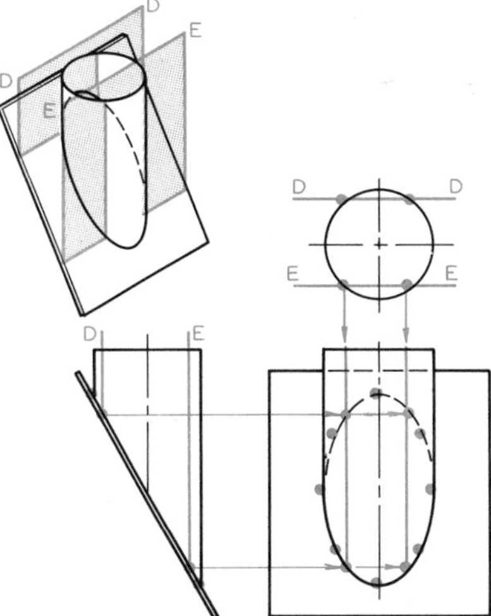

Step 3: Additional cutting planes are used to find more points. These points are connected to give an elliptical line of intersection.

Fig. 11-11. Models are sometimes used to refine a design of a complicated installation. Cylindrical shapes are prominent in this design. (Courtesy of Standard Oil Company of New Jersey.)

The more cutting planes that are used, the more accurate will be your solution. The line of intersection will be an ellipse.

A number of planes intersecting cylinders are shown in Fig. 11-11. This is a model of a refinery that has been constructed to analyze the relationships of the components and to serve as a guide during construction.

A similar problem is solved in Fig. 11-12, in which the plane is oblique in the principal views.

Vertical cutting planes are passed through the vertical cylinder and the oblique plane in the top view to find points of intersection that can be projected to the front view. This process is repeated until a sufficient number of points are found to draw the elliptical line of intersection in the front view.

FIGURE 11-12. INTERSECTION OF A CYLINDER AND AN OBLIQUE PLANE

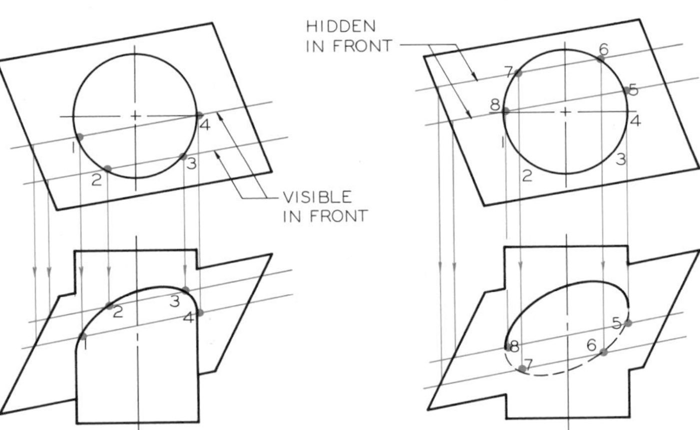

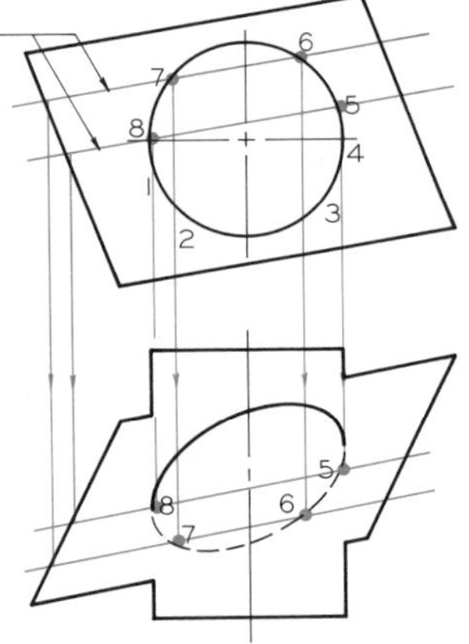

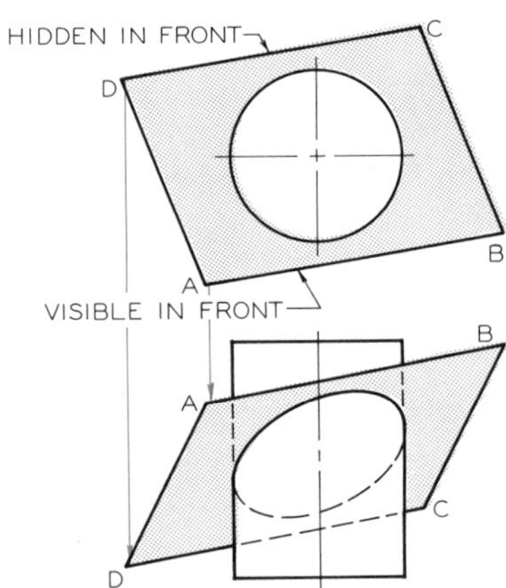

Step 1: Vertical cutting planes are passed through the cylinder in the top view to establish elements on its surface and lines on the oblique plane. Piercing points 1, 2, 3, and 4 are projected to the front view to their respective lines and are connected with a visible line.

Step 2: Additional cutting planes are used to find other piercing points—5, 6, 7, and 8—which are projected to the front view to their respective lines on the oblique plane. These are connected with a hidden line by inspection of the top view.

Step 3: Visibility of the plane and cylinder is completed in the front view. Line *AB* is found to be visible by inspection of the top view, and *CD* is found to be hidden.

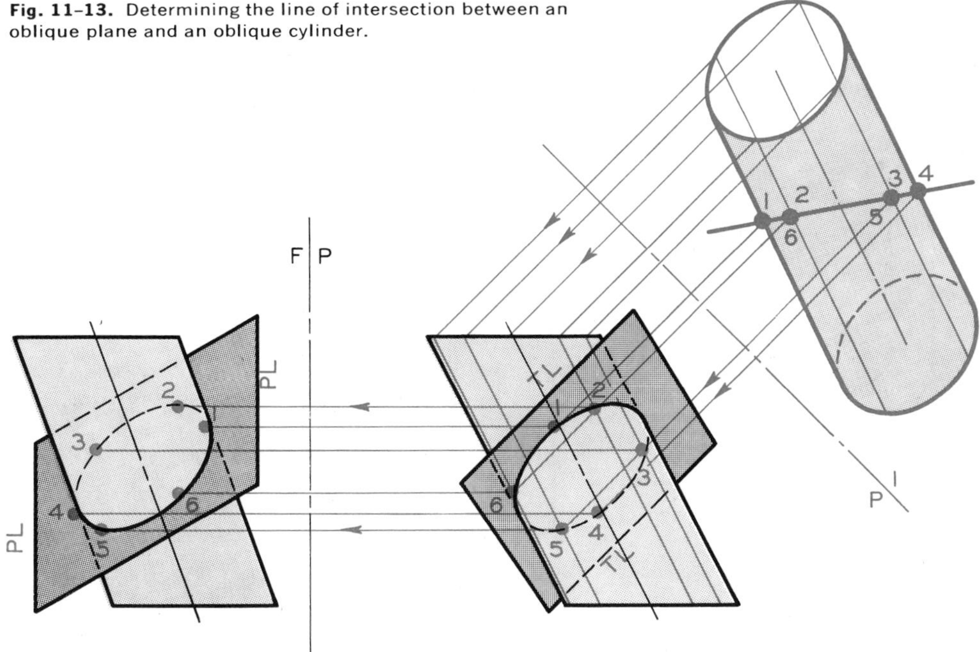

Fig. 11–13. Determining the line of intersection between an oblique plane and an oblique cylinder.

The general case for the intersection between an oblique plane and an oblique cylinder is shown in Fig. 11–13, in which the cylinder does not appear true length, and the plane does not appear as an edge. The line of intersection between these forms is determined by finding an edge view of the plane in a primary auxiliary view, where the projection of the cylinder is foreshortened. Cutting planes are used to establish lines on the surface of the cylinder in the primary auxiliary view. These lines are found to intersect the edge view of the plane at points 1, 2, 3, 4, 5, and 6. The lines on the surface of the cylinder are projected from the auxiliary view to the profile view. Each of the points of intersection found in the auxiliary view is projected to its respective line in the profile view. These points are connected to establish the elliptical line of intersection. Visibility is shown. The line of intersection is found in the front view by transferring measurements of points from the primary auxiliary view to the front view using dividers.

Aircraft designs require the solution of many intersection problems because of the many intersecting geometric forms. Examples of intersections can be seen in the F-105 shown in Fig. 11–14. In addition to the intersections made by the tail assembly and the wings with the fuselage, the cockpit represents the principle of a cone intersecting an approximate cylinder.

Fig. 11–14. The F-105 fighter-bomber is composed of many intersections between a variety of geometric shapes. (Courtesy of Republic Aviation Corporation.)

FIGURE 11-15 INTERSECTION BETWEEN A CYLINDER AND A PRISM

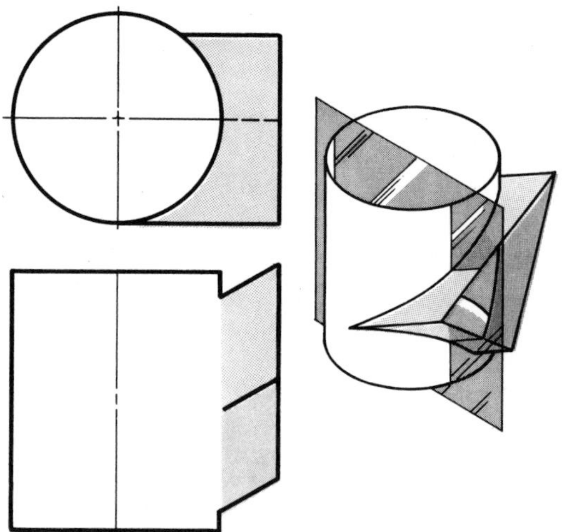

Given: The top and front views of an intersecting cylinder and prism.
Required: Find the line of intersection between the cylinder and prism.
Reference: Article 11-5.

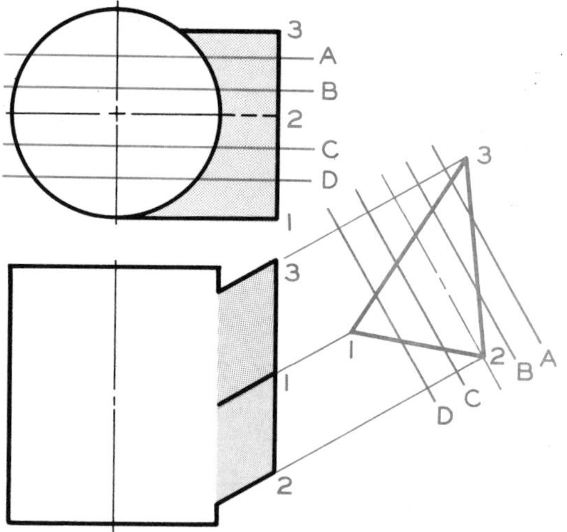

Step 1: Project an auxiliary view of the triangular prism from the front view to show three of its surfaces as edges. Pass frontal cutting planes through the top view of the cylinder and project them to the auxiliary view. The spacing between the planes is equal in both views.

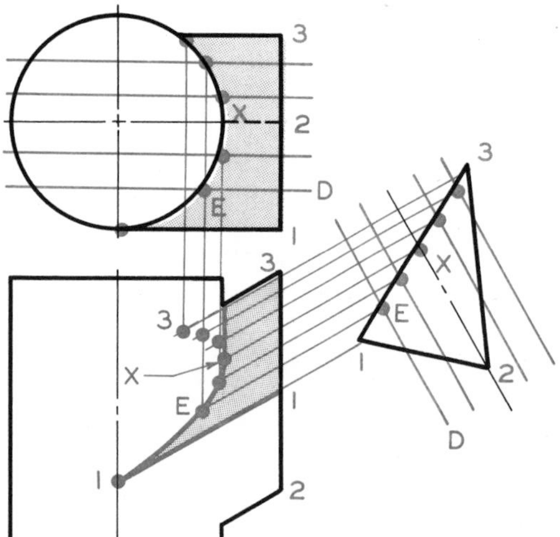

Step 2: Locate points along the line of intersection of the cylinder and plane 1-3 in the top view and project them to the front view. The intersection of these projectors with those coming from the auxiliary view establishes points on the line of intersection in the front view. *Example:* Point *E* on cutting plane *D* is found in the top and primary auxiliary views and projected to the front view where the projectors intersect. Point *X* on the center line is the point where visibility changes from visible to hidden in the front view.

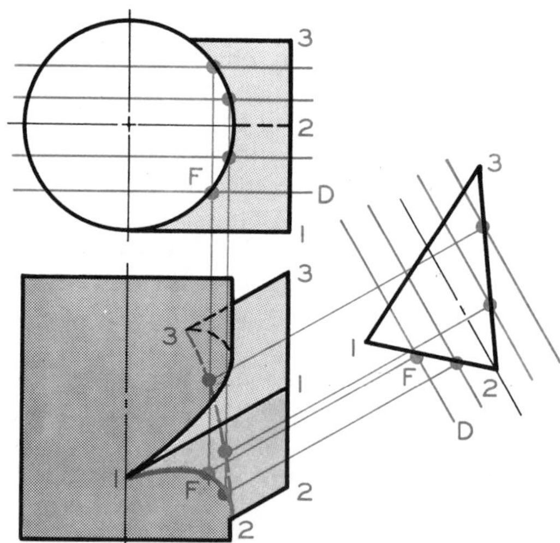

Step 3: Determine the remaining points of intersection by using the same cutting planes. Point *F* is shown in the top and primary auxiliary views and is projected to the front view on line of intersection 1-2. Connect the points and determine visibility. Judgment should be used in spacing the cutting planes so that they will produce the most accurate representation of the line of intersection.

11-5 INTERSECTION BETWEEN A CYLINDER AND A PRISM

A series of cutting planes are used in Fig. 11-15 to establish lines that lie on the surfaces of the cylinder and the prism. Since these lines lie in a common cutting plane, they will intersect where they cross in the views of projection. A primary auxiliary view is necessary to locate the lines on the surface of the prism in the front view (step 1). Rather than attempting to find the lines of intersection of two or more planes simultaneously, we shall analyze each plane independently. The line of intersection is projected from the edge view of plane 1-3 in the auxiliary view to the front view in step 2. A plane intersects a curved surface with a curved line. Note that the change in visibility of a line passing around a cylinder in the front is found to be point *X* in the top view. Step 3 is a continuation of this system of locating points until the final line of intersection is found with the visibility shown.

A practical example of intersections such as we have been discussing can be seen in an electric coffee pot. The lines of intersection made by the spout and handle with the cylindrical body of the container can be determined by constructing a series of horizontal cutting planes and projecting points of intersections to the other views. Determining these lines of intersection is a preliminary step in designing the components for accurate assembly.

11-6 INTERSECTION BETWEEN TWO CYLINDERS

The intersection between the two cylinders shown in Fig. 11-16 is found with the cutting-plane method. Frontal cutting planes are drawn in the top view to establish points common to each cylinder. For example, the locations of points 1 and 2 in the front view are determined by the intersections of the projectors coming from the top and primary auxiliary views where plane *D* intersects the cylinders. These points are on the line of intersection in the front view. The trace of the cutting plane *D* is shown in the front view to illustrate the path of the cutting plane. Additional points are found and connected to find the complete line of intersection. Visibility is indicated in the front view.

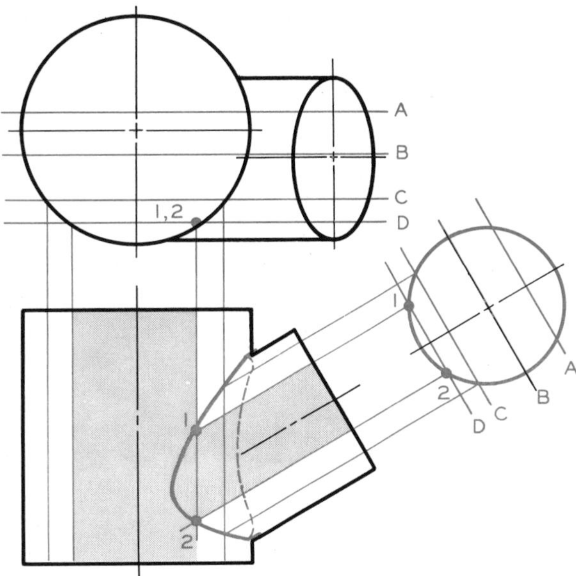

Fig. 11-16. Determining the intersection between cylinders.

Fig. 11-17. Many intersections between cylinders can be seen in this gas processing plant. (Courtesy of Humble Oil and Refining Company.)

Many intersections between cylinders are shown in Fig. 11-17, in which a thermometer at an Oklahoma gas-processing plant is being checked. Intersections of this type must be found to permit the shapes to be formed for proper joining on the site.

FIGURE 11-18. INTERSECTION OF A PLANE AND A CONE

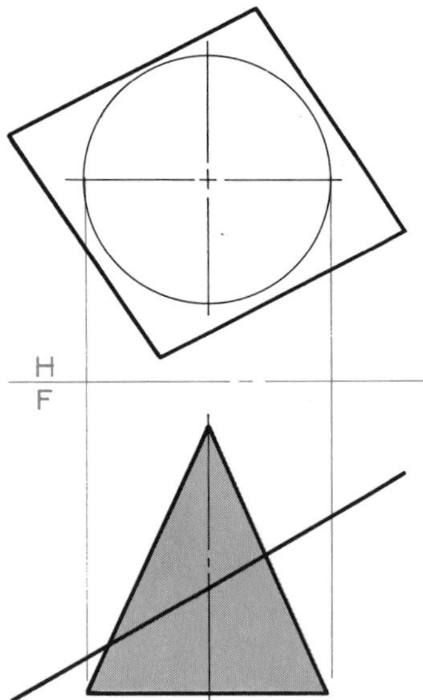

Given: The top and front views of a cone and an intersecting plane.
Required: Find the line of intersection of the two geometric shapes.

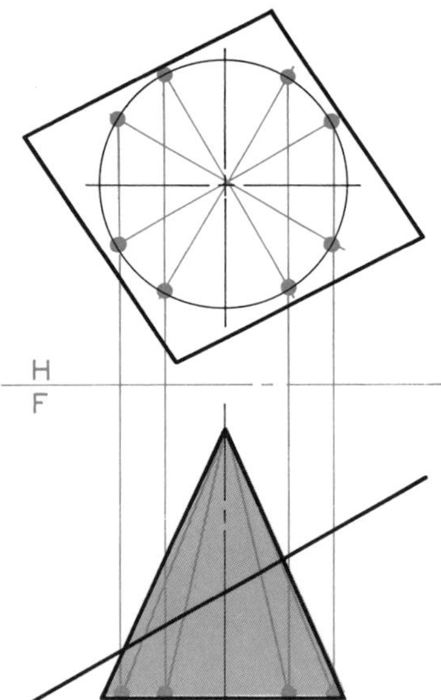

Step 1: Divide the base into even divisions in the top view and connect these points with the apex to establish elements on the cone. Project these to the front view.

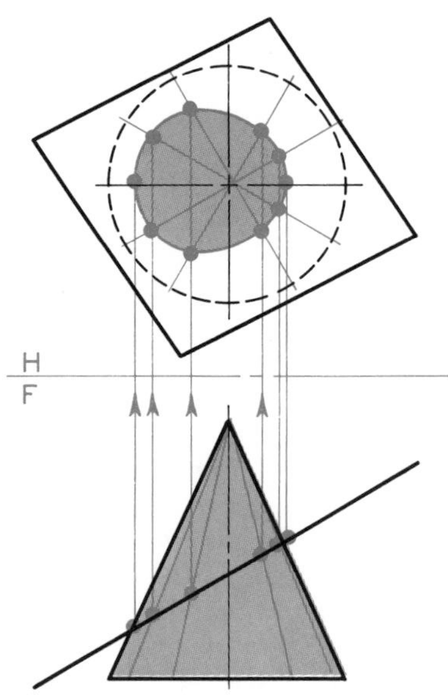

Step 2: The piercing point of each element on the edge view of the plane can be found in the front view. These points are projected to the top view to the same elements, where they are connected to form the line of intersection. Visibility is shown to complete the drawing.

11-7 INTERSECTION BETWEEN A PLANE AND A CONE

A cone is a geometric shape which is used in many engineering designs in combination with other forms. The determination of the intersection of a plane with a cone is shown in Fig. 11-18.

In this case, a series of radial lines from the cone's apex to its base (elements) is used to find the line of intersection. These elements cross the edge view of the plane in the front view to locate piercing points that are projected to the top view of these elements. The points are connected to find the line of intersection.

A cone and an oblique plane are given in Fig. 11-19, in which the line of intersection is determined with a series of cutting planes.

Horizontal cutting planes are used in the front view to give easy-to-draw circular sections in the top view. Also, these cutting planes will locate lines on the oblique plane that will intersect the same circular sections cut by each respective cutting plane. The points of intersection are projected to the adjacent view.

The cutting-plane method could have been used to solve the example shown in Fig. 11-18 as an alternative method. Most descriptive geometry problems have more than one method of solution.

Figure 11-20 illustrates the utilization of conical shapes in the configuration of a launch escape vehicle. Points of intersection, as well

FIGURE 11-19. INTERSECTION OF AN OBLIQUE PLANE AND A CONE

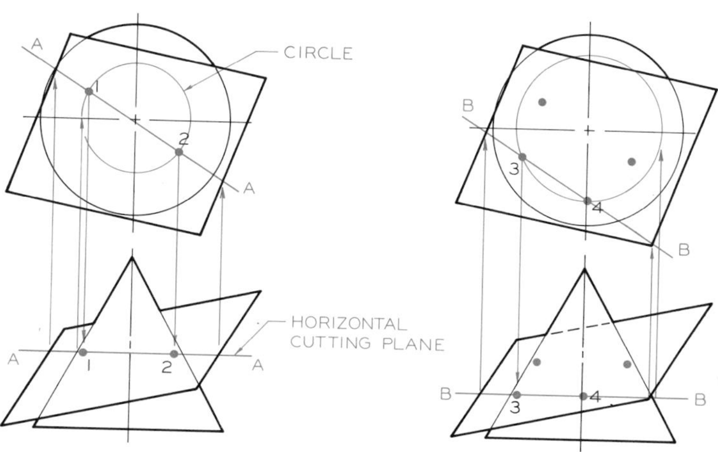

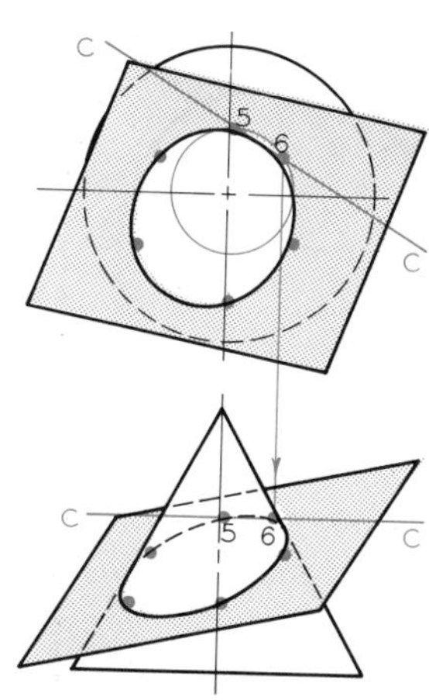

Step 1: A horizontal cutting plane is passed through the front view to establish a circular section on the cone and a line on the oblique plane in the top view. The piercing point of this line must lie on the circular section if the line intersects the cone. Piercing points 1 and 2 are projected to the front view.

Step 2: Horizontal cutting plane B–B is passed through the front view in the same manner to locate piercing points 3 and 4 in the top view. These points are projected to the horizontal plane in the front view from the top view.

Step 3: Additional horizontal planes are used to find sufficient points to complete the line of intersection. Determination of the visibility completes the solution.

as lines of intersection, were determined in the final refinement of this spacecraft.

11-8 INTERSECTION BETWEEN A CONE AND A PRISM

A primary auxiliary view is drawn in Fig. 11-21 to show the lateral planes of the prism as edges so that the line of intersection between the prism and cone may be found. Cutting planes that radiate from the apex of the cone in the

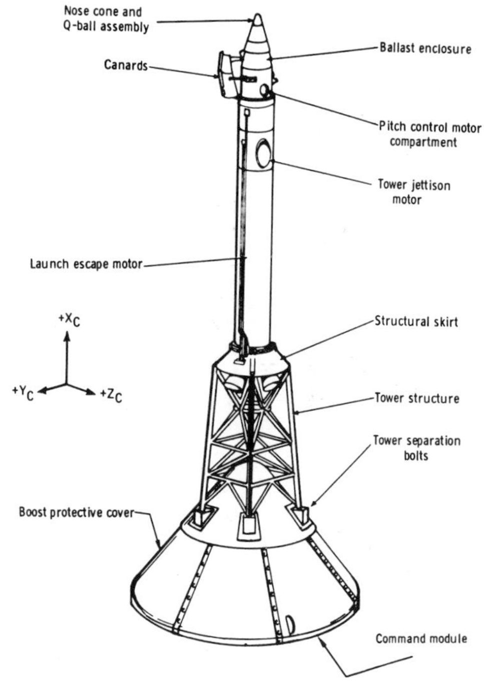

Fig. 11-20. Intersections with a conical shape were solved in designing the launch escape vehicle. (Courtesy of the National Aeronautics and Space Administration.)

FIGURE 11-21. INTERSECTION BETWEEN A CONE AND A PRISM

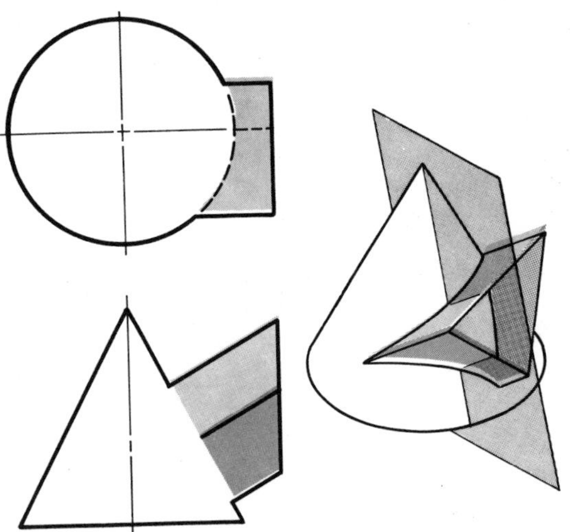

Given: The top and front views of a cone intersecting with a prism.
Required: Find the line of intersection between the cone and prism and determine visibility.
Reference: Article 11-8.

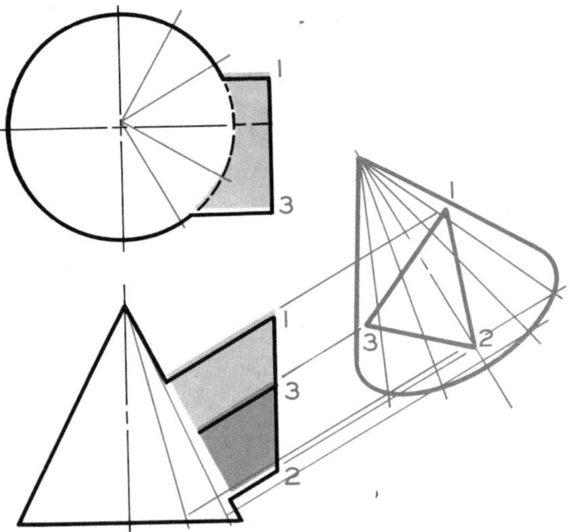

Step 1: Construct a primary auxiliary view to obtain the edge views of the lateral surfaces of the prism. In the auxiliary view pass cutting planes through the cone which radiate from the apex to establish elements on the cone. Project the elements to the principal views.

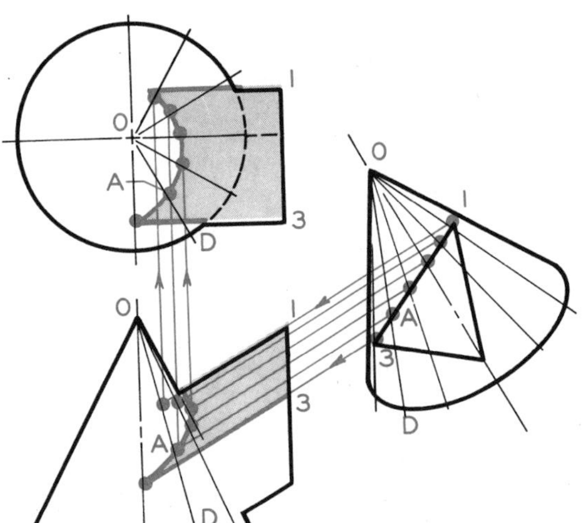

Step 2: Locate the piercing points of the cone's elements with the edge view of plane 1-3 in the primary view and project them to front and top views. *Example:* Point *A* lies on element *OD* in the primary auxiliary, so it is projected to the front and top view of element *OD*. Locate other points along the line of intersection in this manner.

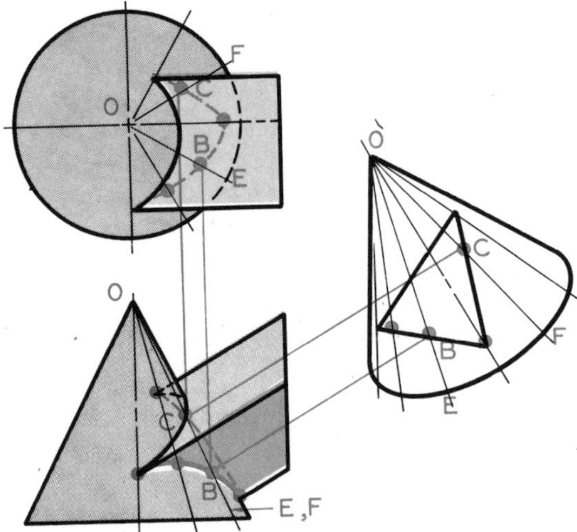

Step 3: Locate the piercing points where the conical elements intersect the edge views of the other planes of the prism in the primary auxiliary. *Example:* Point *B* is found on *OE* in the primary auxiliary and is projected to the front and top views of *OE*. Show visibility in each view after the location of a sufficient number of points.

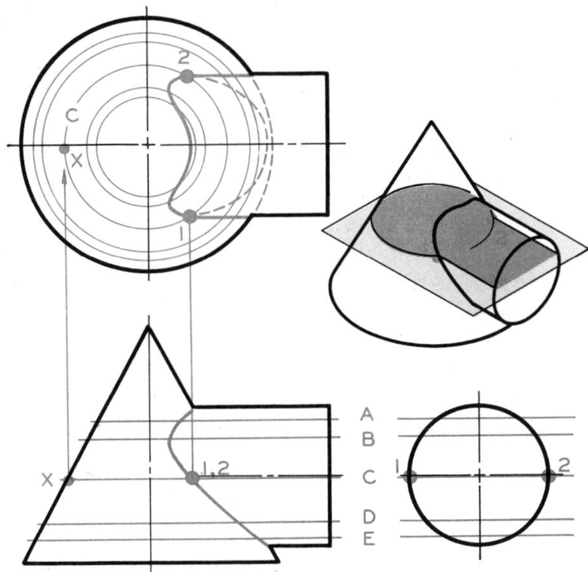

Fig. 11-22. Intersection between a cone and a cylinder.

Fig. 11-23. This electrically operated distributor illustrates intersections between a cone and a series of cylinders. (Courtesy of GATX.)

primary auxiliary view are used to establish lines lying on the surface of the cone and the surface of the prism, as shown in step 1. Inspection of the auxiliary view in step 2 shows that point *A* lies on cutting plane *OD*. Point *A* is projected to the front and top views of element *OD*, which was established on the surface of the cone by the cutting plane.

Other piercing points are found by repeating this system on the other two planes of the prism in step 3. All projections originate in the auxiliary view, where the cutting planes and the planes of the prism appear as edges.

The horizontal cutting-plane method for finding the line of intersection between a cylinder and a cone is shown in Fig. 11-22. This is not a feasible method if the axis of the intersecting cylinder is not horizontal and the axis of the cone not vertical, since the sections cut by the cutting planes would be irregular in shape and would require the tedious plotting of many points.

An unusual example of cylinders intersecting a cone can be seen in Fig. 11-23. The lines of intersection between the cones of this distributor housing were determined through the use of the auxiliary view method, as illustrated in Fig. 11-21.

11-9 CONIC SECTIONS

Conic sections—the parabola, hyperbola, ellipse, and circle—are, in effect, intersections of a plane with a cone. These are basic mathematical figures that can be found graphically as well as mathematically. The graphical method of finding the line of intersection between the imaginary plane and the cone is illustrated in the following examples.

Parabola. The parabola is the line of intersection formed by a cutting plane that passes through the cone, making the same angle with the cone's base as with its elements, as illustrated in Fig. 11-24A. This figure can be described mathematically as a plane curve, each point of which is equidistant from a directrix (a straight line) and its focal point.

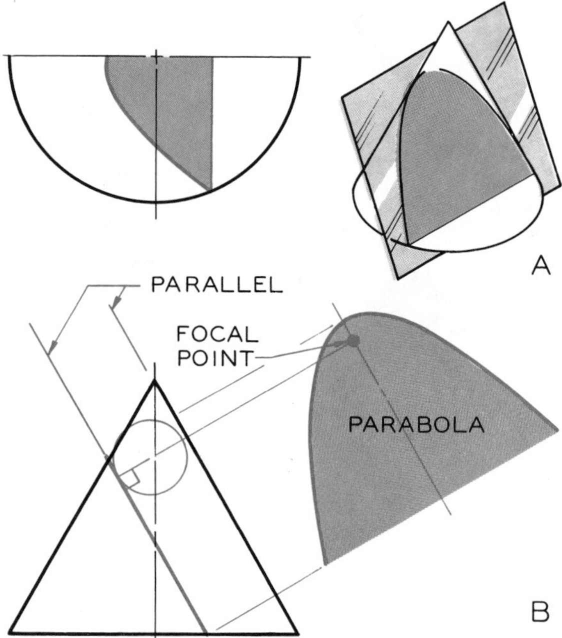

Fig. 11-24. Constructing a parabolic section of a cone.

Fig. 11-25. This tracking antenna is an application of a parabolic shell. (Courtesy of Ryan Aeronautics.)

The edge view of the cutting plane is drawn in the front view of the cone in part B of the figure, and it is projected to the top view by using a series of horizontal cutting planes, as introduced in Fig. 11-19. Having the top view of the line of intersection, it is now possible to find the true-size view of the parabola by a primary auxiliary view that is projected perpendicularly from the edge view of the cutting plane. The circle drawn at the apex of the cone represents a sphere that is drawn tangent to the cone and to the edge view of the parabola. The point of tangency of the sphere with the edge view of the parabola locates the focal point of the parabola. All lines entering the open end of the parabola parallel to its axis of symmetry will be reflected to a common point called the focal point. This shape is used for light reflectors, in which the bulb is located at the focal point, resulting in emission of parallel beams of light from the parabola. It is also used in the design of huge tracking antennas which send radio signals millions of miles into space and receive signals from satellites in space (Fig. 11-25).

The equation of a parabola can be written in the following form:

$$y = ax^2 + bx + c, \qquad \text{when } a \neq 0.$$

When the parabola's equation is known, it can be plotted on grid paper by substituting values for x and y.

Hyperbola. The hyperbola is the line of intersection that is formed by a cutting plane which is passed through a cone in a manner such that it intersects the cone's base at an angle of 90° or less and makes an angle greater than the angle made by the elements with the base. Figure 11-26A illustrates a hyperbola constructed by the intersection of a cutting plane with two cones.

The edge view of the cutting plane is drawn in the front view of part B of the figure. The line of intersection of this cutting plane is found in the top view by using horizontal cutting planes, as shown in Fig. 11-19. An auxiliary view, a right side view in this case, is used to find the true size of the hyperbola. A circle is constructed at the apex of the cone to be tangent to the hyperbola and to the sides of the cone in the front view. The point where the circle is tangent to the plane is the focal point.

A hyperbola is defined as the path of a point which moves in a direction such that the difference of its distances from the two focal points is constant. Its mathematical equation is written in the following form:

$$\frac{x^2}{a^2} - \frac{y^2}{b^2} = 1, \qquad \text{where} \qquad a, b \neq 0.$$

Ellipse. The line of intersection of a plane that cuts across the axis of a cone at an angle other than 90° above the base is an ellipse (Fig. 11-27). An ellipse is the path of a point which is moving in such a way that the sum of the distances from two focal points is a constant.

The edge view of the cutting plane is passed through the cone in part B of the figure, and the top view of the line of intersection is found by projecting points which are established by the projections of horizontal cutting planes to the top view. The auxiliary view results in a true-size view of the plane of the ellipse. The focal points are located by drawing two circular arcs in the front view which represent spheres that are tangent to the cone and to the plane of the ellipse. The points where the spheres are tangent to the ellipse are the focal points. These are projected to the auxiliary view.

An ellipse is also formed by passing an oblique plane through the axis of a cylinder at an angle other than 90°. This principle is employed in experimental designs of ditches at the sides of highways which are to lessen the impact of cars leaving the highway at an angle at high speeds (Fig. 11-28). Mathematics and the laws of motion can be applied to determine the effect on acceleration and deceleration caused by the curvature of the bottom of the ditch. The actual path of the car can be plotted graphically in an auxiliary view, which would show the true size of the plane of the elliptical path.

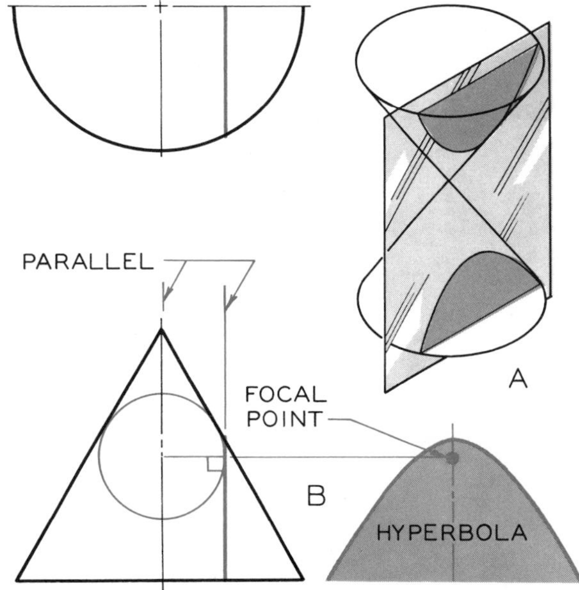

Fig. 11-26. Constructing a hyperbolic section of a cone.

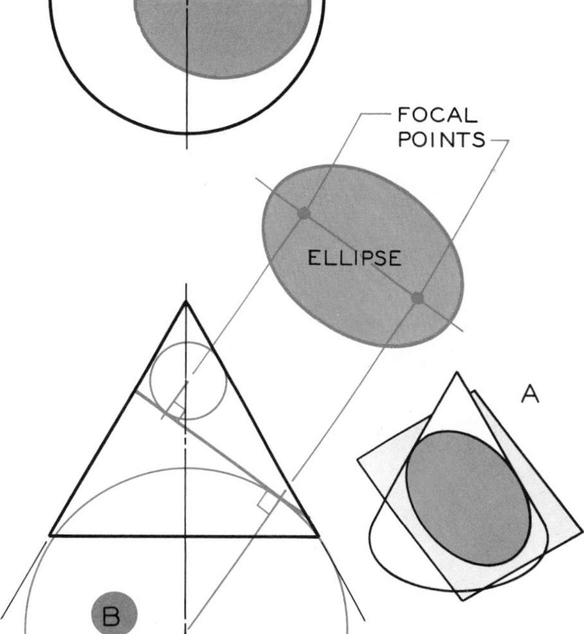

Fig. 11-27. Constructing an elliptical section of a cone.

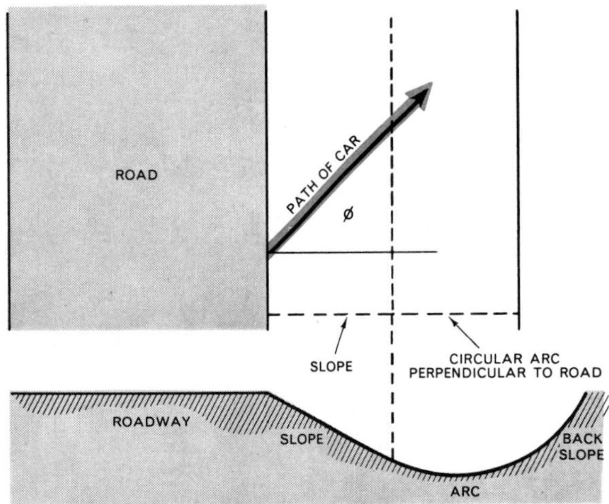

Fig. 11-28. A side ditch which has a circular cross section causes a wayward car to assume an elliptical path. This ditch configuration is effective in safely decelerating the vehicle. (Courtesy General Motors Corporation.)

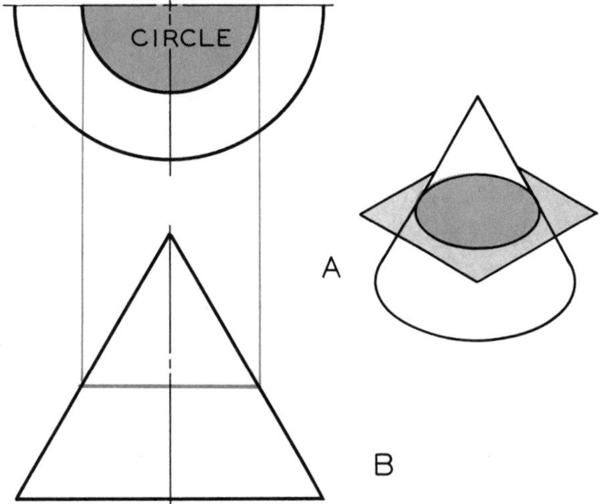

Fig. 11-29. Constructing a circular section of a cone.

The equation of the ellipse can be written in the following form:

$$\frac{x^2}{a^2} + \frac{y^2}{b^2} = 1, \quad \text{where} \quad a, b \neq 0.$$

When the equation is written in this form, a and b are equal to the major and minor diameters of the ellipse, respectively.

Circle. The line of intersection of a plane that is passed through a cone perpendicular to its axis is a circle (Fig. 11-29A). The circle is the path of a point which is moving in a direction such that its distance from the center is a constant. Its equation is written in the following form:

$$\frac{x^2}{r^2} + \frac{y^2}{r^2} = 1, \quad \text{where} \quad r \neq 0.$$

In this form, r is equal to the radius of the circle. The circular intersection formed by the cutting plane is shown in Fig. 11-29B.

11-10 INTERSECTION BETWEEN A PYRAMID AND A PRISM

The intersection between a prism and pyramid can be found by a method similar to that used in Fig. 11-21. An auxiliary view is constructed to show the lateral planes of the prism as edges in step 1 of Fig. 11-30. Cutting planes are drawn to radiate from apex 0 through the corner edges of the prism in the auxiliary view (step 2). Lines $0A$ and $0B$ are found in the principal views by projection. The lateral edges of the prism are projected to these lines in steps 2 and 3 to find piercing points, which are connected to determine the line of intersection. A pictorial located adjacent to step 1 illustrates the cutting-plane principle used in solving this intersection problem.

The intersection between a horizontal prism and a pyramid is determined in Fig. 11-31 through the use of the horizontal cutting-plane method. An auxiliary view is projected from the top view to find the edge views of the lateral surfaces of the prism. Horizontal cutting planes are passed through the front and auxiliary

FIGURE 11-30. INTERSECTION BETWEEN A PRISM AND A PYRAMID

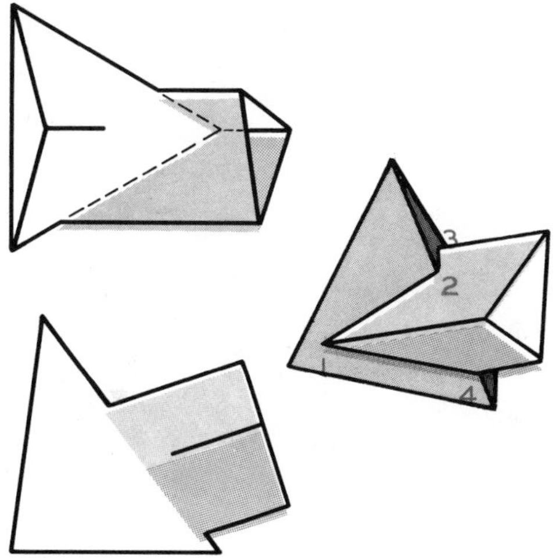

Given: Top and front views of a prism intersecting a pyramid.
Required: Find the line of intersection between the two geometric shapes.
Reference: Article 11-10.

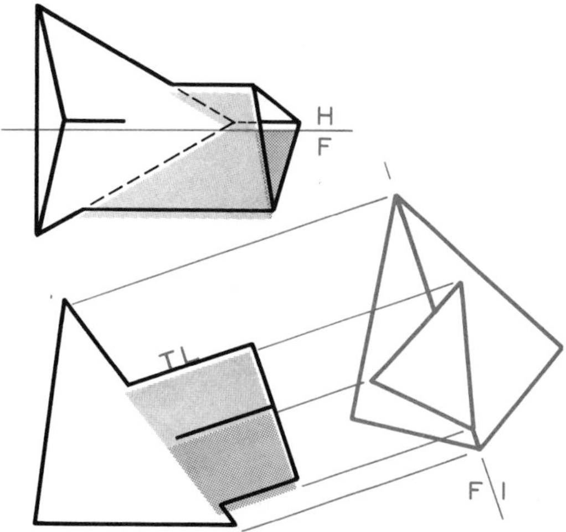

Step 1: Find the edge view of the surfaces of the prism by projecting an auxiliary view from the front view. Project the pyramid into this view also. Only the visible surfaces need be shown in this view.

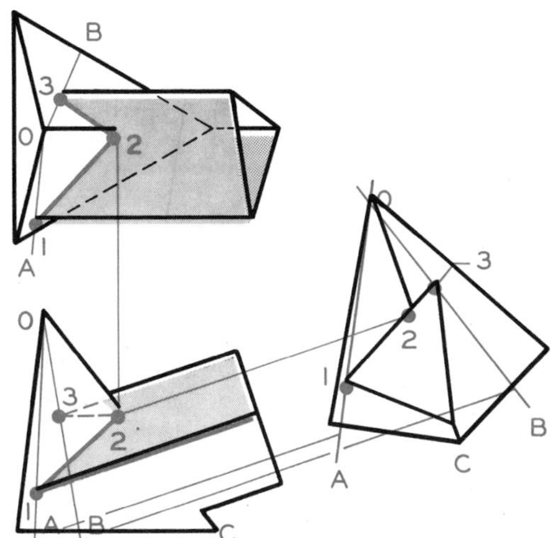

Step 2: Pass planes *A* and *B* through apex 0 and points 1 and 3 in the auxiliary view. Project the intersections of the planes *OA* and *OB* on the surfaces of the pyramid to the front and top views. Project points 1 and 3 to *0A* and *0B* in the principal views. Point 2 lies on line 0*C*. Connect points 1, 2, and 3 to give the intersection of the upper plane of the prism with the pyramid.

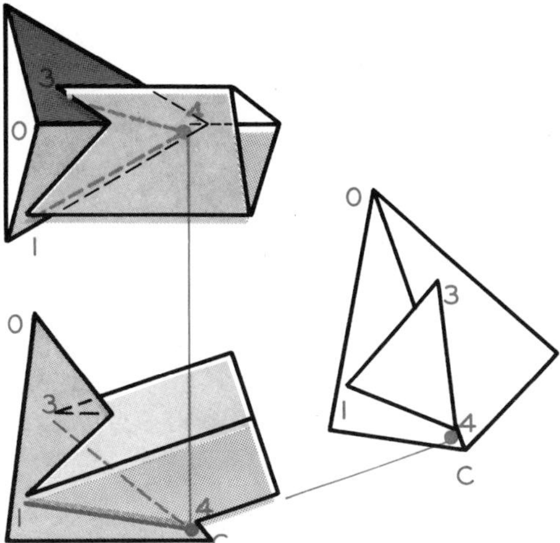

Step 3: Point 4 lies on line 0*C* in the auxiliary view. Project this point to the principal views. Connect point 4 to points 3 and 1 to complete the intersections. Visibility is indicated. Note that these geometric shapes are assumed to be hollow as though constructed of sheet metal.

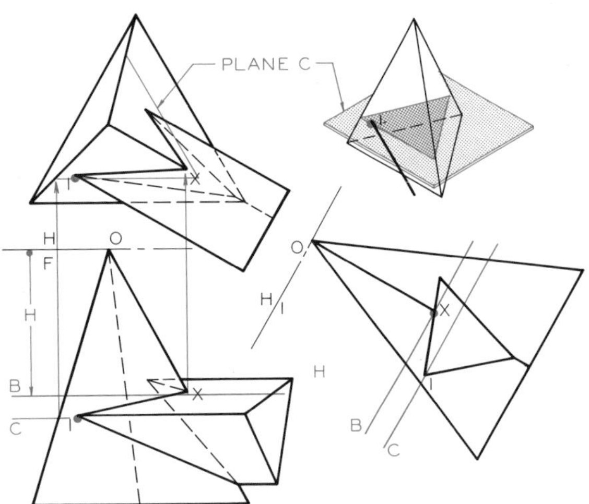

Fig. 11-31. Determining the line of intersection between a pyramid and a prism by horizontal cutting planes.

Fig. 11-32. Examples of intersections of a variety of geometric shapes can be seen in this compressor station installation. (Courtesy of Trunkline Gas Company.)

FIGURE 11-33. INTERSECTION OF A SPHERE AND A PLANE

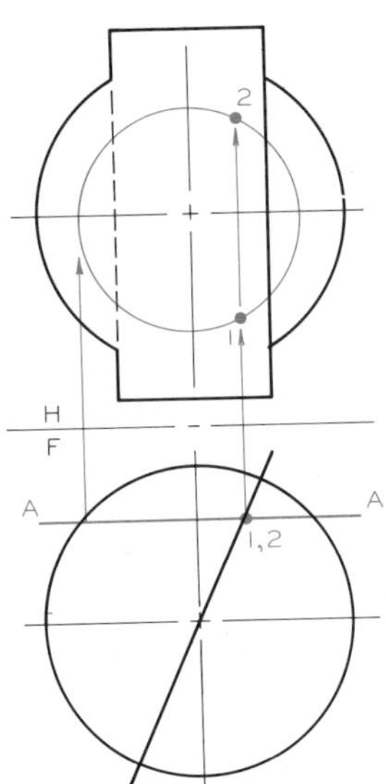

Step 1: Horizontal cutting plane A–A is passed through the front view of the sphere to establish a circular section in the top view. Piercing points 1 and 2 are projected from the front view to the top view, where they lie on the circular section.

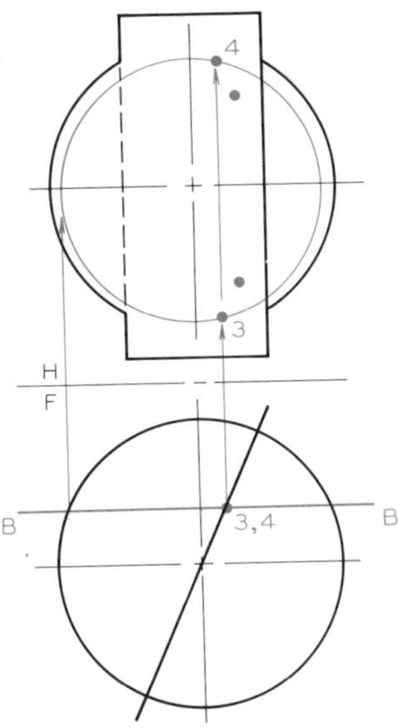

Step 2: Horizontal cutting plane B–B is used to locate piercing points 3 and 4 in the top view by projecting to the circular section cut by the plane in the top view. Additional horizontal planes are used to find sufficient points in this manner.

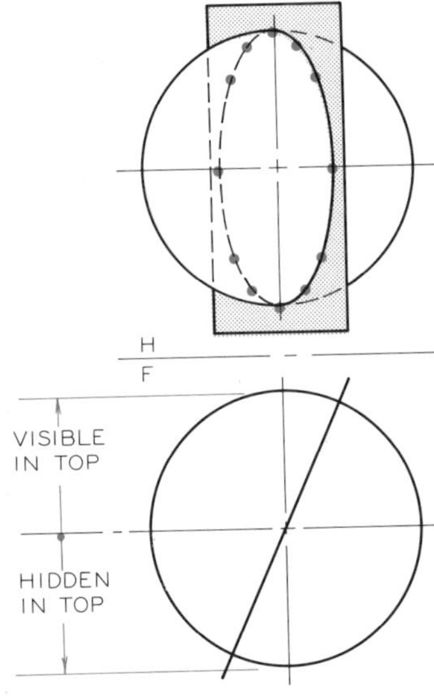

Step 3: Visibility of the top view is found by inspection of the front view. The upper portion of the sphere will be visible in the top view and the lower portion will be hidden.

views, where they appear as edges that are parallel to the horizontal. These planes will cut triangular sections in the top view which have sides that are parallel to the base of the pyramid. Note that these planes are drawn to pass through the given corner edges of the prism. Each corner edge is extended in the top view to the point of intersection with the section of the pyramid formed by the cutting plane passed through that particular line. Plane *B* is used to locate point *X* in the auxiliary view, which is where the line of intersection 1–*X*–3 bends at line 0–2. Visibility is determined in each view.

The intersection could have been found by using radial cutting planes, as in Fig. 11–30. As can be seen in these examples, the use of a systematic lettering procedure to plot each important point is helpful in intersection problems.

Figure 11–32 shows the interior of a compressor station where natural gas is compressed for transmission through pipelines over long distances. Many intersection problems are apparent in this complex facility. Complicated layouts of this type are presented in combinations of drawings and models to improve visualization and communication of spatial relationships.

11–11 INTERSECTION OF A SPHERE AND PLANE

The sphere is a shape that has many engineering applications, from petroleum storage tanks to the plotting of the paths of satellites traveling in space. An example of the determination of the intersection between a plane and a sphere is shown in Fig. 11–33. The resulting line of intersection will be an ellipse in the top view, but a circle when the line of sight is perpendicular to the intersecting plane.

The ellipse could have been drawn with an ellipse template which was selected by measuring the angle between the edge view of the plane in the front view and the projections coming from the top view. The major diameter of the ellipse would be equal to the true diameter of the sphere, since the plane passes through the center of the sphere.

In the partially constructed Unisphere® shown in Fig. 11–34, the structural members represent intersections between imaginary cutting planes and the surface of the sphere. All the circles passing through the poles are equal in size, while those passing perpendicularly to the axis of the sphere vary in size. Straight members are used to approximate the spherical shape in which it appeared in its finished form (Fig. 11–35). The paths of the satellites, depicted by metal rings, can be projected to the surface to the globe to form circular paths that would appear as ellipses in the view shown.

Fig. 11–34. Structural members of this spherical shape represent the intersection between imaginary cutting planes and the sphere. (Courtesy of U. S. Steel Corporation.)

Fig. 11-35. The orbital paths depicted by metal rings which encircle the sphere can be projected to the surface of the sphere to locate support brackets. (Courtesy of U. S. Steel Corporation.)

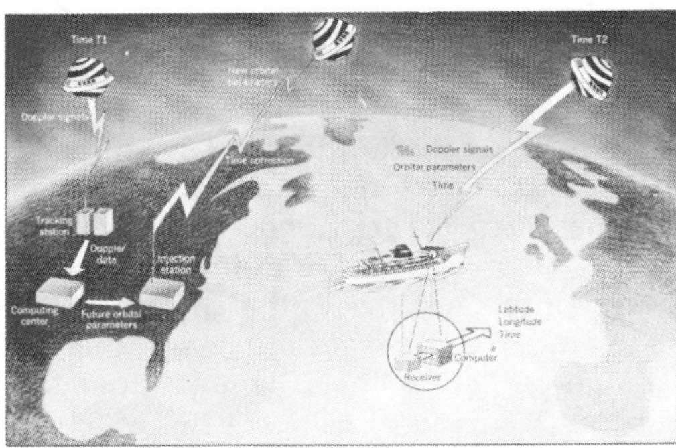

Fig. 11-37. Tracking stations are used to project the path of a satellite to the spherical surface of the earth. (Courtesy of the Coast and Geodetic Survey.)

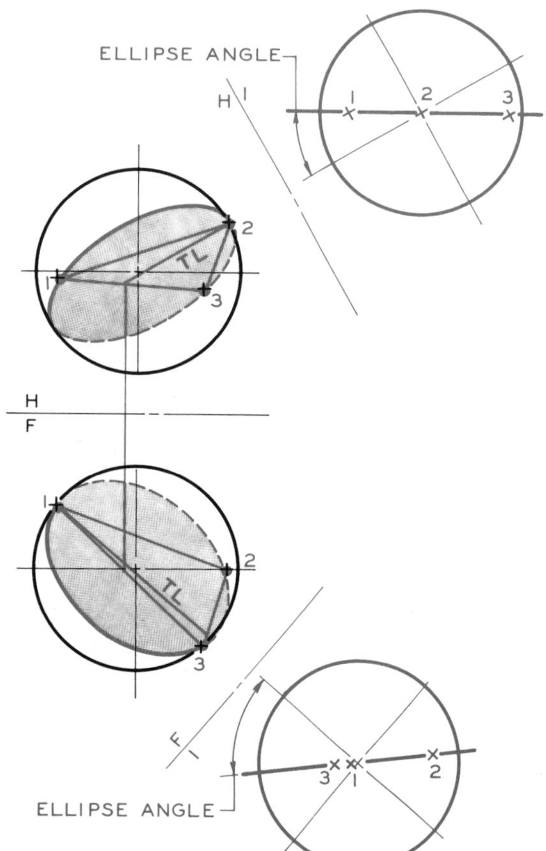

Fig. 11-36. Determining the location of an orbital path on a sphere.

The sphere in Fig. 11-36 has three points, 1, 2, and 3, located on its surface. A circle is to be drawn through these points so that it will lie on the surface of the sphere. This problem is solved by drawing the plane of the circle, plane 1-2-3, in the top and front views. The plane is found as an edge in the primary auxiliary view when projected from the top and front views as shown. The circle on the sphere cut by plane 1-2-3 will appear as an ellipse in the top and front views. The ellipse-guide angle for each view is found by measuring the angle made by the projectors with the edge view of the plane in the primary auxiliary view. The major diameters of the ellipse are drawn parallel to the true-length lines on plane 1-2-3 in the top and front views.

Satellites circling the earth are tracked by determining the lines of intersection made by the planes of their flight with the surface of the earth. Tracking stations (Fig. 11-37) receive signals from the satellite that give its location in space at a particular instant. Additional locations in space establish its plane of travel and, consequently, its projected path on the earth's surface. The intersection of the plane of a satellite's orbit with the surface of the earth is shown in Fig. 11-38. The path on the earth is found by projecting the orbital path toward the center of the earth to locate points *M* and *P*.

11-12 INTERSECTION BETWEEN A SPHERE AND A PRISM

A prism which intersects a sphere is shown in Fig. 11-39. Cutting planes are passed through the sphere in the top and side views so that they are parallel to the frontal plane; they appear as circles in the front view. In the side view, the intersections made by the cutting planes with the edges of the prism are projected to the front view, where they are found to intersect with their respective circles, i.e., those formed by the same cutting plane. *Example:* points 1 and 2 are found to lie on cutting plane *A* in the side view. These are projected to the front view to circle *A*, which was established by cutting plane *A*. Point *X* in the side view locates the point where the visibility of the intersection in the front view changes. Point *Y* in the side view is the point where the visibility of the intersection changes in the top view. Note that both these points lie on center lines of the sphere in the side view.

11-13 INTERSECTION BETWEEN TWO OBLIQUE CYLINDERS

To determine the line of intersection of two cylinders, as shown in Fig. 11-40, a plane must be drawn in space such that it is parallel to both cylinders. This will be the case if the plane contains lines that are parallel to the axes of each cylinder, as shown in step 1. It is necessary that the planes be passed through the top views of the intersecting cylinders as cutting planes; consequently, a line is constructed in the plane that is parallel to the edge view of the base planes of the cylinder in the front view. This line is projected to the top view, where its direction will represent the line of intersection of the cutting planes on the circular bases of the cylinders in the top view. A series of planes is passed through the bases, as shown in step 1, where the elements are formed on the surface of the cylinders parallel to their axes, as shown in stop 2. Elements that lie in common cutting planes establish points on the line of intersection when they cross in the top view. A systematic lettering procedure will assist in plotting the points as they are found. The points are con-

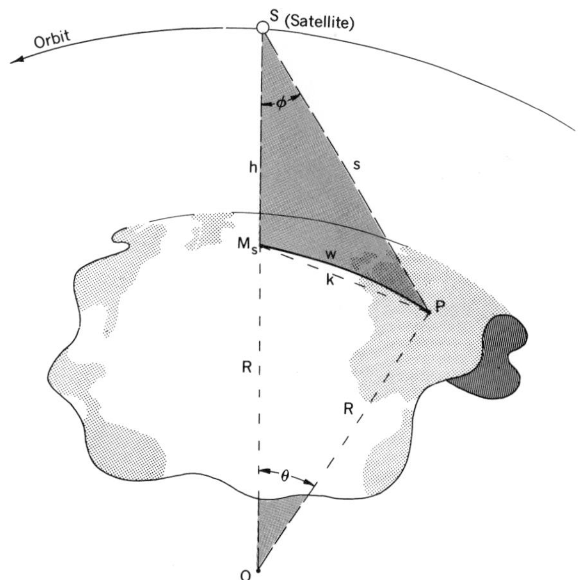

Fig. 11-38. The projection of a satellite's path to the surface of the earth. (Courtesy of the Coast and Geodetic Survey.)

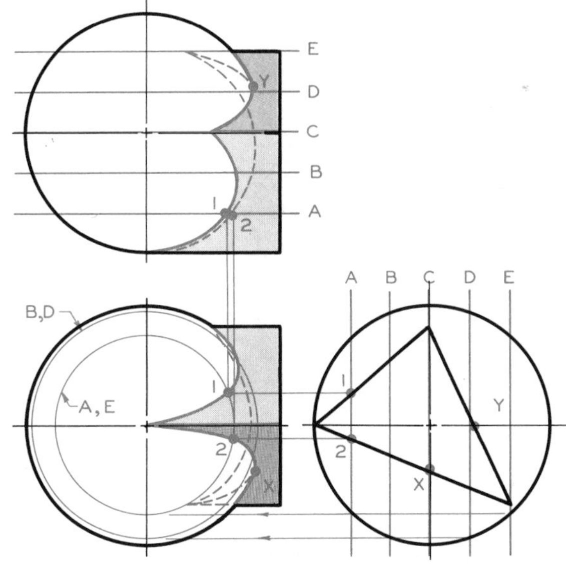

Fig. 11-39. Determining the intersection between a sphere and prism.

FIGURE 11-40. INTERSECTION BETWEEN OBLIQUE CYLINDERS

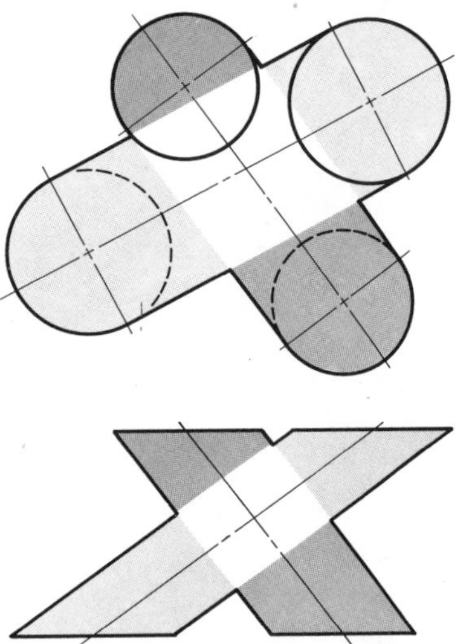

Given: The top and front views of two intersecting cylinders.
Required: Determine the line of intersection between the two cylinders in both views.
Reference: Article 11-13.

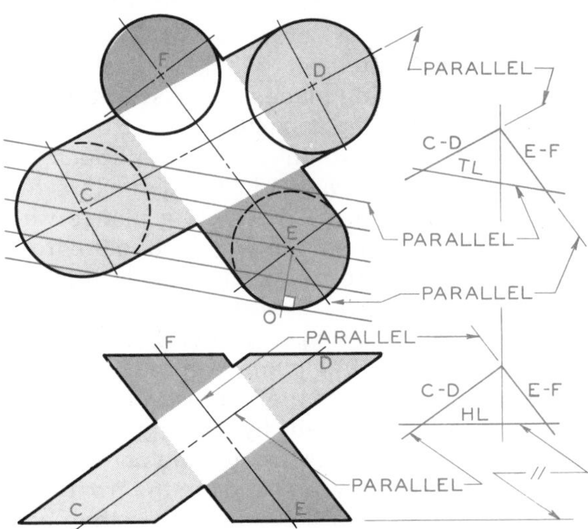

Step 1: Construct a triangular plane so that it will contain lines which are parallel to both axes of the cylinders. Draw a horizontal line in the front view of the triangular plane so that it lies in the base plane of the cylinders. Project this line to the triangular plane in the top view, where its direction is used as the direction for the cutting planes that will be drawn in the top view to pass parallel to the axes of the cylinders.

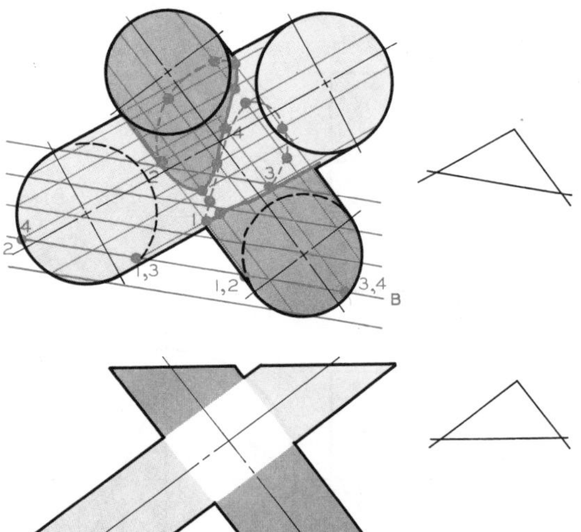

Step 2: Where the cutting planes intersect the bases of cylinders in the top view, elements are formed on the cylinders and they are parallel to the axes of each cylinder. Note that four elements are cut by each cutting plane. Where these common elements intersect, a point on the line of intersection is found. These points should be labeled, as are the four example points shown.

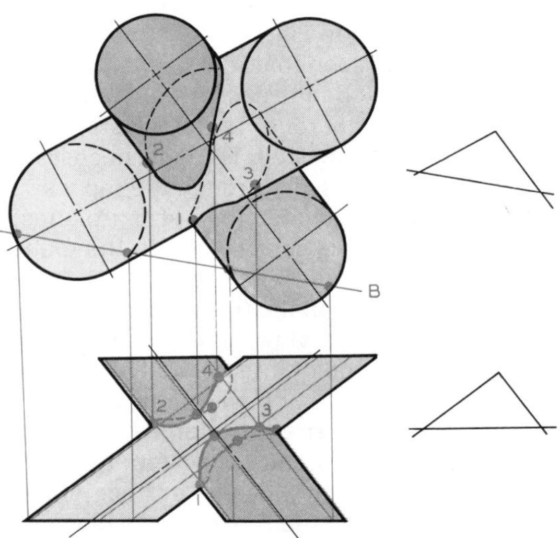

Step 3: Project the elements on the cylinders from the top view to the front view. The points found to lie on specific elements in the top view are projected to their respective elements in the front view. Several points have been projected as examples. Visibility in this view is determined by analysis of the top view.

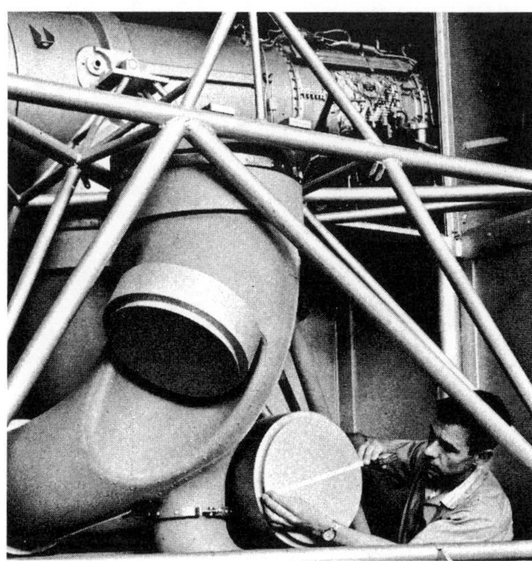

Fig. 11-41. The intersection between these cylindrical shapes is an example of the principle covered in Article 11-13. (Courtesy of Ryan Aeronautical Company.)

nected in sequence to obtain the continuous lines of intersection shown in step 2 in the top view.

The elements on each cylinder are projected to the front view, where they will be parallel to the axes of both cylinders. The points on the lines of intersection lying on the cutting planes are projected to the front view and connected to form the desired lines of intersection. The visibility of each is determined by examining each pair of intersecting elements. If both elements are visible, their points of intersection will be visible. If only one element is visible, the point of intersection is hidden.

The ducts which intersect at unusual angles in Fig. 11-41 require the same type of analysis as that covered in Fig. 11-40. The lines of intersection were used to design the joints of the intersecting ducts.

11-14 INTERSECTING CONES

We are required to determine the line of intersection between the two cones shown in Fig. 11-42. A series of cutting planes is needed to cut elements on each cone, which can be used to find piercing points on the lines of intersection. A plane drawn to contain a line that passes through both apexes of the cone and a line passing through both bases of the cones will cut elements in each cone. Such a plane is established in step 1. Five cutting planes are drawn in step 2, where line *OA* is a common side and the base lines radiate from point *O*. Elements established by the cutting planes are projected to their points of intersection. Note that cutting plane 3 is used to plot points *E*, *F*, *G*, and *H*. All points are connected in sequence to form the lines of intersection of the two cones in the top view.

The elements formed by the cutting planes are projected to the front view so that the front views of the points that have been projected from the top views may be located. Points *J* and *K* are projected to the front view as an example. Visibility is determined in each view by analyzing the elements that were used to plot the points. Both elements must be visible in a view before the point at their intersection can be visible.

11-15 SUMMARY

It can be seen from the examples given in this chapter that principles of intersection have many applications to engineering, technology, and science. Use of the principles of intersections involves most of the previously covered techniques of descriptive geometry and orthographic projection. Piercing points and visibility analysis can be reviewed in Chapter 7 to assist in a better understanding of intersections. Auxiliary views—primary and secondary—are used to find intersections of geometric shapes, as was covered in Chapters 8 and 9.

The fundamental principles covered in this chapter are basic to practically any problem that involves intersections. An attempt should always be made to identify an intersection in terms of its geometric elements. Perhaps several shapes are joined in combination to form the configuration of a design. The intersections will be easier to find if the problem is

FIGURE 11-42. INTERSECTING CONES

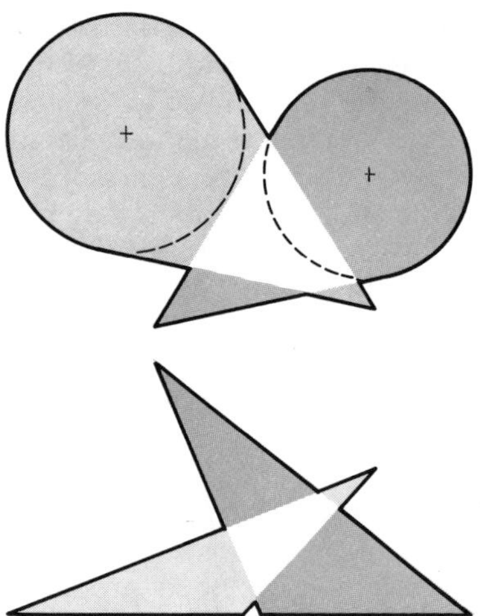

Given: The top and front views of two intersecting cones.
Required: Find the lines of intersection between the two cones in each view.
Reference: Article 11-14.

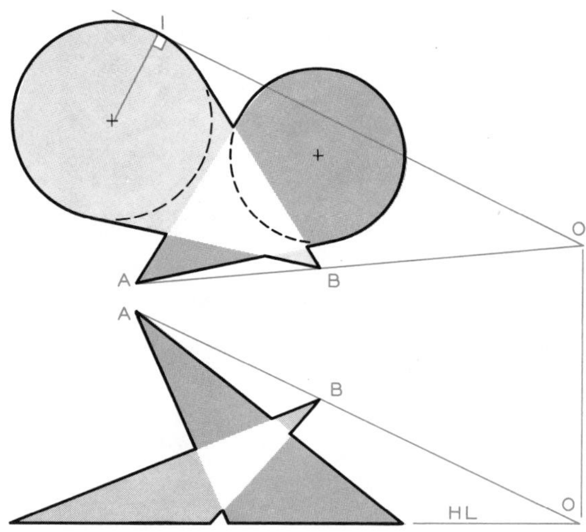

Step 1: Draw a line through apexes *A* and *B*, and extend it to point *O* on the plane of the bases of the two cones in the front view. Project line *ABO* to the top view, and draw line *O*-1 to intersect the two bases, as shown. This plane will cut elements on each cone, since the apexes lie on a common line. Note that line *OC* is tangent to cone *B*.

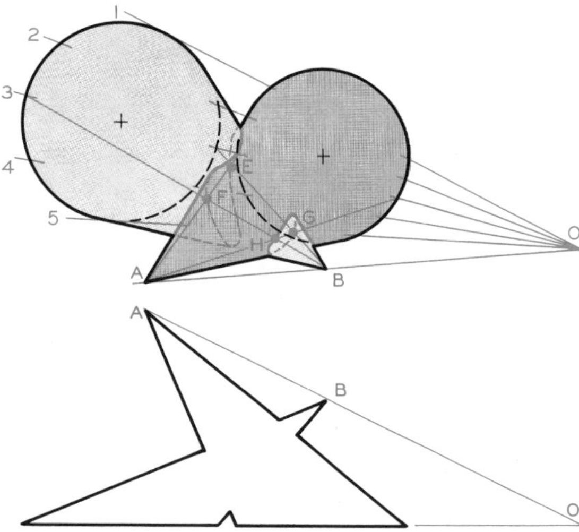

Step 2: Draw a series of planes with line *AO* common to each plane and to a second line in the horizontal plane of the cone bases. These cutting planes establish four elements on each cone, which are connected as illustrated where points *E*, *F*, *G*, and *H* are found at the intersection of common elements. Locate additional points and connect them to form the two lines of intersection.

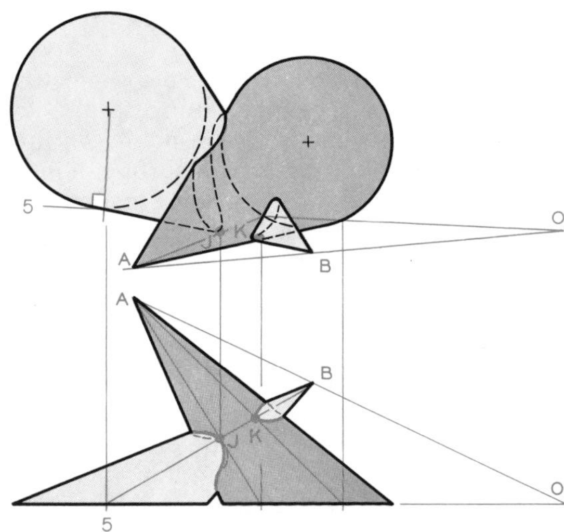

Step 3: Project the elements used in the top view to the front view and project the points lying on them in the top view to the front views of these elements. Points *J* and *K* on plane *AO*5 are projected to illustrate this technique of finding the line of intersection in the front view. Determine the visibility. Cutting plane *AO*5 establishes only two points, since it is tangent to one of the cones.

treated as though it involved an intersection between two geometric elements, then two more, etc., in sequence, until the complete line is found.

The student must understand intersection principles before proceeding to Chapter 12, which deals with developing flat patterns that are used to fabricate products that are composed of geometric shapes. Many of these shapes will be intersected by other forms; consequently, the lines of intersection must be found before the patterns can be completed.

PROBLEMS

General

The problems for this chapter should be constructed from the given sketches with *instruments* on $8\frac{1}{2}'' \times 11''$ sheets, as illustrated in the accompanying figures. For laying out the problems on grid or plain paper, assume that each grid represents $\frac{1}{4}''$. All reference planes and figure points should be labeled, using $\frac{1}{8}''$ letters with guide lines. Solutions should be sufficiently noted and labeled to explain all construction. Refer to Article 1–19.

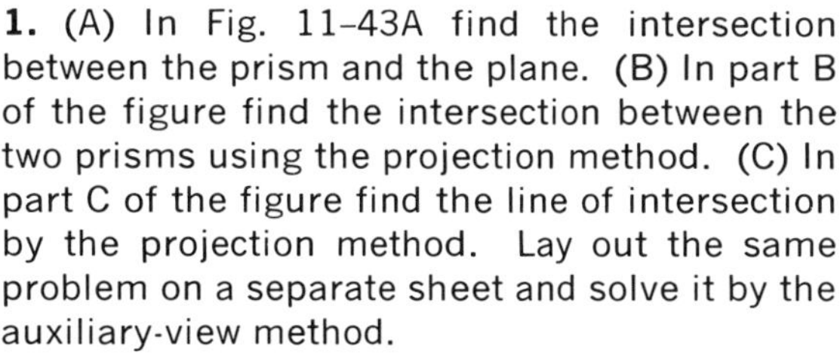

1. (A) In Fig. 11–43A find the intersection between the prism and the plane. (B) In part B of the figure find the intersection between the two prisms using the projection method. (C) In part C of the figure find the line of intersection by the projection method. Lay out the same problem on a separate sheet and solve it by the auxiliary-view method.

2. (A) In Fig. 11–44A find the intersection between the cylinder and the plane. (B) In part B of the figure find the intersection between the cylinder and the prism.

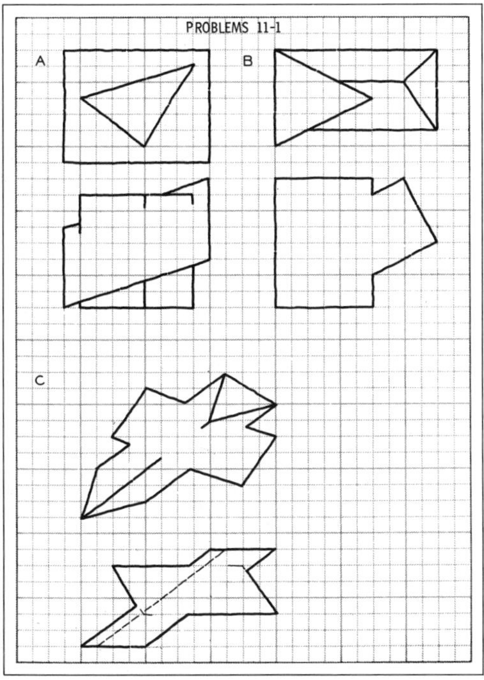

Fig. 11–43. Intersections of planes and prisms.

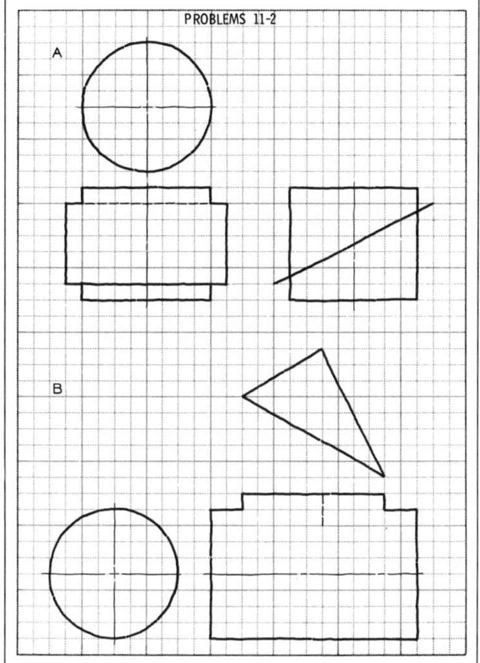

Fig. 11–44. Intersections of cylinders and planes.

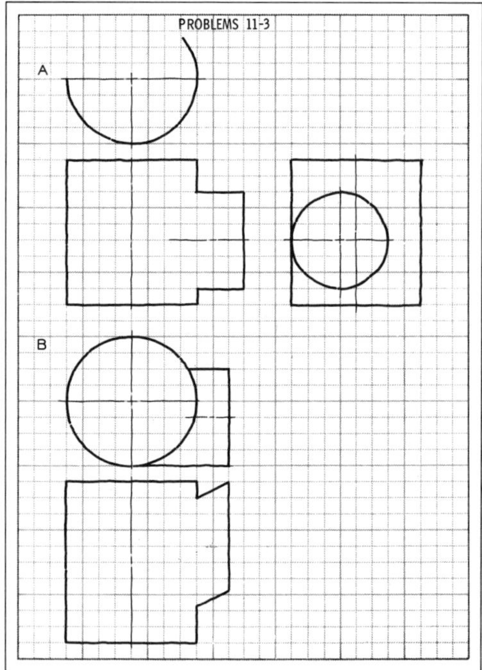

Fig. 11–45. Intersections of cylinders.

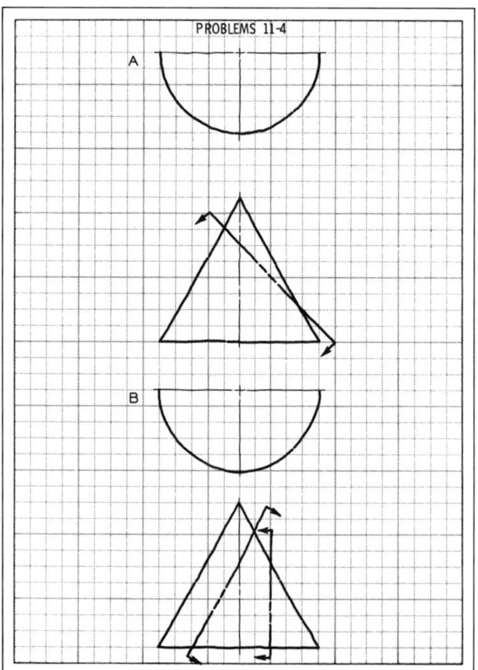

Fig. 11–46. Conic sections.

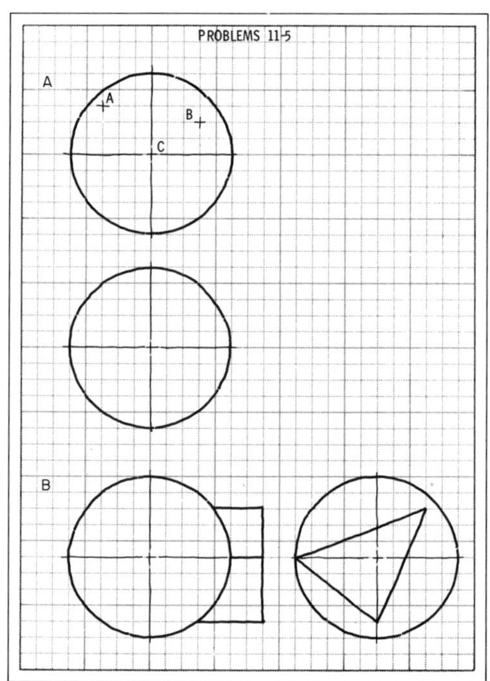

Fig. 11–47. Spherical intersections.

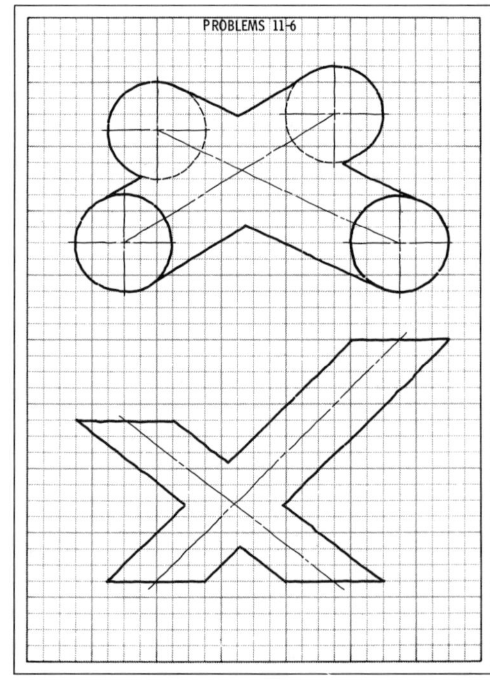

Fig. 11–48. Intersection between oblique cylinders.

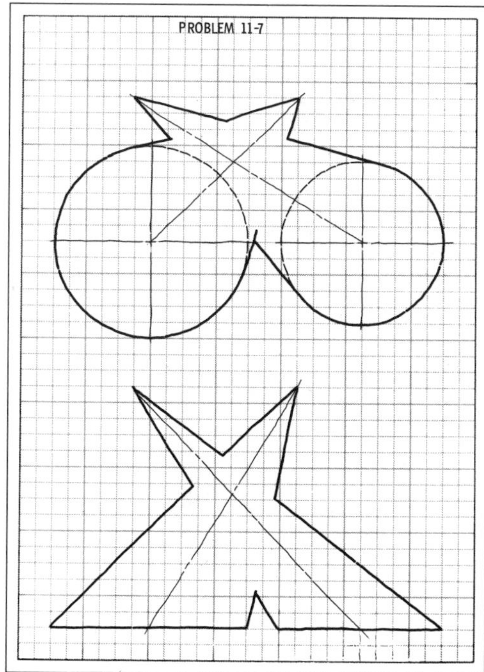

Fig. 11–49. Intersection between oblique cones.

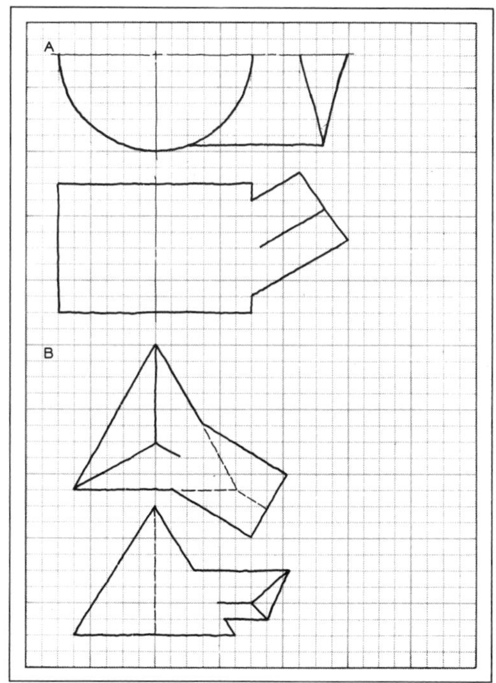

Fig. 11–50. Intersections.

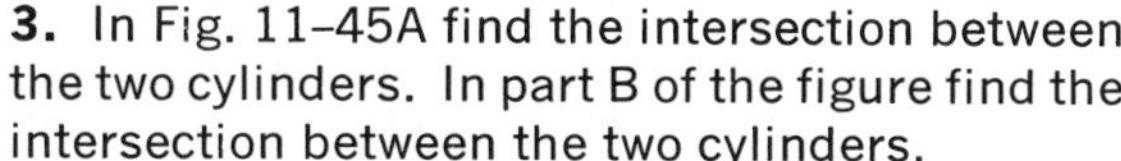
3. In Fig. 11–45A find the intersection between the two cylinders. In part B of the figure find the intersection between the two cylinders.

4. (A) In Fig. 11–46A find the top view of the intersection formed by the cutting plane, and construct the auxiliary view of the section. What type of conic section is this? (B) In part B of the figure find the intersections formed by the cutting planes in the front view. Construct the sections indicated by the cutting planes. Identify the types of conic sections in each case.

5. (A) Two views of a sphere are given in Fig. 11–47A, in which points *A* and *B* are located on the upper surface and point *C* is located at the sphere's center. Find the line of intersection formed by a plane that passes through these points and extends through the surface of the sphere. Show the line of intersection in all views. (B) In part B of the figure find the intersection between the prism and the sphere.

6. In Fig. 11–48 determine the line of intersection of the two oblique cylinders in both views.

7. Determine the lines of intersection of the two oblique cones in Fig. 11–49. Show these in both views and determine visibility.

8. Construct the lines of intersection in parts A and B of Fig. 11–50. Determine visibility and show in all views.

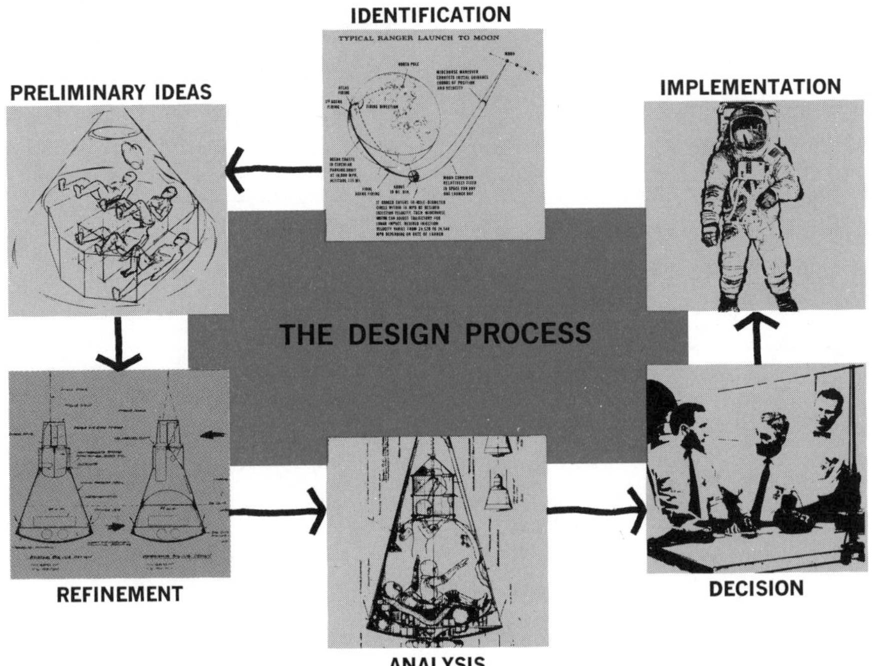

12 DEVELOPMENTS

12-1 INTRODUCTION

The Supersonic F-105 Thunderchief shown in Fig. 12-1 is an example of a highly complicated shape that has been formed with sections of flat sheet metal. This chapter is concerned with the geometric principles and techniques used in the fabrication of such a shape from flat materials.

Creating a flat pattern for a three-dimensional object involves a *development* ("unfolding") of the object. Developments are closely related to the intersections we studied in Chapter 11, since provision for the joining of component parts must be made in the flat pattern of an object.

We may make developments for all applications, from small, simple shapes made of thin sheet metal to sophisticated pieces of hardware such as space capsules, which must be fabricated within a high degree of accuracy. The model of the processing plant shown in Fig. 12-2 illustrates a wide variety of shapes that must be designed, developed, and specified by the designer. Whether the design is fabricated by bending flat metal or by casting a solid object, the designer must have a grasp of development principles. This chapter will cover the fundamentals of this area, and will relate these principles to industrial applications where possible.

12-2 DEVELOPMENT OF A PRISM

A cylinder or a prism (Fig. 12-3) can be laid out to result in either an inside or an outside pattern. An inside development is more frequently desired, because (1) most bending machines are designed to fold metal such that the markings are folded inward, and (2) markings and lines etched on the patterns will be hidden when the development is assembled into its finished

Fig. 12-1. The surface of this F-105 Thunderchief is an application of developed surfaces which were designed to conform to a specified shape. (Courtesy of Republic Aviation Corporation.)

Fig. 12-2. Many examples of intersections and developments can be seen in this model of a processing installation. (Courtesy of Bechtel Corporation.)

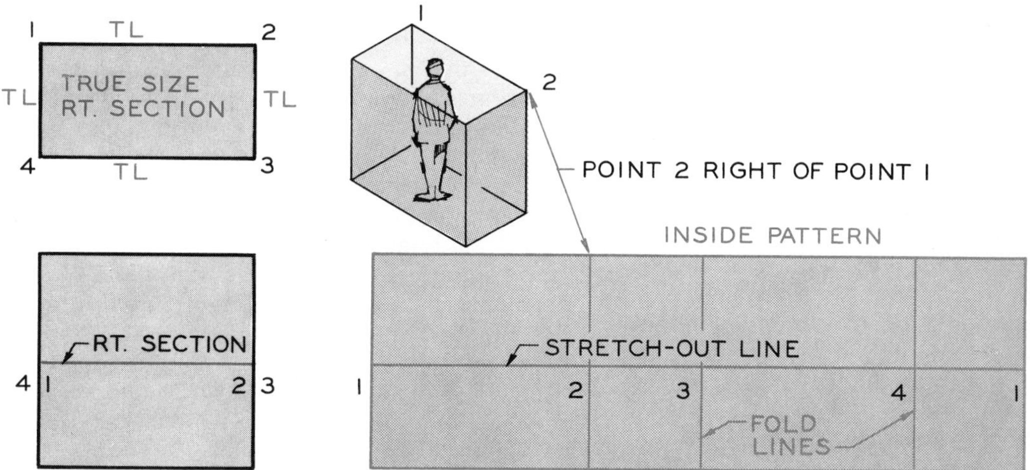

Fig. 12-3. The development of a rectangular prism to give an inside pattern.

form. Whether the pattern is an inside or an outside pattern will depend upon the material and the equipment being used. In any case, it is important that the pattern *always* be labeled as inside or outside when presented. The patterns in the following examples will be inside patterns, since these are the most common; however, the principles for finding inside patterns can be applied to outside patterns.

The following rules apply generally to cylinders and prisms. These should be reviewed as example problems are studied. The most important rule in developing patterns is that *all lines of a development must be true length.*

Rules for Developing Cylinders or Prisms

1. Find the view in which the right section appears as an edge.

2. Lay out the stretch-out line of the development parallel to the edge view of the right section.
3. Locate the distances between the lateral corner edges by measuring from the true-size views in the right section and transferring these measurements to the stretch-out line. Letter these points.
4. Construct the lateral fold lines perpendicular to the stretch-out line.
5. Establish the lengths of the fold lines by projecting from the view in which the right section appears as an edge.
6. Make sure that the line where the development will be spliced is the shortest line, so that the least amount of welding or joining effort will be required.
7. Connect all points in the proper sequence to give the complete pattern.
8. Verify that the point where the development ends is the same point as the beginning point on the right section.
9. Indicate by a note whether the development is an inside or an outside pattern.

These rules have been applied to the problem in Fig. 12–3. Note that the lateral fold lines of the prism are true length in the front view and that the right section appears as an edge in this view also. The stretch-out line is drawn parallel to the edge view of the right section, beginning with point 1. If an inside pattern is desired, it is necessary to select the point that lies to the right of point 1, since the development will be laid out in this direction. The observer assumes that he is inside the prism, as illustrated pictorially in Fig. 12–3, and that he is looking at the inside view of fold line 1. Note that the top view of the prism can be used for this analysis. Point 2 is seen to lie to the right of line 1 whereas line 4 is to the left; consequently, distance 1–2 is transferred from the top view to the stretch-out line, with point 2 to the right of point 1. Note that all lines on the surface of the right section are true length in the top view. Lines 2–3, 3–4, 4–1 are then laid out in sequence along the stretch-out line. The length of each fold line is found by projecting its true length from the front view. The ends of the fold lines are connected to form the limits of the developed surface. Fold lines are drawn as thin lines on the development.

The body of the toaster shown in Fig. 12–4 is an example of the application of the principle of developments in the design of a household appliance. Construction is more economical when it consists of forming one continuous piece of material that is bent into shape than it is when the operation demands joining a series of sections together. The forms that are used for the pouring of concrete are applications of developments of a different type.

A prism with a beveled end can be developed in the same manner as was the example in Fig. 12–3, except that the lengths of the fold lines will have to be determined by projecting from the front view. In this case, the lines will be unequal in length, resulting in a pattern such as that shown in Fig. 12–5. The use of a lettering system will assist in identifying the points of projection, as shown in this example. Note that the right section is used for the direction of the stretch-out line and as a source of measurements for determining the space between fold lines.

The mammoth coal hauler in Fig. 12–6 was developed as a flat pattern and joined to form this finished shape. Regardless of the size of the problem, the principles of solution are identical. The material used in this example was sheet aluminum, which can support ten times its weight.

12–3 DEVELOPMENT OF OBLIQUE PRISMS

The standard views of an oblique prism may be presented in a preliminary sketch which must be analyzed for further refinement. For example, an inclined prism might not show the right section as an edge nor a surface area as true size in the standard views. If this is the case, an auxiliary view must be used to provide the additional information necessary to complete the development.

Fig. 12-4. The surface of this toaster is an application of the development of a rectangular shape. (Courtesy of General Electric Company.)

Fig. 12-6. The all-aluminum body of this coal hauler is an example of an industrial development application. (Courtesy of ALCOA.)

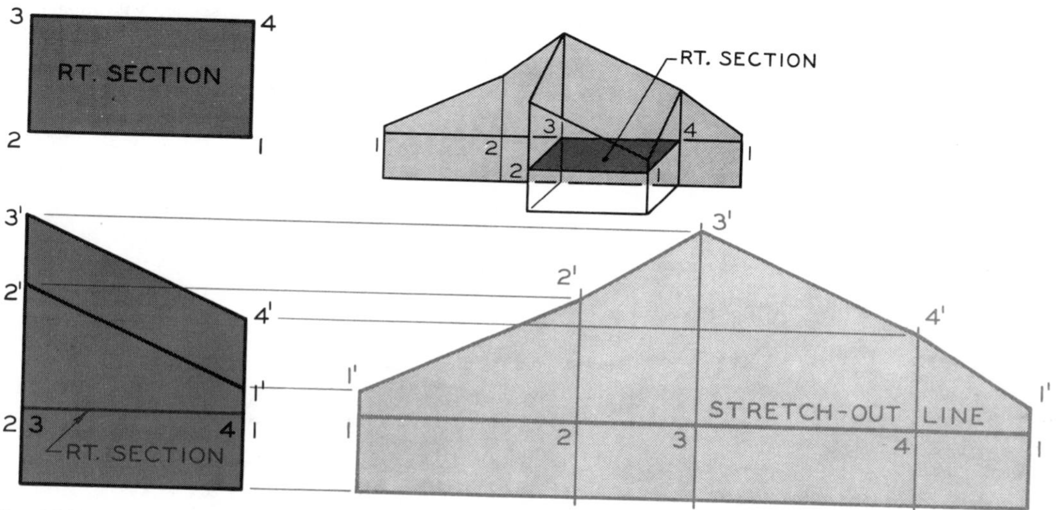

Fig. 12-5. The development of a rectangular prism with a beveled end to give an inside pattern.

A prism is shown inclined to the horizontal plane, but parallel to the frontal plane, in Fig. 12-7. The lateral corner edges of the prism appear true length in the front view, in which they are frontal lines. The right section can be drawn as an edge in the front view perpendicular to the fold lines. An auxiliary view of the edge view of the section will show the true size of the right section (step 1). The pattern is laid out in the conventional manner, which was covered in Article 12-2, and the stretch-out line is drawn parallel to the edge view of the right section in the front view. The measurements between the fold lines are transferred from the true sizes of the right section to the development (step 2). The developments of the end pieces can be found by a secondary auxiliary view, which is projected perpendicular to the edge view of the end of the prism. These projections are drawn as part of the total pattern in the developed view.

A prism which does not project true length in either view, but which is oblique to the principal planes, can be developed as illustrated in

FIGURE 12-7. DEVELOPMENT OF AN OBLIQUE PRISM

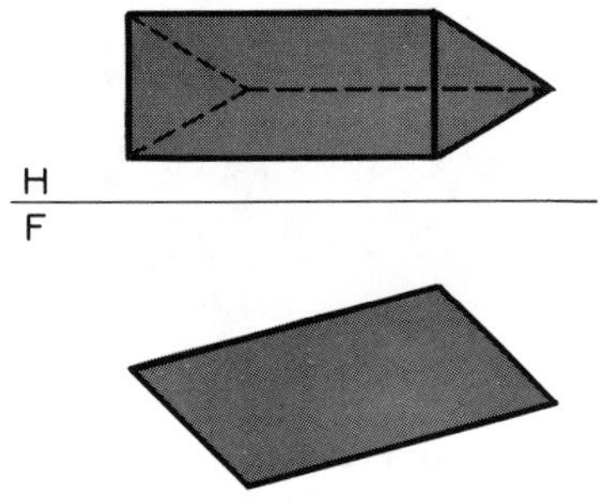

Given: The top and front views of an oblique prism.
Required: The inside pattern of the developed surface of the prism and the end sections.
Reference: Article 12-3.

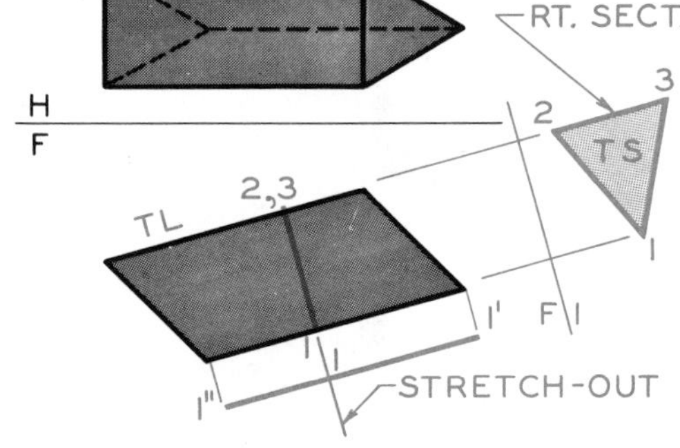

Step 1: The edge view of the right section will appear as perpendicular to the true-length axis of the prism in the front view. Determine the true-size view of the right section by constructing an auxiliary view. Draw the stretch-out line parallel to the edge view of the right section. Project bend line 1′-1″ as the first line of the development.

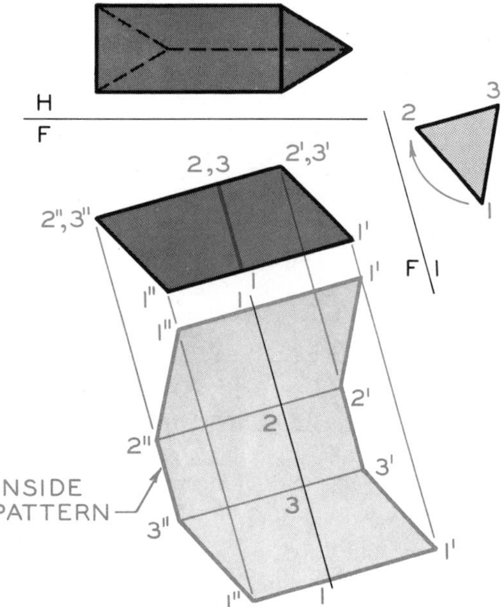
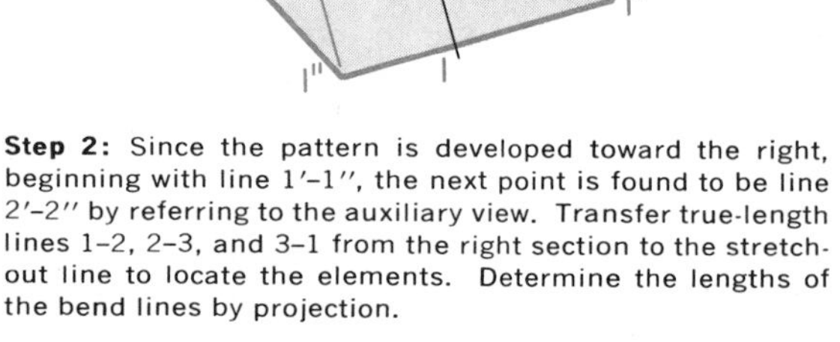

Step 2: Since the pattern is developed toward the right, beginning with line 1′-1″, the next point is found to be line 2′-2″ by referring to the auxiliary view. Transfer true-length lines 1-2, 2-3, and 3-1 from the right section to the stretch-out line to locate the elements. Determine the lengths of the bend lines by projection.

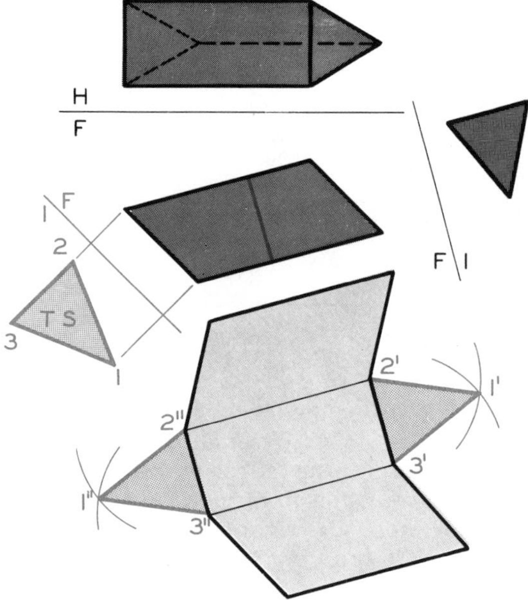

Step 3: Find the true-size views of the end pieces by projecting auxiliary views from the front view. Connect these surfaces to the development of the lateral sides to form the completed pattern. Fold lines are drawn with thin lines, while outside lines are drawn as regular object lines.

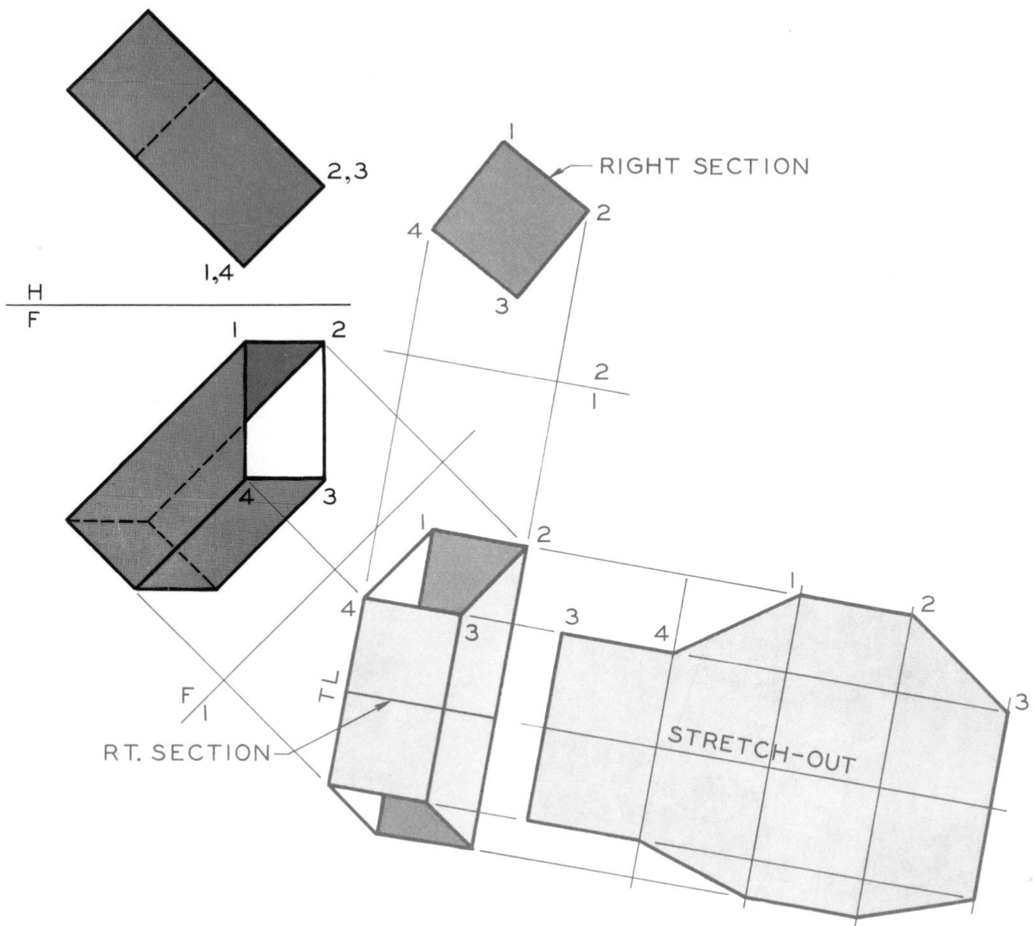

Fig. 12-8. The development of an inside pattern of an oblique prism.

Fig. 12-8. From the front view we find the true length of the lateral corners by projecting them to an auxiliary view in a direction perpendicular to that of the lateral corners in the front view. The right section will appear as an edge in the primary auxiliary view. The stretch-out line is drawn parallel to this edge view. The true size of the right section is found in an auxiliary projected perpendicularly from the edge view of the right section. The fold lines are located on the stretch-out line by measuring around the right section in the secondary auxiliary view. The lengths of the fold lines are then projected to the development from the primary auxiliary view.

12-4 DEVELOPMENT OF CYLINDERS

Cylinders are basic shapes that are used extensively in practically all areas of technology. The large storage tanks shown in Fig. 12-9 are typical of the cylindrical developments that can be found in the petroleum industry. These tanks are efficient and economical vessels for

Fig. 12-9. Storage tanks are designed through the use of cylindrical developments. (Courtesy of Shell Oil Company.)

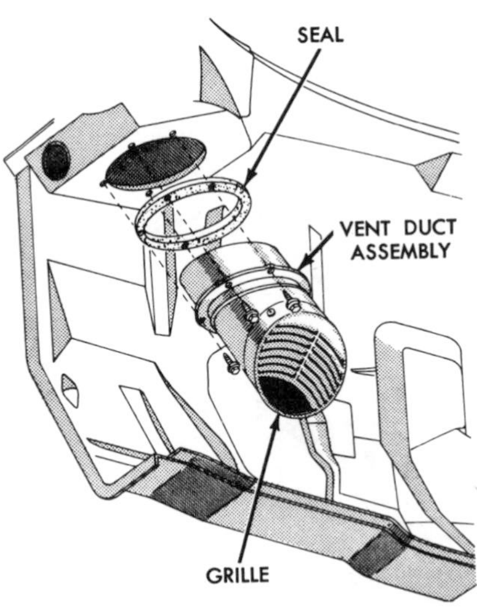

Fig. 12-11. This ventilator air duct was designed through the use of development principles. (Courtesy of the Ford Motor Company.)

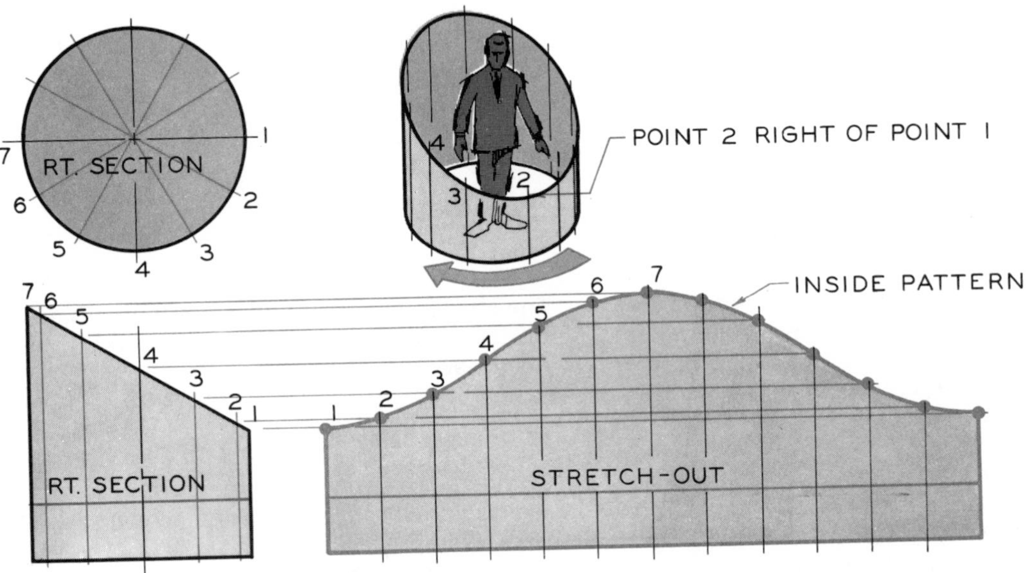

Fig. 12-10. The development of a cylinder.

storage of petroleum products. Note that these cylinders have no fold lines, since their surfaces are smooth and curving; however, they were developed by using a series of lines on their surface as though they were fold lines.

The example in Fig. 12-10 illustrates the manner in which an inside pattern of a cylinder is developed. The axis of the cylinder appears true length in the front view, which allows the right section to be seen as an edge, since it is perpendicular to the axis. The stretch-out line is drawn parallel to the edge view of the section, and point 1 is chosen as the beginning point, since it is on the shortest possible line on the surface. Since an inside pattern is desired, the observer must assume that he is standing inside the cylinder in the top view, as illustrated pictorially in Fig. 12-10. The pattern will be laid out to the right, so the observer is interested in determining which lines are to the right of point 1. The first point to the right of point 1 is point 2, which establishes the sequence of points to be followed in laying out the distances between the lines in the development along the stretch-out line. These distances are transferred from the true-size right section in the top view as chordal distances to approximate the circumference around the cylinder. The closer the intervals between the lines on the right section, the closer the graphical solution will be to the theoretical circumference. If accuracy is a critical factor, the circumference can be determined mathematically, laid out true length along the stretch-out line, and divided into the number of divisions desired. The ends of the lines on the surface are projected from the top to the front view. The ends of these lines on the beveled end of the cylinder are projected to their respective lines in the developed view, where they are then connected with a smooth curve.

A practical application of this principle is shown in Fig. 12-11, in which an air-conditioning vent duct is shown as used on an automobile. This vent was developed through the use of the same principles as those covered in this article. The Hydra 5 test vehicle (Fig. 12-12) is composed of a number of cylindrical developments that required graphical solutions.

Gun ranges that are used to simulate meteoroid impact on spacecraft utilize cylindrical forms, as shown in Fig. 12-13. Other applications of cylindrical developments can be seen in the background of this laboratory.

Fig. 12-12. Cylindrical developments were necessary in the design of the Hydra 5 launch vehicle. (Courtesy of the U. S. Navy.)

Fig. 12-13. Gun ranges, which are used to simulate meteoroid impact on aircraft, are examples of cylindrical developments. (Courtesy of Arnold Engineering Development Center.)

FIGURE 12-14. DEVELOPMENT OF AN OBLIQUE CYLINDER

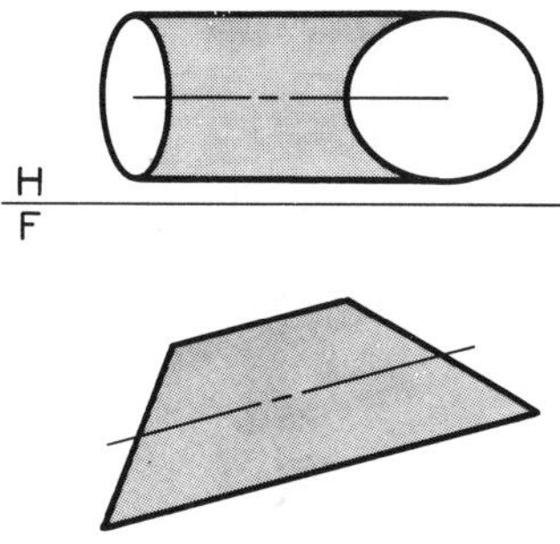

Given: The top and front views of an oblique cylinder.
Required: Find an inside development of the cylinder and its end pieces.
Reference: Article 12-5.

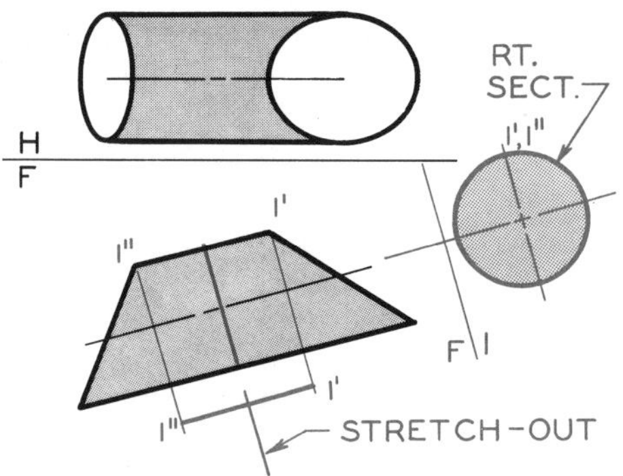

Step 1: The right section appears as an edge in the front view, in which it is perpendicular to the true-length axis. Construct an auxiliary view to determine the true size of the right section. Draw a stretch-out line parallel to the edge view of the right section. Locate element 1′-1″.

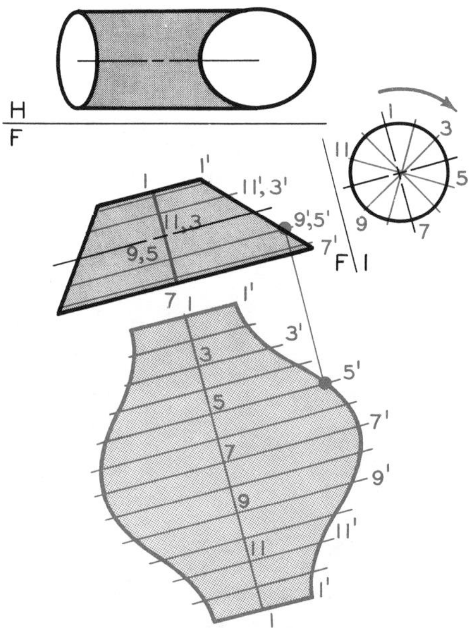

Step 2: Divide the true-size right section into equal points which represent the point views of elements on the cylinder's surface. Project these elements to the front view. Transfer measurements between the lines from the auxiliary view to the stretch-out line to locate the elements in the development. Determine the lengths of the elements by projection to complete the development.

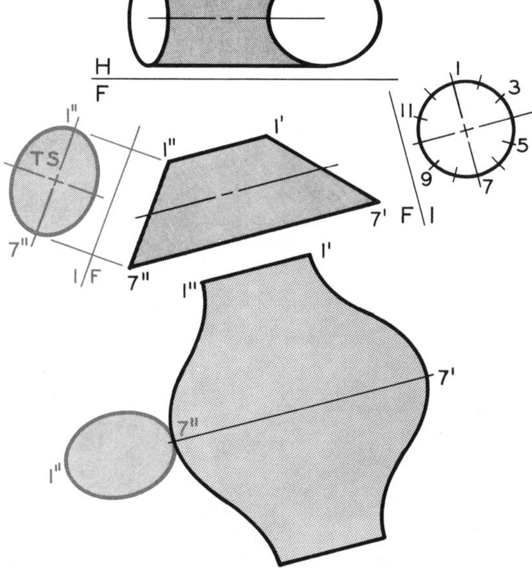

Step 3: The development of the end pieces will require auxiliary views that project these surfaces as ellipses, as shown for the left end. Attach this true-size ellipse to the pattern at a point on the pattern. Note that the line of departure for the pattern was made along line 1″-1′, the shortest element, for economy.

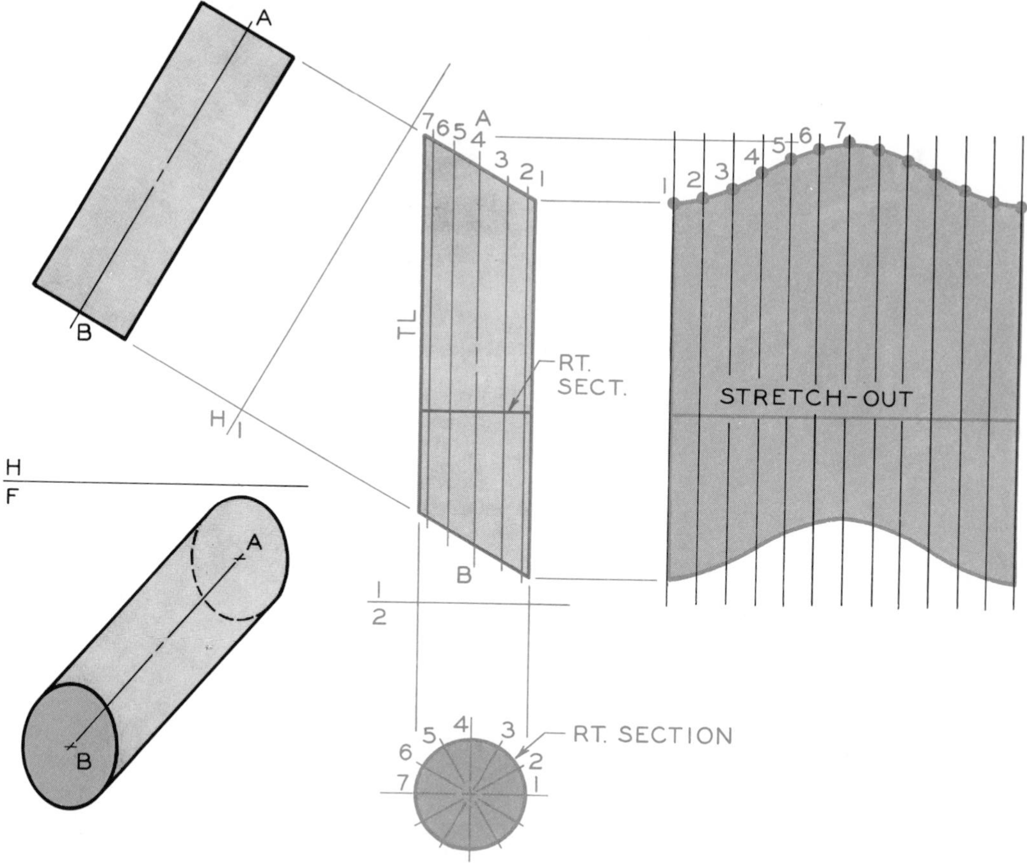

Fig. 12-15. The development of an inside pattern of an oblique cylinder.

12-5 DEVELOPMENT OF OBLIQUE CYLINDERS

The oblique cylinder in Fig. 12-14 appears true length in the front view, in which its right section projects as an edge that is perpendicular to its center line. The stretch-out line for the development is drawn parallel to the edge view of the right section (step 1). The true-size view of the right section is found in an auxiliary view. Lines lying on the surface of the cylinder are projected from the right section to the front view. These elements are spaced the same distance apart on the stretch-out line in the development view as they were in the right section in the auxiliary view. All element lengths are projected to the development from the front view, where they are true length. The ends of the elements are connected with a smooth curve (step 2). The true size of one elliptical end of the cylinder is found by auxiliary view, as shown in step 3. This shape is drawn attached to the development. The development of the opposite end can be found by auxiliary view in the same manner.

Figure 12-15 is an example of a cylinder that is oblique to the principal planes in both views. The edge view of the right section is found in an auxiliary view, where the elements on the surface of the cylinder project true length. The stretch-out line is drawn parallel to this

Fig. 12-16. Cylindrical developments are used to design electronic components. (Courtesy of ITT.)

Fig. 12-17. Wind tunnels are designed through the extensive application of cylindrical developments. (Courtesy of Arnold Engineering Development Center.)

edge view. The elements are separated on the stretch-out line by the distance between the point views of the elements in the secondary auxiliary view, where the right section appears true size. The lengths of the elements in the developments are found by projecting from the true-length view of the elements in the primary auxiliary view. These points are connected by a smooth curve. The elliptical development of the beveled end can be found by a secondary auxiliary view which is projected from the primary auxiliary view in a manner similar to that shown in step 3 of Fig. 12-14.

Applications of cylindrical developments vary in size from small to large. Cylindrical developments are necessary for the construction of electronic components such as those shown in Fig. 12-16. On the larger side, the 16′ wind tunnels shown in Fig. 12-17 are also examples of the application of development principles. Regardless of their size, however, all applications of cylindrical developments are solved in the same manner.

12-6 DEVELOPMENT OF PYRAMIDS

The development of a pyramid is given in Fig. 12-18 through a series of steps. Since all fold lines will have point 0 as a common point, the stretch-out line will not be used on this type of problem; instead, a series of adjacent triangles will be drawn in the development.

Recall that *all lines* in a development must be true length. Lines 1-0 and 2-0 are revolved into the frontal plane in the top view so that their true length will be seen in the front view, as shown. All bend lines are equal in length, since the pyramid is a right pyramid; consequently, in the development line 1-0 is used as a radius for constructing an arc that will contain all corner points lying on the base of the pyramid. The lines of the base appear true length in the top view since the base is a horizontal plane. Distance 1-2 is measured in the top view and transferred to the development, where it is a chord on the arc from point 1 to point 2. Lines 2-3, 3-4, and 4-1 are found in the same manner. The bend lines are drawn with thin lines from the base to the apex, point 0.

A variation of this problem is given in Fig. 12-19, in which the pyramid has been truncated or cut at an angle to its axis. The development of the inside pattern is found in the same manner as covered previously; however, an additional step is required to establish the upper lines of the development. The development is first laid out as though it were a continuous pyramid from the apex 0, to the base. The true-

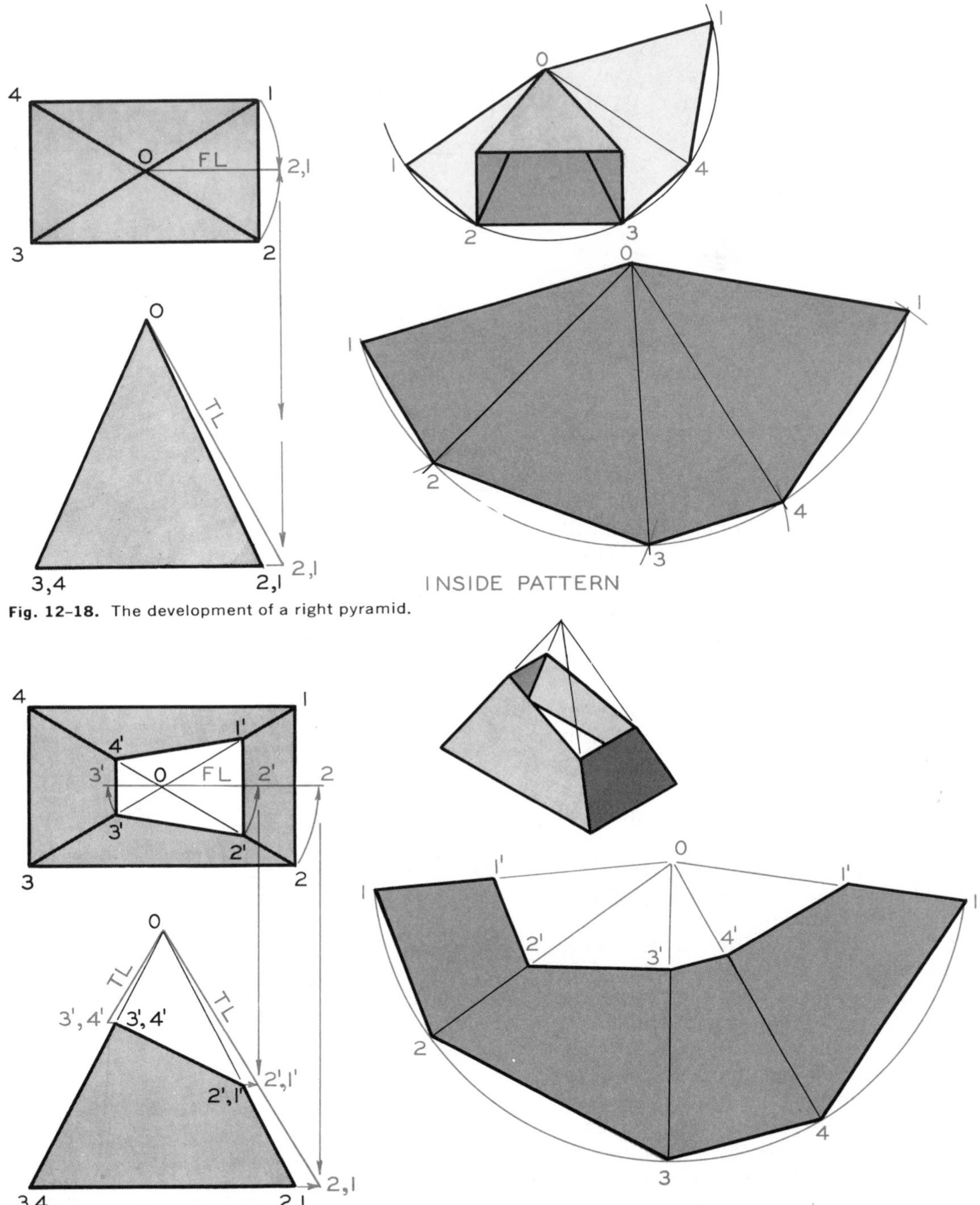

Fig. 12-18. The development of a right pyramid.

Fig. 12-19. The development of an inside pattern of a truncated pyramid.

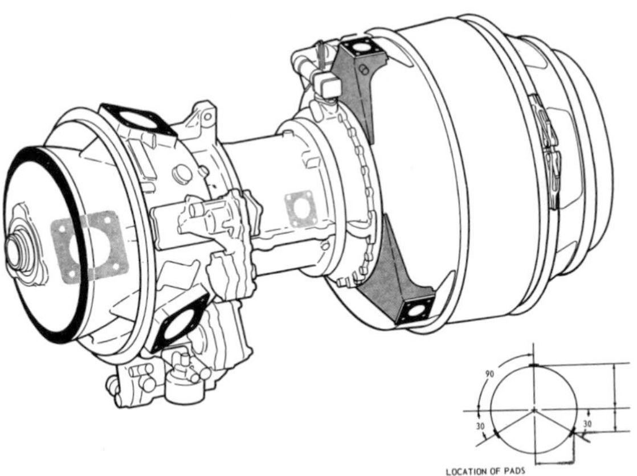

Fig. 12-20. Examples of pyramid shapes in the design of mounting pads for an engine. (Courtesy of Lycoming Division of the Avco Corporation.)

length lines from the apex to points 1′, 2′, 3′, and 4′ are found by revolution, as shown. These true-length distances are measured along their respective lines from point 0 to locate the upper limits of the development. These points are then connected to complete the inside development of the truncated pyramid.

The mounting pads in Fig. 12-20 are sections of pyramids that intersect an engine body. This is an example of a design problem involving both intersections and developments.

An oblique pyramid is developed in sequential steps in Fig. 12-21 to illustrate the procedure for constructing the development. The true lengths of all bend lines are determined in step 1 by revolving the lines into the frontal plane and projecting them to the front view. These lines are found to vary in length since the pyramid is not a right pyramid. The planes of each triangular surface of the pyramid are shown true size in the development by triangulation, in which the revolved lengths and the true-length base lines taken from the top view are used. The triangles are drawn adjacent to each other, with point 0 common to each (step 2). To determine the upper limits of the developed surface (step 3), we find the true-length distances from point 0 to points 1′, 2′, 3′, and 4′

FIGURE 12-21. DEVELOPMENT OF AN OBLIQUE PYRAMID

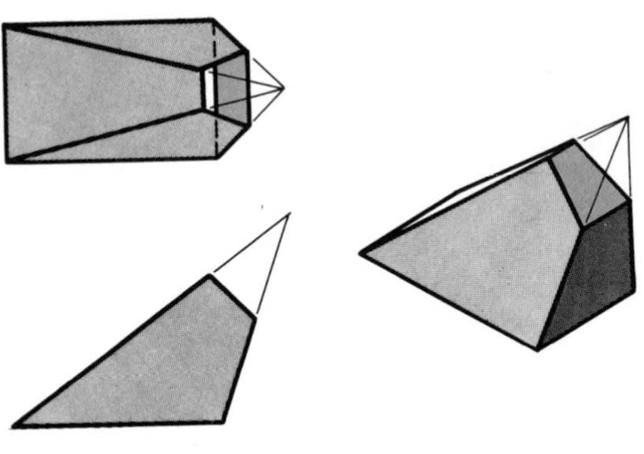

Given: The top and front views of an oblique, truncated pyramid.
Required: Find the inside development of the pyramid's surface.
Reference: Article 12-6.

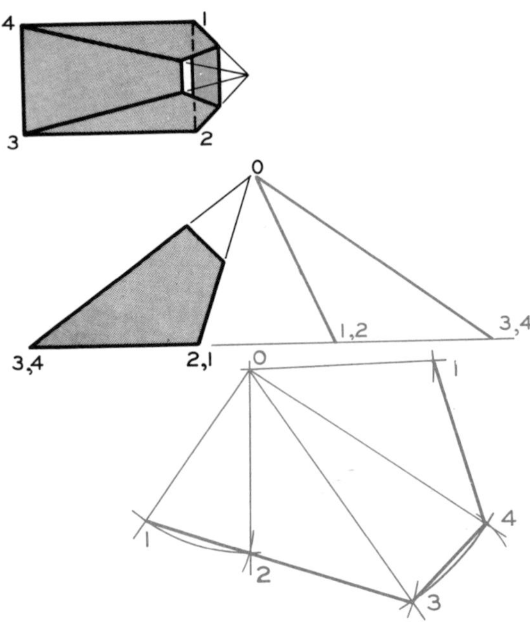

Step 2: The base lines appear true length in the top view. Using these true-length lines from the top view and the revolved lines in the front view, draw the development triangles. All triangles have one side and point 0 in common. This gives a development of the surface, excluding the truncated section.

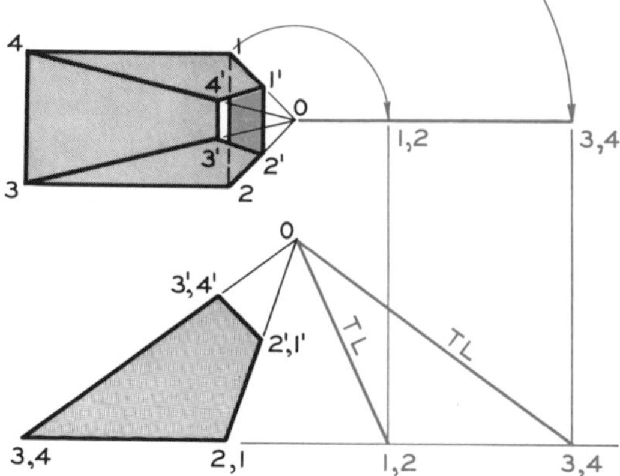

Step 1: Revolve each of the bend lines in the top view until they are parallel to the frontal plane. Project to the front view where the true-length views of the revolved lines can be found. Let point 0 remain stationary but project points 1, 2, 3, and 4 horizontally in the front view to the projectors from the top view.

Fig. 12–22. The Apollo command module is an example of a conical development. (Courtesy of the National Aeronautics and Space Administration.)

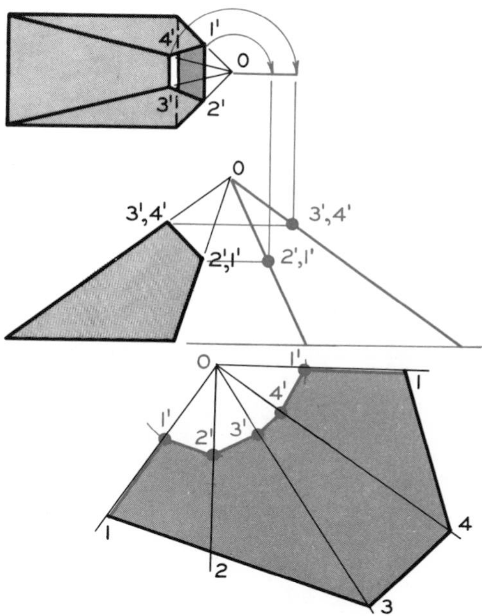

Step 3: The true lengths of the lines from point 0 to the points 1′, 2′, 3′, and 4′ are found by revolving these lines. These distances are laid off from point 0 along their respective lines to establish points along the upper edge of the developed pattern. The points are then sequentially connected by straight lines to complete the development.

by revolution and transfer these lengths to the respective bend lines in the developed view. The limits of the development are connected with straight lines, and fold lines are indicated with thin lines.

12–7 DEVELOPMENT OF CONES

The Apollo command module, shown in Fig. 12–22, is an example of a conical development. Many other examples of cones and other irregular shapes can be seen in the Charger and its missiles, shown in Fig. 12–23. Development principles are used to fabricate these irregular shapes from flat materials.

Cones are developed by a procedure similar to that used to develop pyramids. A series of triangles is constructed on the surface through the use of the elements of the cone and a chordal connection between points on the base of the cone. Figure 12–24 illustrates the division of the surface of the cone into triangular sections in the top and front views. The element 0–10 appears true length in the front view since it is a frontal line in the top view. All elements on a right cone are equal; therefore, line 0–10 will be used to construct the arc upon which the developed base will lie. The inside pattern of

Fig. 12-23. The body of this aircraft and the irregularly shaped missiles were fabricated through the application of development principles. (Courtesy of General Dynamics Corporation.)

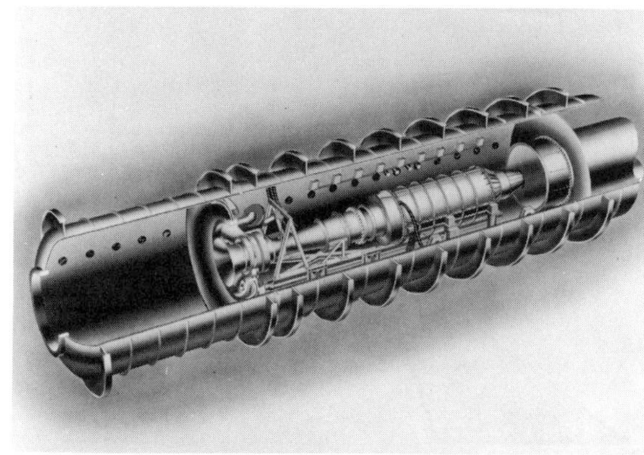

Fig. 12-25. Conical developments were used as an integral part of this wind tunnel design. (Courtesy of Arnold Engineering Development Center.)

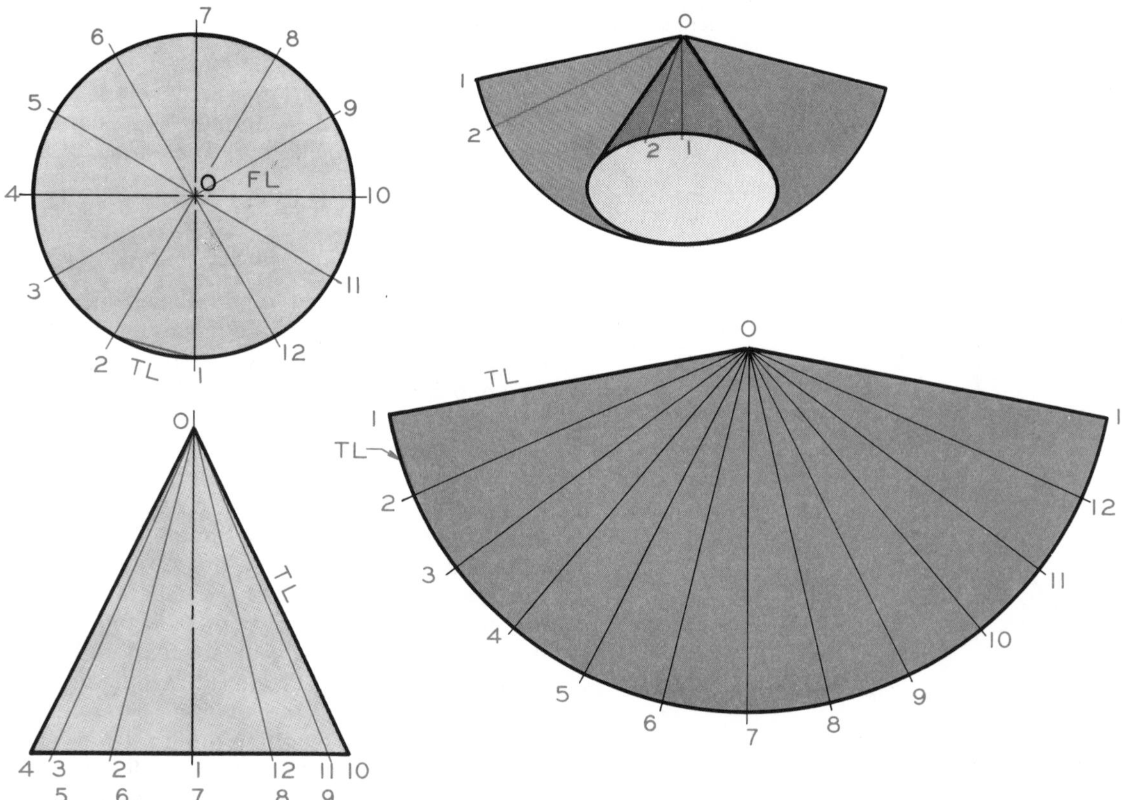

Fig. 12-24. The development of an inside pattern of a right cone.

the cone is drawn beginning with point 1 and moving toward the right. The point to the right of point 1 is point 2, which is found by inspection of the top view and the pictorial view of the cone. Point 2 is found in the top view and in the development by measuring the true-length chordal distance from point 1 along the arc. Successive triangles are found in this manner until point 1 is again reached at the extreme edge of the development. The base of the development is drawn as an arc rather than a series of chords along the arc that were connected by triangulation.

A more accurate approximation of the distance between the base points on the arc can be determined by finding the circumference of the base by mathematics and laying off this distance in equal increments along the arc formed by radius 0–1. The graphical approximation is sufficient in most cases.

Conical developments are used as an integral part of the wind tunnel design shown in Fig. 12–25. Cylindrical and spherical sections were also developed during the design of this facility.

A cone that has been truncated as shown in Fig. 12–26 can be developed by applying the principles illustrated in Fig. 12–24. It is advisable to construct the total development as though it were a complete cone that had not been modified. This portion of the development is identical to that shown in Fig. 12–24. A conical section has been removed from the upper

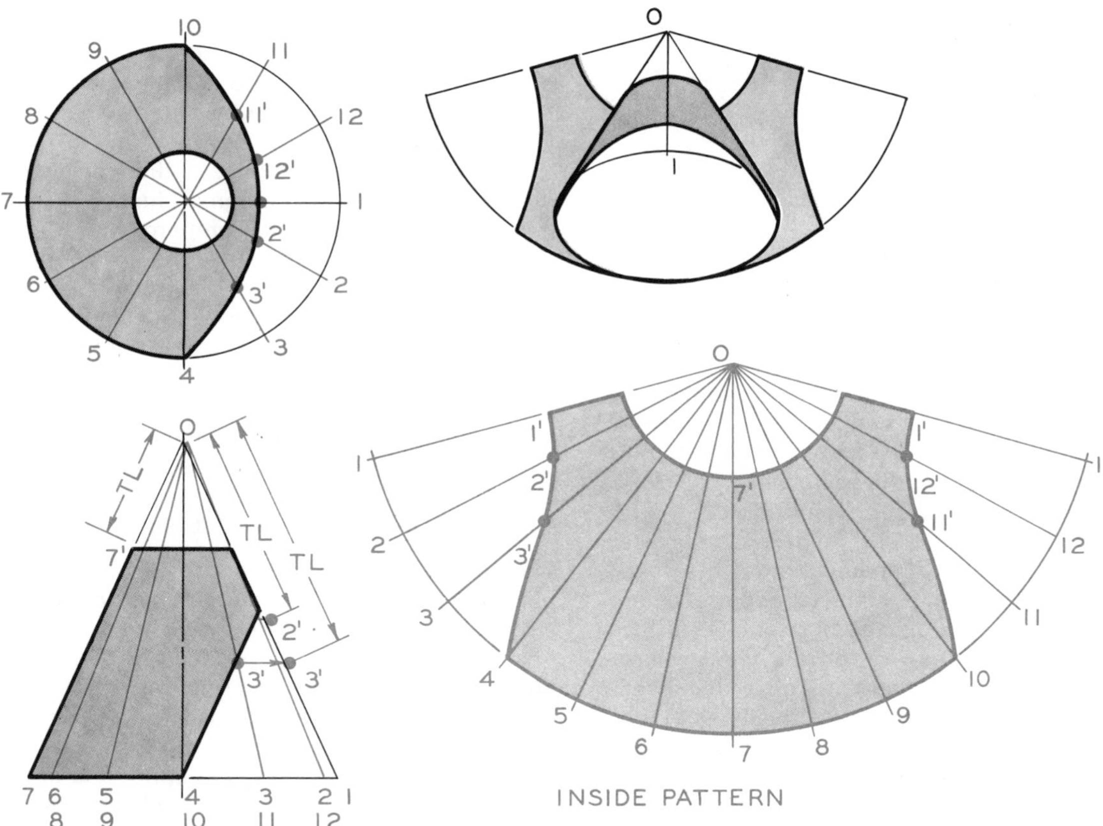

Fig. 12–26. The development of a conical surface with a side opening.

Fig. 12–27. Huge conical developments are used in the construction of a blast furnace. (Courtesy of Jones & Laughlin Steel Corporation.)

portion of the cone. This part of the pattern can be removed by constructing an arc in the development, using as the radius the true-length line 0–7′, which is found in the front view. The true-length measurements from point 0 to the limits of the development, on the hyperbolic surface that is formed by the modification of the cone in the front view, are found by revolution. Lines 0–2′ and 0–3′ are projected horizontally to the extreme element, 0–1 in the front view, where they will appear true length. These distances are measured along their respective lines in the development to establish points through which the smooth curve will be drawn to outline the development.

Huge conical developments are necessary in the construction of a blast furnace (Fig. 12–27). Cylindrical developments are also frequently used in structures of this type. The developments must be carefully constructed to enable on-the-site assembly with considerable accuracy.

The development of an oblique cone is shown in Fig. 12–28. Elements on this cone are of varying lengths, but the resulting development will be symmetrical, since the top view is symmetrical. Elements in the given views are revolved into the frontal plane, as shown, so that their true lengths can be determined in the front view. The development is begun by constructing a series of triangles which are composed of elements and the chordal distances found on the base. The line of separation for the cone is chosen to be 0–1, since this is the shortest line on the cone's surface. The base is connected with a smooth curve. The true-length lines from apex 0 to the upper surface of the approximate cone are found by projecting from the front view to the true-length diagram. Points 1′ and 7′ are projected from the front view to their true-length lines in the true-length diagram found by revolution. Lines 0–1′ and 0–7′ are shown in the development, where they are used to locate points along the upper edges of the developed surfaces. These points are connected with a smooth line, but this line will not be an arc, since the geometric shape is not a true right cone and the edge view of the plane through points 7′ and 1′ in the front view is not perpendicular to the axis of the cone.

12–8 DEVELOPMENT OF WARPED SURFACES

The geometric shape shown in Fig. 12–29 is an approximate cone with a warped surface and is similar to the oblique cone shown in Fig. 12–28. The development of this surface will be merely an approximation, since a truly warped surface cannot be laid out on a flat surface. The surface is divided into a series of triangles in the top and front views by dividing the upper and lower views as shown. The true lengths of all lines are found in the true-length diagrams, which are drawn on each side of the front view, by project-

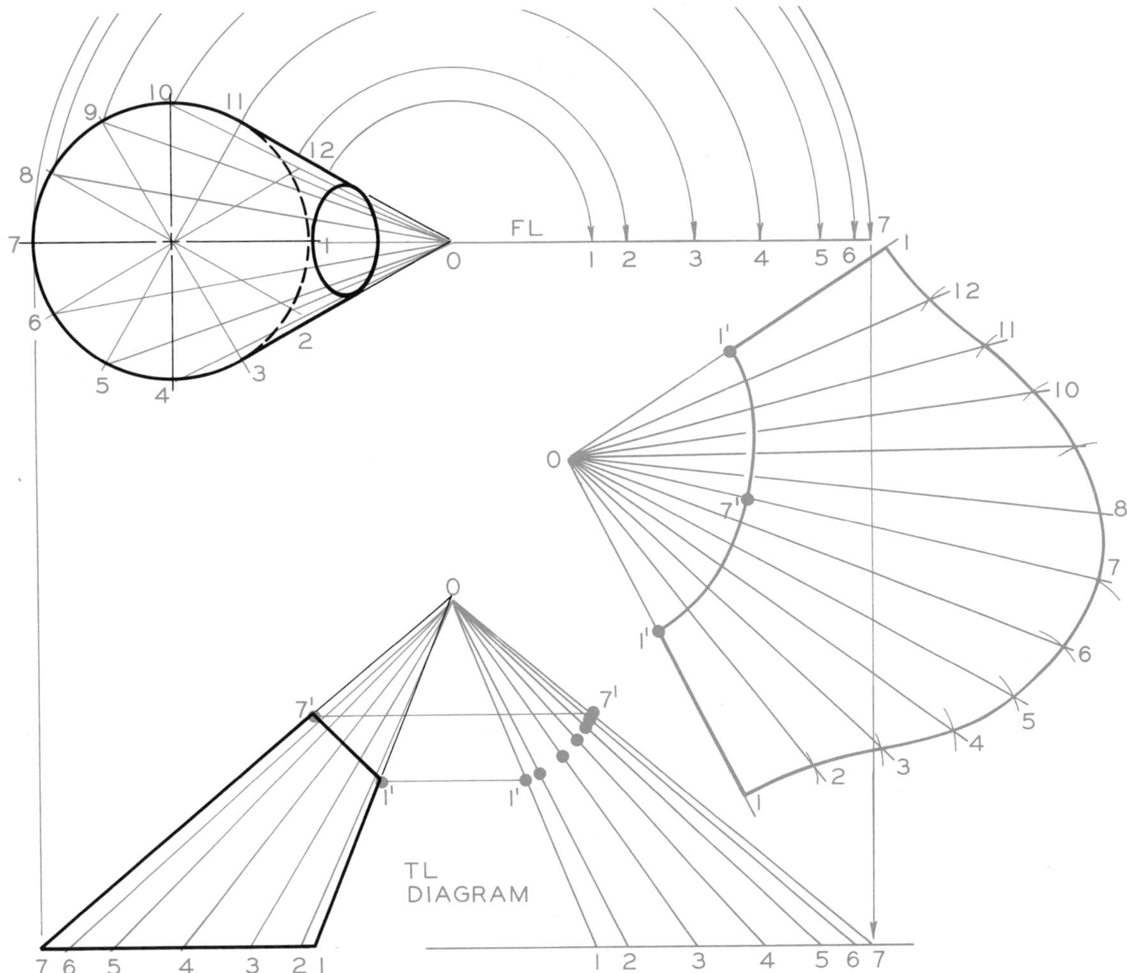

Fig. 12-28. The development of an oblique cone.

ing horizontally from the front view the vertical distances between the lines. To complete the true-length views of the lines, the horizontal distance between the ends of the lines is measured along the actual projection of the top view of the lines. A true-length line found in this manner is equivalent to a line that has been revolved, such as those illustrated in Fig. 12-28.

The chordal distance between the points on the base appears true-length in the top view since the base is horizontal. The chordal distance between the points on the upper edge of the lateral surface will appear true-length in a view that shows a true-size plane of this end. The developed surface is found by triangulation using true-length lines from (1) the true-length diagram, (2) the horizontal base in the top view, and (3) the primary auxiliary view. Each point should be carefully lettered to facilitate construction in all views.

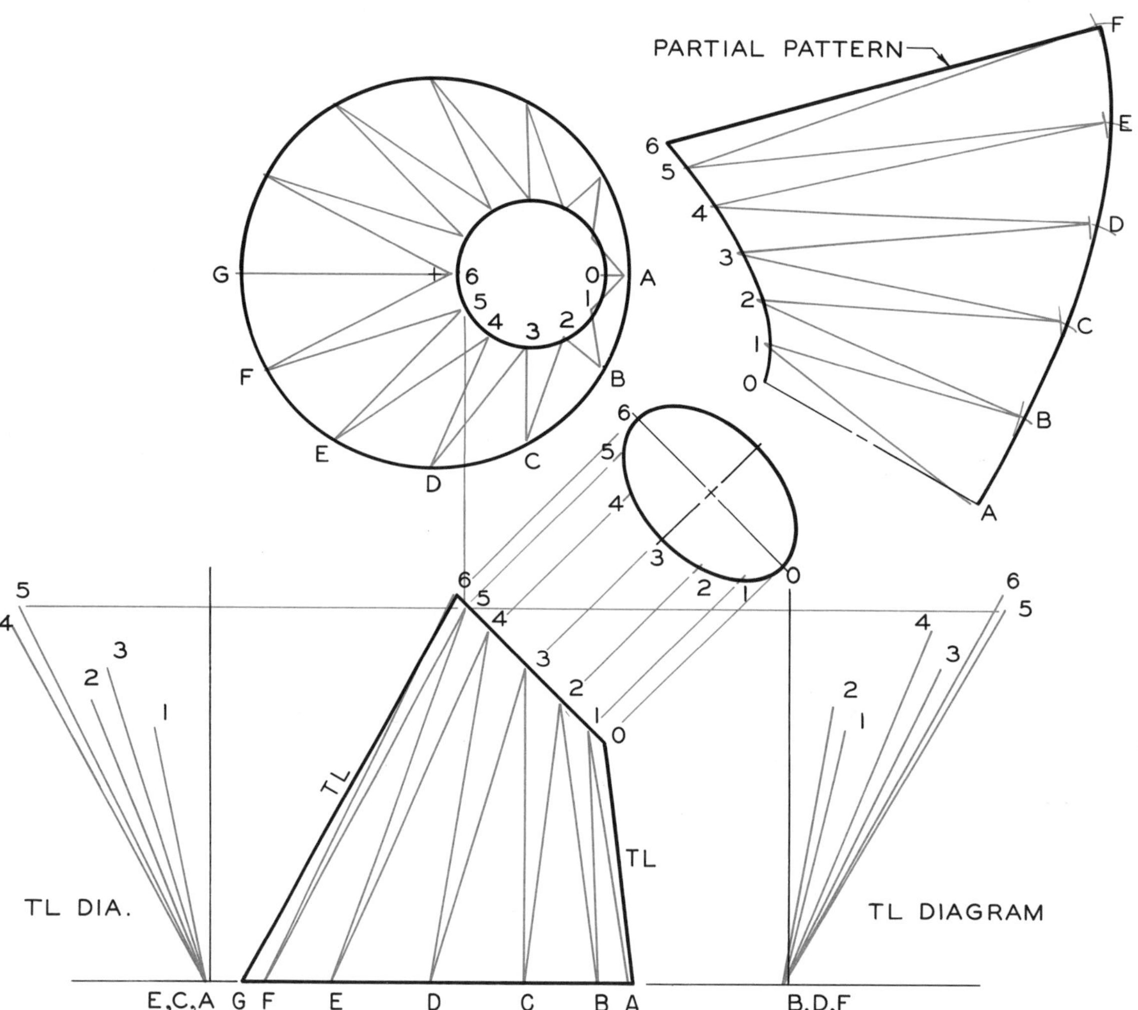

Fig. 12-29. The development of a partial inside pattern of a warped surface.

12-9 DEVELOPMENT OF TRANSITION PIECES

A transition piece is a figure that transforms its section at one end to a different shape at the other. This change is made gradually and uniformly. A duct with a rectangular cross section is connected to a cylinder with a transition piece in Fig. 12-30. Another example of a transition piece is the interior of the supersonic circuit of the wind tunnel shown in Fig. 12-31. Note that the cross section of the tunnel is changed from a rectangle to a circle at this point with a transition piece. Many other examples of these shapes can be seen in concrete structures.

The problem in Fig. 12-32 is solved by steps. The circular view of the transition piece is divided into equal units from which radial lines are

Fig. 12–30. Transition-piece developments are used to join a circular shape with a rectangular section. (Courtesy of Western Precipitation Group, Joy Manufacturing Company.)

Fig. 12–31. An example of a transition application is the interior of this supersonic circuit of a wind tunnel. (Courtesy of Arnold Engineering Development Center.)

drawn to each corner of the base. The true lengths of these lines are found by revolution (step 1). The chordal lines between the points on the circular section appear true length and the lines on the rectangular base appear true length, since these planes are horizontal. The line of separation for the development is line 1–*A*, the shortest line.

A portion of the development is laid out by triangulation in step 2, utilizing the true lengths of the lines. The remaining planes of the surface are found in step 3 to complete half of the symmetrical development. The upper points are connected with a smooth curve and the points on the base are connected with straight lines. Thin fold lines are given to indicate the curving surface at the corners.

Transition pieces and other examples of intersections and developments can be seen in Fig. 12–33. All of these components were developed and constructed through the use of the principles of intersections and developments.

12–10 DEVELOPMENT OF SPHERES

Among the applications of spherical developments, an important one is the projection and preparation of maps used to chart the surface of the earth. No ideal development has been found that will permit the earth's surface to be projected without distortion on a two-dimensional surface. The globe therefore remains the most satisfactory surface on which to represent the areas of the earth. Nevertheless, the limitations of this surface are rather obvious: Spherical surfaces are unwieldy and bulky when drawn at sufficiently large scales to permit the analysis of a relatively small area, as represented on most charts. The advent of space travel has increased interest in charting spherical paths. Spherical developments are also used in the study of domes and geodesic structures, such as that shown in Fig. 12–34. The sphere is used as an efficient storage vessel, as illustrated in Fig. 12–35. Undersea diving capsules are designed as spheres to take advantage of the sphere's ability to withstand the excessive pressures to which a diving capsule is subjected in the depths of the ocean.

An understanding of spherical surfaces will permit the designer to lay out developments for constructing an approximately true sphere with flat materials. Two methods of development are presented below.

FIGURE 12–32. DEVELOPMENT OF A TRANSITION PIECE

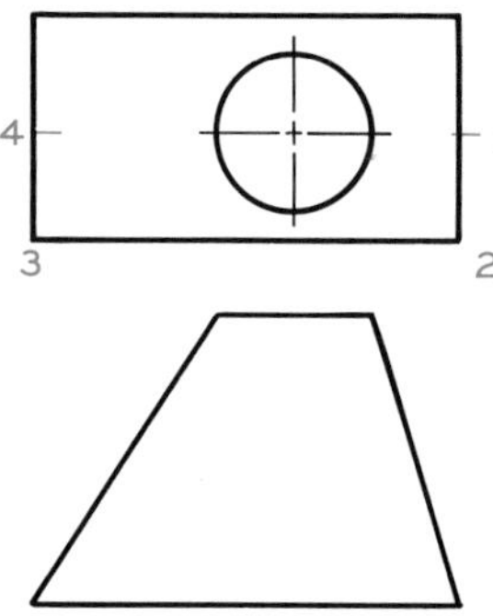

Given: The top and front views of a transition piece.
Required: Find an inside development of the surface from point 1 to point 4.
Reference: Article 12–9.

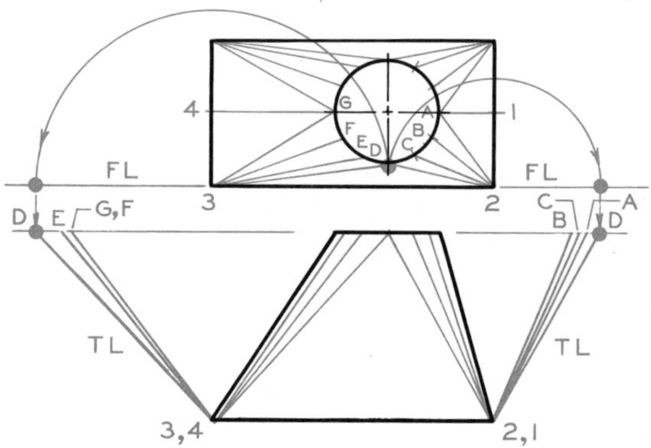

Step 1: Divide the circular edge of the surface into equal parts in the top view. Connect these points with bend lines to the corner points, 2 and 3. Find the true length of these lines by revolving them into a frontal plane and projecting them to the front view. These lines represent elements on the surface of an oblique cone.

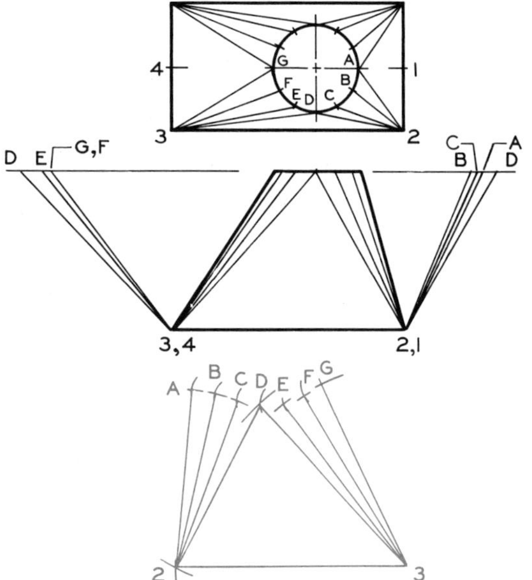

Step 2: Using the true-length lines found in the TL-diagram and the lines on the circular edge in the top-view, draw a series of triangles, which are joined together at common sides, to form the development. *Example:* arcs 2*D* and 2*C* are drawn from point 2. Point *C* is found by drawing arc *DC* from point *D* to find point *C*. *DC* is true length in the top view.

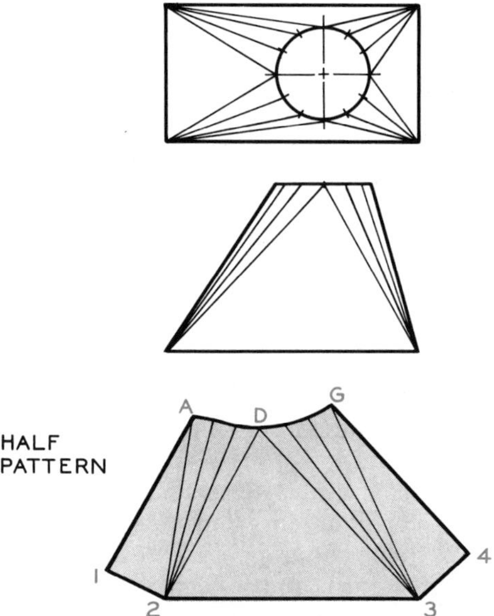

Step 3: Construct the remaining planes, *A*–1–2 and *G*–3–4, by triangulation to complete the inside, half pattern of the transition piece. Draw the fold lines as thin lines at the places where the surface is to be bent slightly. The line of departure for the pattern is chosen along *A*–1, the shortest possible line, for economy.

Fig. 12-33. Transition pieces and other examples of intersections and developments can be seen in this industrial installation. (Courtesy of Kirk and Blum Manufacturing Company.)

Fig. 12-34. An all-aluminum spherical shape is being assembled as a corn storage and conditioning unit. (Courtesy of ALCOA.)

Fig. 12-35. These spherical tanks, which were constructed through developments, make efficient storage tanks. (Courtesy of Shell Oil Company.)

12-11 SPHERICAL DEVELOPMENT—ZONE METHOD

The zone method is a conventional method of developing a sphere on a flat surface. A series of parallels, called latitudes in mapping, are drawn in the front view of Fig. 12-36. The parallels are spaced so that they establish equal arcs, D, on the surface of the sphere in the front view. Note that unit D was determined mathematically and set off on the sphere. This was done to establish uniformity in the development so that each of the developed zones would be equal in breadth. Cones are passed through the sphere's surface so that they form truncated cones in which one parallel serves as a base of a cone, and the other as the truncated top. The largest cone, which has an element equal to R_1, is found by extending line R_1 through the points where the equator and the next parallel intersect the sphere's surface in the front view, until R_1 intersects the extended center line of the sphere. Spherical elements R_2, R_3, and R_4 are found by repeating this process. The development is begun by laying out the largest zone, using R_1 as the radius of an arc which represents the base of an imaginary cone. The breadth of the zone

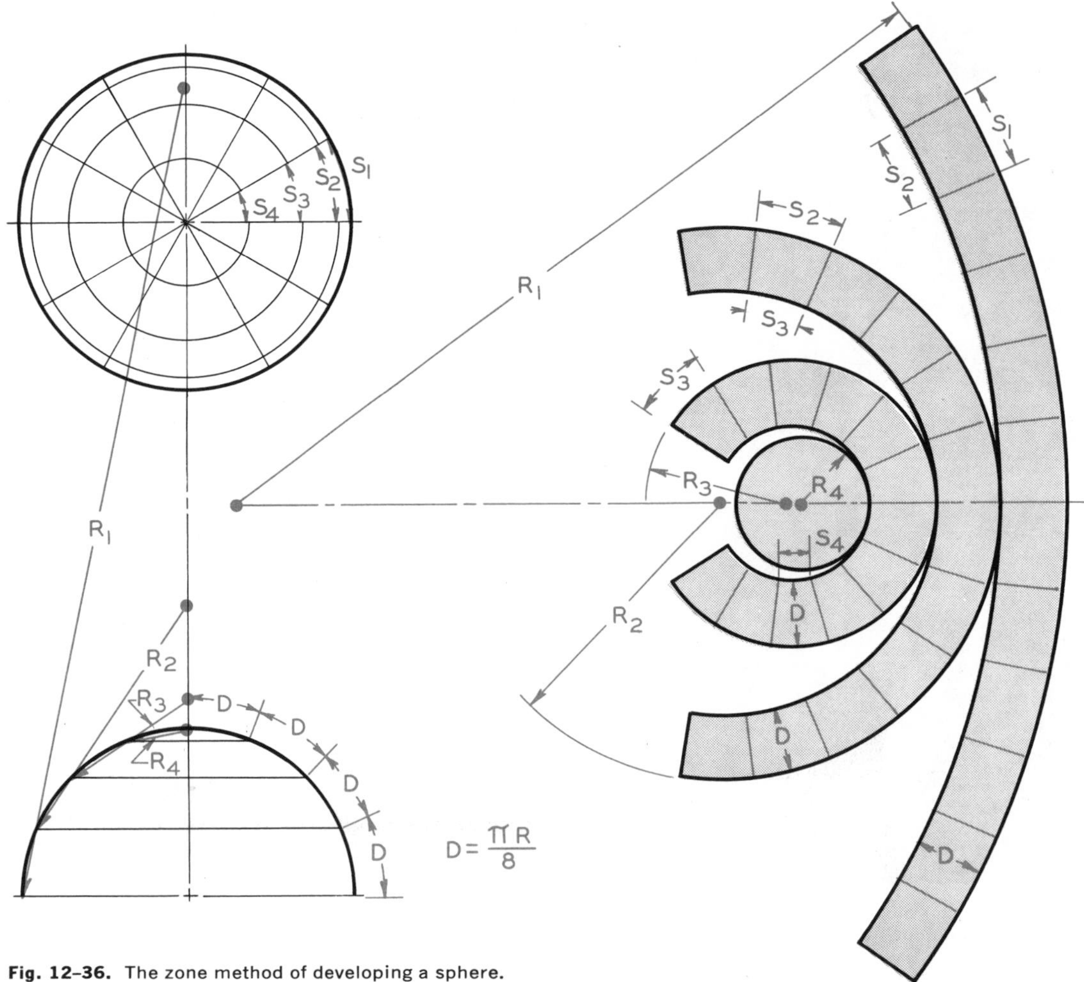

Fig. 12-36. The zone method of developing a sphere.

is found by transferring distance D from the front view to the development and drawing the upper portion of the zone with a radius equal to R_1–D, using the same center. No regard is given to finding the arc lengths at this point. The next zone is drawn using the radius R_2 with its center located on a line through the center of arc R_1. The center of R_2 is positioned along this line such that the arc to be drawn will be tangent to the preceding arc, which was drawn with radius R_1–D. The upper arc of this second zone is drawn with a radius R_2–D. The remaining zones are constructed successively in this manner. The last cone will appear as a circle with R_4 as its radius.

The lengths of the arcs can be established by dividing the top view with vertical cutting planes that radiate through the poles. These lines, which lie on the surface of the sphere, are called longitudes in cartography. Arc distances S_1, S_2, S_3, and S_4 are found on each parallel in the top view. These distances are measured off on the

Fig. 12-37. The giant dome of the United States Exhibit at Expo 67 is an example of a geodesic dome formed by straight structural members. (Courtesy of Rohm and Haas Company.)

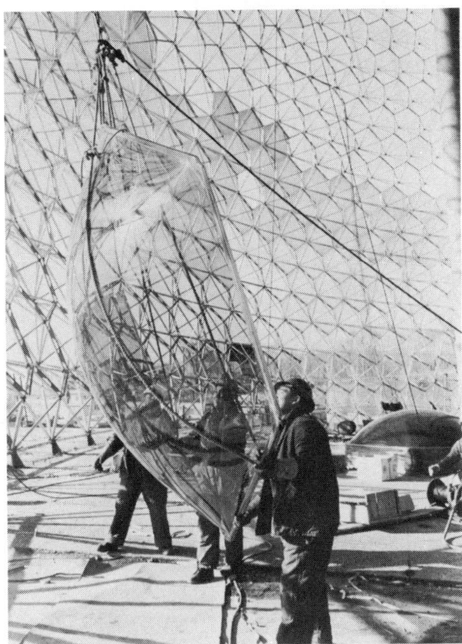

Fig. 12-38. Individual panels of Plexiglas® are installed in the giant dome. (Courtesy of Rohm and Haas Company).

constructed arcs in the development. In this case, there are twelve divisions, but smaller divisions would provide a more accurate measurement. A series of zones found in this manner can be joined to give an approximate sphere.

The giant dome of the United States Exhibit at the International Exhibition in Montreal is an example of a geodesic dome formed by straight structural members. This dome, shown in Fig. 12-37, is 250′ in diameter and 187′ high. Individual panels of Plexiglas® are shown being installed in Fig. 12-38. Most panels measured 10′ by 12′. This dome is another example of a unique application of the sphere. Domes of this type have been considered as possible enclosures for entire cities to control weather conditions and environment.

12-12 SPHERICAL DEVELOPMENT—GORE METHOD

Figure 12-39 is an alternative method of developing a flat pattern for a sphere. This method uses a series of spherical elements called gores. Equally spaced vertical cutting planes are passed through the poles in the top view. Parallels are located in the front view by dividing the surface into equal zones of dimension D. A front view of one of the gores is projected to the front view. A true-size view of one of the gores is developed by projecting from the top, which represents an approximation of the surface between two of the vertical cutting planes. Dimensions can be checked mathematically at all points. A partial pattern of the sphere is shown, in which the gores are drawn tangent to each other at the equator.

The Unisphere® was designed by determining chordal lengths of longitudes and latitudes on the surface of the sphere, as shown in Fig. 12-40. The chordal lengths made it possible to fabricate the structure with straight members. The land areas attached to the sphere were developed by a method similar to the gore method. Segments of these surfaces can be seen in Fig. 12-41, where they are being attached to the framework for later assembly on the site.

πR

0 1 2 3 4

D D D D

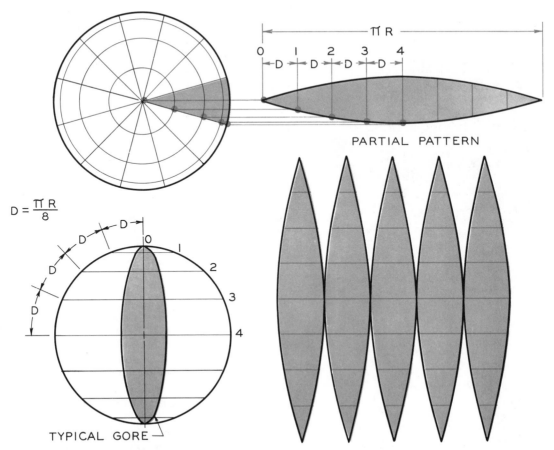

PARTIAL PATTERN

$D = \frac{\pi R}{8}$

D D D D

0 1 2 3 4

TYPICAL GORE

Fig. 12-39. The gore method of developing a sphere.

Fig. 12-40. The Unisphere® was designed by determining chordal lengths of longitudes and latitudes on the surface of the sphere. This method is similar to the gore method of development. (Courtesy of U. S. Steel Corporation.)

Fig. 12-41. Surface areas are being attached to the structural frame of the Unisphere®. (Courtesy of U. S. Steel Corporation.)

FIGURE 12-42. STRAP DEVELOPMENT

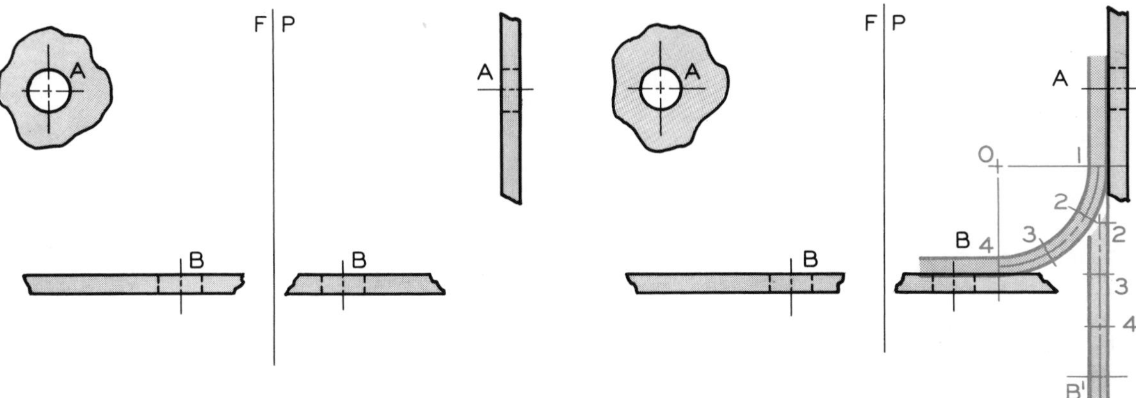

Given: The front and side views of two planes that are to be connected at points *A* and *B* with a metal strap.
Required: Find the true development of the strap and show it in both views.
Reference: Article 12-13.

Step 1: Construct the edge view of the strap in the side view using the specified radius of bend. Locate points 1, 2, 3, and 4 on the neutral axis at the bend. Revolve this portion of the strap into the vertical plane and measure the distances along this view of the neutral axis. Check the arc distances by mathematics. The hole is located at *B′* in this view.

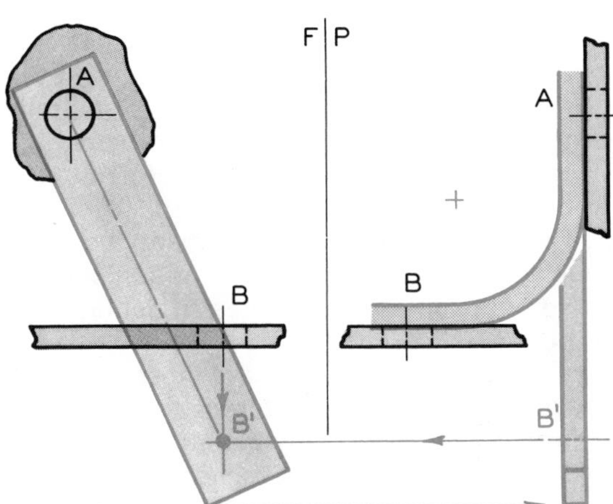

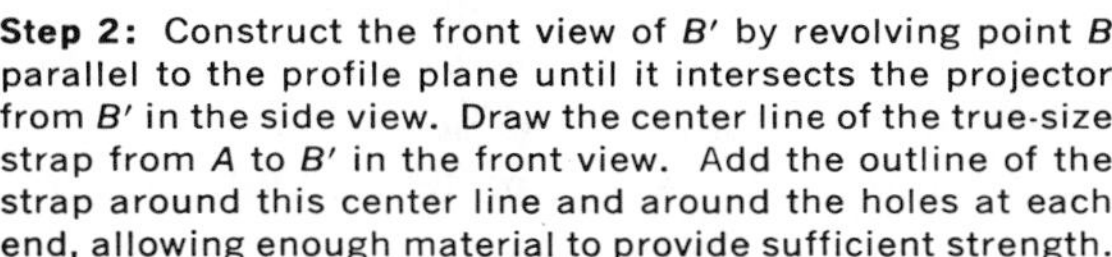

Step 2: Construct the front view of *B′* by revolving point *B* parallel to the profile plane until it intersects the projector from *B′* in the side view. Draw the center line of the true-size strap from *A* to *B′* in the front view. Add the outline of the strap around this center line and around the holes at each end, allowing enough material to provide sufficient strength.

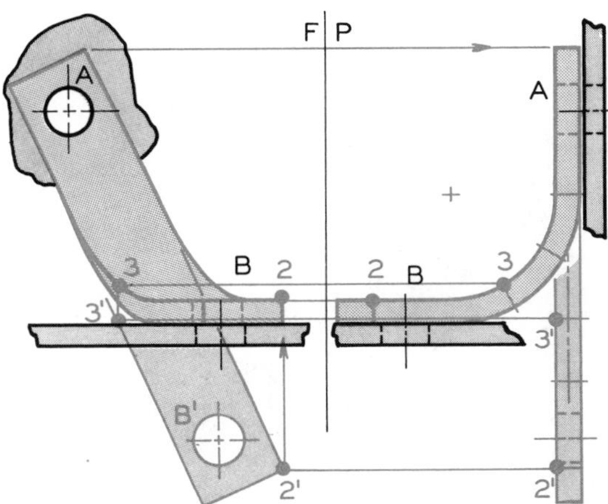

Step 3: Determine the projection of the strap in the front view by projecting points from the given views. Points 3 and 2 are shown in the views to illustrate the system of projection used. The ends of the strap are drawn in each view to form true projections.

12-13 DEVELOPMENT OF A SUPPORT STRAP

Strap metal is universally used in mass-produced products such as brackets, connectors, and supports. It is more economical to form these shapes to the desired configuration by stamping and bending than by any other fabrication method. Almost all designs contain a variety of oblique surfaces and structures which must be connected by brackets that have been stamped. Figure 12-42 illustrates the steps necessary to the design of a developed view of a support bracket. The bracket is to connect two surfaces in different planes whose points of connection are oblique to each other. The strap is drawn in the view in which the planes appear as edges (step 1), using the specified radius of bend. The arc of the bend is divided into smaller arcs and developed as a straight strap without a bend in the side view. Point *B'* is found in this view to indicate the location of the hole. The hole in the front view, shown at *B*, is projected to its position on the developed strap, as shown in step 2. This permits the true-size development of the strap to be drawn, and allowance to be made for the appropriate amount of metal on each side of the hole for strength. The projected front view of the strap in its bent position is constructed in step 3 to indicate its final configuration. An accurate design that reduces surplus material would result in considerable savings when mass-produced.

Observe that principles of revolution have been applied to this development, as well as the techniques of three-view projection. Most industrial problems tend toward a combination of graphical principles rather than the application of a single concept. Mathematics could also be used to verify the arc measurements in step 2. The designer should develop versatility in applying every tool at his disposal to the solving and checking of problems.

Figure 12-43 illustrates many examples of stamped metal components used in the body of an automobile. Each of these components was developed during the design process to obtain flat patterns from which the finished shapes could be fabricated.

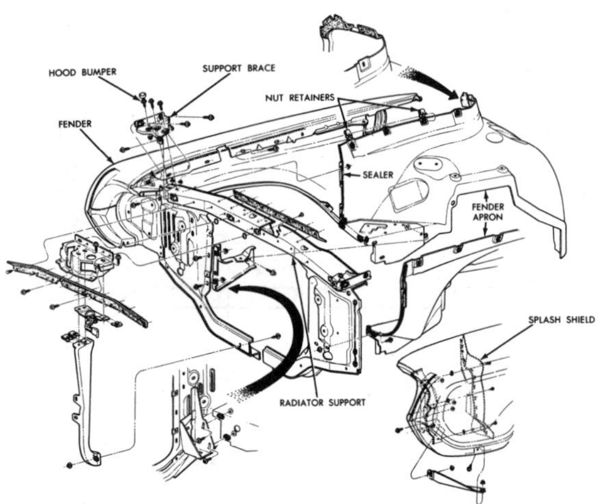

Fig. 12-43. Many examples of stamped metal developments can be seen in this exploded assembly drawing of a portion of an automobile body. (Courtesy of the Ford Motor Company.)

12-14 SUMMARY

The examples and applications covered in this chapter should serve to illustrate the many uses of the principles of developments. Essentially all engineering and technological problems are concerned with a wide assortment of geometric shapes that must be constructed from flat materials. Developments are made possible through the application of basic graphical and descriptive geometry principles in conjunction with mathematics.

Principles of intersections are closely related to developments, since different shapes must be joined together in many instances. Any development problem will be easier to solve if it is first resolved into its basic geometric elements; this process will facilitate the application of the principles covered in this chapter. A lettering system should be utilized in laying out a pattern, to avoid confusion with the projections and constructions.

PROBLEMS

General

The problems for this chapter should be constructed with *instruments* from the given sketches on $8\frac{1}{2}'' \times 11''$ sheets, as illustrated in the accompanying figures. Each grid represents $\frac{1}{4}''$. All reference planes and figure points should be labeled, using $\frac{1}{8}''$ letters with guidelines. Solutions should be sufficiently noted and labeled to explain all construction.

1. (A through C) Using Fig. 12–44, lay out an inside pattern for the prisms in parts A, B, and C of the figure. Number representative points.

2. (A and B) Using Fig. 12–45, lay out an inside pattern for each of the prisms in parts A and B of the figure. Show all construction and number the points.

3. (A through C) Lay out an inside half pattern for each cylinder in parts A, B, and C of Fig. 12–46.

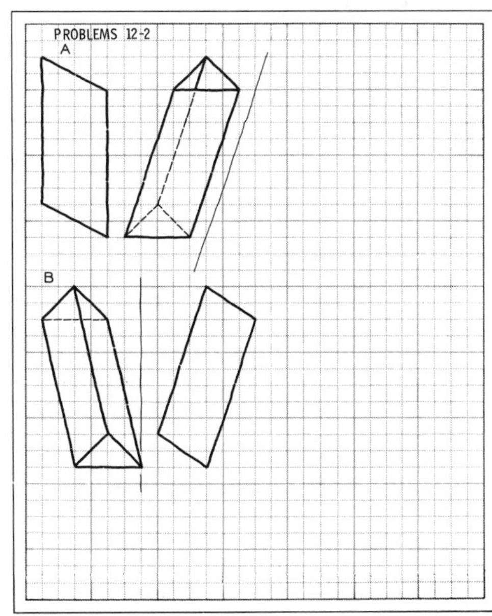

Fig. 12–45. Development of prisms.

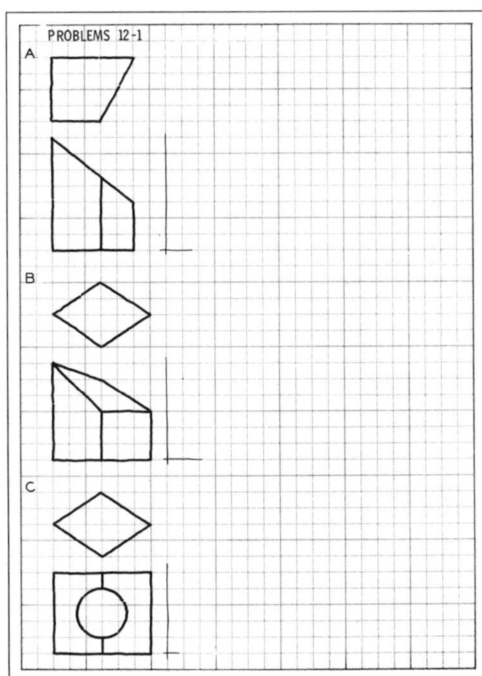

Fig. 12–44. Development of prisms.

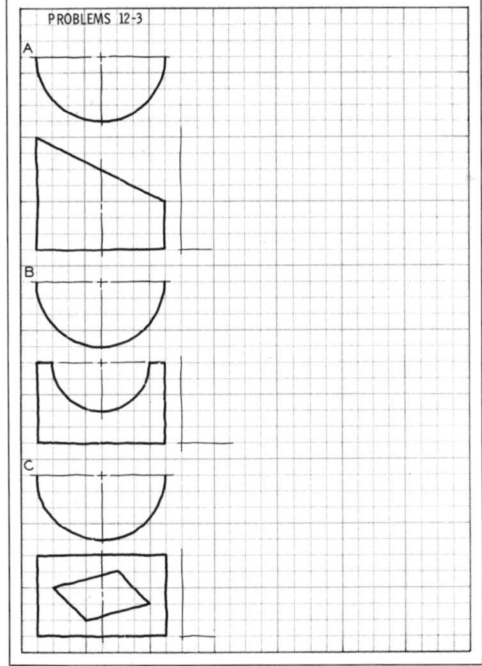

Fig. 12–46. Development of cylinders.

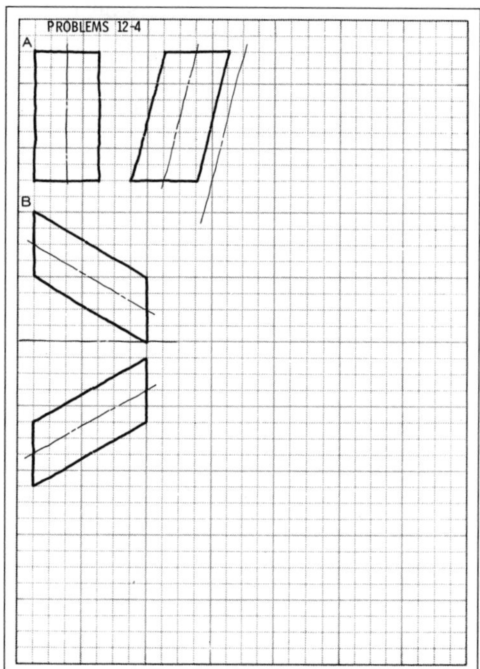

Fig. 12–47. Development of cylinders.

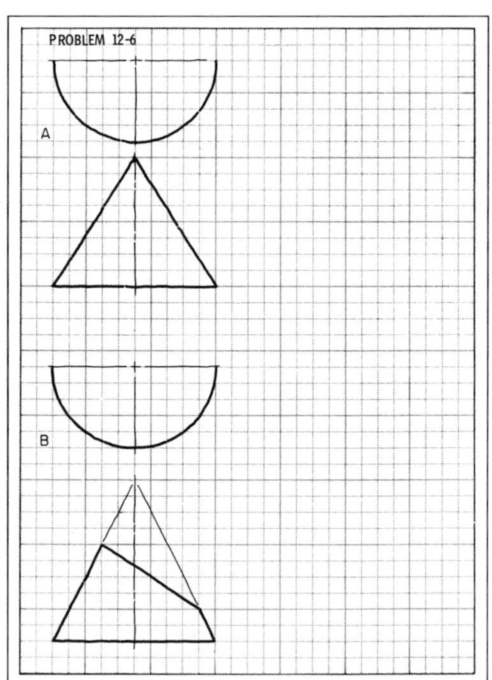

Fig. 12–49. Development of a cone.

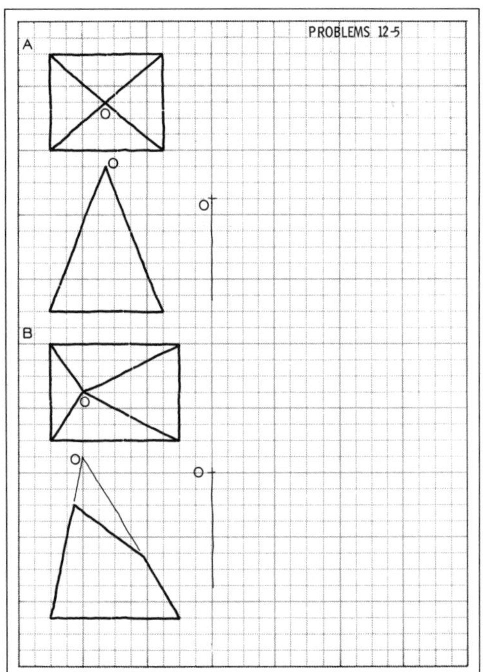

Fig. 12–48. Development of pyramids.

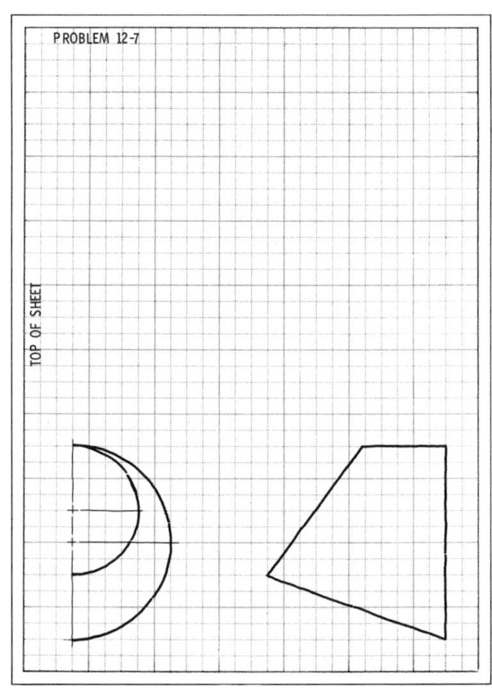

Fig. 12–50. Development of warped surface.

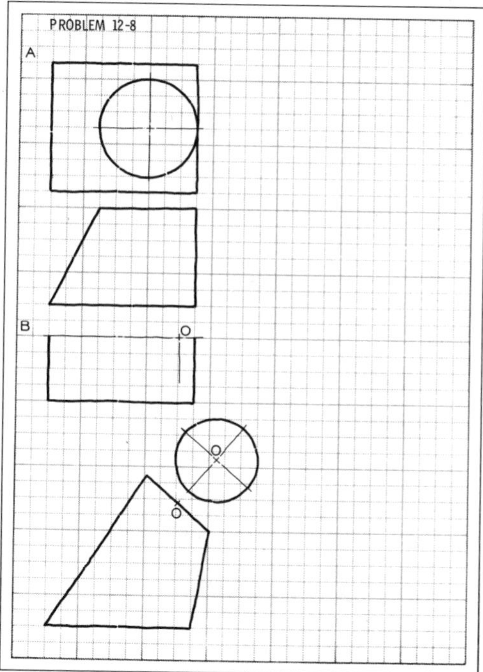

Fig. 12–51. Development of transition pieces.

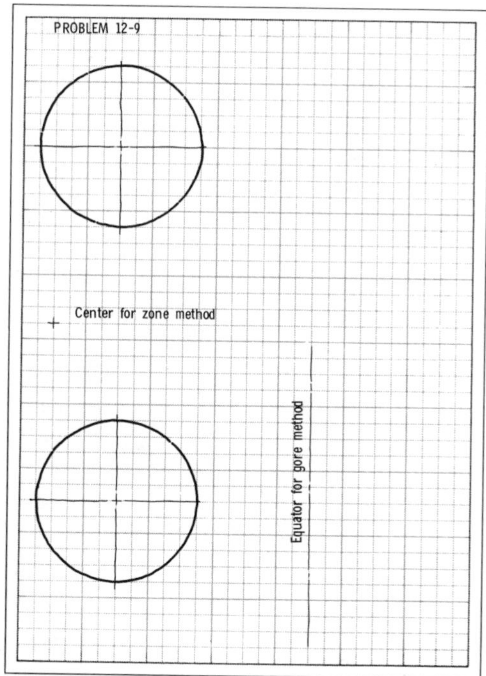

Fig. 12–52. Development of a sphere.

4. (A and B) Lay out an inside pattern for each cylinder in parts A and B of Fig. 12–47. Show all construction and number the points.

5. (A and B) Lay out an inside half pattern for each pyramid in parts A and B of Fig. 12–48.

6. (A and B) In Fig. 12–49 lay out inside half patterns for each of the cones in parts A and B.

7. Lay out an inside pattern for the warped surface in Fig. 12–50. Show a half development.

8. (A and B) Lay out inside half patterns for the transition pieces in parts A and B of Fig. 12–51.

9. (A) Lay out an inside developed pattern of the sphere in Fig. 12–52 using the gore method. (B) Using a separate sheet of paper, lay out an inside developed pattern of the sphere in Fig. 12–52 by the zone method.

10. Complete the front and side views of the $1\frac{1}{4}''$ strap which is shown in Fig. 12–53 bent into position at holes *A* and *B*. Give the complete development of the strap, including squared-off ends that extend $\frac{3}{4}''$ beyond the center line of the holes.

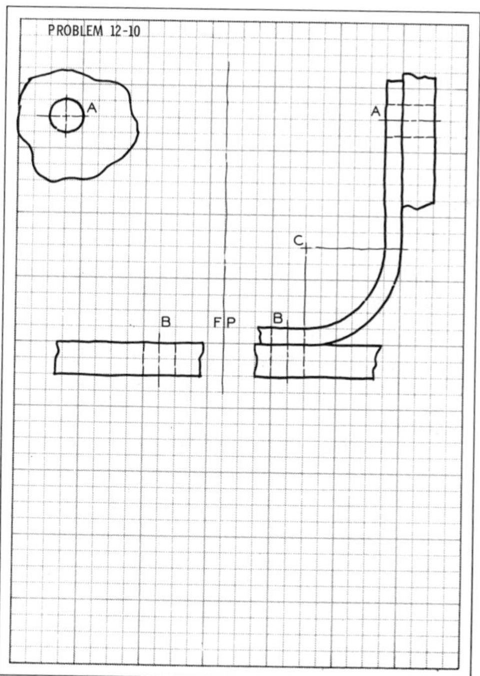

Fig. 12–53. Development of a strap.

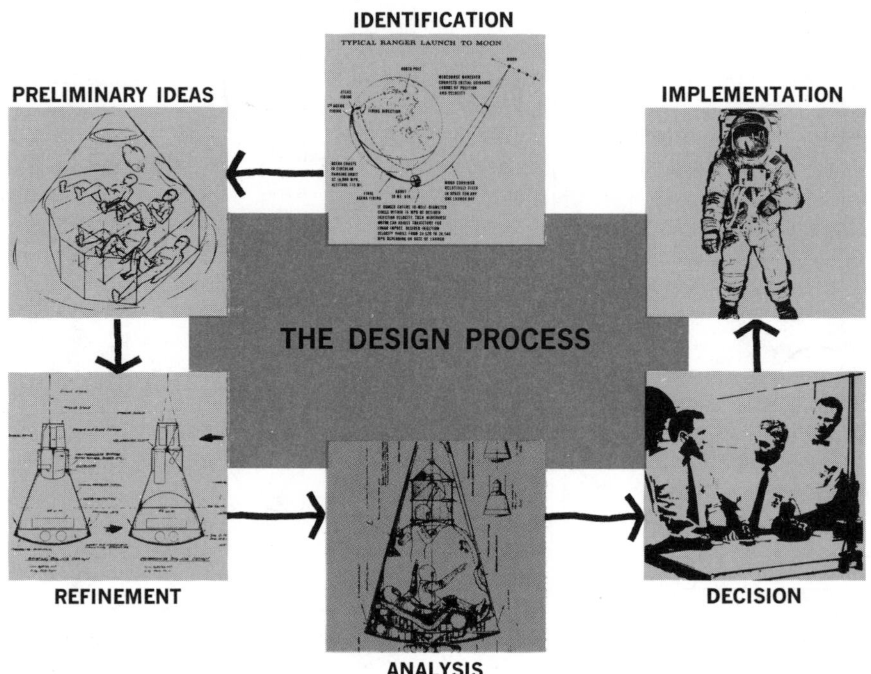

13 DESIGN ANALYSIS

13-1 INTRODUCTION

Analysis is the process most commonly associated with traditional engineering. A given design or given design elements must at some point be isolated for evaluation, to determine feasibility with regard to their purposes and in the circumstances of their proposed use. For example, a bridge is designed to span a river and support a given load; the structural members of the bridge are designed to support the bridge under given conditions. Before the design can be accepted or developed further, each structural component of the bridge must be analyzed to determine its suitability in supporting the assigned loads.

Analysis, then, is the process of evaluation and study of the set of conditions that determine the feasibility of a proposed design. This stage is characterized by objective thinking and the application of factual information, whereas the previous stages of design effort have been primarily concerned with freedom of thought and imagination, in hopes of extending a design concept beyond existing designs. Although the designer is subconsciously aware of physical limitations in the early stages of design development, he does not let these restrictions inhibit his design concepts. As he refines his design, he becomes more aware of the physical laws that will influence his final design. Finally, however, he must thoroughly analyze his proposed design, applying every evaluation technique accessible to him.

13-2 TYPES OF ANALYSIS

The analysis process must be applied to all aspects of a design. A product which has been designed to be operational at a highly efficient level may be unacceptable if it is uncomfortable or unsafe when used by the operator for whom it was designed. Similarly, many designs never come into being due to an excessive cost of manufacturing. Of course, no design can ever be considered perfect or totally acceptable in all aspects. The purpose of analysis is to discover whether a design is the most satisfactory design possible, and the one with the fewest shortcomings or objections. This is called the *optimum* design. In his analysis, therefore, the engineer must determine the requirements that should be met by the most acceptable design, in those areas of analysis considered to be the most critical.

General areas of analysis are: (1) human engineering, (2) market and product analysis, (3) prototype and model analysis, (4) physical quantities, (5) strength analysis, (6) functional analysis, and (7) economic analysis. It would be impossible to assign a fixed order in which to consider these areas of analysis, since each design problem will vary and have different requirements. However, each area must be studied individually and then in combination with others before a truly satisfactory design that will give the optimum result can be obtained.

Function. If any single design characteristic is more important than the others, it is function, or performance of the tasks for which a product was designed. A door knob that will not open a door is unacceptable in design regardless of the other features it may have. Similarly, a motorcycle that is unsatisfactory for transportation is not a good product. An example of a functional motorcycle is shown in Fig. 13-1.

But only seldom does a design result in a product that will not function at all. In assessing the functional capabilities of a design the question is, rather, what degree of function is provided by a given design. A bathroom faucet handle may regulate the flow of water, but does

Fig. 13-1. The primary criterion of a good design, as in this motorcycle, is function. Regardless of its other desirable features, a design is unsatisfactory if it does not do what it was designed to do. (Courtesy of Yamaha International Corporation.)

it work *as well* as another design, and in all circumstances? Obviously, the best handle design would be the one that functions the best under the various conditions existing during operation.

Human Engineering. All designs must ultimately serve man in some respect. He will use the product, travel on it or in it, or profit from its existence. Thought must therefore be given to human needs and to the physical, mental, and emotional characteristics of the use of the product. This important area of study is covered in Article 13-5.

Market and Product Analysis. The market for which a product is designed is usually studied in considerable detail during the initial stages of its development (Chapters 3 and 4) and prior to its production, after the design has been generally formulated. The initial market survey is performed to determine consumer attitude toward a proposed product. Product analysis at the latter stage determines the public's acceptance of the specific design being proposed. Analysis is extended to determine advertising outlets and shipping requirements, and to anticipate what quantities of the product will be needed. This area of analysis will be discussed in greater detail in Article 13-8.

Prototype and Model Analysis. The proposed design is not usually produced in quantity until a nearly complete model or prototype has been constructed for visual inspection and analysis. Extensive tests may be run on a functional design to gather information on its performance that would serve to support a final decision on its acceptance or rejection. Analysis of models will be covered in Article 13–9.

Physical Quantities. All designs must be thoroughly analyzed to determine important physical quantities that would affect the practicality of a design. Descriptive geometry methods have been employed in the previous chapters to determine lengths, areas, shapes, angles, and other physical information that would be critical to a design. But now, still other characteristics must be determined, such as weight, volume, and types of material. Completed designs will be accompanied by specifications which give the weight, shipping weight, overall dimensions, capacities, and general physical properties of the products (Fig. 13–2). These properties must be evaluated for their application to a desired requirement. It is important, for example, that a component designed for an aircraft be as light as possible, while offering the required features. Most design problems, in fact, require solutions that offer maximum strength and utilization with a minimum of weight.

Strength Analysis. A proposed design must be sufficiently strong to support the maximum design load that can be expected. Strength is closely associated with function—if the design is not adequate to withstand the expected stresses, it cannot be considered a functional design. Strength analysis is therefore a major area of engineering analysis. Graphical methods can be used as an efficient tool with which to analyze structural systems for behavior under stress. Applications of graphical and descriptive geometry principles to stress analysis are given in Chapter 14.

Economic Analysis. Regardless of the desirable features of a design, economy will always be a major factor in its final acceptance for production. Essentially all engineering projects are undertaken with profit as a major incentive. Designs that are unduly expensive have smaller chances of being profitable in the face of the competition existing in a free enterprise system. For this reason the designer must consider economy and type of fabrication as his design nears the completion stage. He should approximate the total cost of his design by considering all aspects, including materials, labor, and fabrication processes. Such an analysis is necessary whether approval will come from the engineering organization or from a client employing the organization.

13–3 ANALYSIS AND ENGINEERING

Traditional engineering analysis, which requires the application of scientific and physical principles, is used more in the analysis stage of the design process than at any other step. When preliminary design concepts and refinements are being developed, the designer shows only a secondary concern for the physical and scientific limitations of his design, knowing that they will be evaluated at later stages. In the early stages of design, engineering graphics is the fundamental tool used to assist in the creative process; in analysis, however, many other disciplines are required. The engineer must have a general background in the areas of science, physics, mathematics, and other areas of engineering science (Fig. 13–3).

Sometimes analysis reveals that the proposed design is entirely inadequate for its design specifications. In that case, the entire design process must be repeated. However, a designer can usually anticipate potential trouble in advance of this stage. The analysis process is therefore usually concerned with determining what design will function with the highest efficiency and have the most favorable features.

As we stated earlier, analysis is less creative than the earlier stages of design development. It is restricted to the proven, accepted methods of engineering analysis, applied with the minimum of latitude in subjective judgment.

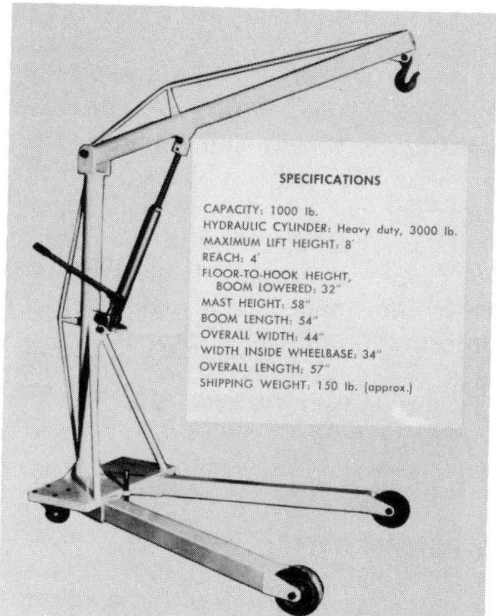

Fig. 13–2. Designs must be analyzed to determine their physical properties, including dimensions, weights, capacities, and other data of this nature. (Courtesy of Air Technical Industries.)

Fig. 13–3. In the analysis stage of the design process, mathematics and engineering sciences are applied more than at any other step. The engineer must be able to use every analytical tool available to him. (Courtesy of AT&T Long Lines.)

13–4 APPLICATION OF ENGINEERING GRAPHICS

Engineering graphics and descriptive geometry are valuable to the analysis of a design in determining stresses and in evaluating laboratory and experimental data. Often systems of forces can be solved graphically in considerably less time than would be taken by the analytical method employed in engineering. For best results, systems of forces, which are called vector systems, should be solved both graphically and analytically. In this manner each method serves as a check on the other.

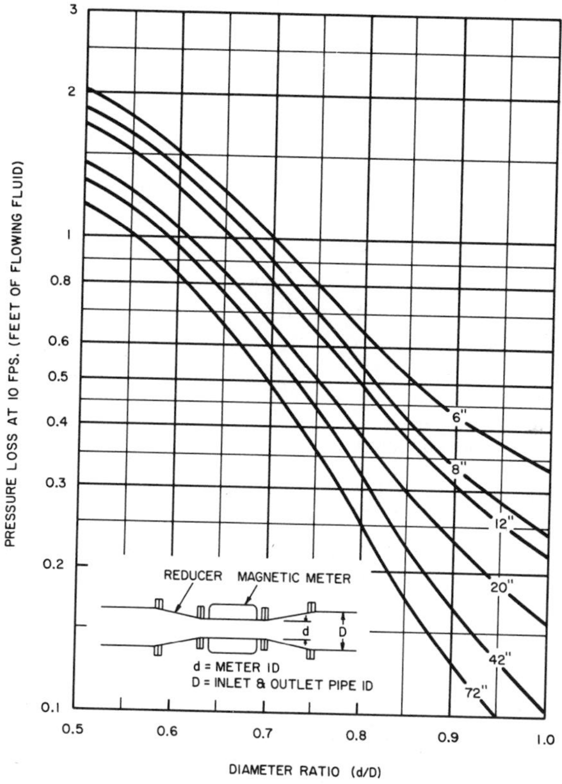

Fig. 13–4. Empirical data obtained from laboratory experiments can be analyzed more effectively by graphical techniques than through mathematical methods. (Courtesy of Fischer and Porter Company.)

Empirical data obtained from laboratory experiments can be transformed from raw data into algebraic equations by the means of graphical techniques (Fig. 13-4). Data expressed in the form of an equation become easier to analyze through the use of mathematics. Mathematical evaluation can also be handled graphically; there is even a graphical calculus. Graphical calculus comes into use when the data do not assume the form of an equation, but instead are plotted as an irregular curve. A solution can be obtained by graphically integrating and differentiating without applying numerical procedures.

Clearance between functional parts and linkage systems is more efficiently found through the graphical process (Fig. 13-5) than by the construction of mathematical models. Even if mathematical principles are applied, it is advantageous to determine graphically a close approximation of the clearance in question prior to attempting a mathematical solution. An accurate drawing of the relative parts can often simplify mathematical solutions that will be used to supplement the graphical solutions.

Data of a less technical nature, such as market surveys, populations, trends, and changes in physical elements, can best be presented graphically. Tabular data that are presented in columns of numbers do not give a clear picture of the basic trends reflected by the data. Interpretation of tabular data requires much effort and concentration to draw a significant conclusion with regard to the total meaning. On the other hand, graphical techniques can convey an instantaneous understanding of the data at a glance. A graphical format of this type is a definite aid to the analysis and evaluation of pertinent information. All well-prepared technical reports make ample use of graphical presentation of data for easy analysis.

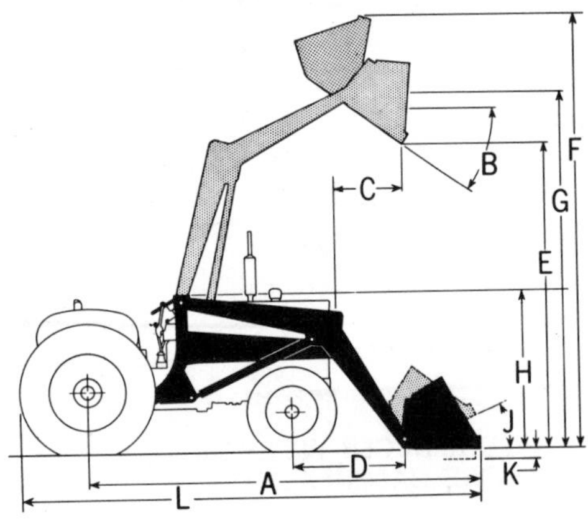

Fig. 13-5. Clearances between functional parts and linkage systems can be analyzed efficiently through the use of graphical methods. (Courtesy of International Harvester Company.)

13-5 HUMAN ENGINEERING

Human engineering is a relatively new field that has gained significant status in recent years. This area of study is concerned with the adaptation of any given design to the needs of man. Woodson[28] gives the following as a definition to human engineering:

> "The design of human tasks, man-machine systems, and specific items of man-operated equipment for the most effective accomplishments of the job, including displays for presenting information to the human senses, controls for human operation, and complex man-machine systems. In the design of equipment, human engineering places major emphasis upon efficiency, as measured by speed and accuracy of human performance, in the use and operation of equipment. Allied with efficiency are the safety and comfort of the operator."

Essentially all designs will be related to some extent to man and his physical relationship to them; consequently, these factors must be considered in developing the most efficient relationship possible. The standard drawing table used by the engineer and technician could probably be improved if more attention were given to human dimensions, comfort, vision, and movements. The handle of a lever must be designed to conform to a variety of hand sizes for maximum comfort and efficiency. The placement and the limiting movements of a lever also require the application of human engineering principles.

Human engineering has always been a prominent factor in the design process. Leonardo da Vinci analyzed body dimensions and proportions in approximately 1473 (Fig. 13–6). These body dimensions could be used to design apparatus for which the human is the limiting factor that influences the operational efficiency of the completed design. A close similarity to Leonardo's study can be seen in Fig. 13–7, where human factors are being measured to determine the restriction of human mobility by a radiation protection garment that will be used by astronauts in space travel.

Human factors are a major consideration in the space program, since an entirely new environment must be related to the activities and movements of astronauts. Because conservation of weight and space are critical to a successful space flight, a thorough investigation of the relationship of an astronaut to his space vehicle must be made. The astronaut must be able to reach the critical gauges and manually-operated controls with the maximum efficiency under the anticipated conditions. Space must be provided to permit him to move within the vehicle to make necessary control adjustments and to maintain body circulation, which would be limited if he were confined to one position. A graphical analysis of some human engineering factors is shown in Fig. 13–8. This is a preliminary drawing prepared by the National Aeronautics and Space Administration to evaluate the space relationships within a capsule.

The design of the display panel of a simulator used to train astronauts is shown in Fig. 13–9. This simulator is used to condition astronauts to the operation of a spacecraft and, at the same time, serves as a means of determining weaknesses in the design of the display system. A typical display panel for the Gemini-15 controls is shown in Fig. 13–10. It should be obvious that the locations of the various gauges and control actuators were planned to conform to human factors, to ensure that operation would be as functional as possible under the expected con-

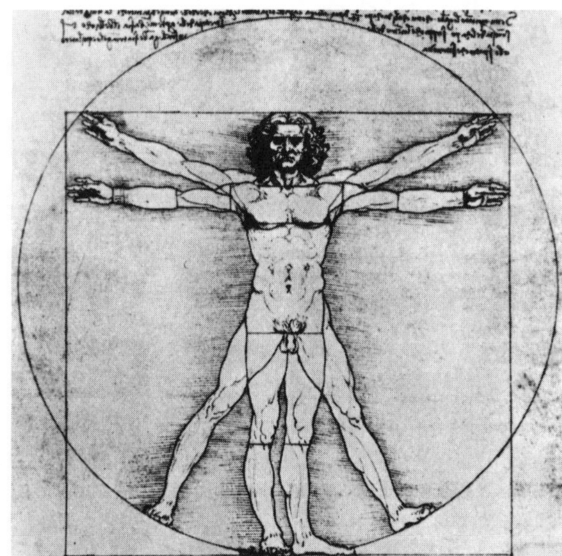

Fig. 13–6. Leonardo da Vinci analyzed body dimensions and proportions in approximately 1473.

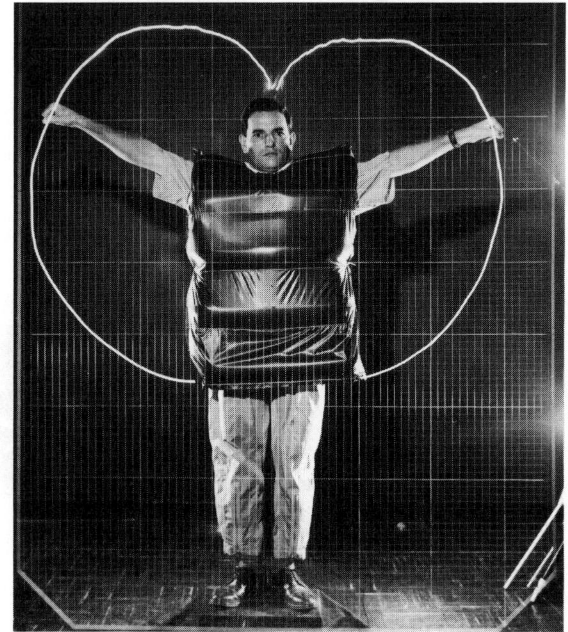

Fig. 13–7. Body dimensions and movements are measured to analyze human mobility as restricted by a radiation protection garment used by astronauts in space travel. (Courtesy of General Dynamics Corporation.)

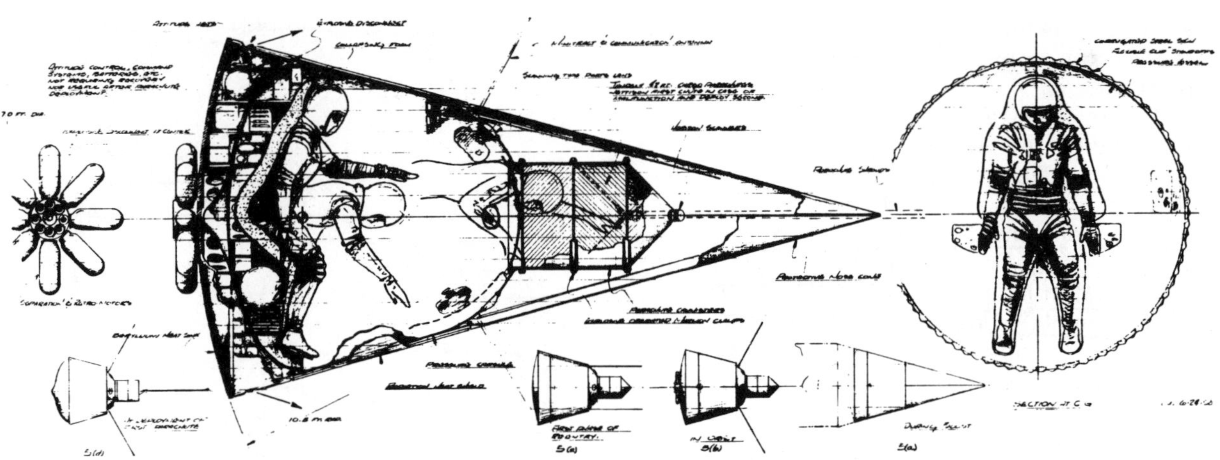

Fig. 13-8. Analysis of a space capsule. (Courtesy of the National Aeronautics and Space Administration.)

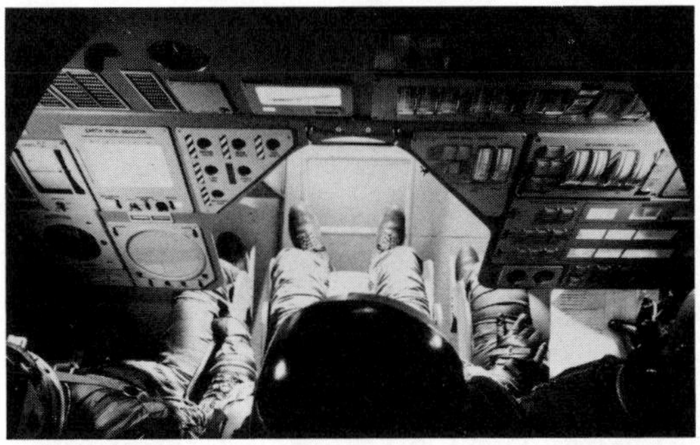

Fig. 13-9. The display panel of this spacecraft simulator was designed to afford the astronauts the functional arrangement of flight information. (Courtesy of General Dynamics Corporation.)

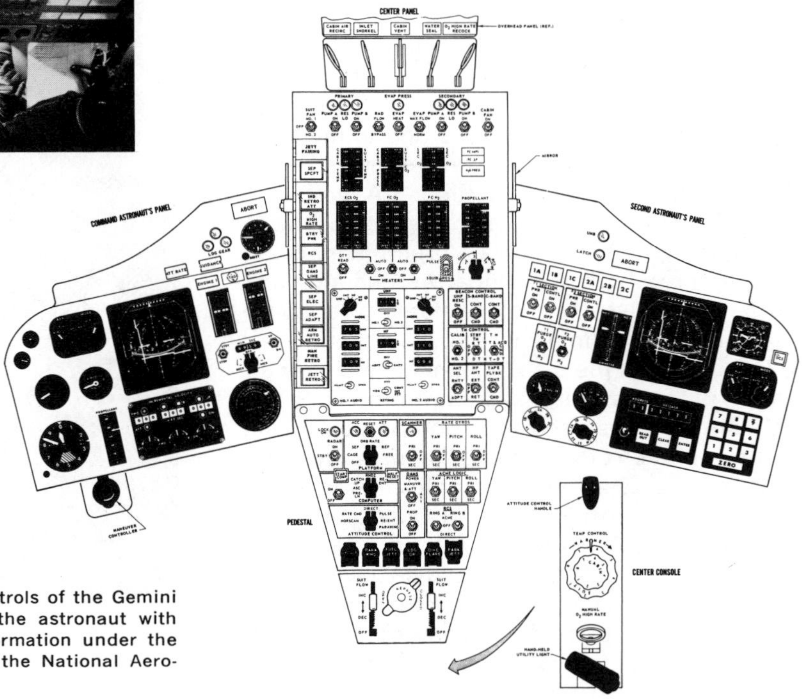

Fig. 13-10. The display panel and controls of the Gemini spacecraft were designed to provide the astronaut with immediate access to controls and information under the most severe conditions. (Courtesy of the National Aeronautics and Space Administration.)

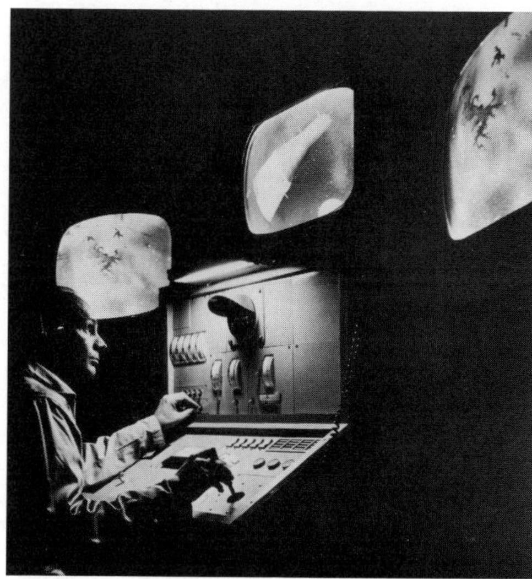

Fig. 13–11. A control panel of a manned spacecraft simulator is used by an astronaut to practice guiding his craft to a rendezvous with another spacecraft in flight. The efficiency of this manuever will depend greatly on the adaptation of the controls to normal human reflexes. (Courtesy of General Dynamics Corporation.)

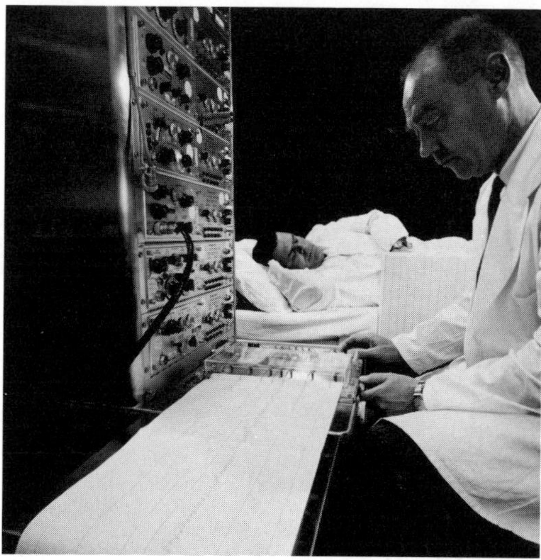

Fig. 13–12. A flight surgeon studies a subject's pulse and respiration rates as they are recorded by a new remote biomonitoring device which permits the gathering of physiological data without the need for contact sensors. (Courtesy of General Dynamics Corporation.)

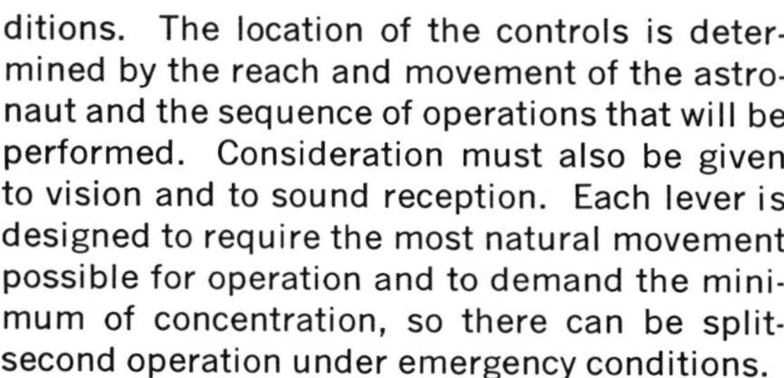

ditions. The location of the controls is determined by the reach and movement of the astronaut and the sequence of operations that will be performed. Consideration must also be given to vision and to sound reception. Each lever is designed to require the most natural movement possible for operation and to demand the minimum of concentration, so there can be split-second operation under emergency conditions.

The manned spacecraft simulator shown in Fig. 13–11 allows an astronaut to practice guiding his craft to a rendezvous with another spacecraft in flight. In designing the control panel and information display, detailed attention must be given to the human reactions and physical movements required to successfully maneuver a craft traveling in space at high speeds. Physiological and physical tests (Fig. 13–12) are used to learn more of human reactions under given conditions. This device is used to monitor an astronaut's heartbeat and respiration rates, among other data, without subjecting him to the discomfort that would be caused by attaching electrodes to his body.

Environmental conditions that will be experienced in space travel must be considered in relationship to every action that will be performed by the astronaut. A state of weightlessness will change the performance of the most simple operations. Simply turning a wrench could cause the astronaut to spin in space as a reaction to the force he applies. Eating will require an entirely different process than it does under atmospheric conditions on the earth.

Exploration of the sea is almost as unusual in terms of normal human functions as is space travel, and the design of craft for undersea exploration involves problems in human engineering that relate to those in space exploration. The one man submarine shown in Fig. 13–13 must have a self-contained atmosphere and complete operational systems in which a man can perform his tasks under the ocean at great depths. He must have ample space for comfort

Fig. 13–13. Star 1, the one-man research submarine, practices fastening to a simulated hatch on the ocean floor. The submarine's environment and space arrangement were based on human requirements. (Courtesy of General Dynamics Corporation.)

Fig. 13–14. The configuration of the Explorer IV was based to a considerable extent upon human dimensions and functions. (Courtesy of Rohm and Haas Company.)

and the movements necessary in his activities. Adequate visibility inside and out of the submarine is another human engineering problem that must be overcome for efficient maneuverability. The occupant of a submarine is used as the basis for the development of the entire craft, and all the submarine's systems are considered in relation to his physical and psychological limitations.

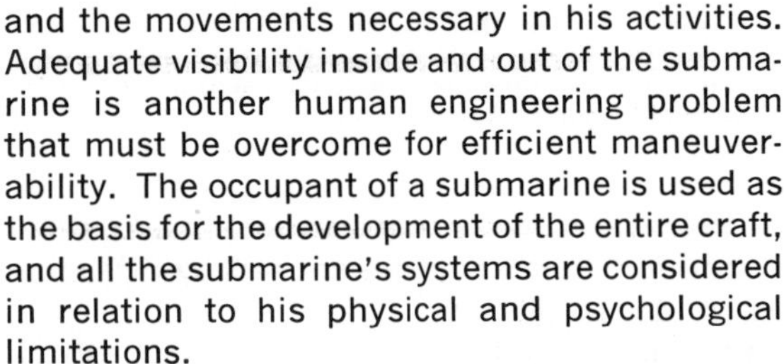

Everyday furniture, hand tools, office equipment, and even textbooks have been designed with human factors as the major guide. Some seats are comfortable for certain sizes of people while other designs are reasonably comfortable for most people regardless of size. This is no accident. Considerable research is required to establish the optimum design, the one that will provide the greatest comfort for the largest number of people who will be using the finished product. Figure 13–14 is a prototype of the Explorer IV, which was designed by the Rohm and Haas Company as an introduction to new concepts in automotive design using Plexiglas® and other acrylics. The exterior and interior of an automobile are influenced by the mechanical equipment necessary for its operation and the space required for the driver and passengers for whom the automobile was designed. To retard fatigue during long drives, the interior seats (Fig. 13–15) are dimensioned to offer the greatest comfort possible for the occupants. Footroom is provided to meet the needs of most passengers. The control panel is conveniently located to afford easy manipulation of the devices that control the car and regulate internal atmosphere, including sound and temperature (Fig. 13–16). The dashboard display has been designed to provide maximum visibility of the gauges for the occupants day or night. Each of the gauges and dials (Fig. 13–17) has been designed to communicate the necessary information as easily as possible with the minimum of study. The configurations of the passenger compartment, headroom space, and all accessories were designed to conform to human needs and limitations.

The principles of human engineering receive primary consideration in the design of appliances and products that are to be operated by hand. An example of a product of this type is the mixer shown in Fig. 13–18. The operational components are housed in an attractive enclosure to appeal to the aesthetic sense of the consumer. The mechanism is designed to balance in the hand with a minimum of effort when in operating position. The handle is designed to

Fig. 13-15. Seating and leg room for an automobile must conform to body dimensions to prevent premature fatigue while driving. (Courtesy of Rohm and Haas Company.)

Fig. 13-16. Controls are located within the operational range of the human body for ease of manipulation. (Courtesy of Rohm and Haas Company.)

Fig. 13-17. Instrument panels must be designed to afford instant communication of significant information through their arrangement, lighting, and coloration. (Courtesy of Rohm and Haas Company.)

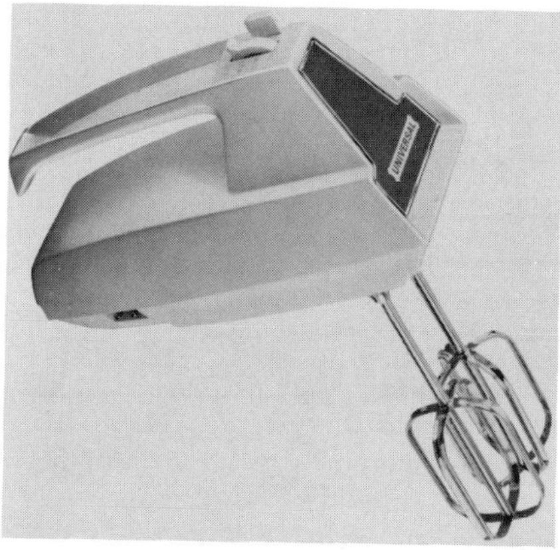

Fig. 13-18. A product that is to be operated or held in the hand should be designed to fit the hand and to have good balance and fingertip controls. (Courtesy of General Electric Company.)

fit any hand with a maximum of comfort. The controls are placed on the handle so that they require only a fingertip adjustment. The entire design is adapted to the user in an effort to appeal to his needs, his desire for comfort, and his appreciation of appearance and styling.

13-6 BODY DIMENSIONS AND HUMAN FACTORS

The previous paragraphs have attempted to identify general, broad areas of human engineering in rather simple terms. This field of study is undergoing a continuous input of new information gathered through basic research and laboratory experimentation. The material covered in this volume is a brief review of the total area of study in human engineering and should not be taken as a complete discussion of the field. We should also point out that human engineering is not the sole domain of engineering or of any other particular field of study. It has, in general, been closely associated with the fields of industrial design, psychology, and industrial engineering. However, designers in all fields of engineering and technology must utilize principles of human engineering frequently when developing designs for human relationship.

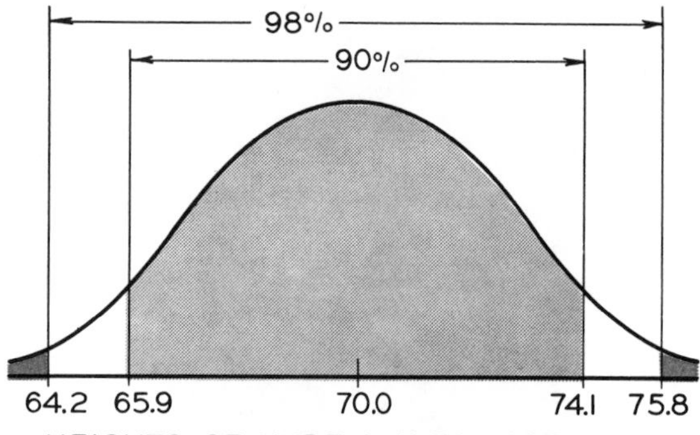

Fig. 13-19. Distribution of the average heights in inches of males 18–22 years of age. (Based on data gathered by B. D. Corpinos, *Human Biology*, **30**, 292.) Fifty percent of males in this age range are taller than 70″, while 50 percent are shorter.

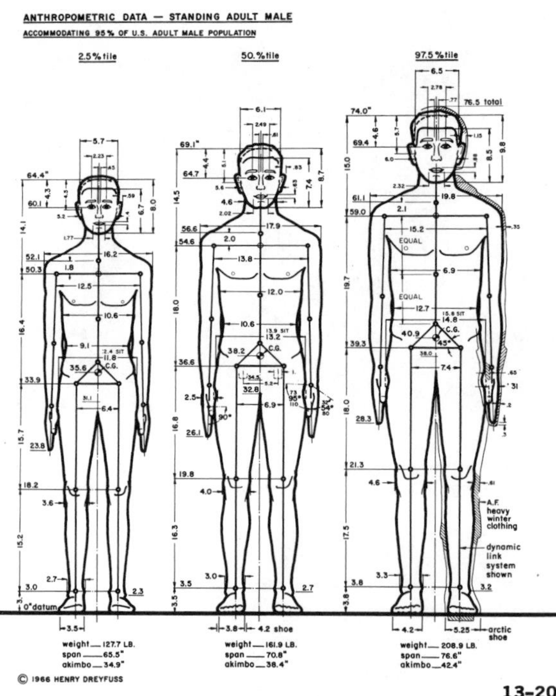

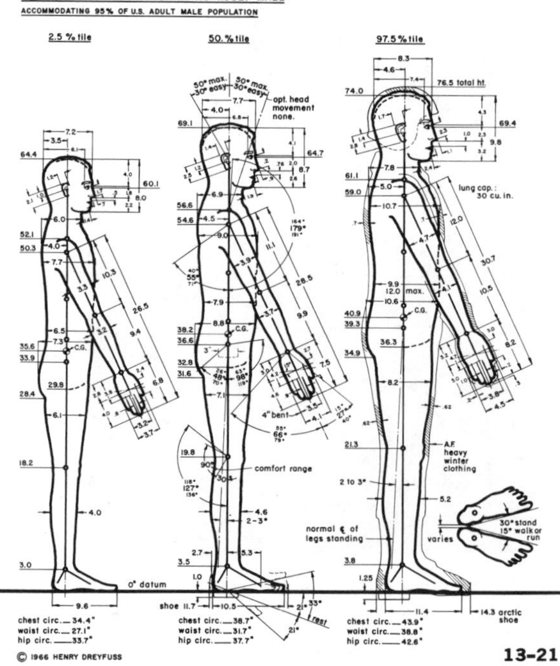

When a design is being developed for general use, it must take into account the dimensions and ranges of manipulation of the person who will be using the finished product. Instead of being concerned with the requirements of a single person, the designer must think in terms of designing for the average size of the persons who will use the design. Information is gathered and recorded by military and governmental agencies to arrive at a set of dimensions that describe the average man and woman. Variations in most natural characteristics tend to conform to the normal distribution curve shown in Fig. 13-19. In this example, male heights are plotted against their frequency of occurrence in a typical sample of American men. Note that the average is 5′-10″.

According to the laws of probability and statistical inference, 90 percent of army males will have a height between 5′-6″ and 6′-2″. This measurement and other body measurements are used as standards for the design of equipment to give optimum efficiency.

Figs. 13-20 through 13-23. Front and profile body measurements of the adult male and female. The measurements describe 95 percent of the U.S. adult population. (Courtesy of Henry Dreyfuss and the Whitney Library of Design, from *The Measure of Man*, New York, 1967.)

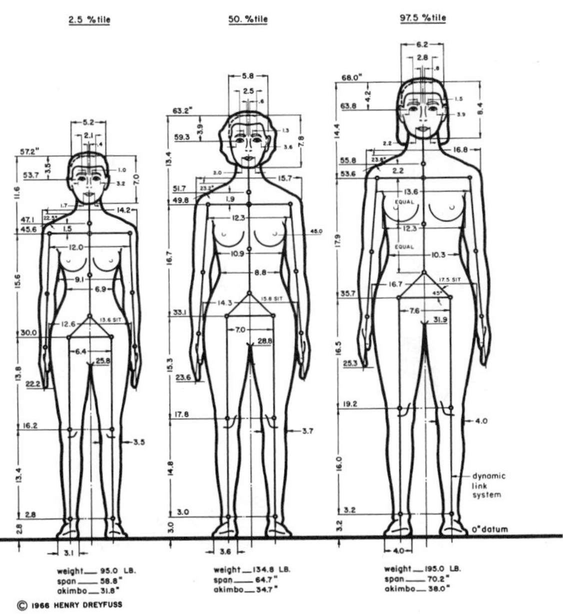

13–22

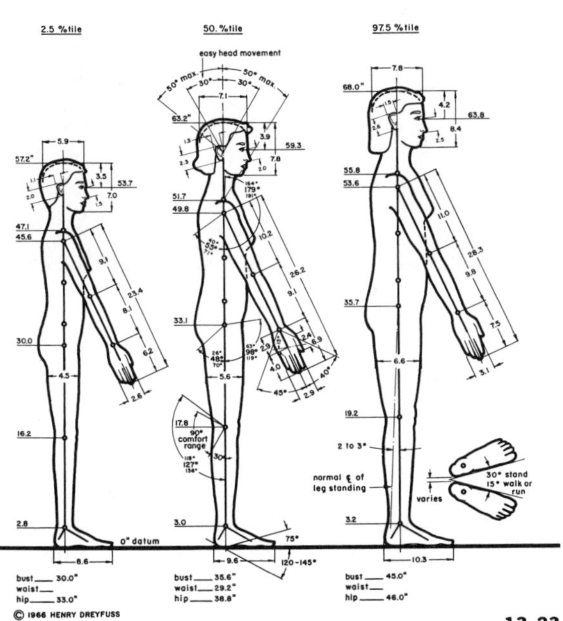

13–23

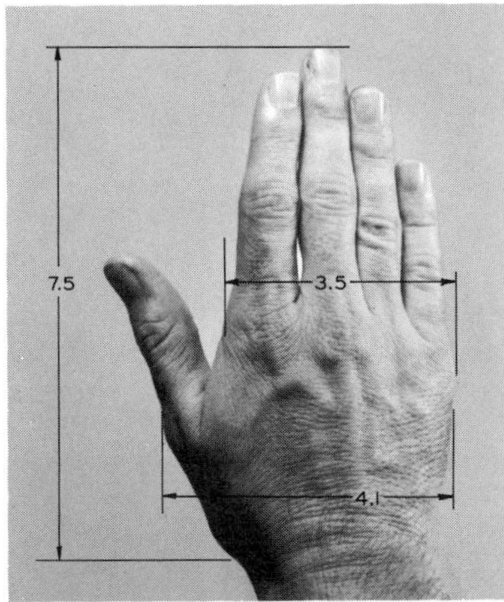

Fig. 13–24. Dimensions of the average adult male's hand. These dimensions control the sizes of hand-operated levers and controls. (Based on data from *Human Engineering Guide to Equipment Design* by Morgan, Cook, Chapanis, and Lund. New York: McGraw-Hill, 1963.)

Typical body dimensions that can be assumed for the average American male are shown in Figs. 13–20 and 13–21. The measurements were determined by Henry Dreyfuss[8] to be used for industrial designs that require a close adaptation to human factors. The average female body dimensions are given in Figs. 13–22 and 13–23. This tabulation of average body dimensions has been extended to include the hands, feet, legs, and arms and other parts of the body, since many designs involve multiple motions—for example, coordinated foot and hand movements. Hand measurements, such as those given in Fig. 13–24, are useful as standards in designing equipment that involves manual operation using hand motion or grip.

Examples of the consideration of human engineering in designs for mass-produced products can be seen in the series of photos beginning with Fig. 13–25. Car seat A, which is designed for a child, has a safety bar positioned to encircle the child's body for support and safety. This bar can be lifted to clear the child's head and thus permits him to dismount easily from

13-25

13-26

Fig. 13-25. Car-seat design A has a safety bar to encircle the child's body for safety.

Fig. 13-26. The safety bar of car-seat design A can be revolved over the child's head for exit from the seat.

Fig. 13-27. Car seat design B is designed primarily for use in a back seat. The safety bar encircling the child is somewhat smaller than that shown in design A.

Fig. 13-28. The method of attachment and the size of the safety bar on design B does not permit the bar to clear the child as in design A.

Fig. 13-29. It is necessary for the child to be lifted from the design B seat or to crawl from it as shown.

13-27

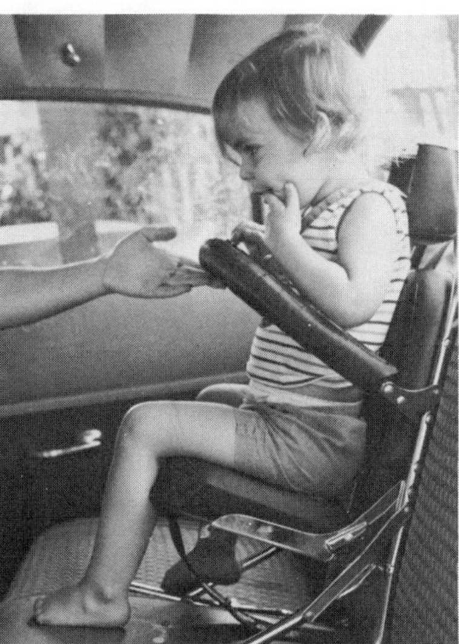
13-28

13-29

the seat (Fig. 13-26). Car seat B (Fig. 13-27) also has a safety bar to encircle the child's body much in the same manner as in seat A. However, this bar cannot be lifted to clear the child's head (Fig. 13-28); therefore it would be difficult for the child to dismount without assistance (Fig. 13-29). This could be an advantage in the case of a child riding unattended in the back seat. The functional difference in these two designs consists in the location of the pivot point of the safety bar and the configuration of the bar. In design A the bar is intentionally curved to provide adequate clearance when lifted, whereas in design B the bar is shaped to provide a close fit. Human factors were a major consideration in the design of these seats so that each would properly fulfill the desired function.

13-7 FACTORS AFFECTING HUMAN ENGINEERING

Human measurements and human comfort have been discussed briefly in relationship to man-machine design. Other major considerations are body motion, vision, sound transmission and reception, and the working environment.

Body Motion. Body motion is related to the body dimensions previously covered and to the effective ranges of operation of the various parts of the body. An example of this human engineering factor is the range of operation of a man while he is sitting at a work area performing a specific function. The study of body motion also includes attention to the amount of force that must be applied to perform a given task, in relationship to the strength of the operator.

Body motion on the lunar surface is especially critical, since the astronaut is entering a new environment. Preparations for this experience can be best achieved by testing under simulated conditions. The astronaut in Fig. 13-30 is testing a Luna-Walker on the lava beds of McKenzie Pass, Oregon, under the surveillance of members of crew support teams. In Fig. 13-31 astronaut William Cunningham tests the functional value of a pressurized suit to determine its adaptation to normal body activities while using the Jacob's Staff. Only through simulated tests of this type can designers and researchers arrive at final conclusions concerning the utility of a particular suit or walking apparatus.

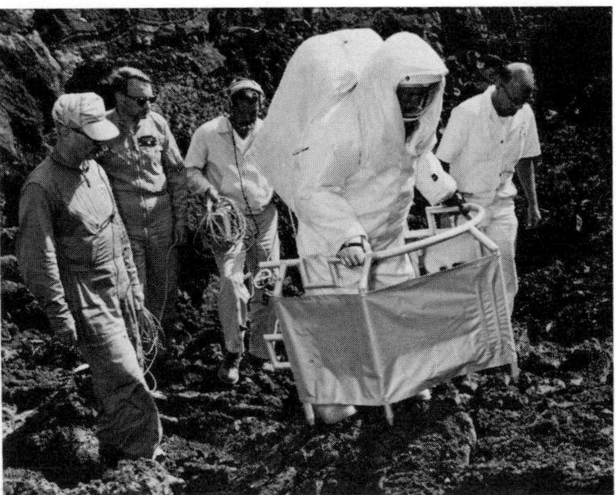

Fig. 13-30. A Luna-Walker is tested on the lava beds of McKenzie Pass to determine how well it functions. (Courtesy of the National Aeronautics and Space Administration.)

Fig. 13-31. Astronaut Walter Cunningham tests the maneuverability of a pressurized suit while using a Jacob's Staff. (Courtesy of the National Aeronautics and Space Administration.)

Vision. Practically all designs involving manual operation utilize visual gauges, controls, and components. The use of colored lights to convey information necessitates the selection of colors which would be most recognizable to the average person. Control panels, such as that shown in Fig. 13-17, are designed to conform to the visual ranges of the average person. The consideration of visual ranges in highway design is extremely important. An example is given in Fig. 13-32, which shows a parapet with maximum visibility. The concrete portion of the parapet is designed to divert the automobile rather than allowing it to crash through the parapet, which would cause more serious injury.

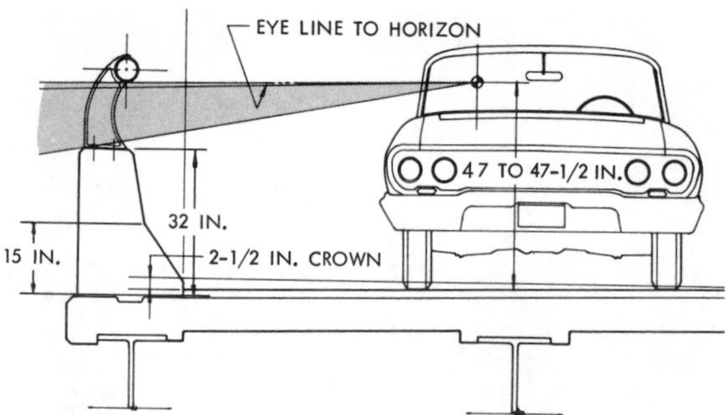

Fig. 13-32. The 32″ parapet height required to prevent impacting vehicles from climbing over the wall also provides adequate visibility for the car's occupants. The 15″ elevation eliminates sheet-metal contact with the upper portion of the parapet should a vehicle wheel contact the base of the barrier. (Courtesy of General Motor's *Engineering Journal*.)

Sound. Sound must be received within specified frequencies to be clearly audible under a given set of circumstances. Much research is being conducted on the human engineering aspects of sound and sound control. Figure 13-33 illustrates a unique system that has been tested experimentally to determine how a driver is affected by brief verbal warnings transmitted to him while he is traveling on a toll road. The sound receiver, which can be installed in an automobile in seconds at the start of the toll road, transmits messages that will assist the driver in adhering to the safety regulations. Tests have indicated that a brief vocal message is likely to be more informative and cause drivers to react more quickly than any roadside warning lights or buzzers actuated by radio signals. Since production efficiency is affected by noise control or the lack of it, sound can be closely related to working environment, which is discussed next.

Working Environment. Working environment may include the total industrial plant layout, the conditions in a particular work station, or a specialized location, such as the cockpit of an airplane. The environment includes (1) temperature, (2) lighting, (3) color scheme, (4) sound control, and (5) comfort of operation. This is the most comprehensive area of human engineering, and it involves all the previously covered aspects of this area of analysis. Psychological needs must also be satisfied as well.

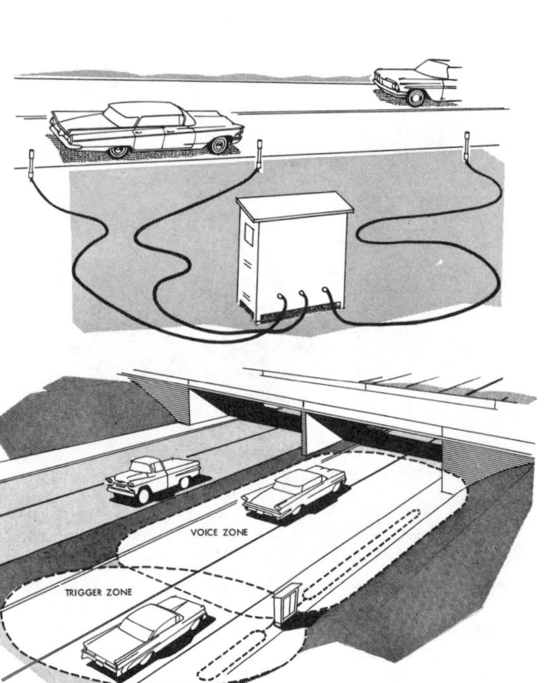

Fig. 13-33. The transmitters of the Hy-Com highway-to-car system can be operated either by ferrite core antennas (top) or by radiating loops laid along the roadside (bottom). With the latter type of installation, a loop is extended about 50′ from the communications enclosure toward oncoming traffic. This length of road is called the trigger zone. As soon as a car enters this zone a signal is picked up that sensitizes the receiver, which was placed inside the car at the beginning of the toll road, to receive a voice message. The message is transmitted as soon as the car enters the voice zone. The loop radiating the voice message can extend any reasonable distance. For a 500′ length, for example, a car traveling 65 mph could receive a six-second message before it passed out of the voice range. (Courtesy of General Motors' *Engineering Journal*.)

Attractive, pleasant surroundings, such as those shown in Fig. 13–34, are more likely to contribute to efficiency than cluttered, distasteful, or noisy environments. Temperature can greatly affect the fatigue limits of the average person performing his tasks. This area is undergoing extensive research so that more definite characteristics of an ideal environment may be identified and thus greater efficiency may be promoted.

Man's environmental comfort zone is based on many interrelated factors which affect his efficiency. The limits of this comfort zone may be depicted graphically as in the diagram by Henry Dreyfuss shown in Fig. 13–35. The inner circle of this diagram represents the comfort zone, while the outer circle is the bearable zone limit. Outside this limit great discomfort or possible damage is encountered. Other considerations that affect man's environment include infrared radiation, ultrasonic vibration, noxious gases, dust, pollen, and heat exchange with liquids and solids. These factors as well as those in the diagram must be considered when designing for human activity and environments.

Fig. 13–34. The working environment has an effect on the work being performed. (Courtesy of the Austin Company.)

13–8 MARKET AND PRODUCT ANALYSIS

A design that has been developed to a point where the final analysis will depend upon its acceptance by the general market must be analyzed with respect to marketability. This analysis will certainly involve the evaluation of the attitude of the potential customer toward it, but this is only a part of the final analysis of a new product. A given product must be analyzed to determine information that relates to all areas of manufacturing and distribution to the market before it is accepted for production. Areas of analysis of a product are: (1) potential-market evaluation, (2) cost analysis, (3) market outlets, (4) advertising, and (5) sales features. These areas apply primarily to commercial products that are developed through engineering and technology; however, these same considerations generally apply to any engineering project to some extent.

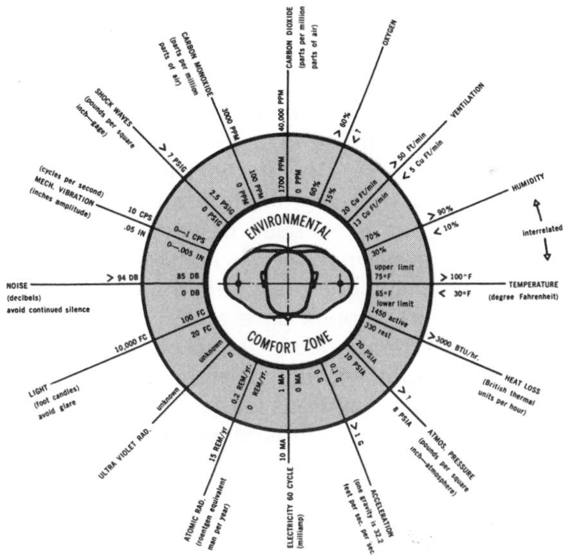

Fig. 13–35. The environment comfort zone is represented by the inner circle while the outer circle is the bearable zone limit of human environment. (Courtesy of Henry Dreyfuss and the Whitney Library of Design from *The Measure of Man*, New York, 1967.)

Fig. 13-36. Market potential must be evaluated before it is possible to proceed with mass production. The potential market for the doll shown here on the production lines was thoroughly investigated before tooling was begun. (Courtesy of Mattel, Inc.)

Potential-Market Evaluation. This information is often determined at the outset of a design project, as was discussed in Chapter 4. Potential-market evaluation will remain a primary consideration during the entire design process if the design is intended for consumption by the general market. It is very helpful to test consumer reaction to several alternative designs if the prototypes have been developed and are available; in this manner it is possible to choose the most acceptable design among those offering satisfactory appearance and function. The consumer's choice can be obtained by contacting samples of potential consumers and tabulating their reactions to the various features that have been incorporated in each design.

General information about the market should be determined, including predicted age groups, income levels, geographical locations, and other characteristics of the consumer who would purchase this product. This information will be helpful in modifying the design to meet the requirements of the market. Secondary markets can be evaluated on the same basis. These are markets in which the product may be used for an application other than the one for which it was designed. Market information will also be helpful in planning advertising campaigns to reach and appeal to the consumer. Failure to thoroughly analyze the market potential could be extremely costly, especially in the production of products for the general market, such as the toy industry (Fig. 13-36).

Market Outlets. The market survey, discussed in Chapter 4, suggests major distribution outlets through which the product can be made available to the market. Rather than being distributed through existing retail outlets, specialized products may require the establishment of a separate sales organization related to the manufacturer which would be responsible for supplying technical assistance and information to the customer. For example, electronic computers are not suitable for distribution through conventional retail outlets; instead, technical representatives work as consultants with the client who will use the equipment. On the other hand, a camping seat or other unique item to be used by the sportsman can be sold effectively through department and sporting-goods outlets with little need for technical representatives.

The designer must work closely with the marketing and sales people of his organization when he is developing a consumer product, in order to provide the best relationship between the product and the user. Market experience and research can be applied to the design so that as many of the desirable features as possible can be incorporated to ensure a marketable product.

Unique Features. To have a high probability for success, an item which is developed to compete with existing designs must incorporate unique features that are more attractive to the consumer than those available in competing products. A listing of unique features should be maintained throughout the design process to support the feasibility of the proposed design. These unique features will be used to stimulate interest in the product and to attract consumers through emphasis given in advertising publicity.

Economy of purchase and ease of operation are vital features to any design. Any of the characteristics of compactness, flexibility, attractiveness, mobility, stability, etc., may be very important to some designs and quite unimportant to others. Consequently, the needs of the design must always be clearly established in a designer's mind to prevent a loss of effort through misdirection.

Advertising. When the market has been evaluated, market outlets recommended, and unique features described, the method of introduction to the market must be considered. This is usually an advertising problem that is handled by an agency. Nevertheless, the total requirements of a market-and-product analysis should be the designer's concern as well. Advertising can be conducted through personal contact, direct mail contact, or advertising through the news media —radio, television, newspapers, and periodicals. The particular medium through which to advertise should be carefully chosen. A product developed for the housewife can be advertised through magazines that appeal to this market; however, a product designed for the professional man would be much less effectively advertised through the same medium. Selection of the appropriate medium must also be measured with regard to the comparative costs for the advertising desired. Timing is important for products that tend to be used on a seasonal rather than a year-round basis.

Cost Analysis. An estimated retail price can be derived after analysis of the preceding data, but a firm retail price cannot be established until a thorough cost analysis has been completed. Expenses to be considered in the cost analysis include those for production, raw materials, advertising, shipping, storage and warehousing, salary overhead, sales commissions for the sales outlet, and other miscellaneous expenditures.

Commissions vary with the nature of the product; however, most consumer products sold through the usual retail outlets allow between 20 and 50 percent markup. For example, an item that retails for $10 will give the retailer a $4 commission when a 40 percent markup is allowed. The manufacturer will receive only $6, from which the product manufacturing and promotional costs must be paid. The freight from the factory to a distributor elsewhere in the country may be either a negligible amount or a considerable sum. The methods of shipment must be studied to permit a reasonable estimate to be made and included in the cost of the product.

A manufacturer must provide storage space for warehousing an inventory of products that will be distributed as needed by his distributors. Warehousing can be an expensive item unless the product incorporates features that permit it to be stored unassembled, in which state it will require less space. Usually, an easily assembled design is also more easily packaged for shipment, and overhead expenses are correspondingly lower. The designer should keep such facts in mind throughout the design process and incorporate as many economical features as possible. This will help to ensure a sufficient profit margins for the producer and retailer, while keeping the product economically priced for the consumer. A general price estimate for a product can be obtained from evaluating the costs of other products on the market having similar characteristics, materials, and production requirements.

Market and product information should be compiled in good form for presentation through the use of graphical methods. Chapter 16 discusses the technical report that will be used as the basis for a final decision on a given design. Graphs should be prepared to present an understandable picture of the potential of the product for acceptance. The accompanying text should analyze the data and point out significant trends and findings that will contribute to the success of the design.

13-9 MODELS

Models are effective aids not only in analyzing a design in preliminary stages, but also in presenting the finished product or system in a three-dimensional form for easy comprehension. A design should be studied for proportion, operation, size, function, and efficiency through scale models, which can vary from a fraction of

Fig. 13-37. A full-scale model of a rapid-transit car made from aluminum. (Courtesy of ALCOA.)

Fig. 13-38. Strain gauges are attached to a lucite model of a structure to determine strains under various loadings in a test laboratory. (Courtesy of Bureau of Reclamation.)

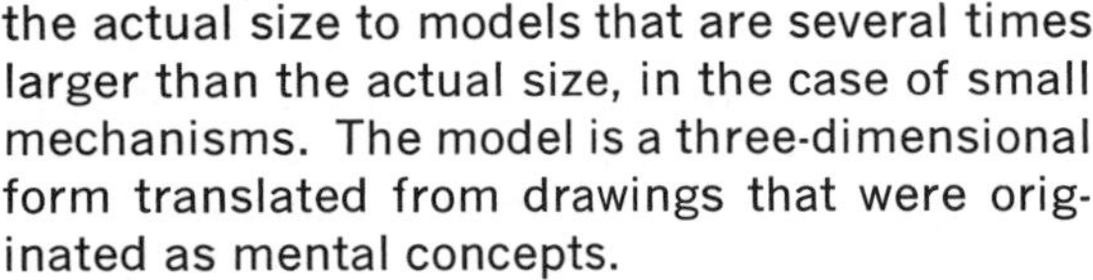

the actual size to models that are several times larger than the actual size, in the case of small mechanisms. The model is a three-dimensional form translated from drawings that were originated as mental concepts.

The analysis of a model can be used to determine clearances or relationships that affect the interaction between parts. A better idea of proportions can be determined when the actual-size design is studied respective to its use by constructing a full-scale mock-up, such as that as shown in Fig. 13-37. Actual components of the proposed design can be constructed and tested under repetitive tests to determine the strength capabilities and the fatigue limits of the design. In the example of laboratory testing shown in Fig. 13-38 a component is being tested to determine its characteristics of performance under severe conditions. Data gathered from experimental tests can be used to predict the probability of success of a given design. This method of analysis will be discussed in Chapter 15.

Models will vary in scale and in the detail of presentation, depending on the purpose of the model. The materials can also vary from paper and balsa wood to the actual specified materials. In general, the basic types of models are:

1. Preliminary models
2. Scale models
3. Mock-ups
4. Prototypes
5. System layout models

Preliminary Models. A preliminary model is a rough model that is made by the designer at any stage of the design process to help him analyze a design feature (Fig. 13-39). Models of this type are primarily for the designer's own use rather than as a means of presenting his ideas. Preliminary models may incorporate only a single feature of the total design to gain a better understanding of its shape, operation, or fabrication; they can be made of any material.

Scale Models. Scale models are constructed for analysis or for the presentation of a refined design. Balsa wood and the usual model materials can be used to good advantage in developing a scale model. The scale selected should be sufficiently large to permit the operations and movements of the design to be demonstrated. A one-twentieth-size engineering model of the Apollo Block-1 Spacecraft Command Module is shown in Fig. 13-40.

Fig. 13–39. This preliminary model of a processing plant is an engineering tool whereby the designer, by using basic design data and flow sheets, can quickly assemble alternative arrangements of equipment and related facilities in three-dimensional form. (Courtesy of Bechtel Corporation.)

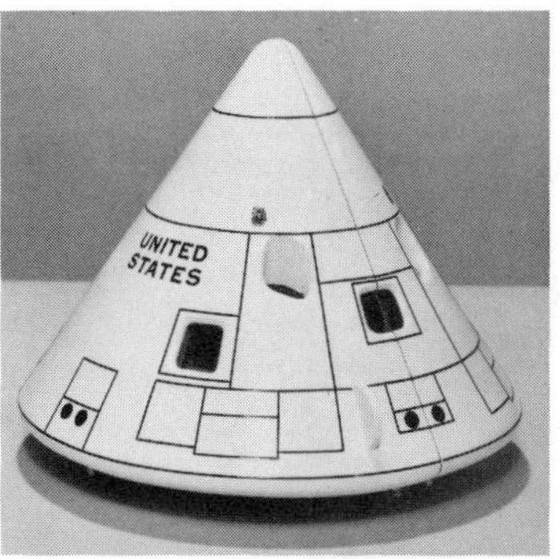

Fig. 13–40. A one-twentieth-size engineering model of the Apollo Block-1 Spacecraft 012 Command Module. (Courtesy of the National Aeronautics and Space Administration.)

Mock-ups. Mock-ups are full-size "dummies" of the finished design that will give the general appearance of the total product. Mock-ups are constructed more for size, shape, appearance, and component relationships than for operational movements. Modifications in size and configuration can be determined by studying the full-size mock-up.

Automobile manufacturers use mock-ups to aid in the styling of auto bodies. In Fig. 13–41 designers at the Ford Motor Company prepare a full-size mock-up of a body design to permit a more thorough evaluation. Interiors are also modeled in clay to give the final impression (Fig. 13–42). Drawings, sketches, and artistic renderings are prepared in great detail to serve as guides in the preparation of these highly realistic mock-ups.

Fig. 13–41. A full-size mock-up in clay of a new body style is used to analyze its appearance. (Courtesy of Ford Motor Company.)

Prototypes. A prototype is a full-size working model that follows the final specifications in all respects. The only exceptions may be in the use of materials. A prototype is made mostly by hand prior to acceptance for mass production; consequently, materials that are easier to fabricate by hand are used in place of those that will

Fig. 13–42. Automobile interiors are modeled in clay to simulate the final design. (Courtesy of Ford Motor Company.)

Fig. 13-43. A systems layout model is used to analyze the details of construction. (Courtesy of E. I. Du Pont de Nemours and Company.)

Fig. 13-44. Models may be used to supplement working drawings and can serve as a means of developing the finished drawings. (Courtesy of E. I. Du Pont de Nemours and Company.)

Fig. 13-45. Models whose purpose is to show the general relationship between buildings or large structures are built at a small scale. (Courtesy of Esso Research, New Jersey.)

be used in final production. The prototype is the last chance for variation in design. Sometimes prototypes of an operational design provide data that can be used for analysis, as will be discussed in Chapter 15.

System Layout Models. System layout models are a special kind of scale model, and are used to show relationships between buildings, manufacturing systems, traffic systems, or industrial processes. Models of refineries are often constructed to supplement working drawings during construction. Models of this type are also used to help the designer determine the clearances necessary for a functional system. Examples of refinery and processing systems are shown in Figs. 13-43 and 13-44. Photographs of detailed sections of models can be superimposed on working drawings to explain certain complicated features that would otherwise require considerable study for comprehension.

The scale selected for the system layout model will depend on the purpose of the finished model. If the model will show only a general relationship between buildings or large structures, a rather small scale of about $\frac{1}{16}''$ per foot or less is used. An example of this type of model is the system layout in Fig. 13-45. If the model is to be used for accurate analysis of clearance between related parts that will be used in the final design, the scale should be somewhat larger. The scale model of the Hoover Dam, shown in Fig. 13-46, was used for analysis and presentation to describe the final appearance of the dam and the surrounding terrain.

Interiors of manufacturing plants or other architectural interior systems are built at a scale of $\frac{1}{4}''$ per foot. These models conform to the usual scale used in the working drawings. Architectural models can be built from commercially available components that add realism and reduce model construction time.

13-10 MODEL CONSTRUCTION

The student should develop preliminary models as a means of evaluating his design and analyzing its function. The same models can be used to aid in the decision process (Chapter 18), when the design concept is presented to a group. Models can give a designer a "feel" for scale, appearance, and proportion that cannot be achieved through other methods. Models prepared by students to represent design solutions can be made with a minimum of expense.

Model Materials. Most communities have model supply dealers who will probably be able to furnish most of the materials required for a student model. Balsa wood is commonly used in such models because it can be easily shaped as desired, with the minimum of equipment. Razor blades and simple model tools are more than ample for model construction with balsa wood, and balsa-wood parts can be easily glued to form completed shapes.

Standard parts such as wheels, tubing, scale figures, dowels, and other structural shapes used in model construction can be purchased commercially to reduce construction time and effort. The designer may need some special parts that cannot be found in the model shop. In some cases, he can find the appropriate components, wheels, or mechanisms on a readily available toy that can be purchased at a nominal cost. There are few set rules as to how the model builder should achieve his completed model, so this entire area is open to his innovation and imagination.

Other workable materials that can be used for models are aluminum, clay and plaster, and wood. Aluminum sheets and tubing are usually used for special components rather than for an entire model. Clay and plaster are effective in molding a plastic shape, such as the automobile body illustrated in Fig. 13–41. Plywood and solid wood have many applications in larger models and in working models which have movable parts. Wood, even a soft wood like pine, requires more specialized tools than balsa wood since it is considerably harder and is therefore more difficult to carve or cut.

When they are to be used in the presentation portion of the design process, models should be finished to give a faithful impression of the finished design. In other cases, such as when

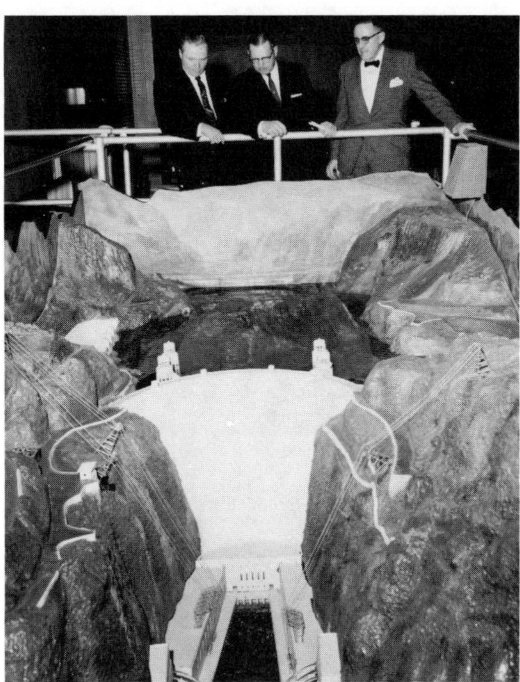

Fig. 13–46. This working scale model of the Hoover Dam was built to show the final appearance of the dam and surrounding terrain. (Courtesy of the Bureau of Reclamation, Department of Interior.)

Fig. 13–47. A $\frac{1}{8}$-size model of the Mariner spacecraft. (Courtesy of the National Aeronautics and Space Administration.)

Fig. 13-48. A student model of a design for a portable home caddy in its collapsed position.

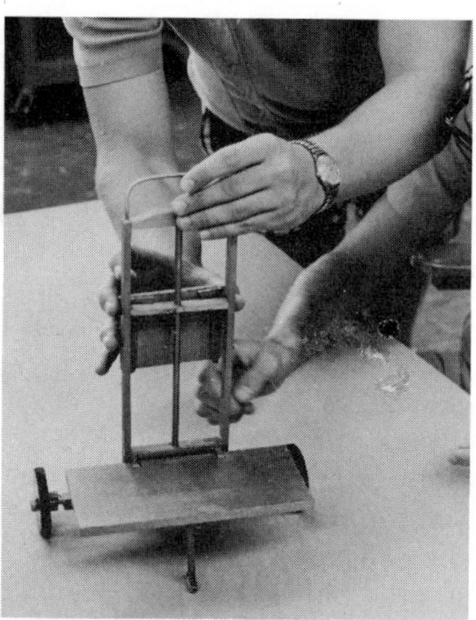

Fig. 13-49. The home caddy in an operating position.

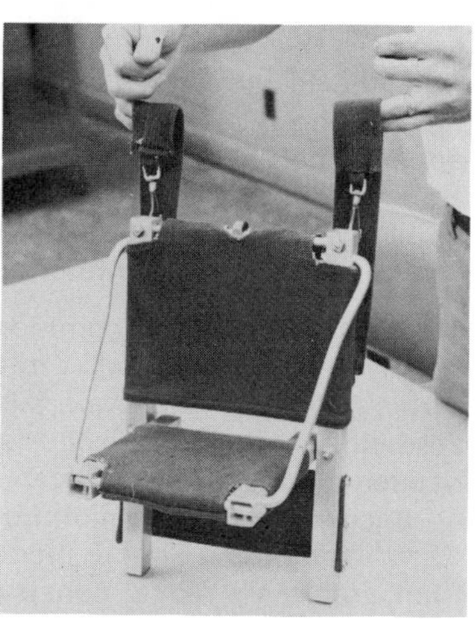

Fig. 13-50. A scale model of a student team's preliminary design of a hunting seat to be attached to a tree.

the model is constructed to analyze function, this will not be as important. An excellent example of a model that is both functional and representative of the final design is the Mariner model, which is constructed at $\frac{1}{8}$-size (Fig. 13-47). Details are shown to completely explain all portions of the design. Student models can effectively be finished by sanding all surfaces and painting the model to simulate the materials that will be used in the final product.

Model Scale. The scale selected by the designer will have a significant effect on the final result and the value of his model. A model that is used to analyze moving parts of a functional product should be scaled such that the smallest moving part may be analyzed. An example of a student model is the portable home caddy shown in Figs. 13-48 and 13-49. This simple balsa-wood model features a linkage system that permits the wheels to be collapsed into a flat position, thereby reducing the amount of storage space required. The wheels are controlled by the knob at the handle. Although this model is relatively small, the linkage system can be operated in the same way as in the completed product. As a general rule, models should be constructed to be at least 12" in overall size. By necessity, models of systems, such as those covered in Article 13-9, need to be considerably larger to depict sufficient detail.

Model Analysis. A student model of the hunting seat introduced in Chapter 2 is shown in its preliminary form in Fig. 13-50. It was constructed of canvas and aluminum scraps obtained from a local manufacturer; the design specifies that the final product also be made of aluminum and canvas. Details of fabrication that could be improved or modified became apparent from studying this scale model. These changes were incorporated in the full-scale prototype shown in Fig. 13-51. Human factors affecting the comfort and function of the seat could be identified by testing the model in actual use. A secondary use of the seat as a back pack could also be studied for comfort as could the method of securing the pack to the hunter's back (Fig. 13-52). The system of anchoring the seat to the tree could be tested and modified by actual application, a necessity since this could not be determined otherwise with complete assurance.

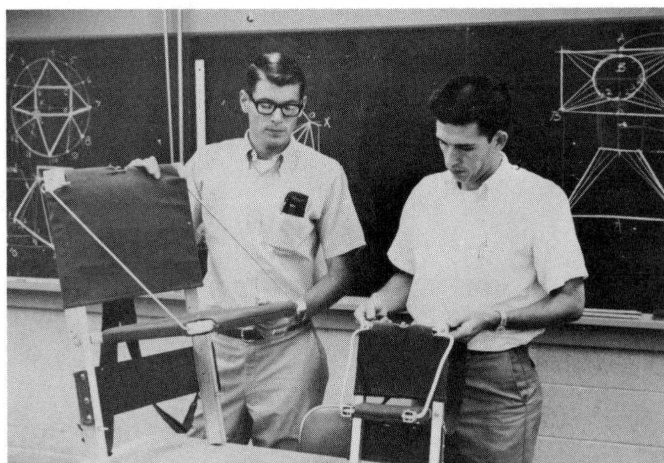

Fig. 13-51. An analysis of the scale model resulted in the development of a full-size prototype for detailed analysis, held here by designers Keith Sherman and Larry Oakes.

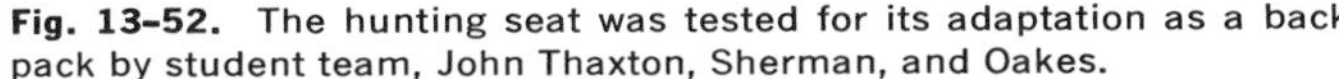

Fig. 13-52. The hunting seat was tested for its adaptation as a back pack by student team, John Thaxton, Sherman, and Oakes.

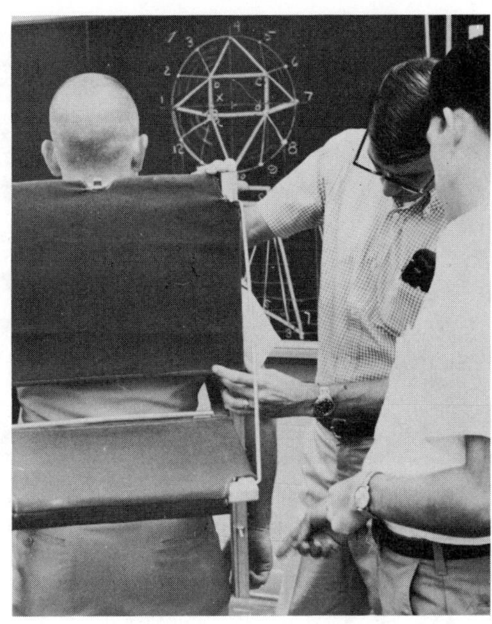

Manufacturing methods of assembling and fabricating the seats are easily improved upon when the completed model was available at the time of consultation with manufacturer's representatives, who are experienced in mass-production.

Models can also be used to test the consumer's reaction to a new product before proceeding with production. Although drawings, photographs, and artistic sketches are helpful in communicating concepts to the general public, the true test of acceptance can come only from reaction to the actual product. As we mentioned previously, it is advantageous to present more than one design to the public to determine preferences for details that would influence the mass production of the product.

A student will find it a profitable experience to carry his design from his initial mental concept through the appropriate drawings to a completed scale model that will demonstrate his design in a tangible form. By this process he will gain exposure to as much of the complete design process as he can without actually being involved in a manufacturing situation. The development of a finished, working model requires that he cope successfully with design problems during the formulation stage; otherwise his design will not function. With this as a test of his effort, he approaches his design under realistic conditions which will provide challenges similar to those he will encounter as a practicing engineer.

13-11 ANALYSIS BY COMPUTER

The computer has been utilized to solve increasingly more of the engineer's problems, providing him with additional time for truly creative engineering work. Computers provide the designer with quick answers to programmed equations and rapid recall of information stored in the computer's memory bank. Initially, computers were used primarily to solve problems in terms of numbers, and little graphical representation was possible; however, graphical representations are now possible on many models (Fig. 13-53).

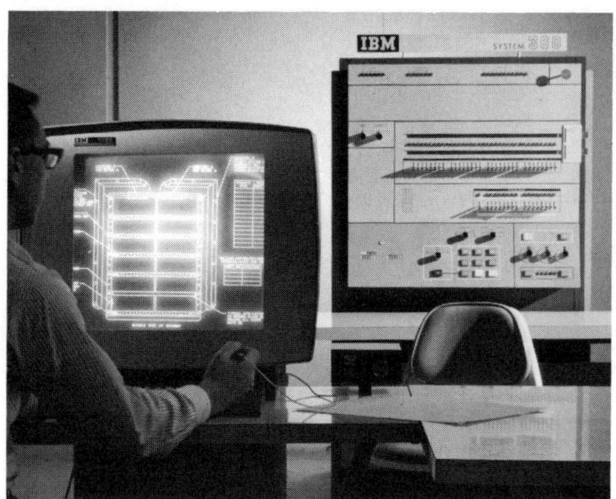

Fig. 13-53. Analysis by a System 360 Model 44 computer allows a graphic display of scientific problems. (Courtesy of IBM.)

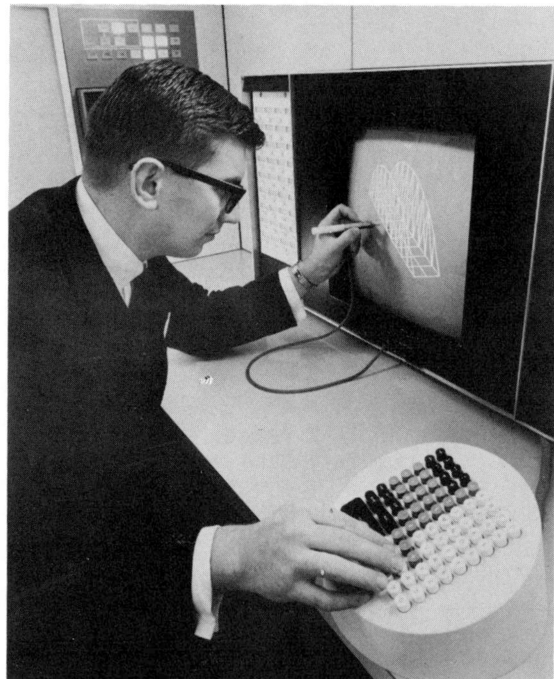

Fig. 13-54. Using a light pen, a sensitized cathode-ray tube (CRT), and the full power of a large-scale computer, a designer can draw a design and finish it in seconds, whereas the conventional method would have taken hours. (Courtesy of IBM.)

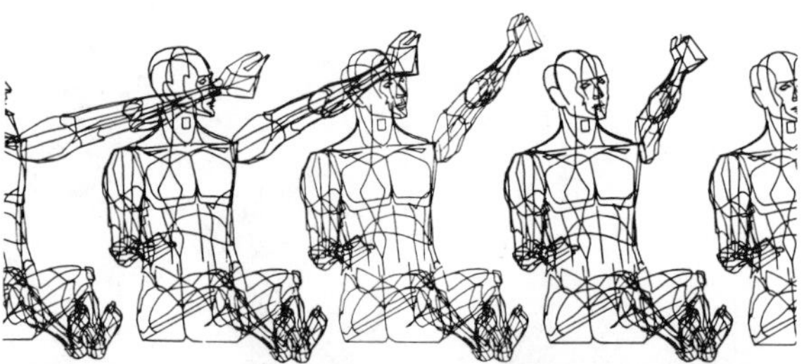

Fig. 13-55. The Boeing Company has successfully programmed an average human figure that can be drawn by a computer-driven plotter in an infinite number of positions for analysis of human factors. (Courtesy of the Boeing Company.)

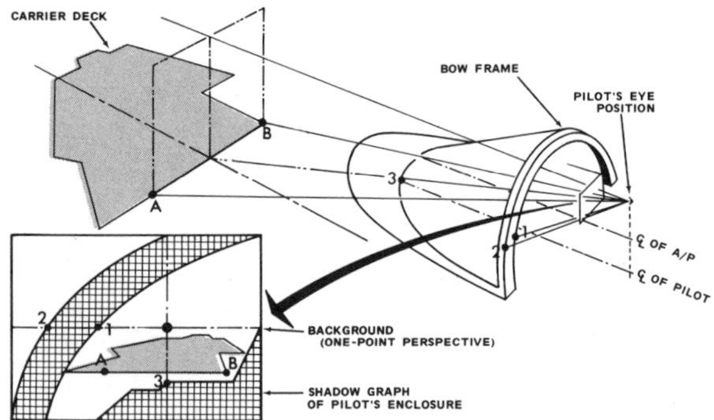

Fig. 13-56. Computer graphics has been used to simulate a pilot's vision of an aircraft carrier's deck through a series of perspectives. (Courtesy of General Dynamics Corporation.)

Three-dimensional displays have been developed to provide the designer with an actual picture of his design that he can modify as he desires (Fig. 13–54) with a light pen on a sensitized cathode-ray tube. This system permits him to revolve the design in space and actually see it from any desired angle so that he can further analyze the design. Human factors have been programmed into the computer graphics system operated by the Boeing Company to permit the analysis of an average man in various positions (Fig. 13–55). Commands to the computer can place the man in an infinite number of positions, and in postures typical of those he would assume during the performance of his tasks. Similar applications have been made of computer graphics by General Dynamics in analyzing the effect on visibility caused by the configuration of an aircraft windshield at different levels of approach to a carrier landing deck (Fig. 13–56). Computer constructed perspectives are programmed from different positions to provide the views the pilot will have of the aircraft carrier from the usual landing approach until touchdown. A series of these computer generator drawings can be sequenced together and filmed to give a realistic animation of the pilot's view of his landing as if photographed with a motion picture camera. Manual solution to a problem of this type would require unlimited time and expense, and would therefore be impractical.

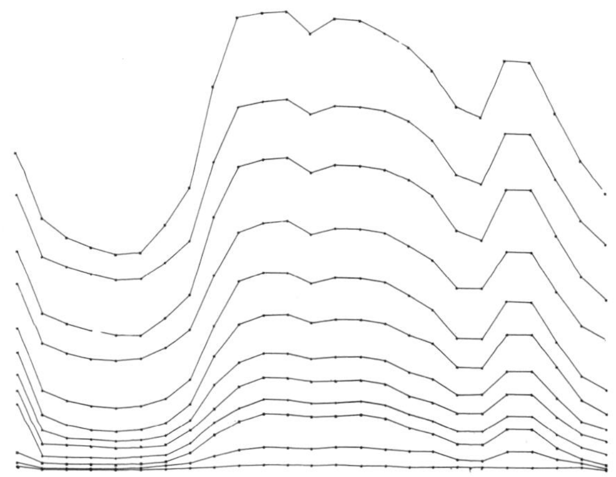

Fig. 13–57. A computer's plot to analyze power consumption versus time at half-hour intervals during a 24-hr monitoring period. (Courtesy of Electronic Associates, Inc.)

An example of two-dimensional computer graphics is illustrated in Fig. 13–57 where the plots of power consumption versus time have been recorded for a number of power stations. The data are presented graphically to provide immediate analysis of the results of the monitoring during a 24-hr period. The plotting was done in three minutes by the Dataplotter of Electronic Associates. This plotter can also be used to plot perspectives, such as that in Fig.

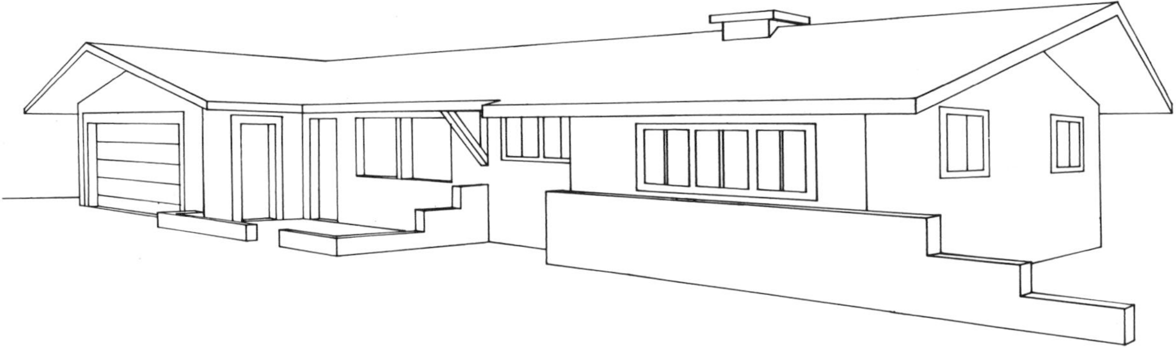

Fig. 13–58. This ranch house was plotted from data read from a punched tape. Each *X*- and *Y*-coordinate was presented as three decimal digits plus a sign. (Courtesy of Electronic Associates, Inc.)

Fig. 13-59. A typical computer system for graphical displays. This is a TR-20 desk-top analog computing system with a Variplotter (*X–Y* recorder) and scope display. (Courtesy of Electronic Associates, Inc.)

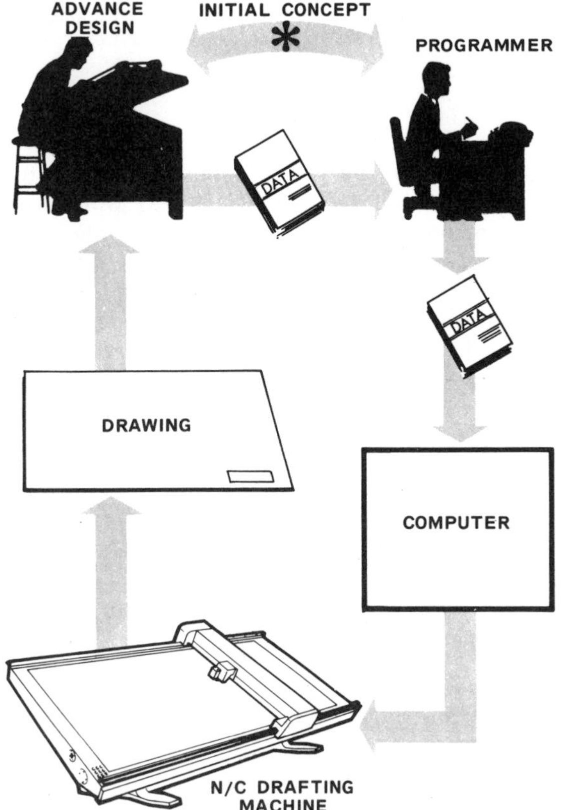

Fig. 13-60. A schematic depicting the relationship between the computer and designer, working in conjunction with a numerical control system. (Courtesy of General Dynamics Corporation.)

13-58, or highway cross sections, which are necessary for highway design. The computing system shown in Fig. 13-59 is typical of those utilized in engineering design.

The computer has been applied for design assistance as a time-saving tool in many industries. An example of the relationship between the computer and the designer can be seen in the schematic in Fig. 13-60. The designer develops a new design concept and works in conjunction with a programmer, who provides him with computer techniques to assist with the formulation of the design. The designer furnishes the data and specifications to the programmer, who in turn supplies the data in computer language to the computer. The computer processes the data and feeds them to a numerically controlled drafting machine that will prepare a drawing. The designer checks this drawing for correctness and then analyzes the initial design and modifies it if necessary. This loop is repeated until the designer arrives at the optimum design to meet his requirements.

A further extension of this designer-computer relationship can be seen in Fig. 13-61. The initial loop is continued until the designer is satisfied with his design. At this point, the drawing produced by the numerically controlled drafting machine is returned to the designer or to his section to be reviewed and completed by adding dimensions, notes, and other specifications. The finished drawings and a numerical-control dimensioned drawing are used by the tool-programming group to program cutter paths for a machined part in terms of tool dimensions, feeds, speeds, and machine requirements. These data are fed to the computer and finally released to the milling machine that will produce the machined part.

The computer has released the designer and engineer from many repetitive chores which have reduced his creative productivity in the past. He can now function much more effectively, since he can use the computer as an aid for retrieval of stored knowledge and drawings, for solving problems, and for performing logic operations. However, the data and graphical

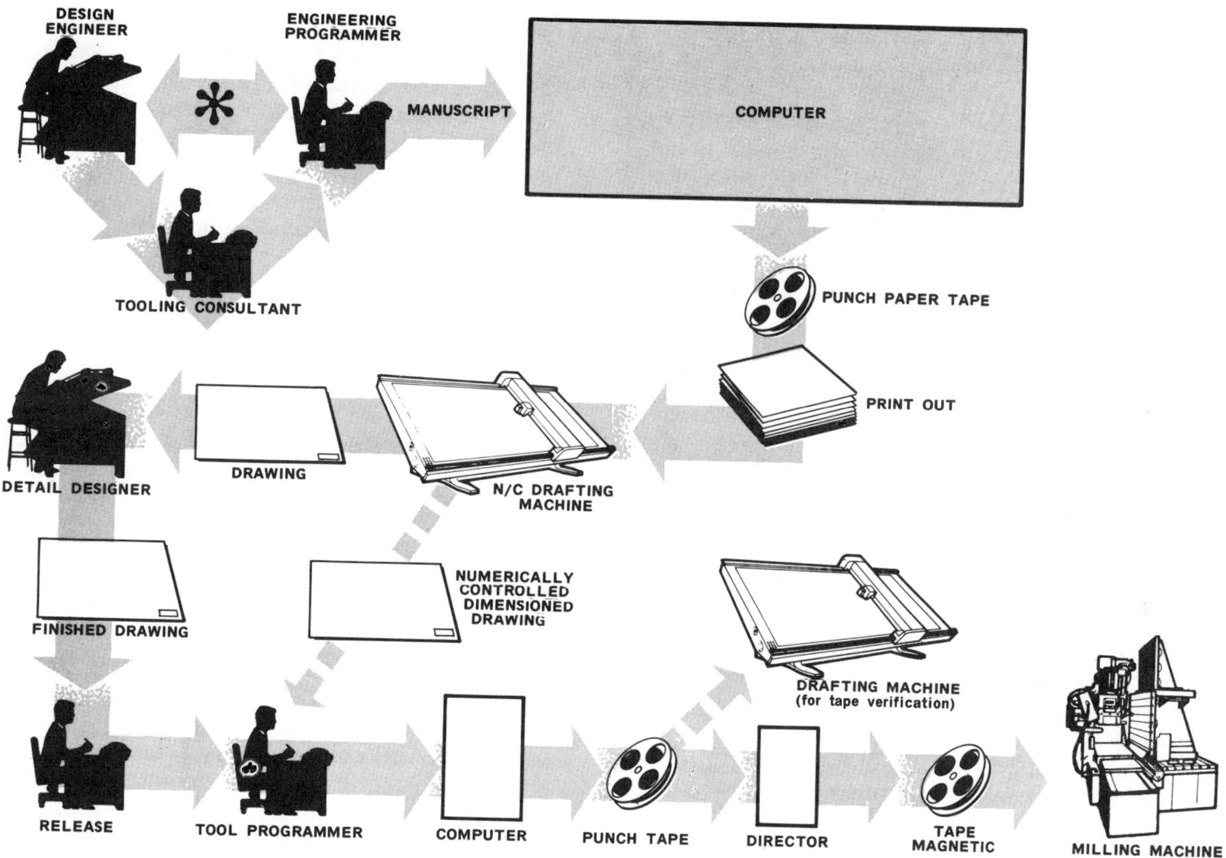

Fig. 13-61. The total system of a numerically controlled machining operation, from the designer to the milling machine. (Courtesy of General Dynamics Corporation.)

information supplied by a computer will only be as accurate as the data fed into it; consequently, the engineer must develop the ability to evaluate this output for its level of correctness. And although the computer has many unique applications, it cannot think. Therefore, the engineer must continue to rely on his own mental processes. It is he, not the computer, who is responsible for the final acceptance or rejection of a design concept. He will base his decision not only on information supplied from the computer and other sources, but also on his own past experience.

13-12 RELATIONSHIP OF GRAPHICS TO COMPUTERS

Much time is saved by computer-aided graphics. The engineer and draftsman are relieved of the necessity of hand producing many drawings that can be made by the computer. However, this does not lessen the engineer's need for knowledge of the principles of graphical representation. In fact, he must have a *better* understanding of the theory of graphics and descriptive geometry before he can successfully program these relationships into a computer. The computer produces drawings in much the same manner as a draftsman would produce them and, as is true with any engineering project, the responsibility for checking and approving a drawing lies with the engineer assigned to that particular project. An incomplete or unclear drawing can cause expensive mistakes. The engineer must have a command of the graphical language and an understanding of spatial relationships in order to check a computer drawing.

It should be stressed that true creative design cannot be performed by a computer. The computer is best suited for repetitive operations based on factual information and specific equations. It can merely provide combinations of information that have previously been fed to it, and is incapable of generating original concepts of its own. The graphical process, then, is used to create the initial ideas, and the computer is used to reduce time and effort in carrying out those ideas.

13-13 PRODUCT DESIGN—ANALYSIS

In previous chapters, examples of a product design problem and a systems design problem have been used to illustrate methods of solution through the application of the principles given in each chapter. The last stage we discussed for the product design—a hunting seat—was refinement (Chapter 6). The hunting-seat design poses a considerable number of human engineering problems that must be solved, since the sole purpose of the seat is to provide safety and comfort to a hunter who is hunting from a tree. Graphical methods are very helpful in preparing drawings that conform to body dimensions and positions, but in all cases dealing with human engineering, there is no substitute for actual testing of the finished product. In classes that have worked on the hunting-seat problem, this testing was conducted by the student team assigned to the project.

The hunting seat was developed from a preliminary model (Fig. 13-50) into a full-scale prototype (Fig. 13-51). The small-scale model was helpful in analyzing the linkage system and the methods of fabrication, while the full-scale prototype was necessary to test for human engineering considerations. Since the seat had a dual role as a back-pack and seat, it was also tested for carrying comfort and adaptation to the human back (Fig. 13-52). Further analysis of this design and model involved graphical evaluation of the vector forces present in each structural member when the seat was attached to a tree and a hunter was in position. This will be covered in greater detail in Chapter 14.

13-14 SYSTEMS DESIGN—ANALYSIS

Human engineering and other areas of analysis can be applied to the parking lot design which was first introduced in Chapter 2. This problem is restated here:

Parking Lot Design. Select a building on your campus that is in need of an improved parking lot to accommodate the people who are housed in the building. This may be a dormitory, an office building, or a classroom building. Design a combination traffic and parking system that will be adequate for the requirements of the building. The solution of this problem must adhere to existing limitations, regulations, and policies of your campus in order that the problem may be as realistic as possible.

The analysis of a parking lot problem will include most of the items covered in this chapter, but it will utilize descriptive geometry less than the hunting-seat problem did. Analysis of the parking space width is illustrated in Fig. 13-62 as an example of how an optimum dimension for the width is verified. If a space of 8.5′ were selected for a car 6.5′ wide, this would allow a space of 2′ on either side of the car when each car is parked in the center of its space. Of course, it is understood that this will not always be the case. Therefore, the extreme condition must be analyzed. As shown in the second part of this work sheet, this condition exists when the two outside cars crowd a middle parking space to the limit. If the middle car is maneuvered to park on the right side of the space, this will allow room for the driver to exit, but not the passengers on the right side of his car. Furthermore, the driver of the car at the

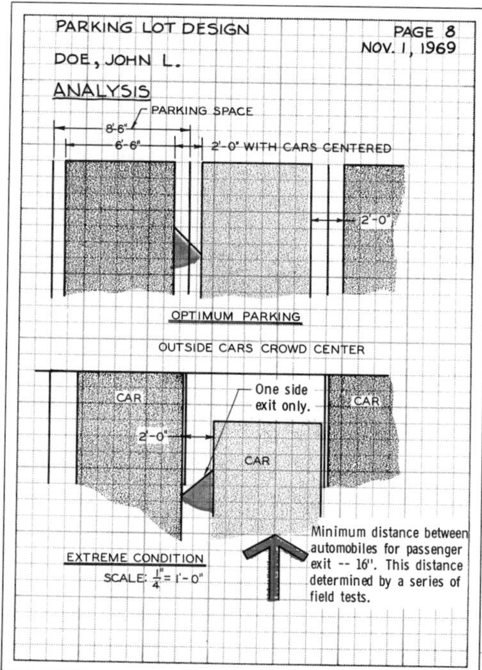

Fig. 13–62. An example analysis work sheet for the parking lot design problem introduced in Chapter 2.

right will find it necessary to enter his car from the right side, since the center car has parked as close as possible to the driver's side of the right car.

A series of field tests has been conducted to determine the minimum opening through which a passenger can exit from a car. These tests were made by parking at various distances from another parked car and having a passenger exit as he would normally. It was found that 16″ is about the minimum distance that will allow comfortable exit.

Other analyses of a graphical nature should also be performed. For example, attention should be given to the path of a car as it backs out of a space and the leeway for turning of corners when all spaces are full. An analysis would have to be made of the ability of cars to back from a space at the optimum parking condition and at the extreme parking condition, using the outside drive radius of 29′ as established on previous work sheets of this problem. This analysis will assure that the spaces and driving areas are adequate.

The analyses outlined thus far involve human engineering in relation to physical properties. Another indispensable analysis would be the comparison of costs for each proposed design in relationship to the convenience offered by each. This requires the engineer to exercise subjective judgment; there are no rules. Only through experience and observation of similar systems can he best make this assessment.

We have not discussed all analyses that would be needed for the refined parking lot designs. For example, perhaps a more extensive analysis of the number of spaces provided in the proposed lots would be worth while at this point. This would ensure that the lot was adequate without being excessive in size. All analysis work sheets should be added to the accumulation of materials for this problem.

13–15 SUMMARY

Once preliminary ideas have been conceived and developed, they must be analyzed to determine which of them provides the most acceptable design solution. The process of analysis can take many forms and utilize many principles. The general areas of analysis discussed in this chapter are: (1) human engineering, (2) market and product analysis, (3) prototype and model analysis, (4) physical quantities, (5) strength analysis, (6) function, and (7) economic analysis.

Human engineering is concerned with the adaption of designs to satisfy human needs of comfort and efficiency. The purpose of most designs is to serve man's needs; consequently, man's characteristics, measurements, and movements will be the limiting factors in selecting the best design. Market and product analysis is a continuation of the evaluation of the potential market for the product being designed; this area was introduced in Chapter 4. Regardless of the merits of the design, it must have sufficient acceptance to justify production or construction, and market analysis will give an indication of this important factor.

Model analysis is an effective method of studying a design for function, scale, and appearance. Tests can be made to gather experimental data for further analysis, as will be covered in Chapter 15. The analysis of physical quantities has been discussed in Chapters 6 through 12, where methods were introduced for finding lengths, sizes, angles, and other properties essential to the analysis of a design. Strength analysis and the application of vectorial methods to this area will be covered in Chapter 14. Function and economy are integral parts of the development and analysis of any design, and cannot be separated from the other steps. Consideration must be given to the efficiency of a design and to its possibilities of giving a profitable return to the manufacturer.

Engineering sciences and principles are used extensively to translate design properties into equations that can be analyzed in as many respects as possible. Graphical methods have valuable applications to each type of analysis.

In many cases, a graphical analysis may be a more convenient method of solving a given problem. The engineer should be proficient in graphical methods so that he may function effectively with as many tools of analysis at his disposal as possible. Chapters 14 and 15 will introduce applications of graphical methods to the analysis step of the design process.

PROBLEMS

The following problems should be solved on $8\frac{1}{2}'' \times 11''$ paper, accompanied by the necessary drawings, notes, and text. Answers to essay problems can be typed or lettered. All sheets should be stapled together or included in a binder or folder. Refer to Article 1-19.

General

1. Make a list of human factors that must be considered in the design of the following items: a canoe, a hairbrush, a water cooler, an automobile, a wheelbarrow, a drawing table, a study desk, a pair of binoculars, a baby stroller, a golf course, the seating in a stadium.

2. What physical quantities would have to be determined in the designs listed in Problem 1?

3. Select one of the items given in Problem 1 and make an outline of the various steps that should be taken to satisfy the following areas of analysis: (1) human engineering, (2) market analysis, (3) prototype analysis, (4) physical quantities, (5) strength, (6) function, and (7) economy.

Human Engineering

4. Using your body as the average, make a drawing to indicate the optimum working areas for you when in a sitting position at a drawing table. Assume that you are to use your measurements as a basis for a drawing table design to satisfy the needs of your class. This table will be marketed to schools similar to yours. Your reach, posture, and vision will have considerable effect upon the dimensions. Your finished drawing should give three views of the ideal working area for you while drawing; the drawing should also show the most efficient positioning of instruments for working. Experiment with the angle of tilt of the table top to determine the most comfortable position for working.

5. Using the dimensions for the average person given in this chapter, design a stadium seating arrangement that will serve the optimum needs of the spectators. Determine the dimensions shown in Fig. 13-63. A primary consideration will be the slope of the stadium seating, which should be designed to provide adequate vision of the playing field. The comfort of the average spectator and provision for traffic between seats must also be considered. It is desirable to get as many people in the stadium as possible while providing adequate comfort. Use the average dimensions given in this chapter and your own body dimensions to simulate these conditions in your classroom.

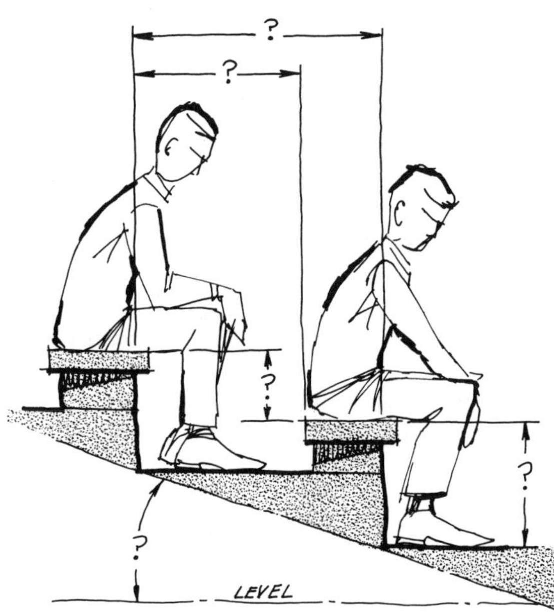

Fig. 13–63. Human engineering applied to stadium seating.

Fig. 13–64. Optimum size for a manhole access.

6. Compare the dimensions of the students in your class with the standards given in the Article 13–6. For example, compare the average height of your class with the national standard height.

7. Design a back pack that will be used on a camping trip. Decide what are the minimum belongings a camper should carry, and use their weights and volumes in establishing the design criteria. Make sketches of the pack and the method of attaching it to the body to provide the optimum in mobility, comfort, and capacity. Determine the optimum load a camper could carry on his back during a hike lasting several hours.

8. Establish the dimensions, facilities, and other provisions that would be needed in a one-man bomb shelter to provide protection for a period of 48 hr. Make sketches of the interior in relationship to a man and his supplies. How will ventilation, water, food, and other vital resources be provided? Explain your design as it relates to human engineering needs.

9. As an engineer you must design a manhole access to an underground facility (Fig. 13–64). What must the diameter of the manhole be to permit a man to climb a ladder for a distance of 10′ with freedom of movement? Make a sketch of your design and explain your method of solving your problem.

10. Assume that you are assigned to design a one-man facility for temporary observation service in the Arctic. This facility is to be absolutely as compact as possible to provide for the needs of a single man during 72-hr periods while he serves as an observer and operates a radio. Determine the facilities and provisions that he would need, including heat, ventilation, and insulation. Make sketches of your design and explain items that you consider to be essential to the human engineering aspects of the problem.

11. Design a configuration for an automobile steering wheel that would differ from present designs, but be just as functional. Base your design on human factors such as arm position, grip, and vision. Make sketches of your design and list items that you considered.

12. Make sketches to indicate safety features that could be built into your automobile to reduce the seriousness of injury caused by accidents. Explain your ideas and the advantages of your designs. Primary consideration should be given to the human aspects of the designs.

13. Assume that you prefer to alternate between a sitting and a standing position when working at a drawing table. Determine the ideal height of the table top for work in each position. Indicate how a table could be devised to permit instant conversion from the height for standing to the height for sitting.

14. Identify some human engineering problems that you recognize as being in need of solution. Present several of these to your instructor for his approval. Solve the problems he approves. Make a series of sketches and notes to explain your approach.
explain your approach.

Market Analysis

15. Assume that you are responsible for conducting a market analysis of the mixer shown in Fig. 13–18. Include in your analysis all of the areas covered in Article 13–8. Assume that this product is new and has never been introduced in an electrically powered form before. Outline the steps you would take in conducting this product and market analysis.

16. Make a product and market analysis of the hunting seat illustrated in Figs. 13–50 through 13–52, following the steps suggested in Article 13–8. Arrive at a market value that you feel would be satisfactory, and determine the outlets and other information of this type that would be important to your analysis.

17. Assume that the following cost estimates of producing hunting seats were given: 100 seats, $35 each; 200 seats, $20 each; 400 seats, $10 each; 1000 seats, $8.50 each. Using these figures, determine the price at which you could introduce the seats to the market on a trial basis and still have some financial protection. Explain your plan.

18. List as many unique features of the hunting seat as you possibly can that would be important to a sales campaign and to advertising. Make sketches and notes to explain these features.

Models

19. Give examples of items for which it would be necessary to build full-size prototypes for detailed analysis and testing before the product was produced. Give examples of products or designs that would not require a full-scale prototype, since a small-scale model could serve for analysis. Explain your answers.

20. List the scales and the materials that you would use to construct models of the items given in Problem 1. Explain your choices.

21. List several types of designs that you think would be most effectively presented in model form to a group of stockholders for possible financial help. Explain your choices. Give examples of projects whose positions would not be improved by presentation of a model. Explain.

Analysis by Computer

22. Write a report on the current applications of computers to the analysis of a design. Information can be obtained from local sources, your library, and brochures from companies specializing in computer equipment.

23. The use of the computer in the solution of engineering and mathematical problems has increased considerably during the last few years. The computer has a capacity to solve problems involving numbers with great ease and in a fraction of the time required for solution by the conventional manual methods of the engineer. How will the effectiveness of this method in solving mathematical problems affect the role of mathematics as a college subject? Since the computer can handle these problems, should mathematics continue to be taught as a fundamental course in engineering? Explain.

24. State for which of the following types of problems a computer will be most helpful: the design of a handle and locking system for a car trunk, the design of a protective football helmet, the design of a truss of standard configuration, the design of an aircraft's landing gear, the design of a road base for specified loads.

BIBLIOGRAPHY AND SUGGESTED READING

1. Baker, C. H., and W. F. Grether, *Visual Presentation of Information*, WACD Tech. Rpt. 54–160. Wright Patterson Air Force Base, Ohio: Wright Air Development Center, 1954.
2. Bennett, E. M., J. Degan, and J. Spiegel, *Human Factors in Technology*. New York: McGraw-Hill, 1963.
3. Chapanis, A., Garner, and C. T. Morgan, *Applied Experimental Psychology: Human Factors in Engineering Design.* New York: Wiley, 1949.
4. Committee on Undersea Warfare, *Human Factors in Undersea Warfare*. Washington, D. C.: National Research Council, 1949.
5. Damon, A., H. W. Stoudt, and R. A. McFarland, *The Human Body in Equipment Design.* Cambridge, Mass.: Harvard University Press, 1966.
6. DeFries, M. G., *Sizing of Cosmetic Hands to Fit the Child and Adult Amputee Population*. Tech. Rpt. 5441. Washington, D. C.: Walter Reed Army Medical Center, 1954.
7. Dreyfuss, H., *Designing for People.* New York: Simon & Schuster, 1955.
8. ——, *The Measure of Man*. New York: The Whitney Library of Design, 1967.
9. Ely, J. E., R. M. Thomson, and J. Orlansky, "Design of Controls," Chapter VI of *Joint Services Human Engineering Guide to Equipment Design*, WADC Tech. Rpt. 56–172. Wright Patterson Air Force Base, Ohio: Wright Air Development Center, 1956.
10. ——, "Layout of Work Places," Chapter V, *ibid.*, WADC Tech. Rpt. 56–171.
11. Eckenrode, R. T., *The Response of Man to His Environment*. Stamford, Conn.: Dunlap & Associates, 1958.
12. Floyd, W. F., and Roberts, *Anatomical, Physiological, and Anthropometric Principles in the Design of Office Chairs and Tables,* BS 3044. London: British Standards Institute, 1958.
13. Floyd, W. F. and A. T. Welford, "Symposium on Human Factors in Equipment Design," *Ergonomics Research Soc. Proc.* **2.** London: H. K. Lewis, 1954.
14. *Human Body Size and Capabilities in the Design and Operation of Vehicular Equipment.* Boston: Harvard School of Public Health, 1953.
15. *Human Conditioning in the Factory.* Cambridge: Harvard Graduate School of Business Administration, 2nd Year Students, 1953.
16. *Human Factors Engineering Design Criteria for Nike-X System Development.* U. S. Army Material Command, 1963.
17. *Human Factors in the Design of Highway Transport Equipment.* Boston: Harvard School of Public Health, 1953.
18. Javitz, A. E., *Human Engineering in Equipment Design,*" Electrical Manufacturing," Combined Reprint. New York: Gage, 1952, 1954, 1955, 1956.
19. Luckiesh, M., *Visual Illusions.* New York: Dover, 1965.
20. Martin, E. W., *Basic Body Measurements of School Age Children.* Washington, D. C.: U. S. Dept. of Health, Education, and Welfare, 1953.
21. McCormick, E. J., *Human Engineering.* New York: McGraw-Hill, 1957.
22. ——, *Human Factors Engineering*, 2nd ed. New York: McGraw-Hill, 1964.
23. McFarland, R. A., *Human Factors in Air Transportation: Occupational Health and Safety.* New York: McGraw-Hill, 1953.
24. ——, *The Application of Human Body Size Data to Vehicular Design,* SP-142. New York: Society of Automotive Engineers, 1955.
25. Morgan, C. T., J. S. Cook, A. Chapanis, and M. W. Lund, *Human Engineering Guide to Equipment Design.* New York: McGraw-Hill, 1963.
26. Panero, J., and N. Repetto, *Anatomy for Interior Designers,* 3rd ed. New York: Whitney Library of Design, 1962.
27. Woodson, W. E., and D. W. Conover, *Human Engineering Guide,* 2nd ed. Los Angeles: University of California Press, 1964.
28. Woodson, W. E., *Human Engineering Guide for Equipment Designers.* Berkeley, Calif.: University of California Press, 1954.

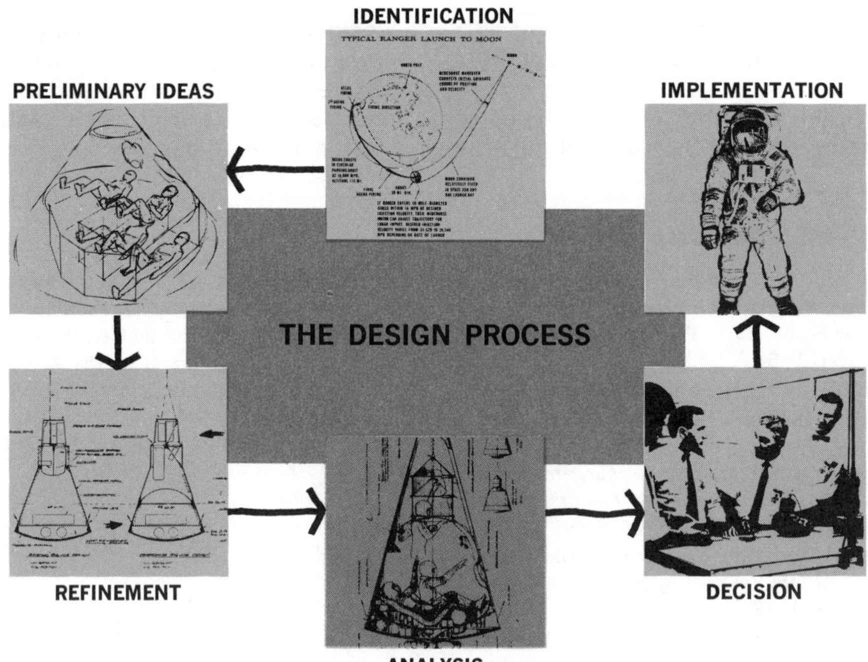

14 VECTOR ANALYSIS

14–1 INTRODUCTION

After a design of a structural system has been refined and drawn to scale, and angular and linear dimensions have been determined, it is necessary to analyze the system for strength and stresses. When the stresses are known, members of an appropriate size may be selected to withstand the forces within the system. Principles of strength of materials can be applied to the graphical solutions in selecting the shapes and sizes of the structural members used in the final design.

In analyzing a system for strength it is necessary to consider the forces of tension and compression within the system. These forces are represented by vectors. Vectors may also be used to represent other quantities. For example, they can represent distance, velocity, and electrical properties.

Graphical methods are useful in the solution of vector problems, which are often very complicated to solve by conventional trigonometric and algebraic methods. This does not mean that only the graphical method should be used. The designer should strive to integrate all methods available to him in solving problems. Each method can serve as an effective check on the solutions determined by other methods.

14–2 BASIC DEFINITIONS

A knowledge of the terminology of graphical vectors is prerequisite to an understanding of the techniques of problem solving with vectors. The following definitions will be used throughout this chapter.

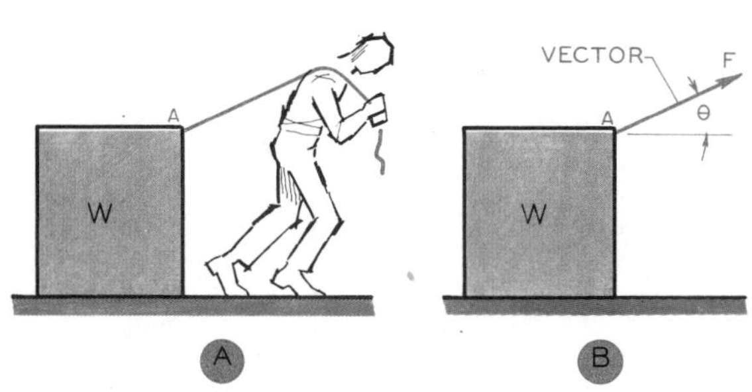

Fig. 14–1. The representation of a force by a vector.

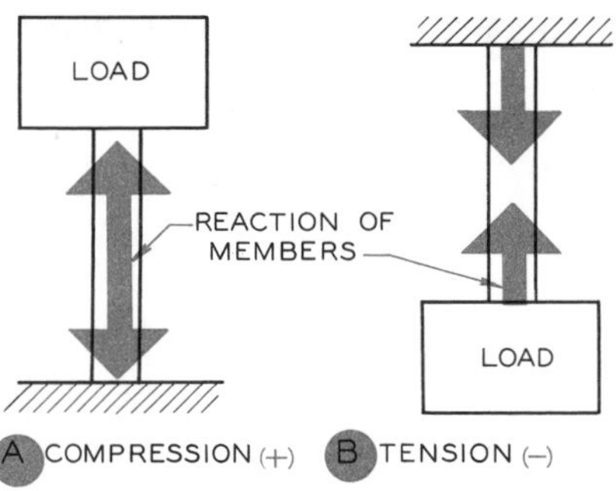

Fig. 14–2. A comparison of tension and compression in a member.

Force: A push or a pull that tends to produce motion. All forces have (1) magnitude, (2) direction, (3) a point of application, and (4) sense. A force is represented by the rope being pulled in Fig. 14–1A.

Vector: A graphical representation of a quantity of force which is drawn to scale to indicate magnitude, direction, sense, and point of application. The vector shown in Fig. 14–1B represents the force of the rope pulling the weight, *W*.

Magnitude: The amount of push or pull. In drawings, this is represented by the length of the vector line. Magnitude is usually measured in pounds of force.

Direction: The inclination of a force (with respect to a reference coordinate system).

Point of application: The point through which the force is applied on the object or member. This is point *A* in Fig. 14–1A.

Sense: Either of the two opposite ways in which a force may be directed, i.e., toward or away from the point of application. The sense is shown by an arrowhead attached to one end of the vector line. In Fig. 14–1A, the sense of the force is away from point A. It is shown in part B of the figure by the arrowhead at *F*.

Compression: The state created in a member by subjecting it to opposite pushing forces. A member tends to be shortened by compression (Fig. 14–2A). Compression is represented by a plus sign (+).

Tension: The state created in a member by subjecting it to opposite pulling forces. A member tends to be stretched by tension, as shown in Fig. 14–2B. Tension is represented by a minus sign (—).

Force system: The combination of all forces acting on a given object. Figure 14–3 shows a force system.

Resultant: A single force that can replace all the forces of a force system and have the same effect as the combined forces.

Equilibrant: The opposite of a resultant; it is the single force that can be used to counterbalance all forces of a force system.

Components: Any individual forces which, if combined, would result in a given single force. For example, Forces *A* and *B* are components of resultant R_1 in step 1 of Fig. 14–3.

Space diagram: A diagram depicting the physical relationship between structural members. The force system in Fig. 14–3 is given as a space diagram.

Vector diagram: A diagram composed of vectors which are scaled to their appropriate lengths to represent the forces within a given system. The vector diagram is used to solve for unknowns that are required in the solution of the problem.

FIGURE 14-3. RESULTANT BY THE PARALLELOGRAM METHOD

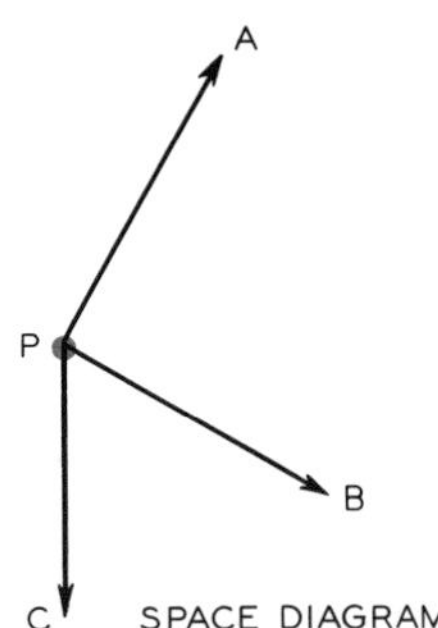

Required: Find the resultant of this coplanar, concurrent force system by the parallelogram method.

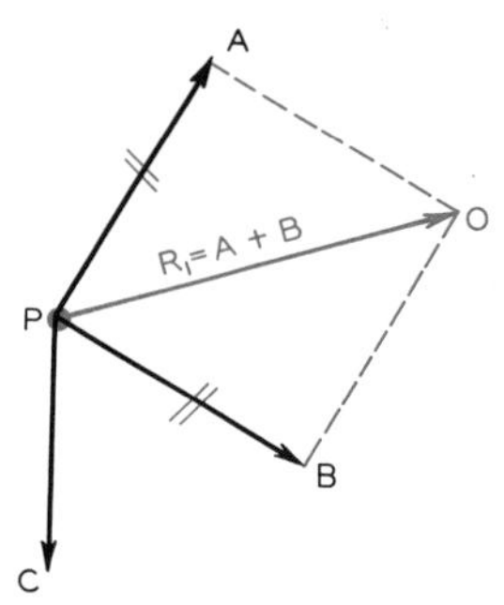

Step 1: Draw a parallelogram with its sides parallel to vectors *A* and *B*. The diagonal, R_1, drawn from *P* to *O* is the resultant of forces *A* and *B*.

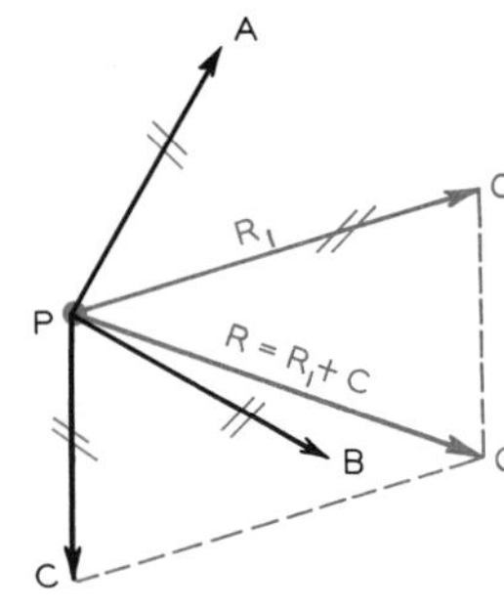

Step 2: Draw a parallelogram using vectors R_1 and *C* to find diagonal *R* from *P* to *Q*. This is the resultant that can replace forces *A*, *B*, and *C*.

A vector diagram may be a polygon or a parallelogram.

Statics: The study of forces and force systems that are in equilibrium.

Additional definitions will be introduced throughout the chapter at appropriate times. The terms given above will be more extensively defined when applied to actual examples.

14-3 COPLANAR, CONCURRENT FORCE SYSTEMS

When several forces, represented by vectors, act through a common point of application, the system is said to be *concurrent.* Vectors *A*, *B*, and *C* act through a single point in Fig. 14-3; therefore this is a concurrent system. When only one view is necessary to show the true length of all vectors, as in Fig. 14-3, the system is *coplanar.*

Engineering designs are analyzed to determine the total effect of the forces applied in a system. Such an analysis requires that the known forces be resolved into a single force—the *resultant*—that will represent the composite effect of all forces on the point of application. The resultant is found graphically by two methods—(1) the parallelogram method and (2) the polygon method. In either case, the selection of a proper scale is important to the final solution. A larger drawing will result in a higher degree of accuracy.

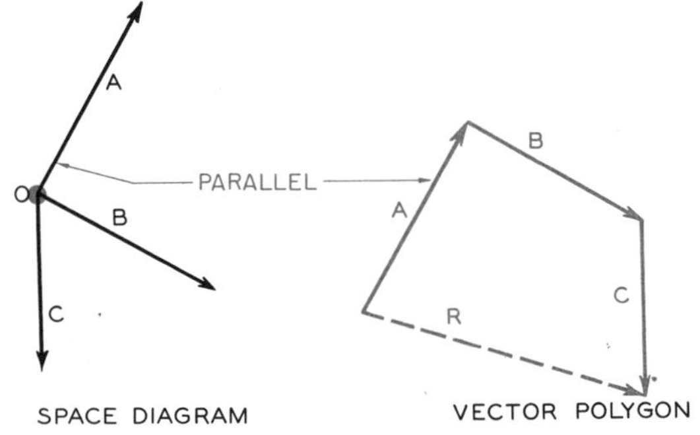

Fig. 14-4. The resultant of a coplanar, concurrent system as determined by the polygon method.

14-4 RESULTANT OF A COPLANAR, CONCURRENT SYSTEM—PARALLELOGRAM METHOD

In the system of vectors shown in Fig. 14-3, all the vectors lie in the same plane and act through a common point. The vectors are scaled to a known magnitude.

The vectors for a force system must be known and drawn to scale in order to apply the parallelogram method to determine the resultant. Two vectors are used to find a parallelogram; the diagonal of the parallelogram is the resultant of these two vectors and has its point of origin at point *P* (Fig. 14-3). Resultant R_1 can be called the *vector sum* of vectors *A* and *B*.

Since vectors A and B have been replaced by R_1, they can be disregarded in the next step of the solution. Again, resultant R_1 and vector C are resolved by completing a parallelogram, i.e., by drawing a line parallel to each vector. The diagonal of this parallelogram, PQ, is the resultant of the entire system and is the vector sum of R_1 and C. This resultant, R, can be analyzed as though it were the only force acting on the point; therefore the analysis of a particular point-of-force application is simplified by finding the resultant.

14-5 RESULTANT OF A COPLANAR, CONCURRENT SYSTEM—POLYGON METHOD

The system of forces shown in Fig. 14-3 is shown again in Fig. 14-4, but in this case the resultant is found by the polygon method. The forces are drawn to scale and in their true directions, with each force being drawn head-to-tail to form the polygon. In this example, the vectors are drawn in a counterclockwise sequence, beginning with vector A. Vector B is drawn with its tail at the arrowhead end of vector A and vector C is similarly attached to B. Note that the polygon does not close; this means that the system is not in *equilibrium*. In other words, it would tend to be in motion, since the forces are not balanced in all directions. The resultant R is drawn from the tail of vector A to the head of vector C to close the polygon. It can be seen by inspection that the resultant is equal in length, direction, and sense to the resultant found by the parallelogram method of the previous article.

14-6 RESULTANT OF A COPLANAR, CONCURRENT SYSTEM—ANALYTICAL METHOD

Vectors can be solved analytically by application of algebra and trigonometry. The graphical method is generally much faster, and presents less chance of error due to an arithmetical mistake. The designer should, however, be well-versed in all methods, since each will have advantages over the others in certain situations. The example in Fig. 14-5 is given to afford a comparison between the graphical and analytical methods.

FIGURE 14-5. RESULTANT BY THE ANALYTICAL METHOD

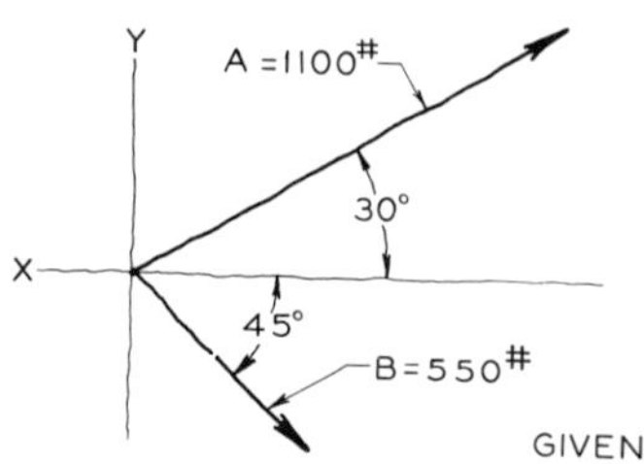

Required: An unscaled, freehand sketch of two forces is given. Find the resultant using the analytical method.

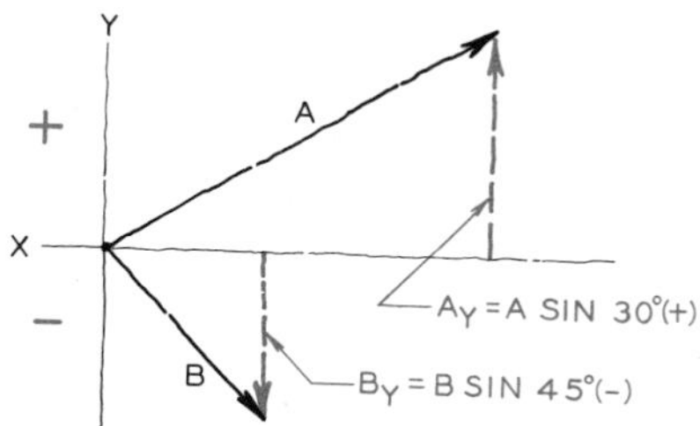

Step 1: The Y-components (vertical components) are found to be the sine functions of the angles the vectors make with the X-axis. The Y-component of A is positive and the Y-component of B is negative.

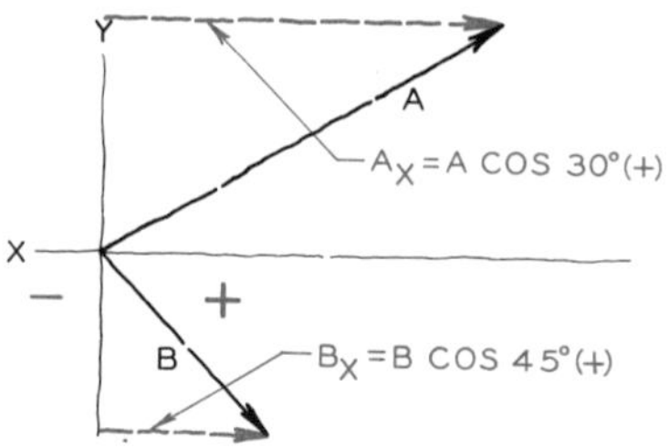

Step 2: The X-components (horizontal components) are the cosine functions of 30° and 45° in this case, both in the positive direction.

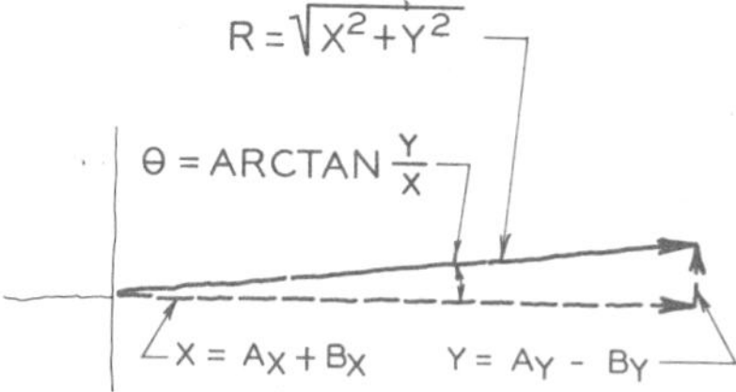

Step 3: The Y-components and X-components are summed to find the components of the resultant, X and Y. The Pythagorean theorem is applied to find the magnitude of the resultant. Its angle with the X-axis is the arctangent of Y/X.

Since the analytical approach will be used, it is unnecessary for the vectors and angles to be drawn accurately to scale. A freehand sketch is sufficient. However, it is advantageous if the sketch approximates the true measurements.

In step 1, the vertical components, which are parallel to the Y-axis, are drawn from the ends of both vectors to form right triangles. The lengths of these components are found through the use of the trigonometric functions of the angles the vectors make with the X-axis. The vertical component of vector A is found to be $A_y = A \sin 30°$ in a positive sense. The vertical component of B is $B_y = B \sin 45°$ in a negative sense.

The horizontal component of each vector is drawn parallel to the X-axis through the end of each vector. The lengths of these components are found to be the cosine functions of the given vectors. The horizontal component of vector A is $A_x = A \cos 30°$ in a positive sense. The horizontal component of vector B is $B_x = B \cos 45°$ in a positive sense.

The Y-components of each vector, A_y and B_y, can be added, since each lies in the same direction. The resulting value is $Y = A_y - B_y$, since the components have opposite senses. The horizontal component is $X = A_x + B_x$, since both components have equal directions and senses. A right triangle is sketched using the X- and Y-distances that were found trigonometrically. The vertical and horizontal components are laid off head-to-tail and the head of the horizontal component is connected to the tail of the vertical to form a three-sided polygon of forces. The resultant is the hypotenuse of the triangle. The magnitude of the resultant is found by the Pythagorean theorem,

$$R = \sqrt{X^2 + Y^2}.$$

The direction of the resultant is

$$\text{angle } \theta = \arctan Y/X,$$

and it is measured from the horizontal X-axis. The sense is determined by the hypotenuse, and it runs from the point of application to the head of the vertical component. All measurements and magnitudes are found mathematically, so no graphical measurements are needed. The diagrams used to analyze the system of forces need not be drawn to scale when the problem is solved in this manner.

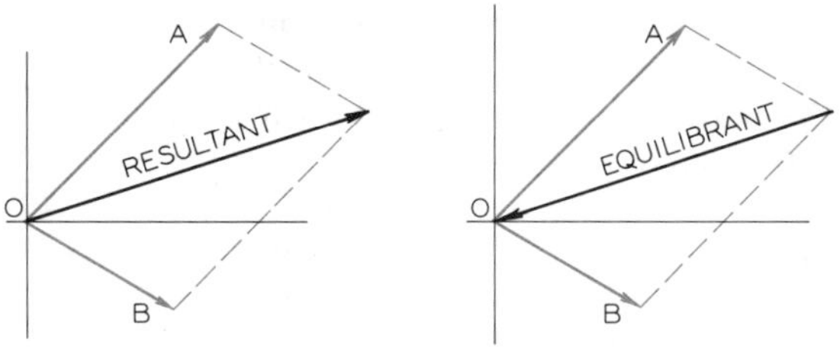

Fig. 14-6. The resultant and equilibrant are equal in all respects except in sense.

It can be seen in this example that a system of only two forces requires a considerable degree of mathematical manipulation to arrive at the resultant. Although these manipulations are relatively simple, there are many possibilities for making a mistake that would nullify the entire sequence of calculations. Errors are often difficult to detect when the solution is derived in this manner. A quickly drawn vector polygon can be used as a readily available method of checking analytical answers in the minimum of time. Graphical solutions can be made with the same degree of accuracy as slide-rule solutions, provided that the appropriate scale is chosen.

An *equilibrant* has the same magnitude, direction, and point of application as the *resultant* in any system of forces. The difference is the sense. Note that the resultant of the system of forces shown in Fig. 14-6 is solved for through the parallelogram method. The sense of the resultant is toward point C along the direction

FIGURE 14–7. RESULTANT BY THE PARALLELOGRAM METHOD

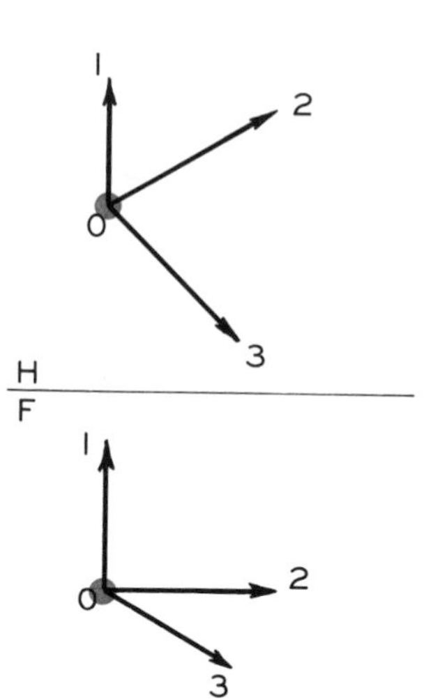

Required: Find the resultant of this noncoplanar, concurrent system of forces by the parallelogram method.

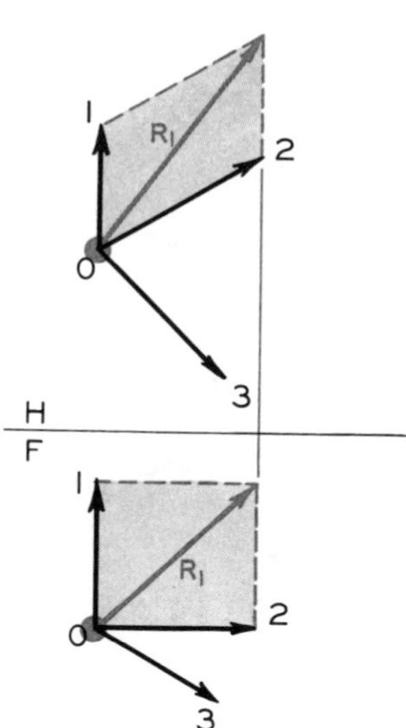

Step 1: Vectors 1 and 2 are used to construct a parallelogram in the top and front views. The diagonal, R_1, is the resultant of these two vectors.

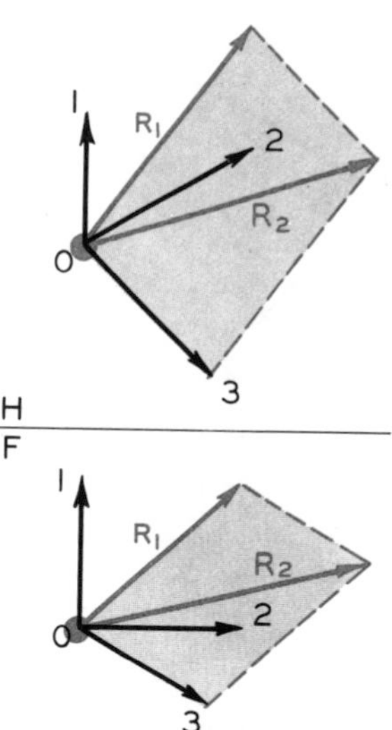

Step 2: Vectors 3 and R_1 are used to construct a second parallelogram to find the overall resultant, R_2.

OC, the diagonal of the parallelogram. The equilibrant is drawn so that its arrowhead is at the opposite end, toward point *O*. The equilibrant can be applied at point *O* to balance the forces *A* and *B* and thereby cause the system to be in a state of equilibrium.

14–7 RESULTANT OF NONCOPLANAR, CONCURRENT FORCES—PARALLELOGRAM METHOD

When vectors lie in more than one plane of projection, they are said to be *noncoplanar;* therefore more than one view is necessary to analyze their spatial relationships. The resultant of a system of noncoplanar forces can be found, regardless of their number, if their true projections are given in two adjacent orthographic views. The solution of an example of this type is shown through sequential steps of the parallelogram method in Fig. 14–7.

Vectors 1 and 2 are used to construct the top and front views of a parallelogram. The diagonal of the parallelogram, R_1, is found in both views. As a check, the front view of R_1 must be an orthographic projection of its top view; if it is not, there is an error in construction. Since R_1 is used to replace vectors 1 and 2, they may be omitted in further construction.

In step 2, resultant R_1 and vector 3 are resolved to form resultant R_2 by the parallelogram method in both views. The top and front views of R_2 must project orthographically if there is no error

FIGURE 14-8. RESULTANT BY THE POLYGON METHOD

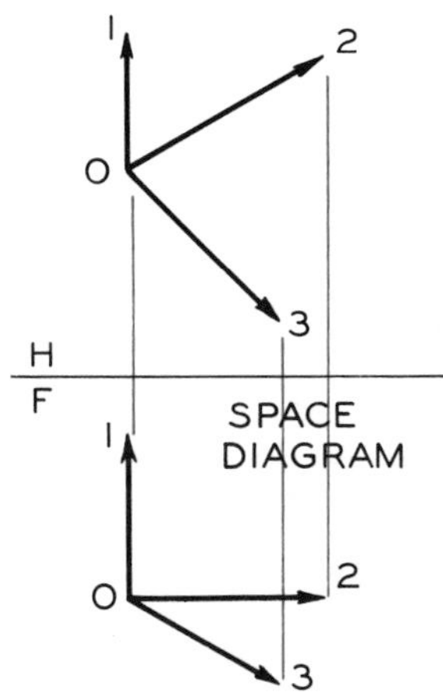

Required: Find the resultant of this system of concurrent, noncoplanar forces by the polygon method.

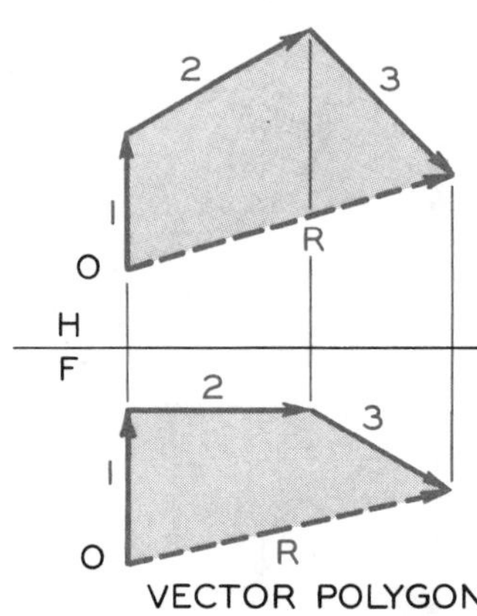

Step 1: Each vector is laid head-to-tail in the same order for both views. The resultant is the vector drawn from point *O* to the head of vector 3.

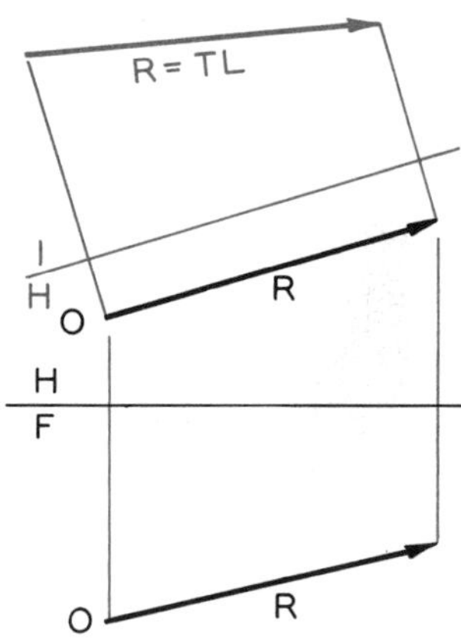

Step 2: The resultant is not true length in the given views; an auxiliary view is used to find it true length where it can be measured.

in construction. Resultant R_2 can be used to replace vectors 1, 2, and 3. Since R_2 is an oblique line that is not true length, its true length can be found by auxiliary view, as shown in Fig. 14-8 or by revolution, as previously covered.

14-8 RESULTANT OF NONCOPLANAR, CONCURRENT FORCES—POLYGON METHOD

The same system of forces that was given in Fig. 14-7 is given in Fig. 14-8. In this instance, we are required to solve for the resultant of the system by the polygon method.

In step 1, the given orthographic views of the vectors are transferred to a vector polygon, in which each vector is laid head-to-tail in a clockwise direction, beginning with vector 1. The vectors are drawn in each view to be orthographic projections at all times. Since the vector polygon did not close, the system is not in equilibrium. The resultant *R* is constructed from the tail of vector 1 to the head of vector 3 in both views.

Resultant *R* is an oblique line and so requires an auxiliary view to find its true length. The magnitude of the resultant can be measured in the true-length auxiliary view by using the same scale as was used to draw the original views. This method could have been used to find the resultant in Fig. 14-7.

14-9 RESULTANT OF NONCOPLANAR, CONCURRENT FORCES—ANALYTICAL METHOD

The same system of forces that was given in Fig. 14-7 is given in Fig. 14-9. We are required to solve for the resultant of the system by the analytical method, using trigonometry and algebraic equations. The projected lengths of the vectors are known in both views, as indicated in Fig. 14-9.

FIGURE 14–9. RESULTANT BY THE ANALYTICAL METHOD

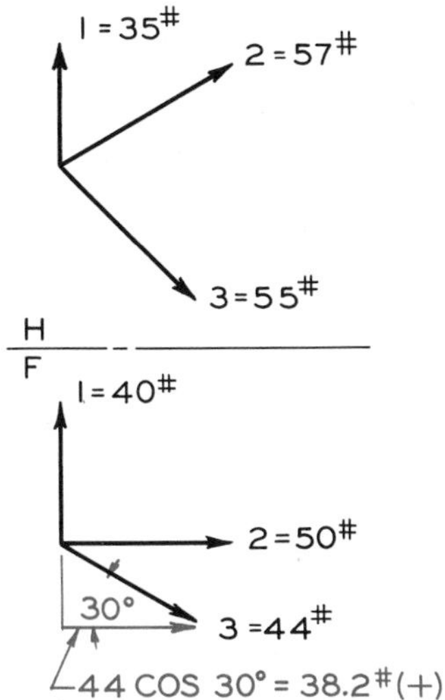

Step 1: The X-component is found in the front or top view. The X-components are found to be: force 1, 0 lb; force 2, 50 lb; force 3, 44 lb cos 30°. These values are positive.

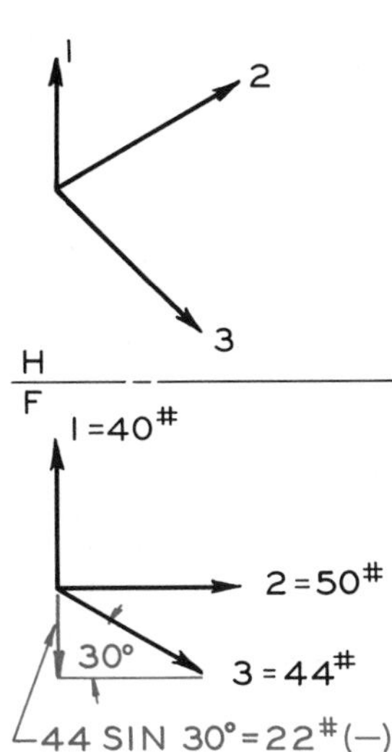

Step 2: The Y-component must be found in the front view. The Y-components are found to be: force 1, 40 lb; force 2, 0 lb; force 3, 44 lb sin 30°.

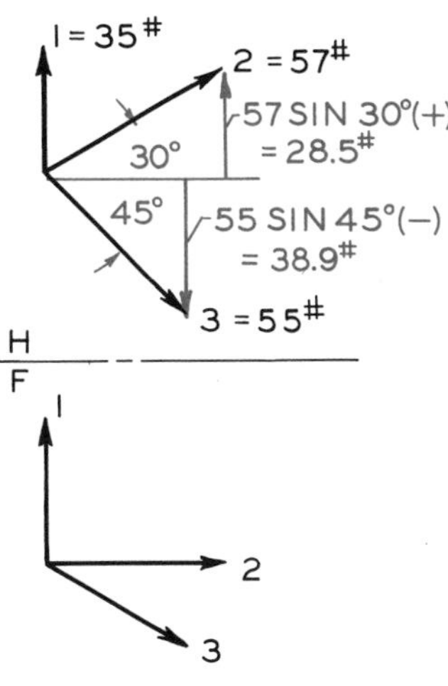

Step 3: The Z-component must be found in the top view. The Z-components are found to be: force 1, 35 lb; force 2, 57 lb sin 30°; force 3, 55 lb sin 45°. The resultant is found in Fig. 14–10.

In step 1, the summation of the forces in the X-direction is found in the front view. Since this left and right direction can be seen in either the top view or front view, either view can be used for finding the X-component of the system. The summation in the X-direction is expressed in the following equation:

$$\begin{aligned}\sum F_x &= (2) + (3)\cos 30^\circ \\ &= 50 + 44\cos 30^\circ = 88.2 \text{ lb } (+).\end{aligned}$$

The X-component is found to be 88.2 lb in the positive direction, which is considered to be to the right. Vector 1 is vertical and consequently has no component in the X-direction.

The summation of forces in the Y-direction is found in the front view. This summation is expressed in the following equation:

$$\begin{aligned}\sum F_y &= (1) - (3)\sin 30^\circ \\ &= 40 - 44\sin 30^\circ = 18 \text{ lb } (+).\end{aligned}$$

Vector 2 is horizontal and has no vertical component.

The summation of forces in the Z-direction is found in the top view. Positive direction is considered to be backward and negative, to be forward. This summation is expressed in the following equation:

$$\begin{aligned}\sum F_z &= (1) + (2)\sin 30^\circ - (3)\sin 45^\circ \\ &= 35 + 57\sin 30^\circ - 55\sin 45^\circ \\ &= 24.6 \text{ lb } (+).\end{aligned}$$

The resultant that can be used to replace vectors 1, 2, and 3 can be found from these three components. The true-length of a line can be determined from these three components by the following equation:

$$R = \sqrt{X^2 + Y^2 + Z^2}.$$

By substitution of the X-, Y-, and Z-components found in the three previous summations, the equation can be solved as follows:

$$R = \sqrt{88.2^2 + 18^2 + 24.6^2} = 93.3 \text{ lb}.$$

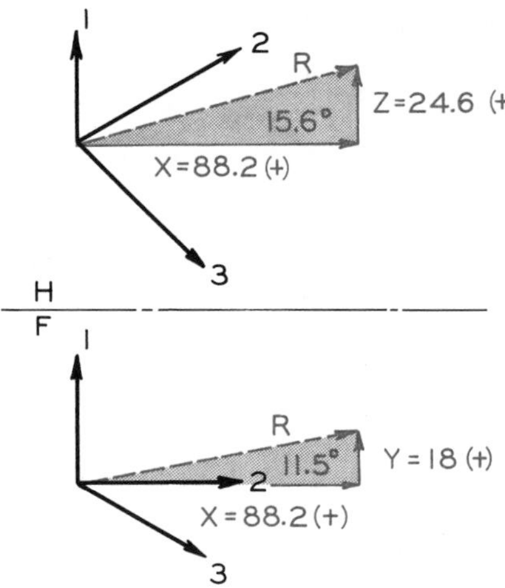

Fig. 14-10. The three components, X, Y, and Z, found in Fig. 14-9 are used to find the resultant, $R = \sqrt{X^2 + Y^2 + Z^2}$.

The resultant force of 93.3 lb is of no value unless its direction and sense are known. To find this information, we must refer to the two orthographic views of the force system, as shown in Fig. 14-10. The X- and Z-components, 88.2 lb and 24.6 lb, are drawn to form a right triangle in the top view. The hypotenuse of this triangle depicts the direction and sense of the resultant in the top view. The angular direction of the top view of the resultant is found in the following equation:

$$\tan \theta = \frac{24.6}{88.2} = 0.279; \qquad \theta = 15.6°.$$

The angular direction of the resultant is found in the front view by constructing a triangle with the X- and Y-components, 88.2 lb and 18 lb. The hypotenuse of this right triangle is the direction of the resultant. The direction of the resultant in the front view is expressed in the following equation:

$$\tan \phi = \frac{18}{88.2} = 0.204; \qquad \phi = 11.5°.$$

These two angles, found in the top and front views, establish the direction of the resultant vector, whose sense can be described as upward, to the right, and back. The force system and the various steps of solution need not be drawn to scale for analytical solution, since no attempt is made to measure lines or angles.

The advantages of the graphical solution of this problem should be apparent after this example is completed in its entirety. Errors are more likely in the analytical solution due to the number of components involved. The accuracy of both methods is essentially the same if a sufficiently large scale is selected for the graphical solution. Both methods should be used in combination for the most satisfactory solution.

14-10 STRUCTURES IN EQUILIBRIUM

In all the previous examples, the vectors were drawn from given or known magnitudes and directions. The same principles can be applied to structural system in which the magnitudes and senses are not given. All engineering structures are analyzed for their loads as the first step in designing and selecting members to adequately support the loads for which the structure is designed. An example of coplanar structures in equilibrium can be seen in the loading cranes in Fig. 14-11, which are used for the handling of cargo on board ship. These can be considered as coplanar, concurrent force systems. The forces in the members are dependent on the magnitude of the loading and the position of the members.

The coplanar, concurrent structure given in Fig. 14-12A is designed to support a load of $W = 1000$ lb. The maximum loading in each is used to determine the type and size of structural members used in the structural design.

In step 1, the only known force, $W = 1000$ lb, is laid off parallel to the given direction. Unknown forces A and B are drawn as vectors that are acting at a common point of application. The sense of these vectors can be determined so as to balance the system. Note that if either force A or B had been drawn with an opposite sense, the system could not be in equilibrium. The

Fig. 14–11. The cargo cranes on the cruise ship "Santa Rosa" are examples of coplanar, concurrent force systems that are designed to remain in equilibrium. (Courtesy of Humble Oil and Refining Company.)

magnitude of these vectors is not known, but their directions must lie along the lines of the structural members.

In step 2, force *W* is drawn to a convenient scale as a vector. Forces *A* and *B* are laid off head-to-tail parallel to their given views to close the polygon formed by the three lines. The resulting polygon can be scaled to give the magnitude of vectors *A* and *B* by applying the same scale as that used for drawing vector *W*. The structural lengths of the members do not affect the forces derived in the polygon. A column 3 ft long may support the same weight as a column 30 ft long. The length versus the cross section of a member will be considered when selecting a member, but the determination of force in the member is found in the same manner in the vector polygon regardless of member length.

Tension is a force tending to stretch a member while compression is a force tending to shorten a member. A rope is a member that is in tension when in use, while a car jack is a mechanism that is in compression when in use. When the sense of a vector is toward the point of application, an object is in compression; when its sense is away from the point, the object is in tension.

The members in Fig. 14–12A can be analyzed to determine whether they are in tension or compression by inspecting the diagram drawn in step 1. Vector *A* can be compared with the member it represents. The sense of this vector is away from the point of application; therefore the member is in tension. Vector *B* has its sense toward the point of application, indicating that the member is in compression. Compression and tension can also be determined by visually relating the vector polygon in step 2 to the given structural diagram.

A similar example of a force system involving a pulley is solved in Fig. 14–12B to determine the loads in the structural members caused by the weight of 100 lb. The only difference between this solution and the previous one is the construction of two equal vectors to represent the loads in the cable on both sides of the pulley.

14–11 FORCES IN EQUILIBRIUM—ANALYTICAL SOLUTION

The force system shown in Fig. 14–12A has been sketched in Fig. 14–13 for solution by the analytical method. The load *W* must be known

FIGURE 14-12A. COPLANAR FORCES IN EQUILIBRIUM

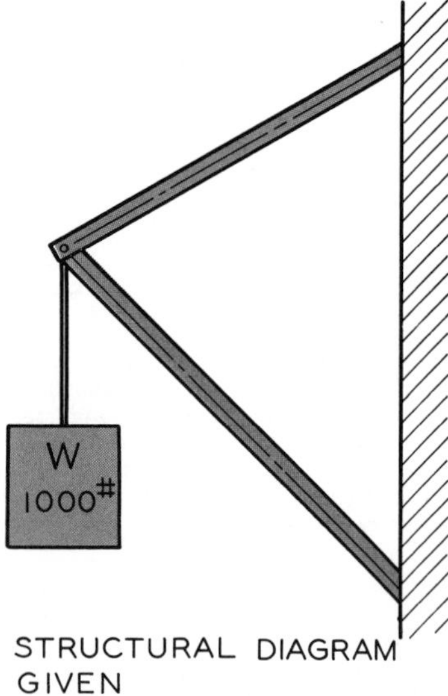

STRUCTURAL DIAGRAM GIVEN

Required: Find the forces in the two structural members caused by the load of 1000 lb.

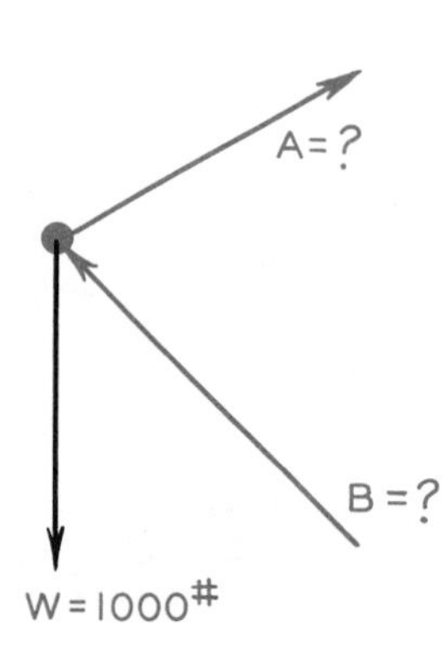

SPACE DIAGRAM

Step 1: Convert the members into a space diagram showing the reactions at the point of application.

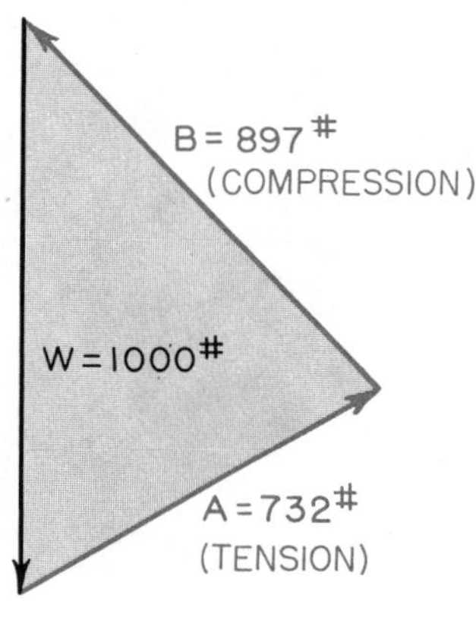

VECTOR POLYGON

Step 2: The known load of 1000 lb is drawn as a vector. The other two forces are drawn from each end of *W* parallel to their directions in the space diagram. Arrowheads are drawn head-to-tail. The sense of *A* is away from the point of application, and *A* is in tension; *B* is toward the point and is in compression.

FIGURE 14-12B. DETERMINATION OF FORCES IN EQUILIBRIUM

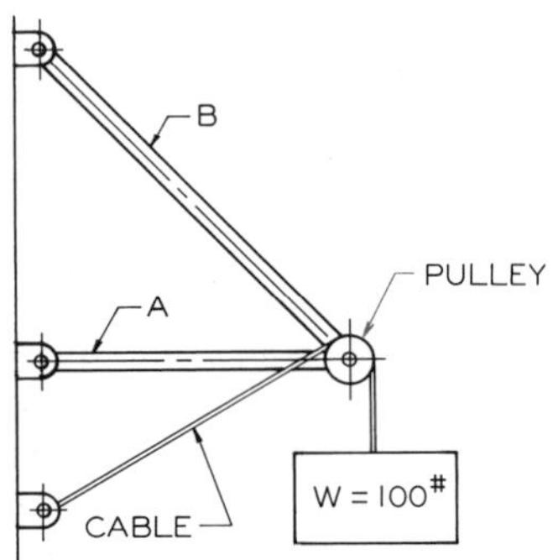

Required: Find the forces in the members caused by the load of 100 lb supported by the pulley.

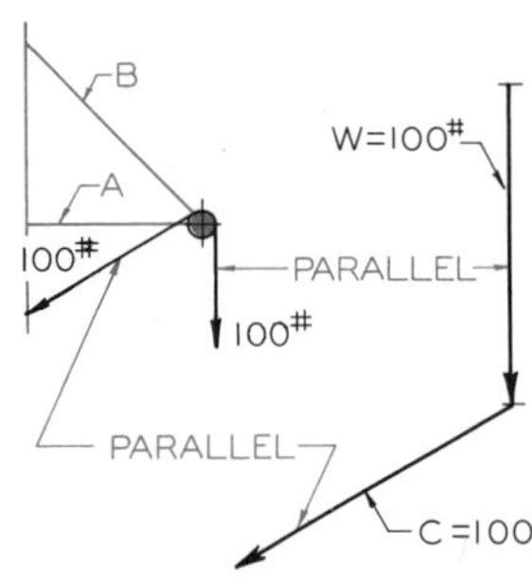

Step 1: The force in the cable is equal to 100 lb on both sides of the pulley. These two forces are drawn as vectors head-to-tail parallel to their directions in the space diagram.

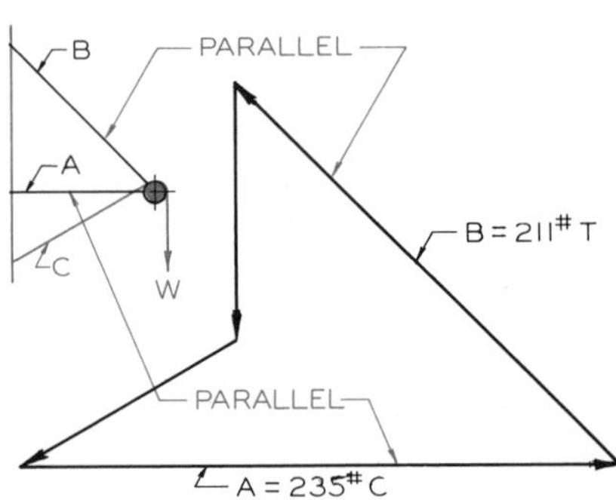

Step 2: The remaining unknowns, *A* and *B*, are drawn to close the polygon, and arrowheads are placed to give a head-to-tail arrangement. The sense of *A* is toward the point of application, and *A* is in compression; *B* is away from the point and is in tension.

along with the angular directions of members A and B. Forces A and B are unknown; however, they can be used in the equations where the X- and Y-forces will be summed. Since the system is in equilibrium, the summation of forces in any direction will equal zero, which indicates balance or equilibrium. The summation of forces in the Y-direction and X-direction can be expressed in the following equations:

(1) $\sum F_y = A \sin 30° + B \sin 45° - 1000 = 0.$

(2) $\sum F_x = A \cos 30° - B \cos 45° = 0.$

We can solve Eq. (2) for A by rearranging the equation to the following form:

(3) $$A = \frac{B \cos 45°}{\cos 30°} = 0.816\ (B).$$

When Eq. (3) is substituted into Eq. (1), the equation can be rewritten as:

(4)
$$\sum F_y = 0.816\ (B) \sin 30° + B \sin 45° - 1000 = 0 = 0.408\ B + 0.707\ B - 1000;$$

$$B = \frac{1000}{1.115} = 897 \text{ lb.}$$

The value of $B = 897$ lb is substituted into Eq. (2) so that we may solve for A in the following manner:

$$\sum F_x = A \cos 30° - 897 \cos 45° = 0,$$

$$A = \frac{897 \cos 45°}{\cos 30°} = 732 \text{ lb.}$$

In comparing the graphical and analytical methods, we should note that both methods are limited to two unknowns. Although we obtained the same answer by the analytical method as we did by the graphical method, there was a considerably greater chance of error in the analytical approach.

14-12 TRUSS ANALYSIS

Vector polygons can be used to analyze a structural truss to determine the loads in each member by two graphical methods: (1) joint-by-joint analysis, and (2) Maxwell diagrams.

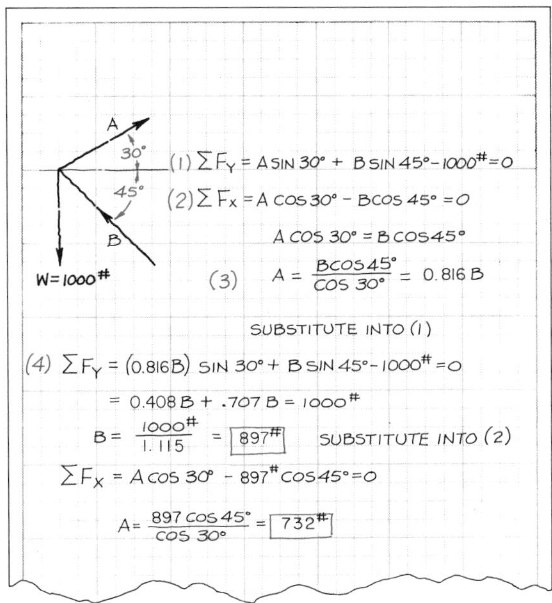

Fig. 14–13. Analytical determination of the forces in a concurrent, coplanar system in equilibrium.

Joint-by-Joint Analysis. The truss shown in Fig. 14–14 is called a Fink truss, and is loaded with forces of 3000 lb that are concentrated at joints of the structural members. A special method of designating forces, called *Bow's notation,* is used. The exterior forces applied to the truss are labeled with letters placed between the forces. Numerals are placed between the interior members.

Each vector used to represent the load in each member is referred to by the number on each of its sides. For example, the first vertical load at the left is called AB, with A at the tail and B at the head of the vector.

The first joint that is analyzed is the one at the left, where the reaction of 4500 lb (denoted by #) is known. This force, reading in a clockwise direction about the joint, is called EA with an upward sense. The tail is labeled E and the head A. Continuing in a clockwise direction, the next force is A–1 and the next 1–E, which closes the polygon and ends with the beginning letter, E.

FIGURE 14–14. JOINT ANALYSIS OF A TRUSS

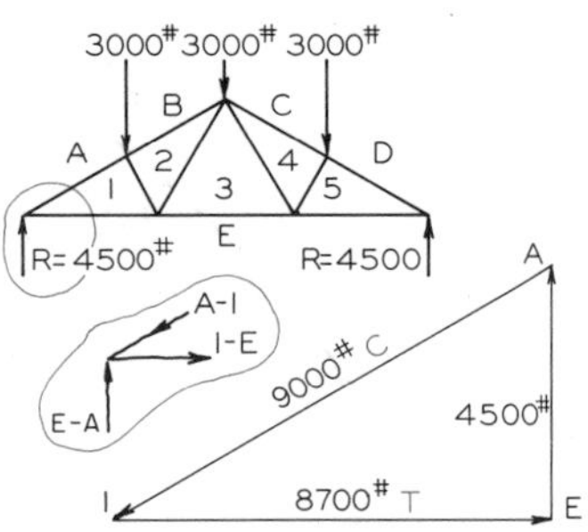

Step 1: The truss is labeled using Bow's notation, with letters between the exterior loads and numbers between interior members. The lower left joint can be analyzed, since it has only two unknowns, *A*–1 and 1–*E*. These vectors are found true length by drawing lines that are parallel to the unknown vectors and meet both ends of the known reaction of 4500 lb. The sense of vector *EA* is upward; this establishes the sense of the other vectors, which are laid off in a head-to-tail order.

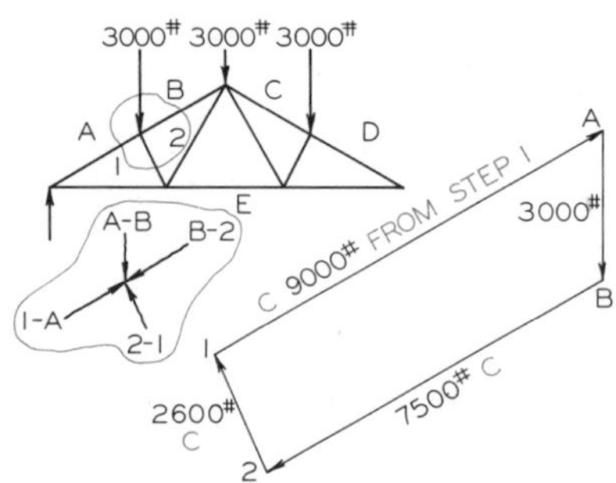

Step 2: Using the vector of 1–*A* found in step 1 and load *AB*, the two unknowns *B*–2 and 2–1 can be found. The known vectors are laid out beginning with vector 1–*A* and moving clockwise about the joint. Vectors *B*–2 and 2–1 close the polygon. If the sense of a vector is toward the point of application, it is in compression; if away from the point, it is in tension.

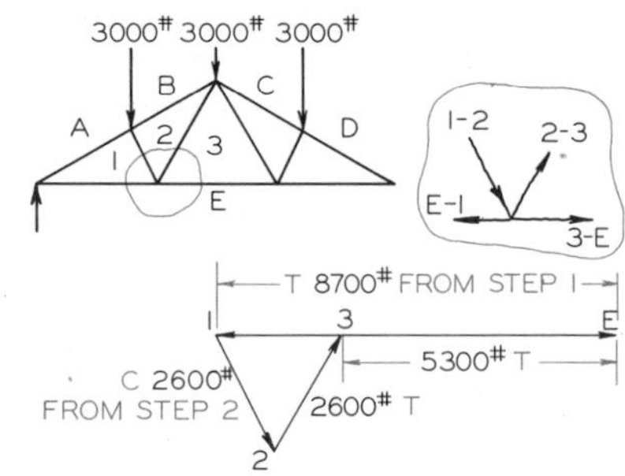

Step 3: The third joint can be analyzed by laying out the vectors *E*–1 and 1–2 from the previous steps. Vectors 2–3 and 3–*E* close the polygon and are parallel to their directions in the space diagram. The senses of 2–3 and 3–*E* are away from the point of application; these vectors are in tension.

The arrows are placed, beginning with the known vector *EA*, in a head-to-tail arrangement. Tension and compression can be determined by relating the sense of each vector to the original joint. For example, *A*–1 has a sense toward the joint and is in compression, while 1–*E* is away and in tension.

Since the truss is symmetrical and equally loaded, the loads in the members on the right will be equal to those on the left.

The other joints are analyzed in the same manner in steps 2 and 3; the procedure is to begin with known vectors found in the previous polygons and then solve for the unknowns. Note that the sense of the vectors is opposite at each end. Vector *A*–1 has a sense toward the left in step 1, and toward the right in step 2.

Maxwell Diagrams. The Maxwell diagram is exactly the same as the joint-by-joint analysis except that the polygons are positioned to overlap, with some vectors common to more than one polygon; separate polygons are not used for each joint. Again, Bow's notation is used to good advantage.

The first step (Fig. 14–15) is to lay out the exterior loads beginning clockwise about the truss—*AB*, *BC*, *CD*, *DE*, and *EA*—head-to-tail. A letter is placed at each end of the vectors. Since they are parallel, this polygon will be a straight line.

The structural analysis begins at the joint through which reaction *EA* acts. A free-body diagram is drawn to isolate this joint for easier analysis. The two unknowns are members *A*–1 and 1–*E*. These vectors are drawn parallel to their direction in the truss in step 1 of Fig. 14–15, with *A*–1 beginning at point *A* and 1–*E* beginning at point *E*. These directions are extended to a point of intersection, which locates point 1. Since this joint is in equilibrium, as are all joints of a system in equilibrium, the vectors must be drawn head-to-tail. Because resultant *EA* has an upward sense, vector *A*–1 must have its tail at *A*, giving it a sense toward point 1. By relating this sense to the free-body diagram, we can see that the sense is toward the point of application, which means that *A*–1 is a compression member. Vector 1–*E* has a sense away from the joint, which means that it is a tension mem-

FIGURE 14–15. TRUSS ANALYSIS

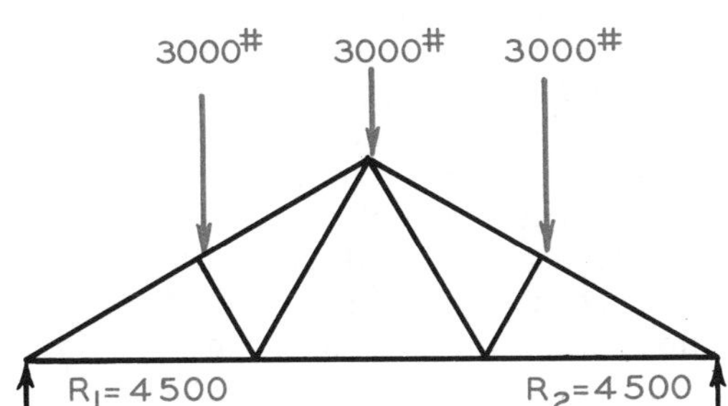

Given: A Fink truss loaded as shown.
Required: Find the stresses in each member of the truss and indicate whether each member is in compression or tension.
Reference: Article 14–12.

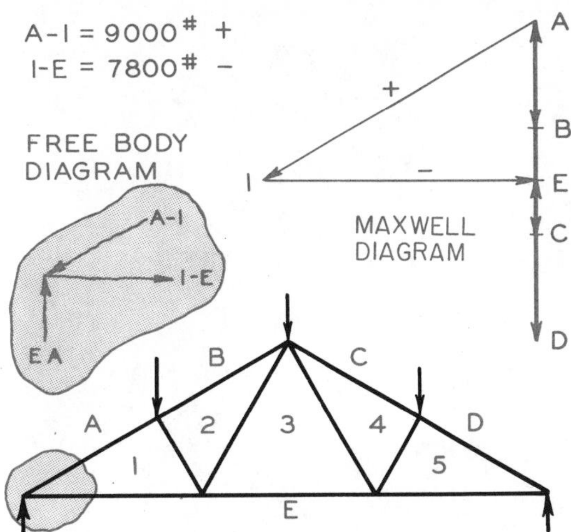

Step 1: Label the portions of supports between the outer forces of the truss with letters and the internal portions with numbers, using Bow's notation. Add the given load vectors graphically in a Maxwell diagram, and sketch a free-body diagram of the first joint to be analyzed. Using vectors *EA*, *A*–1, and 1–*E* drawn head-to-tail, draw a vector diagram to find their magnitudes. Vector *A*–1 is in compression (+) because its sense is toward the joint, and 1–*E* is in tension (—) because its sense is away from the joint.

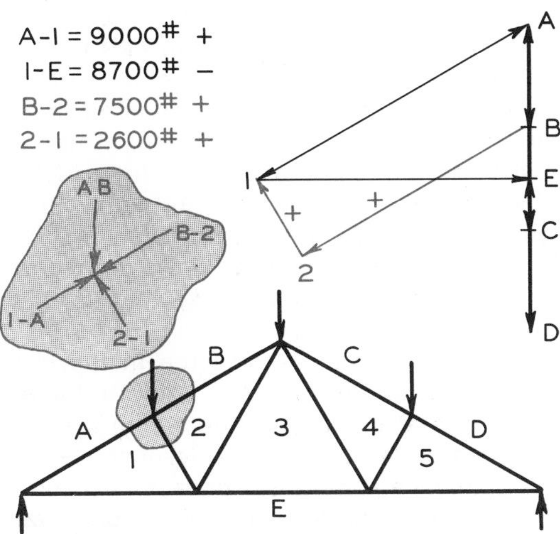

Step 2: Draw a sketch of the next joint to be analyzed. Since *AB* and *A*–1 are known, we have to determine only two unknowns, 2–1 and *B*–2. Draw these parallel to their direction, head-to-tail, in the Maxwell diagram using the existing vectors found in step 1. Vectors *B*–2 and 2–1 are in compression since each has a sense toward the joint. Note that vector *A*–1 becomes 1–*A* when read in a clockwise direction.

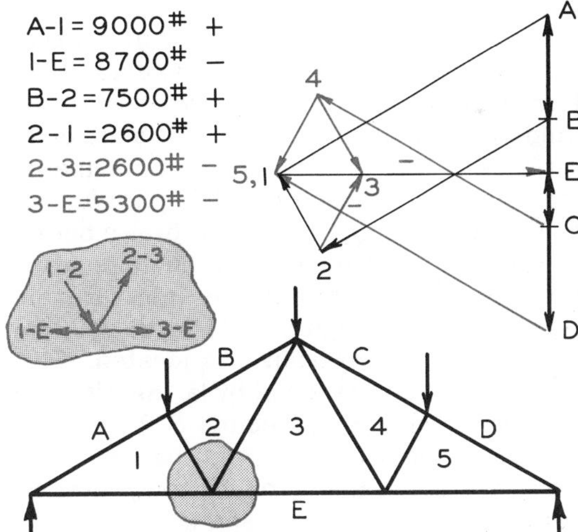

Step 3: Sketch a free-body diagram of the next joint to be analyzed. The unknowns in this case are 2–3 and 3–*E*. Determine the true length of these members in the Maxwell diagram by drawing vectors parallel to given members to find point 3. Vectors 2–3 and 3–*E* are in tension because they act away from the joint. This same process is repeated to find the loads of the members on the opposite side.

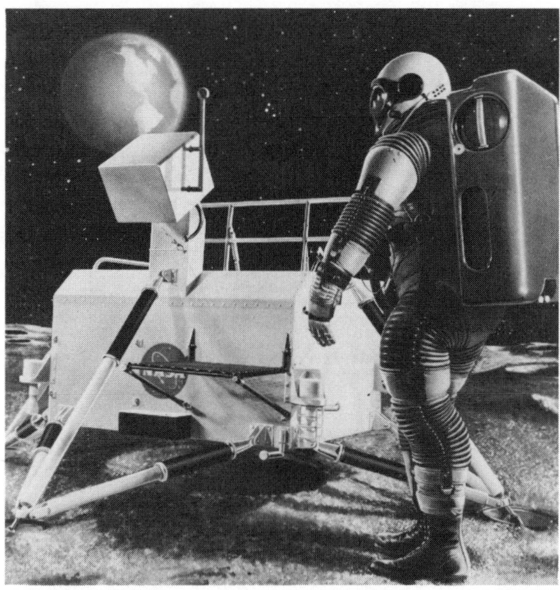

Fig. 14–16. The structural members of this tripod support for a moon vehicle can be analyzed graphically to determine design loads. (Courtesy of National Aeronautics and Space Administration.)

ber. The vectors are coplanar and can be scaled to determine their loads as tabulated.

In step 2 we select the next adjacent joint to take advantage of the load found in vector *A*–1. Vectors *A*–1 and *AB* are known, while vectors *B*–2 and 2–1 are unknown. Since there are only two unknowns it is possible to solve for them. A free-body diagram showing the joint to be analyzed is sketched. Vector *B*–2 is drawn parallel to the structural member through point *B* in the Maxwell diagram and the line of vector 2–1 is extended through point 1 until it intersects with *B*–2, where point 2 is located. The sense of each vector is found by laying off each vector head-to-tail. Both vectors *B*–2 and 2–1 have a sense toward the joint in the free-body diagram; therefore, they produce compression. Their magnitudes are scaled and tabulated.

The next joint is analyzed in sequence to find the stresses in 2–3 and 3–*E*. This construction is shown in the stress diagram in step 3. The truss will have equal forces on each side, since it is symmetrical and is loaded symmetrically. The total Maxwell diagram is drawn to illustrate the completed work in step 3. If all the polygons in the series do not close at every point with perfect symmetry, there is an error in construction. If the error of closure is very slight, it can be disregarded, since safety factors are generally applied in derivation of working stresses of structural systems to assure safe construction.

The analytical solution to this problem could be found by applying algebraic and trigonometric methods, as discussed in Article 14–11. Besides being a more tedious process, there are many possibilities for carrying an error through the series of joint analyses that would nullify all subsequent solutions. The graphical method gives a visible indication of error in projection when the polygons do not close.

14–13 NONCOPLANAR STRUCTURAL ANALYSIS —SPECIAL CASE

Structural systems that are three-dimensional require the use of descriptive geometry, since it is necessary to analyze the system in more than one plane. The manned flying system (MFS) in Fig. 14–16 can be analyzed to determine the forces that exist in the support members when on the surface of the moon (Fig. 14–17). Weight on the moon can be found by multiplying earth weight by a factor of 0.165. A tripod that must support 182 lb on earth has to support only 30 lb on the moon. This is a special case that will serve as an introduction to the general noncoplanar problem. Since members *B* and *C* lie in the same plane and appear as an edge in the front view, we need to determine only two unknowns; that is what makes this a special case.

A vector polygon is constructed in the front view in step 1 of Fig. 14–17 by drawing force *F* as a vector and using the other vectors as the other sides of the polygon. One of these vectors is actually a summation of vectors *B* and *C*. The top view is drawn using the vectors *B* and *C* to close the polygon from each end of vector *A*. In step 2, the point of intersection between the vectors in the top view is projected to the front view, where the magnitudes of vectors *B* and *C* are found. The forces are drawn to scale in the top and front views of the vector polygon,

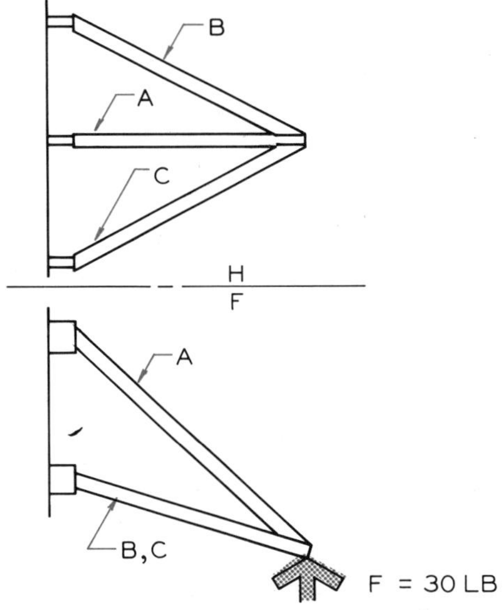

Given: The top and front views of a structural landing gear to support a portion of a craft on the moon. This footing must support 30 lb of force.
Required: Find the forces in each of the structural members *A*, *B*, and *C*.
Reference: Article 14–13.

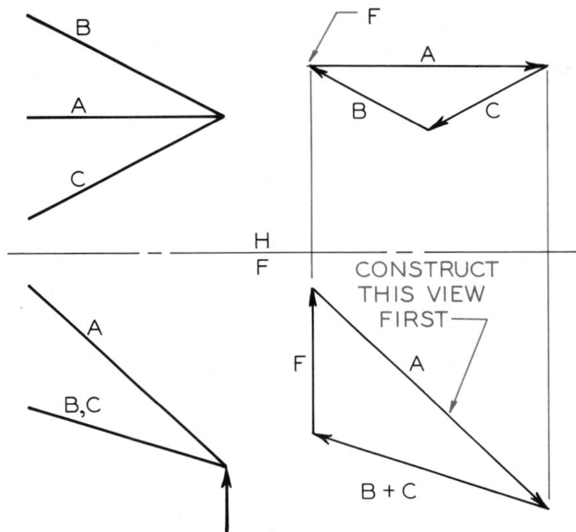

Step 1: Two forces, *B* and *C*, coincide in the front view, resulting in only two unknowns in this view. Vector *F* (30 lb) is drawn, and the other two unknowns are drawn parallel to their front view to complete the front view of the vector polygon. The top view of *A* can be found by projection, from which vectors *B* and *C* can be found.

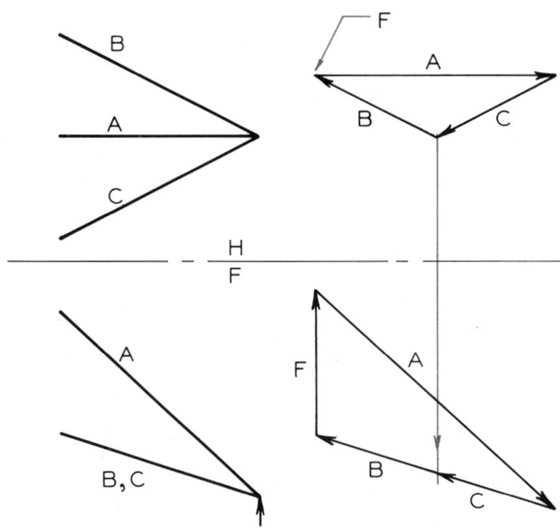

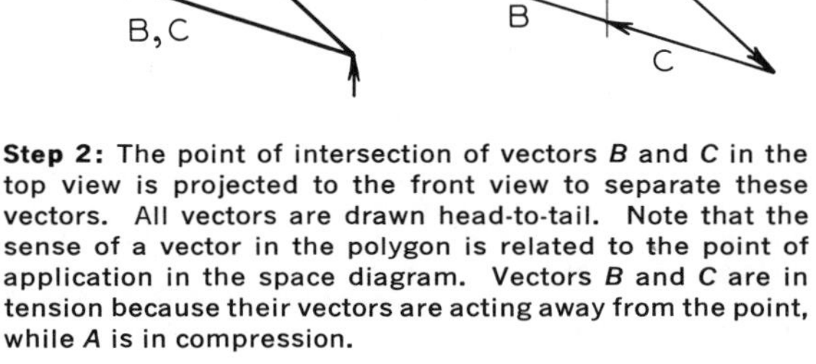

Step 2: The point of intersection of vectors *B* and *C* in the top view is projected to the front view to separate these vectors. All vectors are drawn head-to-tail. Note that the sense of a vector in the polygon is related to the point of application in the space diagram. Vectors *B* and *C* are in tension because their vectors are acting away from the point, while *A* is in compression.

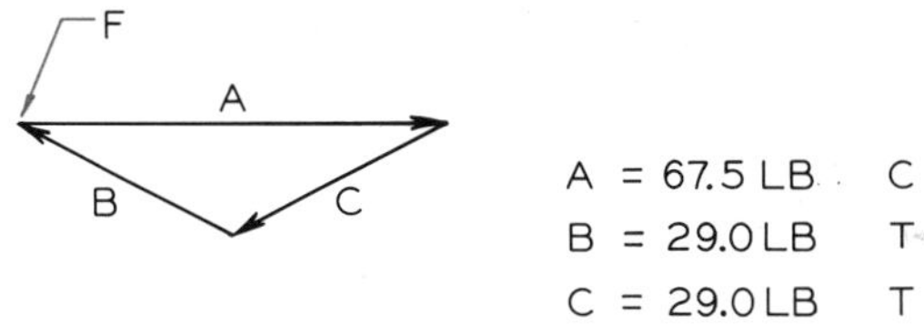

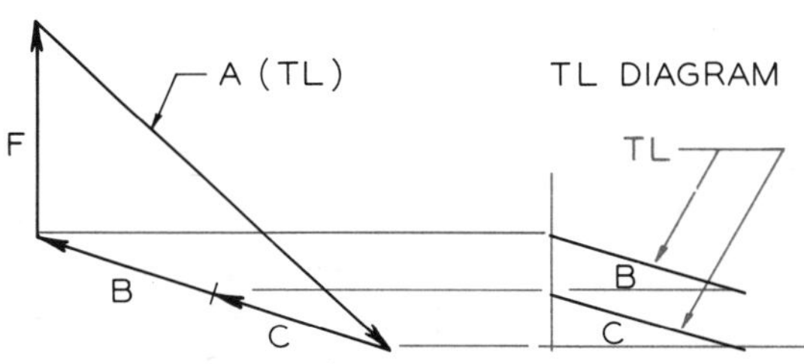

Step 3: The completed top and front views found in step 2 do not give the true lengths of vectors *B* and *C*, since they are oblique. The true lengths of these lines are determined by a true-length diagram. These lines are scaled to find the forces in each member. Refer to Article 8–6 for a review of TL diagrams.

FIGURE 14–18. NONCOPLANAR STRUCTURAL ANALYSIS—GENERAL CASE

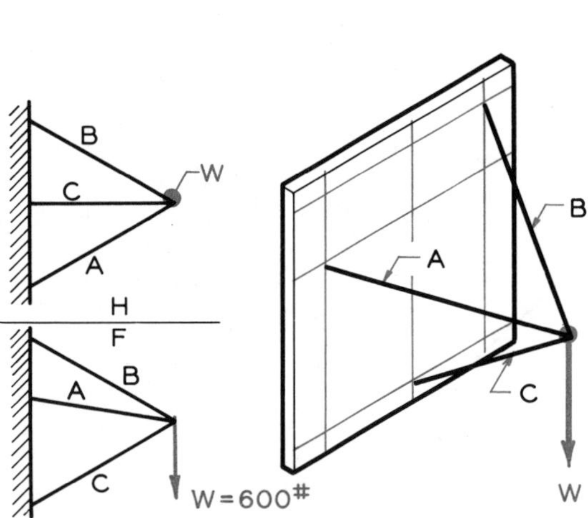

Given: The top and front views of a three-member frame which is attached to a vertical wall in such a way that it can support a maximum weight of 600 lb.
Required: Find the loads in the structural members.
References: Articles 14–12, 14–14.

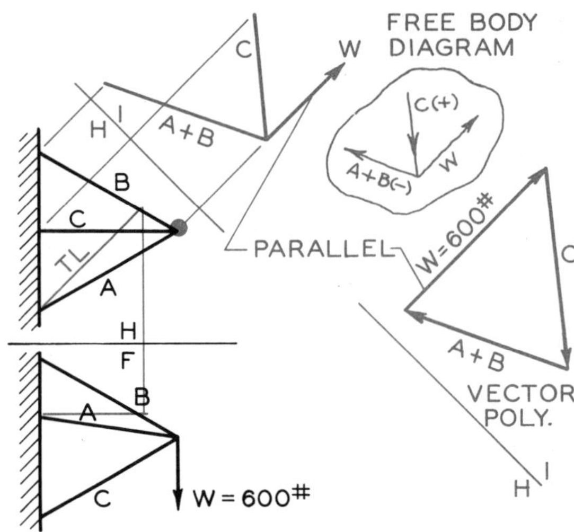

Step 1: To limit the unknowns to two, construct an auxiliary view to find two vectors lying in the edge view of a plane. Use the auxiliary view and top view in the remainder of the problem. Draw a vector polygon parallel to the members in the auxiliary view in which $W = 600$ lb is the only known vector. Sketch a free-body diagram for preliminary analysis.

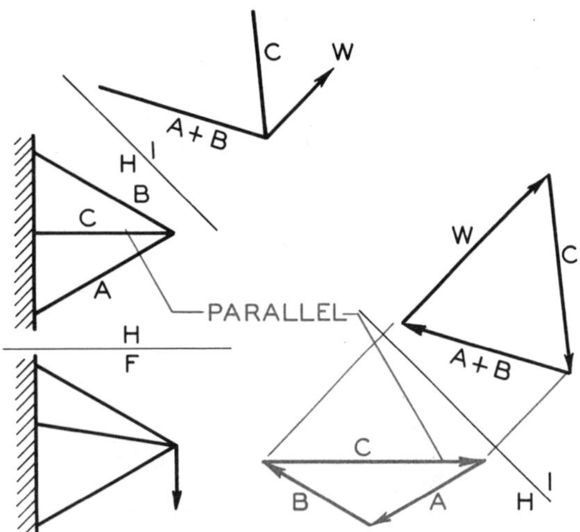

Step 2: Construct an orthographic projection of the view of the vector polygon found in step 1 so that its vectors are parallel to the members in the top view. The reference plane between the two views is parallel to the H–1 plane. This portion of the problem is closely related to the problem in Fig. 14–17.

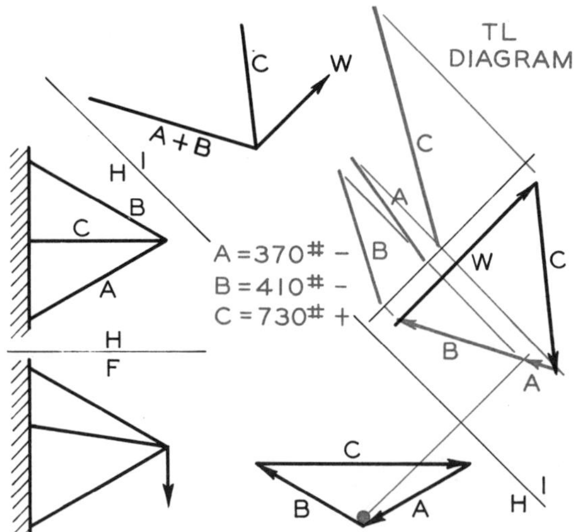

Step 3: Project the intersection of vectors A and B in the horizontal view of the vector polygon to the auxiliary view polygon to establish the lengths of vectors A and B. Determine the true lengths of all vectors in a true-length diagram and measure them to determine their magnitudes. Analyze for tension or compression, as covered in Article 14–12.

but they cannot be measured since they are oblique and foreshortened.

The true lengths of the vectors are found in a true-length diagram in step 3. (Refer to Article 8–6 if necessary, to review construction of true-length diagrams.) The vectors are measured to determine their loads. Vector *A* is found to be in compression because its sense is toward the point of concurrency. Vectors *B* and *C* are in tension.

14–14 NONCOPLANAR STRUCTURAL ANALYSIS —GENERAL CASE

The structural frame shown in Fig. 14–18 is attached to a vertical wall to support a load of $W = 600$ lb. The loads in each member must be determined prior to the selection of the structural shapes. Since there are three unknowns in each of the views, we are required to construct an auxiliary view that will give the edge view of a plane containing two of the vectors, thereby reducing the number of unknowns to two (step 1). Once the top and primary auxiliary views are constructed by following the general steps as illustrated in the special case in Fig. 14–17, we no longer need to refer to the front view. A vector polygon is drawn by constructing vectors parallel to the members in the auxiliary view (step 1). An adjacent orthographic view of the vector polygon is also drawn by constructing its vectors parallel to the members in the top view (step 2). These two views of the vector polygon give the spatial orientation of the vectors; however, they are foreshortened in both views. A true-length diagram is used in step 3 to find the true length of the vectors so they can be scaled to determine their magnitudes.

The cranes on the huge construction barges shown in Fig. 14–19 are examples of noncoplanar, concurrent structural systems that can be solved by application of the previously covered principles. The loads in each of these members will vary as the position of each member changes. Other examples of a three-dimensional system are the side-boom tractors used for lowering pipe into a ditch during pipeline construction (Fig. 14–20).

Fig. 14–19. The cranes on huge construction barges represent force systems whose member loads can be solved for by vectors. (Courtesy of Humble Oil and Refining Company.)

Fig. 14–20. Tractor sidebooms represent noncoplanar, concurrent systems of forces that can be solved graphically. (Courtesy of Trunkline Gas Company.)

FIGURE 14–21. RESULTANT OF NONCONCURRENT FORCES

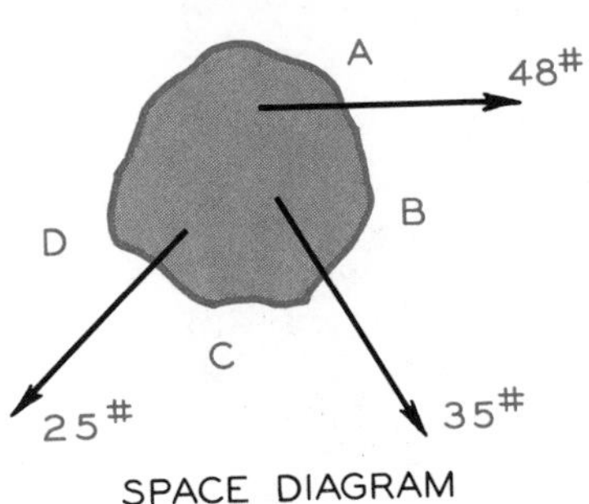

SPACE DIAGRAM

Required: Find the resultant of the known forces applied to this object. The forces are nonconcurrent.

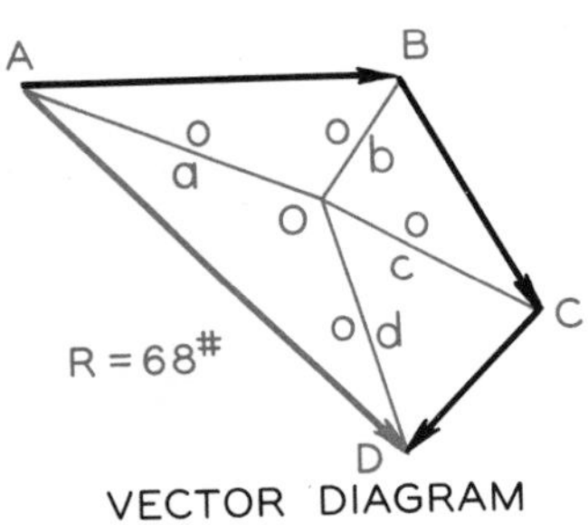

VECTOR DIAGRAM

Step 1: The vectors are drawn head-to-tail to find resultant *R*. Point *O* is conveniently located for the construction of strings to the ends of each vector.

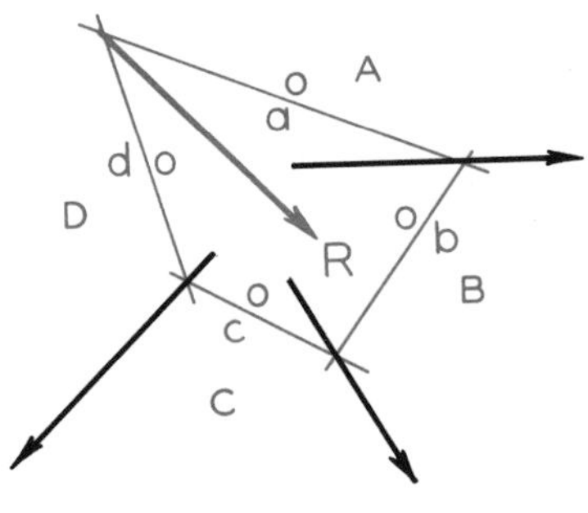

FUNICULAR DIAGRAM

Step 2: Each string is drawn between the two vectors to which it applies in the original space diagram. *Example: o–c* between *BC* and *CD*. These strings are connected in sequence until the strings *o–a* and *o–d* establish the position of *R*, which was found in step 1.

Fig. 14–22. Handwheels are designed for operation by the application of forces in the form of couples. (Courtesy of Standard Oil Company.)

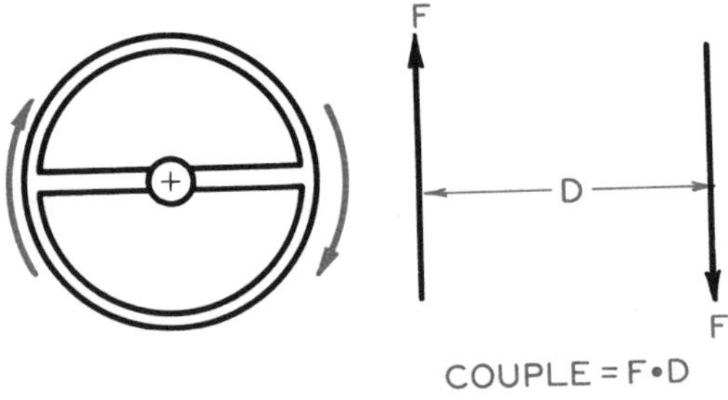

Fig. 14–23. Representation of a couple or moment.

14–15 NONCONCURRENT, COPLANAR VECTORS

Forces *may* be applied in such a manner that they are not concurrent, as illustrated in Fig. 14–21. Bow's notation can be used to locate the resultant of this type of nonconcurrent system.

In step 1, the vectors are laid off to form a vector diagram in which the closing vector is the resultant, $R = 68$ lb. Each vector is resolved into two components by randomly locating point *O* on the interior or exterior of the polygon and connecting point *O* with the end of each vector. The components, or strings, from point *O* are equal and opposite components of adjacent vectors. For example, component *o–b* is common to vectors *AB* and *BC*. Since the strings from point *O* are equal and opposite, the system has not changed statically.

FIGURE 14-24. COUPLE RESULTANTS

SPACE DIAGRAM

10#

A B C D

4# 6#

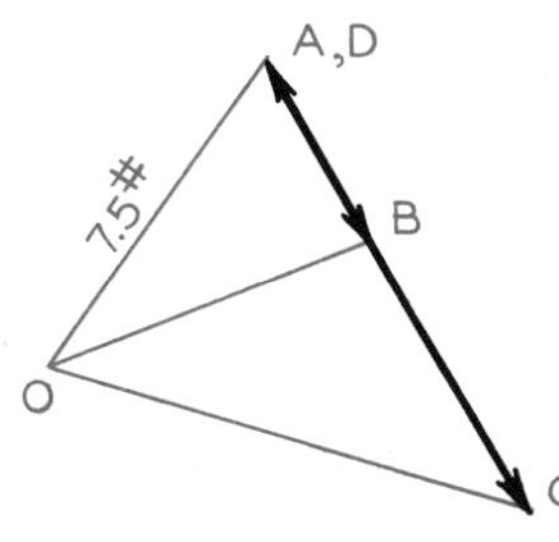

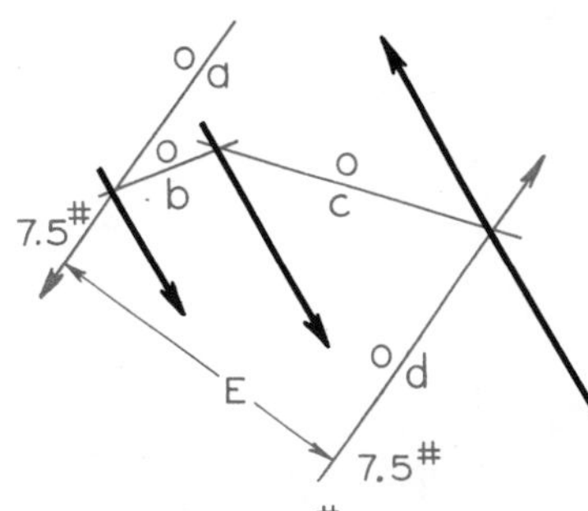

Required: Find the resultant of these nonconcurrent forces applied to this beam.

Step 1: The spaces between each force are labeled in Bow's notation.

Step 2: The vectors are laid out head-to-tail; they will lie in a straight line since they are parallel. Pole point *O* is located in a convenient location and the ends of each vector are connected with point *O*.

Step 3: Strings *o–a*, *o–b*, *o–c*, and *o–d* are successively drawn between the vectors to which they apply. Since strings *o–a* and *o–d* are parallel, the resultant will be a couple equal to 7.5 lb × *E*, where *E* is the distance between *o–a* and *o–d*.

In step 2, each string is transferred to the space diagram of the vectors where it is drawn between the respective vectors to which it applies. (The figure thus produced is called a funicular diagram.) For instance, string *o–b* is drawn in the area between vectors *AB* and *BC*. String *o–c* is drawn in the *C*-area to connect at the intersection of *o–b* and vector *BC*. The point of intersection of the last two strings, *o–a* and *o–d*, locates a point through which the resultant *R* will pass. The resultant has now been determined with respect to magnitude, sense, direction, and point of application, thus completing the solution of the problem.

14-16 NONCONCURRENT SYSTEMS RESULTING IN COUPLES

A *couple* is the descriptive name given to two parallel and equal but opposite forces which are separated by a distance and applied to a member in such a manner that they cause the member to rotate. The handwheels in Fig. 14-22 are examples of mechanical systems which take advantage of this method of force application.

An important quantity associated with a couple is its *moment.* The moment of any force is a measure of its rotational effect. An example is shown in Fig. 14-23, in which two equal and opposite forces are applied to a wheel. The forces are separated by the distance *D*. The moment of the couple is found by multiplying one of the forces by the perpendicular distance between it and a point on the line of action of the other: $F \times D$. If the force is 20 lb and the distance is 3 ft, the moment of the couple would be given as 60 ft-lb.

A series of parallel forces is applied to a beam in Fig. 14-24. The spaces between the vectors

Fig. 14–25. The boom of this crane can be analyzed for its resultant as a parallel, nonconcurrent system of forces when the cables have been disregarded.

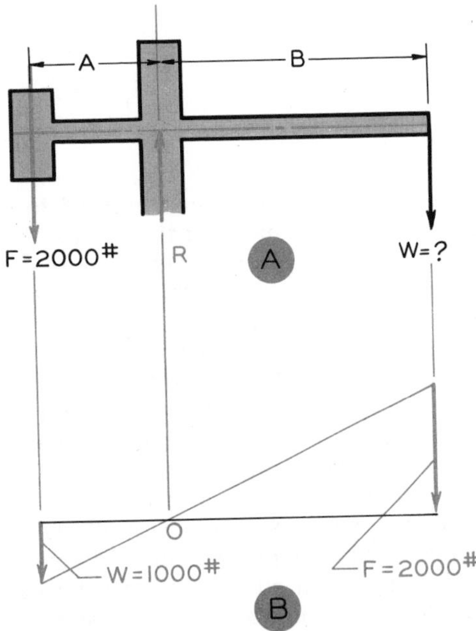

Fig. 14–26. Determining the resultant of parallel, nonconcurrent forces.

are labeled with letters which follow Bow's notation. We are required to determine the resultant.

After constructing a vector diagram, we have a straight line which is parallel to the direction of the forces and which closes at point *A*. We then locate pole point *O* and draw the strings of a funicular diagram.

The strings are transferred to the space diagram, where they are drawn in their respective spaces. For example, *o–c* is drawn in the *C*-space between vectors *BC* and *CD*. The last two strings, *o–d* and *o–a* do not close at a common point, but are found to be parallel; the result is therefore a couple. The distance between the forces of the couple is the perpendicular distance, *E*, between strings *o–a* and *o–d* in the space diagram, using the scale of the space diagram. The magnitude of the force is the scaled distance from point *O* to *A* and *D* in the vector diagram, using the scale of the vector diagram. The moment of the couple is equal to 7.5 lb × *E* in a counterclockwise direction.

14–17 RESULTANT OF PARALLEL, NONCONCURRENT FORCES

Forces applied to beams, such as those shown in Fig. 14–25, are parallel and nonconcurrent in many instances, and they may have the effect of a couple, tending to cause a rotational motion. When the loads exerted on the beams are known, the magnitude and location of the total resultant or equilibrant can be found. This will provide the designer with a better understanding of where supports should be placed.

The beam in Fig. 14–26 is on a rotational crane that is used to move building materials in a limited area. The magnitude of the weight *W* is unknown, but the counterbalance weight is known to be 2000 lb; column *R* supports the beam as shown. Assuming that the support cables have been omitted, we desire to find the weight *W* that would balance the beam.

This problem can be solved by the application of the law of moments, i.e., the force is multiplied by the perpendicular distance to its line of action from a given point, or $F \times A$. If the beam is to be in balance, the total effect of the moments must be equal to zero, or $F \times A = W \times B$. Since W is the only unknown, we may solve for it algebraically. This equation is an inverse proportion that can also be solved graphically.

The graphical solution (Fig. 14–26B) is found by constructing a line to represent the total distance between the forces F and W. Point O is projected from the space diagram to this line. Point O is the point of balance where the summation of the moments will be equal to zero. Vectors F and W are drawn to scale at each end of the line by transposing them to the opposite ends of the beam. A line is drawn from the end of vector F through point O and extended to intersect the direction of vector W. This point represents the end of vector W, which can be scaled, resulting in a magnitude of 1000 lb. This method of construction could also be used to locate the position of a resultant and to determine its magnitude if only the applied forces, F and W, were known.

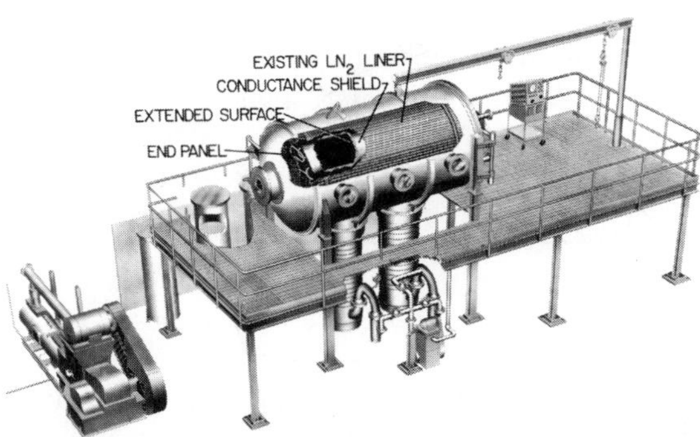

Fig. 14–27. The forces applied to the overhead beam can be analyzed graphically. (Courtesy of Arnold Air Force Station, Aro Inc.)

14–18 RESULTANT OF PARALLEL, NONCONCURRENT FORCES ON A BEAM

When two or more forces are applied to a beam that is supported at more than one point, such as the overhead beam in the aerospace research facility shown in Fig. 14–27, a somewhat different approach is taken to locate the resultant of the system. However, we shall use both a funicular diagram and Bow's notation to aid in the solution.

The beam given in Fig. 14–28 is supported at each end and must in turn support three given loads. We are required to determine the magnitude of each support, R_1 and R_2, along with the resultant of the loads and its location. The spaces between all vectors are labeled in a clockwise direction with Bow's notation in the space diagram in step 1.

In step 2 the lines of force in the space diagram are extended and the strings from the vector diagram are drawn in their respective spaces, parallel to their original direction. *Example:* String *oa* is drawn parallel to string *OA* in space *A* between forces *EA* and *AB*, and string *ob* is drawn in space *B* beginning at the intersection of *oa* with vector *AB*. The last string, *oe*, is drawn to close the funicular diagram. The direction of string *oe* is transferred to the force diagram, where it is laid off through point *O* to intersect the load line at point *E*. Vector *DE* represents support R_2 (refer to Bow's notation as it was applied in step 1). Vector *EA* represents support R_1. This is the method for finding the resultants at each end of the beam.

The magnitude of the resultant of the loads (step 3) is the summation of the vertical downward forces, or the distance from *A* to *D*, or 500 lb. The location of the resultant is found by extending the extreme outside strings in the funicular diagram, *oa* and *od*, to their point of intersection. The resultant is discovered to have a magnitude of 500 lb, a vertical direction, a downward sense, and a point of application established by $\overline{X}$. This location would be important to an engineer if he intended to locate a third support under the beam.

FIGURE 14–28. BEAM ANALYSIS WITH PARALLEL LOADS

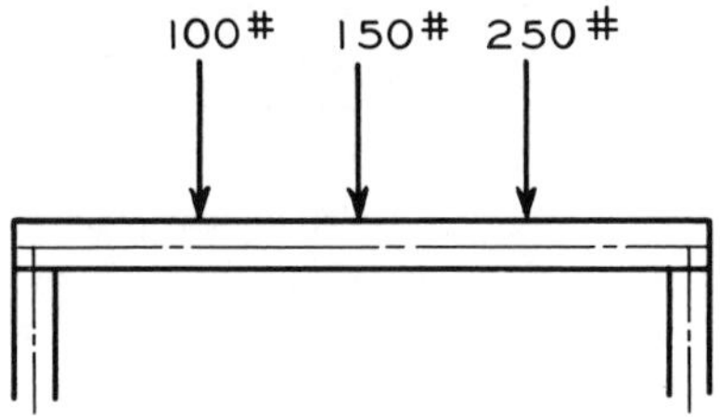

Given: A beam that is loaded with three parallel, unequal loads.
Required: Find the reactions R_1 and R_2 and the total resultant that will replace the parallel loads.
Reference: Article 14–18.

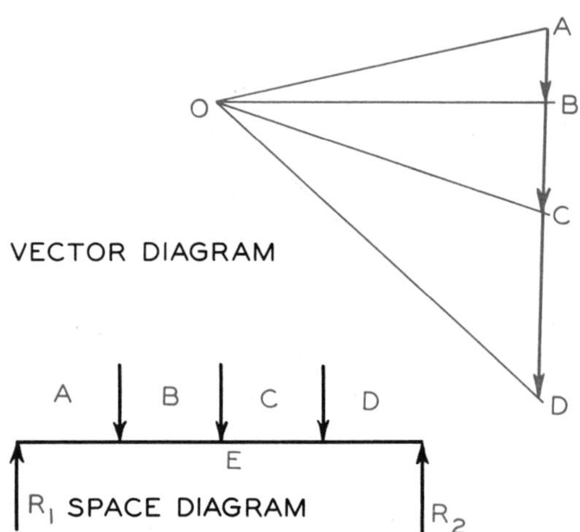

Step 1. Letter the spaces between the loads with Bow's notation. Find the graphical summation of the vectors by drawing them head-to-tail in a vector diagram at a convenient scale. Locate pole *O* at a convenient location and draw strings from point *O* to each end of the vectors.

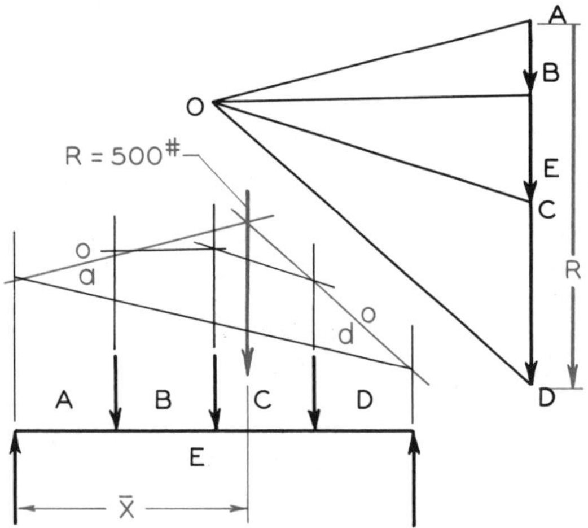

Step 2: Extend the lines of force in the space diagram, and draw a funicular diagram with string *oa* in the *A*-space, *ob* in the *B*-space, *oc* in the *C*-space, etc. The last string, which is drawn to close the diagram, is *oe*. Transfer this string to the vector polygon and use it to locate point *E*, thus establishing the lengths of R_1 and R_2 which are *EA* and *DE*, respectively.

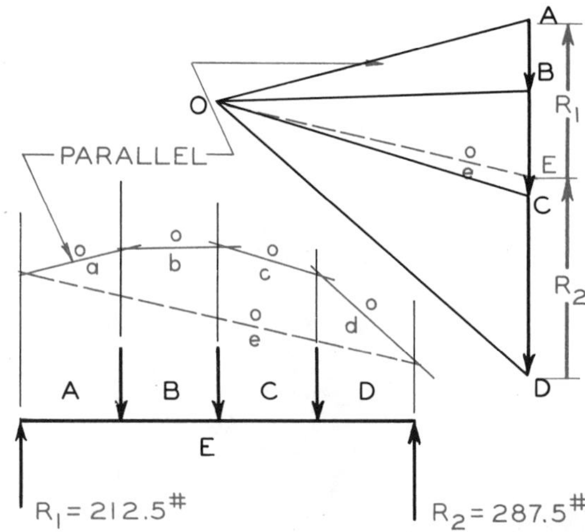

Step 3: The resultant of the three downward forces will be equal to their graphical summation, line *AD*. Locate the resultant by extending strings *oa* and *od* in the funicular diagram to a point of intersection. The resultant $R = 500$ lb, will act through this point in a downward direction. $\overline{X}$ is a locating dimension.

Figure 14-29 shows a number of beams that had to be analyzed to determine their resultants and reactions. In a structure of this type, most of the forces applied are in a vertical direction, and the support members are also vertical.

Fig. 14-29. Structural beams are examples of parallel, nonconcurrently loaded beams. (Courtesy of Jones and Laughlin Steel Corporation.)

14-19 PRODUCT DESIGN—ANALYSIS

The product design example which has been used to illustrate the application of principles covered in each chapter is used here to illustrate the application of graphical principles to its analysis. The problem is restated below.

Hunting seat problem. Many hunters, especially deer hunters, hunt from trees to obtain a better vantage point. Sitting in a tree for several hours can be uncomfortable and hazardous to the hunter, thus indicating a need for a hunting seat that could be used to improve this situation. Design a seat that would provide the hunter with comfort and safety while he is hunting from a tree and that would meet the general requirements of economy and limitations of hunting.

The refinement of the design was discussed in Chapter 6 to illustrate how graphical methods apply to that stage of the design process. Worksheets 6 and 7 were shown in Fig. 6-21 and 6-22. The dimensions that were determined during refinement in Fig. 6-22 are now used as a basis for the vector analysis. These dimensions have been used on work sheet 8 (Fig. 14-30) to construct a space diagram from which a vector analysis of the seat's support system will be made. Only line representations are needed at this stage, since the structural system was determined in preliminary form in the refinement step. Lines will represent the center lines of the support members, which will be converted to vectors in the manner illustrated in this chapter.

It is assumed that a hunter weighing 210 lb, including hunting gear, is to be supported in the seat suspended from a tree by a cable attached at point O. This means that an opposite and equal force of 210 lb must be exerted at point O in an upward direction. This force is scaled as a vector, which is drawn adjacent to the front view. Since all support members lie

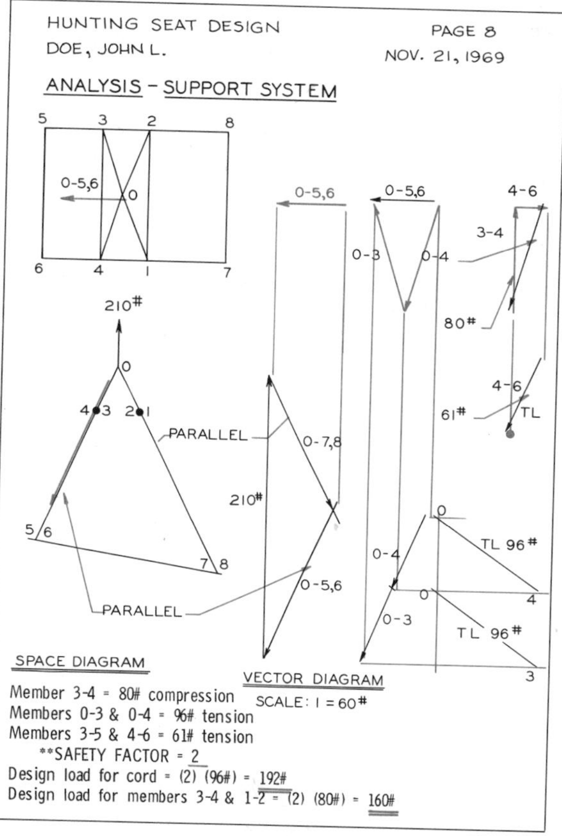

Fig. 14-30. Analysis work sheet of the hunting seat design.

in two planes that appear as edges in the front view, it is possible to determine the portion of the total load that will be supported by the left and right sides as shown in the vector diagram. It can be seen that the left side carries a greater load than the right side, since point *O* is off center and to the left. The vector which represents the load to be supported by the left side of the support system is not equal to the force in any single member, but is a frontal vector that will be divided into components, as shown in the vector diagram in the center of the work sheet. The top and front views of the vector polygon give the components of the resultant force, which are measured to be 96 lb in the true-length diagram. This is the load in both members *O*–4 and *O*–3. Using vector *O*–4, it is possible to determine, by a third vector polygon, the two unknown vectors that are concurrent at point 4 in the top view of the space diagram. Members 4–6 and 3–4 are found, thus completing the analysis of forces on the heavier-loaded side.

This is a special problem since the forces are symmetrical about a frontal plane, through point *O*, which appears as an edge in the top view of the space diagram. A safety factor of 2 is used to ensure that adequate strength is provided to support the seat. The greatest load in single members, with a safety factor of 2, is in members *O*–3 and *O*–4, which have a design load of 192 lb. The load of the single cable supporting the system is 210 lb, or 420 lb when a factor of 2 is applied. The intermediate cords should be selected to withstand 192 lb. The stiffener, 3–4, should be selected to withstand 160 lb of compression.

Other analyses of this type can be applied to other components of the seat's structural system. Only this work sheet is shown as an example of the application of graphical methods. It would be beneficial to check this problem by the mathematical method to compare the results of each approach.

14–20 SUMMARY

The analysis of forces is a prominent part of engineering and technology. It can be seen from the examples in this chapter that graphical methods have many applications in this area of analysis. In fact, the graphical method frequently has advantages over the conventional mathematical approach to the analysis of forces. The graphical method is much faster and presents fewer chances for errors that accumulate, as in the analytical method.

A number of more sophisticated graphical methods are available for solving advanced problems; however, these solutions are based almost entirely on the fundamental problems covered in this chapter. A mastery of the fundamentals will provide a broad background for grasping the principles of complex problems which will be encountered in more advanced courses.

PROBLEMS

General

Problems should be presented *in instrument drawings* on $8\frac{1}{2}'' \times 11''$ paper, grid or plain, using the format introduced in Article 1–19. Each grid square represents $\frac{1}{4}''$. All notes, sketches, drawings, and graphical work should be neatly prepared in keeping with good practices. Written matter should be legibly lettered using $\frac{1}{8}''$ guide lines.

1. In Fig. 14–31(A), determine the resultant of the force system by the parallelogram method at the left of the sheet. Solve the same system using the vector polygon method at the right of the sheet. Scale: $1'' = 100$ lb (note that each gird square equals $\frac{1}{4}''$). (B) In part B of the figure, determine the resultant of the concurrent, coplanar force system shown at

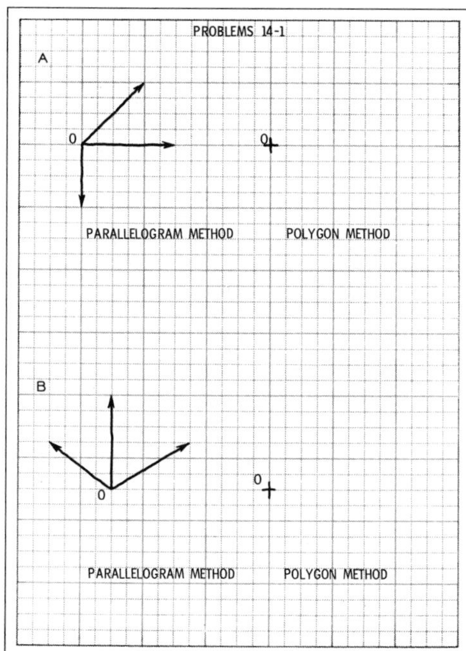

Fig. 14–31. Resultant of concurrent, coplanar vectors.

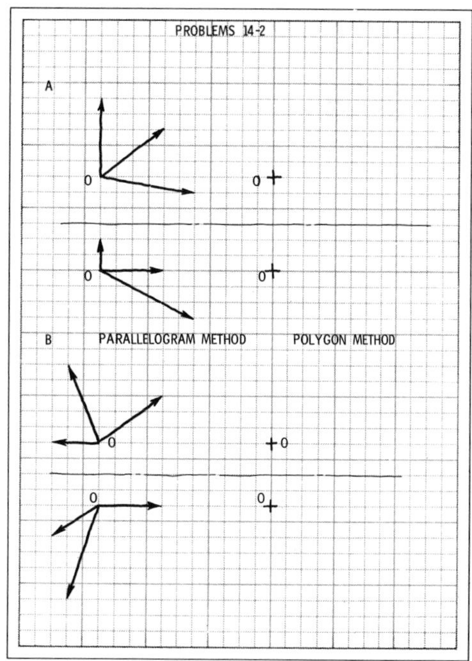

Fig. 14–32. Resultant of concurrent, noncoplanar vectors.

the left of the sheet by the parallelogram method. Solve the same system using the polygon method at the right of the sheet. Scale $1'' = 100$ lb.

2. (A and B) In Fig. 14–32, solve for the resultant of each of the concurrent, noncoplanar force systems by the parallelogram method at the left of the sheet. Solve for the resultant of the same systems by the vector polygon method at the right of the sheet. Find the true length of the resultant in both problems. Letter all construction. Scale: $1'' = 600$ lb.

3. (A and B) In Fig. 14–33, the concurrent, coplanar force systems are in equilibrium. Find the loads in each structural member. Use a scale of $1'' = 300$ lb in part A and a scale of $1'' = 200$ lb in part B. Show and label all construction.

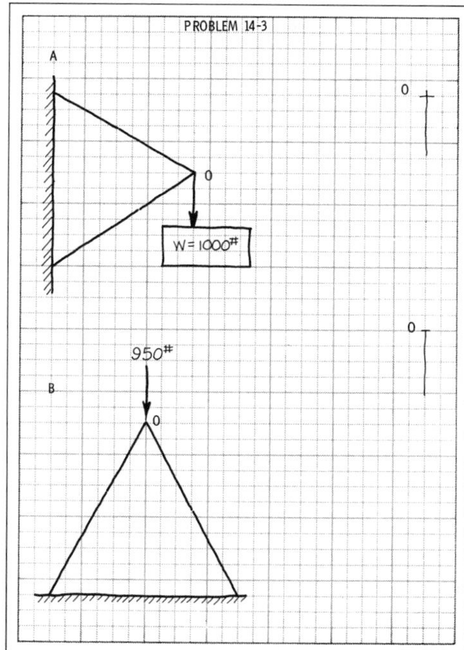

Fig. 14–33. Coplanar, concurrent forces in equilibrium.

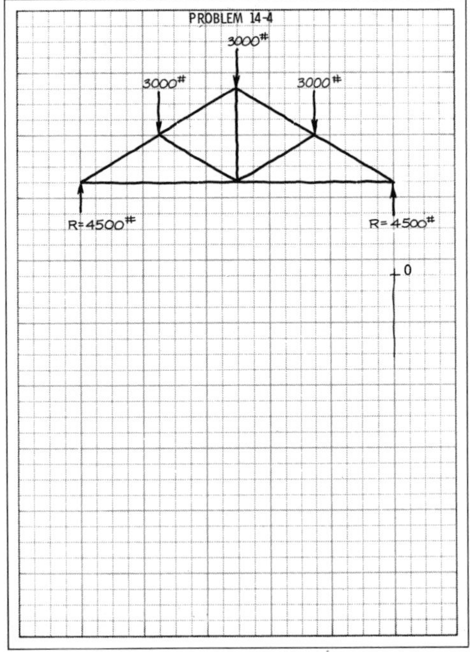

Fig. 14–34. Truss analysis.

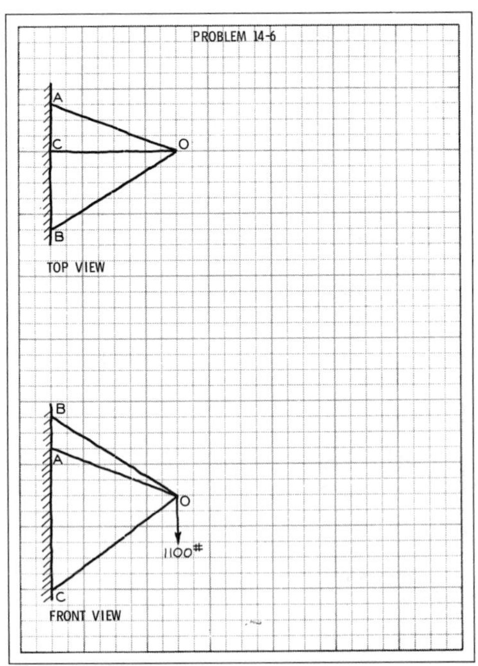

Fig. 14–36. Noncoplanar, concurrent forces in equilibrium.

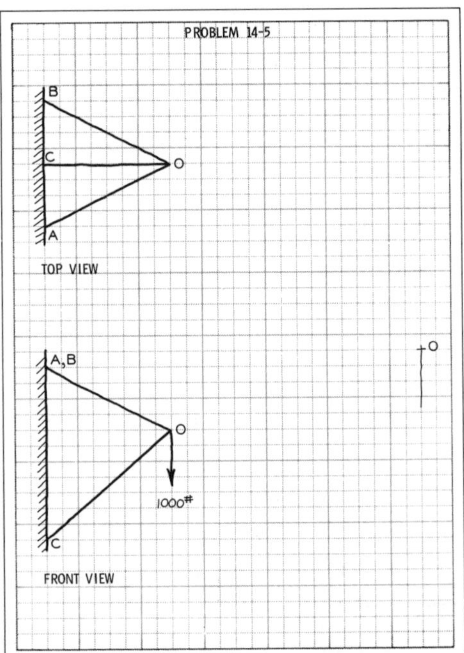

Fig. 14–35. Noncoplanar, concurrent forces in equilibrium.

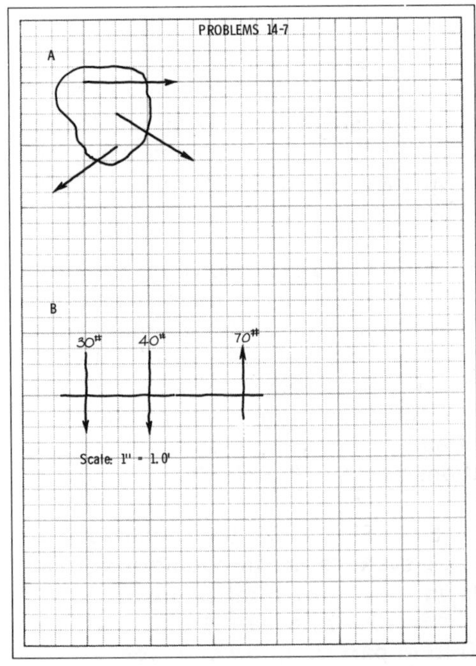

Fig. 14–37. Coplanar, nonconcurrent forces.

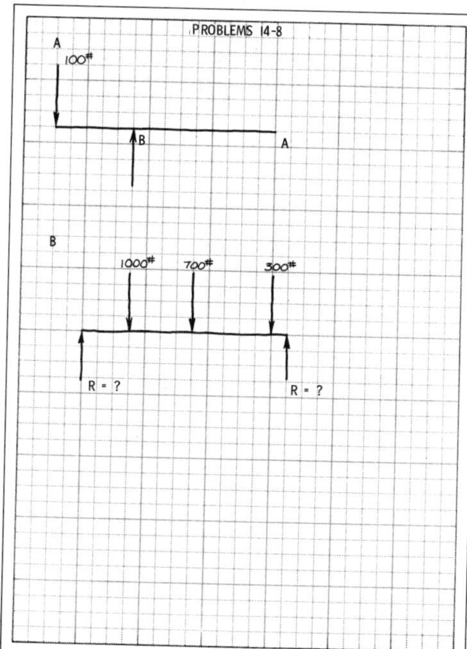

Fig. 14–38. Beam analysis.

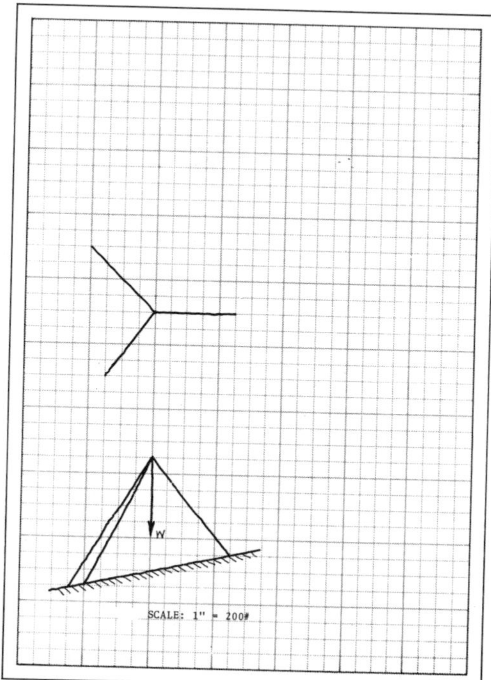

Fig. 14–39. Beam analysis.

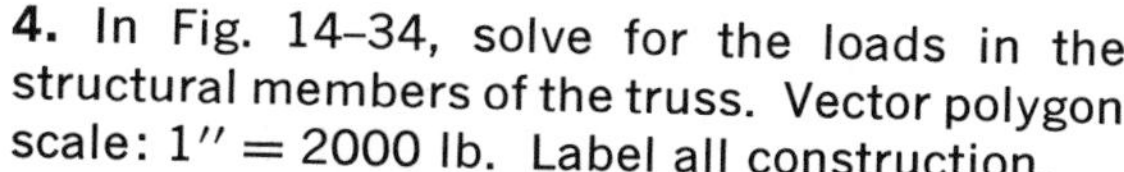

4. In Fig. 14–34, solve for the loads in the structural members of the truss. Vector polygon scale: $1'' = 2000$ lb. Label all construction.

5. In Fig. 14–35, solve for the loads in the structural members of the concurrent, noncoplanar force system. Find the true length of all vectors. Scale: $1'' = 300$ lb.

6. In Fig. 14–36, solve for the loads in the structural members of the concurrent, noncoplanar force system. Find the true length of all vectors. Scale: $1'' = 400$ lb.

7. (A) In Fig. 14–37, find the resultant of the coplanar, nonconcurrent force system. The vectors are drawn to a scale of $1'' = 100$ lb. (B) In part B of the figure, solve for the resultant of the coplanar, nonconcurrent force system. The vectors are given in their true positions and at the true distances from each other. The space diagram is drawn to scale of $1'' = 1.0'$. Draw the vectors to a scale of $1'' = 30$ lb. Show all construction.

8. (A) In Fig. 14–38, determine the force that must be applied at *A* to balance the horizontal member supported at *B*. Scale $1'' = 100$ lb. (B) In part B of the figure, find the resultants at each end of the horizontal beam. Find the resultant of the downward loads and determine where it would be positioned. Scale: $1'' = 600$ lb.

9. Determine the forces in the three members of the tripod in Fig. 14–39. The tripod supports a load of $W = 250$ lb. Find the true lengths of all vectors.

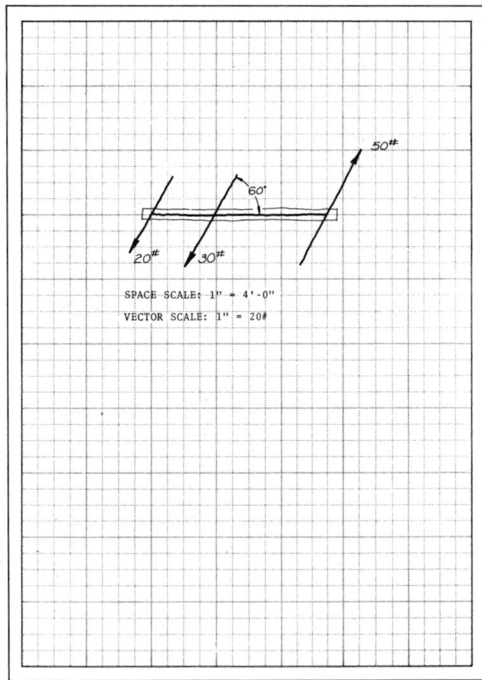

Fig. 14–40. Noncoplanar, concurrent forces in equilibrium.

10. The vectors in Fig. 14–40 each make an angle of 60° with the structural member on which they are applied. Find the resultant of this force system. Refer to Article 14–16.

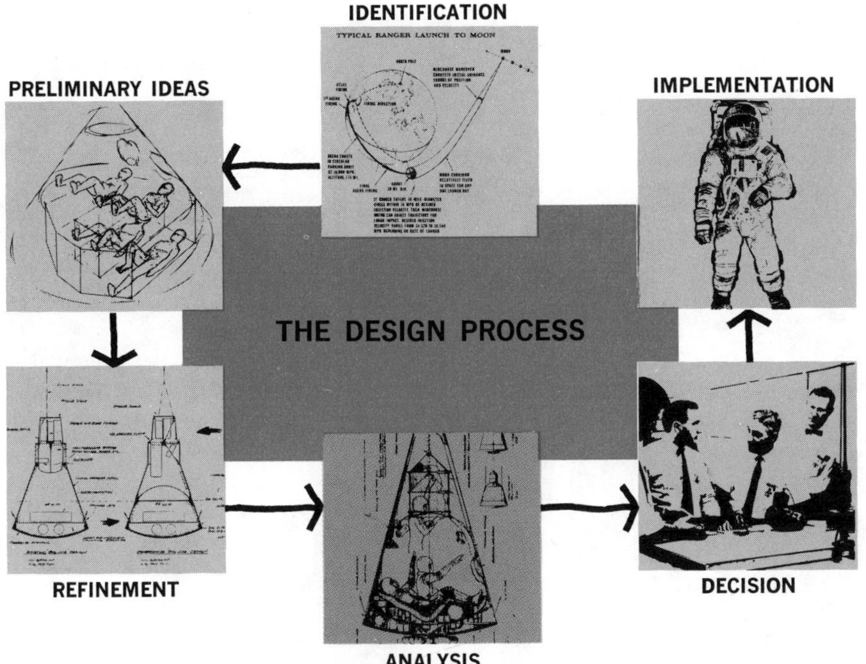

15 ANALYSIS OF DESIGN DATA

15–1 GENERAL

Before a proposed design is accepted, it must be subjected to a careful analysis. During this process, data provided in many forms must be evaluated and interpreted. Most frequently, data are submitted in numerical form whose interpretation is often a lengthy and difficult procedure. Thus, to ensure that each member of the design team understands all aspects of the project (Fig. 15–1), it is customary to convert numerical data to a more convenient form.

Design information may be analyzed in a variety of forms. The more fundamental ones are: (1) graphs, (2) empirical equations, (3) mechanisms, (4) graphical calculus, and (5) nomograms. We shall discuss these areas of analysis to determine whether the presentation of data can be made easier through the use of graphics, since the graphic portrayal of tabular data allows a review of a large amount of data at a glance. Many data that are obtained from laboratory experiments or physical relationships can be expressed in terms of mathematical equations. This approach is helpful in that it establishes mathematical relationships that might not be apparent in the initial data. Graphical techniques can be used to advantage in determining the equation form of empirical data when such an equation exists. Using mathematical and analytical procedures (Fig. 15–2), mechanisms can be analyzed graphically for motion, function, clearance, and interference. Calculus problems can be solved graphically within the limits of reasonable accuracy. Thus the designer has at his disposal a variety of graphical procedures to supplement his analytical approach to studying a design.

15-1

15-2

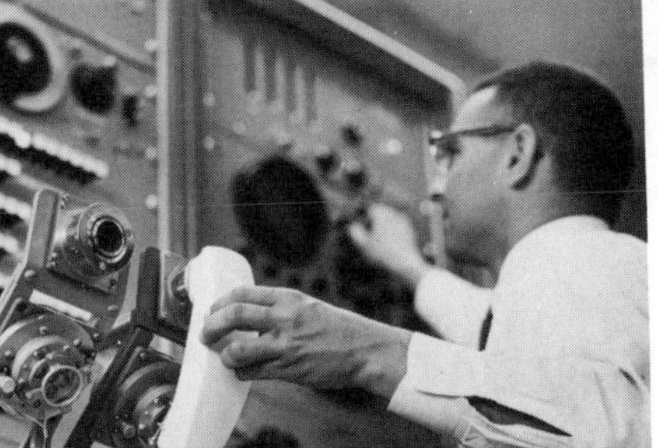

15-3

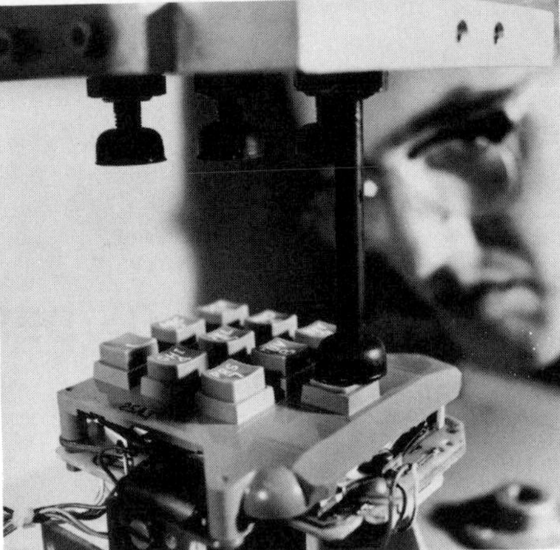

15-4

Fig. 15-1. Engineering aspects of a toy engine are discussed by an industrial team. All aspects of the design and its analysis must be considered in detail before the design can be accepted for mass production. (Courtesy of Mattel, Inc.)

Fig. 15-2. Most products are tested extensively as a means of gathering data for analysis of the design; this testing is also important to effective quality control. (Courtesy of Mattel, Inc.)

Fig. 15-3. A prototype of a Dial-In-Handset telephone is tested with special sound equipment to determine its transmission qualities. (Courtesy of Bell Telephone Laboratories.)

Fig. 15-4. A Touch-Tone dial button tester is used to test the operational effectiveness of a telephone unit. (Courtesy of Bell Telephone Laboratories.)

15-2 INTRODUCTION TO GRAPHS

Any design can be evaluated to a considerable degree by reviewing the data that pertain to it. These data may fall into many different categories. Some of the basic ones are: (1) field data, (2) market data, (3) design-performance data and (4) comparative data.

Field data may affect a design directly or indirectly. A traffic engineer must gather information about traffic flow, driving habits, peak periods of volume, and traffic speed before he can prepare a new design for a traffic system at a given location. On-the-site observations and counts are made during representative periods and tabulated. It is also advisable to gather data on current designs that are believed to be satisfactory, to verify whether or not they are indeed as functional as they appear. Often, field data can be obtained from existing agencies. For instance, records of average temperatures, rainfall, and other weather data are usually maintained by local weather departments.

Market data are evaluated to determine the probable acceptance of an engineering project whether it is a supersonic aircraft or a household appliance; they serve as a guide in arriving at decisions concerning the market of a product. It is necessary to obtain information about the characteristics of the prospective users of the design, such as numbers, needs, average incomes, etc. Data about existing competition in the field are also of considerable value. No company will wish to produce a product for the general market that is too expensive for the typical consumer. Likewise, it would be poor planning to invest engineering funds in a public project that would not serve enough people. Data concerning populations, incomes, areas of population density, and statistical information are available from the Department of Labor and the U. S. Census Bureau, as well as state and local agencies. However, market data are meaningless unless they are presented in an understandable form which clarifies trends and existing situations.

Design performance must be studied to determine the effectiveness of a finished design. Frequently, a prototype is constructed specifically for testing the operation of the design prior to all-out production (Fig. 15–3). Most products are continuously evaluated through the process of quality control, and improvements are made in the basic design to eliminate weaknesses. Failure of certain components under imposed conditions calls for modifications to improve existing designs (Fig. 15–4). Extreme conditions that a design is likely to be exposed to must be simulated prior to actual exposure, since it may not be possible to test the product under actual conditions without considerable danger and expense. The space program presents many examples of this requirement, since prior to actual flights many simulated tests have to be conducted and many data gathered to permit a sound evaluation of the limitations under which space exploration operates. The organization of these data into graphical form permits efficient analysis and evaluation.

Comparative data are used to establish relationships between two or more variables to improve the chances for making a correct decision. For example, to choose between two machines that will be used to produce the same product, one will compare the operational expenses required by each and their relative outputs, as well as the predicted life of each machine and its estimated maintenance expense. For specific applications, one may compare the advantages of one material versus those of another or the effectiveness of one fuel versus that of another.

15–3 TYPES OF GRAPHS

The nature of the data to be presented will determine the type of graph that will give the clearest picture of the information. The types of graphs emphasized in this chapter are primarily those used to analyze data that will aid in the final decision on a design. Although graphs do not make decisions or solve problems, they give the designer a picture of the background information and thus help him to familiarize himself with all aspects of the problem.

The basic types of graphs are:

1) linear (including rectangular, logarithmic, and semilogarithmic grids),
2) bar graphs,
3) pie or circular graphs,
4) polar graphs,
5) schematics and graphical diagrams,
6) computation graphs and nomograms.

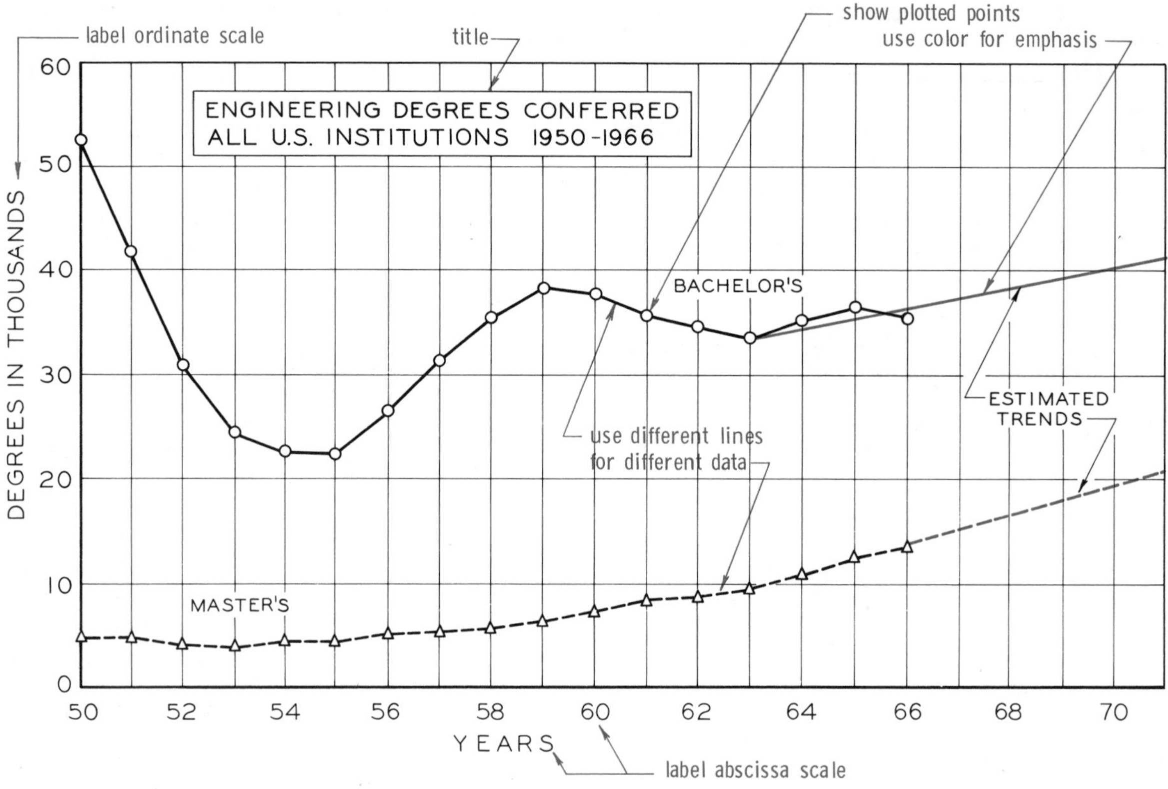

Fig. 15-5. The typical layout of a rectangular graph.

FIGURE 15-6. CONSTRUCTION OF A BROKEN-LINE GRAPH

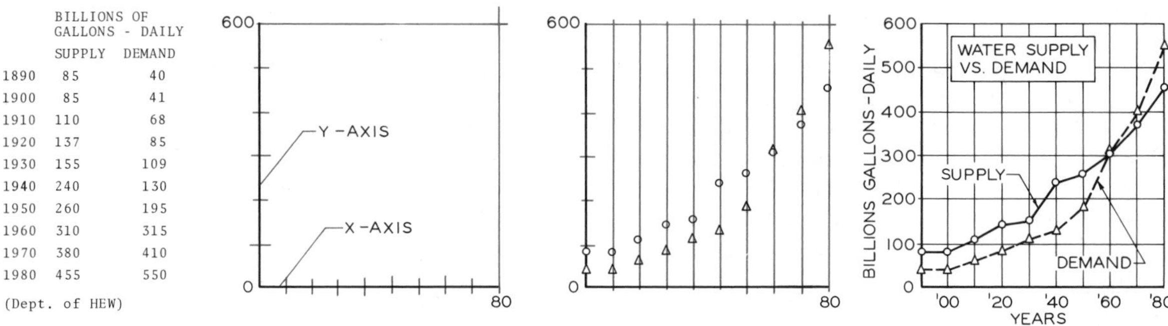

	BILLIONS OF GALLONS - DAILY SUPPLY	DEMAND
1890	85	40
1900	85	41
1910	110	68
1920	137	85
1930	155	109
1940	240	130
1950	260	195
1960	310	315
1970	380	410
1980	455	550

(Dept. of HEW)

Given: A record of water supply and water demand since 1890 has been obtained to determine the future relationships that may occur. These data are to be plotted as a line graph.

Step 1: The vertical and horizontal axes are laid off to provide adequate space for the years and the largest values.

Step 2: The points are plotted directly over the respective years. Different symbols are used for each curve.

Step 3: The data points are connected with straight lines, the axes are labeled, the graph is titled, and the lines are strengthened.

15-4 LINEAR GRAPHS—RECTANGULAR GRIDS

The linear graph is the one most commonly used to present information either to the general public or to a group of technically oriented people. Graphs of this kind may be drawn in their entirety, including the grid, or the data may be plotted on commercially prepared graph paper. A typical graph is shown in Fig. 15-5; the more important parts are properly labeled. A graph should be prepared with the same care and precision that would be exercised in any other portion of the design. The steps required to draw a graph are discussed in the following article.

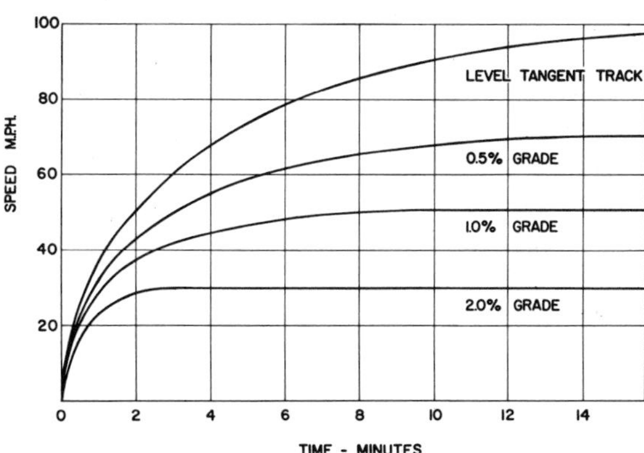

Fig. 15-7. A rectangular graph for presenting continuous data is connected with a smooth curve. (From *General Motors Engineering Journal*, **3**, No. 4 (1956), p. 15.)

15-5 DRAWING A LINEAR GRAPH

A graph similar to the example in Fig. 15-5 is drawn in Fig. 15-6 to illustrate the steps of construction and the important elements of a rectilinear graph. The data for this graph are given in tabular form in the first part of the figure.

A. Selection of Grid. A graph can be drawn on commercially printed graph paper, or the grid may be drawn to fit the specific needs of a particular graph. If the graph is to be reproduced in a formal report or a report that is to be published in large quantities, the entire graph should be drawn in ink.

To permit easy analysis and a minimum of clutter, only important divisions on the graph should be shown. Judgment must be used in selecting the scales to be assigned along the horizontal axis (abscissa or *X*-axis) and the vertical axis (ordinate or *Y*-axis). Variation in either of these scales can exaggerate or minimize fluctuations.

B. Plotting the Data. The data should be plotted on the graph with symbols such as circles, triangles, rectangles, or crosses to indicate the actual data values used. These symbols should be drawn with a template to ensure uniformity.

C. Drawing the Curve. The data presented on a linear graph will be in either of two forms, *discrete* or *continuous*. Discrete data are connected with straight lines to give a broken-line appearance. The data in Fig. 15-6 are discrete because there is no continuous change in the given data from year to year between the plotted points; that is, we do not know how the supply and demand changed within each ten-year period. Consequently the points are connected with straight lines. The discrete data points of Fig. 15-5 were also connected with straight lines, since no uniform rate of change between points on the graph could be assumed. For example, when you say that 52,000 students graduated in 1950 and 42,000 in 1951 you cannot assume that there was a uniform, continuous reduction of students during this one-year period.

Continuous data are connected with a smooth curve from point to point, rather than a broken-line curve. The curves in Fig. 15-7 represent continuous data, since it is understood that there is an infinite number of speeds between 30 mph and 31 mph, for example, 31.01 mph, 31.02 mph, 31.03 mph, and so on. To attain a speed of 30 mph, one must pass through every speed from 0 to 30 mph in a continuous order.

When a curve is drawn through points on a graph, the line of the curve should not overlap the symbols so that they cannot be seen. Each symbol, such as a circle, should be left open and the curve should stop at each side of the symbol.

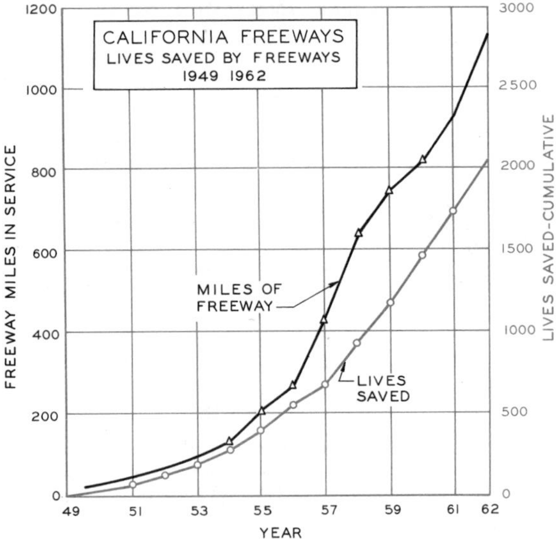

Fig. 15-8. A typical rectangular graph with composite scales to compare discrete data. (Courtesy of the California Highway Department.)

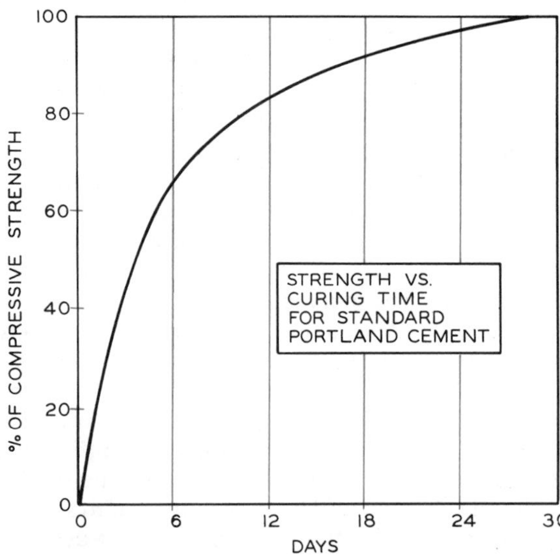

Fig. 15-9. When the process that is graphed involves gradual, continuous changes of relationships, the curve should be drawn as a smooth line.

D. Labeling the Axes. The independent variable is customarily plotted along the horizontal axis, and the dependent variable along the vertical axis. The dependent variable is best evaluated if its initial point, where the two axes intersect, is zero. Making this point represent zero will give the best comparison of trends.

Only the important divisions on a graph should be labeled. The values to be labeled should be chosen so that interpolation of values between those that are labeled will be easy. Familiar multiples of numbers should be used, such as 2, 4, 6, etc., or 0, 5, 10, 15, etc. In addition, each axis should be labeled in general terms to define clearly what the units represent. In Fig. 15-6 these axes are labeled "Billions Gallons—Daily" and "Years."

E. Title. All graphs should have a title (or caption) that will clearly identify the graph and its contents. Data are often reviewed long after they were graphed; hence, it is important that a title be available to identify the graph.

The title can usually be placed within the grid area of the graph to conserve space and to give a pleasing appearance. When placed on the grid, the title should be surrounded by a box (Fig. 15-6). Where space does not permit inclusion within the grid area, the title should be located prominently at the top or the bottom of the graph.

15-6 APPLICATIONS OF LINEAR GRAPHS WITH RECTANGULAR GRIDS

General Graphs. In Fig. 15-8, construction of freeways in California is compared to the estimated number of lives that have been saved as a result of the freeways. Note that this graph has separate scales of different units on each ordinate—distance of freeways in miles and number of lives saved. Although the units are different, it is possible to compare the relationships between the two factors. It can be seen that approximately the same direct relationship exists between freeway miles and the number of lives saved, lending strong support to the effectiveness of freeways. These data are represented by a broken line, since roads are opened one section at a time rather than in a continuous manner.

The graph in Fig. 15-9 is an example of continuous data plotting. The percent of compressive strength is plotted against the number of days of curing time for portland cement. This is a gradual, continuing process; therefore, the data are continuous and the points are connected with a smooth curve.

The design of an automobile's power system is easily analyzed by referring to Fig. 15-10. Four types of data are compared to indicate the usable horsepower available at various velocities. The horsepower *available* at the rear wheels versus the horsepower *required* at the rear wheels is the critical information that must receive first study, since this factor will determine the performance of the automobile. The optimum speed is between 50 and 65 mph, which is the average driving speed. This provides the driver with a reserve of horsepower for quick acceleration and maneuverability to afford safety when most needed. This margin of horsepower reduces sharply after 80 mph and approaches zero at 110 mph where deceleration is the only possibility for change in speed in case of an emergency.

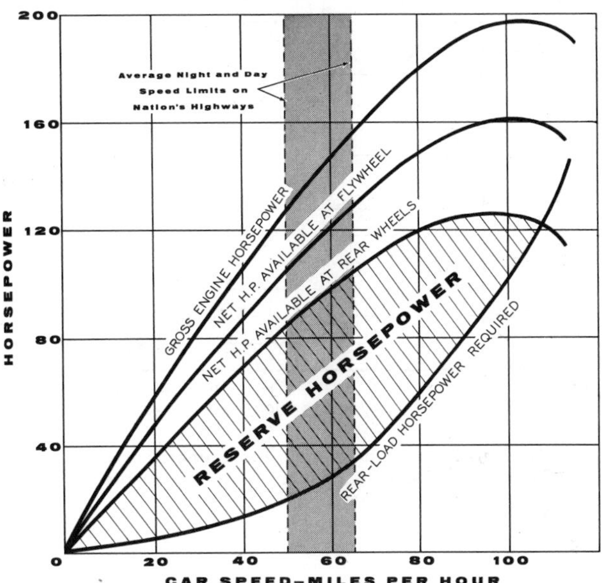

Fig. 15-10. A rectangular graph used to analyze data affecting the design of an automobile's power system. (Courtesy of General Motors Corporation.)

The Best Curve. Some data points may have built-in errors due to the measuring instruments used or to slightly faulty methods of collecting the data. When it is known that the data should produce a smooth, continuous relationship, the curve is drawn as the *best curve*. The best curve cannot pass through each point that has been plotted; instead, it represents an approximation of the data as if there were no errors.

The data points plotted in Fig. 15-11 are experimental data obtained from field tests of two engines. The engines are compared in terms of the miles-per-gallon efficiency. To obtain a smooth curve, it was necessary to draw the curve through some of the points and near others. The compressive strength of structural clay tile is related to the absorption characteristics of this material in Fig. 15-12. The curve of this graph does not pass through the points, but represents the average trend shown by the somewhat scattered data.

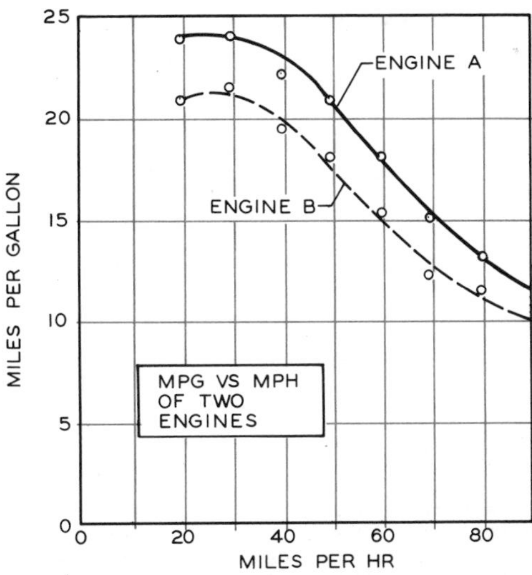

Fig. 15-11. These curves are "best curves," which approximate the data without necessarily passing through each data point.

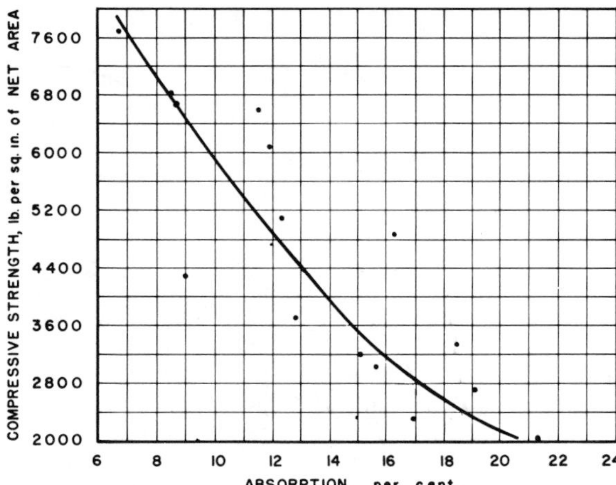

Fig. 15–12. An example of an approximate curve that represents scattered data points. (Courtesy of the Structural Clay Products Institute.)

Break-even Graphs. Rectilinear graphs are useful in analyzing the marketing and manufacturing costs that will be involved in the development of a product. A type of break-even graph is constructed in steps in Fig. 15–13. The *Y*-axis represents thousands of dollars; and the *X*-axis, units in thousands to be manufactured. Once the cost of development, design, and planning has been figured ($20,000 in this case), it can be plotted. The manufacturer estimates that he can produce the product at $1.50 per unit if 10,000 are produced. Thus the amount of $15,000 is added to the $20,000 cost at the 10,000-unit division in step 1. If the manufacturer wishes to break even after 10,000 are sold, the selling price must be $3.50 each. The break-even point is plotted, and a straight line is drawn connecting this point to the origin. This line is extended past the break-even point to the edge of the grid and is labeled "Gross Income." The manufacturer's losses and profits are plotted in step 3. If zero units are produced, the cost will be the $20,000 spent on development. At the break-even point, by definition, the cost will equal the gross income. Consequently a line connecting the $20,000 point on the *Y*-axis with the break-even

FIGURE 15–13. BREAK-EVEN GRAPH

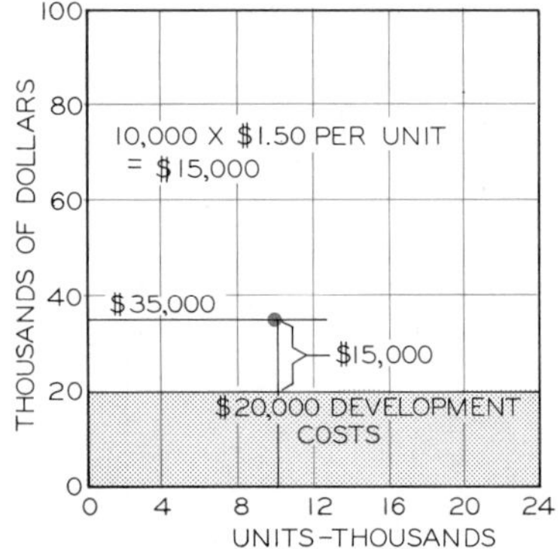

Step 1: The graph is drawn to show the cost ($20,000 in this case) of developing the product. It is determined that each unit would cost $1.50 to manufacture if the total quantity were 10,000. This is a total investment of $35,000 for 10,000 units.

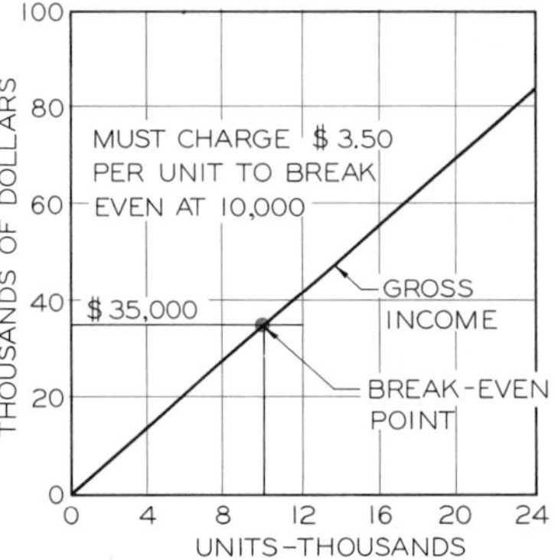

Step 2: In order for the manufacturer to break even at 10,000, the units must be sold for $3.50. Draw a line from zero through the break-even point for $35,000.

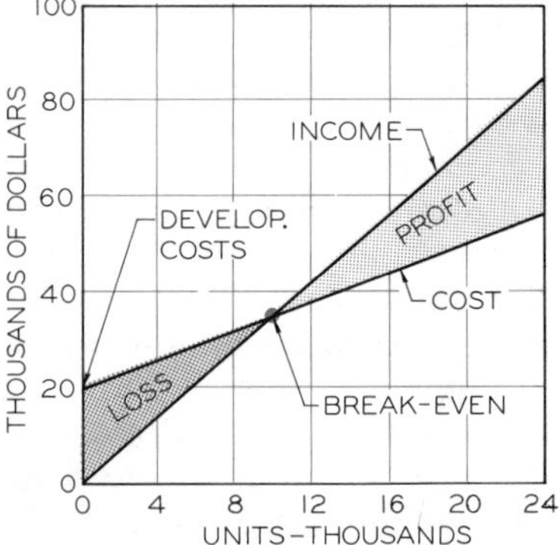

Step 3: The manufacturer's loss is $20,000 at zero units and becomes progressively less until the break-even point is reached. The profit is the difference between the cost and income to the right of the break-even point.

point will represent the manufacturer's costs as the number of units produced is increased from 0 to 10,000. This cost line should be extended to the opposite edge of the grid. The distances between the income and cost lines represent the manufacturer's losses and profits.

A second type of break-even graph (Fig. 15-14) uses the cost of manufacture per unit of a product versus the number of units produced. In this example the development costs must be incorporated into the unit costs. The manufacturer can determine how many units must be sold to break even at a given price, or the price per unit if a given number is selected. In this example, a sales price of 80¢ requires that 8400 units be sold to break even.

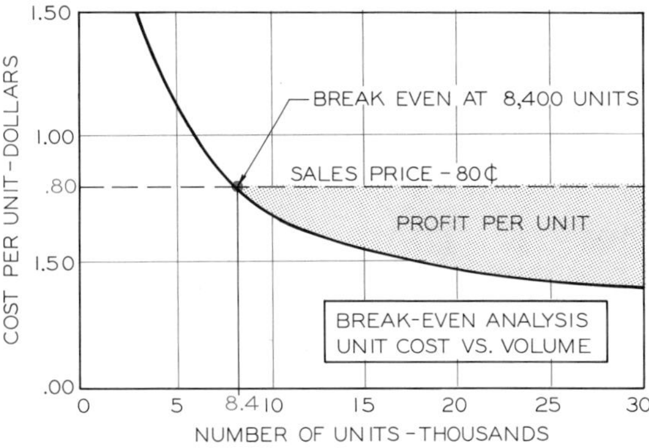

Fig. 15-14. The break-even point can be found on a graph that shows the relationship between the cost per unit, which includes the development cost, and the number of units produced. The sales price is a fixed price. The break-even point is reached when 8400 units have been sold at 80¢ each.

15-7 LOGARITHMIC GRAPHS

The logarithmic graph is a type of rectangular graph in which the scales are graduated with logarithmic divisions along the ordinate and the abscissa. Commercially prepared logarithmic graphs are available in many forms and cycles to fulfill most needs. These graphs have definite uses in the analysis of empirical data (see Article 15-13).

Data that vary from small to very large numbers can be presented on logarithmic graphs in less space than would be required by a conventional rectangular grid. There is no zero point on this type of graph, just as there is no zero on a slide rule scale. Each cycle is raised by a factor of ten. For example, in Fig. 15-15, the ordinate begins at 10 and ends at 100 for the first cycle. The second cycle is from 100 to 1000, but only 200 is shown at the top of the graph. The abscissa is a two-cycle grid.

The curves plotted in this graph were derived from a number of calculations involving the geometry of standard railroad tracks and the sizes of cars used on them. The graph can be used to determine the relationship of various curves in a railroad to the lengths of railroad cars if a maximum projection width of 12 ft is allowed. This information can be helpful in planning the maximum sizes of loads that can be shipped via a plant's railroad siding.

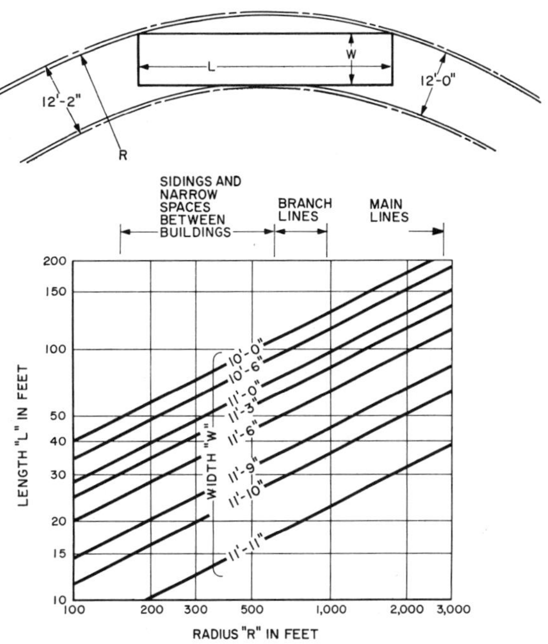

Fig. 15-15. This logarithmic graph shows the maximum load projection of 12 ft in relation to the length of a railroad car and the radius of the curve. (Courtesy of *Plant Engineering.*)

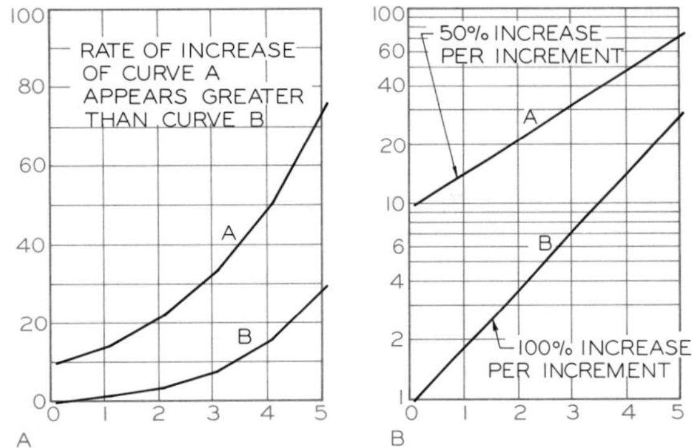

Fig. 15-16. When plotted on a standard grid, curve *A* appears to be increasing at a greater rate than curve *B*. However, the true rate of increase can be seen when the same data are plotted on a semilogarithmic graph in part B.

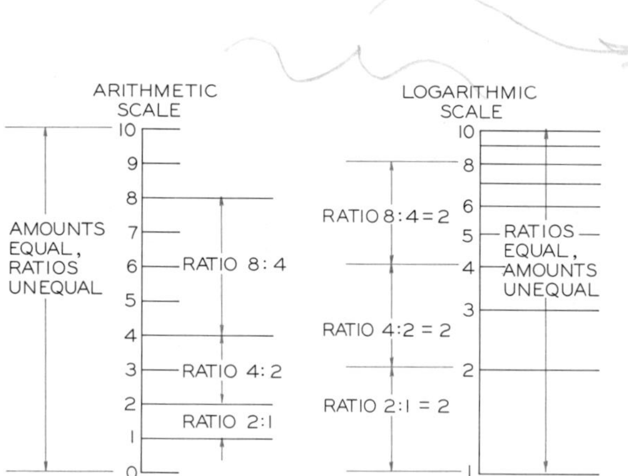

Fig. 15-17. The spacings on an arithmetic scale are equal, with unequal ratios between points. The spacings on logarithmic scales are unequal, but equal spaces represent equal ratios.

15-8 SEMILOGARITHMIC GRAPHS

The semilogarithmic graph is referred to as a ratio graph or a rate-of-change graph, because one scale, usually the vertical scale, is logarithmic, while the other, usually the horizontal scale, is arithmetic (divided into equal divisions). Whereas the arithmetic graph gives a picture of absolute amounts of change, the semilogarithmic graph shows the relative rate of change. These two types of graphs are shown in Fig. 15-16, where the same data are plotted on each type of grid. The rate of change on the arithmetic graph can be computed from a common base point, but not from point to point as in the case of the semilogarithmic graph. Note that curve *A* in Fig. 15-16A appears to be increasing at a greater rate than curve *B*; however, the true comparison between the rates of changes of the two curves is shown in part B of the figure. Curve *A* increases 50 percent each increment marked on the *X*-axis and 125 percent each double period. Curve *B* increases 100 percent each period, 300 percent each double period.

The relationship between the arithmetic scale used on the conventional rectilinear graph and the logarithmic scale used on the semilogarithmic graph can be seen in Fig. 15-17. Note that the equal amounts along the arithmetic scale have unequal ratios, and that the unequal amounts along the logarithmic scale have equal ratios. For data with a considerable variance from small numbers to relatively large numbers, commercially printed semilogarithmic grid paper is available in several cycles. Examples of three-cycle, two-cycle, and one-cycle grids are shown in Fig. 15-18. Each cycle increases in magnitude by a factor of ten. When logarithmic scales are needed on a graph, commercially printed grid paper can be used in transferring dimensions to a scale of any length, as shown in Fig. 15-18C.

It can be seen in Fig. 15-19A that the numbers along a logarithmic scale are separated by the difference of their logarithms. The length of the scale is multiplied by the log of each number to find its location above the number one. This makes it possible to determine the angle of the line which represents the rate of change of the data. It can be seen in Fig. 15–19B that the rate of change is equal at any position on the graph; this was not the case with the arithmetic graph in Fig. 15–16A.

The semilogarithmic graph has certain fundamental advantages and disadvantages that must be considered before the type of grid best suited to the purpose is chosen. The advantages are:*

1) The semilogarithmic graph presents a picture that cannot be shown on an arithmetic scale chart;
2) it converts absolute data into a relative comparison, without computing;
3) it shows the relative change from any point to any succeeding point in a series;
4) it retains the actual units of measurement of the absolute data;
5) it reveals whether or not the data follow a consistent relative-change pattern.

The disadvantages must also be considered:*

1) The semilogarithmic graph presents a picture that many people misunderstand and mistakenly read as an arithmetic graph;
2) it cannot be used for data that include a zero or a negative value;
3) it does not provide a scale from which percentage changes can be read directly;
4) it requires a comparison of angles of change, which are difficult to compare by eye;
5) it gives a percentage decrease at a different angle of change than the same percentage increase.

The same general methods that are used to construct a rectilinear arithmetic graph are applied to a semilogarithmic graph (Article 15–5). Plotted points should be indicated on the graph by circles or other geometric symbols to provide a visual impression of the actual data. Semilogarithmic graphs will be covered in Article 15–16, in which we shall show how they

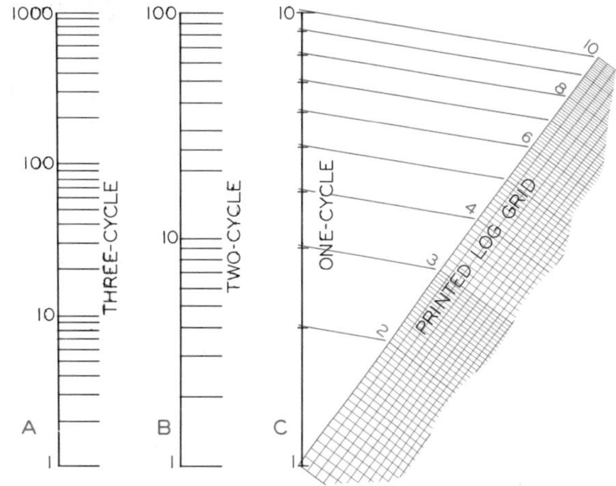

Fig. 15–18. Logarithmic paper can be purchased or drawn using several cycles. Three-, two-, and one-cycle scales are shown here. Calibrations can be drawn on a scale of any length by projecting from a printed scale as shown in part C.

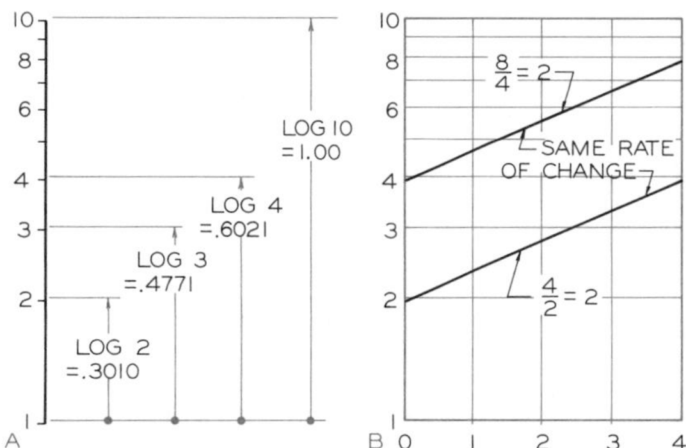

Fig. 15–19. A number's logarithm is used to locate its position on a log scale (A). This makes it possible to see the true rate of change at any location on a semilogarithmic graph (B).

*Extracted from ANSI Time-Series Charts (ANSI Y15.2-1960).

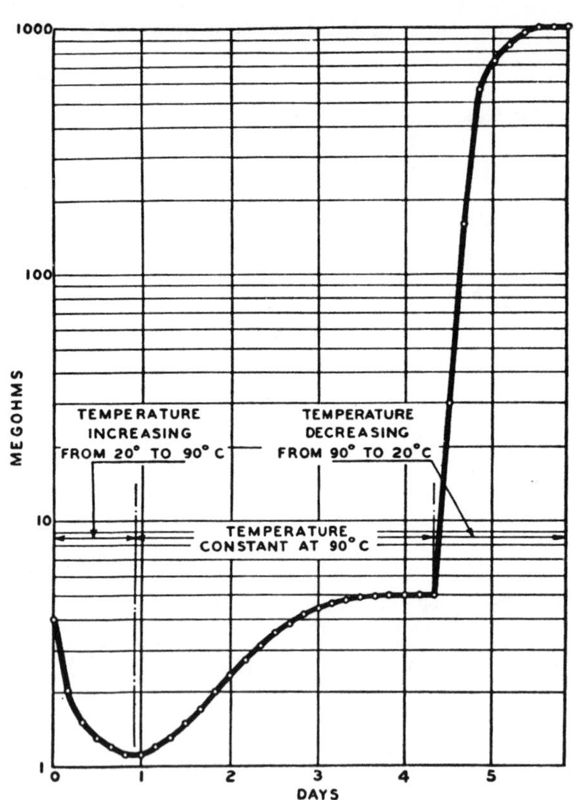

Fig. 15-20. A semilogarithmic graph is used to show how resistance changes as the armature of a dc motor dries out. (Courtesy of James G. Biddle Co.)

can be used to set up equations from empirically derived data.

An example of a semilogarithmic graph is given in Fig. 15-20. Experience and knowledge of the data will dictate the construction and layout of the graph in specific applications.

Percentage Charts. Special applications of semilogarithmic grids can take advantage of the logarithmic plots of the data. The percent that one value is of another value on the graph can be determined with a pair of dividers, with no calculations. Likewise, the percent of increase of one value with respect to another value can be found with similar ease.

Data are shown plotted in step 1 of Fig. 15-21. To find the percent that 30 is of 60, measure the vertical distance between these two points. This distance is the difference between the logarithms of these numbers; it is transferred with dividers and is subtracted from the log of 100 at the right of the graph. This gives a value

FIGURE 15-21. PERCENTAGE GRAPHS

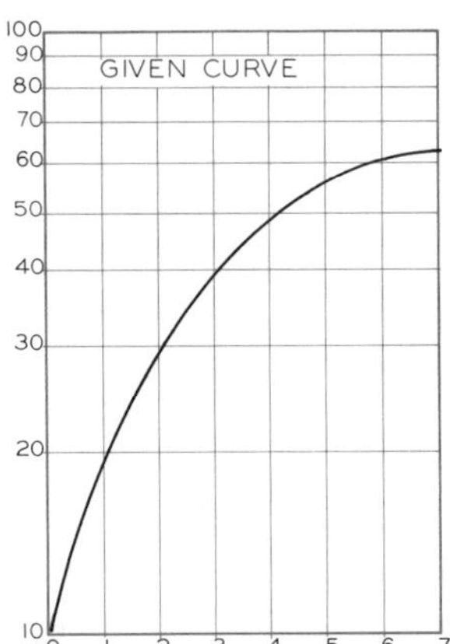

Given: The data are plotted on a semilogarithmic graph to enable you to determine percentages and ratios in much the same manner that you use a slide rule.

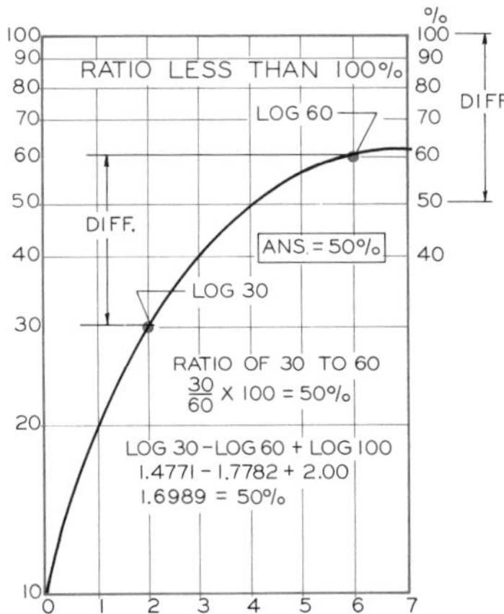

Step 1: In finding the percent that a smaller number is of a larger number, you know that the percent will be less than 100%. The log of 30 is subtracted from the log of 60 with dividers and this dimension is transferred to the percent scale at the right, where 30 is found to be 50% of 60.

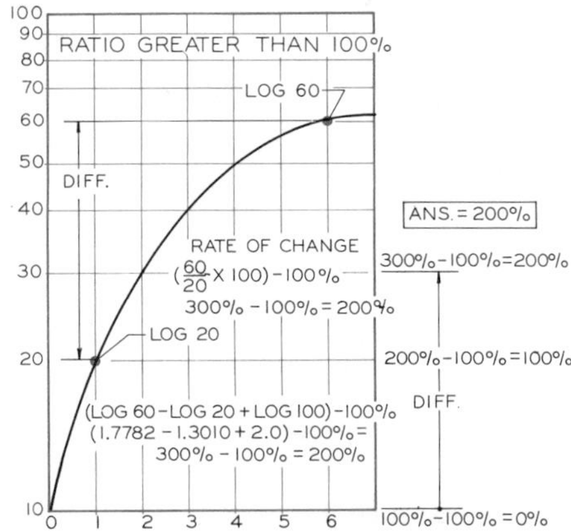

Step 2: To find the rate of increase, a smaller number is divided into a larger number to give a value greater than 100%. The difference between the logs of 60 and 20 is found with dividers, and this distance is measured upward from 100% at the right, to find that the rate of increase is 200%.

of 50%, which is obviously correct. Relate this procedure to the operation of the log scales of your slide rule, which gives the same answer.

In step 2, the rate of increase is found in much the same manner, but the percent increase is measured upward from the other end of the log scale, since the increase will be greater than 100%. The origin is considered to be 100%; consequently 100% is substracted from the percent of increase that is found at the right of the scale.

You can see that for a working graph used to determine percentage relationships, this ease of calculations has many advantages.

15-9 BAR GRAPHS

Bar graphs are commonly used to compare a wide variety of variables, since they are readily understood by the general public. The bars may be vertical or horizontal (Fig. 15-22). Bar graphs are easier to interpret if the bars are arranged either in descending or ascending order according to their lengths or in chronological order. Often the amounts represented by the bars are also given numerically to provide exact information. The steps of constructing a bar graph are illustrated in Fig. 15-23.

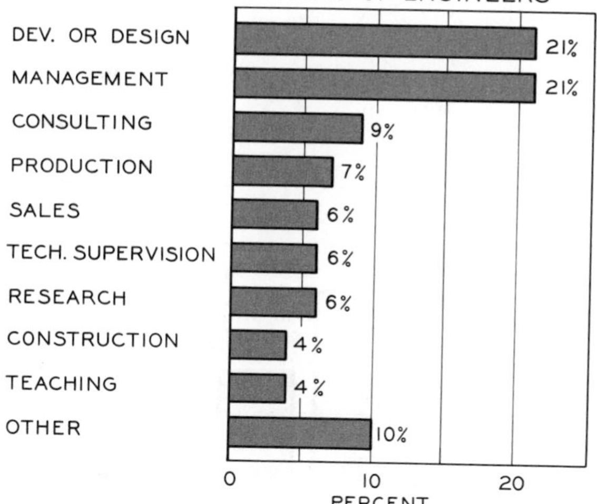

Fig. 15-22. The employment functions of engineers are shown in a bar graph. (Courtesy of the U. S. Department of Labor.)

FIGURE 15-23. CONSTRUCTION OF A BAR GRAPH

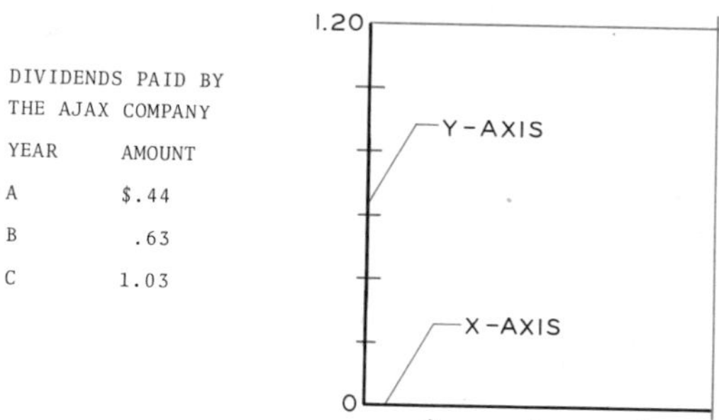

DIVIDENDS PAID BY THE AJAX COMPANY

YEAR	AMOUNT
A	$.44
B	.63
C	1.03

Given: These data are to be plotted as a bar graph.

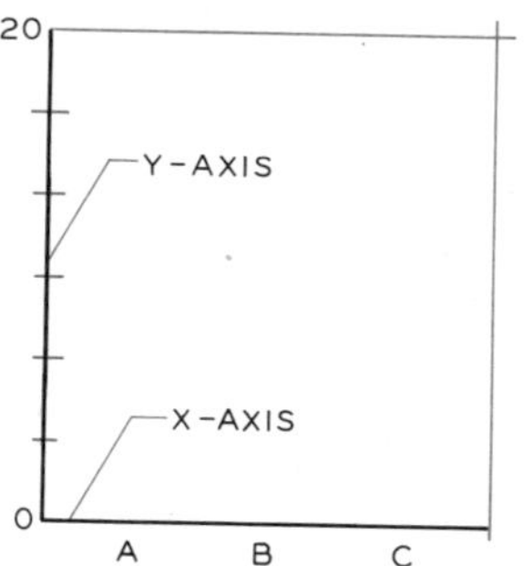

Step 1: Lay off the vertical and horizontal axes so that the data will fit on the grid. Make the bars begin at zero.

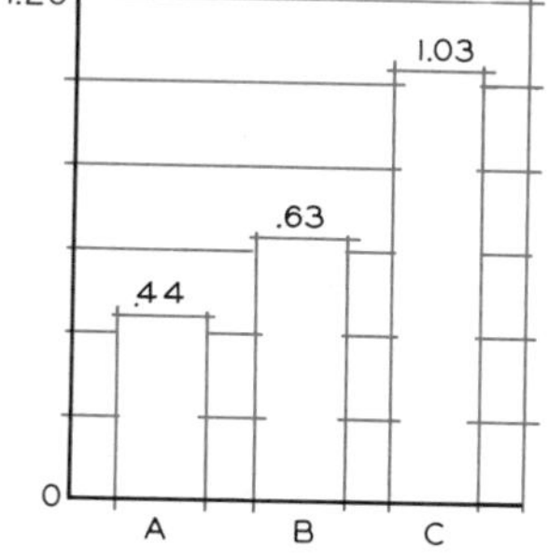

Step 2: Construct and label the bars. The width of the bars should be different from the space between the bars. Horizontal grid lines should not pass through the bars.

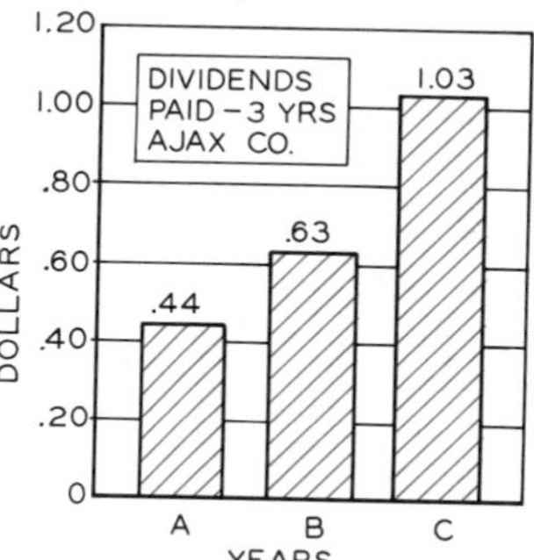

Step 3: Strengthen lines, title the graph, label the axes, and crosshatch the bars.

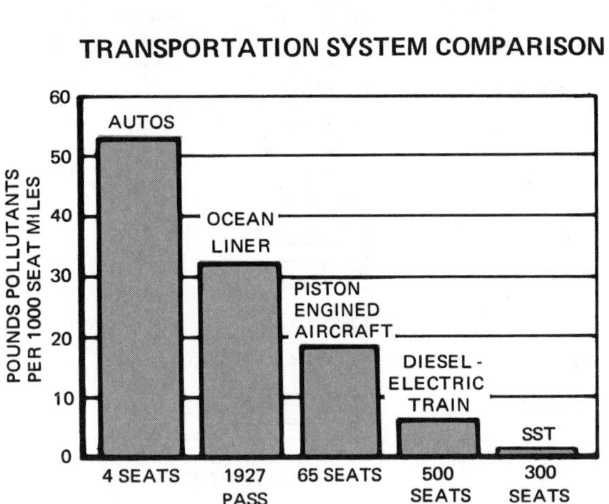

Fig. 15-24. A bar graph is used here to compare the pollution caused by various types of transportation systems. (Courtesy of Boeing.)

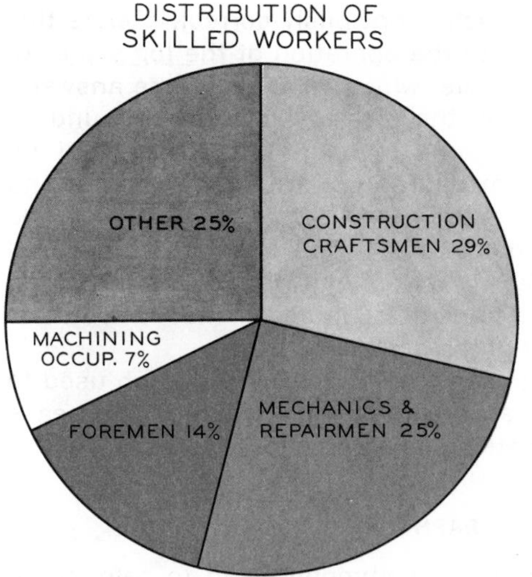

Fig. 15-25. The distribution of skilled workers presented in a pie graph. (Courtesy of U.S. Department of Labor.)

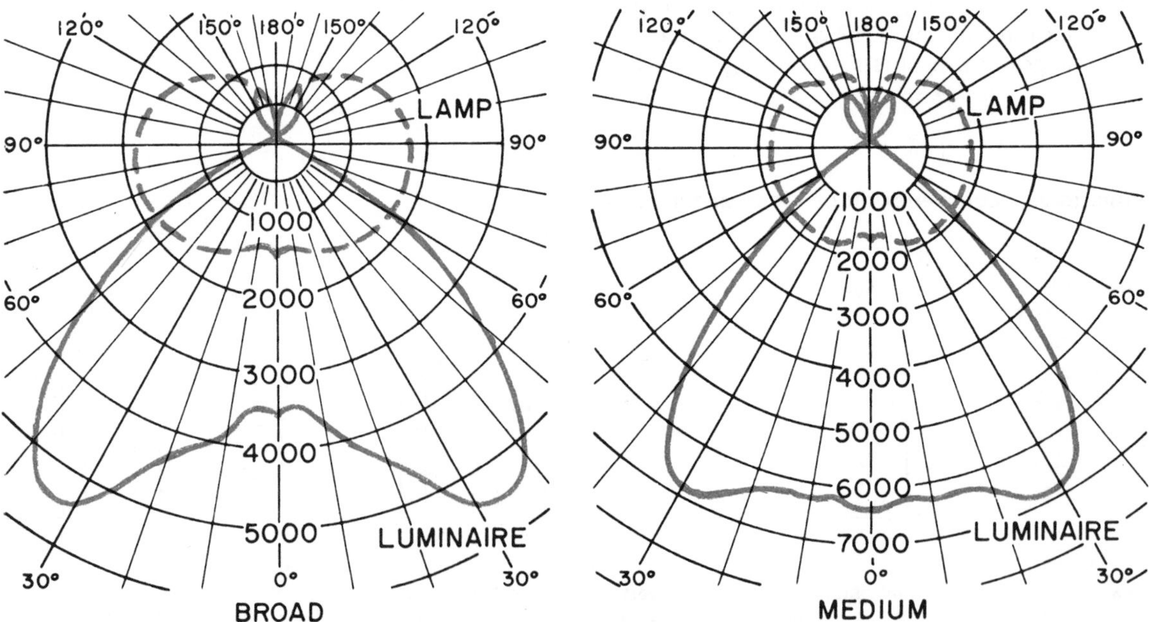

Fig. 15-26. A polar graph is used to show the illumination characteristics of luminaires.

Figure 15-24 is an application of a bar graph to performance levels of various transportation systems. The space between the bars and the widths of the bars should *not* be the same, so that the bars can easily be distinguished.

15-10 PIE GRAPHS

Pie graphs are used to compare the relationship of parts to a whole when there are not too many parts. Figure 15-25 shows the distribution of skilled workers employed in industry. The sectors are found by determining the percentage each part is of the whole and multiplying by 360°. For example, 25 percent of 360° is 90°, which is the size of the sector for mechanics and repairmen. To facilitate lettering within narrow spaces, the narrow sectors should be placed in a horizontal position. Where there is not enough space, labels may be placed outside the sector. The actual percentages should be given in all cases, and, depending on the use of the graph, it may be desirable to give the actual numbers involved. Pie graphs are often used to present the expenditure of budgeted funds and other information to the general public.

15-11 POLAR GRAPHS

Polar graphs are composed of a series of concentric circles with the origin at the center. Lines are drawn from the center toward the perimeter of the graph where data can be plotted through 360° by measuring quantities from the origin. The illumination of two lamps is shown in Fig. 15-26. The maximum lighting of the first lamp is 550 lumens at 35° from vertical. This form of graph is commonly used to plot the areas of illumination of lighting fixtures. Polar graph paper is available commercially.

15-12 SCHEMATICS

Designs and complicated systems may be more easily analyzed if schematics are used to separate major components. Figure 15-27 is a block diagram schematic that is useful in describing steps of a project. The diagram in

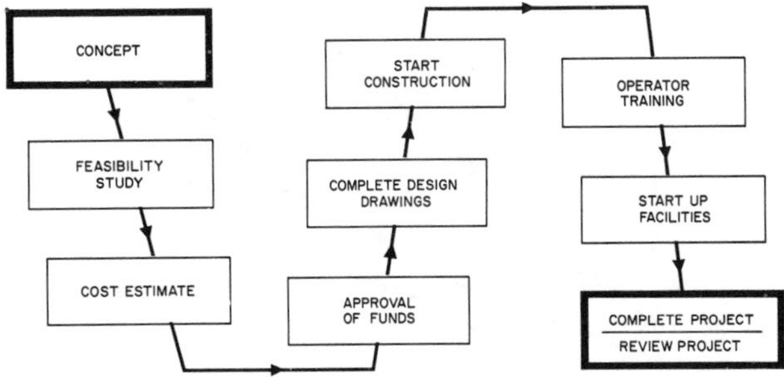

Fig. 15-27. This schematic shows a block diagram of the steps required to complete a project. (Courtesy of *Plant Engineering.*)

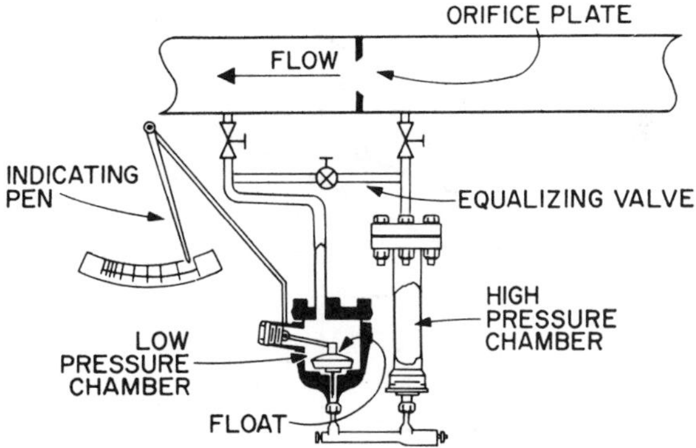

Fig. 15-28. A schematic showing the components of a gauge that measures the flow in a pipeline. (Courtesy of *Plant Engineering.*)

Fig. 15-28 illustrates the design of a pressure gauge. Note that neither of these diagrams is drawn to scale or with any great degree of detail. Instead, they are kept simple and symbolic in order to emphasize the relationship of the components of the system. Similar schematics can be used to present more detailed components within each major section of the schematic. Diagrams of this type are used to illustrate various steps in production, or personnel organization, or any related sequence of components or activities.

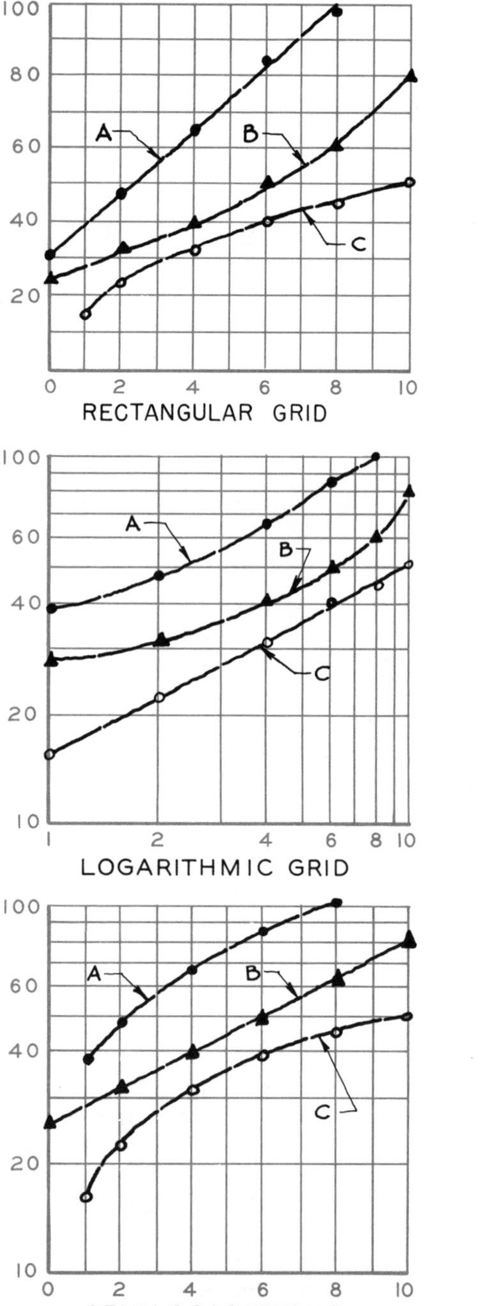

Fig. 15-29. Empirical data are plotted on each of these types of grids to determine which will render a straight-line plot. If the data can be plotted as a straight line on one of these grids, their equation can be found.

15-13 EMPIRICAL DATA

Data gathered from laboratory experiments and tests of prototypes or from actual field tests are called empirical data. Although in some instances there is no advance knowledge as to whether or not specific scientific relationships exist, in many cases the nature of the data makes it possible to set up equations that can be used to mathematically evaluate the data characteristics. Empirical data can be transformed to equation form by means of one of three types of equations to be covered here.

The analysis of empirical data begins with the plotting of the data on rectangular grids, logarithmic grids, and semilogarithmic grids. Curves are then sketched through each point to determine which of the grids renders a straight-line relationship (Fig. 15-29). We wish to determine a straight-line relationship so that we may find an equation for the data. Note that in the figure three sets of empirical data are plotted and that curves are sketched to connect them. Each curve appears as a straight line in one of the graphs. We use this straight-line curve to write an equation for the data.

15-14 LINEAR EQUATIONS: $Y = MX + B$

The curve fitting the experimental data plotted in Fig. 15-30 is a straight line; therefore, we

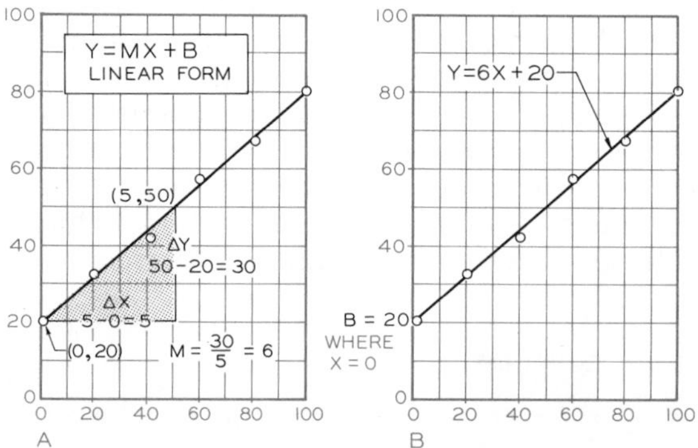

Fig. 15-30. (A) A straight line on an arithmetic grid will have an equation in the form $Y = MX + B$. The slope, M, is found to be 6. (B) The intercept, B, is found to be 20. The equation is written as $Y = 6X + 20$.

FIGURE 15–31. THE POWER EQUATION: $Y = BX^M$

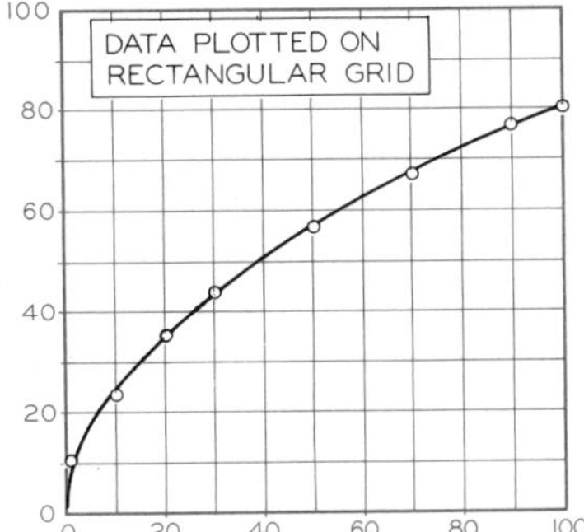

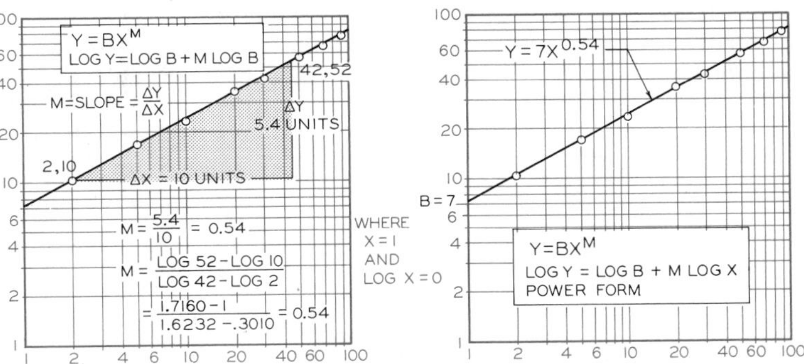

Given: The data plotted on the rectangular grid give an approximation of a parabola.

Step 1: The curve of the data forms a straight line on a logarithmic grid, making it possible to find the equation of the data. The slope, M, can be found graphically with an engineers' scale, setting dX at 10 units and measuring the slope directly (dY) using the same scale. Logarithms are also used as a check to verify the answer.

Step 2: The intercept $B = 7$ is found where $X = 1$. The slope and intercept are substituted into the equation, which then becomes $Y = 7X^{0.54}$.

may assume that these data are linear, meaning that each measurement along the Y-axis is directly proportional to X-axis units. We may use the slope-intercept form or the selected-points method to illustrate one method of writing the equation for the data.

In the slope-intercept method two known points are selected along the curve. The vertical and horizontal differences between the coordinates of each of these points are determined to establish the right triangle shown in part A of the figure. In the slope-intercept equation, $Y = MX + B$, M is the tangent of the angle between the curve and the horizontal, B is the intercept of the curve with the Y-axis where $X = 0$, and X and Y are variables. In this example $M = \frac{30}{5} = 6$ and the intercept is 20. If the curve had sloped downward to the right, the slope would have been negative. By substituting this information into the slope-intercept equation, we obtain $Y = 6X + 20$, from which we can determine values of Y by substituting any value of X into the equation.

The selected-points method could also have been used to arrive at the same equation if the intercept were not known. By selecting two widely separated points such as (2, 32) and (10, 80), one can write the equation in this form:

$$\frac{Y - 32}{X - 2} = \frac{80 - 32}{10 - 2},$$

which results in the same equation as was found by the slope-intercept method ($Y = MX + B$).

15–15 THE POWER EQUATION $Y = BX^M$

Since the data shown plotted on a rectangular grid in Fig. 15–31 do not form a straight line, they cannot be expressed in the form of a linear equation. However, when the data are plotted on a logarithmic grid, they are found to form a straight line (step 1). Therefore, we express the data in the form of a power equation in which Y is a function of X raised to a given power or $Y = BX^M$. The equation of the data is obtained in much the same manner as was the linear equation, using the point where the curve intersects the Y-axis where $X = 0$, and letting M equal the slope of the curve. Two known points are selected on the curve. Any linear scale in decimal units, such as the 20-scale on the engineers' scale, can be used, when the cycles along the X- and Y-axes are equal, to measure the vertical and horizontal differences between the coordinates of the two points.

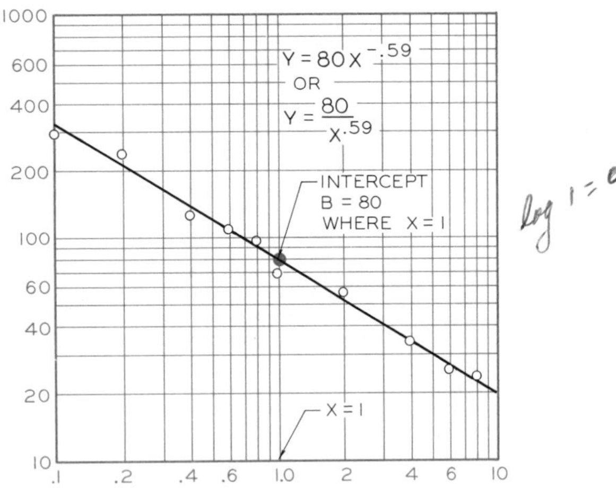

Fig. 15–32. When the slope-intercept equation is used, the intercept can be found only where $X = 1$. Therefore, in this example the intercept is found at the middle of the graph.

If the horizontal distance of the right triangle is drawn to be 1 or 10 or a multiple of 10, the vertical distance can be read off directly. In step 2, the slope M (tangent of the triangle) is found to be 0.54. The intercept B is 7; thus the equation is $Y = 7X^{0.54}$, which can be evaluated for each value of Y by converting this power equation into the logarithmic form of log Y:

$$\log Y = \log B + M \log X,$$
$$\log Y = \log 7 + 0.54 \log X.$$

Note that, when the slope-intercept method is used, the intercept can be found on the Y-axis where $X = 1$. In Fig. 15–32, the Y-axis at the left of the graph has an X-value of 0.1; consequently, the intercept is located midway across the graph where $X = 1.0$. This is analogous to the linear form of the equation, since the log of 1 is 0. The curve slopes downward to the right; thus the slope, M, is negative. The selected-points method can be applied to find the equation of the data as discussed in the previous article.

FIGURE 15–33. THE EXPONENTIAL EQUATION: $Y = BM^X$

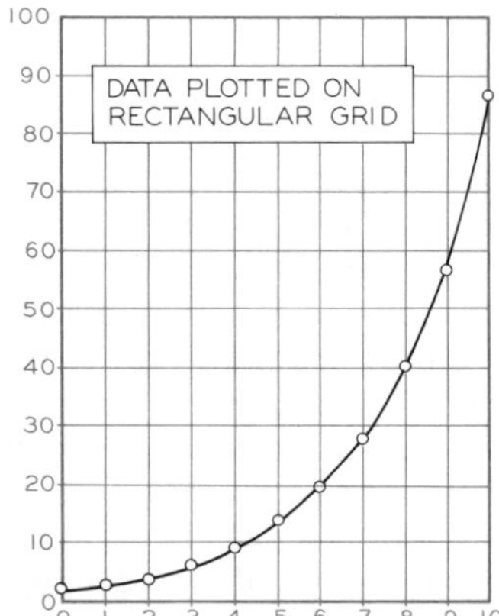

Given: These data do not give a straight line on either a rectangular grid or a logarithmic grid. However, when plotted on a semilogarithmic grid, they do give a straight line.

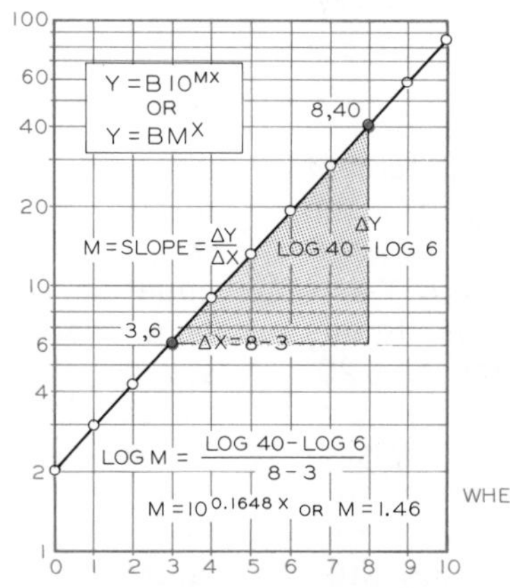

Step 1: The slope must be found by mathematical calculations; it cannot be found graphically. The slope may be written in either of the forms shown here.

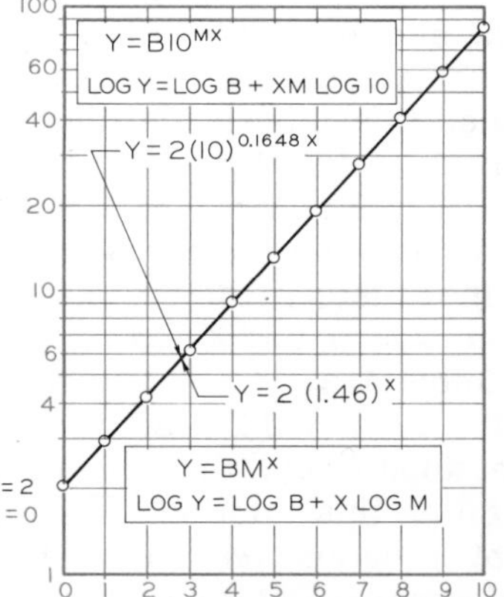

Step 2: The intercept $B = 2$ is found where $X = 0$. The slope (M) and the intercept (B) are substituted into the equation to give $Y = 2(10)^{0.1648X}$ or $Y = 2(1.46)^X$.

Base-ten logarithms are used in these examples, but natural logs could be used with e (2.718) as the base.

15–16 THE EXPONENTIAL EQUATION $Y = BM^X$

The experimental data plotted in Fig. 15–33 form a curve, indicating that they are not linear. When the data are plotted on a semilogarithmic grid, as has been done in step 1 of the figure, they approximate a straight line for which we can write the equation $Y = BM^X$, where B is the Y-intercept of the curve and M is the slope of the curve. The procedure for deriving the equation is shown in step 2, in which two points are selected along the curve so that a right triangle can be drawn to represent the differences between the coordinates of the points selected. The slope of the curve is found to be

$$\log M = \frac{\log 40 - \log 6}{8 - 3} = 0.1648 = (10)^{0.1648}$$

or

$$M = 1.46.$$

The value of M can be substituted in the equation in the following manner:

$$Y = BM^X \quad \text{or} \quad Y = 2(1.46)^X,$$

$$Y = B(10)^{MX} \quad \text{or} \quad Y = 2(10)^{0.1648X}$$

where X is a variable that can be substituted into the equation to give an infinite number of values for Y. We can write this equation in its logarithmic form, which enables us to solve it readily for the unknown value of Y for any given value of X. The equation can be written as

$$\log Y = \log B + X \log M$$

or

$$= \log 2 + X \log 1.46.$$

The same methods are used to find the slope of a curve with a negative slope. The curve of the data in Fig. 15–34 slopes downward to the right; therefore, the slope is negative. Two points are selected in order to find the tangent of the curve (step 1). The slope M can be written as $(10)^{-0.0274}$ or as -1.065, which is the antilog of -0.0274. The intercept, 70, can be combined with the slope, M, to find the final equations as illustrated in step 2 of Fig. 15–34.

15–17 SELECTION OF POINTS ON A CURVE

Two methods of finding the equation of a curve have been mentioned previously: (1) the selected-points method and (2) the slope-intercept method. These are compared on a semilogarithmic graph in Fig. 15–35.

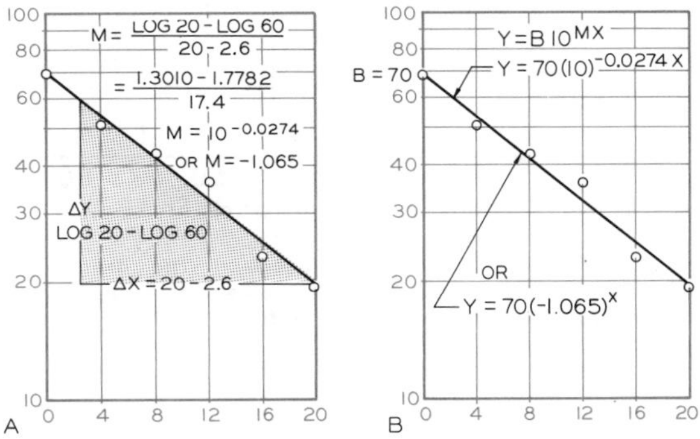

Fig. 15–34. When a curve slopes downward to the right, its slope is negative as calculated in part A. Two forms of the final equation are shown in part B by substitution.

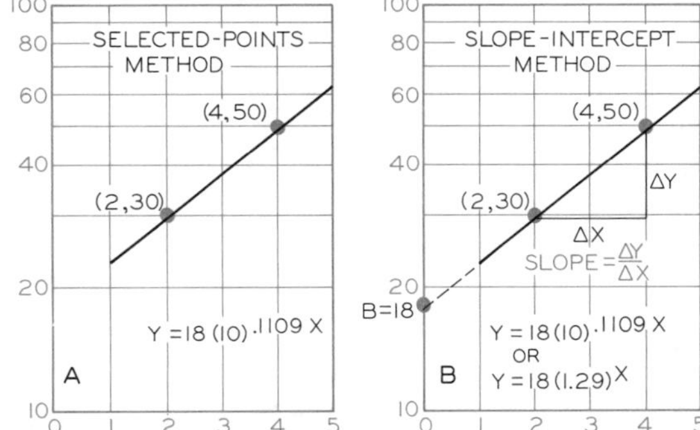

Fig. 15–35. The equation of a straight line on a grid can be determined by selecting any two points on the line (part A). The slope-intercept method requires that the intercept be found where $X = 0$ on a semilog grid (part B). This requires the extension of the curve to the Y-axis.

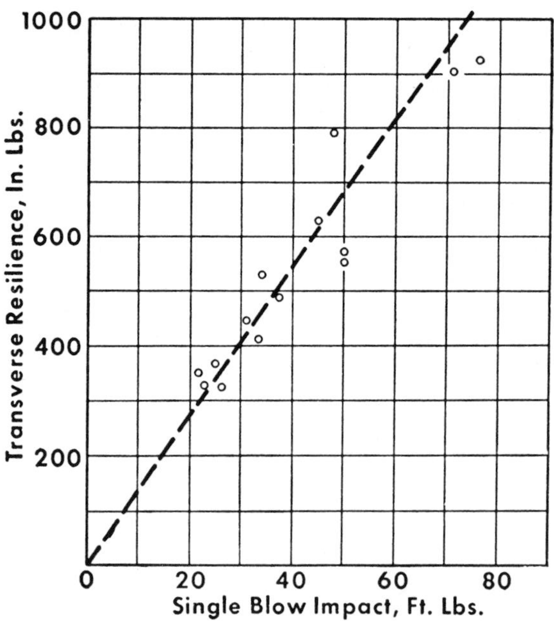

Fig. 15–36. The relationship between the transverse strength of gray iron and impact resistance results in a straight line with an equation of the form $Y = MX + B$.

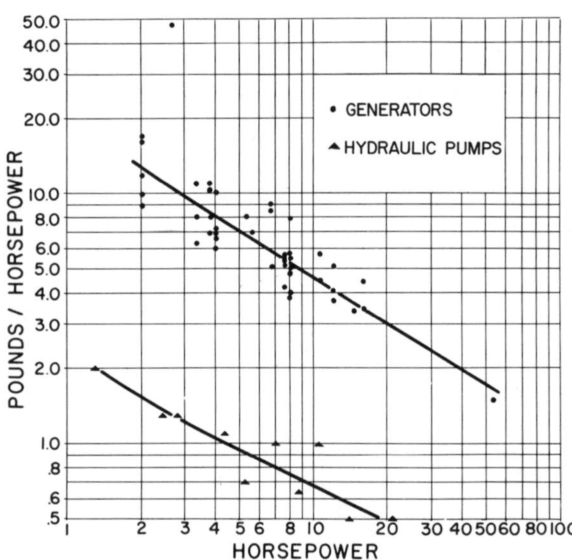

Fig. 15–37. Empirical data plotted on a logarithmic grid, showing the specific weight versus the horsepower of electric generators and hydraulic pumps. The curve is the average of points plotted. (Courtesy of General Motors Engineering Journal.)

Selected-Points Method. Two widely separated points, such as (2, 30) and (4, 50), can be selected on the curve. These points are substituted in the equation below:

$$\frac{\log Y - \log 30}{X - 2} = \frac{\log 50 - \log 30}{4 - 2}.$$

Note that the values in the Y-direction are logarithms and must be handled as such. The resulting equation for the data is

$$Y = 18(10)^{0.1109X}.$$

Slope-Intercept Method. To apply the slope-intercept method, the intercept on the Y-axis where $X = 0$ must be known. If the X-axis is logarithmic, then the log of $X = 1$ is 0 and the intercept must be found above the value of $X = 1$.

In Fig. 15–35B, the data do not intercept the Y-axis; therefore, the curve must be extended to find the intercept $B = 18$. The slope of the curve is found ($\Delta Y/\Delta X$) and substituted into the slope-intercept form to give the equation as

$$Y = 18(10)^{0.1109X} \quad \text{or} \quad Y = 18(1.29)^X.$$

The base-e logarithms can be used just as effectively as the base-10 logarithms, as shown in these examples. Other methods of converting data to equations are used, but the two methods illustrated here make the best use of the graphical process and are the most direct methods of introducing these concepts.

15–18 APPLICATIONS OF EMPIRICAL GRAPHS

Figure 15–36 is an example of how empirical data can be plotted to compare the transverse strength and impact resistance of gray iron. Note that the data are somewhat scattered, but the best curve is drawn. Since the curve is a straight line on a linear graph, the equation of these data can be found by the equation

$$Y = MX + B.$$

Figure 15–37 is an example of how empirical data can be plotted to compare the specific weight (pounds per horsepower) of generators and hydraulic pumps versus horsepower. Note that the weight of these units decreases as linearly as the horsepower increases. Therefore, these data can be written in the form of the power equation

$$Y = BX^{M}.$$

We obtain the equation of these data by applying the procedures covered in Article 15-14 and thus mathematically analyze these relationships.

The half-life decay of radioactivity is plotted in Fig. 15-38 to show the relationship of decay to time. Since the half-life of different isotopes varies, different units would have to be assigned to time along the X-axis; however, the curve would be a straight line for all isotopes. The exponential form of the equation discussed in Article 15-16 can be applied to find the equation for these data,

$$Y = BM^{X}.$$

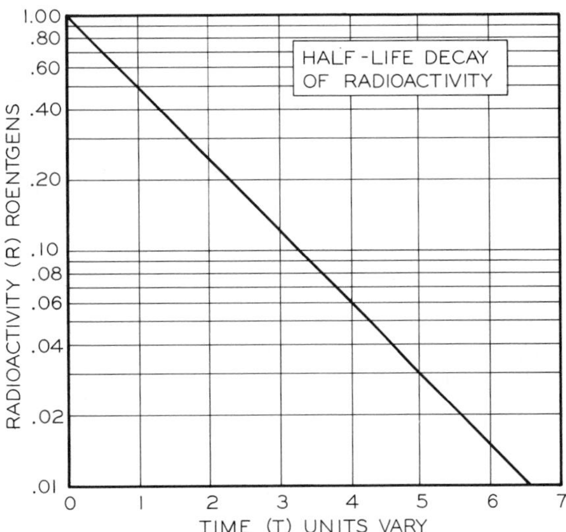

Fig. 15-38. The relative decay of radioactivity is plotted as a straight line on this semilog graph, making it possible for its equation to be found in the form $Y = BM^{X}$.

15-19 INTRODUCTION TO MECHANISMS AND LINKAGES

Mechanisms are used to produce force or motion through a series of interrelated components. A mechanism is a combination of components based on rotation, leverage, or the inclined plane. A linkage is a type of mechanism relying primarily on leverage. An alternative system could be operated electronically with a minimum of mechanical links. Linkages and mechanisms are universally used in machinery (Fig. 15-39), jigs and fixtures, and, to some extent, in practically all designs. The analysis of mechanisms is often referred to as mechanics and is undertaken to determine the effects of forces upon the mechanisms.

The following definitions are fundamental to the study of linkages and mechanisms involved in a design:

Fig. 15-39. This metal-forming machine illustrates the many linkages and mechanisms used in standard equipment. (Courtesy of A. H. Nilson Company.)

Statics. The study of the effect of forces upon bodies or parts which are at rest or moving at uniform velocity.

Dynamics. The study of the effect of forces that cause a change in the motion of machine components or material bodies. Includes *Kinematics* and *Kinetics.*

Kinetics. The study of the effect of forces that cause a change in the motion of machine components or other bodies.

Kinematics. The study of motion without regard to forces.

These areas of analysis are very critical to the final analysis of a design. Complex analytical methods are employed to arrive at the final design configuration that will produce the most effective performance of a mechanism. However, as a supplement to the usual analytical procedures, graphical methods can be used as a basis for initial steps toward analyzing a design. This chapter will be confined to graphical applications that can be used advantageously in this phase of analysis; no attempt will be made to cover the whole area of mechanics.

The mechanisms that are graphically analyzed in this chapter are cams and linkages. Several examples are given that are closely related to variations of rotary motion coupled with linkages. This motion is plotted on rectangular graphs to permit analysis.

15-20 CAMS

Cams (grooved cams, plate cams, or cylindrical cams) are components that produce motion in a single plane, usually up and down (Fig. 15-40). A plate cam with a knife-edge follower is illustrated in Fig. 15-45. The cam revolving about an eccentric center produces a rise and fall in the follower during rotation. The configuration of the cam is analyzed graphically prior to the preparation of the specifications for its manufacture. Only plate cams are covered in the brief review of this mechanism. Cams utilize the principle of the inclined wedge, with the surface of the cam causing a change in the slope of the plane, thereby producing the desired motion.

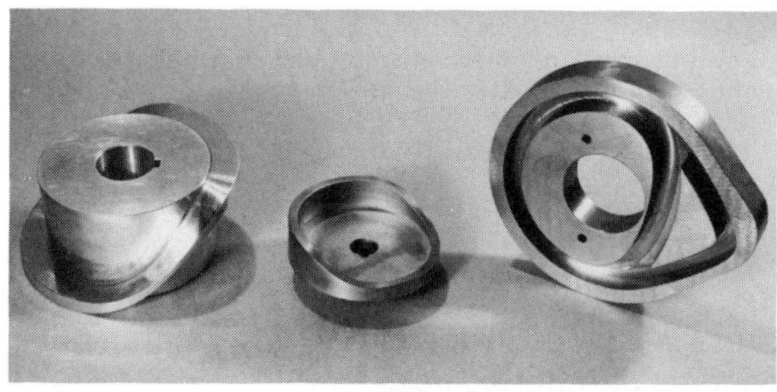

Fig. 15-40. Examples of machined cams. (Courtesy of Ferguson Machine Company.)

15-21 CAM MOTION

Cams are designed primarily to produce (a) uniform or linear motion, (b) harmonic motion, (c) gravity motion, or (d) combinations of these. Some cams are designed to fit special needs that do not fit these patterns, but are instead based on particular design requirements.

Displacement diagrams are used to represent the travel of the follower relative to the rotation of the cam. Construction of a displacement diagram is the first step in cam design.

Uniform motion is shown in the displacement diagram in Fig. 15-41A. Displacement diagrams represent the motion of the cam follower as the cam rotates through 360°. It can be seen that the uniform motion curve has sharp corners, indicating abrupt changes of velocity at two points; this is impractical and inefficient, since it causes the follower to bounce. Hence this motion is usually modified with arcs that tend to smooth this change and thus the operation. The radius of the modifying arc can vary up to a radius of one-half the total displacement of the follower, depending upon the speed of operation. Usually a radius of about one-third to one-fourth total displacement is best.

Harmonic motion, plotted in part B of the figure, is a smooth continuous motion based on the change of position of the points on the circumference of a circle. At moderate speeds, this displacement results in a smooth operation. Note the method of drawing a semicircle to establish points on the displacement diagram.

Gravity motion (uniform acceleration), plotted in part C, is commonly used for high-speed operation. The variation of displacement is analogous to the force of gravity exerted on a falling body, with the difference in displacement being 1;3;5;5;3;1, based on the square of the number. For instance $1^2 = 1$; $2^2 = 4$; $3^2 = 9$.

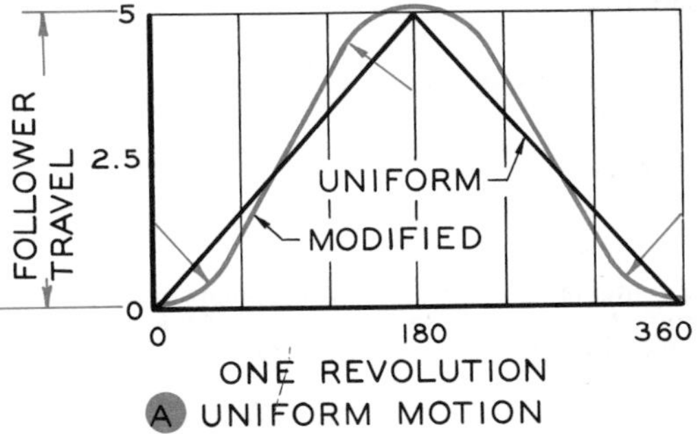

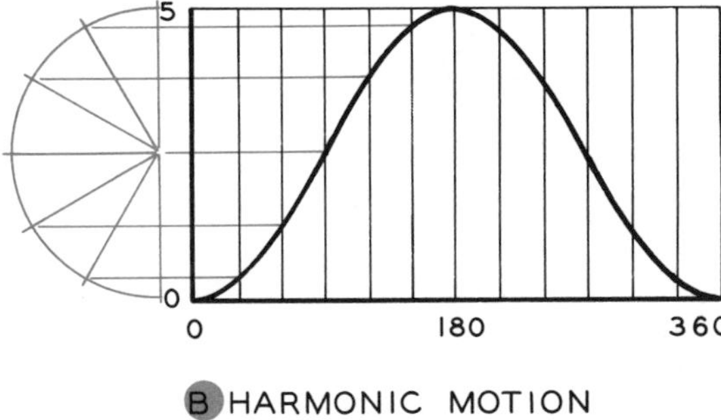

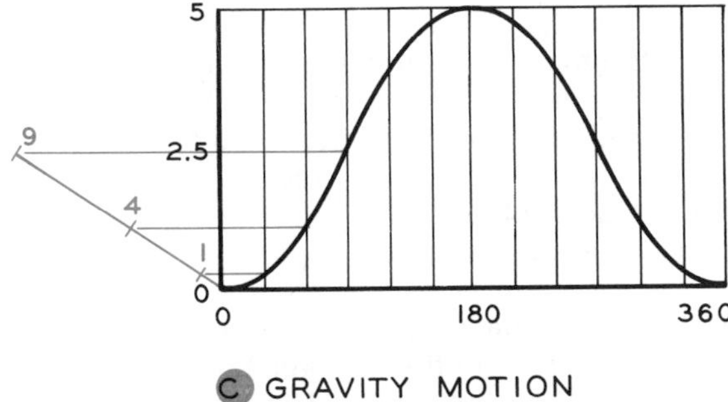

Fig. 15–41. The methods of plotting the three basic motions of cams—uniform, harmonic, and gravity.

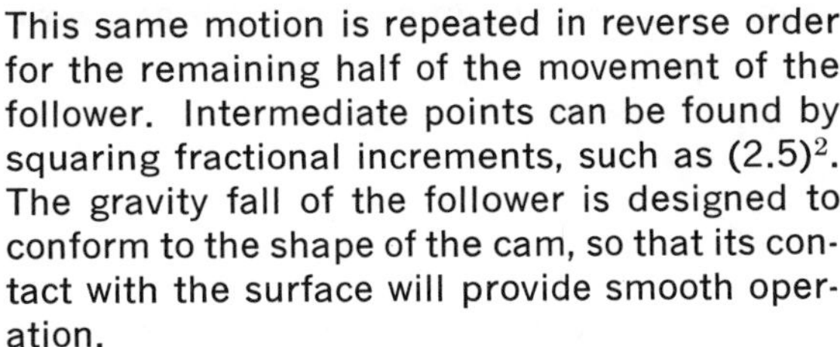

This same motion is repeated in reverse order for the remaining half of the movement of the follower. Intermediate points can be found by squaring fractional increments, such as $(2.5)^2$. The gravity fall of the follower is designed to conform to the shape of the cam, so that its contact with the surface will provide smooth operation.

Cam Followers. Three basic types of cam followers are (A) the flat surface, (B) the roller, and (C) the knife edge, as shown in Fig. 15–42. The flat-surface and knife-edge followers are limited to use with slow moving cams where the minimum of force will be exerted by the friction that is caused during rotation. The roller is the most often used form of follower since it can withstand higher speeds and transmit greater forces.

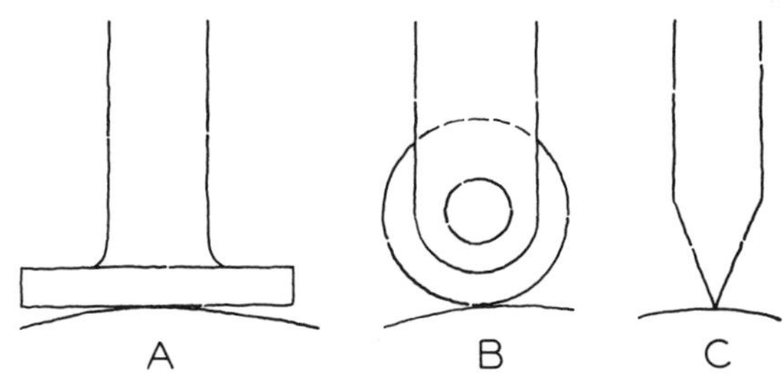

Fig. 15–42. Three basic types of cam followers—the flat surface, the roller, and the knife edge.

15–22 CONSTRUCTION OF A CAM

Plate Cam—Harmonic Motion. The steps of constructing a plate cam with harmonic motion are shown in Fig. 15–43. The draftsman must know certain information before he can design a cam. He must know the desired motion of the follower, the total rise of the follower, the size of the follower and type, the position of the follower, the diameter of the base circle, and the direction of rotation. When this information is available, he proceeds as follows.

FIGURE 15-43. CONSTRUCTION OF A PLATE CAM WITH HARMONIC MOTION

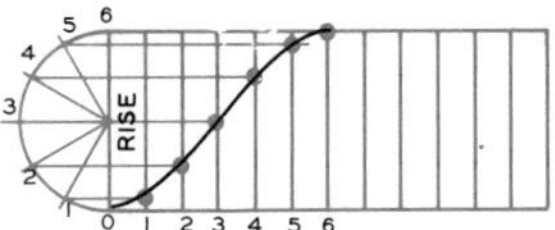

Step 1: Construct a semicircle whose diameter is equal to the rise of the follower. Divide the semicircle into the same number of divisions as there are between 0° and 180° on the horizontal axis of the displacement diagram. Plot half of the displacement curve in the displacement diagram.

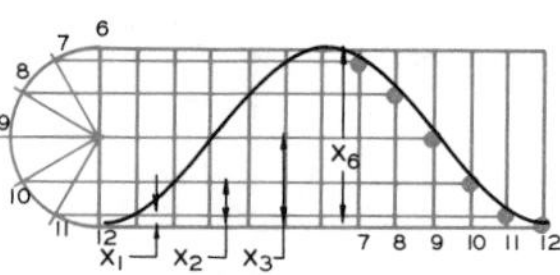

Step 2: Continue the process of plotting points by projecting from the semicircle, starting from the top of the semicircle and proceeding to the bottom. Complete the curve.

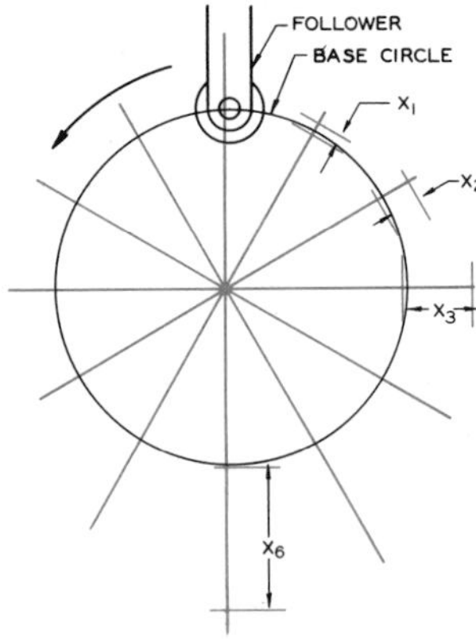

Step 3: Construct the base circle and draw the follower. Divide the base circle into the same number of sectors as there are divisions on the displacement diagram. Transfer distances from the displacement diagram to the respective radial lines of the base circle, measuring outward from the base circle.

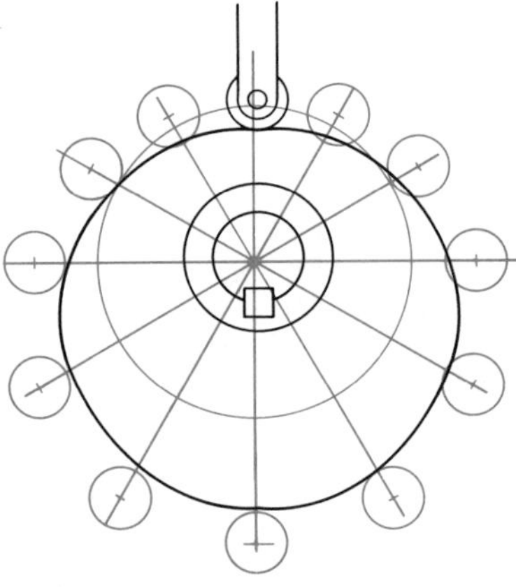

Step 4: Draw circles to represent the positions of the roller as the cam revolves in a counterclockwise direction. Draw the cam profile tangent to all the rollers to complete the drawing.

Step 1. The displacement diagram is laid out. The vertical axis represents the rise of the follower from its lowest point. The horizontal axis is divided into equal divisions representing degrees of rotation of the cam (each division usually represents 15° or 30°). A semicircle with a diameter equal to the rise of the follower is constructed and divided into the same number of equal units as are drawn between 0° and 180° on the horizontal axis of the displacement diagram. The points on the semicircle are projected to their respective lines drawn vertically through the divisions of the horizontal axis. These points are connected with an irregular curve.

Step 2. The same semicircle is used to find points on the curve from 180° to 360° starting from the top of the semicircle (point 6) and proceeding downward to point 12. The points are projected to their respective lines and are connected with a smooth irregular curve. The right side and left side of the displacement diagram are symmetrical.

Step 3. The base circle is drawn from given specifications and the follower is drawn with its center on the base circle. The circle is divided into the same number of sectors as shown on the displacement diagram. There are twelve in this example, since the circle is divided into 30°

FIGURE 15–44. CONSTRUCTION OF A PLATE CAM WITH UNIFORM ACCELERATION

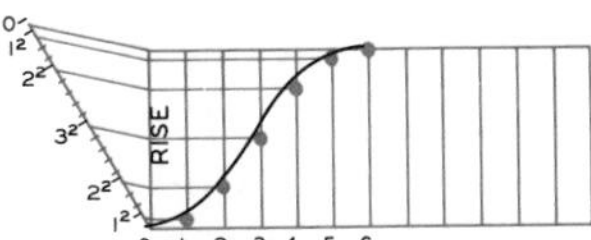

Step 1: Construct a displacement diagram to represent the rise of the follower. Divide the horizontal axis into angular increments of 30°. Draw a construction line through point 0; locate the 1^2, 2^2, and 3^2 divisions and project them to the vertical axis to represent half of the rise. The other half of the rise is found by laying off distances along the construction line with descending values.

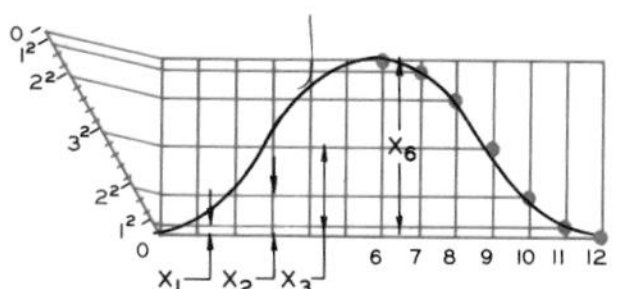

Step 2: Use the same construction to find the right half of the symmetrical curve.

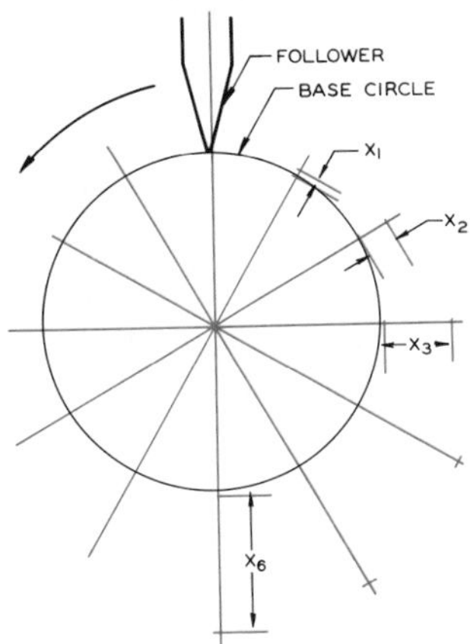

Step 3: Construct the base circle and draw the knife-edge follower. Divide the circle into the same number of sectors as there are divisions in the displacement diagram. Transfer distances from the displacement diagram to the respective radial lines of the base circle, measuring outward from the base circle.

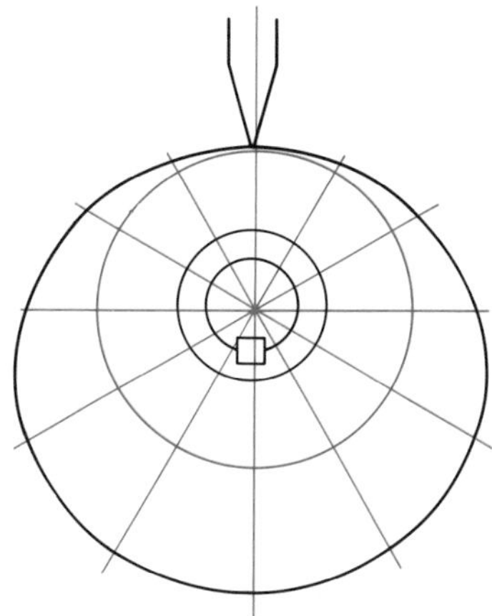

Step 4: Connect the points found in step 3 with a smooth curve to complete the cam profile. Show also the cam hub and keyway.

sectors. The displacement of the cam follower is taken from the displacement diagram, and since the motion of the cam is counterclockwise, the displacement is plotted to the right of the follower. For example, the distances X_1, X_2, and X_3 are measured from the base circle outward. Points are located in this manner all the way around the base circle.

Step 4. Construction circles representing the roller follower are drawn with the points plotted in Step 3 as centers. The profile of the cam is drawn with an irregular curve to be tangent to each of the roller constructions. Additional intervals can be found to construct a more accurate profile. The cam hub and keyway are drawn to given specifications.

Plate Cam—Uniform Acceleration. This construction is the same as the previous example except for the displacement diagram and the knife-edge follower. The steps involved in constructing a plate cam with uniform acceleration are shown in Fig. 15–44.

Step 1. The displacement diagram is drawn with each division on the horizontal axis representing 30° and with the vertical axis equal to the rise of the follower. The rate of travel of the follower changes constantly, producing accel-

FIGURE 15-45. CONSTRUCTION OF A PLATE CAM WITH COMBINATION MOTIONS

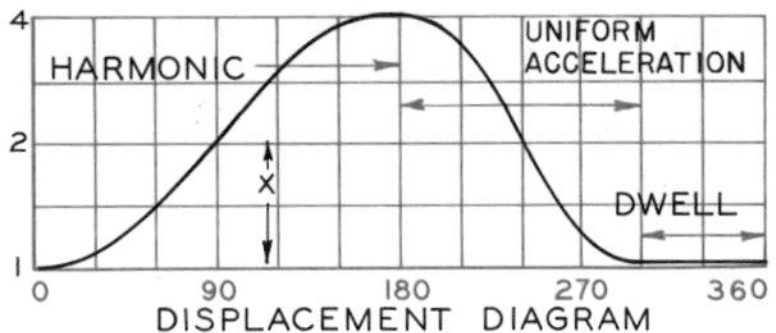

Step 1: The cam is to rise 4″ in 180° with harmonic motion, fall 4″ in 120° with uniform acceleration, and dwell for 60°. These motions are plotted on the displacement diagram.

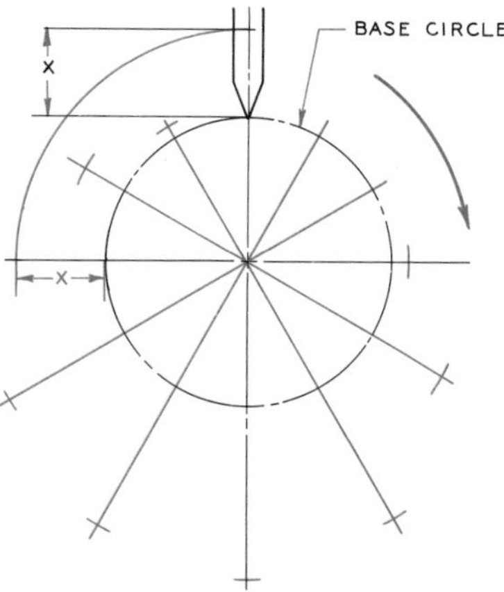

Step 2: Construct the base circle and draw the knife-edge follower. Transfer distances from the displacement diagram to the respective radial lines of the base circle, measuring outward from the base circle.

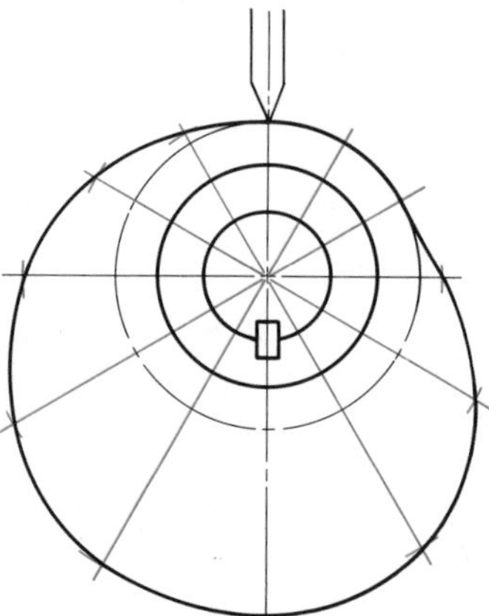

Step 3: Draw a smooth curve through the points found in step 2 to complete the profile of the cam. Show also the cam hub and keyway.

eration and deceleration. The changes in rise are based on the square of each division. Note that these divisions are laid off on the construction line and are projected back to the vertical axis. The follower accelerates from 0° to 180° and decelerates from 180° to 360°. One half of the curve is plotted as an irregular curve.

Step 2. The same construction is used to find the displacement curve from 180° to 360° to complete the symmetrical curve.

Step 3. The base circle is drawn to represent the lowest position of the knife-edge follower. The circle is divided into 30° sectors—the same number of divisions as in the displacement diagram. Since the rotation of the cam is counterclockwise, the displacement is plotted outward from the base circle to the right of the follower in a clockwise direction.

Step 4. The profile of the cam is drawn with an irregular curve through the plotted points. The cam hub and keyway are added to complete the drawing.

Plate Cam—Combination Motion. In Fig. 15-45 a knife-edge follower is used with a plate cam to produce harmonic motion from 0° to 180°, uniform acceleration from 180° to 300°, and dwell (no follower motion) from 300° to 360°. We are to draw a cam that will give this motion from the given base circle.

Step 1. The harmonic portion of the displacement diagram is constructed by drawing a semicircle whose circumference is divided into the same number of equal parts as there are horizontal divisions on the displacement diagram between 0° and 180°—six in this case (Fig. 15-45). Refer to Fig. 15-41B. The uniform acceleration (four divisions in Fig. 15-45) of the follower is found by dividing the number of horizontal divisions by 2; that is, $4 \div 2 = 2$. Then 1^2 would give a travel of 1 during the first 30°, and 2^2 would give a travel of 4 from the peak, or a fall of 3 units between 210° and 240°. The units are laid off as shown in Fig. 15-45C. From 300° to 360°, where a dwell condition exists, the follower does not move; consequently, this portion of the curve is a horizontal line.

Step 2. Radial lines are drawn from the center of the base circle to correspond to the intervals used on the horizontal scale of the displacement diagram. The displacement is measured outward along the radial lines from the base circle with dividers. Distance *X* is shown as an example.

Step 3. The points on the radial lines are connected with a smooth curve to form the cam profile that will produce the specified motion. The hub and keyway are drawn to complete the construction.

15-23 CONSTRUCTION OF A CAM WITH AN OFFSET ROLLER FOLLOWER

The cam in Fig. 15-46 is required to produce harmonic motion through 360°. This motion can be plotted directly from the follower rather than on a displacement diagram, since there are no combinations of motion involved. A semicircle is drawn with its diameter equal to the total motion desired in the follower. In this case, the base circle is the center of the roller of the follower. The center line of the follower is extended down, and a circle is drawn with its center at the center of the base circle so that it is tangent to the extension of the follower center line. This circle is divided into 30° intervals to establish points of tangency for all positions of the follower as it revolves through 360°. These tangent lines can be accurately constructed by drawing them perpendicular to the 30° interval lines extended from the center of the circle to the points on the circumference. The distances are transferred from the harmonic motion diagram to each subsequent tangent line. Distance *X* is located as an example of this procedure. The circular roller is drawn in all views and the profile of the cam is constructed to be tangent to the rollers at all positions, as shown.

15-24 OTHER APPLICATIONS OF CAMS

The latching pawl shown in Fig. 15-47A is an example of a cam used to apply pressure to se-

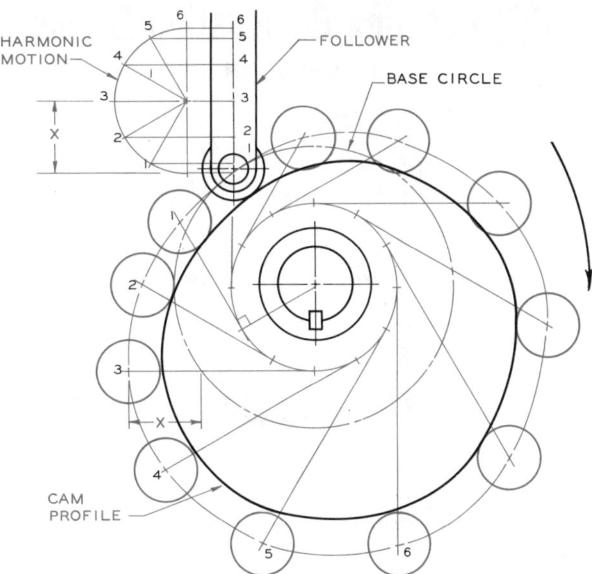

Fig. 15-46. Construction of a plate cam with an offset roller follower.

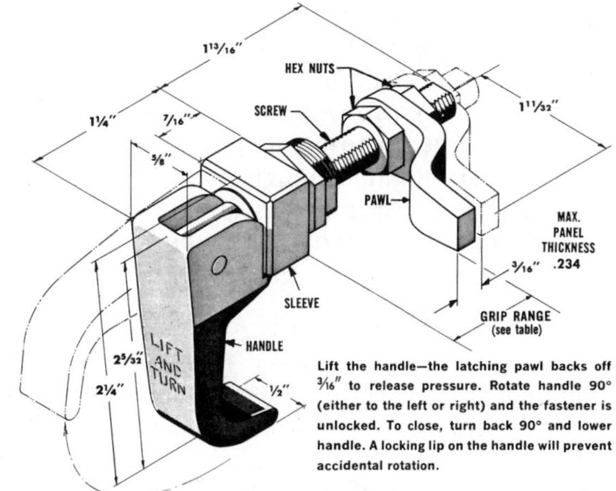

Fig. 15-47A. An application of a cam to a latching pawl which secures a door. (Courtesy of South Chester Corporation.)

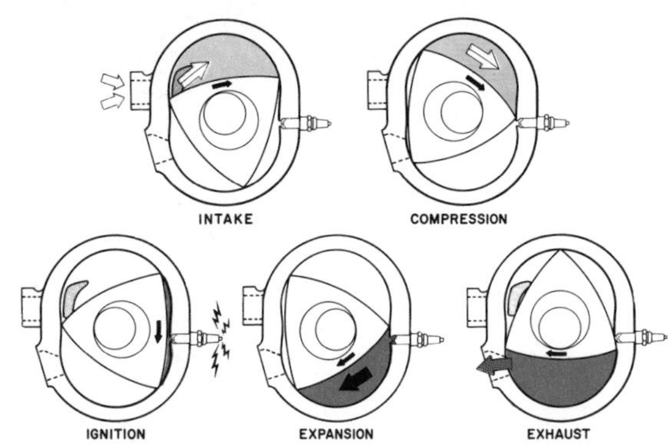

Fig. 15–47B. The combustion cycle of the experimental engine, RC6. (Courtesy of Curtiss-Wright Corporation.)

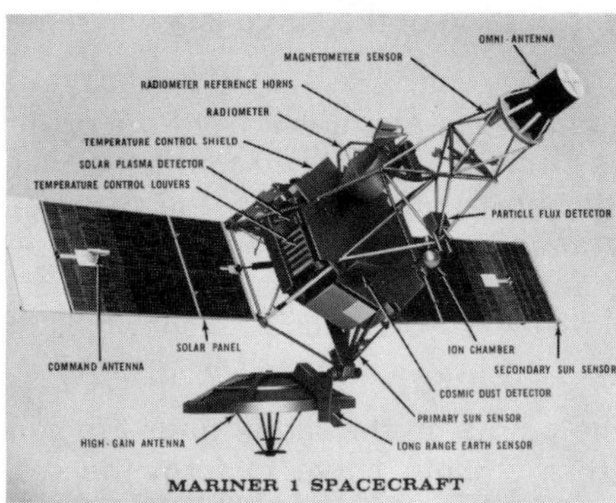

Fig. 15–48A. The Mariner I Spacecraft uses a linkage system that allows the craft to be collapsed into a minimum of space during its flight through the earth's atmosphere. (Courtesy of the National Aeronautics and Space Administration.)

cure a door that has been latched. This design could probably use an arc of a circle to serve the same purpose. However, as leverage becomes more critical, it is necessary to apply the principles of cam motion to provide the most efficient application of force and operation.

An application closely related to the principle of cam motion is shown in Fig. 15–47B, which illustrates the rotary mechanism of a combustion engine that utilizes an eccentrically mounted rotor that performs the same function as the piston in a conventional four-stroke combustion engine. The combustion cycle of this revolutionary engine is illustrated in a sequence of revolutions. Graphics is an important tool for developing a design of this type.

Fig. 15–48B. This portable taper is composed of a combination of mechanisms and linkages. (Courtesy of the 3M-Company.)

15–25 LINKAGES

The spacecraft shown in Fig. 15–48A employs a unique linkage system which is used to position the long-range earth sensor and the solar panels after the vehicle is in space. These linkages must be designed so that the components can be withdrawn into a position that will require minimum space during launching. The portable taper shown in Fig. 15–48B is a combination of gears, cams, and linkages. The hydraulic pusher

Fig. 15–48C. This pusher, which is used to force pipes under roadways, is a linkage system that uses hydraulic power. (Courtesy of Arnold Engineering Development Center.)

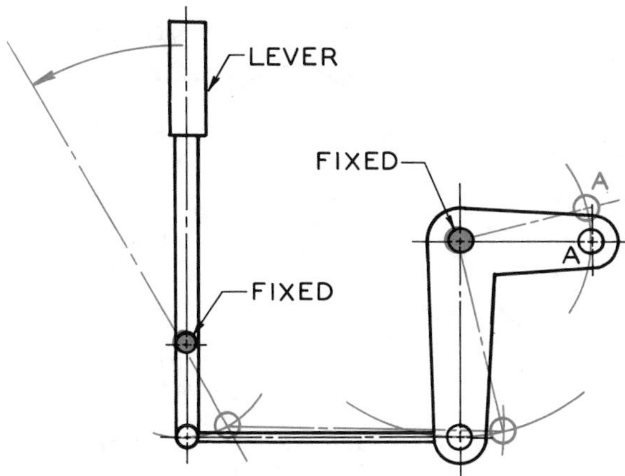

Fig. 15–49. A basic three bar linkage.

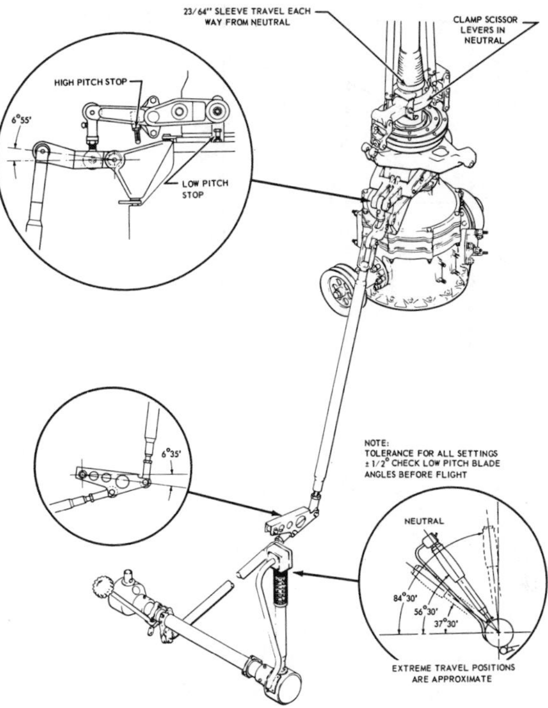

Fig. 15–50. An example of a linkage system used to control the blade pitch on helicopters. (Courtesy of Bell Helicopter Corporation.)

in Fig. 15–48C which was designed to force pipe under roadways, is based on a linkage system utilizing hydraulic power. Linkages are universally used in mechanisms of all sizes. The initial analysis of a linkage system can be approached graphically, prior to the final mathematical analysis.

15–26 A BASIC LINKAGE SYSTEM

The simple linkage system shown in Fig. 15–49 illustrates the graphical analysis of a linkage, in which fixed points are given from which the components must pivot. The motion in this case is transmitted through levers to produce motion of point *A*. To locate the linkage components, all measurements are made by swinging arcs from the fixed pivot points. This is a three-bar linkage composed of three moving parts. An application of this type of system is shown in Fig. 15–50, which illustrates the linkage control system for a helicopter. To ensure proper power transmission and correct motion at the output, the designer must not only graphically analyze but also apply principles of mechanics to a linkage design of this type. Another application of a linkage system of this type is shown in Fig. 15–51.

Fig. 15–51. This gate lock utilizes a combination of linkages and cams. (Courtesy of General American Transportation Corporation.)

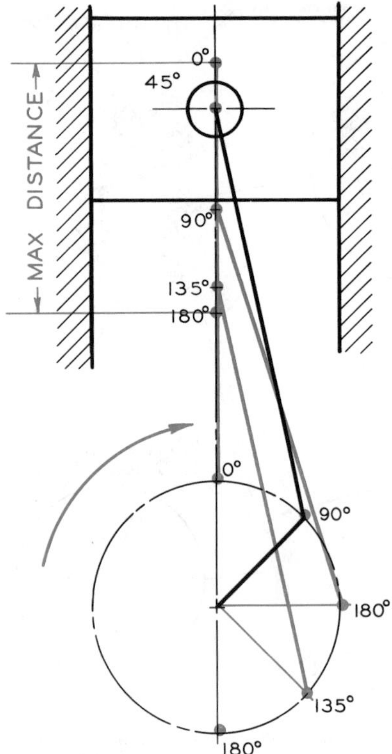

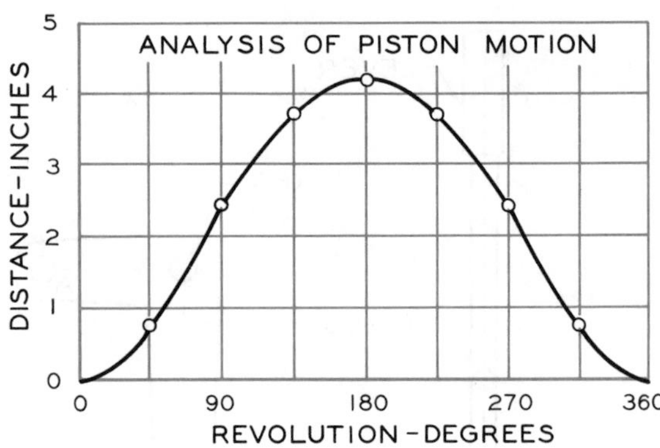

Fig. 15-52. The displacement of the travel of a piston caused by a crankshaft linkage. This is called a slider-crank mechanism.

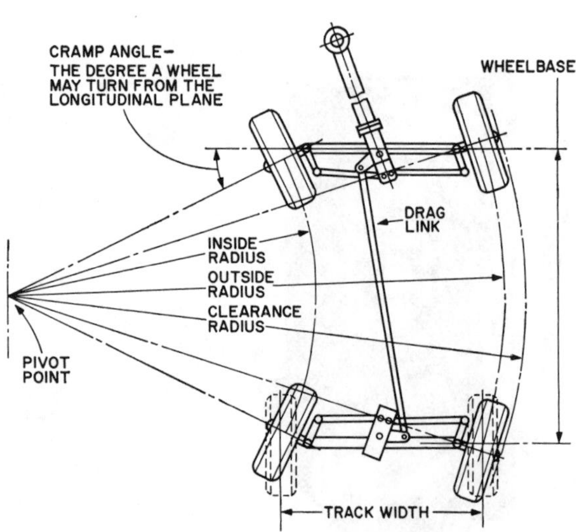

Fig. 15-53. This linkage ensures that an in-plant cargo trailer will tow properly within the available traffic lanes. (Courtesy of *Plant Engineering*.)

15-27 LINKAGE APPLICATIONS

The revolution of a crankshaft is shown in Fig. 15-52, in which a connecting rod and a piston are analyzed for motion in a displacement diagram. This displacement can be found graphically with a high degree of accuracy if a sufficiently large scale is used. The graphical analysis assists the engineer in applying principles of mechanics to the analytical solution. A typical steering linkage system for trailers used in industrial materials handling is shown in Fig. 15-53. Steering systems can be analyzed graphically to determine the motion of the components during the turning process.

15-28 ANALYSIS OF A CLAMPING DEVICE

Many linkage systems are used in the design of clamping mechanisms which, as components of jigs and fixtures, are necessary for holding parts being machined. An example of such a device is shown in Fig. 15-54. The handle is shown in its closed position, position A, and in its revolved position, position B. A partial view of the handle is shown in position C, where the handle makes contact with the working surface. The graphical analysis of the linkage indicates that the plunger will be in its most withdrawn position at position C, where the handle is revolved θ degrees from

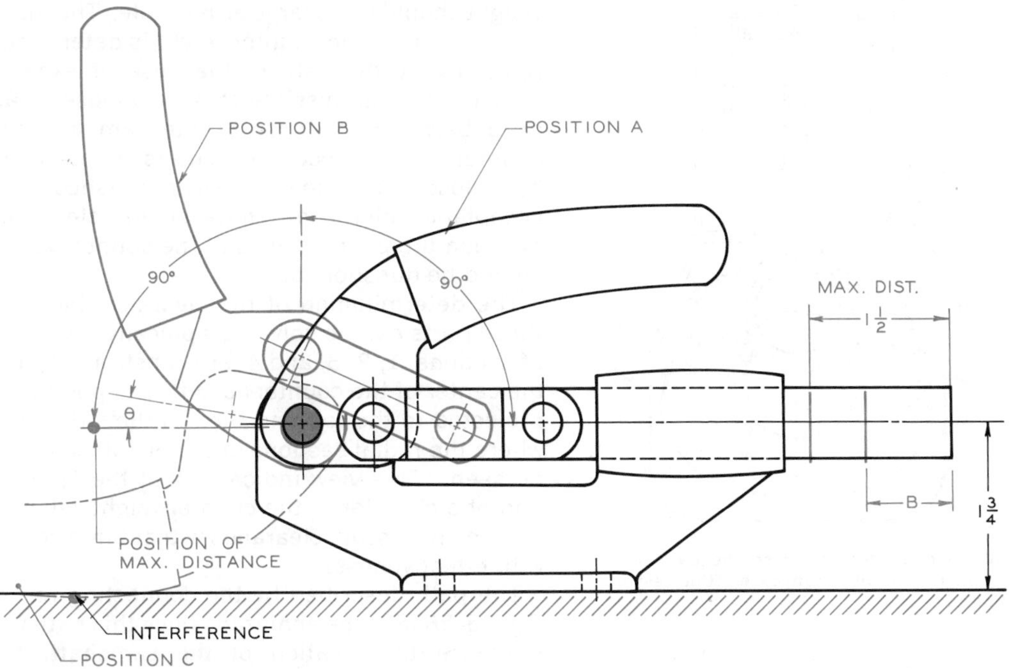

Fig. 15-54. Graphical analysis of a hand-operated clamping device that incorporates linkage principles. (Courtesy of Universal Engineering Corporation.)

the horizontal. If utilization of the maximum travel of the plunger were critical, the handle would have to be modified to permit full operation and hand clearance.

The advantage of the graphical method of analysis of a linkage system of this type is rather obvious. With a minimum of effort, the designer can determine the effects of the dimensions of each link with respect to the motion produced and the available clearance. The design of the handle must consider the position of the operator and the comfort of operation provided by its configuration. Within this framework other linkage systems can be developed that would enable the same clamping action with less movement of the handle if this were necessary.

15-29 ANALYSIS FOR CLEARANCE

A counterweight for an engine is shown in Fig. 15-55. For optimum operation, the counter-

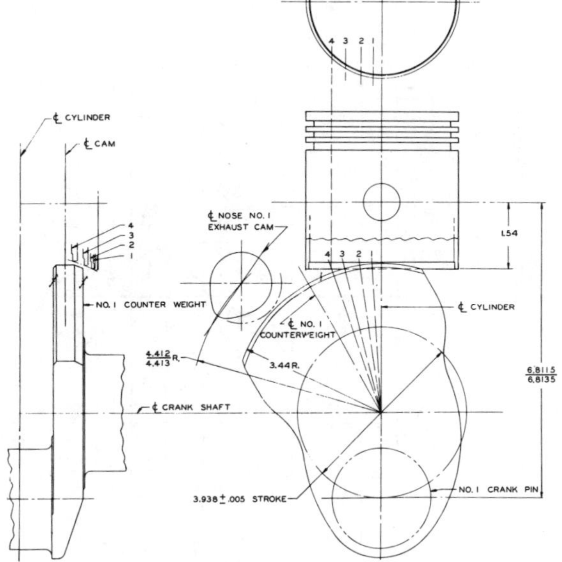

Fig. 15-55. Graphical determination of the clearance between a counterweight and a piston skirt. (Courtesy of Chrysler Corporation.)

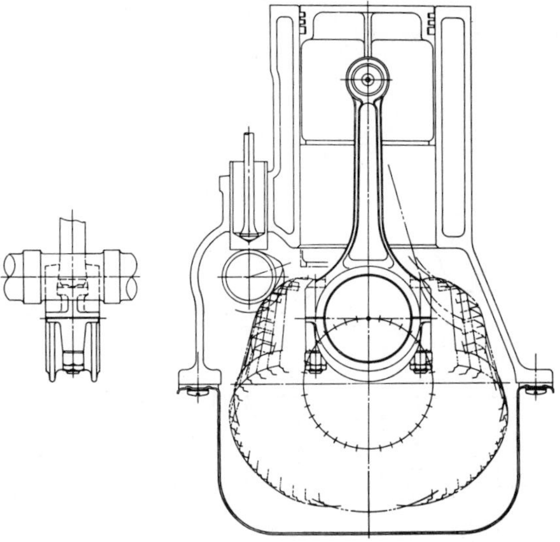

Fig. 15-56. Graphical clearances between the path of a connecting rod and the interior of a crankcase. (Courtesy of Chrysler Corporation.)

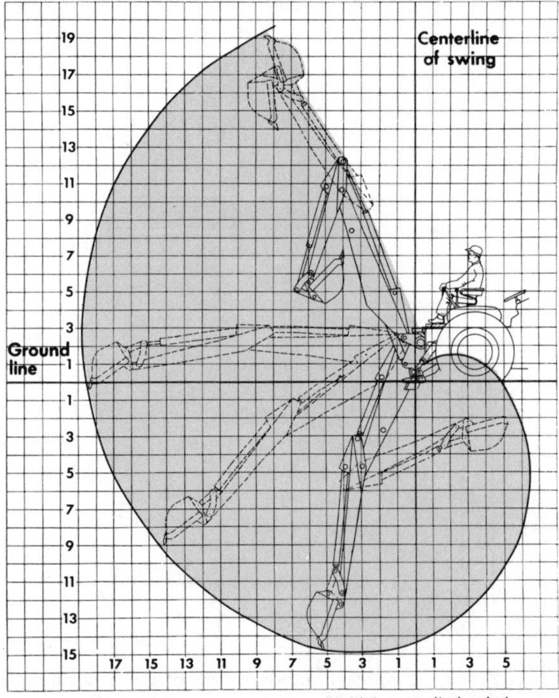
Centerline of swing
Ground line
This digging profile is for backhoe with high capacity bucket.
For digging profile with standard bucket, deduct 4½ inches.

Fig. 15-57. A graphical analysis of the limits of operation of a 3141 Backhoe plotted on graph paper. (Courtesy of the International Harvester Company.)

weight should be as large as possible. The maximum radius of the counterweight is determined primarily by the path of the nose of exhaust cam 1. It is permissible to have a close clearance between the nose of the cam and the counterweight, since the centers of each are held closely, and the surfaces are finished to an acceptable tolerance. However, the clearance between the piston skirt and the counterweight should be questioned.

The determination of the clearance between these parts can be solved graphically. A series of sections, 1, 2, 3, and 4, are constructed from the center of the counterweight. The points are projected to the top and then to the side view, where the radial sections of the piston skirt can be seen. This view indicates that the application of a chamfer to the counterweight will provide the necessary clearance without interfering with effectiveness.

The path described by the connecting rod in Fig. 15-56 must be analyzed, since this path will influence the location of the camshaft, the crankcase walls, the width of oil pans, and other limiting factors. The clearance between the camshaft and the connecting rod bolt head can be close because these are finished surfaces whose centers are closely held. On the other hand, the clearance between the connecting rod and the walls and the oilpan must be somewhat greater to allow for imperfections in the rough forgings and rough crankcase walls. The designer can position the camshaft and establish the size of the crankcase by plotting the extreme path of the connecting rod. The graphical method lends itself to this form of analysis more than any other technique.

In Fig. 15-57, the operating positions for a backhoe are plotted in graphical form to permit visual analysis of its linkage system. The graph-

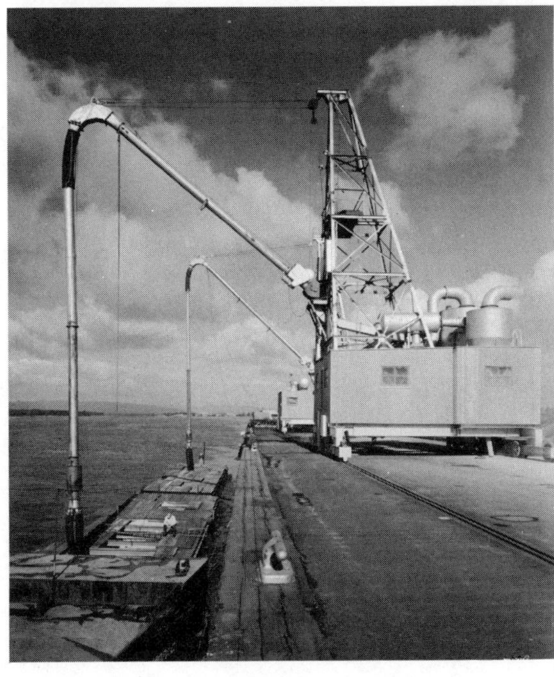

Fig. 15-58. These vacuum systems, which are used for unloading barges, can be analyzed graphically to determine loads and clearances. (Courtesy of General American Transportation Company.)

ical presentation of these positions can be used to communicate its operating characteristics and its limits of efficiency.

15-30 EMPIRICAL ANALYSIS OF A LINKAGE

Linkage systems are often designed to be movable so that the equipment may assume a variety of positions. An example of such a design can be seen in the vacuum booms for unloading barges shown in Fig. 15-58. These booms can be positioned to provide the most effective access to the cargo that is to be moved. When the booms are raised or lowered in different positions, the loads in them and in the support cables will change. The maximum loads that will be supported by the boom, the strength of the cable, and the boom position will affect the limiting positions of the boom within which it can be safely operated. The boom is analyzed graphically in Fig. 15-59 to establish the load in the cable when the boom is in a number of positions. The data thus obtained can be used to determine the safe operating area.

The boom is shown in seven positions in the space diagram loaded with the maximum load of 1000 lb, which will be a vertical force. Force diagrams are drawn for each of the seven positions. For example, when the boom is at 15°, the load in the cable is 360 lb. The stress in the cable versus the position of the boom is plotted in a graph. These points are connected with a smooth curve since the change in load is continuous. Given that the cable is designed for an 1800-lb load, the critical point is found to be at 110°. If the boom is lowered beyond this point, the cable is subject to failure. Inspection of this graph will help the designer select a cable strong enough to withstand the stress imposed if the boom must be designed for lowering beneath the 110° zone. These data are empirical since only selected points were used. It is also customary to use a safety factor with data of this type to avoid variations or defects in the materials used.

15-31 INTRODUCTION TO GRAPHICAL CALCULUS

The engineer, designer, or technician must often deal with relationships between variables that must be solved using the principles of calculus. Data that can be dealt with by calculus and plotted on a graph can be approached graphically. If the equation of the curve is known, traditional methods of calculus will solve the problem. However, many engineering data cannot be converted to standard equations. In these cases, it is desirable to use the graphical method of calculus which provides relatively accurate solutions to irregular problems.

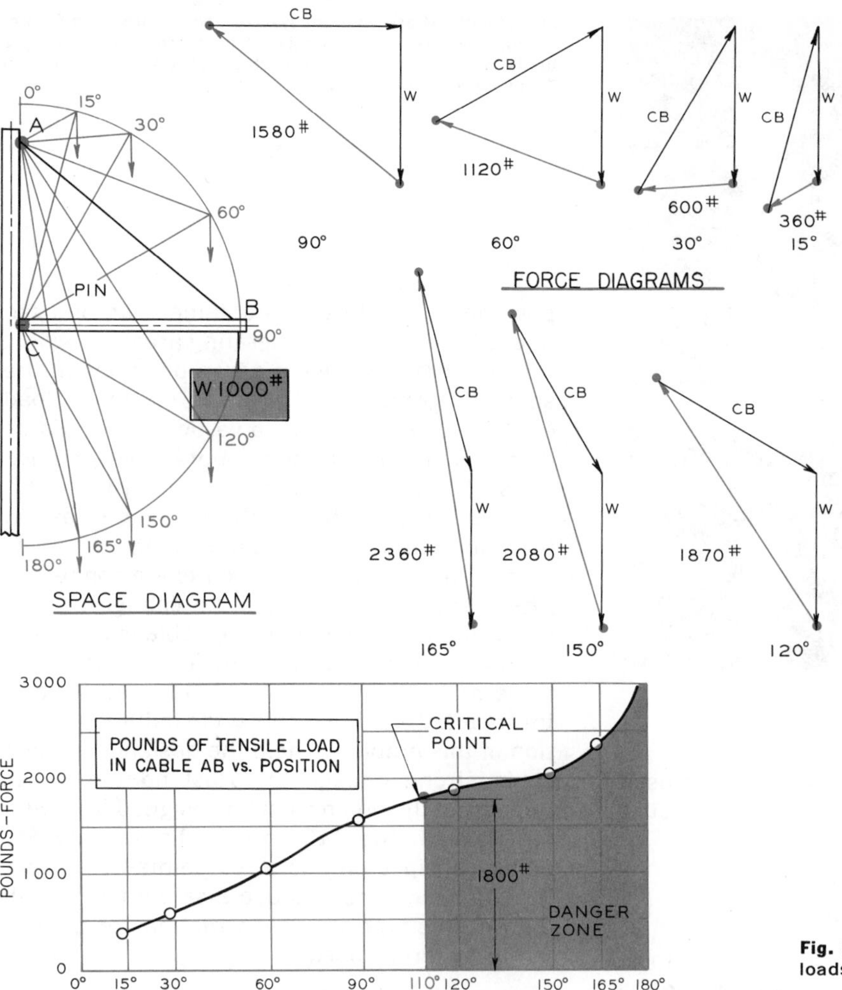

Fig. 15–59. A graphical analysis of the loads in cable *AB* at all positions.

The two basic forms of calculus are (1) differential calculus, and (2) integral calculus. Differential calculus is used to determine the rate of change of one variable with respect to another. For example, the curve plotted in Fig. 15–60 represents the relationship between two variables. Note that the *Y*-variable is increasing as the *X*-variable increases. The rate of change of *Y* relative to *X* is an important characteristic that may influence the design of a mechanism. The rate of change at any instant along the curve is the slope of a line that is tangent to the curve at that particular point. This exact slope is often difficult to determine graphically; consequently, it can be approximated by constructing a chord at a given interval, as shown in Fig. 15–60. The slope of this chord can be measured by finding the tangent of $\Delta Y/\Delta X$. These measurements give a general estimate of the slope of the line through this interval if the intervals are selected to be sufficiently small to minimize error. This slope can represent miles per hour, weight versus length, or a number of other meaningful rates that are important to the analysis of data.

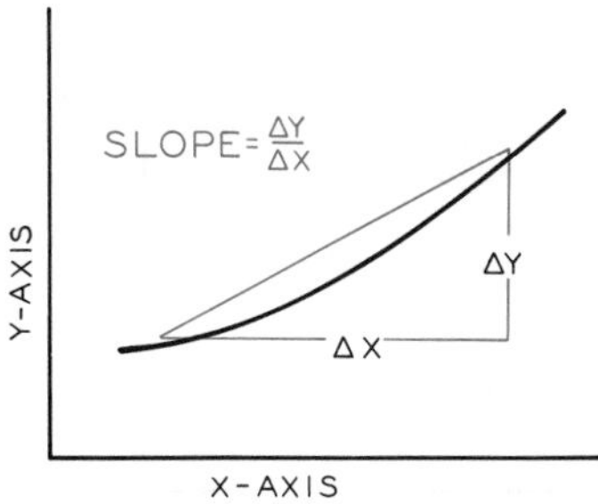

Fig. 15-60. The derivative of a curve is its rate of change at any point, which is the slope of curve, $\Delta Y/\Delta X$.

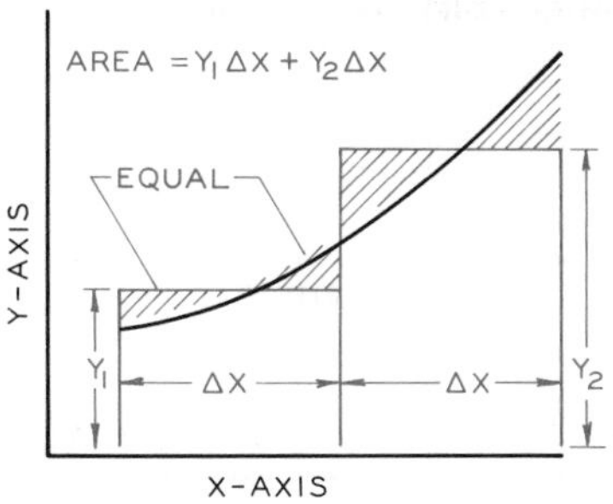

Fig. 15-61. The integral of a curve is the cumulative area enclosed by the curve, which is the product of the two variables.

Integral calculus is the reverse of differential calculus. Integration is the process of finding the area under a given curve, which can be thought of generally as the product of the two variables plotted on the *X*- and *Y*-axes. If one of the variables is area and the other is linear distance, the resulting integral is a volume. The area under a curve is approximated by dividing one of the variables into a number of very small intervals, which become small rectangular areas at a particular zone under the curve, as shown in Fig. 15-61. The bars are extended so that as much of the square end of the bar is under the curve as above the curve and the average height of the bar is therefore near its midpoint. Although this description of integration is the graphical method that will be used, it presents a general idea of the principles of calculus.

15-32 GRAPHICAL DIFFERENTIATION

Graphical differentiation is defined as the determination of the rate of change of two variables with respect to each other at any given point. Figure 15-62 illustrates the preliminary construction of the derivative scale that would be used to plot a continuous derivative curve from the given data.

Step 1. The original data are plotted graphically and the axes are labeled with the proper units of measurement. These grids need not be square, however; the nature of the data will influence the relationship of the *X*- and *Y*-units. The maximum scale required for the ordinate on

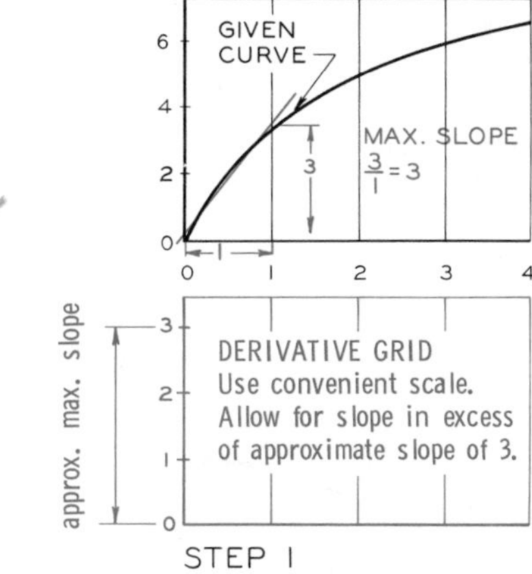

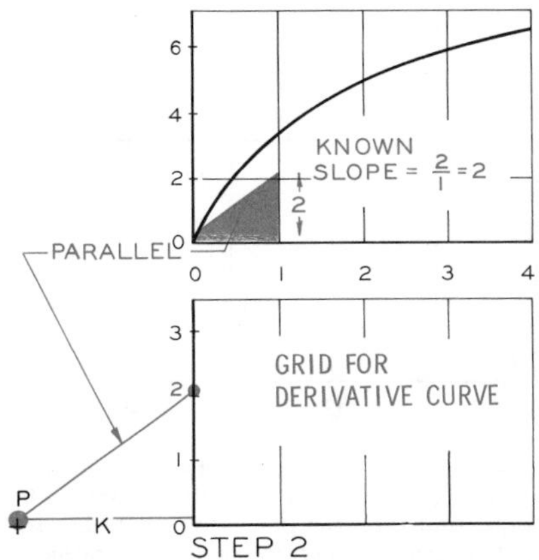

Fig. 15-62. The construction of scales for graphical differentiation.

FIGURE 15–63. GRAPHICAL DIFFERENTIATION

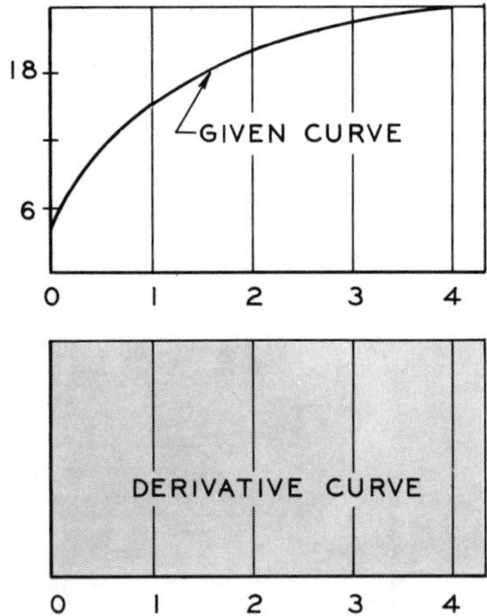

Given: The data plotted in the graph.
Required: Find the derivative curve of the given data.
Reference: Article 15–32.

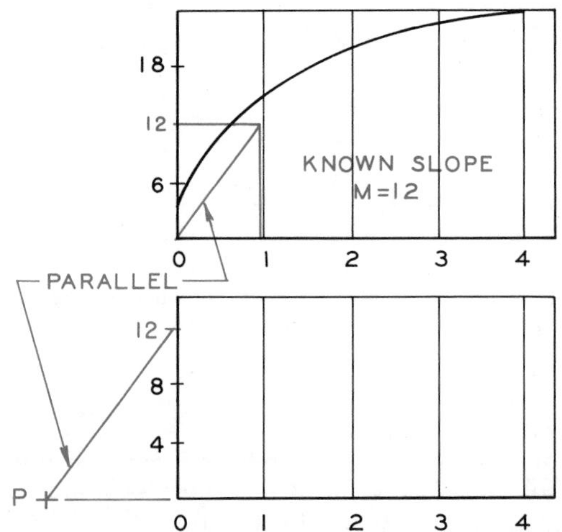

Step 1: Determine the pole distance in the derivative scale by applying the principles covered in Fig. 15–62. Find the known slope of 12 on the given scale, and draw an ordinate scale to provide for slope in excess of 12 on the derivative curve, the maximum estimated slope. Determine point *P* by drawing a slope from the 12 unit mark on the ordinate parallel to the known slope.

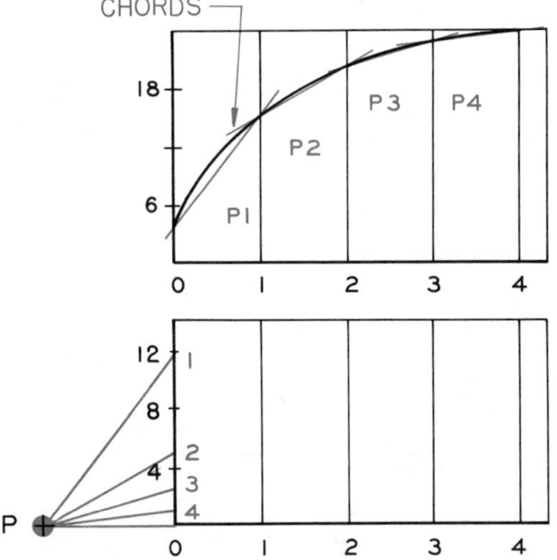

Step 2: Construct a series of chords between selected intervals on the given data curve and draw lines parallel to these chords through point *P* on the derivative grid. Locate points on the ordinate scale where these lines intersect. Shorter chords should be used for greater accuracy where the curve changes sharply.

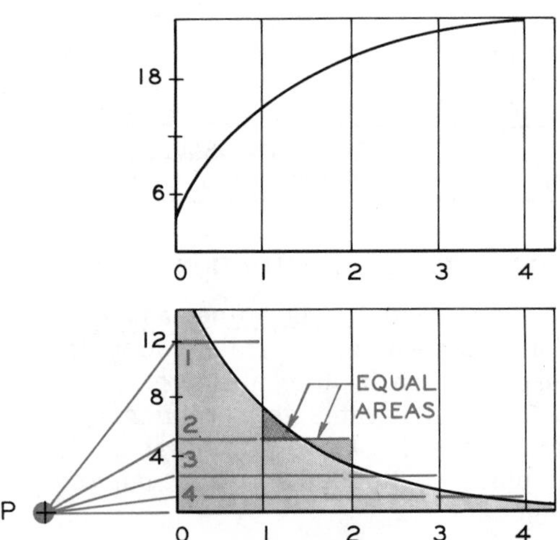

Step 3: Project points 1, 2, 3, and 4 horizontally from the ordinate scale to the intervals through which the chords were drawn. Carefully draw the derivative curve through these intervals near their midpoints. Note that the curve is constructed to have equal areas under and over the horizontal division of the bars. This curve represents the derivatives of the given data.

the derivative grid will be equal to the maximum slope of the original data. A series of chords can be constructed, so that it is possible to estimate the maximum slope by inspection. In the given curve, the maximum slope is estimated to be 3. A vertical scale is constructed in excess of 3 to provide for the plotting of slopes that may exceed the estimate. This ordinate scale is drawn to a convenient scale to facilitate measurement. It should be understood that the ordinate of the derivative scale at any point will be equal to the slope of the given curve, or its rate of change at that point.

Step 2. A known slope is plotted on the given data grid. This slope need not be related to the curve in any way. Construction is simpler if the horizontal interval used in the slope triangle is chosen to be 1, 10, or a multiple of 10, since this will simplify the arithmetic. In this case, the slope can be read directly as 2, since the abscissa spacing is 1 unit. The pole distance K can be found by drawing a triangle from the ordinate of 2 (the known slope) on the derivative scale so that its hypotenuse is parallel to the slope line. These similar triangles are used to obtain the pole distance K, which will be used in determining the derivative curve.

The steps in completing the graphical differentiation are given in Fig. 15-63. Note that the same horizontal intervals used in the given curve are projected directly beneath on the derivative scale. The procedure employed to determine the pole point P (discussed above) is applied in step 1. A known slope of 12 is found on the given grid. The maximum slope of the data curve is estimated to be slightly greater than 12. A scale is selected that will provide an ordinate that will accommodate the maximum slope. A line is drawn from point 12 on the ordinate axis of the derivative that is parallel to the known slope in the given curve grid. The point of intersection of this line and the extension of the X-axis is point P.

A series of chords are constructed on the given curve. These can be varied in length or interval to best approximate the curve. Lines are constructed parallel to these chords through point P and extended to the Y-axis of the derivative grid to locate points 1, 2, 3, and 4. In step 3, these points are projected horizontally across to their respective intervals to give a series of vertical bars. A smooth curve is constructed through the top of these bars in such a manner that the area above the horizontal top of the bar is the same as that below it. This curve represents the derivative of the given data. The rate of change, Y/X, can be found at any interval of the variable X by reading directly from the graph at the value of X in question.

This system of graphical differentiation can be used to find the derivative curve of irregular and empirical data that cannot be expressed by a standard equation. Graphical differentiation is important, since many engineering data do not fit algebraic forms.

15-33 APPLICATIONS OF GRAPHICAL DIFFERENTIATION

The mechanical handling shuttle shown in Fig. 15-64 is used to convert rotational motion into a controlled linear motion. The linkage system for this operation is shown in Fig. 15-65 in pictorial form. A scale drawing of the linkage components is given in an orthographic view in Fig. 15-66, so that graphical analysis can be applied to determine the motion resulting from this system.

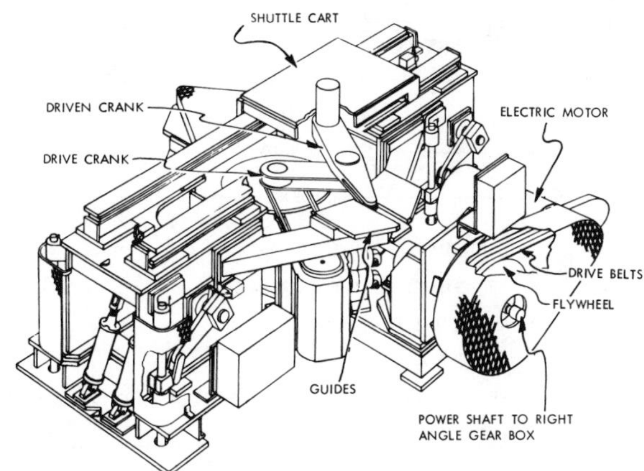

Fig. 15-64. An electrically powered mechanical handling shuttle used to move automobile parts on an assembly line. (Courtesy of General Motors Corporation.)

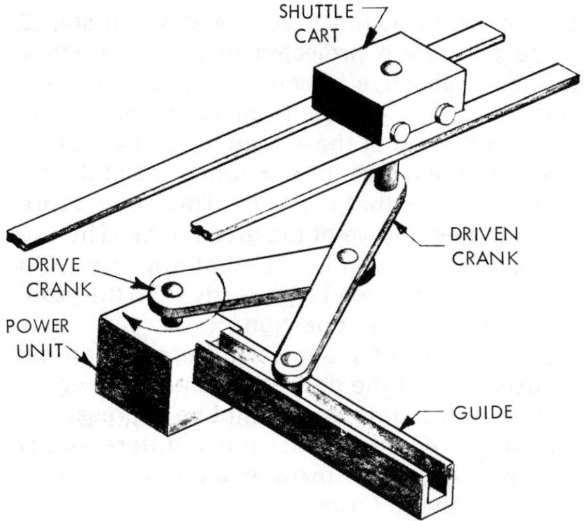

Fig. 15-65. The basic linkage system of the mechanical handling shuttle. (Courtesy of General Motors Corporation.)

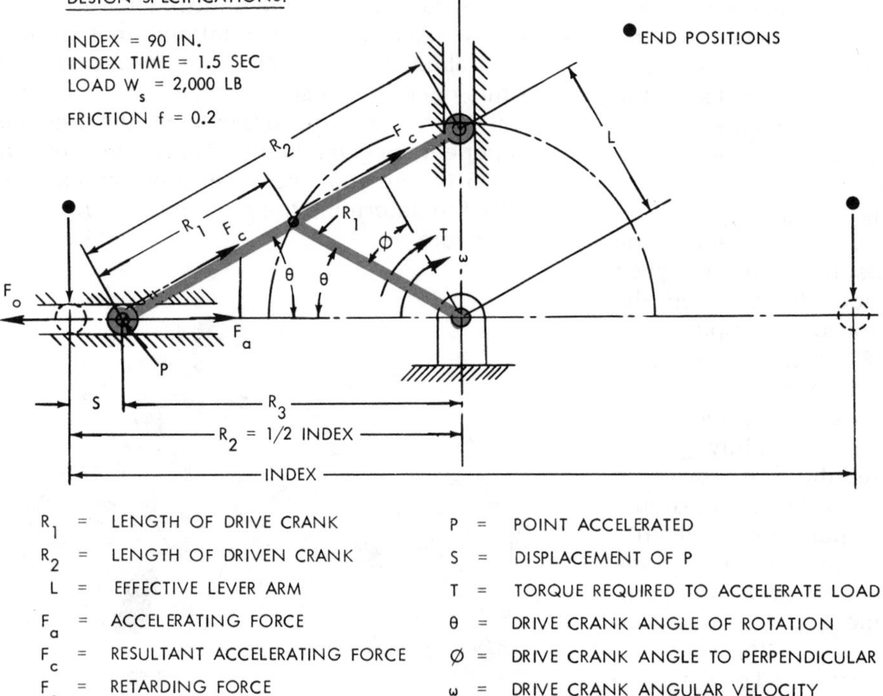

Fig. 15-66. A scale drawing of the linkage system of the mechanical handling shuttle which is used to graphically analyze its motion. (Courtesy of General Motors Corporation.)

The linkage is drawn to show the end positions of point P, which will be used as the zero point for plotting the travel versus the degrees of revolution. Since rotation is constant at one revolution per three seconds, the degrees of revolution can be converted to time, as shown in the data curve given at the top of Fig. 15-67. The drive crank, R_1, is revolved at 30° intervals, and the distance that point P travels from its end position is plotted on the graph, as shown in the given data. This gives the distance-vs.-time relationship. It is desirable to know the velocity and acceleration of the shuttle at various intervals, since these factors will influence the design of the unit. The rate of change of distance vs. time will give velocity, which is in units of inches per second. A derivative curve is needed to determine this rate of change at any instant.

We determine the ordinate scale of the derivative grid by estimating the maximum slope of the given data curve, which is found to be a little less than 100 in./sec. A convenient scale is chosen that will be used for the derivative curve; the maximum limit is 100 units. A slope of 40 is drawn on the given data curve; this will be used in determining the location of pole P in the derivative grid. From point 40 on the derivative ordinate scale, we draw a line parallel to the known slope, which is found on the given grid. Point P is the point where this line intersects the extension of the X-axis. The procedure of determining the pole distance and locating point P can be reviewed by referring to Fig. 15-62.

A series of chords are drawn on the given curve to approximate the slope at various points. In this example, the chords are drawn through the 30° intervals; however, these chords could be drawn through any interval. The intervals need not be equal, but should be spaced so as to give the best approximation to significant rate changes. Lines are constructed through point P of the derivative scale parallel to the chord lines of the given curve and extended to the ordinate scale. The points thus obtained are then projected across to their respective intervals to form vertical bars. A smooth curve is drawn through the top of each of the bars to give an average of the bars (refer to Fig. 15-63). This curve can be used to find the velocity of the shuttle in inches per second at any time interval.

Analysis can also be used to determine the acceleration of the shuttle at various times. The construction of the second derivative curve is very similar to that of the first derivative. By inspecting the first derivative, we estimate the maximum slope to be 200 in./sec/sec. An easily measured scale is established for the ordinate scale of the second derivative curve. Point P is found by constructing a line of a known slope of 60 in the first derivative curve and locating the point where 60 is measured on the second derivative ordinate. From this point a line is drawn parallel to the known slope of 60 to intersect the X-axis; the point of intersection is P.

Chords are drawn at intervals on the first derivative curve. Lines are drawn parallel to these chords from point P in the second derivative curve to the Y-axis, where they are projected horizontally to their respective intervals to form a series of bars. A smooth curve is drawn through the tops of the bars to give a close approximation of the average areas of the bars. Note that a minus scale is given for the acceleration curve to indicate deceleration.

The maximum acceleration is found to be at the extreme endpoints and the minimum acceleration is at 90°, where the velocity is the maximum. It can be seen from the velocity and acceleration plots that the parts being handled by the shuttle are accelerated at a rapid rate until the maximum velocity is attained at 90°, at which time deceleration begins and continues until the parts come to rest. Note that unless there exists a proper relationship between velocity and acceleration, parts will be thrown from the carriage.

Cam displacement diagrams can be analyzed to determine the velocity and acceleration of the follower at any instant during the cam's revolution. The velocity and acceleration of the connecting rod in Fig. 15-52 can be found by graphical differentiation. The process of integration, which is discussed in the following article, can be applied to convert derivative curves to the original data and to find areas and volumes.

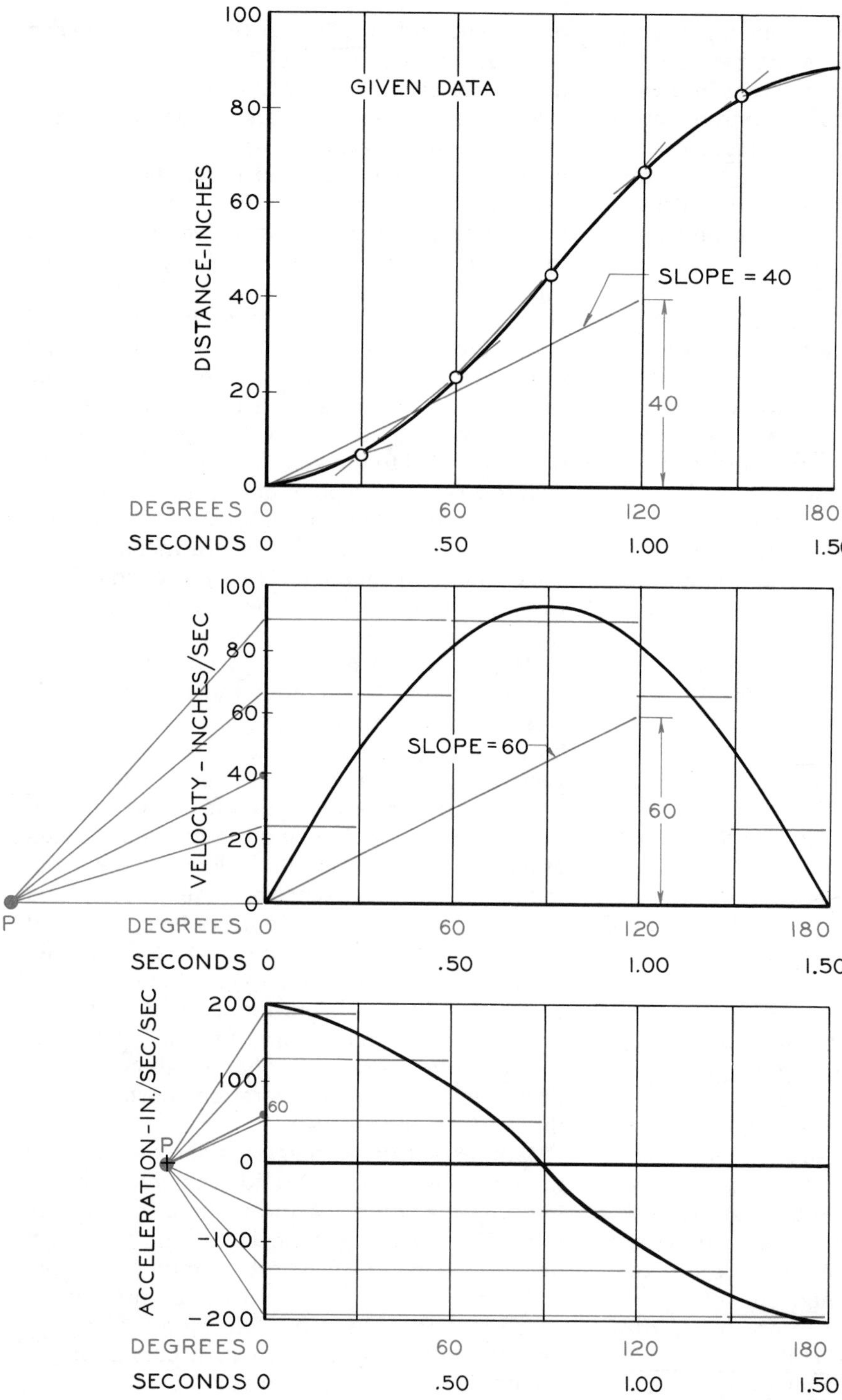

Fig. 15-67. Graphical determination of velocity and acceleration of the mechanical handling shuttle by differential calculus.

15–34 GRAPHICAL INTEGRATION

Integration is the process of determining the area (product of two variables) under a given curve. For example, if the Y-axis were pounds and the X-axis were feet, the integral curve would give the product of the variables, foot-pounds, at any interval of feet along the X-axis. Figure 15–68 depicts the method of constructing scales for graphical integration.

Step 1. The pole distance, K, is found in the given data grid by similar triangles. It is customary to locate the integral curve above the given data curve, since the integral will be an equation raised to a higher power. However, this arrangement is not necessary. A line is drawn through the given data curve to approximate the total area under the curve. This line is estimated to go through point 5 on the ordinate Y-axis to give approximately equal areas above and below the curve. The approximate area is 4×5 or 20 square units of area. The ordinate scale is drawn on the integral curve in excess of 20 units to provide a margin for any overage. The horizontal scale intervals are projected from the given curve to the integral grid. A convenient scale is used for the ordinate axis that will accommodate the size of the graph desired.

Step 2. The ordinate at any point on the integral scale will have the same numerical value as the area under the curve as measured from the origin to that point on the given data grid. A rectangular area is established on the given grid. The ordinate at point 2 on the X-axis directly above the rectangle must be equal to its area of 8. A slope is drawn from the origin to the ordinate of 8. Point P is found by drawing a line from point 4 on the given grid parallel to the slope established in the integral grid. This line intersects the extension of the X-axis at point P. This point will be used to find the integral curve. The procedure is opposite to that used in differentiation.

The technique illustrated in Fig. 15–69 can be applied to most integration problems. The equation of the given curve is $Y = 2X^2$, which

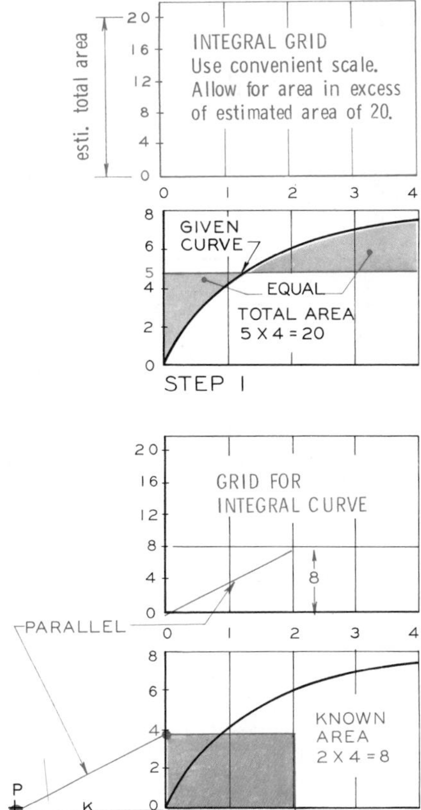

Fig. 15–68. Construction of scales for graphical integration.

can also be integrated mathematically as a check.

From the given grid, the total area under the curve can be estimated to be 40 units. This value becomes the maximum height of the Y-axis on the integral curve. A convenient scale is selected and units are assigned to the ordinate. The pole point, P, is found by constructing a rectangle of known area in the given grid and finding an ordinate in the integral curve above this area to represent the area. A line is drawn from the ordinate, MN, to the origin to give the slope of the line that will be drawn from point R to the extension of the X-axis, where point P is located. This procedure is explained in Fig. 15–68.

FIGURE 15-69. GRAPHICAL INTEGRATION

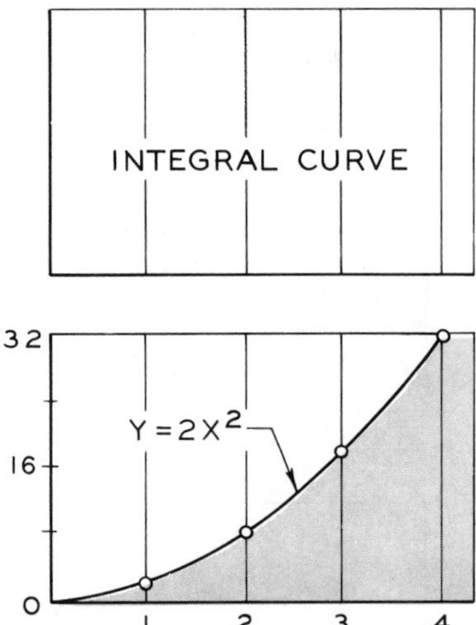

Given: The equation $Y = 2X^2$ plotted in graphical form.
Required: The integral curve of the given data.
Reference: Article 15-34.

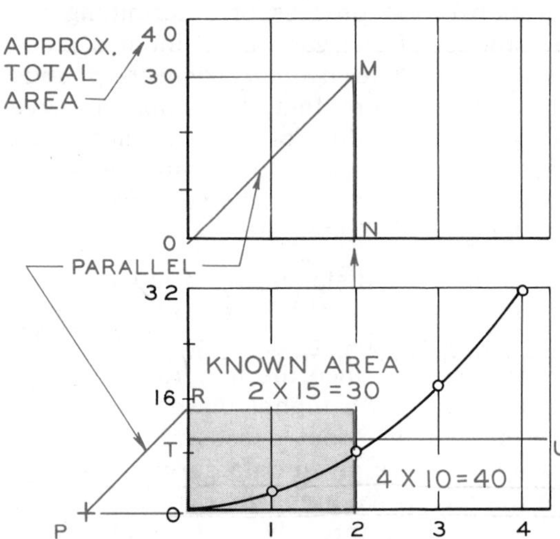

Step 1: The total area under the given curve is estimated to be 40 units by constructing line *TU*. Scale the ordinate on the integral grid to include a maximum of 40 units using a convenient scale. Find a known area of 30 on the given grid. Point *M* is the 30-unit point on the integral curve. Locate point *P* by applying the principles covered in Fig. 15-68.

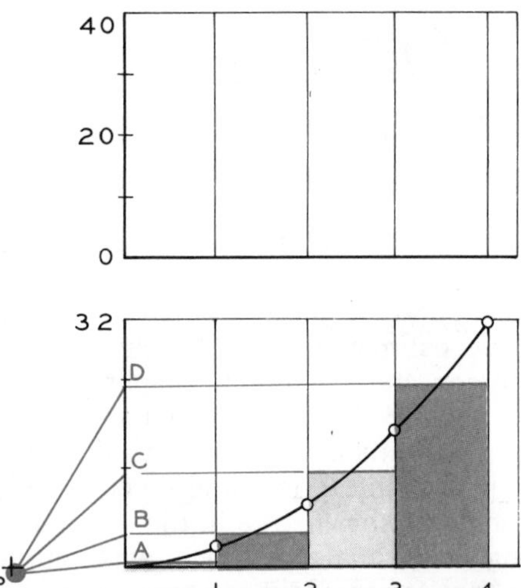

Step 2: Divide the given curve into a series of vertical bars that approximate the area under the curve at given intervals. These intervals need not be equal. Project the heights of the bars to points *A*, *B*, *C*, and *D* on the *Y*-axis and draw rays from these points to point *P*.

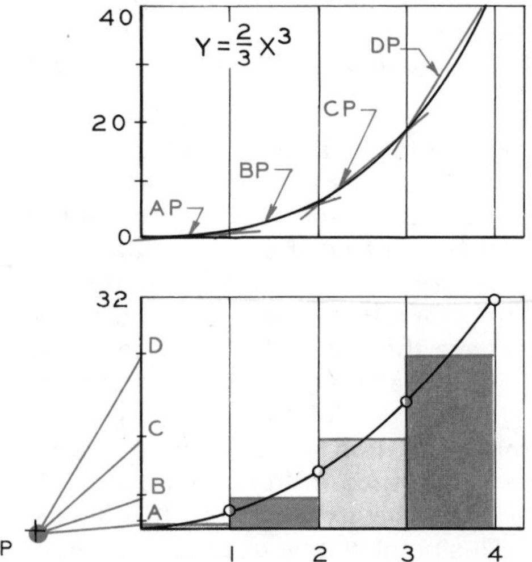

Step 3: Draw lines parallel to these rays in the integral grid at their respective intervals in succession. These sloping lines are drawn to represent the chords of the integral curve. Draw the curve through the chord intersections as shown. The total area under the integral curve from zero to three units can be measured as 18 on the integral graph.

A series of vertical bars are constructed at intervals to approximate the areas under the curve at these intervals. The narrower the bars, the more accurate will be the resulting calculations. The top lines of the bars are extended horizontally to the ordinate Y-axis, where the points are then connected by lines to point P. Lines are drawn parallel to AP, BP, CP and DP in the integral grid to correspond to the respective intervals in the given grid. The intersection points of the chords are connected by a smooth curve—the integral curve. This curve gives the cumulative product of the X- and Y-variables at any value along the X-axis. For example, the area under the curve at $X = 3$ can be read directly as 18.

Mathematical integration gives the following result for the area under the curve from 0 to 3:

$$\text{Area } A = \int_0^3 Y\,dX, \qquad \text{where} \qquad Y = 2X^2;$$

$$A = \int_0^3 2X^2\,dX = \tfrac{2}{3}X^3]_0^3 = 18.$$

15–35 APPLICATIONS OF GRAPHICAL INTEGRATION

Integration is commonly used in the study of the strength of materials to determine shear, moments, and deflections of beams. An example problem of this type is shown in Fig. 15–70, in which a truck exerts a total force of 36,000 lb on a beam that is used to span a portion of a bridge. The first step is to determine the resultants supporting each end of the beam.

A scale drawing of the beam is made with the loads concentrated at their respective positions. A force diagram is drawn, using Bow's notational system for laying out the vectors in sequence. This process can be reviewed by referring to Article 14–12. Pole point O is located, and rays are drawn from the ends of each vector to O. The lines of force in the load diagram at the top of the figure are extended to the funicular diagram. Then lines are drawn parallel to the rays between the corresponding lines of force. For example, ray OA is drawn in the A-interval in the funicular diagram. The closing ray of the funicular diagram, OE, is transferred to the vector diagram by drawing a parallel through point O to locate point E. Vector DE is the right-end resultant of 20.1 kips (one kip equals 1000 lb) and EA is the left-end resultant of 15.9 kips. The origin of the resultant force of 36 kips is found by extending OA and OD in the funicular diagram to their point of intersection.

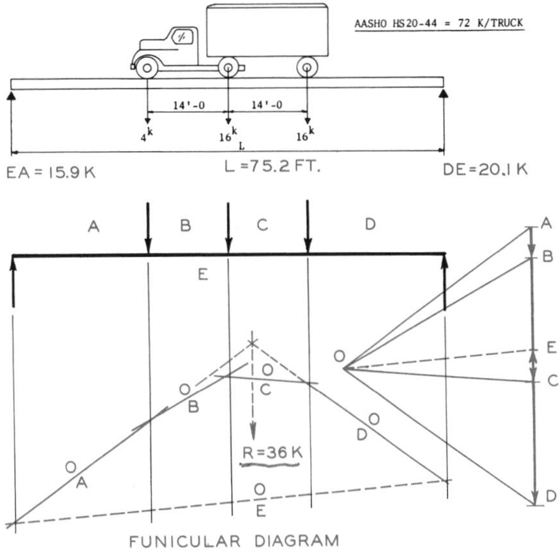

Fig. 15–70. The determination of the forces on a beam of a bridge and its total resultant.

From the load diagram shown in Fig. 15–71 we can, by integration, find the shear diagram, which indicates the points in the beam where failure due to crushing is most critical. Since the applied loads are concentrated rather than uniformly applied, the shear diagram will be composed of straight-line segments. In the shear diagram the left-hand resultant of 15.9 kips is drawn to scale from the axis. The first load of 4 kips, acting in a downward direction, is subtracted from this value directly over its point of application, which is projected from the load diagram. The second load of 16 kips also exerts a downward force and so is subtracted from the 11.9 kips (15.9–4). The third load of 16 kips is also subtracted, and the right-hand resultant will bring the shear diagram back to

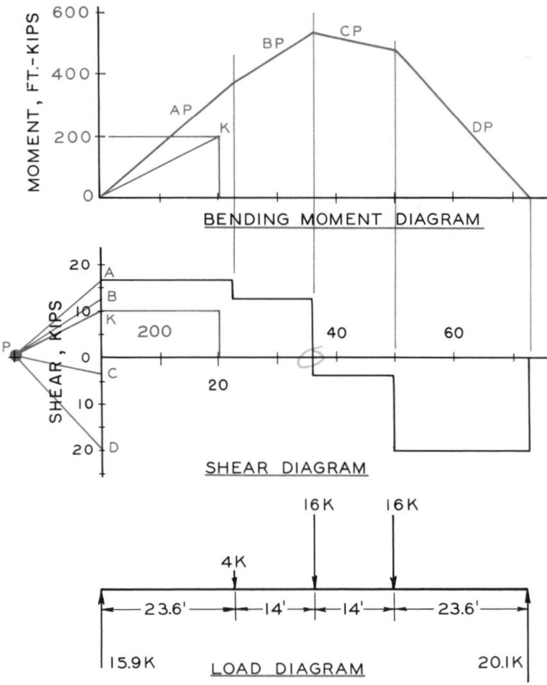

Fig. 15–71. The determination of shear and bending moment by graphical integration.

the *X*-axis. It can be seen that the beam must be designed to withstand maximum shear at each support and minimum shear at the center.

The moment diagram is used to evaluate the bending characteristics of the applied loads in foot-pounds at any interval along the beam. The ordinate of any *X*-value in the moment diagram must represent the cumulative foot-pounds in the shear diagram as measured from either end of the beam.

Pole point *P* is located in the shear diagram by applying the method described in Fig. 15–68. A rectangular area of 200 ft-kips is found in the shear diagram. We estimate the total area to be less than 600 ft-kips; so we select a convenient scale that will allow an ordinate scale of 600 units for the moment diagram. We locate the area of 200 ft-kips in the moment diagram by projecting the 20-ft mark on the *X*-axis until it intersects with a 200-unit projection from the *Y*-axis, locating point *K*. The diagonal, *OK*, is transferred to the shear diagram, where it is drawn from the ordinate of the given rectangle to point *P* on the extension of the *X*-axis. Rays *AP*, *BP*, *CP*, and *DP* are found in the shear diagram by projecting horizontally from the various values of shear. In the moment diagram, these rays are then drawn in their respective intervals to form a straight-line curve that represents the cumulative area of the shear diagram, which is in units of ft-kips. Maximum bending will occur at the center of the beam, where the shear is zero. The bending is scaled to be about 560 ft-kips. The beam selected for this span must be capable of withstanding a shear of 20.1 kips and a bending moment of 560 ft-kips.

15–36 NOMOGRAPHY*

An additional aid in analyzing data is a graphical computer called a *nomogram* or *nomograph.* Basically, a nomogram or "number chart," is any graphical arrangement of calibrated scales and lines which may be used to facilitate calculations, usually those of a repetitive nature. The most frequently used nomograms are the common line graphs previously discussed in this chapter.

The term "nomogram" is frequently used to denote a specific type of scale arrangement called an alignment chart. Typical examples of alignment charts are shown in Fig. 15–72. Many other types are also used which have curved scales or other scale arrangements, for more complex problems. The discussion of nomograms in this chapter will be limited to the simpler conversion, parallel-scale, and N-type charts and their variations.

Using an Alignment Chart. An alignment chart is usually constructed to help solve for one or more unknowns in a formula or empirical relationship between two or more quantities, for example, to convert degrees centigrade to de-

* Articles 15–36 through 15–42 were written by Michael P. Guerard, Engineering Design Graphics, Texas A&M University.

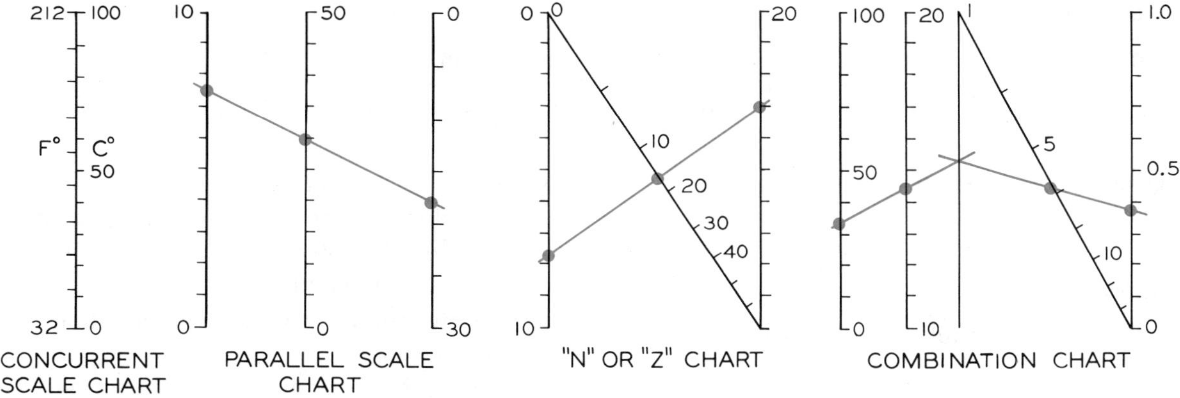

Fig. 15-72. Typical examples of types of alignment charts.

grees fahrenheit, to find the size of a structural member to sustain a certain load, etc. An alignment chart is read by placing a straightedge, or by drawing a line called an *isopleth,* across the scales of the chart, and reading corresponding values from the scales on this line. The example in Fig. 15-73 shows readings for the formula $U + V = W$.

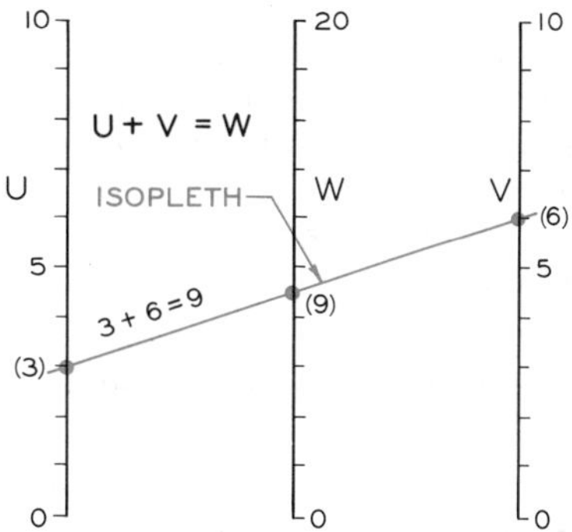

Fig. 15-73. The use of an isopleth to solve graphically for unknowns in the given equation.

15-37 ALIGNMENT CHART SCALES

To construct any alignment chart, we must first determine the graduations of the scales that will be used to give the desired relationships. Alignment-chart scales are called *functional scales*. A functional scale is one that is graduated according to values of some *function* of a variable, but *calibrated* with values of the variable. A functional scale for $F(U) = U^2$ is illustrated in Fig. 15-74. It can be seen in this example that if a value of $U = 2$ was substituted into the equation, the position of U on the functional scale would be 4 units from zero or $2^2 = 4$. This procedure can be repeated with all values of U by substitution.

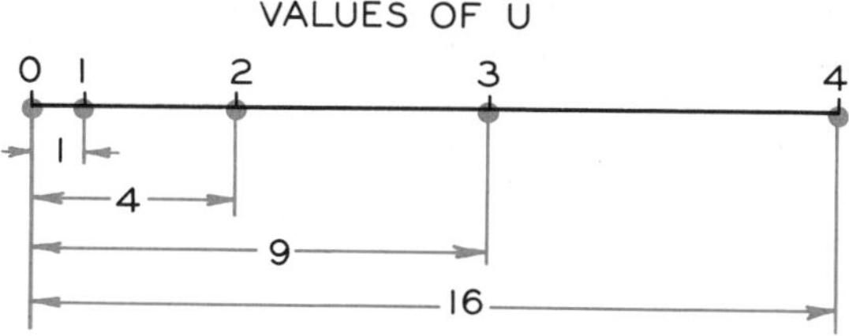

Fig. 15-74. A functional scale for units of measurement that are proportional to $F(U) = U^2$.

The Scale Modulus. Since the graduations on a functional scale are spaced in proportion to values of the function, a proportionality, or scaling factor is needed. This constant of proportionality is called the *scale modulus* and it is

Table 15-1

U	0°	5°	10°	15°	20°	25°	30°	35°	40°	45°
X	0	0.74	1.47	2.19	2.90	3.58	4.24	4.86	5.45	6.00

given by the equation

$$m = \frac{L}{F(U_2) - F(U_1)}, \tag{1}$$

where

m = scale modulus, in inches per functional unit,

L = desired length of scale, in inches,

$F(U_2)$ = function value at end of the scale,

$F(U_1)$ = function value at start of the scale.

For example, suppose that we are to construct a functional scale for $F(U) = \sin U$, with $0° \leq U \leq 45°$ and a scale 6″ in length. Thus $L = 6''$, $F(U_2) = \sin\ 45° = 0.707$, $F(U_1) = \sin\ 0° = 0$. Therefore Eq. (1) can be written in the following form by substitution:

$$m = \frac{6}{0.707 - 0} = 8.49 \text{ inches per (sine) unit.}$$

The Scale Equation. Graduation and calibration of a functional scale are made possible by a *scale equation*. The general form of this equation may be written as a variation of Eq. (1) in the following form:

$$X = m[F(U) - F(U_1)], \tag{2}$$

where

X = distance from the measuring point of the scale to any graduation point,

m = scale modulus,

$F(U)$ = functional value at the graduation point,

$F(U_1)$ = functional value at the measuring point of the scale.

For example, a functional scale is constructed for the previous equation, $F(U) = \sin U$ $(0° \leq U \leq 45°)$. It has been determined that $m = 8.49$, $F(U) = \sin U$, and $F(U_1) = \sin 0° = 0$. Thus by substitution the scale equation, (2), becomes

$$X = 8.49 (\sin U - 0) = 8.49 \sin U.$$

Using this equation, we can substitute values of U and construct a table of positions. In this case, the scale is calibrated at 5° intervals, as reflected in Table 15-1.

The values of X from the table give the positions, in inches, for the corresponding graduations, measured from the start of the scale ($U = 0°$); see Fig. 15-75. It should be noted that the measuring point does *not* need to be at one end of the scale, but it is usually the most convenient point, especially if the functional value is zero at that point.

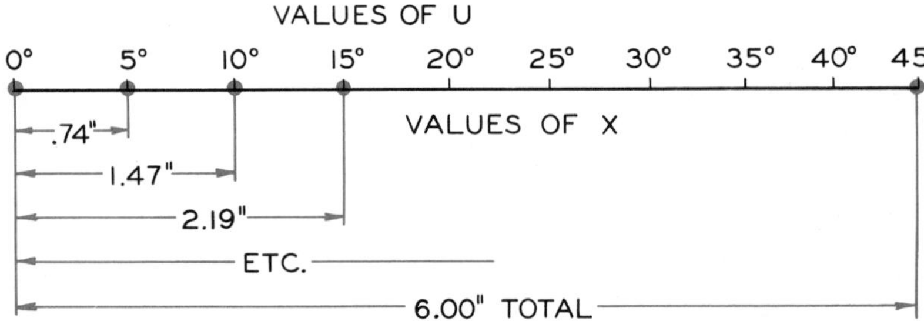

Fig. 15-75. Construction of a functional scale using values from Table 15-1, which were derived from the scale equation.

Table 15-2

r	1	2	3	4	5	6	7	8	9	10
X_r	0	0.15	0.40	0.76	1.21	1.77	2.42	3.18	4.04	5.00

Table 15-3

A	(3.14)	50	100	150	200	250	300	(314)
X_A	0	0.76	1.56	2.36	3.16	3.96	4.76	5.00

15-38 CONCURRENT SCALE CHARTS

Concurrent scale charts are useful in the rapid conversion of one value into terms of a second system of measurement. Formulas of the type $F_1 = F_2$, which relate two variables, can be adapted to the concurrent scale format. Typical examples might be the Fahrenheit-centigrade temperature relation,

$$°F = \tfrac{9}{5}°C + 32,$$

or the area of a circle,

$$A = \pi r^2.$$

Design of a concurrent-scale chart involves the construction of a functional scale for each side of the mathematical formula in such a manner that the *position* and *lengths* of each scale coincide. For example, to design a conversion chart 5″ long that will give the areas of circles whose radii range from 1 to 10, we first write $F_1(A) = A$, $F_2(r) = \pi r^2$, and $r_1 = 1$, $r_2 = 10$. The scale modulus for r is

$$m_r = \frac{L}{F_2(r_2) - F_2(r_1)}$$

$$= \frac{5}{\pi(10)^2 - \pi(1)^2} = 0.0161.$$

Thus the scale equation for r becomes

$$\begin{aligned} X_r &= m_r[F_2(r) - F_2(r_1)] \\ &= 0.0161[\pi r^2 - \pi(1)^2] \\ &= 0.0161\pi(r^2 - 1) \\ &= 0.0505(r^2 - 1). \end{aligned}$$

A table of values for X_r and r may now be completed as shown in Table 15-2. The r-scale can be drawn from this table, as shown in Fig. 15-76. From the original formula, $A = \pi r^2$, the limits of A are found to be $A_1 = \pi = 3.14$ and $A_2 = 100\pi = 314$. The scale modulus for concurrent scales is always the same for equal-length scales; therefore $m_A = m_r = 0.0161$, and the scale equation for A becomes

$$\begin{aligned} X_A &= m_A[F_1(A) - F_1(A_1)] \\ &= 0.0161(A - 3.14). \end{aligned}$$

The corresponding table of values is then computed for selected values of A, as shown in Table 15-3.

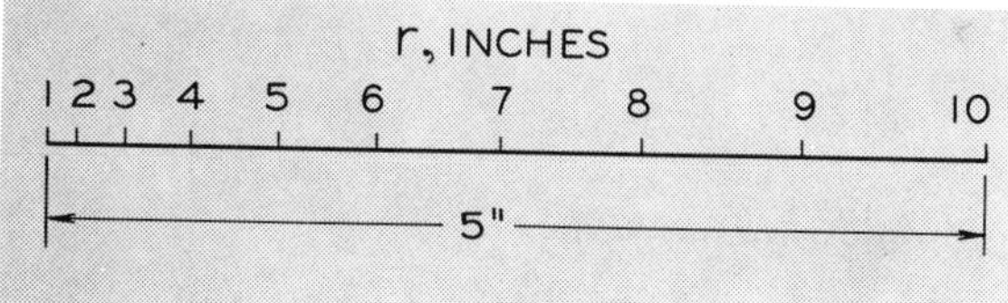

Fig. 15-76. The calibration of one scale of a concurrent scale chart using values from Table 15-2.

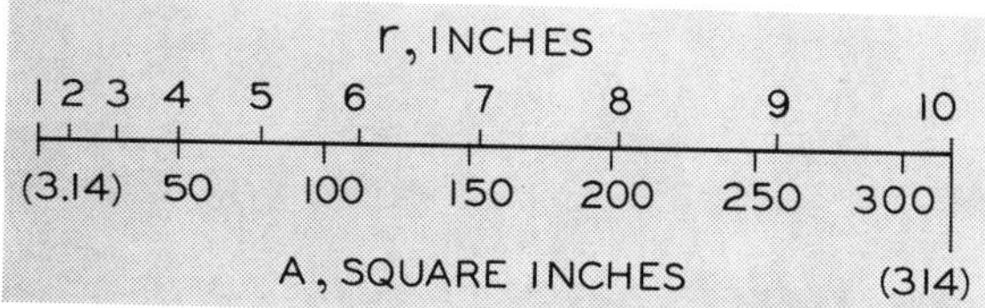

Fig. 15-77. The completed concurrent scale chart for the formula, $A = \pi r^2$. Values for the A-scale are taken from Table 15-3.

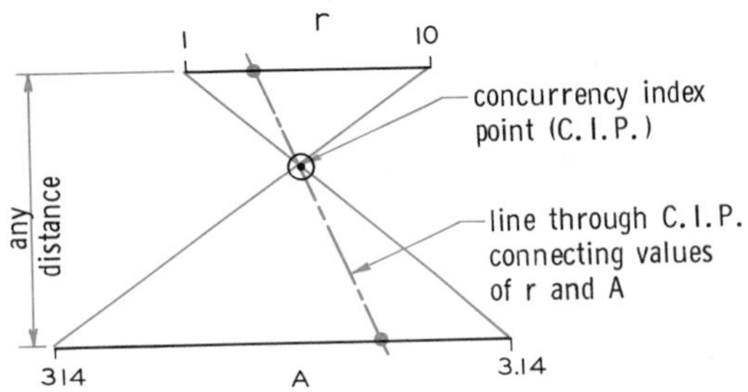

Fig. 15-78. A concurrent scale chart with unequal scales.

The *A*-scale is now superimposed on the *r*-scale; its calibrations have been placed on the other side of the line to facilitate reading (Fig. 15-77). It may be desired to expand or contract one of the scales, in which case an alternative arrangement may be used, as shown in Fig. 15-78. The two scales are drawn parallel at any convenient distance, and calibrated in *opposite* directions. A different scale modulus and corresponding scale equation must be calculated for each scale if they are *not* the same length.

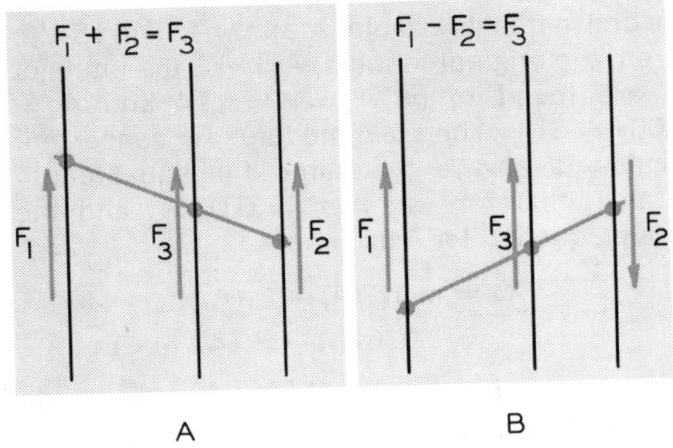

Fig. 15-79. Two common forms of parallel-scale alignment charts.

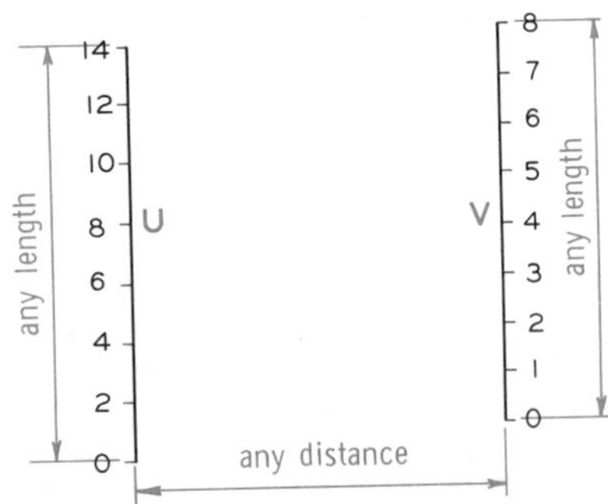

Fig. 15-80. Calibration of the outer scales for the formula $U + 2V = 3W$, where $0 \leq U \leq 14$ and $0 \leq V \leq 8$.

15-39 CONSTRUCTION OF ALIGNMENT CHARTS WITH THREE VARIABLES

For a formula of three functions (of one variable each), the general approach is to select the lengths and positions of *two* scales according to the range of variables and size of the chart desired. These are then calibrated by means of the scale equations, as shown in the preceding section. The position and calibration of the third scale will then depend upon these initial constructions. Although definite mathematical relationships exist which may be used to locate the third scale, graphical constructions are simpler and usually less subject to error. Examples of the various forms are presented in the following articles.

15-40 PARALLEL-SCALE CHARTS

Many engineering relationships involve three variables that can be computed graphically on a repetitive basis. Any formula of the type $F_1 + F_2 = F_3$ may be represented as a parallel-scale alignment chart, as shown in Fig. 15-79A. Note that all scales increase (functionally) in the same direction and that the function of the middle scale represents the *sum* of the other two. Reversing the direction of any scale changes the sign of its function in the formula, as for $F_1 - F_2 = F_3$ in Fig. 15-79B.

To illustrate this type of alignment chart, we shall use the formula $U + 2V = 3W$, where $0 \leq U \leq 14$ and $0 \leq V \leq 8$. First, it is necessary to determine and calibrate the two outer scales for U and V; we can make them any con-

FIGURE 15–81. PARALLEL-SCALE CHART (LINEAR)

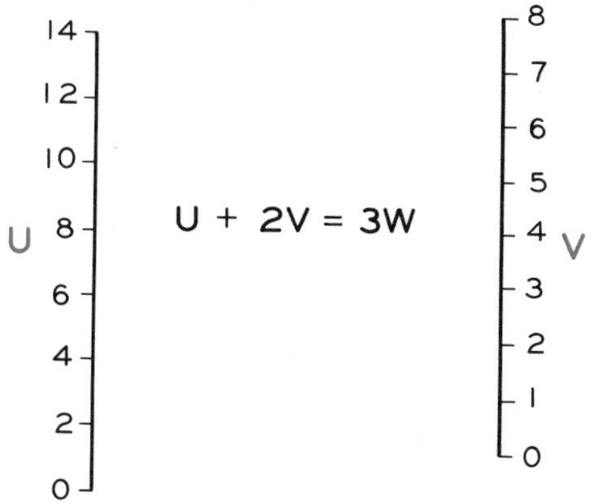

Given: The equation $U + 2V = 3W$ and the two scales constructed in Fig. 15–80.
Required: Construct a parallel-scale chart for determining various solutions of the given formula.
References: Articles 15–36 through 15–40.

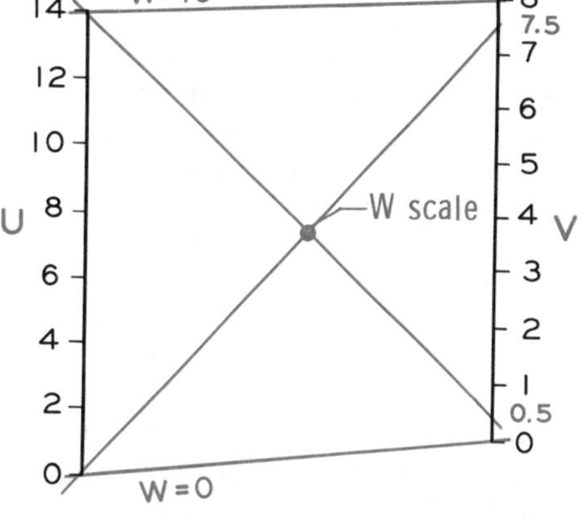

Step 1: Substitute the end values of the *U*- and *V*-scales into the formula to establish the extreme values of the *W*-scale. These values are found to be $W = 10$ and $W = 0$. Select two sets of corresponding values of *U* and *V* that will give the same value of *W*. For example, when $U = 0$ and $V = 7.5$, *W* will equal 5, and when $U = 14$ and $V = 0.5$, *W* will equal 5. Connect these sets of values; the intersection of their lines locates the position of the *W*-scale.

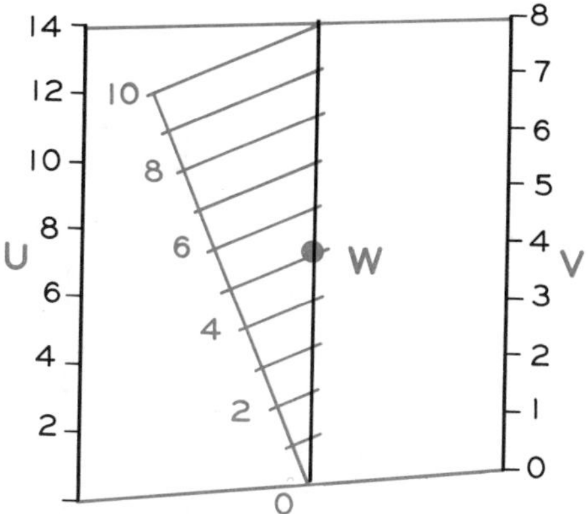

Step 2: Draw the *W*-scale parallel to the outer scales; its length is controlled by the previously established lines of $W = 10$ and $W = 0$. Since this scale is 10 linear divisions long, divide it graphically into ten units as shown. This will be a linear scale. See Article 5–8 to review the method of dividing the *W*-scale.

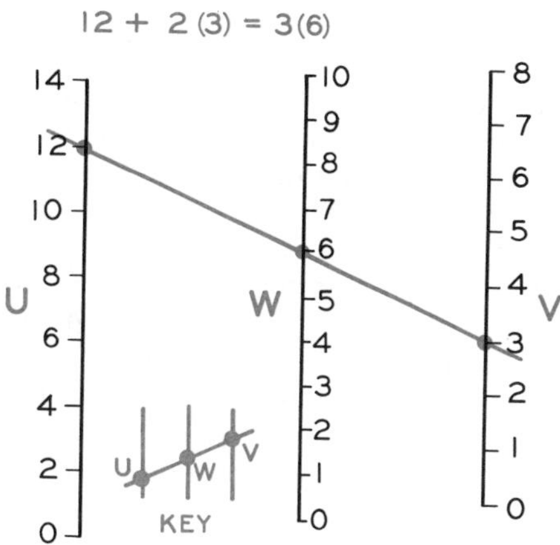

Step 3: The completed nomogram can be used as illustrated by selecting any two known variables and connecting them with an isopleth to determine the third unknown. A key is always included to illustrate how the nomogram is intended to be used. An example of $U = 12$ and $V = 3$ is shown to verify the accuracy of the graph.

venient length, and position them any convenient distance apart, as shown in Fig. 15–80. These scales are used as the basis for the step-by-step construction shown in Fig. 15–81.

The limits of calibration for the middle scale are found by connecting the endpoints of the outer scales and substituting these values into the formula. Here, W is found to be 0 and 10 at the extreme ends (step 1). Two pairs of corresponding values of U and V are selected that will give the *same* value of W. For example, values of $U = 0$ and $V = 7.5$ give a value of 5 for W. We also find that $W = 5$ when $U = 14$ and $V = 0.5$. This should be verified by substitution before continuing with construction. We connect these corresponding pairs of values with isopleths to locate their intersection, which establishes the position of the W-scale.

Since the W-scale is linear ($3W$ is a linear function), it may be subdivided into uniform intervals by the methods commonly used to divide a line into equal parts (step 2). For a nonlinear scale, the scale modulus (and the scale equation) may be found in step 2 by substituting its length and its two end values into Eq. (1) of Article 15–37. The scales can be used to determine an infinite number of problem solutions when sets of two variables are known, as illustrated in step 3.

Parallel-Scale Graph with Logarithmic Scales. Problems involving formulas of the type $F_1 \times F_2 = F_3$ can be solved in a manner very similar to the example given in Fig. 15–81 when logarithmic scales are used. An example of this type of problem is the formula $R = S\sqrt{T}$, for $0.1 \leq S \leq 1.0$ and $1 \leq T \leq 100$. Assume the scales to be 6″ long. These scales need not be equal except for convenience. This formula may be converted into the required form by taking common logarithms of both sides, which gives

$$\log R = \log S + \tfrac{1}{2} \log T.$$

Thus we have $F_1(S) + F_2(T) = F_3(R)$, where

$$F_1(S) = \log S,$$
$$F_2(T) = \tfrac{1}{2} \log T,$$
$$F_3(R) = \log R.$$

The scale modulus for $F_1(S)$ is, from Eq. (1),

$$m_s = \frac{6}{\log 1.0 - \log 0.1} = \frac{6}{0 - (-1)} = 6.$$

Choosing the scale measuring point from $S = 0.1$, we find from Eq. (2) that the scale equation for $F_1(S)$ is

$$X_S = 6(\log S - \log 0.1) = 6(\log S + 1).$$

Similarly, the scale modulus for $F_2(T)$ is

$$m_T = \frac{6}{\frac{1}{2} \log 100 - \frac{1}{2} \log 1} = \frac{6}{\frac{1}{2}(2) - \frac{1}{2}(0)} = 6.$$

Thus, the scale equation, measuring from $T = 1$, is:

$$X_T = 6(\tfrac{1}{2} \log T - \tfrac{1}{2} \log 1) = 3 \log T.$$

The corresponding tables for the two scale equations may be computed as shown in Tables 15–4 and 15–5. We shall position the two scales 5 in. apart, as shown in Fig. 15–82. The logarithmic scales are graduated using the values in Tables 15–4 and 15–5. The step-by-step procedure for constructing the remainder of the nomogram is given in Fig. 15–83 using the two outer scales determined here.

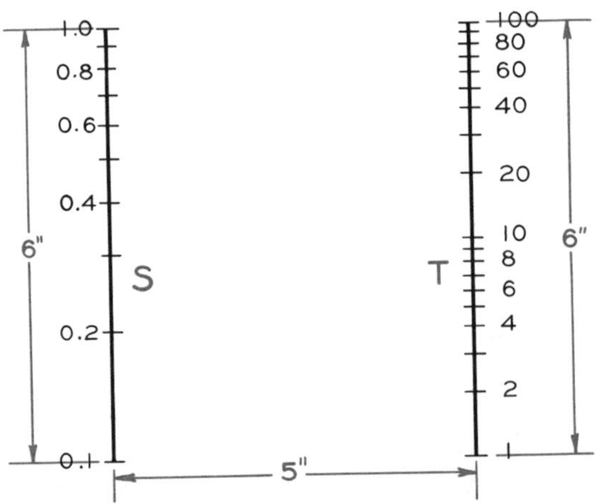

Fig. 15–82. Calibration of the outer scales for the formula, $R = S\sqrt{T}$, where $0.1 \leq S \leq 1.0$ and $1 \leq T \leq 100$.

Table 15–4

S	0.1	0.2	0.3	0.4	0.5	0.6	0.7	0.8	0.9	1.0
X_S	0	1.80	2.88	3.61	4.19	4.67	5.07	5.42	5.72	6.00

Table 15–5

T	1	2	4	6	8	10	20	40	60	80	100
X_T	0	0.91	1.80	2.33	2.71	3.00	3.91	4.81	5.33	5.77	6.00

Table 15–6

R	0.1	0.2	0.4	0.6	0.8	1.0	2.0	4.0	6.0	8.0	10.0
X_R	0	0.91	1.80	2.33	2.71	3.00	3.91	4.81	5.33	5.71	6.00

The end values of the middle (R) scale are found from the formula $R = S\sqrt{T}$ to be $R = 1.0\sqrt{100} = 10$ and $R = 0.1\sqrt{1} = 0.1$. Choosing a value of $R = 1.0$, we find that corresponding value pairs of S and T might be $S = 0.1$, $T = 100$ and $S = 1.0$, $T = 1.0$. We connect these pairs with isopleths in step 1 and position the middle scale at the intersection of the lines connecting the corresponding values. The R-scale is drawn parallel to the outer scales and is calibrated by deriving its scale modulus:

$$m_R = \frac{6}{\log 10 - \log 0.1} = \frac{6}{1 - (-1)} = 3.$$

Thus its scale equation (measuring from $R = 0.1$) is

$$X_R = 3(\log R - \log 0.1) = 3(\log R + 1.0).$$

Table 15–6 is computed to give the values for the scale. These values are applied to the R-scale as shown in step 2. The finished nomogram can be used as illustrated in step 3 to compute the unknown variables when two variables are given.

Note that this example illustrates a general method of creating a parallel-scale graph for all formulas of the type $F_1 + F_2 = F_3$ through the use of a table of values computed from the scale equation. As an alternative method, this center scale may be found graphically once the end values of the scales have been determined. An example of the graphical method is illustrated in Fig. 15–84, in which the scale is calibrated by graphical enlargement or reduction of the desired portions of printed logarithmic scales as found in common logarithmic graph paper.

15–41 N- OR Z-CHARTS

Whenever F_2 and F_3 are linear functions, we can partially avoid using logarithmic scales for formulas of the type

$$F_1 = \frac{F_2}{F_3};$$

instead, we use an N-chart, as shown in Fig. 15–85. The outer scales, or "legs" of the N are

FIGURE 15–83. PARALLEL-SCALE CHART (LOGARITHMIC)

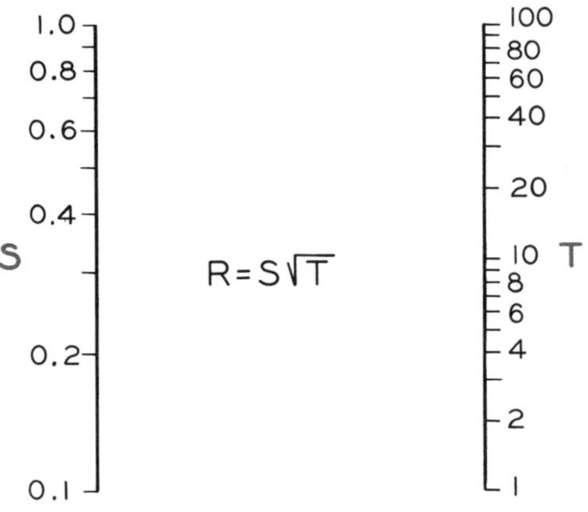

Given: The outer scales of a parallel-scale alignment graph determined in Fig. 15–82.
Required: Construct a parallel alignment chart for solving the equation $R = S\sqrt{T}$.
Reference: Article 15–40.

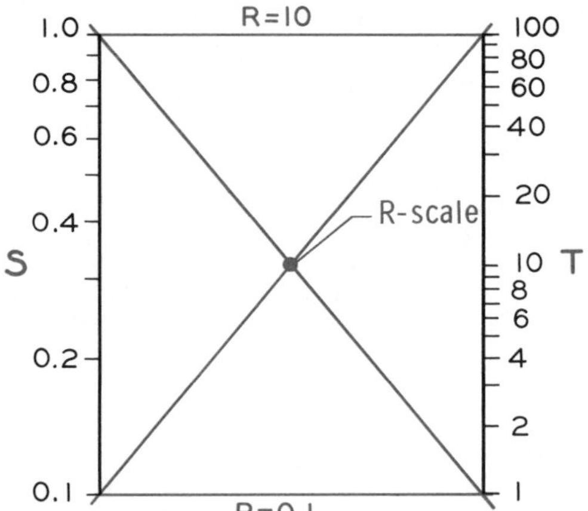

Step 1: Connect the end values of the outer scales to determine the extreme values of the *R*-scale, $R = 10$ and $R = 0.1$. Select corresponding values of *S* and *T* that will give the same value of *R*. Values of $S = 0.1$, $T = 100$ and $S = 1.0$, $T = 1.0$ give a value of $R = 1.0$. Connect the pairs to locate the position of the *R*-scale.

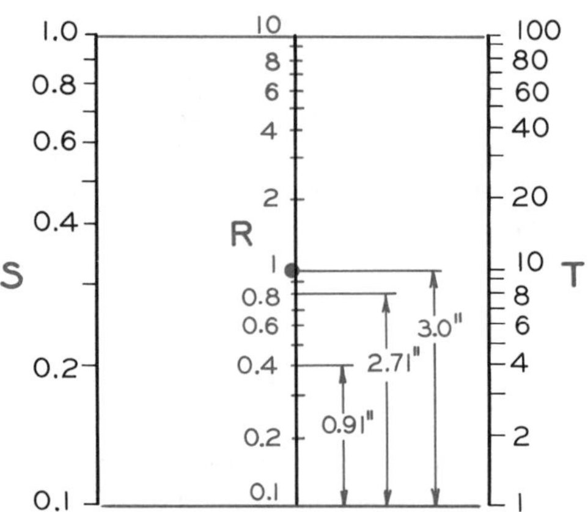

Step 2: Draw the *R*-scale to extend from 0.1 to 10. Calibrate it by substituting values determined from its scale equation. These values have been computed and tabulated in Table 15–6. The resulting tabulation is a logarithmic, two-cycle scale.

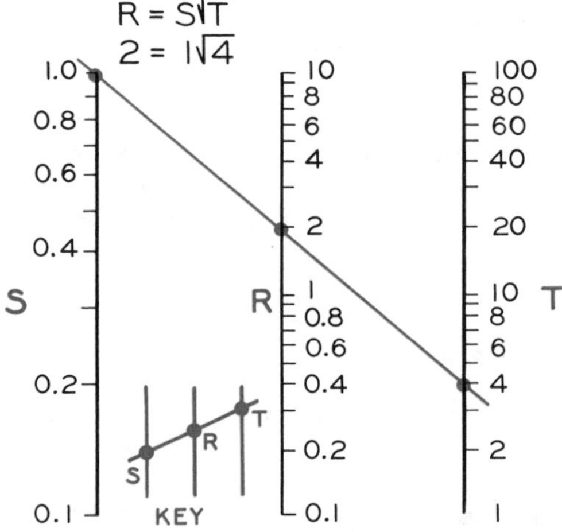

Step 3: Add labels to the finished nomogram and draw a key to indicate how it is to be used. An isopleth has been used to determine *R* when $S = 1.0$ and $T = 4$. The result of 2 is the same as that obtained mathematically, thus verifying the accuracy of the chart. Other combinations can be solved in this same manner.

functional scales and will therefore be linear if F_2 and F_3 are linear, whereas if the same formula were drawn as a parallel-scale chart, all scales would have to be logarithmic.

Some main features of the N-chart are:

1. The outer scales are parallel functional scales of F_2 and F_3.
2. They increase (functionally) in *opposite* directions.
3. The diagonal scale connects the (functional) *zeros* of the outer scale.
4. In general, the diagonal scale is not a functional scale for the function F_1 and is generally nonlinear.

Construction of an N-chart is simplified by the fact that locating the middle (diagonal) scale is usually less of a problem than it is for a parallel-scale chart. Calibration of the diagonal scale is most easily accomplished by graphical methods. To illustrate, an N-chart is constructed for the equation

$$A = \frac{B+2}{C+5},$$

where $0 \leq B \leq 8$ and $0 \leq C \leq 15$. This equation follows the form of

$$F_1 = \frac{F_2}{F_3},$$

where $F_1(A) = A$, $F_2(B) = B + 2$, and $F_3(C) = C + 5$. Thus the outer scales will be for $B + 2$ and $C + 5$, and the diagonal scale will be for A.

The construction is begun in the same manner as for a parallel-scale chart by selecting the layout of the outer scales (Fig. 15-86). As before, the limits of the diagonal scale are determined by connecting the endpoints on the outer scales, giving $A = 0.1$ for $B = 0$, $C = 15$ and $A = 2.0$ for $B = 8$, $C = 0$, as shown in the given portion of Fig. 15-87. The remainder of the construction is given in step form in the figure.

The diagonal scale is located by finding the *functional* zeros of the outer scales, i.e., the points where $B + 2 = 0$, or $B = -2$, and $C + 5 = 0$, or $C = -5$. The diagonal scale may

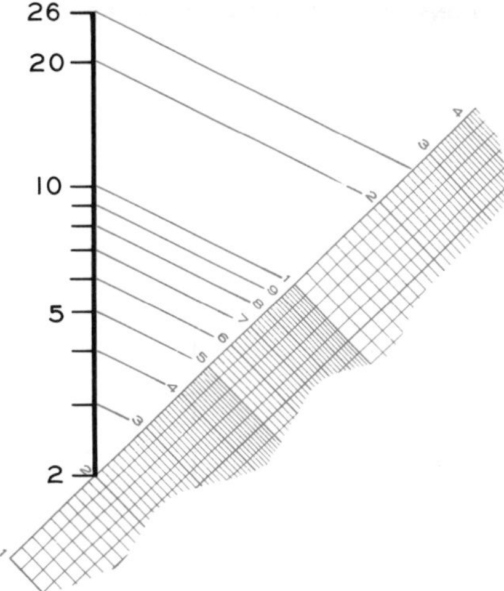

Fig. 15-84. Graphical calibration of a scale using logarithmic paper.

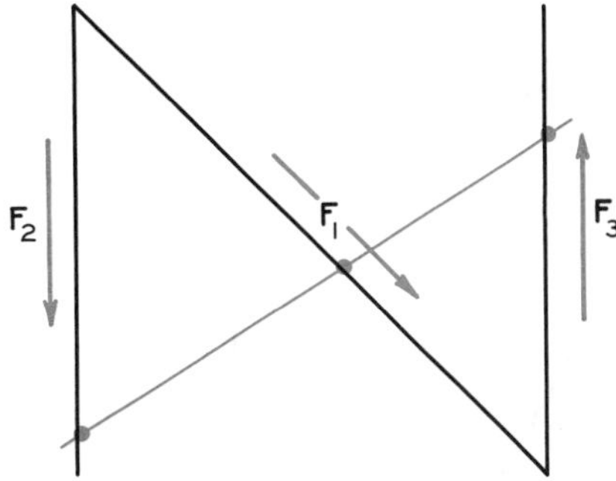

Fig. 15-85. An N-chart for solving an equation of the form $F_1 = F_2/F_3$.

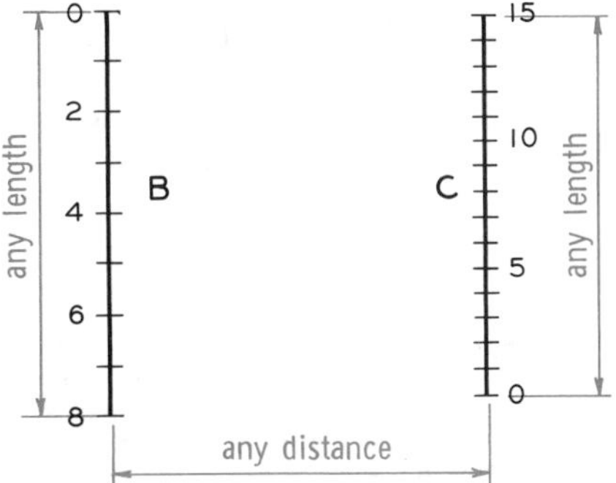

Fig. 15-86. Calibration of the outer scales of an N-chart for the equation $A = (B + 2)/(C + 5)$.

FIGURE 15-87. CONSTRUCTION OF AN N-CHART

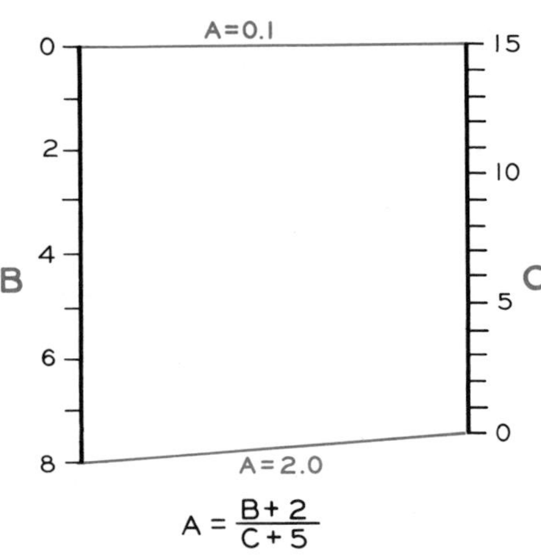

Given: The outer scales of an N-chart as determined in Fig. 15-86.
Required: Complete the N-chart for the formula $A = (B + 2)/(C + 5)$.
Reference: Article 15-41.

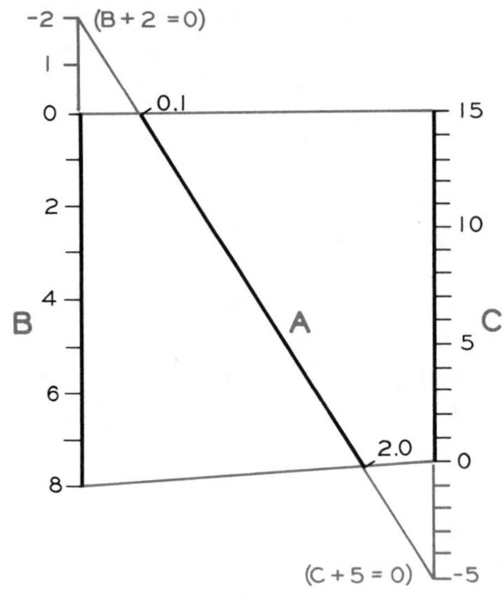

Step 1: Locate the diagonal scale by finding the functional zeros of the outer scales. This is done by setting $B + 2 = 0$ and $C + 5 = 0$, which gives a zero value for A when $B = -2$ and $C = -5$. Connect these points with diagonal scale A.

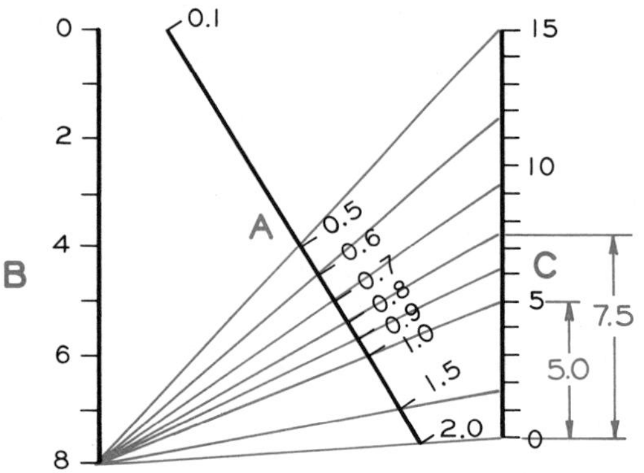

Step 2: Select the upper limit of one of the outer scales, $B = 8$ in this case, and substitute it into the given equation to find a series of values of C for the desired values of A, as shown in Table 15-7. Draw isopleths from $B = 8$ to the values of C to calibrate the A-scale.

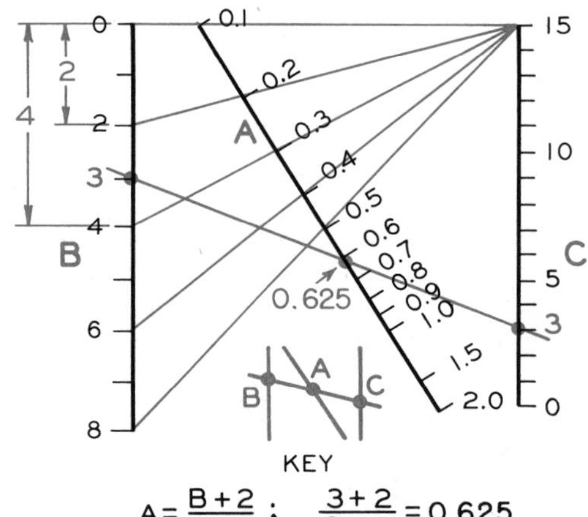

Step 3: Calibrate the remainder of the A-scale in the same manner by substituting the upper limit of the other outer scale ($C = 15$) into the equation to determine a series of values on the B-scale for desired values on the A-scale, as listed in Table 15-8. Draw isopleths from $C = 15$ to calibrate the A-scale as shown. Draw a key to indicate how the nomogram is to be used. Solve an example problem to verify its accuracy.

Table 15-7

A	2.0	1.5	1.0	0.9	0.8	0.7	0.6	0.5
C	0	1.67	5.0	6.11	7.50	9.28	11.7	15.0

then be drawn by connecting these points as shown in step 1. Calibration of the diagonal scale is most easily accomplished by substituting into the formula. Select the upper limit of an outer scale, for example, $B = 8$. This gives the formula

$$A = \frac{10}{C+5}.$$

Solve this equation for the other outer scale variable,

$$C = \frac{10}{A} - 5.$$

Using this as a "scale equation," make a table of values for the desired values of A and corresponding values of C (up to the limit of C in the chart), as shown in Table 15-7. Connect isopleths from $B = 8$ to the tabulated values of C. Their intersections with the diagonal scale give the required calibrations for approximately half the diagonal scale, as shown in step 2 of Fig. 15-87.

The remainder of the diagonal scale is calibrated by substituting the end value of the other outer scale ($C = 15$) into the formula, giving

$$A = \frac{B+2}{20}.$$

Solving this for B yields

$$B = 20A - 2.$$

A table for the desired values of A can be constructed as shown in Table 15-8. Isopleths connecting $C = 15$ with the tabulated values of B will locate the remaining calibrations on the A-scale, as shown in step 3.

15-42 COMBINATION FORMS OF ALIGNMENT CHARTS

The types of charts discussed above may be used in combination to handle different types of formulas. For example, formulas of the type $F_1/F_2 = F_3/F_4$ (four variables) may be represented as *two* N-charts by the insertion of a "dummy" function. To do this, let

$$\frac{F_1}{F_2} = S \qquad \text{and then} \qquad S = \frac{F_3}{F_4}.$$

Each of these may be represented as shown in part A of Fig. 15-88, where one N-chart is inverted and rotated 90°. In this way the charts may be superimposed as shown in part B, if the S-scales are of equal length. The S-scale, being a "dummy" scale, does not need to be calibrated; it is merely a "turning" scale for intermediate values of S which do not actually enter into the formula itself. The chart is read with *two* isopleths which connect the four variable values and cross on the S-scale as shown in part C. Charts of this form are commonly called *ratio charts.*

Formulas of the type $F_1 + F_2 = F_3F_4$ are handled similarly. As in the preceding example, a "dummy" function is used: $F_1 + F_2 = S$, and $S = F_3F_4$. In order to apply the superimposition principle, a more equitable arrangement is obtained by rewriting the equations as $F_2 = S - F_1$ and $F_3 = S/F_4$. These two equations then take the form of a parallel-scale chart and

Table 15-8

A	0.5	0.4	0.3	0.2	0.1
B	8.0	6.0	4.0	2.0	0

FIGURE 15-88. A FOUR-VARIABLE CHART

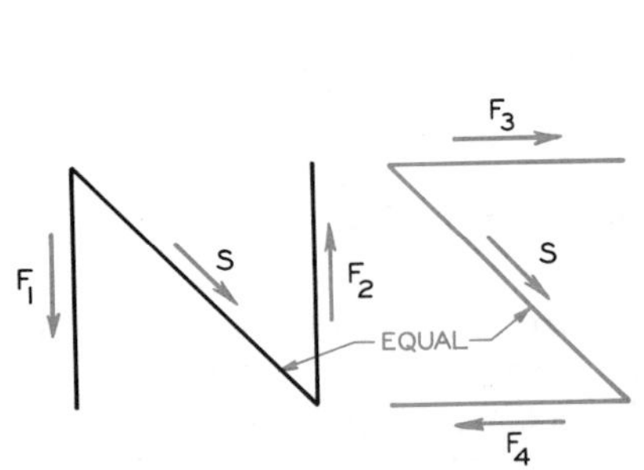

A. A combination chart can be developed to handle four variables in the form $F_1/F_2 = F_3/F_4$ by developing two N-charts in the forms $F_1/F_2 = S$ and $F_3/F_4 = S$, where S is a dummy scale of equal length in both charts.

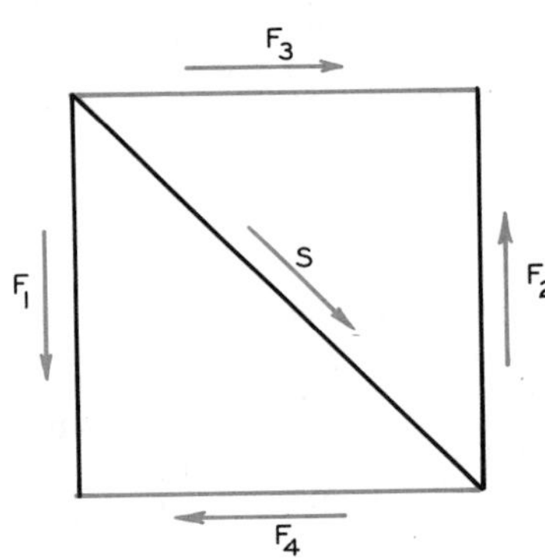

B. If equal-length scales are used in each of the N-charts and if the S-scales are equal, then the charts can be overlapped so that each is common to the S-scale.

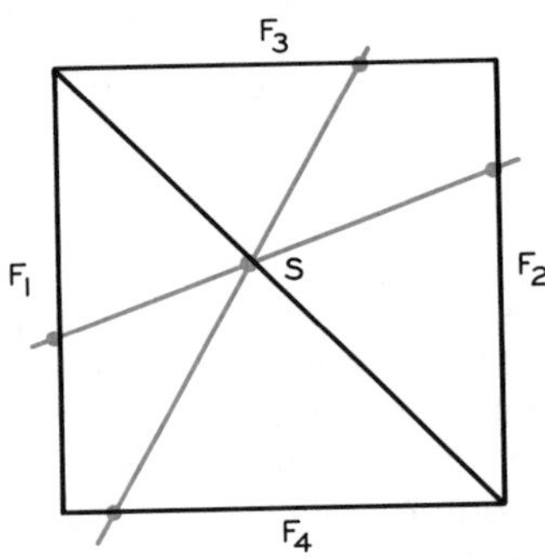

C. Two lines (isopleths) are drawn to cross at a common point on the S-scale. Numerous combinations of the four variables can be read on the surrounding scales. The S-scale need not be calibrated, since no values are read from it.

FIGURE 15-89. A COMBINATION PARALLEL-SCALE CHART AND AN N-CHART

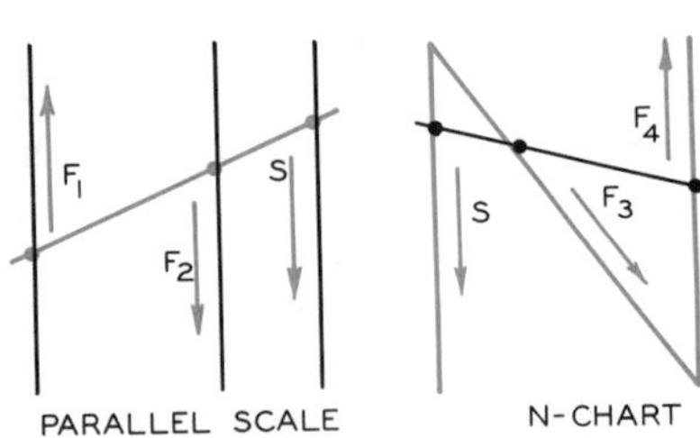

A. Formulas of the type $F_1 + F_2 = F_3F_4$ can be combined into one nomograph by constructing a parallel-scale chart and an N-chart with an equal S-scale (a dummy scale).

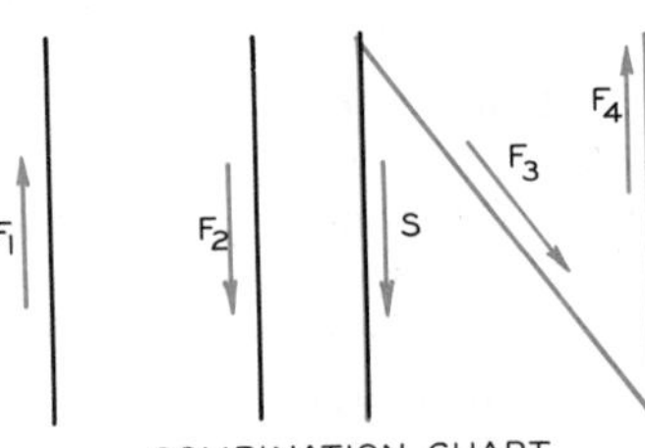

B. By superimposing the two equal S-scales, the two nomograms are combined into a combination chart. The S-scale need not be calibrated, since values are not read from it.

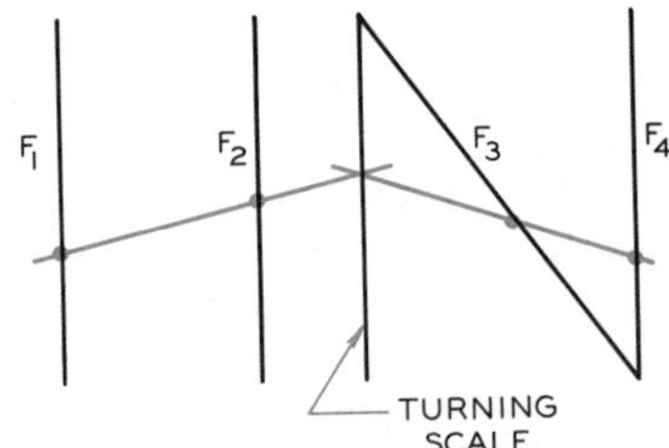

C. The addition of the variables can be handled at the left of the chart. The S-scale is the turning scale from which the N-chart can be used to find the unknown variables.

an N-chart, respectively, as shown in part A of Fig. 15-89. Again, the S-scales must be identical but need not be calibrated. The charts are superimposed in part B. The S-scale is used as a "turning" scale for the two isopleths, as shown in part C. Many other combinations are possible, limited only by the ingenuity of the nomographer in adapting formulas and scale arrangements to his needs.

15-43 SUMMARY

Throughout the design process, graphics has been the primary agent of creativity. Sketches, graphs, and diagrams were used to identify the problem; freehand sketches were made to determine preliminary ideas; the ideas were refined graphically; and the designs were then analyzed for feasibility prior to selection of the best solution. The development process would be virtually impossible without the thinking process being recorded, and even stimulated, by the applications of graphics. Throughout this process, the designer is guided by his knowledge of physical properties, engineering fundamentals, and manufacturing limitations. However, he does not let these limitations confine his thinking or imagination during the creative development stage. The real confrontation with the physical, mathematical, and scientific principles is in the analysis stage of the design process. Many of the data derived from experiments with prototypes and laboratory experiments will be in a numerical form that must be analyzed to provide a total picture of the proposed design.

Various aspects of graphical analysis of data and components were covered in this chapter, including graphs, empirical data, linkages and mechanisms, graphical calculus, and nomography. Each of these areas can be evaluated using formal mathematical and analytical approaches; however, graphical methods are applicable to many problems. In some cases, the graphical technique will offer the best method of solution.

Although conventional engineering methods are probably used more in the analysis phase of the design process than any other, graphical methods can be applied to good advantage in this phase also. The engineer or technician should be sufficiently aware of the applications of graphics to utilize this valuable method of problem solution.

PROBLEMS

General

The following problems are to be solved on $8\frac{1}{2}'' \times 11''$ or on $11'' \times 15''$ paper. The graph problems may be solved on commercially prepared paper or the grid may be constructed by the student. Problems involving geometric construction and mathematical calculations should show the construction and calculations as part of the problem for future reference. If the mathematical calculations are extensive, it may be desirable to include these on a separate sheet. Legible lettering practices and principles of good layout should be followed in these problems, and all notes and constructions should be provided to explain fully the method of solution.

Rectangular Graphs

1. Using the data given in Table 15-9, prepare a rectangular graph to compare the number of Master's and Doctor's degrees granted in the United States from 1920 to 1965. Use these data as a basis for predicting the trend for the period from 1965 to 1980.

2. Using the data given in Table 15-10, prepare a rectangular graph to compare the supply and

Table 15-9

	Master's	Doctor's
1920	5,100	1,700
1930	14,700	3,100
1940	24,500	4,500
1950	64,000	7,800
1960	73,000	9,700
1965	102,000	15,200

Table 15-10

	1890	1900	1910	1920	1930	1940	1950	1960	1970	1980
Supply	80	80	110	135	155	240	270	315	380	450
Demand	35	35	60	80	110	125	200	320	410	550

Table 15–11

Angle with vertical	0	10	20	30	40	50	60	70	80	90
Candlepower (thous.) 2–400W	37	34	25	12	5.5	2.5	2	0.5	0.5	0.5
Candlepower (thous.) 1–1000W	22	21	19	16	12.3	7	3	2	0.5	0.5

Table 15–12

Years after graduation	0	5	10	15	20	25	30
Upper decile	9,800	13,000	17,500	20,500	22,500	23,800	25,000
Upper quartile	8,700	11,900	15,000	17,000	19,000	19,200	18,700
Median	8,000	10,500	13,000	14,500	15,800	15,200	15,000
Lower quartile	7,500	9,750	11,500	12,800	13,000	12,700	12,200
Lower decile	7,000	8,900	10,000	11,000	11,400	11,000	10,500

Table 15–13

F	100	200	500	1000	2000	5000	10,000
A(1)	0.0028	0.002	0.0015	0.001	0.0006	0.0003	0.00013
A(2)	0.06	0.05	0.04	0.03	0.018	0.005	0.001

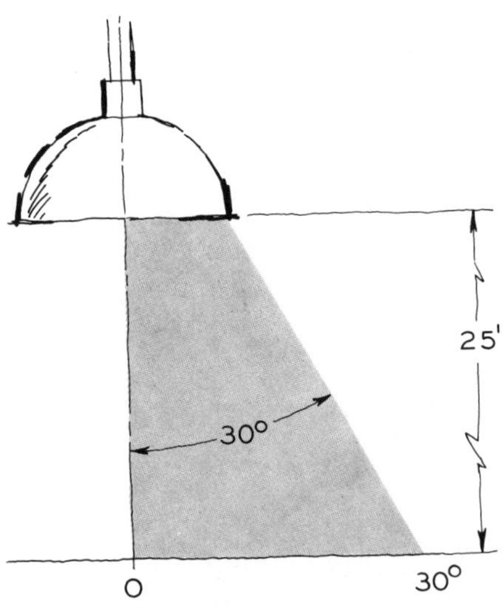

Fig. 15–90. The angular measurement of illumination under a lamp (Problem 3).

demand of water in the United States from 1890 to 1980. Supply and demand are given in units of billions of gallons of water per day.

3. Analyze the data given in Table 15–11 in a rectangular graph to decide which lamps should be selected to provide economical lighting for an industrial plant. You are to decide whether to use single 1000-watt bulbs or twin 400-watt bulbs. The table gives the candlepower directly under the lamps (0°) and at the various angles from the vertical when the lamps are mounted at a height of 25′, as shown in Fig. 15–90.

4. Construct a rectangular grid graph that shows the relationship in energy costs (mills per kilowatt-hour) and the percent capacity of two types of power plants. Plot energy costs along the *Y*-axis and the capacity factor along the *X*-axis. The plotted curve will compare the costs of a nuclear plant with a gas- or oil-fired plant. Data for a gas-fired plant: 17 mills, 10%; 12 mills, 20%; 8 mills 40%; 7 mills, 60%; 6 mills, 80%; 5.8 mills, 100%. Nuclear plant data: 24 mills, 10%; 14 mills, 20%; 7 mills, 40%; 5 mills, 60%; 4.2 mills, 80%; 3.7 mills, 100%.

5. Construct a rectangular grid graph to show the accident experience of Company A from 1953 to 1966. Plot the numbers of disabling accidents per million man-hours of work on the *Y*-axis. Years will be plotted on the *X*-axis. Data: 1953, 1.21; 1954, 0.97; 1955, 0.86; 1956, 0.63; 1957, 0.76; 1958, 0.99; 1959, 0.95; 1960, 0.55; 1961, 0.76; 1962, 0.68; 1963, 0.55; 1964, 0.73; 1965, 0.52; 1966, 0.46.

6. Construct a rectilinear graph that shows the relationship between the transverse resilience in inch-pounds (*Y*-axis) and the single-blow impact in foot-pounds (*X*-axis) of gray iron. Data: 21 fp, 375 ip; 22 fp, 350 ip; 23 fp, 380 ip; 30 fp, 400 ip; 32 fp, 420 ip; 33 fp, 410 ip; 38 fp, 510 ip; 45 fp, 615 ip; 50 fp, 585 ip; 60 fp, 785 ip; 70 fp, 900 ip; 75 fp, 920 ip.

7. Using the data from a 1967 survey (Table 15–12), construct a rectangular graph to reflect the salaries of engineers during successive years after graduation with a bachelor's degree. These salaries are given in averages for deciles (10% intervals) and quartiles (25% intervals). Plot each of these as a separate curve.

Break-even Graphs

8. Construct a break-even graph that shows the earnings for a new product that has a development cost of $12,000. The first 8000 will cost 50¢ each to manufacture, and you wish to break even at this quantity. What would be the profit at a volume of 20,000 and at 25,000?

9. Same as Problem 8 except that the development costs are $80,000, the manufacturing cost of the first 10,000 is $2.30 each, and the desired break-even point is at this quantity. What would be the profit at a volume of 20,000 and at 30,000? What sales price would be required to break even at 10,000 units?

10. A manufacturer has incorporated the manufacturing and development costs into a cost-per-unit estimate. He wishes to sell the product at $1.50 each. Construct a graph of the following data. On the *Y*-axis plot cost per unit in dollars; on the *X*-axis, number of units in thousands. Data: 1000, $2.55; 2000, $2.01; 3000, $1.55; 4000, $1.20; 5000, $.98; 6000, $.81; 7000, $.80; 8000, $.75; 9000, $.73; 10,000, $.70. How many must be sold to break even? What will be the total profit when 9000 are sold?

11. The cost per unit to produce a product by a manufacturing plant is given below. Construct a break-even graph with the cost per unit plotted on the *Y*-axis and the number of units on the *X*-axis. Data: 1000, $5.90; 2000, $4.50; 3000, $3.80; 4000, $3.20; 5000, $2.85; 6000, $2.55; 7000, $2.30; 8000, $2.17; 9000, $2.00; 10,000, $.95.

Logarithmic Graphs

12. Using the data given in Table 15–13, construct a logarithmic graph where the vibration amplitude (*A*) is plotted as the ordinate and vibration frequency (*F*) as the abscissa. The data for curve 1 represent the maximum limits of machinery in good condition with no danger from vibration. The data for curve 2 are the lower limits of machinery that is being vibrated excessively to the danger point. The vertical scale should be three cycles and the horizontal scale two cycles.

13. Plot the data below on a two-cycle log graph to show the current in amperes (*Y*-axis) versus the voltage in volts (*X*-axis) of precision temperature-sensing resistors. Data: 1 volt, 1.9 amps; 2 volts, 4 amps; 4 volts, 8 amps; 8 volts, 17 amps; 10 volts, 20 amps; 20 volts, 30 amps; 40 volts, 36 amps; 80 volts, 31 amps; 100 volts, 30 amps.

Semilogarithmic Graphs

14. Construct a semilogarithmic graph of the data in Problem 7, using the median values to determine the ratios of increase during this time period.

15. Construct a semilogarithmic graph to compare the relative ratios of the Master's and Doctor's degrees granted, as given in Problem 1.

16. Construct a semilog graph with the *Y*-axis a two-cycle log scale from 1 to 100 and the *X*-axis a linear scale from 1 to 7. Plot the data below to show the survivability of a shelter at varying distances from a one-megaton air burst. The data consist of overpressure in psi along the *Y*-axis, and distance from ground zero in miles along the *X*-axis. The data points represent an 80% chance of survival of the shelter. Data: 1 mi, 55 psi; 2 mi, 11 psi; 3 mi, 4.5 psi; 4 mi, 2.5 psi; 5 mi, 2.0 psi; 6 mi, 1.3 psi.

17. The growth of two divisions of a company, Division A and Division B, is given in the data below. Plot the data on a rectilinear graph and on a semilog graph. The semilog graph should have a one-cycle log scale on the *Y*-axis for sales in thousands of dollars, and a linear scale on the *X*-axis showing years for a six-year period. Data in dollars: 1 yr, A = $11,700 and B = $44,000; 2 yr, A = $19,500 and B = $50,000; 3 yr, A = $25,000 and B = $55,000; 4 yr, A = $32,000 and B = $64,000; 5 yr, A = $42,000 and B = $66,000; 6 yr, A = $48,000 and B = $75,000. Which division has the better growth rate?

Percentage Graphs

18. Plot the data given in Problem 7 on a semilog graph in order to determine the rates of increase of salaries. What is the rate of increase of the upper decile between 5 years and 20 years? What percent of the upper-decile salary at 20 years is the lower-decile salary at 20 years?

19. Plot the data given in Problem 2 on a semilog graph in order to determine the percentages and ratios of the data. What is the rate of increase in the demand for water from 1890 to 1920? from 1920 to 1970? What percent of the demand is the supply for the following years: 1900, 1930, and 1970?

20. Using the graph plotted in Problem 17, determine the rate of increase of Division A and Division B from year 1 to year 4. Also, what percent of the sales of Division A are the sales of Division B at the end of year 2 and at the end of year 6?

Table 15–14

Ages	Percent of labor force	
	Graduates, %	Dropouts, %
16–17	18	22
18–19	12.5	17.5
20–21	8	13
22–24	5	9

Bar Graphs

21. Construct a bar graph to depict the unemployment rate of high-school graduates and dropouts in various age categories. The age groups and the percent of unemployment of each group are given in Table 15–14.

22. Prepare a bar graph to compare the number of skilled workers employed in various occupations. Arrange the graph for ease of interpretation and comparison of occupations. Use the following data: carpenters, 82,000; all-round machinists, 310,000; plumbers, 350,000; bricklayers, 200,000; appliance service men, 185,000; automotive mechanics, 760,000; electricians, 380,000; painters, 400,000.

23. Construct a bar graph of the data shown in Table 15–10.

24. Using the data in Table 15–12, construct a bar graph showing the upper- and lower-decile earnings of engineers.

Pie Graphs

25. Prepare a pie chart to compare the areas of employment of male youth between the ages of 16 and 21 as tabulated in 1964: operatives, 25%; craftsmen, 9%; professions, technicals, and managers, 6%; clerical and sales, 17%; service, 11%; farm workers, 11%; laborers, 19%.

Table 15-15

A	X	0	40	80	120	160	200	240	280			
	Y	4.0	7.0	9.8	12.5	15.3	17.2	21.0	24.0			
B	X	1	2	5	10	20	50	100	200	500	1000	
	Y	1.5	2.4	3.3	6.0	9.2	15.0	23.0	24.0	60.0	85.0	
C	X	1	5	10	50	100	500	1000				
	Y	3	10	19	70	110	400	700				
D	X	2	4	6	8	10	12	14				
	Y	6.5	14.0	32.0	75.0	115.0	320	710				
E	X	0	2	4	6	8	10	12	14			
	Y	20	34	53	96	115	270	430	730			
F	X	0	1	2	3	4	5	6	7	8	9	10
	Y	1.8	2.1	2.2	2.5	2.7	3.0	3.4	3.7	4.1	4.5	5.0

26. Make a pie graph to give the relationship between the following members of the scientific and technical team, as listed in 1965: engineers, 985,000; technicians, 932,000; scientists, 410,000.

27. Construct a circle graph of the following percentages of the employment status of the 1969 graduates of two-year technician programs one year after graduation: employed, 63%; continuing full-time study, 23%; considering job offers, 6%; military, 6%; other, 2%.

28. Construct a circle graph that shows the relationship between the types of degrees held by engineers in aeronautical engineering: bachelor's degree, 65%; master's degree, 29%; Ph.D. degrees, 6%.

Polar Graphs

29. Construct a polar graph of the data given in Problem 3.

30. Construct a polar graph of the following illumination, in lumens at various angles, emitted from a luminaire. The zero-degrees position is vertically under the overhead lamp. Data: 0°, 12,000; 10°, 15,000; 20°, 10,000; 30°, 8000; 40°, 4200; 50°, 2500; 60°, 1000; 70°, 0. The illumination is symmetrical about the vertical.

Empirical Data—General Types

31. The data shown in Table 15-15, A through F, have been tabulated from experimental laboratory tests. Plot these data on rectangular, logarithmic, and semilogarithmic graphs and determine the empirical equations of the data. Select the proper graph needed for each set of data.

Empirical Data—Linear

32. Construct a linear graph to determine the equation for the yearly cost of a compressor in relationship to the compressor's size in horsepower. The yearly cost should be plotted on the Y-axis and the compressor's size in horsepower on the X-axis. Data: 0 hp, $0; 50 hp, $2100; 100 hp, $4500; 150 hp, $6700; 200 hp, $9000; 250 hp, $11,400. What is the equation of these data?

33. Construct a linear graph to determine the equation for the cost of soil investigation by boring to determine the proper foundation design for varying sizes of buildings. Plot the cost of borings in dollars along the Y-axis and the building area in sq ft along the X-axis. Data: 0 sq ft, $0; 25,000 sq ft, $35,000; 50,000 sq ft, $70,000; 750,000 sq ft, $100,000; 1,000,000 sq ft, $130,000.

34. Determine the equation of the empirical data plotted in Fig. 15–36.

Empirical Data—Logarithmic Graphs

35. The following empirical data compare input voltage V with the input current I to a heat pump. Find the equation of the data given in Table 15–16.

36. Table 15–17 lists empirical data giving the relationship between the peak allowable current in amperes (I) versus the overload operating time in cycles at 60 cycles per second (C). Place I on the Y-axis and C on the X-axis. Determine the equation for these data.

37. The empirical data given in Table 15–18 for a low-voltage circuit breaker used on a welding machine give the maximum loading during weld in amperes (rms) for the percent of duty cycle (pdc). Determine the equation for these data. Place rms along the Y-axis and pdc along the X-axis.

38. Construct a three-cycle × three-cycle logarithmic graph to find the equation of a machine's vibration during operation. Plot vibration displacement in mills along the Y-axis and vibration frequency in cycles per minute (cpm) along the X-axis. Data: 100 cpm, 0.80 mills; 400 cpm, 0.22 mills; 1000 cpm, 0.09 mills; 10,000 cpm, 0.009 mills; 5000 cpm, 0.0017 mills.

Table 15–16

Y-axis	V	0.8	1.3	1.75	1.85
X-axis	I	20	30	40	45

Table 15–17

Y-axis	I	2000	1840	1640	1480	1300	1120	1000
X-axis	C	1	2	5	10	20	50	100

Table 15–18

Y-axis	rms	7500	5200	4400	3400	2300	1700
X-axis	pdc	3	6	9	15	30	60

39. Determine the equation of the empirical data plotted in Fig. 15–36.

Empirical Data—Semilogarithmic Graphs

40. Construct a semilog graph of the following data to determine their equation. The Y-axis should be a two-cycle log scale and the X-axis a 10-unit linear scale. Plot the voltage (E) along the Y-axis and time (T) in sixteenths of a second along the X-axis to represent resistor voltage during capacitor charging. Data: 0, 10 volts; 2, 6 volts; 4, 3.6 volts; 6, 2.2 volts; 8, 1.4 volts; 10, 0.8 volts.

41. Find the equation of the data in Fig. 15–38.

42. Construct a semilog graph of the following data to determine their equation. The Y-axis should be a three-cycle log scale and the X-axis a linear scale from 0 to 250. These data give a comparison of the reduction factor, R (Y-axis), with the mass thickness per square foot (X-axis) of a nuclear protection barrier. Data: 0, 1.0R; 100, 0.9R; 150, 0.028R; 200, 0.009R; 300, 0.0011R.

Empirical Analysis

43. By determining stresses in the cable at intervals, construct an empirical curve that shows the stresses in relationship to the position of the loading boom (Fig. 15–91). This problem is very similar to the one illustrated in Fig. 15–59. Construct stress diagrams to arrive at the stresses in a number of positions. The boom must permit upward and downward movement of 45° with the horizontal.

Cams

The following cam problems are to be solved on Size B sheets (11″ × 17″) with the following standard dimensions: base circle, 4″; roller follower .75″ diameter; shaft, .75″ diameter; hub, 1.25″ diameter. The direction of rotation is clockwise. The follower is positioned vertically over the center of the base circle except in Problems 52 and 53. Lay out the problems and displacement diagrams as shown in Fig. 15–92.

44. Make a drawing of a plate cam with a knife-edge follower for uniform motion and a rise of $1\frac{1}{4}$″.

45. Make a displacement diagram and a drawing of the cam that will give a modified uniform motion to a knife-edge follower with a rise of 1.5″. Use an arc of one-quarter of the rise to modify the uniform motion in the displacement diagram.

46. Make a displacement diagram and a drawing of the cam that will give a harmonic motion to a roller follower with a rise of $1\frac{3}{8}$″.

47. Make a displacement diagram and a drawing of the cam that will give harmonic motion to a knife-edge follower with a rise of .75″.

48. Make a displacement diagram and a drawing of the cam that will give uniform acceleration to a knife-edge follower with a rise of 1.5″.

49. Make a displacement diagram and a drawing of the cam that will give uniform acceleration to a roller follower with a rise of 1.25″.

50. Make a displacement diagram and a drawing of the cam that will give the following motion to a knife-edge follower: dwell for 90°; rise 1″ with harmonic motion in 100°; fall 1″ with a modified uniform motion in 100°; and dwell for 70°.

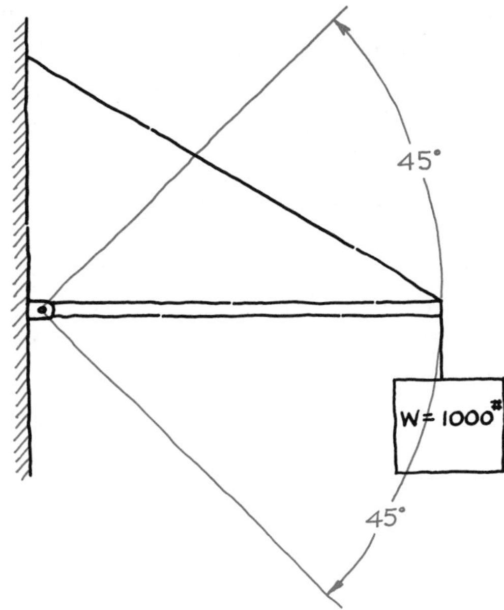

Fig. 15–91. Empirical analysis of stresses (Problem 43).

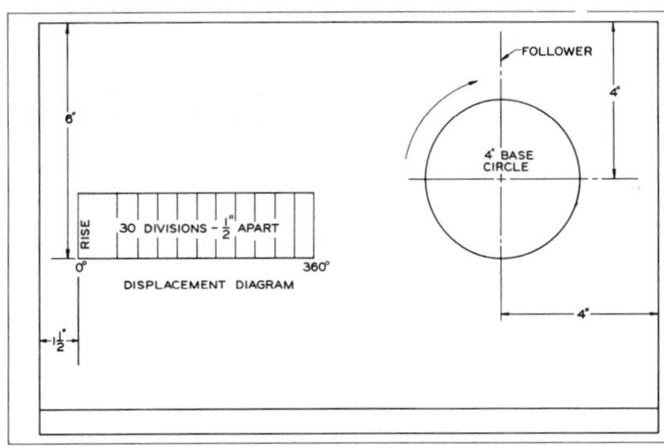

Fig. 15–92. Problem layout for the cam problems on Size B sheets.

51. Make a displacement diagram and a drawing of the cam that will give the following motion to a roller follower: rise 1.25″ with uniform acceleration in 120°; dwell for 120°; and fall 1.25″ with a harmonic motion in 120°.

52. Repeat Problem 44, but offset the follower .75″ to the right of the vertical centerline.

53. Repeat Problem 46, but offset the follower .75″ to the left of the vertical centerline.

Linkages

54. Design and analyze the linkage system for the internal safety valve shown in Fig. 15–93. Use the dimensions given in the table for the particular problem assigned. Determine the *other dimensions* that will permit the operation for the limits given. Show all graphical analysis and the design of the linkage system on 11″ × 15″ tracing paper.

55. Determine the location of the pivot points and the lengths of the linkage members in the clamping device shown in Fig. 15–94 that will raise the bar 90° when the handle is raised 60°. Show all graphical construction and analysis on

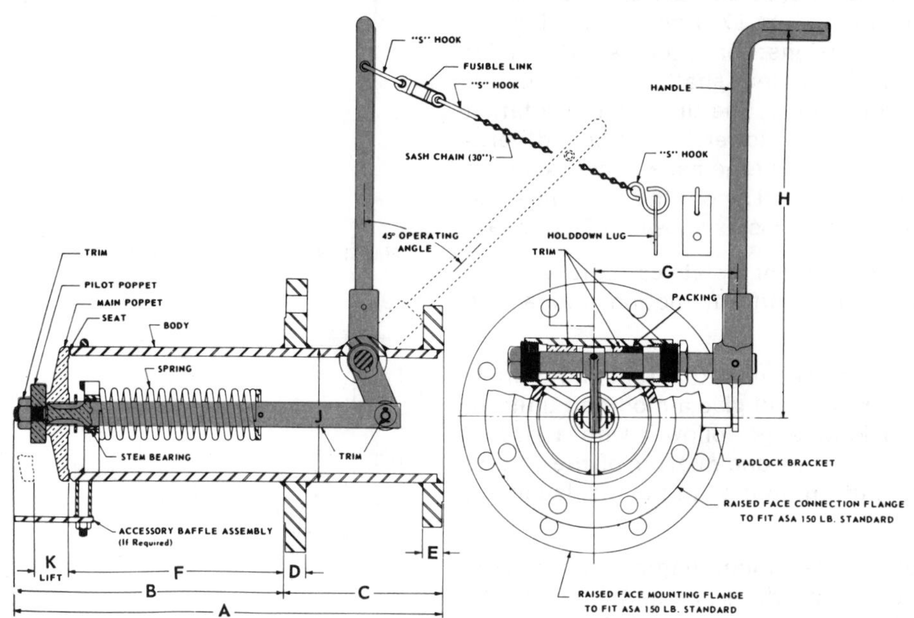

TABLE OF DIMENSIONS																	
VALVE SIZE	CONN. FLANGE SIZE	MOUNTING FLANGE SIZE		A	B	C	D	E	F	G	H	J	K	NET WT. LBS.	SHPG. WT. LBS.	BOX SIZE INCHES
		STANDARD	OVERSIZE													
4"	4"	6"	8"	17	11 5/8	5 3/8	1	15/16	10	6 1/8	12 1/4	4 1/2	1 7/16	78	82	16x17x19
6"	6"	8"	10"	21 3/4	13 3/4	8	1 1/8	1	11	7 1/4	19 1/4	6 5/8	1 3/4	130	136	18x16x23
8"	8"	10"	12"	23 3/4	14 3/4	9	1 3/16	1 1/8	12	8 5/8	31 3/4	8 5/8	2 1/8	173	208	20x17x32
10"	10"	12"	16"	24 3/4	14 3/4	10	1 1/4	1 3/16	12	10 1/8	32 3/4	10 3/4	3 1/2	255	297	24x20x32
12"	12"	14"	18"	24 1/4	14 7/8	9 3/8	1 3/8	1 1/4	12	11 1/8	37	12 3/4	4 3/8	350	402	26x22x32

Fig. 15–93. The linkage system of an internal safety valve (Problem 54). (Courtesy of General Precision Systems, Inc.)

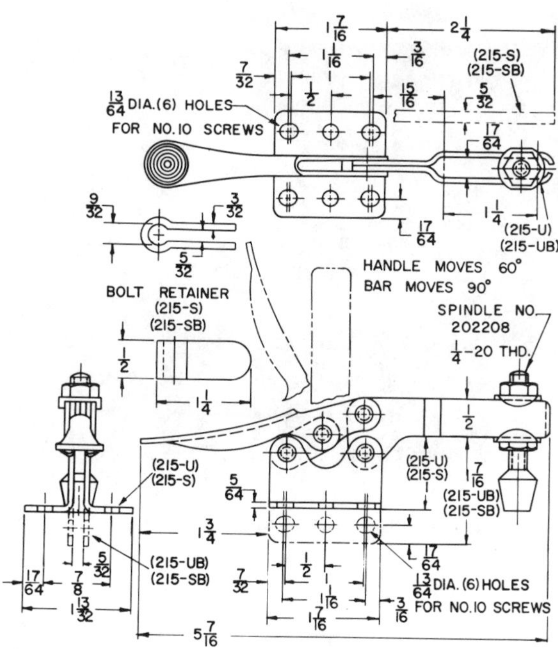

Fig. 15-94. A clamping device linkage (Problem 55). (Courtesy of De-Sta-Co Corporation.)

11″ × 15″ tracing paper. Disregard the details of the specific shapes of the members; be concerned with center-to-center dimensions.

56. Analyze the motion of the piston shown in Fig. 15-52 using the following dimensions: radius of driver, 3.5″; length of piston rod, 9.7″. Plot the distance of travel of the piston for each degree of rotation. The driver is turning at a rate of one revolution per second. Show all construction on a 11″ × 15″ tracing paper.

57. A preliminary sketch and a pictorial of a linkage system to control the pitch of a helicopter blade are shown in Fig. 15-95. The variation in pitch is to be controlled by moving the vertical stick between the vertical and the left. The extreme positions of the stick are vertical and 85° to the left of vertical. The desired out-

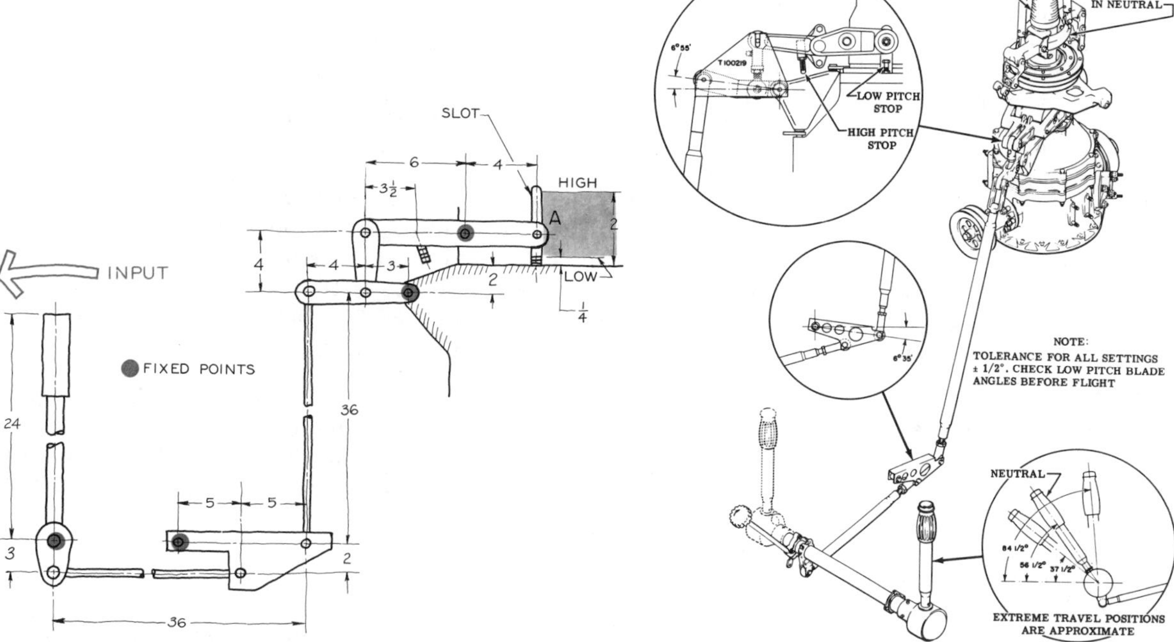

Fig. 15-95. A preliminary sketch and a pictorial of the linkage system to control the pitch on a helicopter (Problem 57). (Courtesy of Bell Helicopter Corporation.)

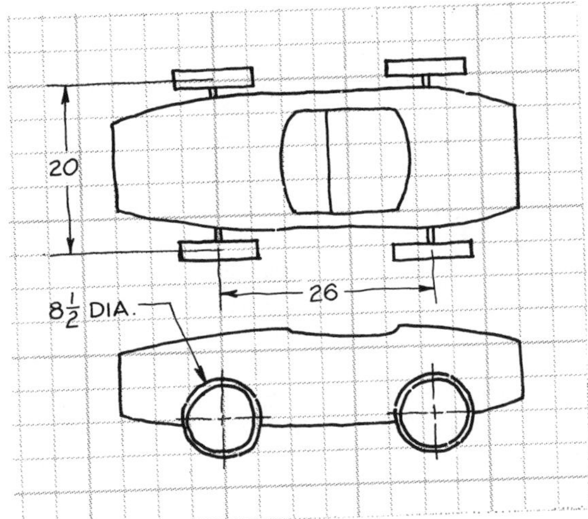

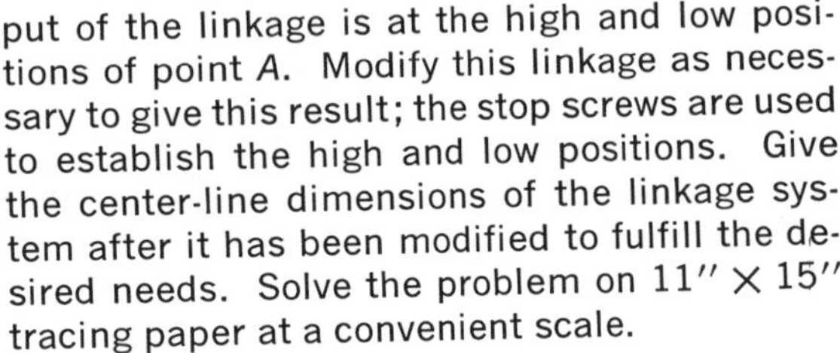

Fig. 15–96. Overall dimensions of a toy racer (Problem 58).

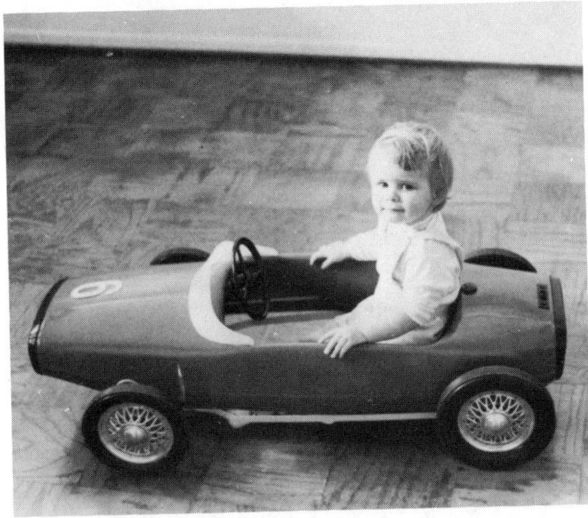

Fig. 15–97. Photograph of the toy car in Problems 58 and 59.

put of the linkage is at the high and low positions of point *A*. Modify this linkage as necessary to give this result; the stop screws are used to establish the high and low positions. Give the center-line dimensions of the linkage system after it has been modified to fulfill the desired needs. Solve the problem on 11″ × 15″ tracing paper at a convenient scale.

58. Design a steering linkage for the toy racer shown in Fig. 15–96 that will be steered by a child. The wheels are 8.5″ in diameter and are 20″ apart. The linkage should be as simple and economical as possible to provide a system that could be mass-produced and assembled cheaply. Show your construction on a 11″ × 15″ sheet of tracing paper.

59. Design a linkage system for the child's racer shown in Fig. 15–97 that will enable the child to pedal the car. The front wheels are separated from the rear wheels by 26″. Estimate other dimensions to complete the linkage. Show your analysis and construction on an 11″ × 15″ sheet of tracing paper.

60. Construct a graph giving the travel of point *P* in Fig. 15–66 versus time in seconds. Use the following dimensions: $R_1 - 20''$, $R_2 - 40''$. Show all construction and analysis on a 11″ × 15″ sheet of tracing paper.

Differentiation

61. Plot the equation $Y = X^3/6$ as a rectangular graph. Graphically differentiate the curve to determine the first and second derivatives.

62. Analyze the motion of the piston discussed in Problem 57. Assume that the crankshaft is turning at a rate of one revolution per second. The piston rod is 9.7″ long, the radius of the input crank is 3.5″. Determine the velocity and acceleration at all intervals.

63. Analyze the motion of the shuttle plotted in Problem 60. Using the rate of revolution as one revolution per three seconds, determine the velocity and acceleration by graphical differentiation.

Integration

64. Plot the equation $Y = X + 2$ on a rectangular graph. Graphically integrate this curve to determine the first and second integrals. Find the area under the curve between $X = 1$ and $X = 7$.

65. Using graphical calculus, analyze a vertical strip 12″ wide on the inside face of the dam in Fig. 15–98. The force on this strip will be 52.0 lb/in at the bottom of the dam. The first graph will be pounds per inch (ordinate) vs. height in inches (abscissa). The second graph will be the integral of the first to give shear in pounds (ordinate) vs. height in inches (abscissa). The third will be the integral of the second graph to give the moment in inch-pounds (ordinate) vs. height in inches (abscissa). Convert these scales to give feet instead of inches.

66. A plot plan shows that a tract of land is bounded by a lake front (Fig. 15–99). By graphical integration, determine a graph that will represent the cumulative area of the land from point *A* to *E*. What is the total area? What is the area of each lot?

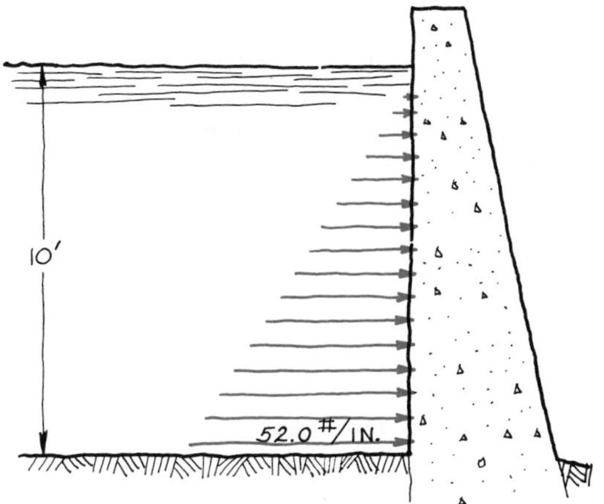

Fig. 15–98. Pressure on a 12″ wide section of a dam (Problem 65).

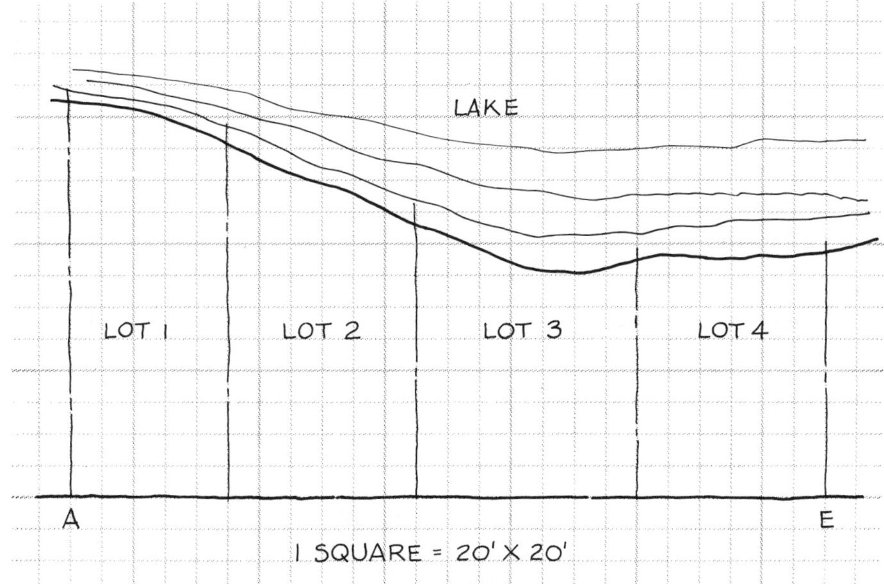

Fig. 15–99. A plot plan of a tract bounded by a lake front (Problem 66).

Nomography

The following problems are to be solved on an $8\frac{1}{2}'' \times 11''$ sheet with the scales selected to be most appropriate for the particular construction. Show all calculations and construction as part of the problems.

Nomography—Conversion Scales

67. Construct a chart that will convert inches to centimeters from 0 to 100 cm given that $1'' = 2.54$ cm.

68. Construct a chart for converting degrees in fahrenheit to degrees in centigrade from 32°F to 212°F using the formula, $°C = \frac{4}{9}(°F - 32)$.

69. Construct a concurrent scale that will convert values of a radius (R) from 1 to 10 to an area (A) of a circle when $A = \pi R^2$.

70. Construct a concurrent scale that will convert numbers from 1 to 10 to their logarithms.

Parallel - Scale Nomograms

71. Construct a parallel-scale chart that will give solutions for the equation $A^2 + B^2 = C^2$ where values of A and B range from 0 to 20.

72. Construct a parallel-scale chart that will give the volume of cones varying in radius r from $1''$ to $10''$ and in height from $1''$ to $30''$. The equation for volume of a cone is $V = (\pi/3)r^2h$.

73. Construct a parallel-scale graph to determine your course grade based on the following equation:

$$\text{Grade } (G) = 0.75 \text{ (test average)} + 0.25 \text{ (final exam)}.$$

Note: Use factors that correspond to those used at your school if different ones are used.

74. Construct a parallel-scale chart that can be used to find how many miles per gallon an automobile will travel. Use the following equation:

$$\text{mpg} = \frac{\text{miles}}{\text{gallon}},$$

where miles vary from 0 to 500 and gallons from 0 to 24.

75. Construct a parallel-scale chart that can be used to find the cost per mile (cpm) of an automobile. Use the following equation:

$$\text{cpm} = \frac{\text{cost}}{\text{miles}},$$

where miles vary from 0 to 500 and cost varies from 0 to $10.00.

N-Charts

76. Using the equation stress $= P/A$, where P ranges from 0 to 1000 psi and A ranges from 0 to 15 in.^{2}, construct an N-chart to determine the stresses on a load-carrying member.

77. Construct an N-chart to determine the relationship of the equation $I = E/R$, where $I =$ amperes of current, $E =$ voltage, and $R =$ resistance in ohms. Ranges: $E = 0$ to 1000 volts and $R = 0$ to 200 ohms.

78. Solve Problem 73 or 74 by using an N-chart.

79. Construct an N-chart to show the volume per 100-ft length of a ditch that is dug as the depth (D in ft) and width (W in ft) vary. The equation of these data is as follows:

$$\text{volume} = 100D \times 100W.$$

[*Hint:* Rewrite this equation in the standard form on an N-chart.]

Combination Charts

80. Construct a combination chart to express the law of sines as expressed in the equation $a/\sin A = b/\sin B$. Assume that a and b vary from 0 to 10, and that A and B vary from 0° to 90°.

81. Construct a combination chart to determine the velocity of sound in a solid, using the formula

$$C = \sqrt{\frac{E + 4\mu/3}{\rho}},$$

where E varies from 10^6 to 10^7 psi, μ varies from 1×10^6 to 2×10^6 psi, and C varies from 1000 to 1500 fps. [*Hint:* Rewrite the formula as $C^2\rho = E + \frac{4}{3}\mu$.]

BIBLIOGRAPHY AND SUGGESTED READING

1. Chambers, S. D., and V. M. Faires, *Analytic Mechanics.* New York: Macmillan, 1949.

2. Hammond, R. H., C. P. Buck, W. B. Rogers, G. W. Walsh, Jr., and H. P. Ackert, *Engineering Graphics for Design and Analysis.* New York: Ronald, 1964.

3. Luzadder, W. J., *Basic Graphics.* Englewood Cliffs, N. J.: Prentice-Hall, 1968.

4. Wellman, B. L., *Introduction to Graphical Analysis and Design.* New York: McGraw-Hill, 1966.

5. Woodward, Forrest, *Graphical Simulation.* Scranton, Pa.: International Textbook, 1967.

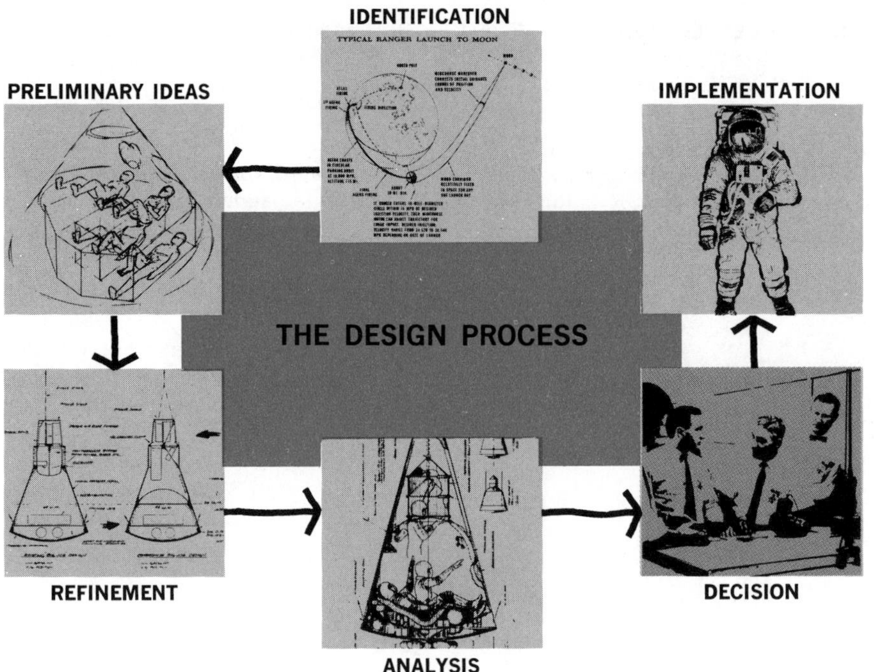

16 DESIGN FINALIZATION

16–1 INTRODUCTION

A good design solution must be accepted before it can be produced; and acceptance, in many cases, will hinge on the skill with which the design is presented. The design process has progressed to its present stage from a roughly outlined set of circumstances that suggested the need for a solution. The designer investigated the background of the problem and the factors affecting it to determine whether the problem was actually in need of a solution and what general type of solution was needed. He then developed preliminary solutions, refined them, determined specific measurements, analyzed his better designs, and has now arrived at the point where he feels qualified to present his design with his recommendations. This is the decision stage of the design process.

By this time, the designer has a complete understanding of the problem, the data and information affecting this thinking, experience with regard to ideas that will not work as well as others, and reasons for his suggested solution. His familiarity with the problem can, in fact, be a handicap to him during the presentation process, because those with whom he is dealing may have only a minimum of background information, and his presentation may not include a sufficiently complete review of the problem and the reasons that made him arrive at a specific solution. However, his associates who are responsible for accepting his proposal for volume production or the expenditure of large sums of capital must have access to a summary of the problem and the reason for the designer's final solution in order to make an informal decision based on facts or experience.

Presentation for the decision phase of the design process can be called the climax of the designer's work. A well-prepared, effectively given presentation will increase the chance for a design to be accepted for further development or immediate implementation. On the other hand, an inferior presentation may kill a superior design; in this case, the preliminary effort invested in the project may be lost.

This type of presentation is referred to as presentation for *decision*. Although decisions on the acceptance of a completed design will usually be made by a group of people, in some cases it will be the *designer* who will make the decision. The process of presentation is much the same in this case; however, the methods used will vary.

The other type of presentation is the presentation for *implementation*—for augmenting a design once a favorable decision has been reached. This will involve all methods available for presenting specifications, working drawings, schematics, diagrams, etc., that completely describe the implementation of the completed design.

16–2 THE DESIGNER'S PRESENTATION TO HIMSELF

On small design projects, the designer himself may have to decide whether or not to accept a design. He will have to review the project in his own mind. Although he may not necessarily prepare charts and other visual aids as he would if he were giving a formal presentation, he must, nevertheless, have access to the same information and data for his own evaluation as would be required in a formal presentation. The designer can easily lose sight of important features and points throughout the design process without realizing the oversight. Consequently, he should frequently refer to early worksheets and preliminary ideas throughout the design sequence to ensure that no idea has been overlooked. All worksheets, as suggested in Chapter 3, should be kept as a permanent record of the designer's progress in arriving at the finished design.

When he has narrowed his final solutions to several designs, he must decide which one to accept for implementation. At times, the solution arrived at may turn out to be neither economically feasible nor sensible; in this case, the designer will regard his findings as valuable background for future projects of a similar nature. Cases of this sort are likely to arise in experimental design projects that are conducted as a form of research.

Although the designer is completely familiar with his project after working with it for a period of time, he will not want to make a final decision without reviewing the entire list of alternatives. A good way for a designer to make a decision is to communicate with himself through sketches, data, notes, or models. He will begin his review by making a list of the favorable features of each design solution and a similar list of the unfavorable features. An example of such a list is given in Fig. 16–1, where two types of hunting seats are evaluated for their advantages and disadvantages. Note that many of the features were listed as previously stated in the preliminary design stages. Such a list forces the designer to review completely the design features of each solution while recalling his previous impressions of each.

Previously gathered data should be evaluated in conjunction with each design solution. Market research data will indicate the price range that would be most acceptable for a product of this type. The consumer's activity when using the hunting seat will affect the designer's decision. Will the hunter walk for long distances carrying the seat and hunting equipment or will he travel by vehicle most of the way? Will he be able to climb a tree or is a self-hoisting mechanism needed? The average age of the hunter for which the seat was designed will answer these questions in part. Older hunters will probably need more comfort, walk less, and be less adept at climbing trees. Available data should be plotted in the form of a graph to allow easy inter-

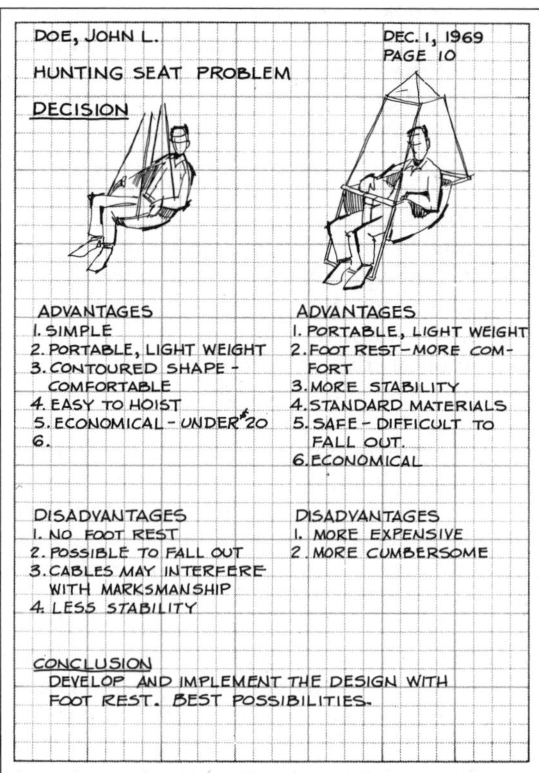

DOE, JOHN L.
DEC. 1, 1969
PAGE 10
HUNTING SEAT PROBLEM
DECISION

ADVANTAGES
1. SIMPLE
2. PORTABLE, LIGHT WEIGHT
3. CONTOURED SHAPE - COMFORTABLE
4. EASY TO HOIST
5. ECONOMICAL - UNDER $20
6.

ADVANTAGES
1. PORTABLE, LIGHT WEIGHT
2. FOOT REST - MORE COMFORT
3. MORE STABILITY
4. STANDARD MATERIALS
5. SAFE - DIFFICULT TO FALL OUT.
6. ECONOMICAL

DISADVANTAGES
1. NO FOOT REST
2. POSSIBLE TO FALL OUT
3. CABLES MAY INTERFERE WITH MARKSMANSHIP
4. LESS STABILITY

DISADVANTAGES
1. MORE EXPENSIVE
2. MORE CUMBERSOME

CONCLUSION
DEVELOP AND IMPLEMENT THE DESIGN WITH FOOT REST. BEST POSSIBILITIES.

Fig. 16-1. A work sheet used by the designer to decide on the best design to implement. This method is used when the decision is made by the designer rather than a group.

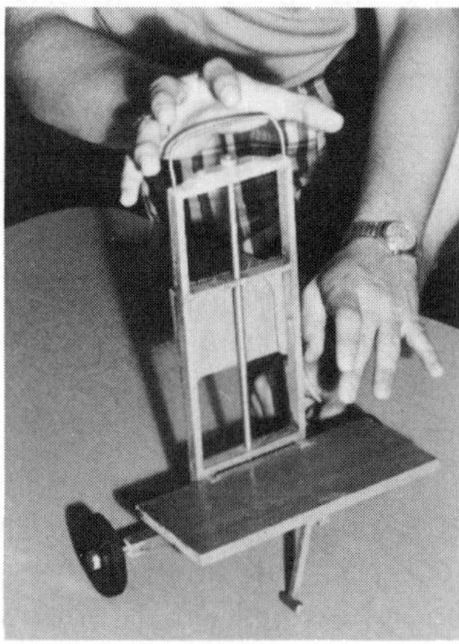

Fig. 16-2. Models, such as this student design for a home caddy, are excellent aids to assist the designer in evaluating a proposed design.

pretation. This information should be added to the list of features of each design. At this point the designer can arrive at his decision.

The designer has been actually communicating with himself by employing graphical methods for recalling his ideas. He may even make pictorial sketches to explain his refined designs more fully to himself. Often it is easier to analyze a pictorial than a two-dimensional orthographic drawing. Principles of pictorial drawing will be covered in Chapter 17; these will be of assistance in presentation for decision *and* for implementation.

The most realistic means of evaluating a design is through a scale model or a prototype, as covered in Chapter 13. Such a model is invaluable in studying features and operational methods to eliminate doubt as to a product's function and other characteristics. Models need not be complicated or expensive to serve their purpose. Commonly available model materials, including balsa wood and even paper, often are sufficient to provide a better understanding of the proposed design. An example of a student model is given in Fig. 16-2, which shows a home-caddy model that demonstrates the functional characteristics of the design. This model was relatively inexpensive to construct but was effective in suggesting further improvements. Models are certainly necessary to the designer in communicating his ideas to others, but they are also valuable for communicating with himself. He is better able to understand his own ideas and to review his design concepts. The design of any product involving a close contact with the human body should be rendered as a full-size model if at all possible to establish the optimum dimensions and other comfort factors that cannot be evaluated without actual testing.

16-3 COMMUNICATION WITH GROUPS

In general, a designer will present his design to several of his associates or perhaps a sizable group before a final decision will be made (Fig. 16-3). This type of presentation will involve the same steps as those outlined in Article

Fig. 16-3. The designer will often present his design concepts to his associates or perhaps to a sizable group before the final decision is made. (Courtesy of Black and Decker Manufacturing Company.)

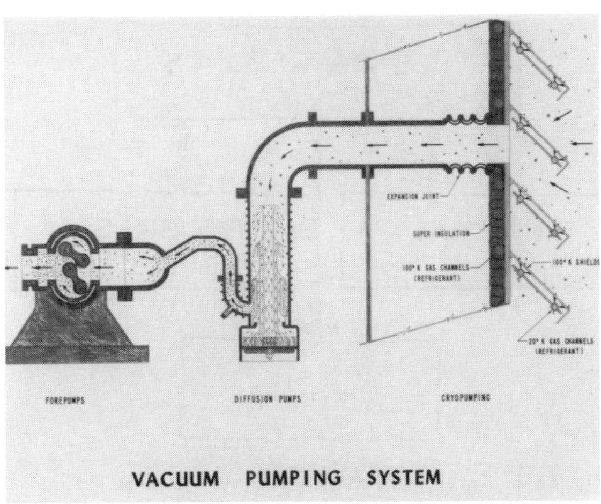

Fig. 16-4. Schematics and diagrams are essential to the explanation of many engineering designs and processes. (Courtesy of Aro, Inc., Arnold Engineering Development Center.)

16-2. He must organize his thoughts and prepare a presentation that will completely cover his design efforts with maximum clarity in minimum time. Obviously a verbal presentation is not as effective as one using visual materials and graphical aids. Technical data and design information must be presented by graphical means in order to provide the clearest picture without necessitating prolonged study of tabular information and complex procedures. In many cases, it is impossible to communicate technical information without graphical aids (Fig. 16-4). The shortcomings of verbal descriptions of even a simple object becomes immediately obvious to anybody who attempts to describe a common object to a person who does not see the object.

Pictorials are more meaningful to the average group than are two view-drawings, regardless of the quality of presentation. Presentations should make good use of as many pictorials as are needed to describe the design being discussed (Fig. 16-5). Such pictorials can be presented as illustrations on flip charts, photographic slides, or as transparencies to be shown

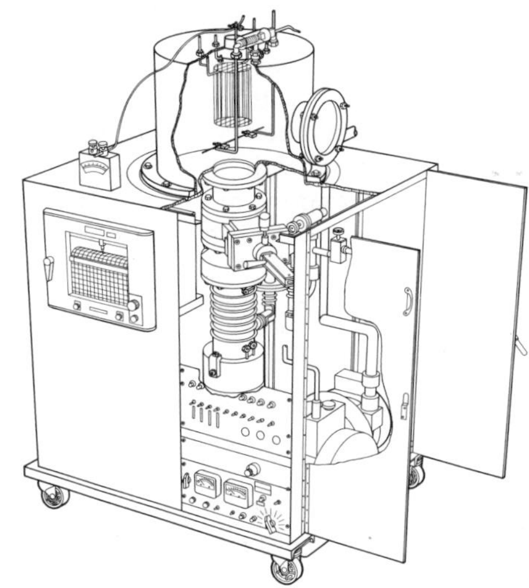

BIG BELL JAR

Fig. 16-5. The finalization of a design is usually much easier when the design can be presented pictorially. (Courtesy of Aro, Inc., Arnold Engineering Development Center.)

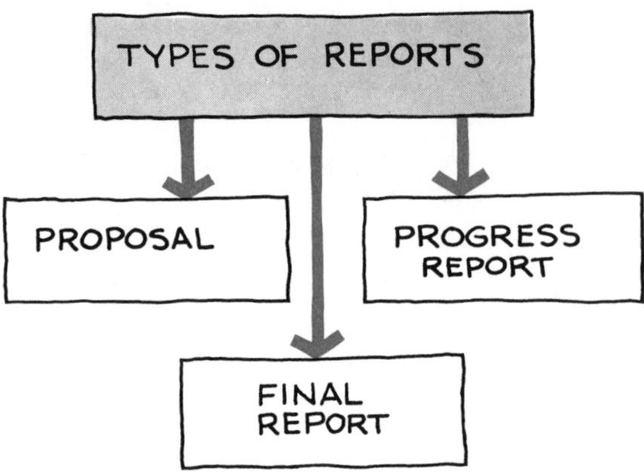

Fig. 16-6. Three basic types of technical reports.

on the overhead projector.

The designer should develop an awareness of the importance of carrying a design through this very critical phase of the decision process. It is not enough to merely have a superior idea —good ideas must be sold with enthusiasm and conviction. Failure to assume the responsibility for good communication with associates and superiors will limit the opportunities of an engineer or technician involved in the development of new designs.

16-4 THE TECHNICAL REPORT

Engineers and technicians at all levels must know how to prepare a written report, since this is the universally used means of transmitting information. Considerable emphasis has been placed on the need to develop writing abilities in order to function as an effective member of the industrial team.

The report can be written for one of the following purposes: (1) proposal for a project, (2) progress report, and (3) a final report (Fig. 16-6). The proposal and final report are usually detailed and formally presented. However, the progress report may be in the form of a letter or a memorandum, depending upon the requirements of the particular project. A letter is usually sent to one or only a few of those who are responsible for, or concerned with, the progress or the status of the project at a given interval.

16-5 THE PROPOSAL

The proposal is a report written to substantiate the need for a given project that will require the authorization of funds and the utilization of manpower within the organization. It could also be a report to be submitted to a client, outlining a recommendation that will necessitate an expenditure of funds. Since a project will not become a reality unless approved by the organization administrators, the proposal is usually written in a very thorough, formal form that reflects sound analysis and thinking.

The proposal is organized to include data, costs, specifications, time schedules, personnel requirements, completion dates, and any specific information that will aid the reader to understand the project. Above all, the purpose and the importance of the proposed project must be clearly stated with emphasis on the benefit of the project to the client or to the organization. For instance, if an industrial engineer suggests a major modification of the manufacturing processes of a company that will cost a considerable amount, he must be able to give a substantiated estimate of the increased production and profits that will offset the initial expense of the modification.

The proposal must be written in the language of the reader. The businessman will be more interested in profits and benefits that a project promises, whereas the chief engineer will be concerned with its feasibility from an engineering standpoint. In some cases, a proposal may begin as a rather technical report that is reviewed by the personnel directly affected by the proposed project. After the report has been approved at this level, the proposal is rewritten to present the overall picture in less technical terms for the investor, client, stockholder, or businessman who may be indirectly involved.

Fig. 16–7. The fundamental divisions of a proposal.

The proposal was mentioned earlier in Chapter 3 as an example of presenting preliminary data in support of a project. Preliminary data should be presented graphically and analyzed in the report to emphasize significant points. Surveys of opinions and field data should be included in graphical form where inspection will be sufficient for comprehension. In a formal proposal, it may be desirable to include the tabular data in the appendix.

A typical proposal (Fig. 16–7) should contain the following elements:

Statement of the problem. The problem is clearly identified to present the purpose of the project. In most cases, about one typewritten page or less will suffice.

Method of approach. The procedures for attacking the problem are outlined and explained in detail. This can be done in outline form for easy review (usually the longest part of a proposal).

Personnel needs and facilities. Requirements for equipment, space, and personnel are itemized.

Time schedule. A time schedule gives an estimate of the completion dates for the various phases of the project. This schedule should be coordinated with any other related activity that may be affected.

Budget. The funds necessary should be presented in sufficiently detailed form to permit analysis by those who review the proposal.

Summary. The report is reviewed to emphasize the important points that are the basis of the proposal. The importance of the project and its contribution to the reviewer should be strongly stated in the summarizing comments.

16–6 THE PROGRESS REPORT

The progress report periodically reviews the status of a project or an assignment that is in progress. Some progress reports may be in the form of a letter to an immediate superior or a memorandum that will be circulated among those interested in the project. More comprehensive projects require a more detailed formal report.

The progress report relates the status of the project to the original time and budget schedule. It usually gives a projection of an increase or decrease in expenditures or time schedules to permit a revision of project plans. These reports are essential to keep top management in touch with any variation or deviation in the operation of a project. The progress report may be used to determine whether or not a project should be continued after the completion of the initial stage of preliminary development.

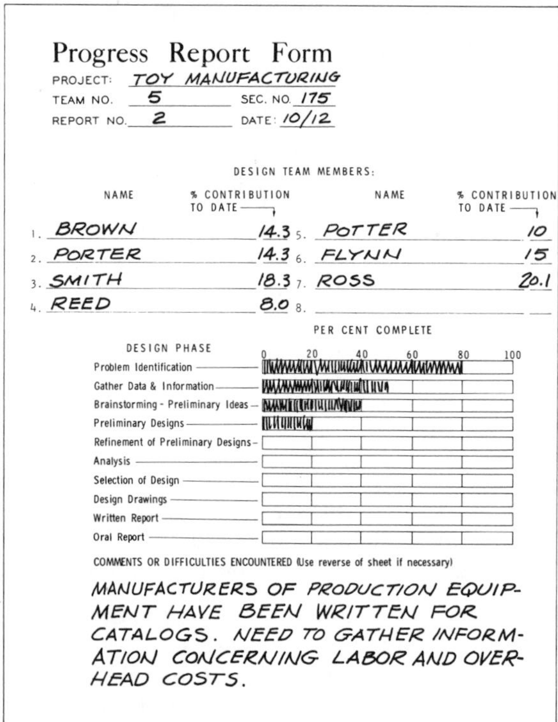

Progress Report Form

PROJECT: TOY MANUFACTURING

TEAM NO. 5 SEC. NO. 175

REPORT NO. 2 DATE: 10/12

DESIGN TEAM MEMBERS:

	NAME	% CONTRIBUTION TO DATE		NAME	% CONTRIBUTION TO DATE
1.	BROWN	14.3	5.	POTTER	10
2.	PORTER	14.3	6.	FLYNN	15
3.	SMITH	18.3	7.	ROSS	20.1
4.	REED	8.0	8.		

PER CENT COMPLETE (0, 20, 40, 60, 80, 100)

DESIGN PHASE
- Problem Identification
- Gather Data & Information
- Brainstorming - Preliminary Ideas
- Preliminary Designs
- Refinement of Preliminary Designs
- Analysis
- Selection of Design
- Design Drawings
- Written Report
- Oral Report

COMMENTS OR DIFFICULTIES ENCOUNTERED (Use reverse of sheet if necessary)

MANUFACTURERS OF PRODUCTION EQUIPMENT HAVE BEEN WRITTEN FOR CATALOGS. NEED TO GATHER INFORMATION CONCERNING LABOR AND OVERHEAD COSTS.

Fig. 16–8. A progress report form for reporting weekly progress by a student team.

Reference to Project Evaluation and Review Techniques (PERT) introduced in Chapter 3 suggests effective methods of reporting the status of a design project. Essentially the same forms used to schedule activities could be submitted as part of a progress report to give an accurate picture of the progress that has been made. A schematic diagram can be used to present the information taken from the Design Schedule and Progress Report for ease of interpretation. This type of progress report is required by many agencies responsible for complex projects. A weekly progress report for student projects is shown in Fig. 16–8.

16–7 THE FINAL REPORT

The final report is the last report written at the conclusion of a project. It must be remembered that the project could be the organization of an engineering plan, a preliminary investigation, or a recommended solution to a problem that must be approved for implementation. This type of report should be well prepared and should include a considerable amount of detail, since it will be kept as a permanent record that may influence future projects. Reference will be made to final reports on many occasions and perhaps many years after completion. The engineer or technician most intimately related to the project should organize and write the report, since he has access to more of the specific details than anyone else.

Conclusions and recommendations are usually the most important element of any report, but probably more important to the final report than to any other. Recommendations in a final report are more conclusive than those in the proposal and progress report, since they are based on the results of the total project rather than on predictions and speculations. These findings are useful for evaluation of subsequent proposals and projects.

16–8 ORGANIZATION OF A TECHNICAL REPORT

A good technical report is composed of the following broad areas: (1) problem identification, (2) method, (3) body, (4) findings, and (5) conclusions and recommendations. The order of presentation of these divisions may vary with the requirements of the governing organization. For instance, some reports are written with the conclusions and recommendations preceding the body of the report so that the reader immediately sees the results of the report. Almost any report will be written to contain these major divisions, although the order of arrangement may be different.

The following article will point out specific points and rules that should be considered when preparing a report.

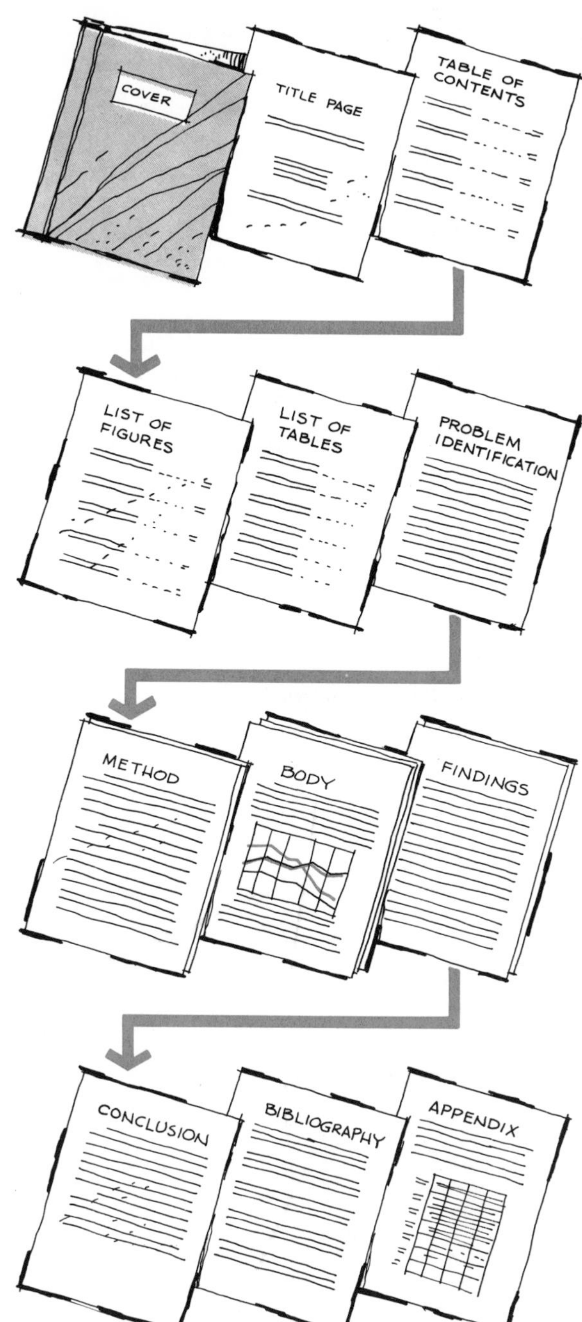

Fig. 16–9. The elements of a technical report.

16–9 FORMAT OF THE REPORT

A general sequence of the contents of a technical report is shown in Fig. 16–9. Portions of a typical student report will be used to illustrate the specific parts.

1. *Cover.* Your finished report should *always* be bound in an appropriate cover, which gives the title of the report and the name of the individual or team that prepared it. The contents should be held firmly in the cover and not simply placed inside loosely.

2. *Evaluation sheet.* The first page of the report should be a standard evaluation sheet of the type shown in Fig. 16–10A. The teacher can record your grades on this sheet after reviewing the report.

3. *Letter of transmittal.* The second page should be a letter of transmittal that briefly describes the contents of the report and the reasons for initiating the project (Fig. 16–10B).

4. *Title page.* The title page should contain the elements shown in Fig. 16–11A.

5. *Table of contents.* The major headings of the report and the corresponding page numbers should be shown (Fig. 16–11B).

6. *Table of illustrations.* This page may be omitted in less formal reports (Fig. 16–11C).

7. *Problem identification.* (Use a heading appropriate for your report rather than this general term.) This section is more than a statement of the problem. It should give a background review of the related facts and information that focuses on the problem and establishes its importance and the need for a solution.

A typical page of a report is shown in Fig. 16–11D, and a page containing a footnote is shown in Fig. 16–11F. You should adhere to the margins shown here for all pages of a report, including those where illustrations are given. Use the third person; do not say, "We investigated the problem and I suggested . . . ."

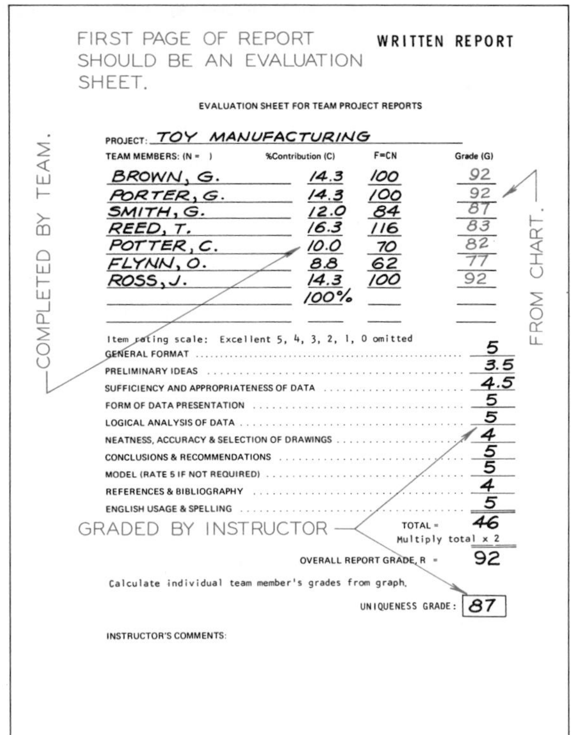

FIRST PAGE OF REPORT SHOULD BE AN EVALUATION SHEET.

WRITTEN REPORT

EVALUATION SHEET FOR TEAM PROJECT REPORTS

PROJECT: TOY MANUFACTURING

TEAM MEMBERS: (N =)	%Contribution (C)	F=CN	Grade (G)
BROWN, G.	14.3	100	92
PORTER, G.	14.3	100	92
SMITH, G.	12.0	84	87
REED, T.	16.3	116	83
POTTER, C.	10.0	70	82
FLYNN, O.	8.8	62	77
ROSS, J.	14.3	100	92
	100%		

Item rating scale: Excellent 5, 4, 3, 2, 1, 0 omitted

GENERAL FORMAT	5
PRELIMINARY IDEAS	3.5
SUFFICIENCY AND APPROPRIATENESS OF DATA	4.5
FORM OF DATA PRESENTATION	5
LOGICAL ANALYSIS OF DATA	5
NEATNESS, ACCURACY & SELECTION OF DRAWINGS	4
CONCLUSIONS & RECOMMENDATIONS	5
MODEL (RATE 5 IF NOT REQUIRED)	5
REFERENCES & BIBLIOGRAPHY	4
ENGLISH USAGE & SPELLING	5
TOTAL =	46
Multiply total x 2	
OVERALL REPORT GRADE, R =	92

Calculate individual team member's grades from graph.

UNIQUENESS GRADE: 87

INSTRUCTOR'S COMMENTS:

Fig. 16–10A. A typical evaluation sheet for a student report.

LETTER OF TRANSMITTAL – SECOND PAGE OF YOUR REPORT. ADDRESS TO YOUR TEACHER.

May 8, 1972

Professor J. T. Coppinger
Engineering Design Graphics Department
Texas A&M University
College Station, Texas 77840

Dear Professor Coppinger:

Attached is our report which outlines our recommendations for the establishment of a manufacturing operation to produce an educational toy at a rate of 5,000 per month.

We have researched and studied this problem very closely, and feel that our conclusions and recommendations are based on sound judgment. We are hopeful that our findings meet with your approval.

Sincerely,

Gerald Brown

Gerald Brown, Chief Designer
Team 5, EDG 105, Section 145

Fig. 16–10B. The letter of transmittal.

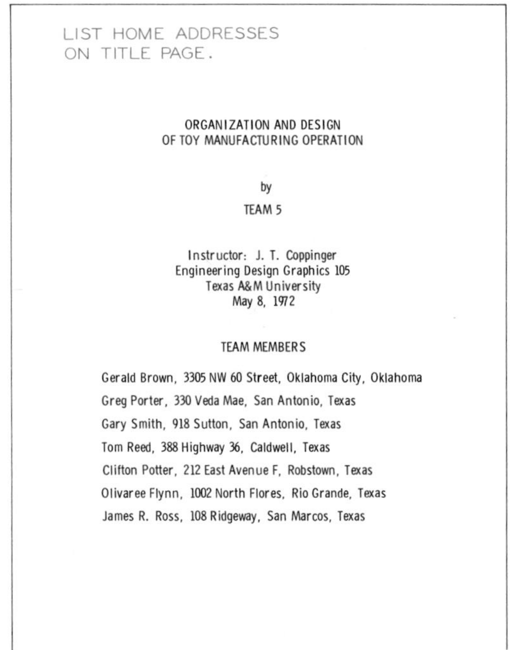

LIST HOME ADDRESSES ON TITLE PAGE.

ORGANIZATION AND DESIGN
OF TOY MANUFACTURING OPERATION

by

TEAM 5

Instructor: J. T. Coppinger
Engineering Design Graphics 105
Texas A&M University
May 8, 1972

TEAM MEMBERS

Gerald Brown, 3305 NW 60 Street, Oklahoma City, Oklahoma
Greg Porter, 330 Veda Mae, San Antonio, Texas
Gary Smith, 918 Sutton, San Antonio, Texas
Tom Reed, 388 Highway 36, Caldwell, Texas
Clifton Potter, 212 East Avenue F, Robstown, Texas
Olivaree Flynn, 1002 North Flores, Rio Grande, Texas
James R. Ross, 108 Ridgeway, San Marcos, Texas

Fig. 16–11A. The title page of team report.

DOUBLE SPACE

TABLE OF CONTENTS

Fig. 16–11B. The table of contents of a report.

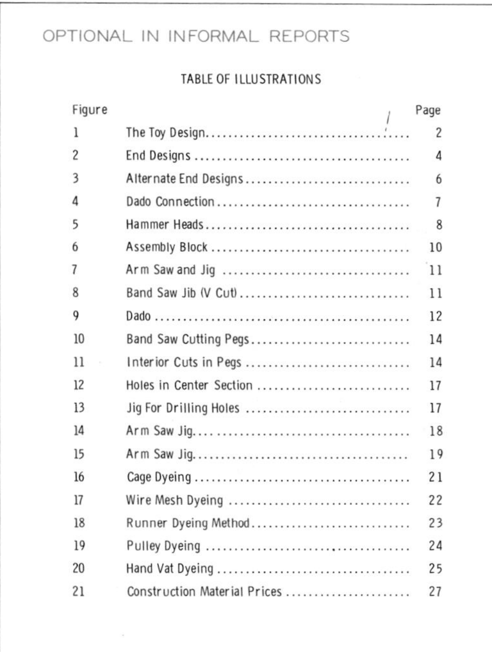

OPTIONAL IN INFORMAL REPORTS

TABLE OF ILLUSTRATIONS

Fig. 16–11C. The table of illustrations. This page can be omitted in less formal reports.

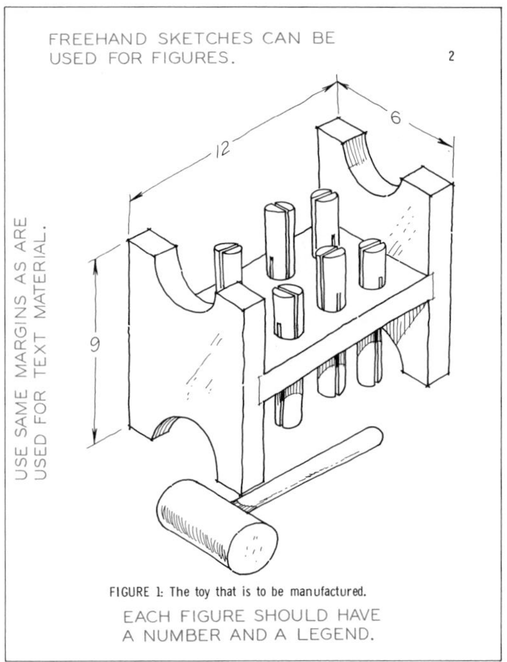

Fig. 16–11E. A freehand sketch used as a figure.

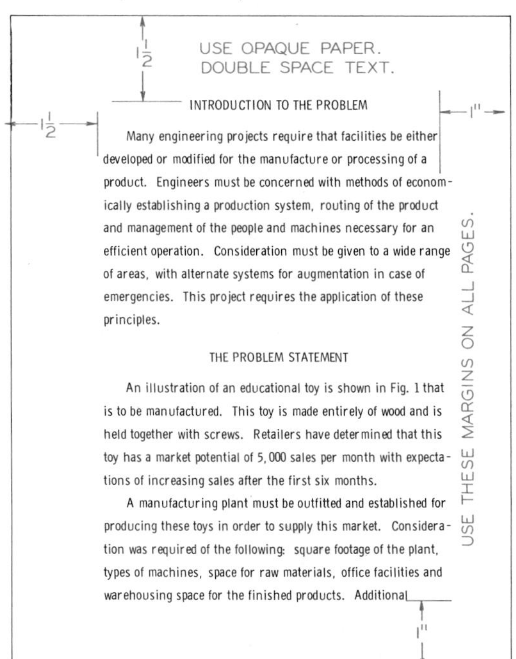

INTRODUCTION TO THE PROBLEM

Many engineering projects require that facilities be either developed or modified for the manufacture or processing of a product. Engineers must be concerned with methods of economically establishing a production system, routing of the product and management of the people and machines necessary for an efficient operation. Consideration must be given to a wide range of areas, with alternate systems for augmentation in case of emergencies. This project requires the application of these principles.

THE PROBLEM STATEMENT

An illustration of an educational toy is shown in Fig. 1 that is to be manufactured. This toy is made entirely of wood and is held together with screws. Retailers have determined that this toy has a market potential of 5,000 sales per month with expectations of increasing sales after the first six months.

A manufacturing plant must be outfitted and established for producing these toys in order to supply this market. Consideration was required of the following: square footage of the plant, types of machines, space for raw materials, office facilities and warehousing space for the finished products. Additional

Fig. 16–11D. A typical page of text material in a report.

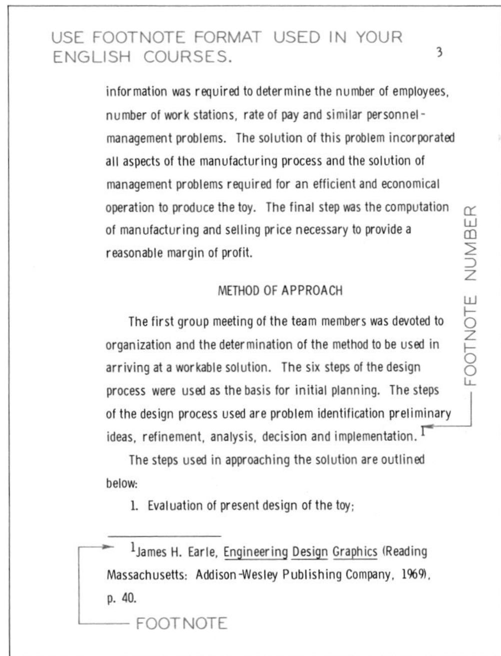

information was required to determine the number of employees, number of work stations, rate of pay and similar personnel-management problems. The solution of this problem incorporated all aspects of the manufacturing process and the solution of management problems required for an efficient and economical operation to produce the toy. The final step was the computation of manufacturing and selling price necessary to provide a reasonable margin of profit.

METHOD OF APPROACH

The first group meeting of the team members was devoted to organization and the determination of the method to be used in arriving at a workable solution. The six steps of the design process were used as the basis for initial planning. The steps of the design process used are problem identification preliminary ideas, refinement, analysis, decision and implementation.[1]

The steps used in approaching the solution are outlined below:

1. Evaluation of present design of the toy;

[1] James H. Earle, Engineering Design Graphics (Reading Massachusetts: Addison-Wesley Publishing Company, 1969), p. 40.

Fig. 16–11F. A page of text with a footnote.

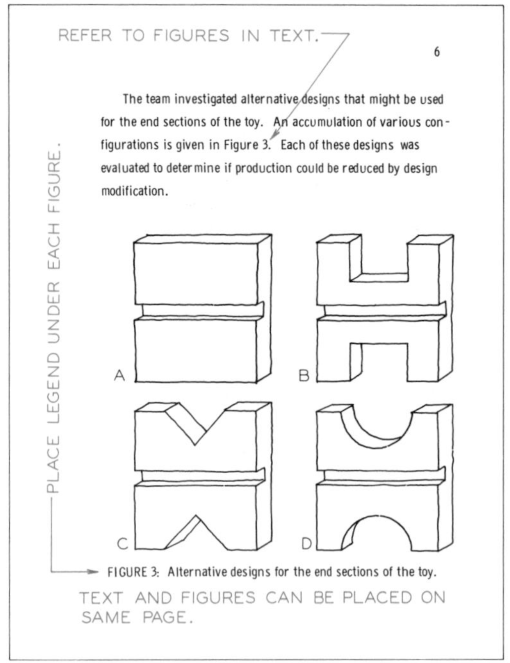

REFER TO FIGURES IN TEXT.

6

The team investigated alternative designs that might be used for the end sections of the toy. An accumulation of various configurations is given in Figure 3. Each of these designs was evaluated to determine if production could be reduced by design modification.

FIGURE 3: Alternative designs for the end sections of the toy.

PLACE LEGEND UNDER EACH FIGURE.

TEXT AND FIGURES CAN BE PLACED ON SAME PAGE.

Fig. 16–11G. A page that contains both text and figures.

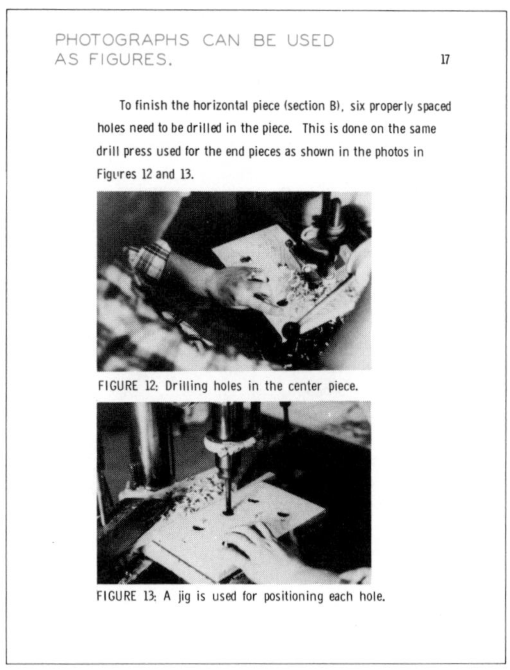

PHOTOGRAPHS CAN BE USED AS FIGURES.

17

To finish the horizontal piece (section B), six properly spaced holes need to be drilled in the piece. This is done on the same drill press used for the end pieces as shown in the photos in Figures 12 and 13.

FIGURE 12: Drilling holes in the center piece.

FIGURE 13: A jig is used for positioning each hole.

Fig. 16–11H. Photographs can be attached to a page with rubber cement and used as figures.

The text should refer to a figure that follows. Example: "The numbers of boats sold between 1950 and 1973 are shown in Figure 6." The figure should be placed immediately after the text that refers to it or on the following page. Figure 16–11E shows a figure that is referred to in Fig. 16–11D.

8. *Method.* (Use a heading appropriate for your report rather than this general term.) This section should cover the general method that will be used in solving the problem. It can be written in outline or essay form.

9. *Body.* (Use a heading appropriate for your report rather than this general term.) This portion elaborates on the solution of the problem. Subheadings should be used to make the parts of the report stand out. Where possible, illustrate your report with sketches, instrument drawings, graphs, or photographs to communicate its contents. Examples of illustrations are shown in Figs. 16–11E, G, H, and K.

Illustrations should be drawn on opaque paper or on tracing paper, and a print should be made for inclusion in the report. Ink illustrations are preferable. If a drawing must be turned lengthwise on the sheet, the top of the figure should be placed toward the left side of the sheet so that it can be read from the right side of the page.

Graphs and illustrations can be drawn proportional to a photographic slide or to an overhead transparency if these will be used in an oral presentation. This will eliminate duplication of effort.

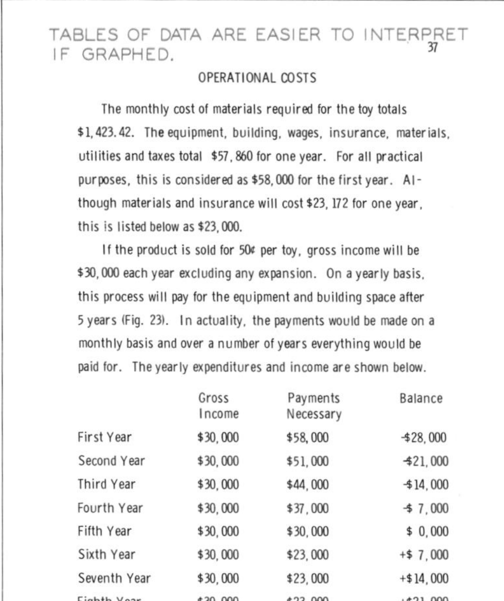

TABLES OF DATA ARE EASIER TO INTERPRET IF GRAPHED.

37

OPERATIONAL COSTS

The monthly cost of materials required for the toy totals $1,423.42. The equipment, building, wages, insurance, materials, utilities and taxes total $57,860 for one year. For all practical purposes, this is considered as $58,000 for the first year. Although materials and insurance will cost $23,172 for one year, this is listed below as $23,000.

If the product is sold for 50¢ per toy, gross income will be $30,000 each year excluding any expansion. On a yearly basis, this process will pay for the equipment and building space after 5 years (Fig. 23). In actuality, the payments would be made on a monthly basis and over a number of years everything would be paid for. The yearly expenditures and income are shown below.

	Gross Income	Payments Necessary	Balance
First Year	$30,000	$58,000	-$28,000
Second Year	$30,000	$51,000	-$21,000
Third Year	$30,000	$44,000	-$14,000
Fourth Year	$30,000	$37,000	-$ 7,000
Fifth Year	$30,000	$30,000	$ 0,000
Sixth Year	$30,000	$23,000	+$ 7,000
Seventh Year	$30,000	$23,000	+$14,000
Eighth Year	$30,000	$23,000	+$21,000

Fig. 16–11J. Tabular data can be given in a report, but are easier to interpret if graphed.

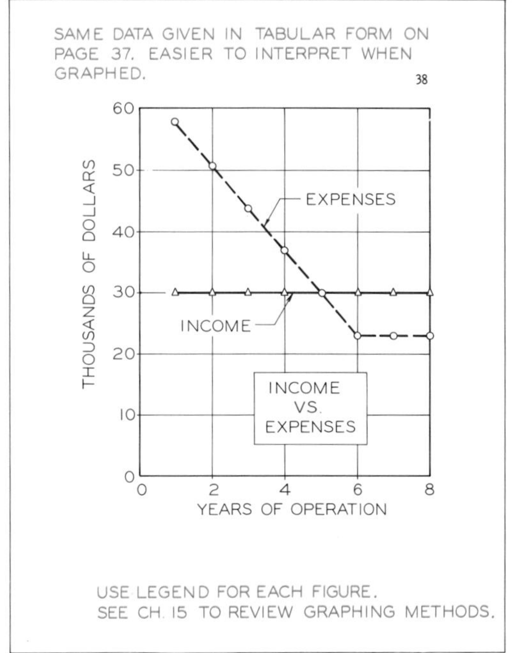

Fig. 16–11K. The data shown in the previous figure are shown as a figure in the form of a graph for easy interpretation.

Large drawings that must be folded for insertion in a report should be folded to $8\frac{1}{2}'' \times 11''$ to allow them to be conveniently unfolded by the reader.

10. *Findings.* (Use a heading appropriate for your report rather than this general term.) The results of the report should be tabulated and presented graphically with explanatory text. The findings should be evaluated and presented for easy interpretation. The data presented in Fig. 16–11J are easier to interpret when graphed as shown in Fig. 16–11K.

11. *Conclusions.* The conclusions should summarize the entire report very briefly and end with specific conclusions and recommendations, either positive or negative. If there are several conclusions, they may be emphasized by a listing in numerical order.

12. *Bibliography.* This is a list of references—books, magazines, brochures, conversations—that were used in the preparation of the report. They are usually listed alphabetically by author (Fig. 16–11L). Refer to your English textbook for the format suitable for your report; several formats are acceptable for footnotes and bibliographies.

13. *Appendix.* The appendix should include less important drawings, sketches, raw data, brochures, letters, and other general information that supports but is not appropriate for inclusion in the main part of the report (Figs. 16–11M and N). Preliminary ideas and student progress reports should be included here.

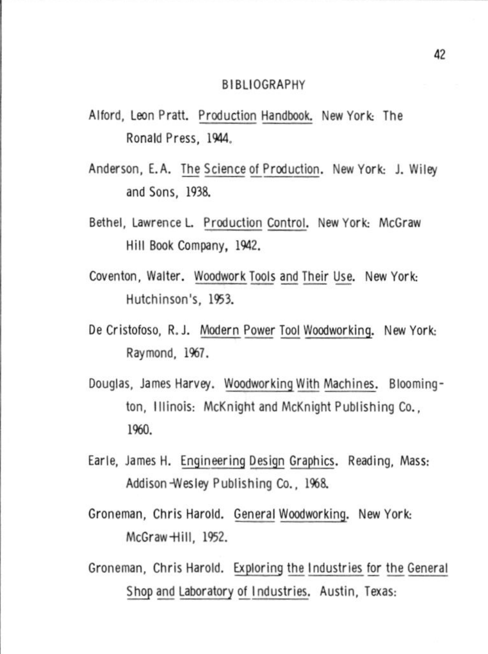

42

BIBLIOGRAPHY

Alford, Leon Pratt. Production Handbook. New York: The Ronald Press, 1944.

Anderson, E.A. The Science of Production. New York: J. Wiley and Sons, 1938.

Bethel, Lawrence L. Production Control. New York: McGraw Hill Book Company, 1942.

Coventon, Walter. Woodwork Tools and Their Use. New York: Hutchinson's, 1953.

De Cristofoso, R. J. Modern Power Tool Woodworking. New York: Raymond, 1967.

Douglas, James Harvey. Woodworking With Machines. Bloomington, Illinois: McKnight and McKnight Publishing Co., 1960.

Earle, James H. Engineering Design Graphics. Reading, Mass: Addison-Wesley Publishing Co., 1968.

Groneman, Chris Harold. General Woodworking. New York: McGraw-Hill, 1952.

Groneman, Chris Harold. Exploring the Industries for the General Shop and Laboratory of Industries. Austin, Texas:

Fig. 16-11L. One form of bibliography listing the references used in composing the report.

APPENDIX MATERIALS INCLUDE RAW DATA, NOTES, SKETCHES, PROGRESS REPORTS, ETC,

44

SUMMARY SHEET
OF OPINION SURVEY
Number of Votes Per Section

Team Member	1	2	3	4	5	6
#1	0	2	7	1	0	0
#2	0	3	3	2	1	1
#3	0	2	6	2	0	0
#4	1	1	5	3	0	0
Totals	1	8	21	8	1	1

Each of the four members interviewed ten people of his choice. Each team member had a data sheet on which he recorded the opinions of the persons interviewed. This data was combined into the chart as shown below.

Piece number 3 received the most votes (21) as the most attractive design.

Fig. 16-11M. Data and survey information can be placed in the appendix for reference at the option of the reader.

Drawings and illustrations that are important to the development of the report should be included in the main portion of the report as numbered figures, with legends to describe them and to relate them to the text.

16-10 COMMON OMISSIONS

Elements that are often omitted from technical reports, but should be included, include cost estimates, overhead expenses, human and psychological factors, shipping costs, packing specifications, method of advertising, sales considerations, and summarizing recommendations. As you prepare your report, assume that you are the reader and that you are unfamiliar with the purpose of the report. Doing this will assist you in critically evaluating its contents and completeness.

16-11 PATENTS

A designer may feel that he has developed a design sufficiently novel and unique in some respects to be patentable. In such cases, he may wish to file for a patent (Fig. 16-12) with the U. S. Patent Office prior to disclosing his invention or design, since premature disclosure may forfeit patent rights. If the invention has been described in a printed publication anywhere in the world, or if it has been in public use or on sale in this country before the date on

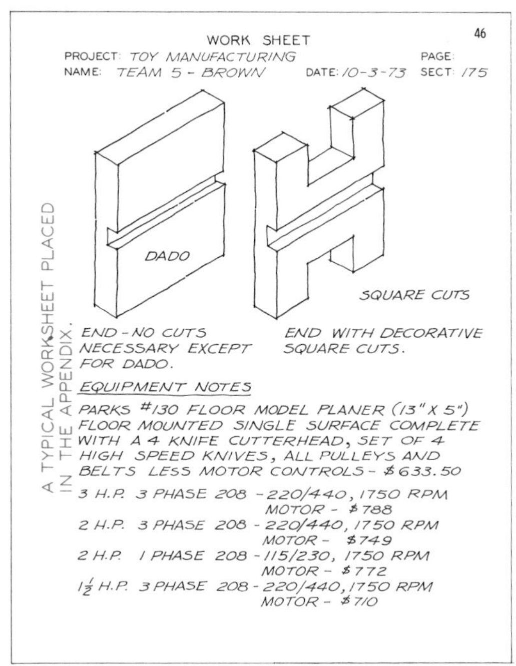

46
WORK SHEET
PROJECT: TOY MANUFACTURING
PAGE:
NAME: TEAM 5 - BROWN
DATE: 10-3-73
SECT: 175
DADO
SQUARE CUTS
END - NO CUTS NECESSARY EXCEPT FOR DADO.
END WITH DECORATIVE SQUARE CUTS.
EQUIPMENT NOTES
PARKS #130 FLOOR MODEL PLANER (13" X 5")
FLOOR MOUNTED SINGLE SURFACE COMPLETE
WITH A 4 KNIFE CUTTERHEAD, SET OF 4
HIGH SPEED KNIVES, ALL PULLEYS AND
BELTS LESS MOTOR CONTROLS - $633.50
3 H.P. 3 PHASE 208 - 220/440, 1750 RPM
MOTOR - $788
2 H.P. 3 PHASE 208 - 220/440, 1750 RPM
MOTOR - $749
2 H.P. 1 PHASE 208 - 115/230, 1750 RPM
MOTOR - $772
1½ H.P. 3 PHASE 208 - 220/440, 1750 RPM
MOTOR - $710
A TYPICAL WORKSHEET PLACED IN THE APPENDIX.

Fig. 16–11N. A typical worksheet, worthy of inclusion in the appendix, showing the preliminary ideas considered.

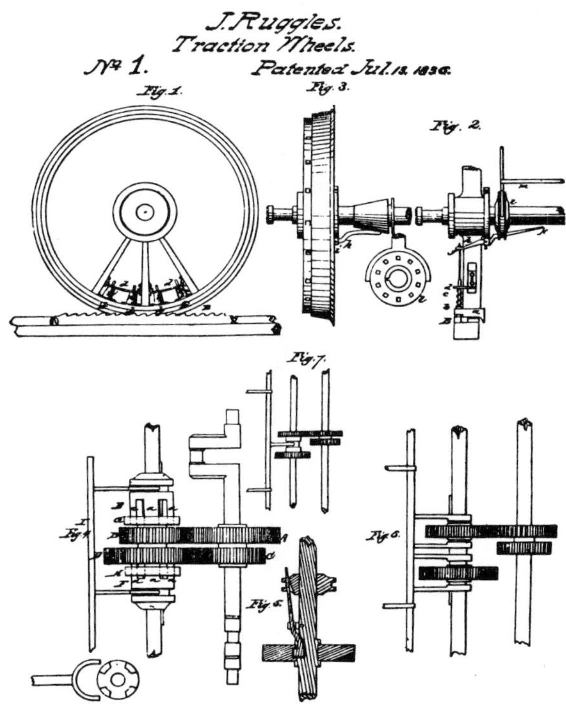

Fig. 16–12. The first patent, which was issued by the U.S. Patent Office in 1836.

which the applicant made his invention, a patent cannot be obtained. Likewise, to obtain a patent, an inventor must file for it within a year after his invention has been described in a printed publication or has been in public use or on sale. Failure to do so within this time limit will result in forfeiture of the right to a patent.

The designer who desires to investigate the patent possibilities of his design can gain valuable information as to the proper procedure by referring to publications available from the Government Printing Office, listed in Article 16–17. These publications provide information that will assist the designer in initiating his application for a patent. Patent attorneys can be of considerable help to the patent applicant to ensure that he receives full protection for his invention that might be lost through an unskillfully prepared application. Patent attorneys or patent agents must be registered by the Patent Office before they are permitted to represent an inventor before the Patent Office. They must be attorneys and/or holders of a college degree in engineering or science and must pass an examination to be admitted to represent cases before the Patent Office.

This portion of the chapter will give a general outline of the process required to apply for a patent. A helpful pamphlet (available free of charge from the Patent Office), *General Information Concerning Patents,* is suggested for more specific details of the patent procedure. (This publication was the primary reference for the information contained in these articles.)

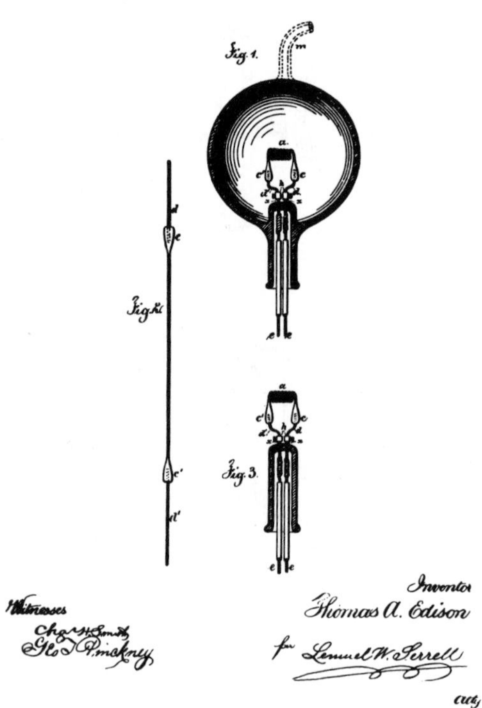

T. A. EDISON.
Electric-Lamp.
No. 223,898.
Patented Jan. 27, 1880.

Fig. 16–13. Thomas Edison's patent drawing for the electric lamp, 1880.

16–12 GENERAL PATENT REQUIREMENTS

The designer must have a general understanding of the patent requirements. He will need to understand what can be patented and who is eligible to apply for a patent. In some cases, it is difficult to ascertain whether or not a design is patentable within the intent of the patent laws.

What Can Be Patented. In the language of the patent law now in effect, any person who "invents or discovers any new and useful process, machine, manufacture, or composition of matter, or any new and useful improvement thereof, may obtain a patent," subject to the conditions and requirements of law. Essentially, these categories include everything made by man and the processes for making them (Fig. 16–13).

Court interpretations of this statute have excluded specific categories of inventions from the field of patentable items. For example, inventions used solely for the development of nuclear and atomic weapons for warfare are not patentable since these are not considered to be "useful." Another example, a design for a functional mechanism that will not operate in keeping with its intended purpose is not patentable. An *idea* for a new invention or machine is not patentable. The specific design and description of the machine must be available before it can be eligible for consideration as a patentable item.

Who Can Apply for a Patent. Only the inventor of a device may apply for a patent. A patent given to a person who was not the inventor would be void, and the person would be subject to prosecution for committing perjury. Application for a patent *can* be made by the executor of a deceased inventor's estate. Two or more persons may apply for a patent as joint inventors, but the person or firm making a financial contribution cannot be joined in the application as an inventor.

Patent Rights. A patent granted to an inventor gives him the right to exclude others from making, using, or selling the invention throughout the United States for a period of 17 years. After expiration of the 17-year patent term, the invention may be made, used, or sold by anyone without authorization from the holder of the patent. The term may not be extended except by special act of Congress.

Patented articles must be marked with the word "Patent" and the number of the patent.

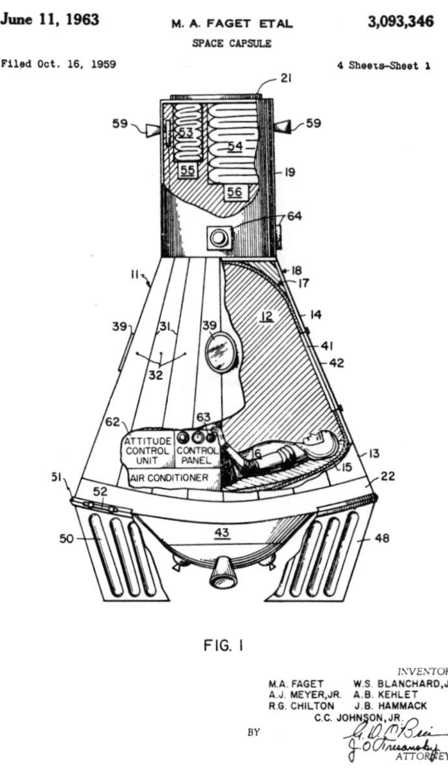

Fig. 16–14. The patent drawing of the space capsule developed by the National Aeronautics and Space Administration.

Failure to mark an item in this manner may forfeit rights to damages if a person infringes on an invention not properly marked and continues to infringe after the application of the proper marking. Markings using the terms "Patent Pending" have no legal effect, since protection does not begin until the actual grant is made.

16–13 APPLICATION FOR A PATENT

An inventor applying for a patent must include the following:

1) A written document which comprises a petition, a specification (description and claims), and an oath or declaration;
2) a drawing in those cases in which a drawing is possible; and
3) the filing fee.

The patent application will not be accepted for consideration unless it is complete and complies with the rules of the Patent Office. The greatest assistance a patent attorney offers is in making sure that these forms are prepared in an acceptable form.

Petition, Oath, or Declaration. The petition and oath are usually combined in one form; on this form, the inventor petitions or requests that he be given a patent on his invention. The oath or declaration is a statement declaring that the inventor believes himself to be the original and first inventor of the invention described in his application. This statement is presented in a form suggested by the Patent Office and sworn to before a notary public.

Specification of the Patent. The specifications or description of a patent must be attached to the application in written form describing the invention in full detail so that a person skilled in the field to which the invention pertains can produce the item. These descriptions should specifically point out features that distinguish the invention from similar patents. Drawings should be referred to in the text by figure and part numbers (Figs. 16–14 through 16–17).

The following format is suggested for the specifications:

a) Title of the invention, or a preamble stating the name, citizenship, and residence of the applicant and the title of the invention.
b) Brief summary of the invention.

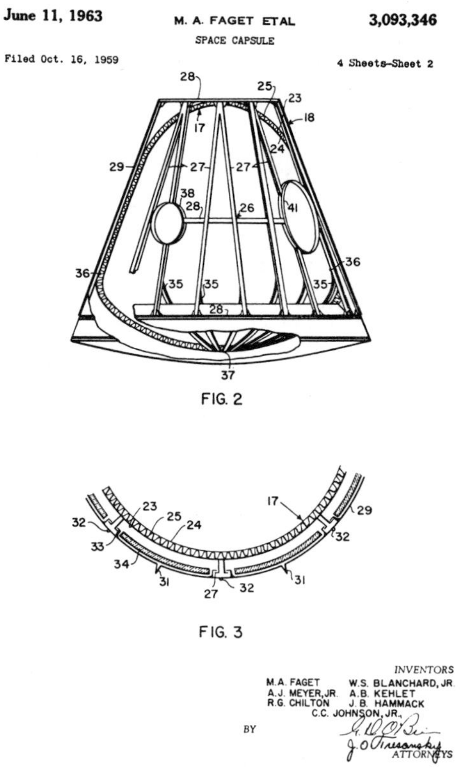

Fig. 16–15. Structural details of the space capsule.

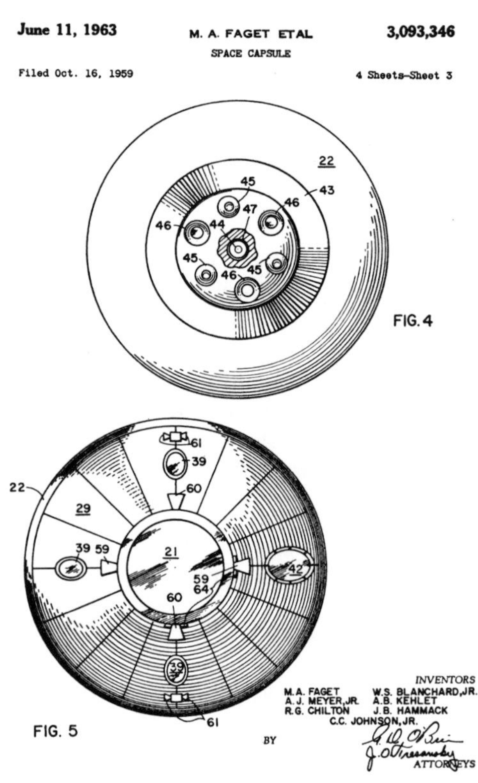

Fig. 16–16. The top and bottom views of the space capsule.

c) If there are drawings, a brief description of the several views given.
d) Detailed description.
e) Claims.

Claims are brief descriptions of the details of the invention that distinguish new features from features of already patented material. The claims are the most significant parts of the patent, since they will be used as the basis to ascertain the novelty and patentability of an invention. A single invention may incorporate a number of features that will be stated as separate claims in the specification. Descriptions of a design should be clear and concise, consistently using proper technical terminology.

Fee. The application for a patent must be accompanied by the filing fee. The basic filing fee is $65.00. An additional charge of $2.00 per claim is made for each claim in excess of ten on any one application. After the application has been accepted, a notice will be sent to the

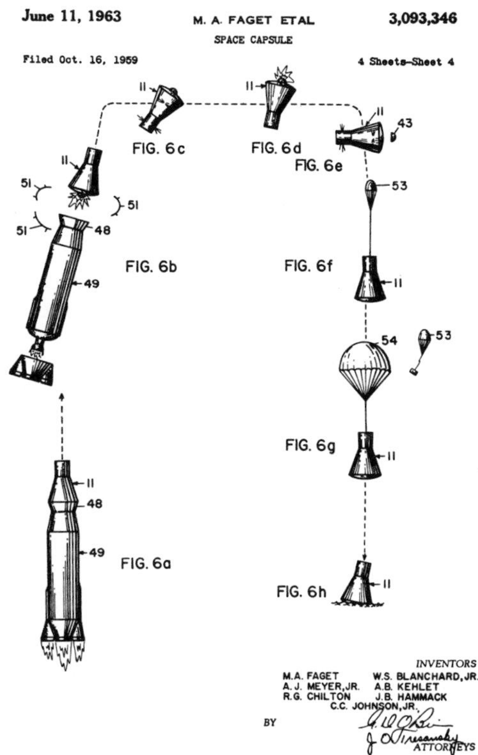

Fig. 16-17. The sequence of events involving the space capsule from launch to landing.

applicant giving him three months from that date to remit an issue fee of $100.00. An additional fee of $10.00 is charged for each page of the specification printed, and $2.00 for each sheet of drawing.

16-14 THE PREPARATION OF PATENT DRAWINGS

When drawings are necessary to describe an invention, the applicant for a patent must submit these drawings with the application. In some cases it may be desirable to prepare flow diagrams, schematics, and similar diagrams. Due to the many thousands of patents that are processed by the Patent Office, it is imperative that all drawings conform to established standards and rules. Drawings not prepared in keeping with these directives are not acceptable.

A booklet, *Guide for Patent Draftsmen,* is available from the U. S. Government Printing Office for 20¢. It outlines the procedures for the preparation of patent drawings. Most of the rules and illustrations included in this booklet are presented in the following articles. In general, most rules are similar to conventional engineering drawing practices. Specific rules concerning sheet size, spacing, and notation are of special importance, since even a well-prepared drawing will be rejected unless the format rules are observed. If the inventor cannot furnish his own drawings, the Patent Office will refer him to a draftsman who can prepare his drawings. This service will be at the expense of the inventor.

16-15 PATENT DRAWING STANDARDS

When the patent is issued, the completed drawing is printed and published. Drawing sheets are reduced about one-third in size; this requires that the original drawings be prepared uniformly to 150%. The quality of the drawings should be excellent. The following rules must be followed as closely as possible to prevent rejection of the application. The example patent drawings reproduced in this portion of the text illustrate the rules.

Paper and Ink. Drawings must be made on pure white paper of thickness corresponding to a two-ply or three-ply Bristol board. The surface must be calendered and smooth to permit erasure and correction. Only India ink will secure perfectly black solid lines. The use of white pigment to cover lines is not acceptable.

Sheet Size and Margins. The sheet size must be exactly $10'' \times 15''$. A margin is drawn exactly $1''$ from each edge to give a working space of $8'' \times 13''$. All work must appear within

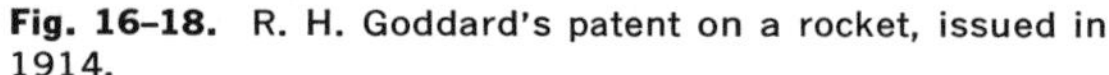

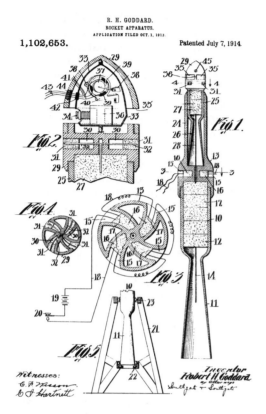

Fig. 16–18. R. H. Goddard's patent on a rocket, issued in 1914.

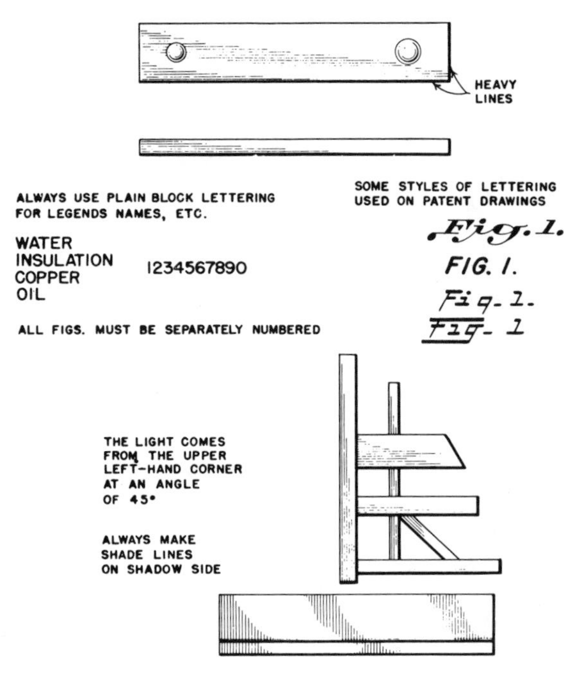

Fig. 16–19. Typical examples of lines and lettering recommended for patent drawings.

these margins. One of the shorter sides of the sheet is regarded as its top. A space of not less than $1\frac{1}{4}''$ is to be measured from the upper margin and left blank for the heading that will be applied by the Patent Office. An example of a heading can be seen in Fig. (16–18).

Character of Lines. All lines and lettering must be absolutely black regardless of how fine the lines may be. All lines should be drawn with instruments. Freehand work should be avoided. Lines should not be crowded.

Hatching and Shading. Hatching lines, used to shade the surface of an object, should be parallel lines not less than about $\frac{1}{20}''$ apart (Fig. 16–20). Heavy lines are used on the shade side of the drawing; however, they should not be used if they are likely to confuse the drawing. The light is assumed to come from the upper left-hand corner at an angle of 45°. Examples of this form of shading are shown in Fig. 16–19. Types of surface delineation are given in Figs. 16–21 and 16–22. Note the method of indicating the bevel in the top view of the object shown in Fig. 16–22. A heavy line is used at the intersection of the horizontal plane and the inclined bevel. The outer line is drawn lightly to simulate the effect of the beveled plane.

Scale. The scale should be large enough to show the mechanism without crowding when the drawing is reduced for reproduction. Certain portions of the mechanism may be drawn

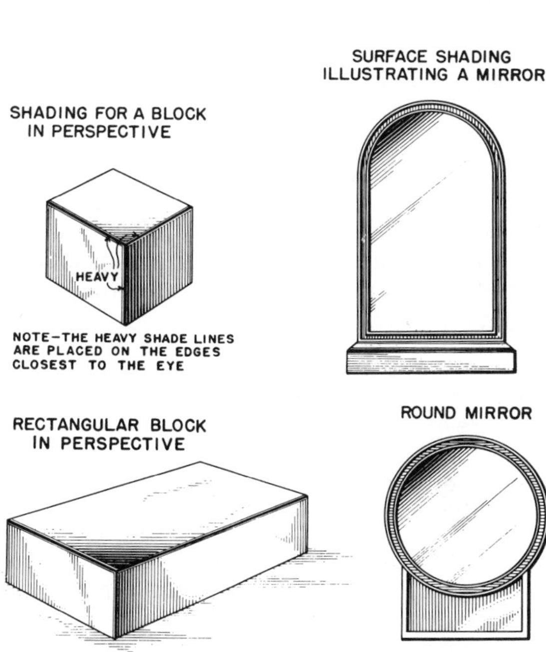

Fig. 16-20. Techniques of shading patent drawings.

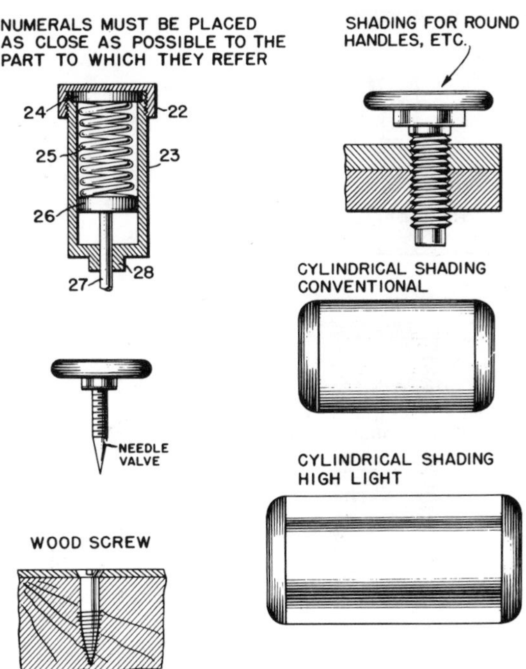

Fig. 16-21. Methods of numbering parts and rendering details for patent drawings.

at a larger scale to show additional details. Additional patent drawings can be used if necessary, but not more should be used than is necessary.

Reference Characters. The different views of a mechanism should be identified by consecutive figure numbers, using plain, legible, and carefully prepared numerals. They should be at least $\frac{1}{8}''$ in height, not encircled, and placed close to the parts to which they apply without confusing the drawing, as shown in Fig. 16-21. A leader is used to indicate the parts to which they refer. Numbers should not be placed on hatched surfaces unless a blank space is provided for them. The same part appearing in more than one view of the drawing should be

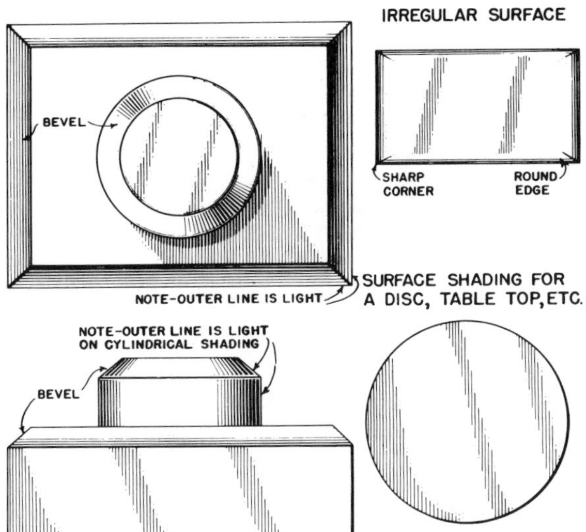

Fig. 16-22. Techniques of representing surfaces and beveled planes on patent drawings.

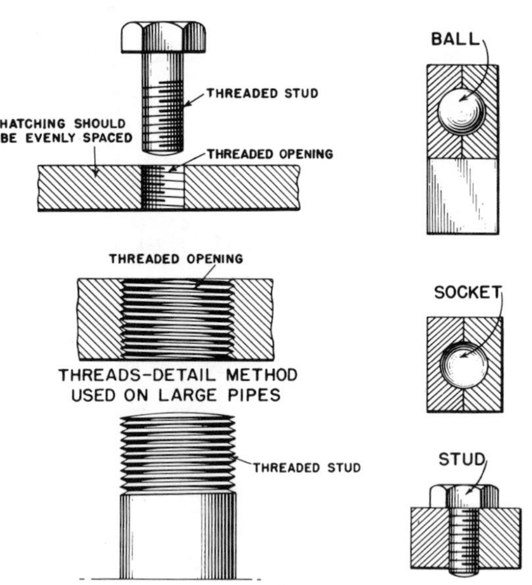

Fig. 16-23. Techniques of representing threads and small components on patent drawings.

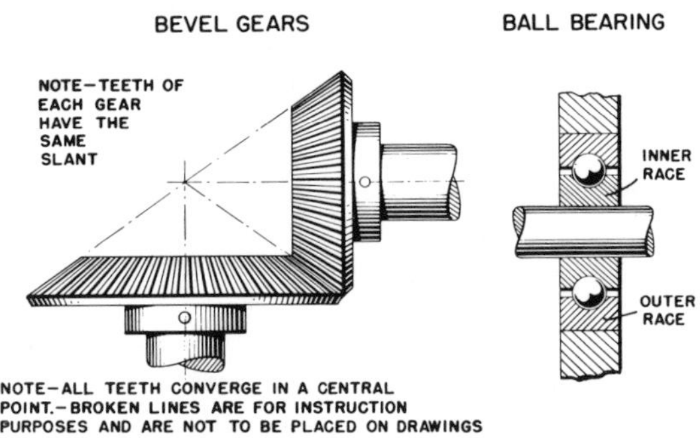

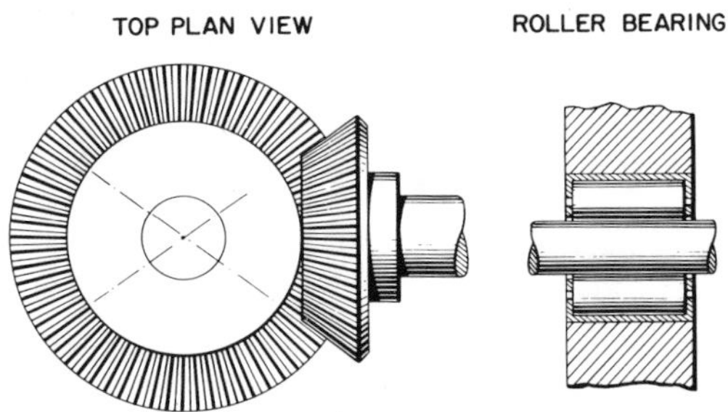

Fig. 16-24. Representation of gears and ball bearings on patent drawings.

designated by the same character, and this character should never be used to designate other parts.

Symbols. Symbols used to represent various materials in sections, electrical components, and mechanical devices are suggested by the Patent Office, but these conform to the usual conventional engineering drawing standards covered in Chapters 5 and 19. All symbols used must be adequately identified in the specifications. Legends may be used on the drawing to explain the symbols used.

Signature and Names. The signature of the applicant or the name of the applicant and the signature of the attorney or agent may be placed in the lower right-hand corner of each sheet within the marginal lines or below the lower marginal lines.

Views. The patent drawing should contain as many figures as are necessary to explain an invention. If possible, the figures should be numbered consecutively in order of their appearance. Figures may be plan, elevation, section, perspective, or detail views. Examples of views used to illustrate patent drawings are shown in Figs. 16-23 and 16-24. Shading is used to show the shape of the components and the details of each part. Exploded views such as those of the Colt Revolving Gun (Fig. 16-25) can be used to advantage to describe the assembly of a number of parts. Large parts may be broken into sections and drawn on several sheets if this approach does not confuse the matter. Removed sections can be used, provided that the cutting plane is labeled to indicate the section by number. Views should not be connected by projection lines. All sheet headings and signatures will be placed in the same position on the sheet whether the drawing is arranged to read from the bottom of the sheet or from the right side of the sheet. It is desirable that the drawing be positioned so that it can be read when the sheet is held in upright; however, in some cases this may not be practical.

No extraneous matter, such as an agent's or attorney's stamp or address, is permitted to

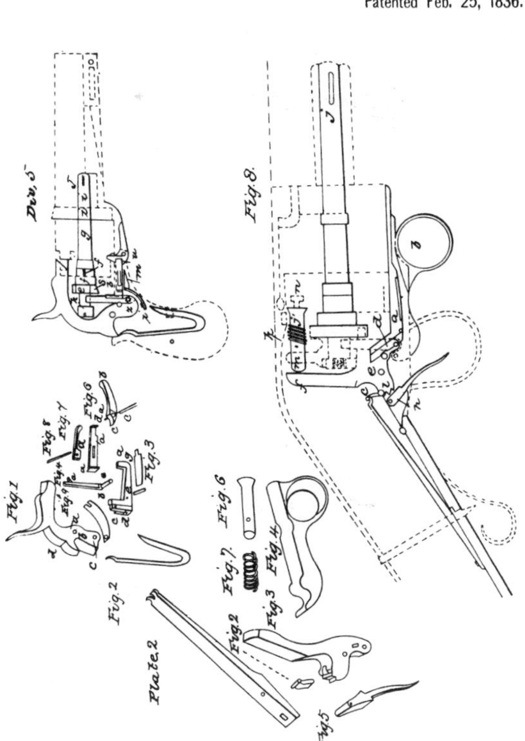

Fig. 16-25. An assembly of parts used to describe the workings of a patent.

appear on the face of the drawing. The completed drawings should be sent flat, protected by heavy board or rolled in a suitable mailing tube. Folded or mutilated drawings must be redrawn. Drawings used for an accepted patent will not be returned to the applicant, but will remain on permanent record.

16-16 PATENT SEARCHES

A patent is not always granted when an application has been filed. A patent can be granted only after the Patent Office examiners have searched existing patents to determine whether the invention has been previously patented. With over 3,000,000 patents on record, a patent search is the most time-consuming portion of the process of obtaining a patent. Many inventors employ patent attorneys or agents to conduct a preliminary search of existing patents to discover whether an invention infringes on another. These preliminary searches serve to establish whether or not a patent application has a chance of success; however, the Patent Office Examiner may find prior patents covering the same invention that were not found during the preliminary search.

Patents are filed in the Search Room of the Patent Office by classes and subclasses according to subject matter. The searcher will review the subclass that covers patents in the field of the application he is working on. However, other seemingly unrelated patents may cover the invention being submitted, thereby disallowing the patent.

16-17 PATENT OFFICE PUBLICATIONS

The Patent Office publications available to the general public are listed below. They are available from the Superintendent of Documents, Government Printing Office, Washington, D. C., 20402. These publications will answer the majority of questions concerning the procedure for obtaining a patent. A brief description of each publication is given to explain the contents of each.*

Patents (50¢ each). The specifications and accompanying drawings of all patents are published on the day they are granted, and printed copies are sold to the public by the Patent Office. Over 3,000,000 patents have been issued. The drawing and specifications of a typical patent available from the Patent Office are shown in Figs. 16-26 and 16-27.

Official Gazette of the United States Patent Office ($50.00 per year). The *Official Gazette* is the official journal relating to patents and trademarks. It has been published weekly since 1872, and is now issued each Tuesday, simul-

---

* These descriptions are from *General Information Concerning Patents.* Washington D.C.: U. S. Department of Commerce, 1966.

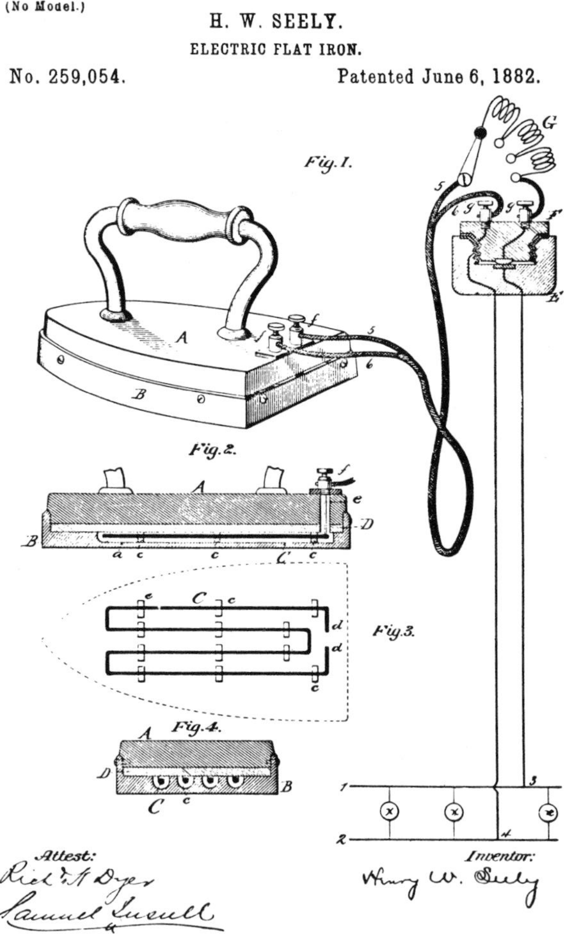

Fig. 16-26. The complete patent drawing for the electric iron.

taneously with the weekly issue of the patents. It contains a claim and a selected figure of the drawings of each patent granted on that day; decisions in patent and trademark cases rendered by the Courts and the Patent Office; notice of patent and trademark suits, indexes of patents and patentees, lists of patents available for license or sale, and other general information.

Index of Patents (price varies): This annual index to the *Official Gazette* contains an alphabetical index of the names of patentees and a list identifying the subject matter of the patents granted during the calendar year.

Decisions of the Commissioner of Patents (price varies): An annually published volume republishing the decisions which have been published weekly in the *Official Gazette.*

Manual of Classification ($8.50): This is a looseleaf book containing a list of all the classes and subclasses of inventions in the Patent Office classification of patents, a subject matter index, and other information relating to classification.

Classification Bulletins: The various changes in classification made from time to time are collected and published in bulletins which give definitions of the new and revised classes and subclasses.

Patent Laws (35¢ each): A compilation of the patent laws in force; revised editions are published from time to time.

Rules of Practice of the United States Patent Office in Patent Cases (50¢ each): This publication contains the rules governing patent procedures which have been adopted by the Commissioner under the authority of the patent statutes and approved by the Secretary of Commerce, and supplementary materials including forms and relevant sections of the patent law.

General Information Concerning Patents (free): This pamphlet is designed for the layman and contains general information (expressed in nontechnical language) concerning the granting of patents.

Patents and Inventions, an Information Aid for Inventors (15¢): The purpose of this pamphlet is to help inventors in deciding whether to apply for patents, in obtaining patent protection, and in promoting their inventions.

UNITED STATES PATENT OFFICE.

HENRY W. SEELY, OF NEW YORK, N. Y., ASSIGNOR OF TWO-THIRDS TO RICHARD N. DYER AND SAMUEL INSULL, OF SAME PLACE.

ELECTRIC FLAT-IRON.

SPECIFICATION forming part of Letters Patent No. 259,054, dated June 6, 1882.

Application filed December 8, 1881. (No model.)

To all whom it may concern:

Be it known that I, HENRY W. SEELY, a citizen of the United States, residing at New York, in the county and State of New York, have invented a new and useful Electric Flat-Iron, of which the following is a specification.

The object of my invention is to utilize electric currents derived from any suitable source of electric energy for the purpose of heating flat-irons, fluting-irons, and other similar utensils. To accomplish this object I place within the iron and close to its face a resistance, preferably of carbon, and of such size and shape that it will heat the face of the iron sufficiently and equally. This resistance has terminals, by means of which it may be connected in an electric circuit, preferably a multiple-arc circuit of an electric lighting system.

In the accompanying drawings, Figure 1 is a perspective view of a flat-iron connected with a multiple-arc system of electric lighting; Fig. 2, a vertical longitudinal section of the iron; Fig. 3, a plan view of the heating-resistance, and Fig. 4 a transverse vertical section of the iron.

Similar letters of reference refer to corresponding parts in all these figures.

The base of the flat-iron is made in two parts, A B, the upper part, A, fitting into the lower one, B. In the interior of B is formed a groove, *a*, whose shape corresponds to that of the carbon resistance C, which is laid in the groove. This resistance is preferably molded or formed as one continuous piece of carbon, though, instead of this, a number of carbon sticks could be laid parallel in grooves connected together by wires electroplated to their ends. To prevent contact between the carbon and the metal below and around it, it is laid in supporting-saddles *c c*, of some suitable non-conducting and non-combustible material.

Above the resistance is placed a layer, D, of an insulating substance, which is also both non-combustible and a poor conductor of heat. This substance is preferably one which can be put in its place while in a soft or plastic condition and then allowed to harden—as, for instance, plaster-of-paris. Before pouring in such substance the grooves and resistance should be covered with a sheet of paper or similar material, in order that the plastic substance may not penetrate between the carbon and the iron, and thus impair the conduction of heat between them. The upper part, A, of the iron is set directly upon the top of the insulating substance D, and is secured to the lower part by rivets, or in any other suitable manner.

If desired, a packing of felt or other substance which is a non-conductor of heat may be placed in the joint between A and B, so that all the heat will be retained in the lower part of the iron.

The ends *d d* of the resistance C are electroplated or otherwise attached to wires which pass up through an aperture, *e*, (being insulated from the iron where they pass through it,) to binding-posts *f f*, attached to a plate of insulating material fastened to the top of the base. By means of these binding-posts connection is made with the wires from any suitable source of electricity.

In Fig. 1 the flat-iron is shown in connection with a multiple-arc system of electric lighting. 1 2 are floor-mains of the system in derived circuits, from which are placed incandescent electric lamps, (represented at *x x*.) 3 4 is a multiple-arc circuit leading to the interior terminals of an ordinary lamp-socket, E. From this the lamp has been removed, and instead a plug, F, having exterior terminals corresponding to the socket-terminals, is placed in the socket. The plug-terminals are connected to binding-posts *g g*, from which flexible conducting-wires 5 6, of sufficient length to allow the iron to be moved back and forth, lead to the binding-posts *f f*.

An adjustable resistance, G, may, if desired, be placed in the circuit between the socket and the iron, in order that the heat of the latter may be properly regulated.

A safety-catch should be provided, preferably located within the plug F, to protect the system in case of a short circuit occurring.

It is evident that my invention could be applied to fluting-irons in which a curved corrugated iron bears on a corrugated base by placing a heating-resistance in the base, or in both the base and the moving iron.

2 259,054

What I claim is—

1. The combination, with a flat-iron or similar utensil, of an electrical resistance located within the same, the face of said iron being heated by radiation from said resistance, substantially as set forth.

2. A chambered flat-iron or similar utensil, in combination with an electrical resistance inclosed entirely thereby, whereby all the heat radiated from such resistance will be utilized, substantially as set forth.

3. A chambered flat-iron or similar utensil, in combination with an electrical resistance inclosed thereby, and a layer of non-heat-conducting material to confine the heat to the face of the iron, substantially as set forth.

This specification signed and witnessed this 6th day of December, 1881.

HENRY W. SEELY.

Witnesses:

RICHD. N. DYER,
SAMUEL INSULL.

Fig. 16 27. The complete patent specifications for the electric iron. Copies of patents are available from the Patent Office.

Roster of Attorneys and Agents Registered to Practice Before the United States Patent Office (70¢ each): This is an alphabetical list of registered attorneys and agents.

Manual of Patent Examining Procedure ($4.00 each): This manual is written for examiners in the Patent Office and gives in great detail the procedures followed by the examiners.

Guide for Patent Draftsmen (15¢ each): A statement of Office requirements for patent drawings. It includes sample illustrations.

How to Obtain Information from United States Patents (20¢ each): This pamphlet contains helpful information on how to best utilize the facilities and publications of the United States Patent Office. It gives the inventor instructions on such subjects as patent search, use of the *Official Gazette,* and obtaining information from Patent Copy Libraries.

16–18 QUESTIONS AND ANSWERS ABOUT PATENTS

This brief review of the general procedures required to obtain a patent is no more than a basic introduction. For best results, patent applications must be handled with the assistance of a qualified patent attorney or patent agent. However, some knowledge of general patent rules are of advantage to anybody who might at some time develop a patentable idea.

As a further help to the potential inventor, the Patent Office has published a pamphlet, *Questions and Answers About Patents.* Most of these questions and answers are listed here to supplement the previous articles on patents.

Nature and Duration of Patents

1. Q. *What is a patent?*
   A. A patent is a grant issued by the U. S. Government giving an inventor the right to exclude all others from making, using, or selling his invention within the United States, its territories and possessions.
2. Q. *For how long a term of years is a patent granted?*
   A. Seventeen years from the date on which it is issued; except for patents on ornamental designs, which are granted for terms of $3\frac{1}{2}$, 7, or 14 years.
3. Q. *May the term of a patent be extended?*
   A. Only by special act of Congress, and this occurs very rarely and only in most exceptional circumstances.
4. Q. *Does the patentee continue to have any control over the use of the invention after his patent expires?*
   A. No. Anyone has the free right to use an invention covered in an expired patent, so long as he does not use features covered in other unexpired patents in doing so.
5. Q. *On what subject matter may a patent be granted?*
   A. A patent may be granted to the inventor or discoverer of any new and useful process, machine, manufacture, or composition of matter, or any new and useful improvement thereof, or on any distinct and new variety of plant, other than a tuber-propagated plant, which is asexually reproduced, or on any new, original, and ornamental design for an article of manufacture.
6. Q. *On what subject matter may a patent not be granted?*
   A. A patent may not be granted on a useless device, on printed matter, on a method of doing business, on an improvement in a device which would be obvious to a person skilled in the art, or on a machine which will not operate, particularly on an alleged perpetual motion machine.

Meaning of Words "Patent Pending"

7. Q. *What do the terms "patent pending" and "patent applied for" mean?*
   A. They are used by a manufacturer or seller of an article to inform the public that an application for patent on that article is on file in the Patent Office. The law imposes a fine on those who use these terms falsely to deceive the public.

Patent Applications

8. Q. *I have made some changes and improvements in my invention after my patent application was filed in the Patent Office. May I amend my patent application by adding a description or illustration of these features?*
A. No. The law specifically provides that new matter shall not be introduced into the disclosure of a patent application. However, you should call the attention of your attorney or patent agent promptly to any such changes you may make or plan to make, so that he may take or recommend any steps that may be necessary for your protection.

9. Q. *How does one apply for a patent?*
A. By making the proper application to the Commissioner of Patents, Washington, D. C., 20231.

10. Q. *What is the best way to prepare an application?*
A. As the preparation and prosecution of an application are highly complex proceedings, they should preferably be conducted by an attorney trained in this specialized practice. The Patent Office therefore advises inventors to employ a patent attorney or agent who is registered in the Patent Office.

11. Q. *Of what does a patent application consist?*
A. An application fee, a petition, a specification, and claims describing and defining the invention, an oath or declaration, and a drawing if the invention can be illustrated.

12. Q. *What are the Patent Office fees in connection with filing of an application for patent and issuance of the patent?*
A. A filing fee of $65 plus certain additional charges for claims, depending on their number and the manner of their presentation, are required when the application is filed. A final or issue fee of $100 plus certain printing charges are also required if the patent is to be granted. The final fee is not required until your application is allowed by the Patent Office.

13. Q. *Are models required as a part of the application?*
A. Only in the most exceptional cases. The Patent Office has the power to require that a model be furnished, but rarely exercises it.

14. Q. *Is it necessary to go to the Patent Office in Washington to transact business concerning patent matters?*
A. No; most business with the Patent Office is conducted by correspondence. Interviews regarding pending applications can be arranged with examiners if necessary, however, and are often helpful.

15. Q. *Can the Patent Office give advice as to whether an inventor should apply for a patent?*
A. No. It can only consider the patentability of an invention when this question comes regularly before it in the form of a patent application.

16. Q. *Is there any danger that the Patent Office will give others information contained in my application while it is pending?*
A. No. All patent applications are maintained in the strictest secrecy until the patent is issued. After the patent is issued, however, the Patent Office file containing the application and all correspondence leading up to issuance of the patent is made available in the Patent Office Search Room for inspection by anyone, and copies of these files may be purchased from the Patent Office.

17. Q. *May I write to the Patent Office directly about my application after it is filed?*
A. The Patent Office will answer an applicant's inquiries as to the status of the application and inform him whether his application has been rejected, allowed, or is awaiting action by the Patent Office. However, if you have a patent attorney or agent the Patent Office cannot correspond with both you and the attorney concerning the merits of your application. All comments concerning your invention should be forwarded through your patent attorney or agent.

18. Q. *What happens when two inventors apply separately for a patent on the same invention?*
A. An "interference" is declared and testimony may be submitted to the Patent Office to determine which inventor is entitled to the patent. Your attorney or agent can give you further information about this if it becomes necessary.

19. Q. *Can the six-month period allowed by the Patent Office for response to an office action in a pending application be extended?*
A. No. This time is fixed by law and cannot be extended by the Patent Office, but it may be reduced to not less than thirty days. The application will be abandoned unless proper response is received in the Patent Office within the time allowed.

20. Q. *May applications be examined out of their regular order?*
A. No; all applications are examined in the order in which they are filed, except under certain very special conditions.

When to Apply for Patent

21. Q. *I have been making and selling my invention for the past 13 months and have not filed any patent application. Is it too late for me to apply for patent?*
A. Yes. A valid patent may not be obtained if the invention was in public use or on sale in this country for more than one year prior to the filing of your patent application. Your own use and sale of the invention for more than a year before your application is filed will bar your right to a patent just as effectively as though this use and sale had been done by someone else.

22. Q. *I published an article describing my invention in a magazine 13 months ago. Is it too late to apply for a patent?*
A. Yes. The fact that you are the author of the article will not save your patent application. The law provides that the inventor is not entitled to a patent if the invention has been described in a printed publication anywhere in the world more than a year before his patent application is filed.

Who May Obtain a Patent

23. Q. *Is there any restriction as to persons who may obtain a United States patent?*
A. No. Any inventor may obtain a patent regardless of age or sex, by complying with the provisions of the law. A foreign citizen may obtain a patent under exactly the same conditions as a United States citizen.

24. Q. *If two or more persons work together to make an invention, to whom will the patent be granted?*
A. If each had a share in the ideas forming the invention, they are joint inventors and a patent will be issued to them jointly on the basis of a proper patent application filed by them jointly. If, on the other hand, one of these persons has provided all of the ideas of the invention, and the other has only followed instructions in making it, the person who contributed the ideas is the sole inventor and the patent application and patent should be in his name only.

25. Q. *If one person furnishes all of the ideas to make an invention and another employs him or furnishes the money for building and testing the invention, should the patent application be filed by them jointly?*
A. No. The application must be signed, executed, sworn to, and filed in the Patent Office in the name of the inventor. This is the person who furnishes the ideas, not the employer or the person who furnishes the money.

26. Q. *May a patent be granted if an inventor dies before filing his application?*
A. Yes; the application may be filed by the inventor's executor or administrator.

27. Q. *While in England this summer, I found an article on sale which was very ingenious and has not been introduced into the United States or patented or described. May I obtain a United States patent on this invention?*
A. No. A United States patent may be obtained only by the true inventor, not by someone who learns of an invention of another.

Ownership and Sale of Patent Rights

28. Q. *May the inventor sell or otherwise transfer his right to his patent or patent application to someone else?*
A. Yes. He may sell all or any part of his interest in the patent application or patent to anyone by a properly worded assignment. The application must be filed in the Patent Office as the invention of the true inventor, however, and not as the invention of the person who has purchased the invention from him.

29. Q. *Is it advisable to conduct a search of patents and other records before applying for a patent?*
A. Yes; if it is found that the device is shown in some prior patent it is useless to make application. By making a search beforehand the expense involved in filing a needless application is often saved.

Patent Searching

30. Q. *Where can a search be conducted?*
A. In the Search Room of the Patent Office in the Department of Commerce Building at 14th and E Street, Northwest, Washington, D.C. Classified and numerically arranged sets of United States and foreign patents are kept there for public use.

31. Q. *Will the Patent Office make searches for individuals to help them decide whether to file patent applications?*
A. No. But it will assist inventors who come to Washington by helping them to find the proper patent classes in which to make their searches. For a reasonable fee it will furnish lists of patents in any class and subclass, and copies of these patents may be purchased for 50 cents each.

Technical Knowledge Available from Patents

32. Q. *I have not made an invention but have encountered a problem. Can I obtain knowledge through patents of what has been done by others to solve the problem?*
A. The patents of the Patent Office Search Room in Washington contain a vast wealth of technical information and suggestions, organized in a manner which will enable you to review those most closely related to your field of interest. You may come to Washington and review these patents, or engage a patent practitioner to do this for you and to send you copies of the patents most closely related to your problem.

33. Q. *Can I make a search or obtain technical information from patents at locations other than the Patent Office Search Room in Washington?*
A. Yes. Libraries have sets of patent copies numerically arranged in bound volumes, and these patents may be used for search or other information purposes as discussed in the answer to Question 34.

34. Q. *How can technical information be found in a library collection of patents arranged in bound volumes in numerical order?*
A. You must first find out from the *Manual of Classification* in the library the Patent Office classes and subclasses which cover the field of your invention or interest. You can then, by referring to microfilm reels or volumes of the Index of Patents in the library, identify the patents in these subclasses and, thence, look at them in the bound volumes. Further information on this subject may be found in the leaflet *Obtaining Information from Patents,* a copy of which may be requested from the Patent Office.

Infringement of Others' Patents

35. Q. *If I obtain a patent on my invention will that protect me against the claims of others who assert that I am infringing their patents when I make, use, or sell my own invention?*
A. No. There may be a patent of a more basic nature on which your invention is an improvement. If your invention is a detailed refinement or feature of such a basically protected invention, you may not use it without the consent of the patentee, just as

no one will have the right to use your patented improvement without your consent. You should seek competent legal advice before starting to make or sell or use your invention commercially, even though it is protected by a patent granted to you.

Enforcement of Patent Rights

36. Q. *Will the Patent Office help me to prosecute others if they infringe the rights granted to me by my patent?*
A. No. The Patent Office has no jurisdiction over questions relating to the infringement of patent rights. If your patent is infringed, you may sue the infringer in the appropriate United States court at your own expense.

Patent Protection in Foreign Countries

37. Q. *Does a United States patent give protection in foreign countries?*
A. No. The United States patent protects your invention only in this country. If you wish to protect your invention in foreign countries, you must file an application in the Patent Office of each such country within the time permitted by law. This may be quite expensive, both because of the cost of filing and processing the individual patent applications, and because of the fact that most foreign countries require payment of taxes to maintain the patents in force. You should inquire of your attorney about these costs before you decide to file in foreign countries.

How to Obtain Further Information

38. Q. *How does one obtain information as to patent applications, fees, and other details concerning patents?*
A. By ordering a pamphlet entitled *General Information Concerning Patents.*

39. Q. *How can I obtain information about the steps I should take in deciding whether to try to obtain a patent, in securing the best possible patent protection, and in developing and marketing my invention successfully?*
A. By ordering a pamphlet entitled *Patents and Inventions, An Information Aid for Inventors.*

16–19 SUMMARY

Communication is a primary responsibility of the engineer or a designer who is presenting a new, original concept. It is relatively easy to describe an object and its details when it is well known to the audience. On the other hand, it is difficult to explain simplest household appliance when one has never before seen the design. Failure to communicate effectively is a handicap that may well lead to the rejection of a superior design.

The two basic types of communication introduced in this chapter were (1) presentation for decision and (2) presentation for implementation. The decision presentation must precede the implementation of a design. When the design is relatively simple and will not be mass-produced on a large scale, the designer may have the responsibility for making the final decision without assistance from others. More usually, however, he will work as a member of a team who communicate with one another throughout the design development. The final decision may lie with other members of the organization who will form their opinion on the basis of the presentation given by the designer or design team. The procedure for organizing the presentation for a group is very similar to that followed when the decision is made by one person. The main difference lies in the preparation of the visual aids that will be used in communicating the ideas.

The engineering report is a very necessary instrument which compiles the results and findings of a research project. In general, engineers are not noted for their writing ability. As a result, they have often encountered unjustified criticism and have failed to accomplish their goals. The types of technical reports are: (1) the proposal, (2) progress report, and (3) the final report. Each of these reports is necessary for the acceptance of a design solution and, in general, for the efficient operation of an engineering organization.

Communication should not be taken for granted—nor should it be oversimplified. Experienced engineers feel that this matter of communication is the most critical problem that the engineering profession faces. Consequently, every effort should be made to achieve the best communication possible.

PROBLEMS

Decision

1. Using the work-sheet method (Fig. 16–1) of evaluating the alternatives of a given situation, arrive at a decision on the following situations. List advantages and disadvantages of each and state your final conclusions. All work should be neatly lettered to facilitate easy reading and review of your ideas. Decide which of the following would be most appropriate for you: the purchase of a car versus a motor scooter; living in an on-campus dormitory versus living off-campus in a private apartment; the merits of pursuing a Master's degree versus working with a Bachelor's degree; the value of an engineering education versus a degree in another field of your interest; the use of an air-cooled automobile engine versus a water-cooled engine. Select a similar set of alternatives for comparison. Submit it to your instructor for approval.

2. Apply the work-sheet evaluation method to a problem that you have developed to decide which solution is most worthy of further development or implementation.

Technical Reports

3. Explain and give examples why it is important for a designer or engineer to develop the ability to communicate ideas to himself and to a group. Do not use more than one typewritten page for your answer.

4. Write a proposal for a design project that you would like to undertake as a class project. Develop your time table to correspond to the time schedule assigned by your instructor. Clarify the significance of this problem and its value if satisfactorily solved. Determine the budget requirements, with your time being the major item of expense. This cost can be estimated by assessing the value of your efforts in comparison to the current pay scale for practicing engineers and technicians in your field. Submit this proposal in a binder to your instructor who will approve or reject your proposal.

5. Submit progress reports on projects being developed at intervals as specified by your instructor. These should be in the form of a memorandum or letter. Include a schematic in the form of PERT to indicate the status of your project.

6. Prepare a technical report to help you better understand your field of study. Follow the format and organization outlined in Articles 16–8 and 16–9. Outline the objectives of your report and review the method you intend to employ in researching the field to arrive at its total evaluation. Charts, graphs, and schematics should be used to present data and statistical figures that are difficult to explain verbally. It is preferable that the report be typed and submitted to your instructor in a binder. Reference should be made to the library, personal acquaintances, periodicals, and interviews with practitioners in the field.

7. Prepare a final report to explain your activities on a design project that you have been assigned as a class project. Present your total activities in the report, including the completed drawings. Include your preliminary sketches and other data of significance in the appendix along with your planning schedule and PERT forms to indicate your planning for the project.

Patents

8. Write for a copy of a patent that would be of interest to you. Make a list of the features that were used as a basis for obtaining the patent.

9. Suggest modifications that could be used to modify the patent mentioned in the previous problem. Make sketches of innovations that would be possible improvements of the patented mechanism.

10. Write the U. S. Patent Office for patent application forms. Prepare a patent application for a simple invention that has been previously patented, such as a fountain pen, drafting instrument, or similar item. Determine what drawings and materials are needed to complete your application.

11. Prepare patent drawings in accordance with the standards established in Article 16–15 to depict a simple patented object, such as those mentioned in Problem 10. Strive for a finished technique that would make your drawing acceptable as a patent drawing.

12. Make a list of ideas that you believe to be patentable. These may be ideas that you have developed during work on design problems assigned in class.

13. Write a technical report investigating the history and significance of the patent system and its role in our industrial society. Consult your library and available government publications on patents. Give information and data that will improve your understanding of patents.

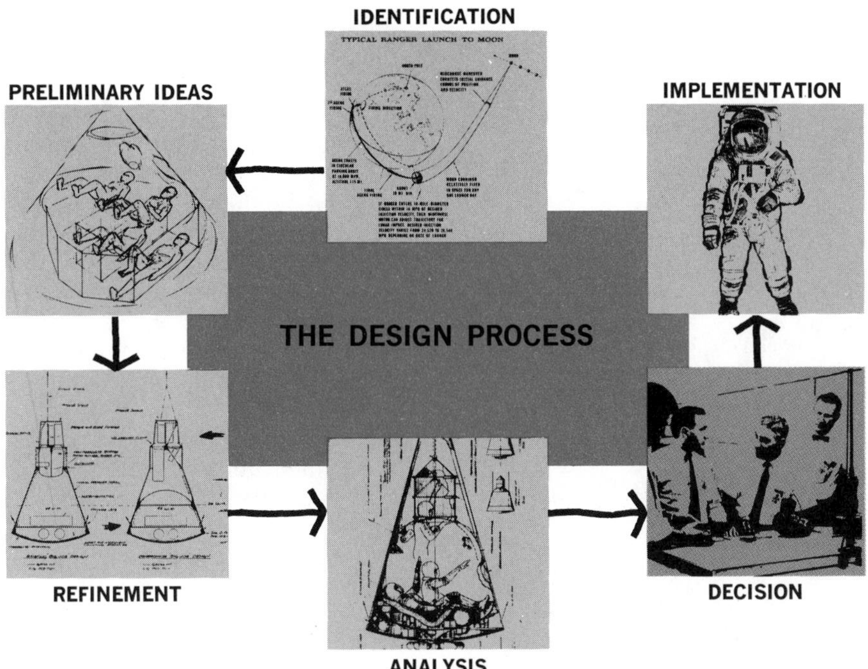

17 PICTORIAL PRESENTATION

17–1 INTRODUCTION

The communication of ideas and concepts is one of modern industry's most pressing needs, since large numbers of people are required to work as a unit toward a common objective. It is impossible for a single individual or a small group of supervisors to communicate ideas and instructions on a man-to-man basis; consequently, engineering drawings and written specifications are universally used for the implementation of a project. Since the complexity of conventional engineering drawings makes interpretation difficult, improved methods of presenting complicated designs are needed. One way of improving communication concerning design details is the use of pictorials which convey ideas clearly and thus reduce the possibility of errors and loss of time. Pictorials can be used to advantage in many types of communication—from technical reports to oral presentations. Pictorials may be line drawings, freehand sketches, or artist's renderings with a high degree of realism. A number of techniques are available for depicting minute details, internal parts, the relationships of components, and many other arrangements that are difficult to comprehend in the typical working drawing.

An ultrahigh altitude rocket cell is shown in schematic form in Fig. 17–1. A schematic of this type, illustrating the major components in block form, is sufficient when the general arrangement is being presented to technical people who are concerned with the system and the relationship of its components. A more complete representation of the completed rocket cell is shown in Fig. 17–2; in this figure, the components are realistically illustrated in an airbrush rendering done by a technical illustrator. Note that sections have been used to

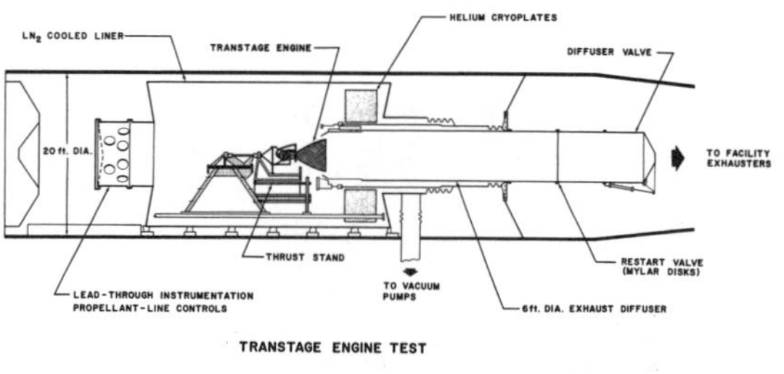

Fig. 17-1. A schematic diagram of an engineering system. (Courtesy of Aro, Inc., Arnold Engineering Center.)

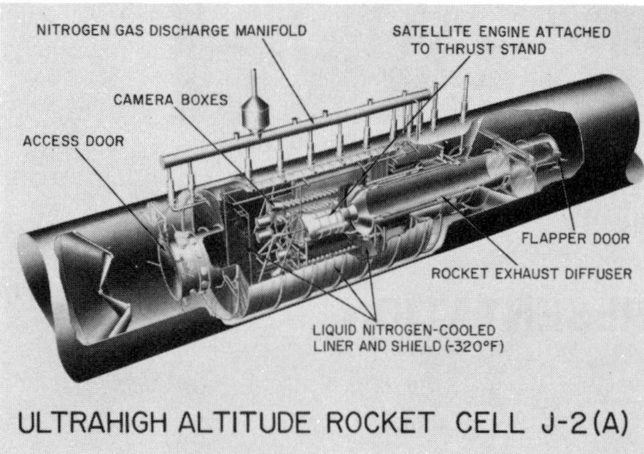

Fig. 17-2. A pictorial representation of the system shown in Fig. 17-1. (Courtesy of Aro, Inc., Arnold Engineering Center.)

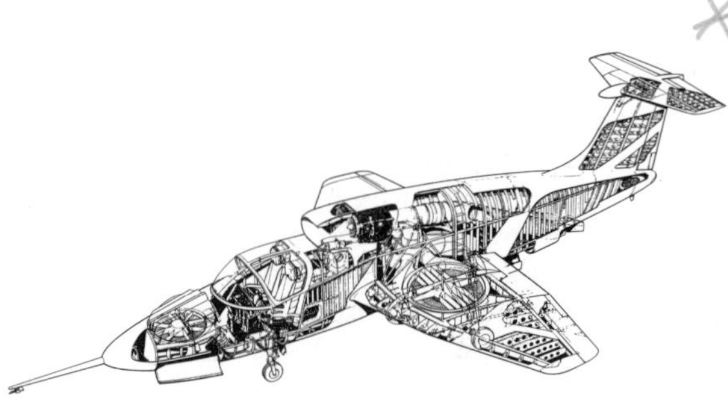

Fig. 17-3. A pictorial showing a complicated aircraft. (Courtesy of Ryan Aeronautics Corporation.)

illustrate the interior features and their assembly. Information and details presented in the pictorial of the rocket cell would be difficult to render by any other means. (An actual photograph of the completed unit would be considerably less effective, since it would not show interior sections.) Similarly, the line drawing of an aircraft, Fig. 17-3, clearly shows the assembly of a highly complicated structure.

Technical illustrations are extensively used to illustrate catalogs, parts manuals, and maintenance publications. Photographs are used in some cases, but pictorial drawings are considered to be the most effective means of depicting the relationship of parts. Figure 17-4 is an illustration from Bell Helicopter Corporation's maintenance and overhaul manual. A pictorial of this type leaves few questions as to the assembly and the name of parts included. Note that this assembly has been exploded to separate the parts for easier interpretation. When there is no loss of clarity, pictorials may show partially assembled arrangements. Another example of a pictorial is shown in Fig. 17-5, which illustrates the clutch adjustments of an automobile. This is typical of the hundreds of pictorials in Ford Shop Manuals, illustrating the various adjustments and assemblies that must be maintained through the life of a vehicle.

Illustrations of this type can be prepared by anyone who understands the principles and theories of engineering graphics, orthographic projection, and pictorial projection covered in this chapter. To illustrate parts or assemblies in pictorial form, one does not need to have artistic abilities. Instead, pictorials can be made by anyone who has mastered the mechanics of pictorial principles and is aware of the many pictorial aids available from commercial sources. Techniques of shading and rendering can be applied to line drawings to improve the realism of a simple drawing.

This chapter will cover the basic types of pictorial drawing systems: (1) isometric drawing, (2) oblique drawing, (3) axonometric projection, (4) oblique projection, and (5) perspective projection. Techniques of rendering will be

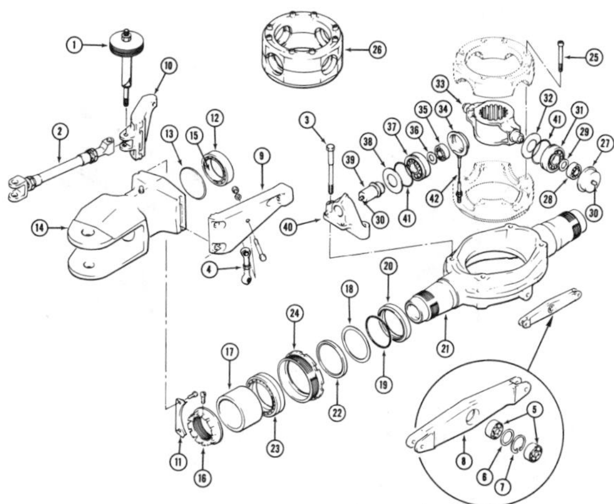

Fig. 17–4. An exploded pictorial such as those extensively used in maintenance catalogs and manuals. (Courtesy of Bell Helicopter Corporation.)

covered as an introduction to shading and the commercial processes available.

17–2 TYPES OF PICTORIALS

The three principal forms of pictorial *projections* are (1) axonometric projection, (2) oblique projection, and (3) perspective projection. These projections are illustrated in Fig. 17–6.

Axonometric projection is a three-dimensional projection of an object on a plane of paper obtained by projecting from the object to a picture plane (Fig. 17–6A). Since the projectors are parallel and perpendicular to the projection plane, axonometric projection is a form of orthographic projection. The mechanics of axonometric projection will be discussed later.

Oblique projection, as the name implies, is a three-dimensional pictorial projected onto a projection plane with parallel projectors *oblique* to the picture plane, as shown in part B of the figure. Any surface parallel to the picture plane will appear true size and shape when projected onto the picture plane.

Perspective projection is the most realistic of the pictorial systems. The projectors are drawn

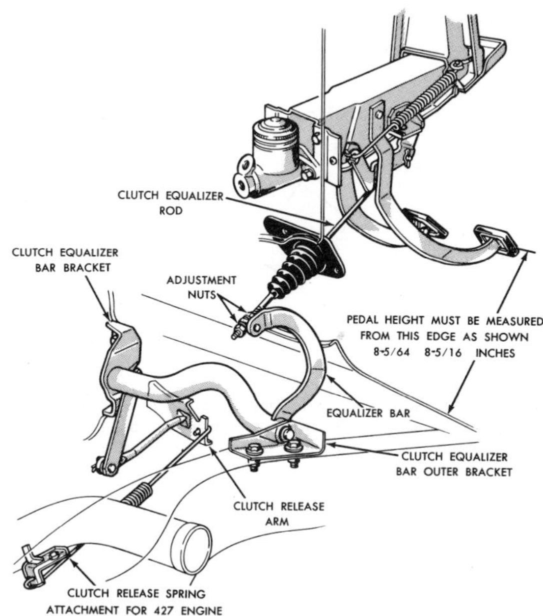

Fig. 17–5. A pictorial taken from a shop manual. (Courtesy of Ford Motor Company.)

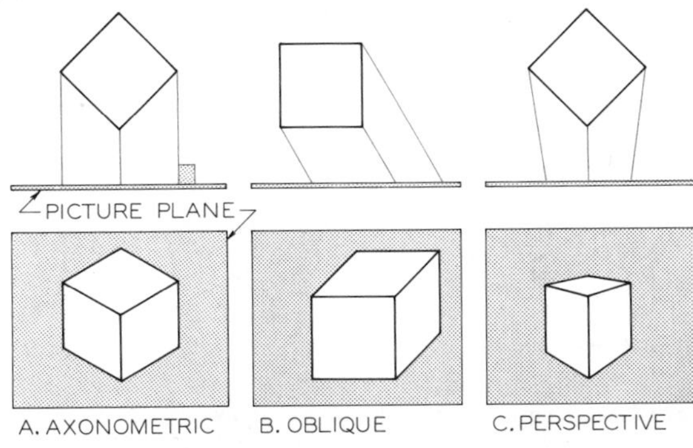

Fig. 17–6. Types of projection systems for pictorials. (A) Axonometric pictorials are formed by parallel projectors perpendicular to the picture plane. (B) Obliques are formed by parallel projectors that are oblique to the picture plane. (C) Perspectives are formed by converging projectors making varying angles with the picture plane.

from the object to converge at the viewer's eye and make different angles with the picture plane (Fig. 17–6C). The horizontal lines tend to converge at the horizon in the front view, where the pictorial is seen in its finished form.

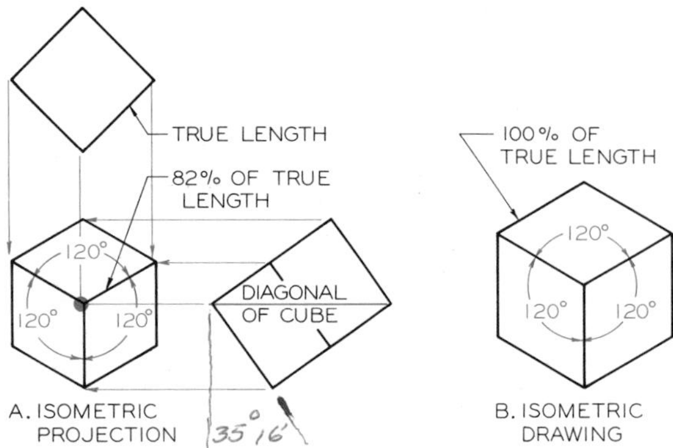

Fig. 17-7. An isometric projection is found by constructing a view where the diagonal of a cube appears as a point. An isometric drawing is not a true projection and is drawn larger than an isometric projection.

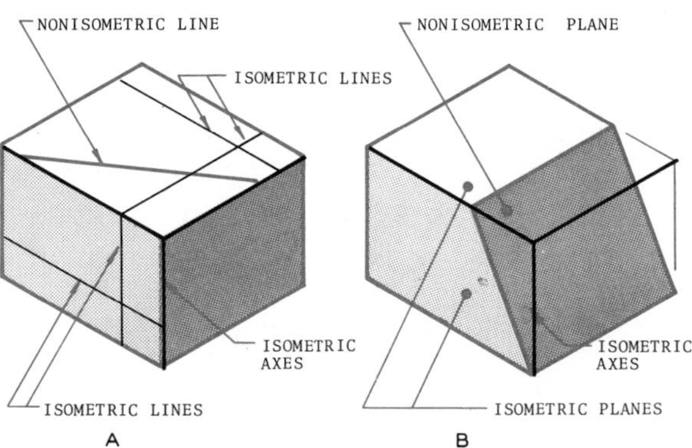

Fig. 17-9. (A) True measurements can be made only along isometric lines (lines that are parallel to the three axes). Lines not parallel to the axes are nonisometric and cannot be measured. (B) Nonisometric planes are planes that are inclined to any of the three planes of a cube in an isometric drawing.

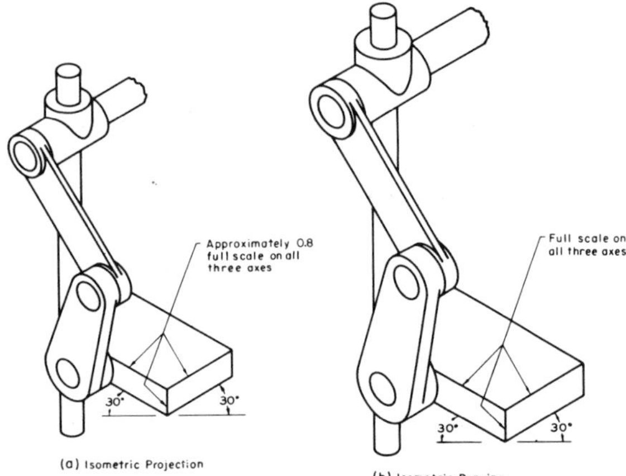

Fig. 17-8. A comparison of an object shown as an isometric projection with one shown as an isometric drawing. (Courtesy of ANSI; Y14.4-1957.)

Each of the three pictorial systems discussed here—axonometric, oblique, and perspective—is a form of *projection* that is constructed by projecting from given views of an object in much the same manner used to find an orthographic view. Other types of pictorial representations commonly used are simplified versions of these systems; they are called *drawings.* These pictorials are discussed in the following articles.

17-3 ISOMETRIC DRAWING

An *isometric projection* (Fig. 17-6A) is a type of orthographic projection in which the projectors are parallel and perpendicular to the picture plane. When the diagonal of a cube is viewed as a point, the resulting projection is an isometric projection with the sides of the cube foreshortened equally to 82 percent of their true length (Fig. 17-7A). The term isometric, which means "equal measurement," is used to describe this type of projection because the three planes of the cubes are equally foreshortened and the three axes of the pictorial are separated by equal angles of 120°.

An *isometric drawing* is very similar to an *isometric projection* except that it is not a true projection, but an approximate method of drawing a pictorial. The only difference is that instead of being drawn parallel to the axes at 82 percent of their true length, the lines are drawn true length (Fig. 17-7B). The axes are also 120° apart. This procedure allows pictorials to be made with full measurements and a 30°-60° triangle. A comparison of the same object drawn by both methods is shown in Fig. 17-8.

FIGURE 17-10. CONSTRUCTION OF AN ISOMETRIC DRAWING

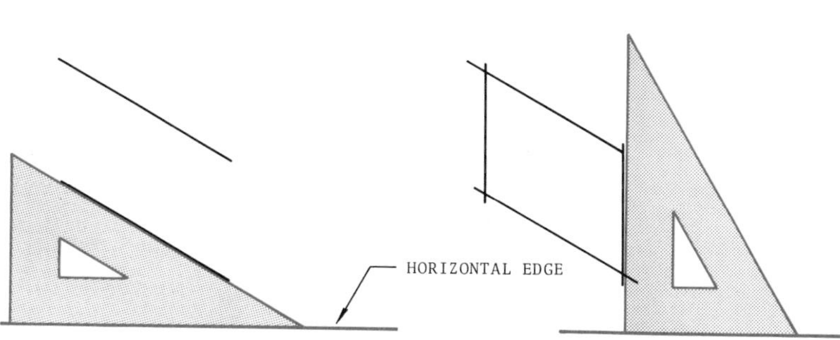

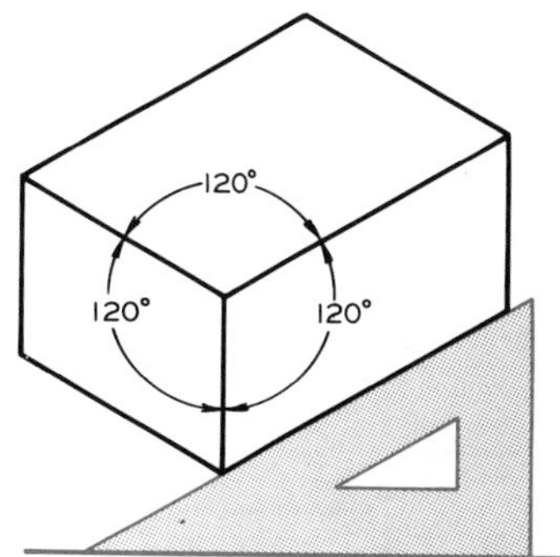

Step 1: A 30°-60° triangle is used in combination with a horizontal straightedge for drawing the initial lines of an isometric.

Step 2: Vertical lines are drawn. Note that parallel lines appear parallel in isometric as well as orthographic views.

Step 3: The final side of the isometric is drawn and the lines are strengthened. The 30°-60° triangle automatically separates the axes of the drawing by 120°.

17-4 CONSTRUCTION OF AN ISOMETRIC DRAWING

The three isometric axes are important in the construction of an isometric pictorial. These lines, and other lines that are parallel to them, are called *isometric lines*. True measurements can be made along these lines using any scale desired. You cannot make true measurements along lines that are *not* isometric lines.

For example, the isometric lines labeled in Fig. 17-9A can be measured just as in an orthographic view. However, a nonisometric line, one that is not parallel to one of the axes, cannot be measured to determine its length, since the scale changes as the direction of the line changes in relation to the isometric axes.

The three surfaces of a cube drawn in isometric are called *isometric planes* (Fig. 17-9B). Planes that are not parallel to these planes are *nonisometric planes*. Measurements on nonisometric planes must be handled differently from measurements on isometric planes.

The basic tools for constructing an isometric drawing, the 30°-60° triangle and a scale, are illustrated in Fig. 17-10. Since the isometric axes are 120° apart, the 30°-60° triangle will automatically give this separation when used with a horizontal base line. Usually the vertical lines of an object are drawn as vertical lines in the isometric drawing.

When working from a multiview drawing such as a working drawing, you can transfer actual dimensions to the isometric drawing to ensure that true proportions are maintained. The construction is simplified if a block is drawn that contains the object; the object's height, width, and depth are used in constructing the block (Fig. 17-11). Other dimensions can be taken from the given views and measured along the isometric axes to locate notches and portions that are to be removed from the "blocked-in" drawing. This process results in the completed pictorial.

Angles in isometric pictorials cannot be measured as true angles, nor can nonisometric lines be measured as true length. The two 30° angles shown in the orthographic views in Fig. 17-12A do not appear as 30° angles in the isometric drawing in part B.

This fact is further illustrated in Fig. 17-13, where an object with nonisometric planes is

FIGURE 17–11. LAYOUT OF AN ISOMETRIC DRAWING

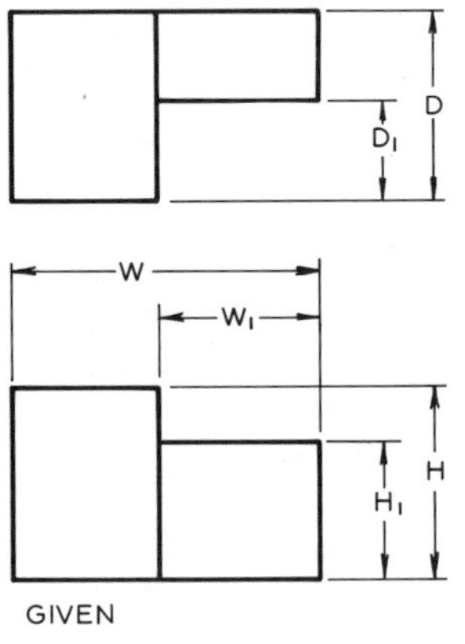

GIVEN

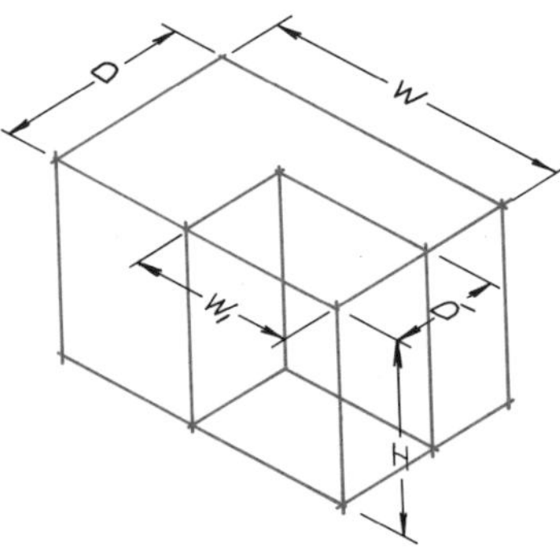

Step 1: The overall dimensions of the object are used to lightly block in the object. One notch is removed by using dimensions taken from the given views.

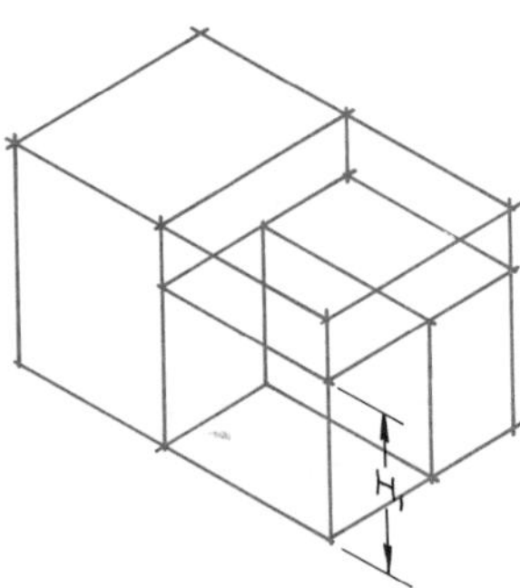

Step 2: The second notch is removed using dimension H_1.

Step 3: The final lines of the isometric are strengthened.

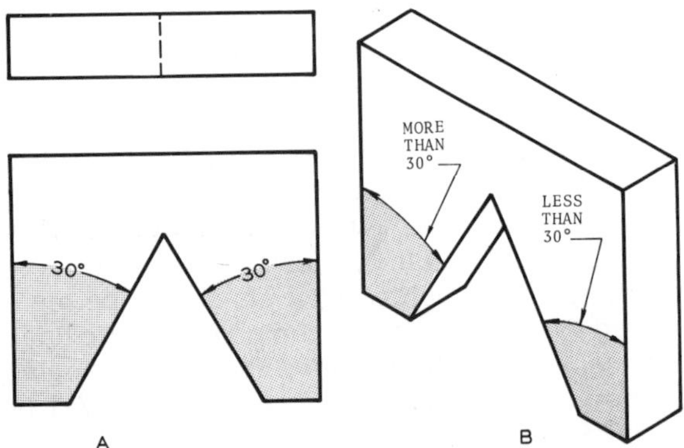

Fig. 17–12. Angular measurements cannot be made in isometric drawings. Angles drawn in isometric are greater and less than the true angles.

drawn in isometric. The lines *AD* and *BC* appear shorter and longer than true length, respectively. Since angles cannot be measured in isometric, points *A* and *B* must be located by measuring distances *D* along the isometric axes.

The technique of constructing a pictorial of an object with an inclined plane is shown in Fig. 17–14. The object is blocked in pictorially and portions are removed. The extreme ends of the inclined plane are located along the isometric axes and these points are connected to complete the pictorial. All construction lines should be drawn lightly so that they need not be erased when the completed pictorial is darkened.

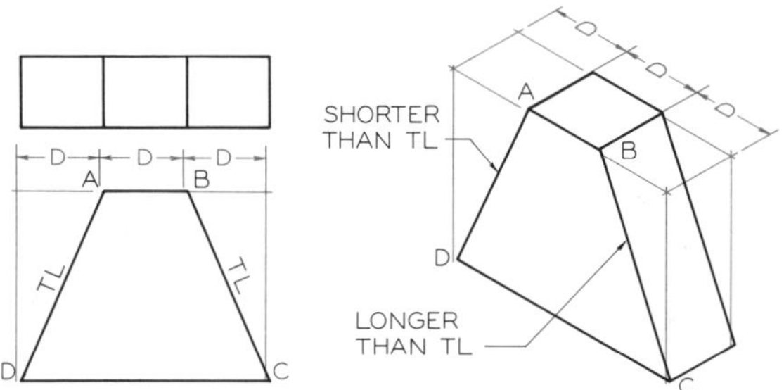

Fig. 17–13. Inclined surfaces must be found by using coordinates measured along the isometric axes. The lengths of angular lines will not be true length in isometric.

FIGURE 17–14. CONSTRUCTION OF AN ISOMETRIC DRAWING WITH AN INCLINED PLANE

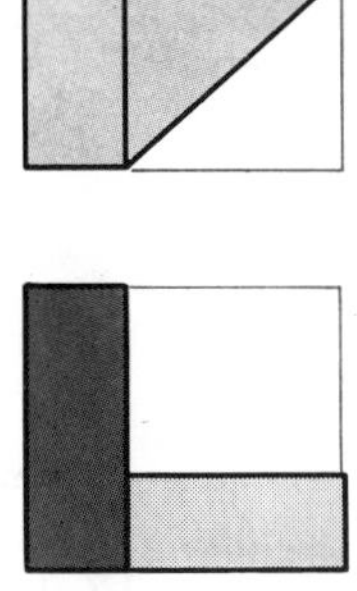

GIVEN

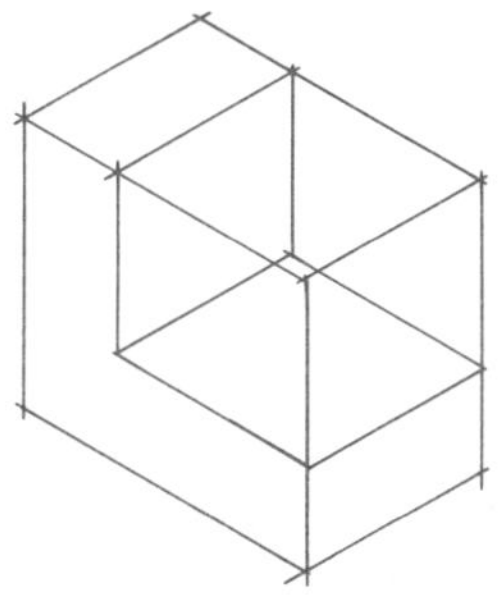

Step 1: The object is blocked in using the overall dimensions. The notch is removed.

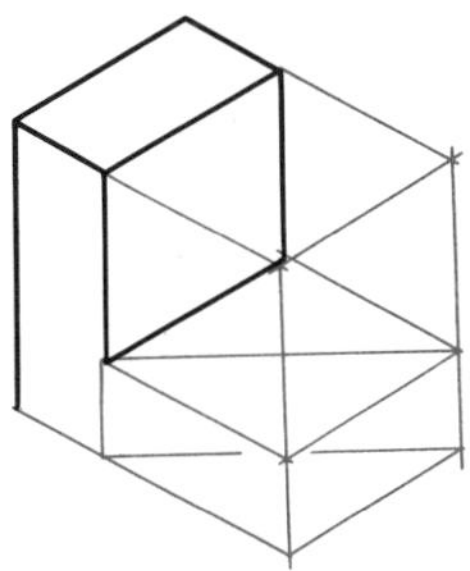

Step 2: The inclined plane is located by establishing its end points.

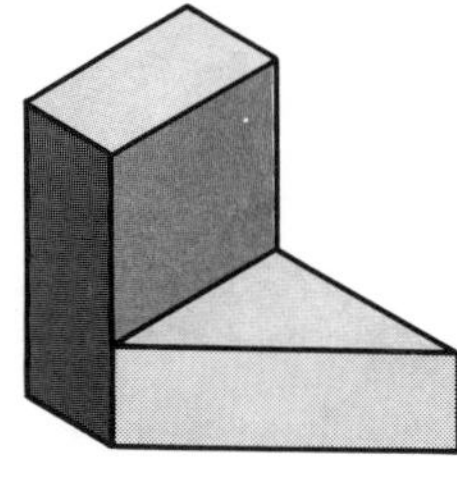

Step 3: The lines are strengthened to complete the drawing.

17–5 CIRCLES IN ISOMETRIC

The most difficult problem of pictorial drawing is that of representing circles by means of ellipses. The pictorial assembly shown in Fig. 17–15 is composed of several circular shapes that are drawn as ellipses.

There are three methods of constructing circles in isometric drawings: (1) point plotting, (2) four-center ellipse construction, and (3) ellipse templates. These three methods will be discussed in the following articles.

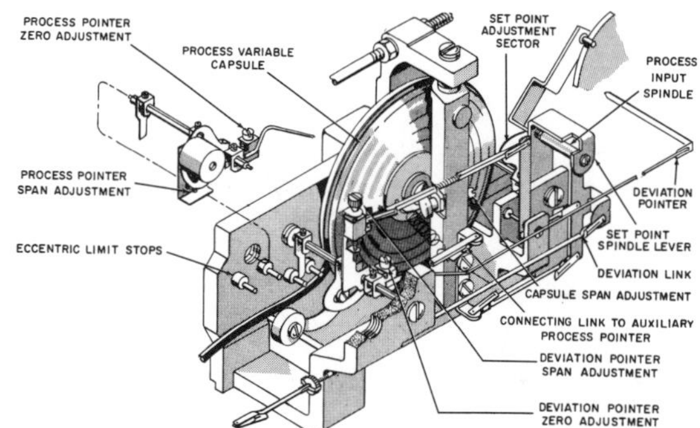

Fig. 17–15. A pictorial of a scale instrument where circular features are drawn in isometric as ellipses. (Courtesy of Fischer and Porter Company.)

17–6 CIRCLES: POINT PLOTTING

When a series of points is located along the circumference of a circle, these points can be located in an isometric pictorial by using two

FIGURE 17–16. PLOTTING CIRCLES

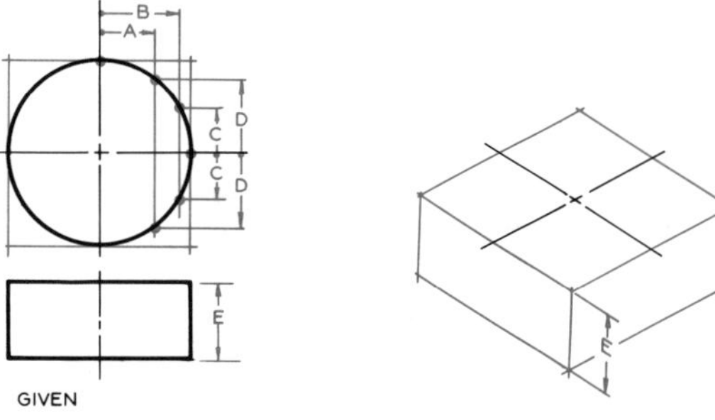

Step 1: The cylinder is blocked in using the overall dimensions. The center lines locate the points of tangency of the ellipse.

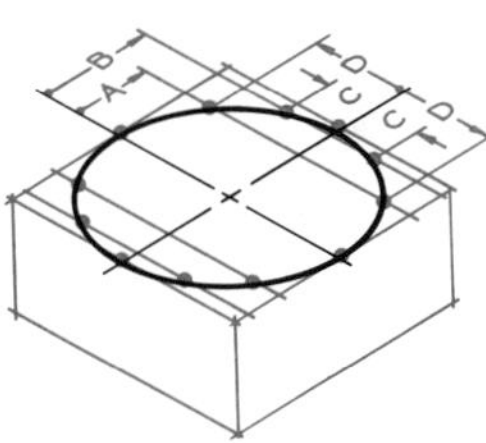

Step 2: Coordinates are used to locate points on the circumference of the circle.

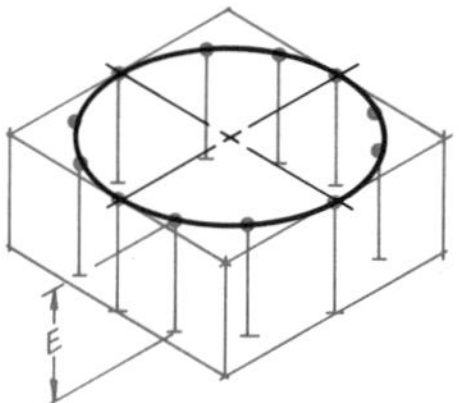

Step 3: The lower ellipse is found by dropping each point a distance equal to the height of the cylinder *E*.

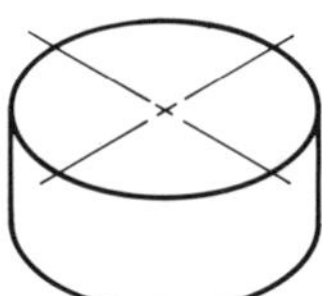

Step 4: The two ellipses can be drawn with an irregular curve and connected with tangent lines to complete the cylinder.

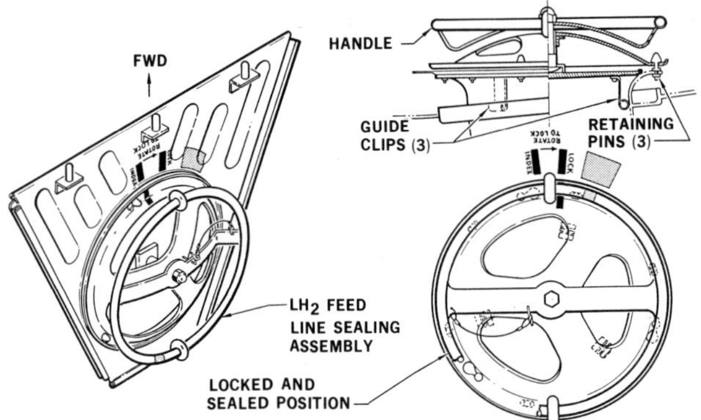

Fig. 17–17. An example of parts that have been drawn using ellipses in isometric to represent circles. This is a handwheel that is proposed for use in an orbital workshop to be launched into space in the future. (Courtesy of the National Aeronautics and Space Administration.)

dimensions parallel to the isometric axes. These two dimensions are called *coordinates*. Examples of coordinates are shown in Fig. 17–16 in the given views of the cylinder.

First the cylinder is blocked in and drawn pictorially, with the center lines added as shown in step 1. The points where the center lines intersect the box are the points of tangency through which the ellipse must pass. Coordinates *A*, *B*, *C*, and *D* are used in step 2 to locate points on the ellipse that can be joined with the aid of an irregular curve. The ellipse shown here is a *true ellipse*.

The lower ellipse that is located on the bottom plane of the cylinder can be found without using a second set of coordinates for each point. Since the upper plane is parallel to the lower plane, the height *E* can be measured below each point on the upper plane (step 3). The completed ellipses can be connected with parallel vertical lines tangent to both ellipses to give the completed drawing in step 4.

This true ellipse corresponds to the ellipse found in ellipse templates. The ellipse template used for true ellipses in isometric drawings is the 35° template.

rhombus - an equilateral parallelogram with oblique angles.

FIGURE 17-18. CONSTRUCTION OF THE FOUR-CENTER ELLIPSE

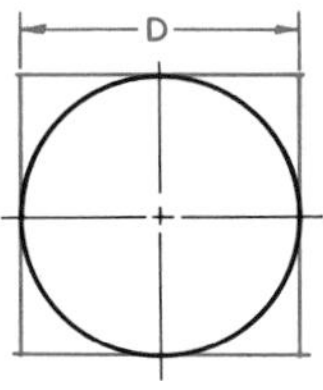

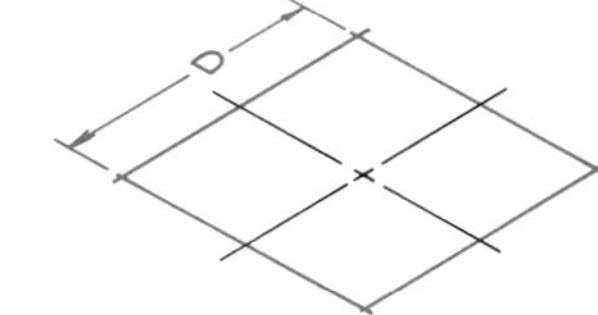

GIVEN

Step 1: The diameter of the circle is used for construction of a rhombus that is tangent to the ellipse.

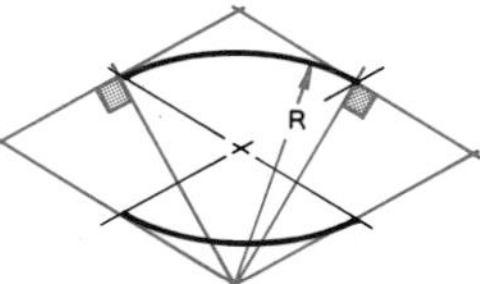

Step 2: Perpendicular lines are drawn from the midpoints of two intersecting sides of the rhombus to locate the center of an arc for drawing one segment of the ellipse. The procedure is repeated on the opposite sides of the rhombus to yield a second segment of the ellipse.

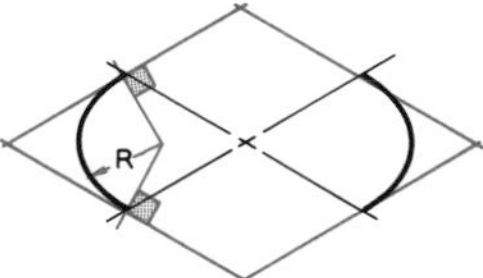

Step 3: The centers for the two remaining arcs are located.

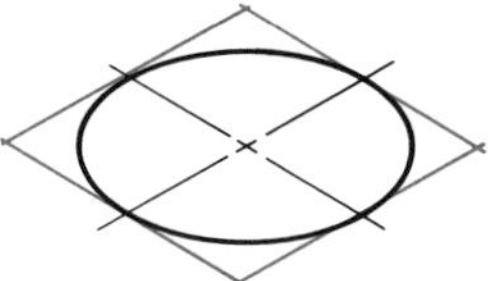

Step 4: When the four arcs have been drawn, the final result is an approximate ellipse.

17-7 CIRCLES: FOUR-CENTER ELLIPSE CONSTRUCTION

A handwheel used in an orbital workshop that will be launched into space is shown in Fig. 17-17 as an isometric drawing. The circular features were constructed using the four-center ellipse method to give an *approximate* ellipse.

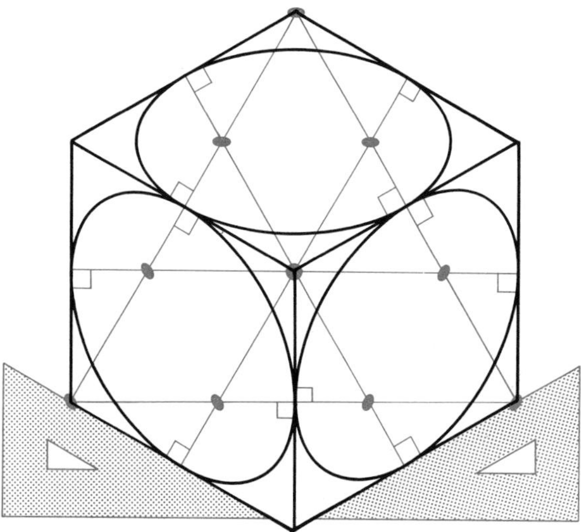

Fig. 17-19. The four-center ellipse construction is used to find an ellipse on each surface of an isometric drawing.

This is a method that is satisfactory for most applications, even though the ellipse is not a true ellipse since it is formed from arcs drawn with a compass.

The construction of a four-center ellipse is shown in four steps in Fig. 17-18. The top view of the circle is blocked in with a square which is tangent to the circle at four points. The isometric drawing of the square results in a rhombus (step 1). We find the center lines by locating the midpoints of the sides of the rhombus. In steps 2 and 3, perpendicular construction lines are drawn from the midpoints of the sides of the rhombus to locate center points for drawing the four arcs that will be tangent to the sides and will form the ellipse. This construction is based on the principle that the perpendicular bisectors of the chords of a circle intersect at the circle's center.

The radii for the arcs are found by measuring from the center points to the midpoints of the sides of the rhombus. The four arcs are drawn separately to give the completed four-center ellipse in step 4. This method can be used on any of the three isometric planes, since all isometric planes are equally foreshortened (Fig. 17-19).

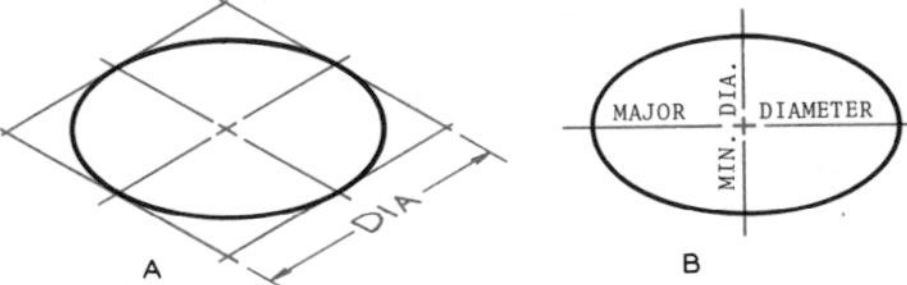

Fig. 17-20. The diameter of the circle is measured along the isometric axes. The major diameter of an ellipse in isometric is greater than the actual diameter of the circle, since it is the diagonal of the rhombus. The minor diameter is perpendicular to the major diameter.

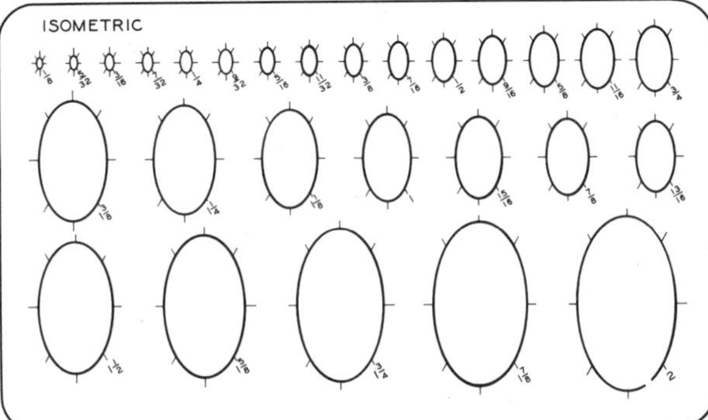

Fig. 17-21. The isometric ellipse template is a special template designed to reduce drafting time. Note that the true diameters of the circles are not the major diameters of the ellipses, but the diameters that are parallel to the isometric axes.

17-8 CIRCLES: ELLIPSE TEMPLATES

Circles in pictorial can be drawn by using ellipse templates, which were discussed in Chapter 9. In order to use an ellipse guide effectively, it is necessary that you understand ellipses and their elements.

When a circle is blocked in (Fig. 17-20A), the diameter of the circle is equal to the length of one of the sides of the rhombus. Note that the longest diameter of the ellipse is greater than the true diameter of the circle. This diameter is called the major diameter (Fig. 17-20B). The minor diameter is the smallest diameter that can be measured. The minor diameter is perpendicular to the major diameter and, like the major diameter, passes through the center of the ellipse.

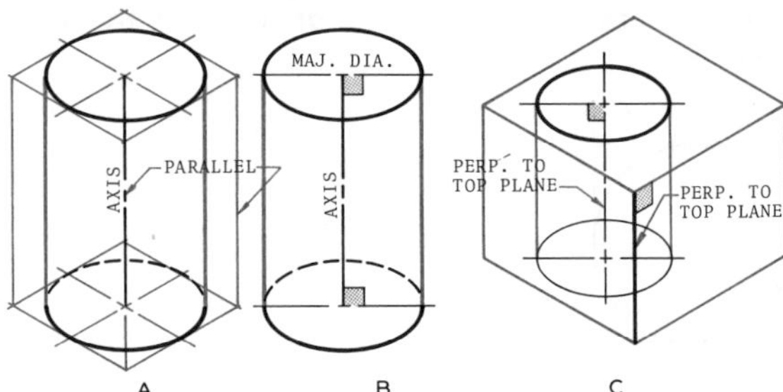

Fig. 17-22. Two methods of drawing cylinders in isometric are shown in A and B. Construction of a cylindrical hole in isometric is shown in C.

A special isometric ellipse template is available for drawing ellipses that lie in isometric planes (Fig. 17-21). Marks are given around the elliptical holes in the template for aligning the guide with the major and minor diameters or the isometric center lines of the circles in isometric.

Two methods of using the isometric ellipse template are illustrated in parts A and B of Fig. 17-22. In A, the cylinder is blocked in and the isometric center lines are drawn. The center lines are used for aligning the ellipse template. The diameter of the circle shown in isometric is shorter than the major diameter of the ellipse. This shorter diameter is the dimension that is labeled on the ellipse template. For example, if the true diameter of the circle is $1\frac{1}{2}''$, then the $1\frac{1}{2}''$ ellipse template is used.

In Fig. 17-22B, the major diameter of the ellipse and the axis of the cylinder are used for constructing the cylinder. The axis of a right cylinder is always perpendicular to the major diameter of the elliptical ends. In this case, the ellipse guide's major diameter is aligned to be perpendicular to the axis. As in part A, you must use the size of ellipse that corresponds to the true diameter of the circle measured in the direction of the isometric axes. The reason for this is that the major diameter of the isometric ellipse is not labeled on the template. The major diameter is greater than the actual diameter of the circle.

FIGURE 17–23. CYLINDERS IN ISOMETRIC

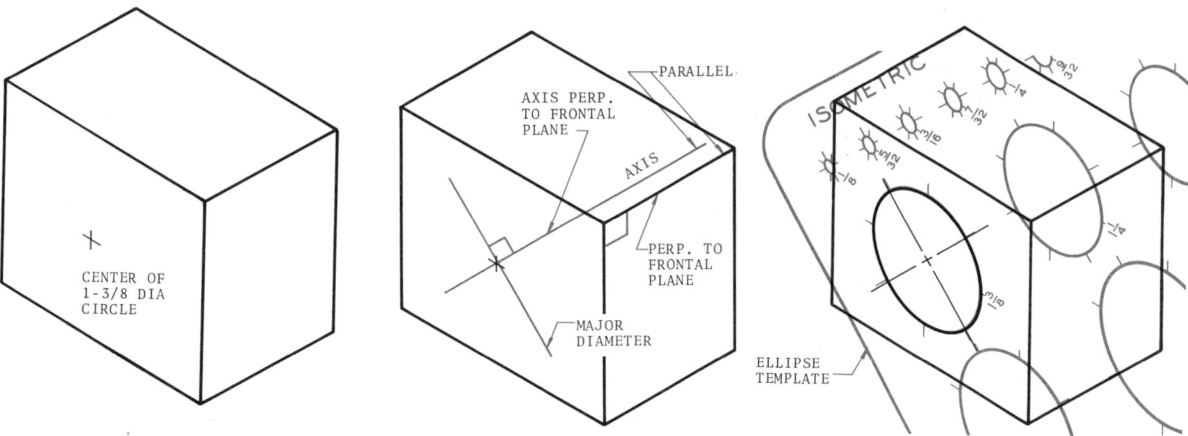

Step 1: The center of the hole with a given diameter is located on a face of the isometric drawing.

Step 2: The axis of the cylinder is drawn from the center parallel to that isometric axis which is perpendicular to the plane of the circle. The major diameter is drawn perpendicular to the axis of the cylindrical hole.

Step 3: The $1\frac{3}{8}''$ ellipse template is used to draw the ellipse by aligning the major and minor diameters with the guidelines on the template.

You can use these principles very conveniently to construct a cylindrical hole through an isometric drawing of a part. Since one isometric axis will always be perpendicular to the plane formed by the other two axes, the axis of a cylindrical hole will be parallel to one of the axes if it is perpendicular to one of the isometric planes. The elliptical view of the cylinder is drawn by placing the major diameter of the ellipse template perpendicular to the axis of the cylinder (Fig. 17–22C).

An example of constructing a cylindrical hole through an isometric view is shown in three steps in Fig. 17–23. The isometric is drawn in step 1 and the center is located on the desired plane (which we shall call the frontal plane). In step 2, the axis of the cylinder is drawn parallel to that isometric axis which is perpendicular to the plane of the circle (i.e., the frontal plane). The minor diameter will be located on this axis. The major diameter is then drawn perpendicular to the axis of the cylinder through its center. Now that the minor and major diameters have been established, an ellipse template can be used to complete the drawing (step 3).

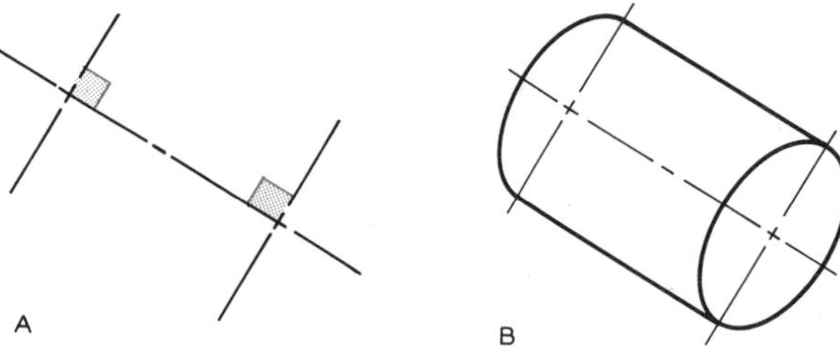

Fig. 17–24. A cylinder can easily be constructed in isometric by drawing the axis to the proper length and constructing major diameters perpendicular to the axis at each end (A). The ellipse templates are selected for the proper size and the circular ends are drawn by aligning the major and minor diameters with the template (B).

The isometric ellipse template can also be used conveniently to draw a cylinder when the length of the axis and the diameter of the circle are known. The axis is drawn as an isometric line and measured to the proper length. The major diameters are drawn perpendicular to the axis at each end (Fig. 17–24A). The ellipse template's major diameter is aligned with the perpendiculars at each end and the ellipses are drawn (part B). If the circular end is 2″ in diam-

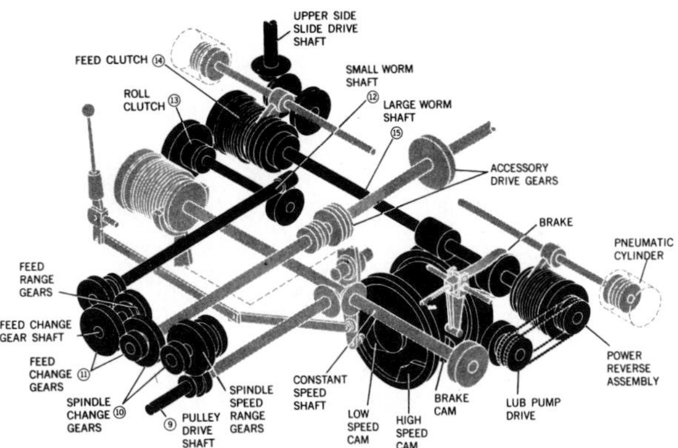

Fig. 17-25A. Examples of ellipses drawn in schematic to illustrate gearing systems of a machine. (Courtesy of the National Acme Company.)

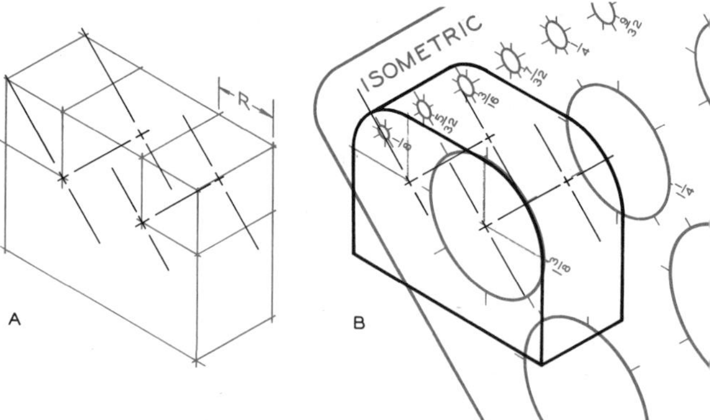

Fig. 17-26. Construction of rounded corners with an ellipse template. The four-center ellipse method could have been used equally well.

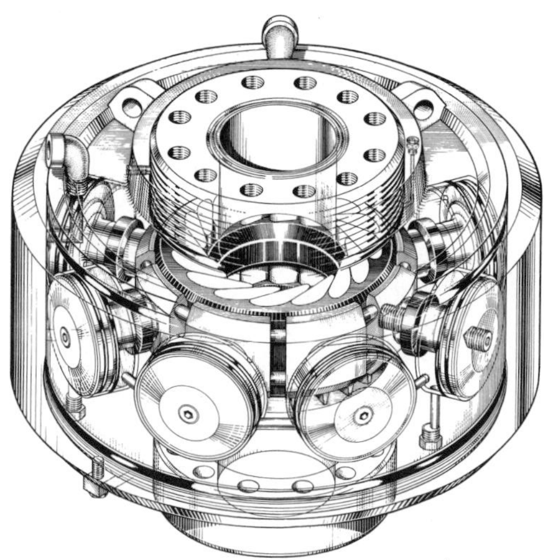

Fig. 17-25B. This diaphanous view of a blowout preventer was drawn using an ellipse template to illustrate the circular features. (Courtesy of Cameron Iron Works, Inc., and L. G. Whitfield.)

eter, then the 2″ ellipse template is used. The elliptical ends of the cylinder are connected with isometric lines that are tangent to the ellipses.

Several examples of ellipses and axes are shown in isometric in Fig. 17-25A. Note that the major diameters are perpendicular to their respective axes. The same principles were applied to the drawing in Fig. 17-25B. The horizontal circles were drawn with isometric ellipse templates, but the cylindrical parts that face in different directions about the center were drawn with different ellipse templates, each with a different angle—30°, 15°, etc.

17-9 PARTIAL CIRCLES IN ISOMETRIC

Partial circles such as fillets and rounds are drawn in isometric using the principles discussed in the previous articles. Any of the methods can be used.

In Fig. 17-26A, an object with rounded corners is blocked in and the center lines are located at each corner that is to be rounded. An ellipse template is used in B to construct the rounded corners on the front and back planes. These rounded corners could have been constructed by the four-center ellipse method or by plotting points on the circles.

17-10 CIRCLES IN NONISOMETRIC PLANES

When a circle or an arc lies on a nonisometric plane, the circle must be plotted point-by-point, since the regular isometric ellipse guide can be used only on isometric planes. Two views of an object having an inclined plane are given in Fig. 17-27. The object is drawn in isometric, and a series of coordinates is used to locate points corresponding to those in the given views. These coordinates are used in step 1 and step 2

FIGURE 17–27. CONSTRUCTION OF ELLIPSES ON AN INCLINED PLANE

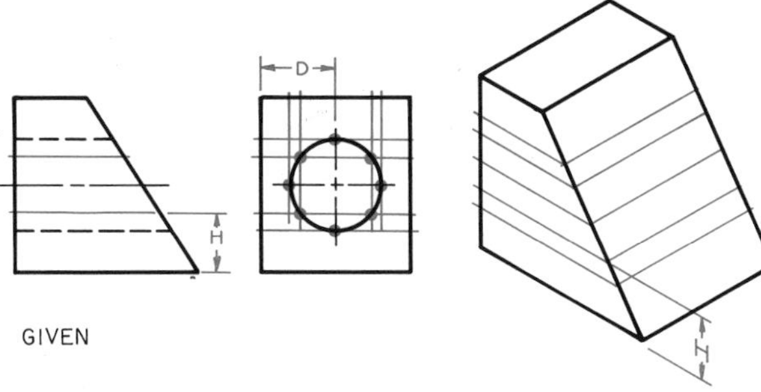

Step 1: Coordinates are established in the orthographic views and corresponding coordinates are located in the isometric drawing. All measurements are made parallel to the isometric axes.

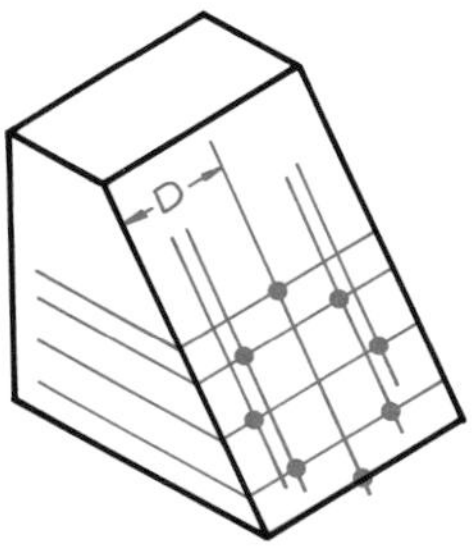

Step 2: The other coordinates are drawn to locate points on the ellipse.

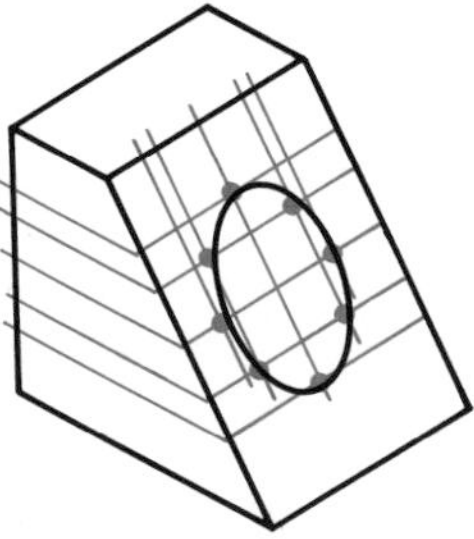

Step 3: The points are connected with an irregular curve, or an ellipse template angle can be selected by trial and error.

to locate a number of points on the ellipse. The points are connected with an irregular curve (step 3) to give the completed ellipse.

The ellipse could have been blocked in and the center lines located on the nonisometric surface. An ellipse-guide angle (other than isometric) could have been determined by trial and error to approximate the ellipse that would be tangent to the blocked-in ellipse. In an isometric drawing, it is not essential that the ellipse be exactly drawn. After all, a pictorial is merely a representation of an object, and a high degree of accuracy is not essential in most cases.

FIGURE 17–28. PLOTTING IRREGULAR CURVES

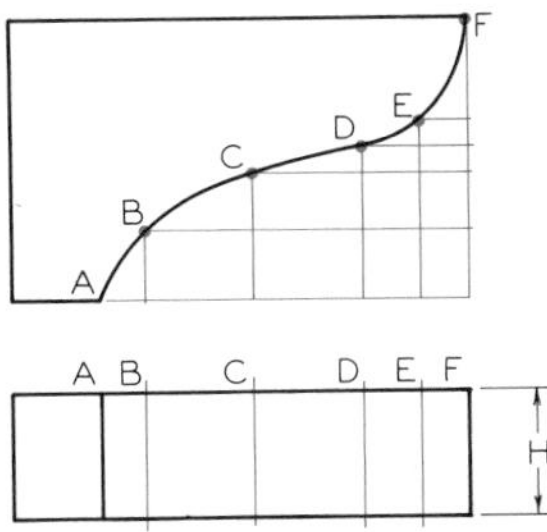

Step 1: Draw two coordinates to locate a series of points on the irregular curve. These coordinates must be parallel to the standard *W*, *D*, and *H* dimensions.

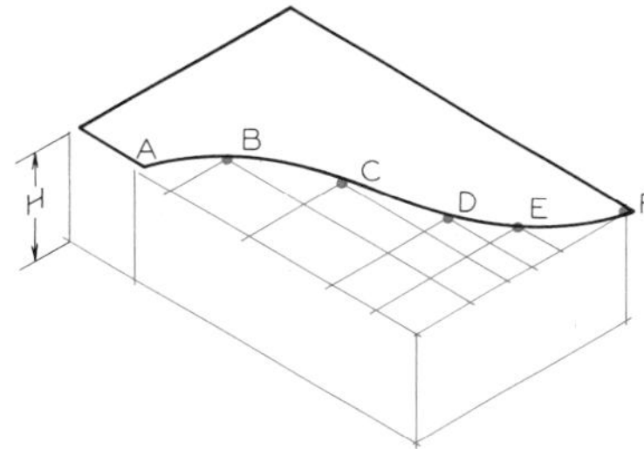

Step 2: Block in the shape using overall dimensions. Locate points on the irregular curve using the coordinates from the orthographic views.

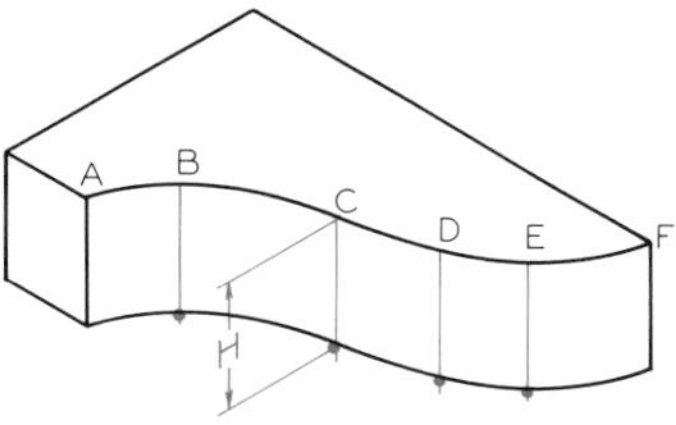

Step 3: Since the object has a uniform thickness, the lower curve can be found by projecting downward the distance *H* from the upper points. Connect the points with an irregular curve.

17–11 IRREGULAR CURVES IN ISOMETRIC

Irregular curves that are not composed of arcs or circles must be plotted point-by-point using

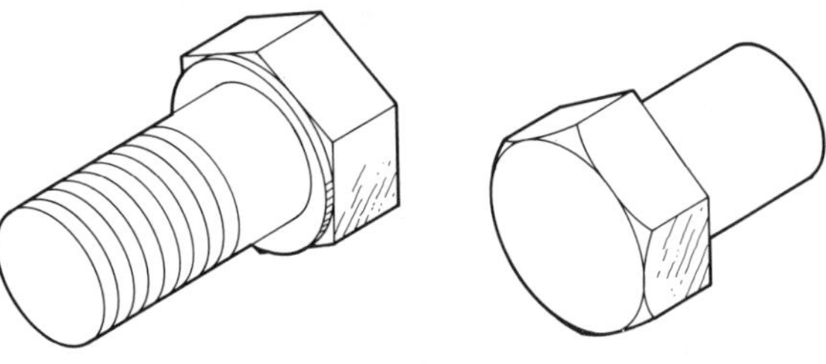

Fig. 17–29. Threads and bolts in isometric.

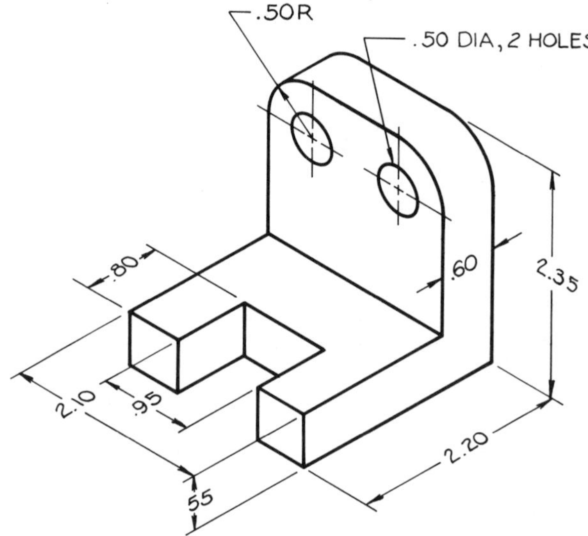

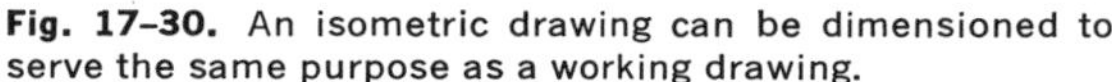

Fig. 17–30. An isometric drawing can be dimensioned to serve the same purpose as a working drawing.

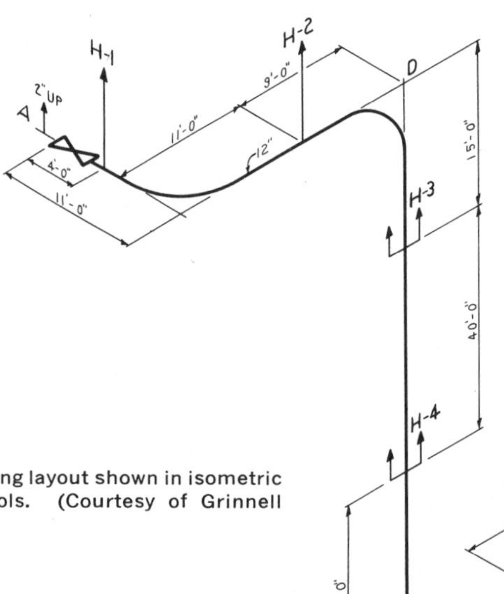

Fig. 17–31. A dimensioned piping layout shown in isometric using single-line piping symbols. (Courtesy of Grinnell Corporation.)

coordinates to locate each point. In Fig. 17–28 points 1 through 5 are located along the irregular curve in the given views with coordinates of width and height. These coordinates are transferred to the isometric drawing and are measured along the isometric axes.

The points are located and are connected with an irregular curve. The curve on the back side of the isometric can be found by projecting each point on the front surface to the rear surface by a distance equal to the depth of the object.

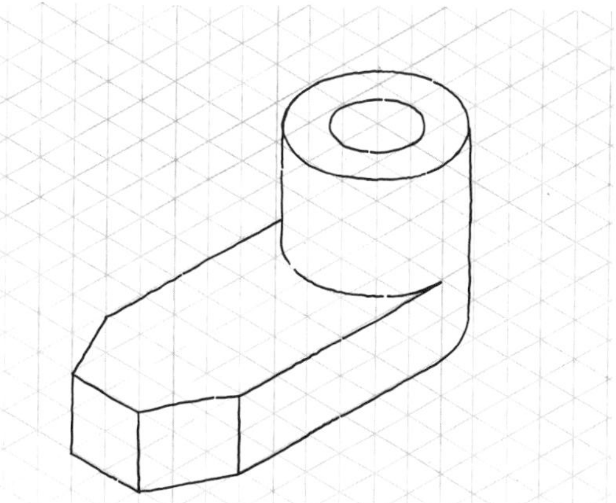

Fig. 17–32. Ideas can be sketched as isometric drawings on isometric grid paper.

17–12 SPECIAL APPLICATIONS OF ISOMETRIC DRAWINGS

Nuts and bolts are often drawn pictorially, since they are commonly used fasteners. Examples of isometric drawings of a bolt and bolt head are shown in Fig. 17–29. Note that the threads are drawn as equally spaced ellipses, as if the threads were concentric circles with their centers along the axis of the bolt.

Isometric drawings can be dimensioned and used effectively as detail drawings (Fig. 17–30) from which the parts can be made. The numerals are positioned to lie in the same plane as the isometric plane being dimensioned. Note, however, that dimensions with leaders, such as the .50 DIA holes, use numerals and letters constructed with horizontal guidelines, instead of being positioned in an isometric plane.

Isometric drawings are used extensively to describe piping layouts (Fig. 17–31). Note that symbols are used to denote the various types of piping components as well as important dimensions. This is a single-line schematic; however, double-line drawings are sometimes used for added realism.

Isometric sketching can aid the designer in developing ideas and making preliminary sketches. Specially printed isometric grid paper can be purchased for rapid sketches (Fig. 17–32). Again, the best way of beginning an isometric sketch is to block in the pictorial by the same technique used for instrument drawings.

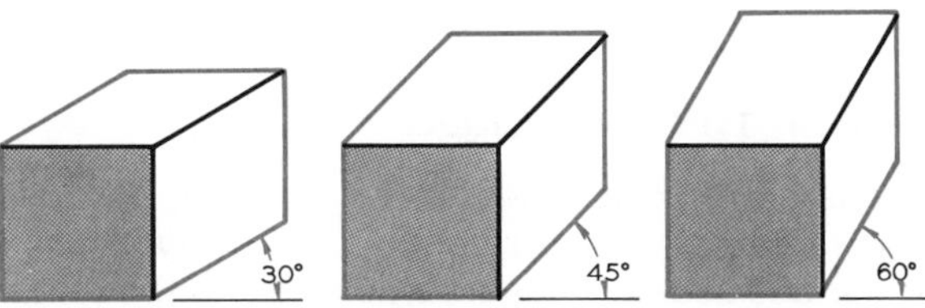

Fig. 17–33. Oblique drawings of the same cube with different angles for the receding axes.

17–13 OBLIQUE DRAWINGS

Although there are similarities between oblique drawings and isometrics, the oblique drawing is based on a different set of principles. Instead of being a type of orthographic projection, as an isometric drawing is, the oblique is usually positioned so as to have one surface of a cube parallel to the projection plane; this surface will appear true size. The receding axis is projected to the picture plane—the plane represented by the sheet of paper—with projectors that are *oblique* to the picture plane. In the case of orthographic projection and isometric projection, the projectors are *perpendicular* to the picture plane.

Three oblique drawings of a cube are shown in Fig. 17–33. It is important to note that the receding axis can be at *any angle*. In each case, one face of the cube is drawn true size and the receding axis is oblique to the true-size surface.

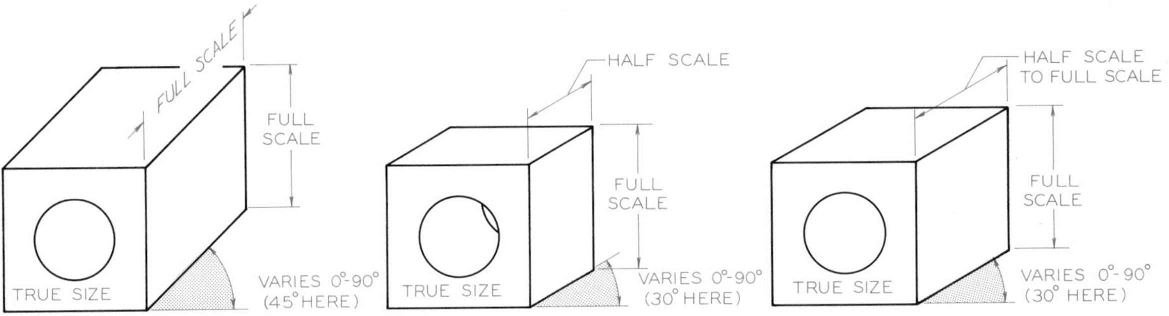

A. The cavalier oblique can be drawn with a receding axis at any angle, but measurements along this axis are true length.

B. The cabinet oblique can be drawn with a receding axis at any angle, but the measurements along this axis are half scale.

C. The general oblique can be drawn with a receding axis at any angle, but the measurements along this axis can vary form half to full scale.

17–14 TYPES OF OBLIQUES

There are three types of obliques: (a) cavalier, (b) cabinet, and (c) general. In all types, one surface usually appears true size and the receding axis can be drawn at any angle. The primary difference is the scale at which the receding axis is drawn (Fig. 17–34).

In *cavalier* obliques the measurements along the receding axis are true length and are equal to the same dimensions in the orthographic views. The reason for this is that the projectors form 45° angles with the picture plane. This does not mean that the angle between the receding axis and the horizontal must be 45°; this angle can vary from 0° to 90°, and in all cases the measurements along the receding axes will be full size (Fig. 17–34A).

In *cabinet* oblique drawings the measurements along the receding axis are half-length. This shortens the drawing and gives it a more realistic appearance (Fig. 17–34B).

In *general* obliques the measurements along the receding axes may be reduced to any proportion between half size and full size (Fig. 17–34C). The angle of the receding axis can vary between 0° and 90°.

A comparison of the most commonly used types of obliques—cavalier and cabinet—is shown in Fig. 17–35. It is apparent that objects

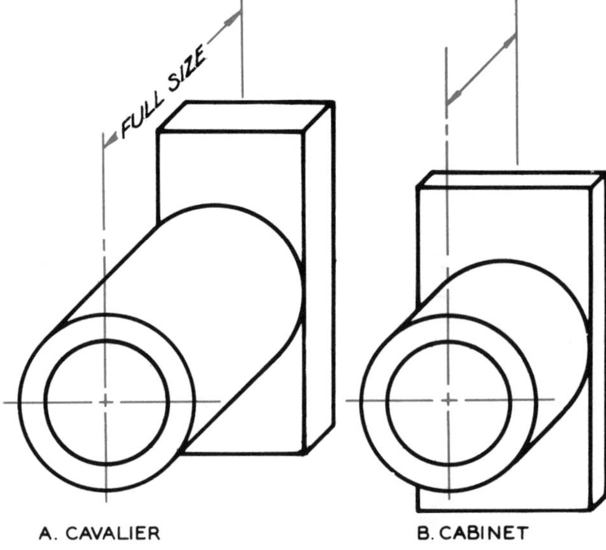

Fig. 17–35. A comparison of cavalier and cabinet oblique.

with long depths appear excessively long when drawn as cavalier obliques. The cabinet oblique gives a much better appearance.

17–15 CONSTRUCTION OF AN OBLIQUE

As in drawing an isometric, it is advisable to construct an oblique by using the height, width,

FIGURE 17-36. OBLIQUE CONSTRUCTION

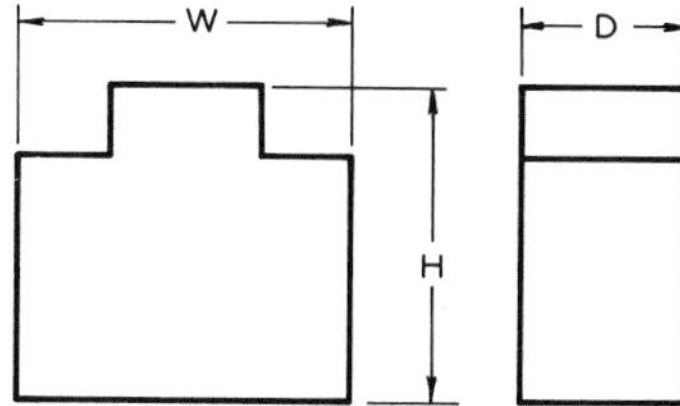

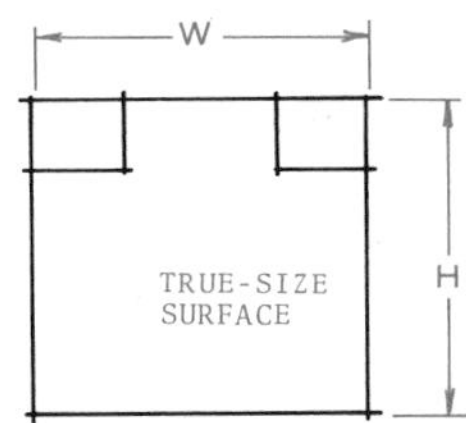

Step 1: The front surface of the oblique is drawn as a true-size plane. The corners are removed.

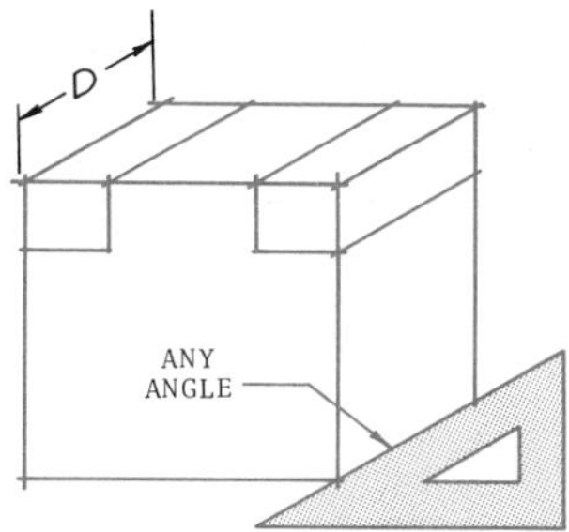

Step 2: The receding axis is selected and the true dimensions are measured along this axis.

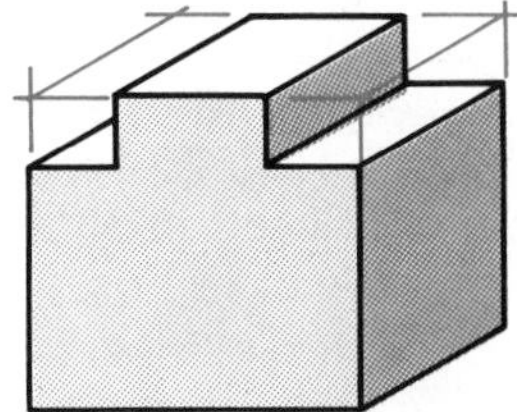

Step 3: The finished cavalier oblique is strengthened to complete the drawing.

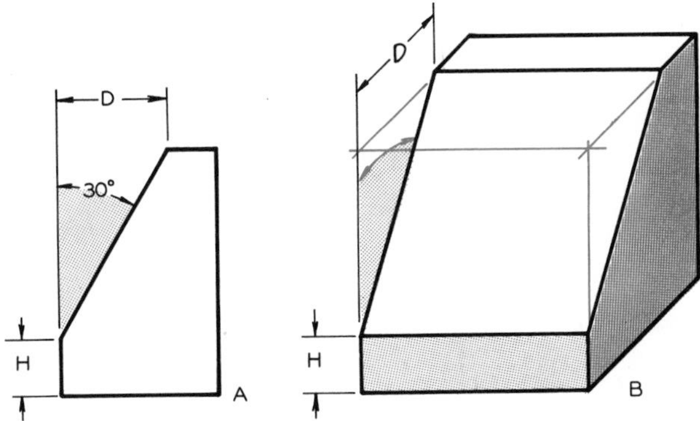

Fig. 17-37. Angles in oblique must be located by using coordinates. They cannot be measured true size.

and depth dimensions to draw a box that contains the object. The front surface is drawn true size in step 1 of Fig. 17-36. In step 2, the receding axis is drawn at any angle—30° in this case. The depth is measured true length along the receding axis; therefore, this is a cavalier oblique drawing. The notches are removed from the blocked-in drawing and the lines are strengthened in step 3 to complete the drawing. The resulting cavalier oblique adequately describes the object in much the same manner as an isometric drawing would.

17-16 ANGLES IN OBLIQUE

Actual measurements can be made in any direction on the true-size plane of an oblique. But on the two other planes of the oblique, true measurements can be made only parallel to the axes of the drawing. In this respect obliques are similar to isometric drawings.

An inclined plane is shown in an orthographic view in Fig. 17-37A. The angle shown here cannot be measured as a 30° angle in the oblique (B). Instead, dimension *D* must be measured along the receding axis to establish the point where the inclined plane will intersect the upper plane of the drawing. Dimension *H* is used to establish the other end of the inclined plane.

Since angles and inclined planes cannot be measured as true angles and true lengths in oblique, it is wise for the draftsman to take ad-

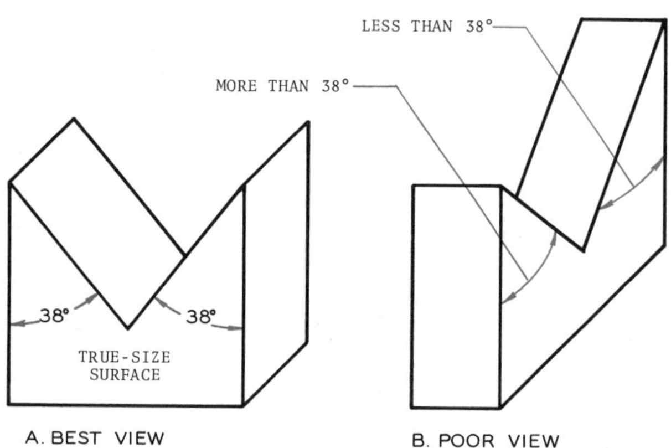

Fig. 17-38. The best view is the view that takes advantage of the ease of construction offered by oblique drawings. The view in B is less descriptive and harder to construct than the view in A.

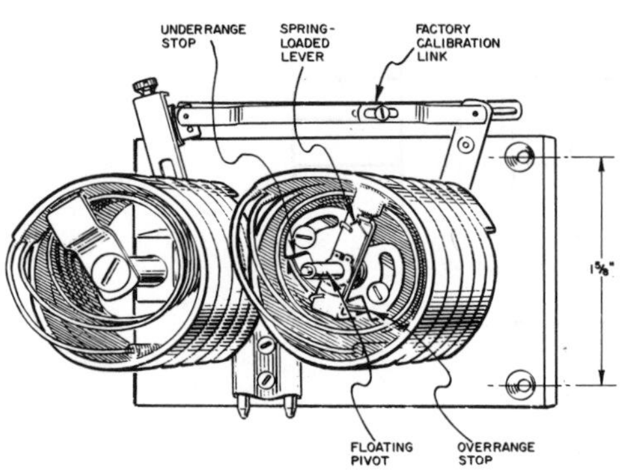

Fig. 17-39. An illustration of circles drawn in oblique as true circles. (Courtesy of Fischer and Porter Company.)

vantage of the benefits of an oblique when laying out a drawing. For example, the oblique drawing in part A of Fig. 17-38 is drawn with the front view as a true-size plane where the true angles can be measured. The drawing in part B is correct, but this view requires more construction than does the drawing in A. In addition, the angles cannot be measured true size since they do not lie in a true-size plane. Nor does the position of the object illustrate its features as well in B as in A.

17-17 CIRCLES IN OBLIQUE

One side of a cube usually shows true size in an oblique drawing; this means that angles and other measurements can be made true size on this surface in any direction. This feature is the greatest advantage of an oblique drawing. It means that circles can be drawn as true circles on the true-size plane. Figure 17-39 is an example of an oblique drawing of a gauging device composed of circular shapes. The circles are drawn as true circles rather than as ellipses. This advantage can also be seen in Fig. 17-34, where the circular ends of the cylinders are drawn as true circles.

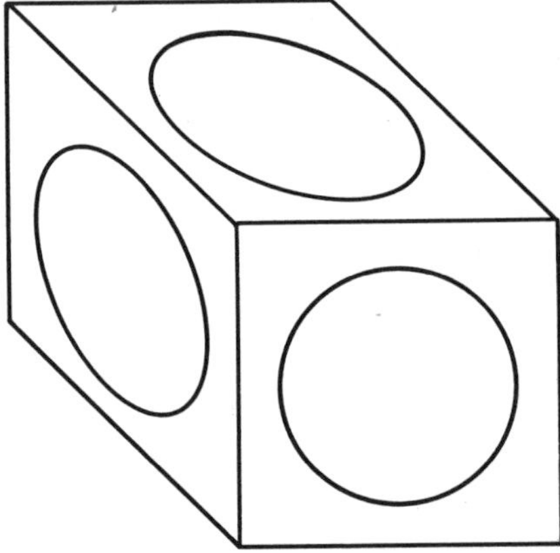

Fig. 17-40. Each of these three circles lies on one of the three planes of an oblique drawing.

Only one plane of an oblique can appear true size; consequently, the circles on the other two planes must be drawn as ellipses (Fig. 17-40). The four-center ellipse method is used to construct these ellipses as in isometric drawings.

The construction of a four-center ellipse to represent a circle on an oblique plane is shown in four steps in Fig. 17-41. The given circle is

FIGURE 17–41. FOUR-CENTER ELLIPSE IN OBLIQUE

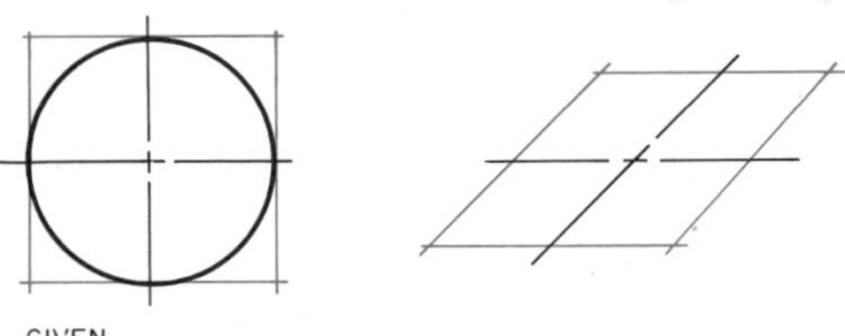

Step 1: The circle that is to be drawn in oblique is blocked in with a square which is tangent to the circle at four points. This square will appear as a rhombus on the oblique plane.

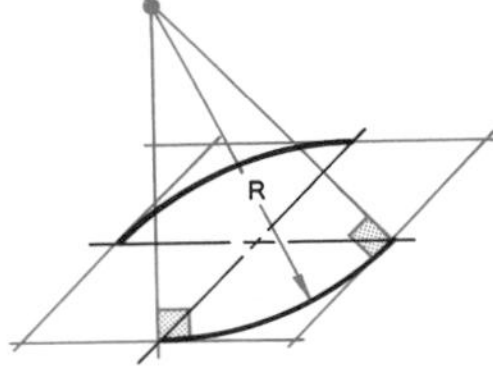

Step 2: Construction lines are drawn perpendicularly from the points of tangency to locate the centers for arcs for drawing two of the four segments of the ellipse.

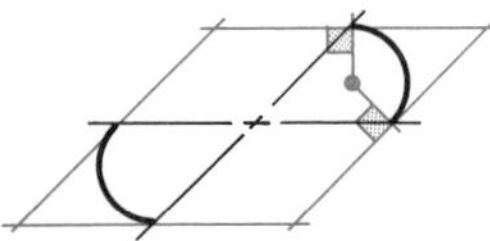

Step 3: The centers for the two remaining arcs are located.

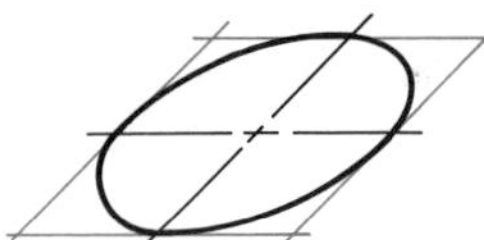

Step 4: When the four arcs have been drawn, the final result is an approximate ellipse.

blocked in with a square that is tangent to the circle at four points. The square is constructed in step 1 as a rhombus with the receding axis set at an angle which corresponds with the angle of the oblique plane on which the circle is drawn. The center lines cross the side of the rhombus at the four points where the ellipse will be tangent. From these points, perpendicular construction lines are drawn to locate the center of an arc that will constitute one-quarter of the ellipse (step 2). This method is again applied to construct the remaining arcs (step 3). The completed ellipse is shown in step 4.

Whenever possible, oblique drawings of objects with circular features should be positioned to have circles drawn on the true-size planes so that they can be drawn as true circles. Unless advantage is taken of this feature, the object might better be illustrated by an isometric drawing.

A wise use of the features of oblique drawings is shown in part A of Fig. 17–42. The circular features here are drawn as true circles. The drawing in part B requires the semicircular feature to be constructed by the four-center ellipse method. Not only does this method require more construction effort, but the view in part B is not as descriptive of the part as is the view in part A.

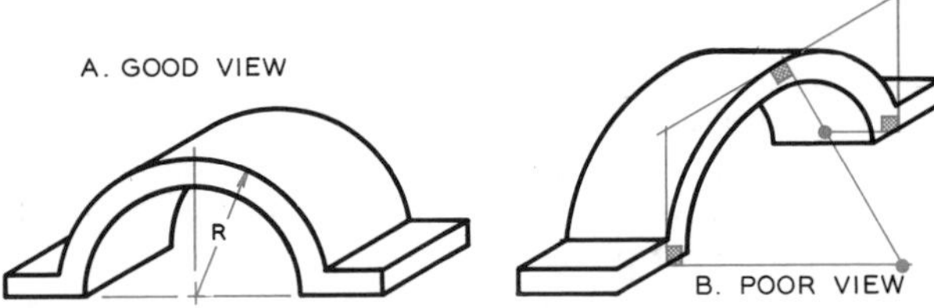

Fig. 17–42. An oblique view should be positioned to enable circular features to be drawn with the greatest of ease.

Circles that are to be drawn on the half-size surfaces of cabinet obliques must be located with coordinates and transferred to the oblique. Since dimensions along the receding axis are half-scale, the four-center ellipse method cannot be used. The type of construction used is illustrated in Fig. 17–43.

A. ORTHOGRAPHIC VIEW

B. CABINET OBLIQUE

TRUE SIZE SURFACE

HALF SCALE

FULL SCALE

Fig. 17-43. The four-center ellipse technique cannot be used to locate circular shapes on the foreshortened surface of a cabinet oblique. These ellipses must be plotted with coordinates.

FIGURE 17-44. CONSTRUCTION OF AN OBLIQUE

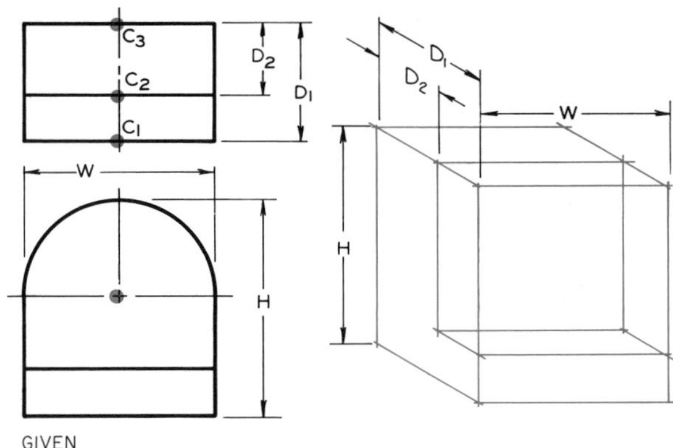

Step 1: The overall dimensions are used to block in the oblique pictorial. The notch is removed.

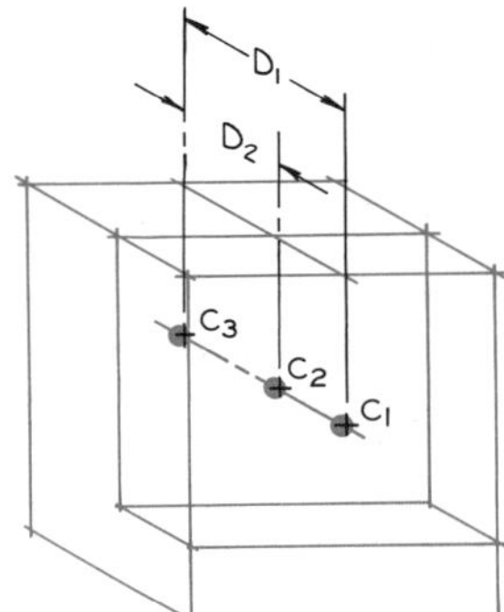

Step 2: The three centers C_1, C_2, and C_3 are located on each of the planes.

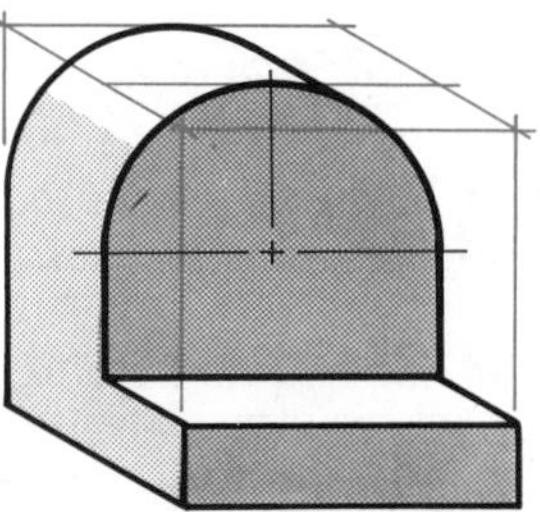

Step 3: The three centers found in step 2 are used to draw the semicircular features of the oblique. Lines are strengthened.

17-18 CIRCULAR FEATURES IN OBLIQUE

An object with a semicircular end is given in Fig. 17-44. The object is drawn as a blocked-in oblique in step 1 with the notch removed. Center C_1 is located on the front plane of the box in step 2. This point is projected back parallel to the receding axis to represent the axis of the cylindrical feature. Center C_2 is located on the middle plane and C_3 is located on the rear plane.

These centers can be used in step 3 for drawing the two arcs needed to represent the semicircular end. To complete the outline of the object, a line is drawn tangent to the two arcs and parallel to the receding axis. The lines are strengthened to complete the drawing. Note that the circular features are drawn as true circles to take advantage of the fact that true-size measurements can be made on one plane of an oblique pictorial.

17-19 IRREGULAR CURVES IN OBLIQUE

As in isometric drawings, irregular curves that do not lie in the true-size plane of an oblique must be plotted point-by-point. An example is shown in Fig. 17-45.

Coordinates are used to locate points along the curve in the orthographic view. These coordinates are transferred to the oblique draw-

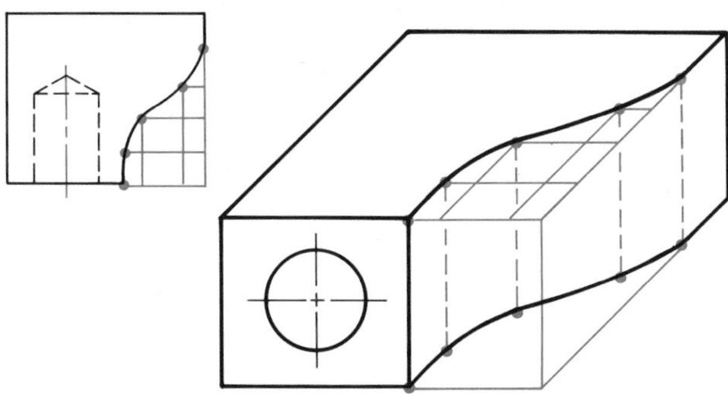

Fig. 17–45. Coordinates are used to establish irregular curves in oblique. The lower curve is found by projecting the points downward a distance equal to the height of the oblique.

ing to locate the points. An irregular curve is used to draw the curving line. The more points that are used, the more accurate the irregular curve will be.

If the object is of a uniform thickness, the lower curve can be found by projecting vertically down from the upper points a distance equal to the height of the object. It is unnecessary to plot each point on the lower surface with coordinates.

17–20 PICTORIAL SECTIONS

Both isometric and oblique drawings can be used to represent sections in pictorial. An isometric half section is shown in Fig. 17–46. An oblique full section is shown in Fig. 17–47. This pictorial section is also dimensioned to make it an effective method of communicating the full description of the part.

17–21 AXONOMETRIC PROJECTION

An *axonometric projection* is a form of orthographic projection in which the object is projected perpendicularly onto the projection plane with parallel projectors. The object is placed in an oblique position to the picture plane to achieve a three-dimensional effect. Three types of axonometric projections are possible: (1) isometric, (2) dimetric, or (3) trimetric. The *isometric projection* is the view obtained when the line of sight is parallel to the diagonal of a cube. In this case, the three planes will be

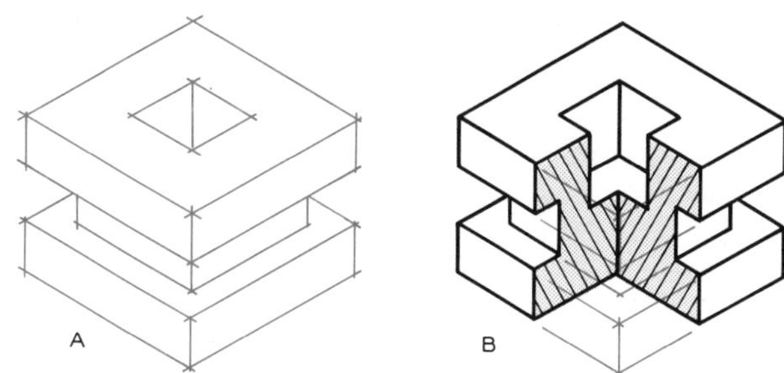

Fig. 17–46. The construction of an isometric half section. The imaginary cutting plane passes halfway through the object to show internal features.

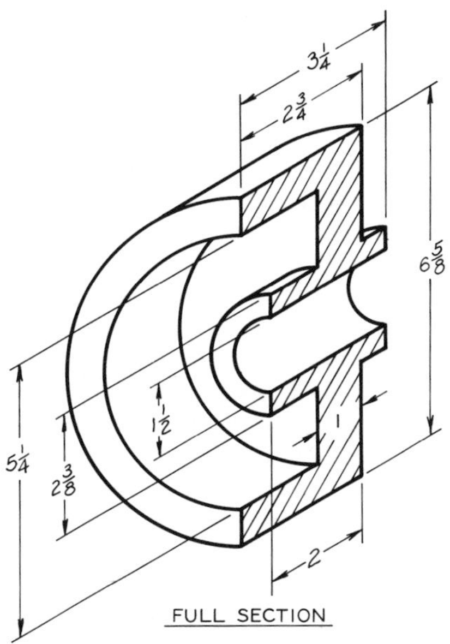

Fig. 17–47. Oblique pictorials can be drawn as sections and dimensioned to serve as working drawings.

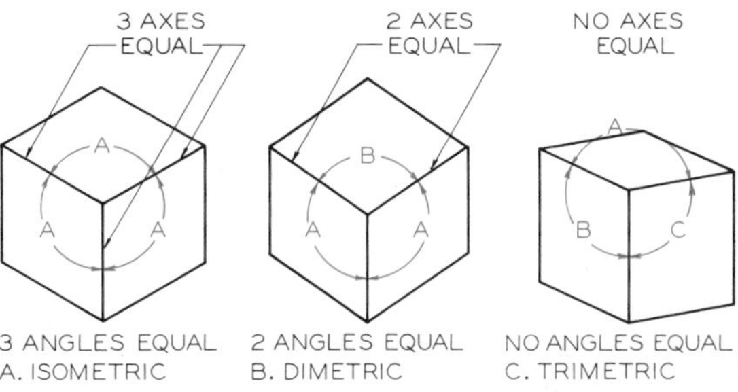

Fig. 17–48. The three types of axonometric projection.

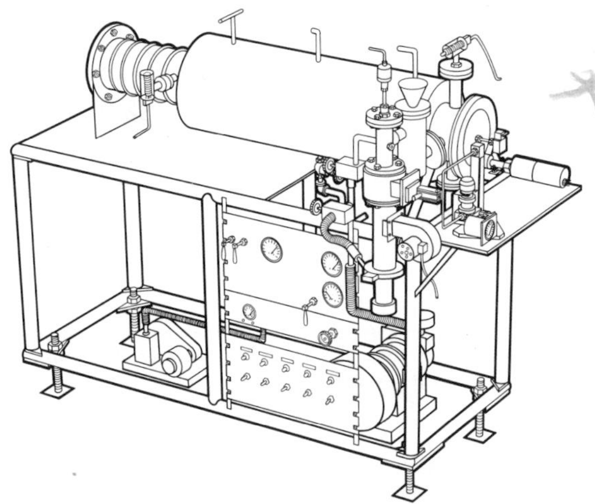

Fig. 17-49. A trimetric projection of a cold diffusion pump. (Courtesy of Aro, Inc., Arnold Engineering Center.)

equally foreshortened and the axes equally spaced 120° apart, as shown in Fig. 17-48A. The measurements along the three axes will be equally foreshortened rather than true length, as in *isometric drawing*. The *dimetric projection* is an axonometric projection in which two planes are equally foreshortened and two of the axes are separated by equal angles (Fig. 17-48B). An infinite number of combinations of angles are available for dimetric projection. The measurements along two axes are equal in a dimetric. In the trimetric *projection*, all three planes are unequally foreshortened; therefore their axes are unequally separated, as shown in Fig. 17-48C. The measurements along the three axes of a cube are unequal in a trimetric. Figure 17-49 is a trimetric projection of a cold diffusion pump.

17-22 AXONOMETRIC CONSTRUCTION

Isometric, dimetric, or trimetric projections are constructed in the same manner, the only difference being the direction of the line of sight. A trimetric projection is constructed by steps in Fig. 17-50 to illustrate a simplified approach to the development of the trimetric scales. These can be used in many cases as permanent measuring aids and thus eliminate the need for repeating the basic construction.

A cube should always be used for establishing the axonometric scales instead of the object to be drawn. In steps 1 and 2, the cube is revolved and tilted at the specified angles. If the top view were revolved 45° and the side view tilted 35° 16′, the projection would be an isometric, since this revolution would give the point view of the cube's diagonal.

The three axes can be enlarged and more units added to form a trimetric scale that can be used for drawing any trimetric at this particular angle. This eliminates the need for duplicating the construction when trimetrics of similar angles are drawn repeatedly during a given project assignment.

A trimetric scale is not complete unless the ellipse guides are found for each plane. The ellipse templates can then be used to draw circular features by simply locating the center point of the circle to be drawn. The ellipse guide will be different for each plane, since each is foreshortened differently. The construction for determining ellipse guides is shown in steps in Fig. 17-51. The trimetric projection of the cube found in Fig. 17-50 is given. The theory discussed in Articles 9-6 and 7-20 must be employed to find the true-size plane, 1-2-3, in step 1. It is known that the three principal planes of a cube are mutually perpendicular; hence we know that *OE* is perpendicular to plane *ABCO*; line *OC* is perpendicular to plane *AFEO*; and line *AO* is perpendicular to plane *EDCO*. A line that is perpendicular to a plane is perpendicular to all of the lines in that plane. Likewise, when two lines are perpendicular to each other, they will project as perpendiculars in the view giving one or both of them as true length. These principles can be used to find a true-length line on each principal plane of the cube. Line 1-2 on plane *ABCO*, which is perpendicular to the extension of line *EO*, is true length. Lines 2-3 and 1-3 are found in the same manner by extending the axes of the cube.

A plane that is true size in the front view must be a frontal plane and will therefore be a vertical edge in the side view. The edge view of plane 1-2-3 is located conveniently in the side view,

FIGURE 17–50. TRIMETRIC-SCALE CONSTRUCTION

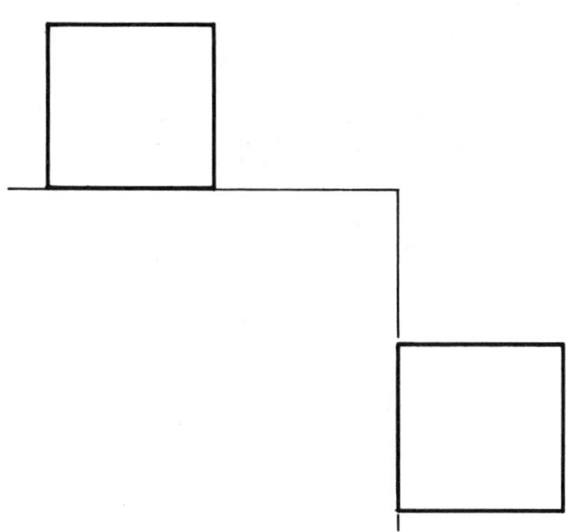

Given: The top and side views of a cube.
Required: Determine a trimetric scale for constructing axonometric projections of various objects. The scales will be found by revolving the top view 30° clockwise and tilting the side view 34°.
Reference: Article 17–22.

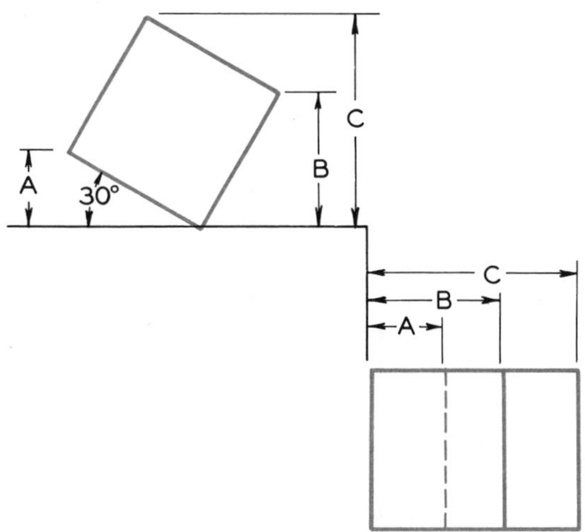

Step 1: Revolve the top view 30° clockwise. Find the side view by transferring dimensions A, B, and C from the top view. If the revolution had been 45° in the top view, the resulting projection would be either a dimetric or isometric.

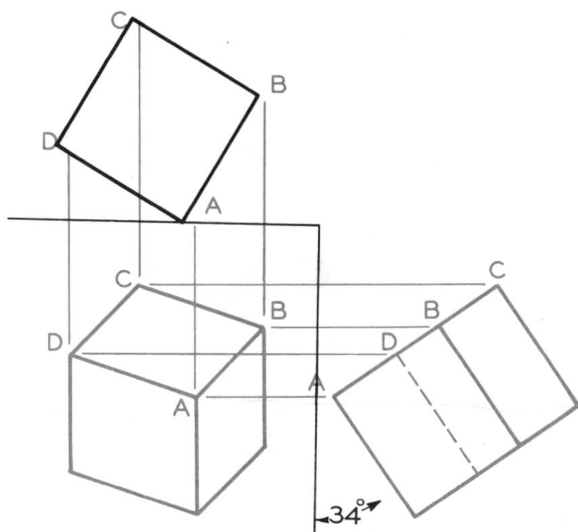

Step 2: Tilt the side view 34°. This will change the projection of the top view, but not the width dimension; consequently, it is unnecessary to change the top view. Determine the trimetric projection of the cube by projecting from the top and side views as in orthographic projection. The resulting pictorial is a trimetric projection.

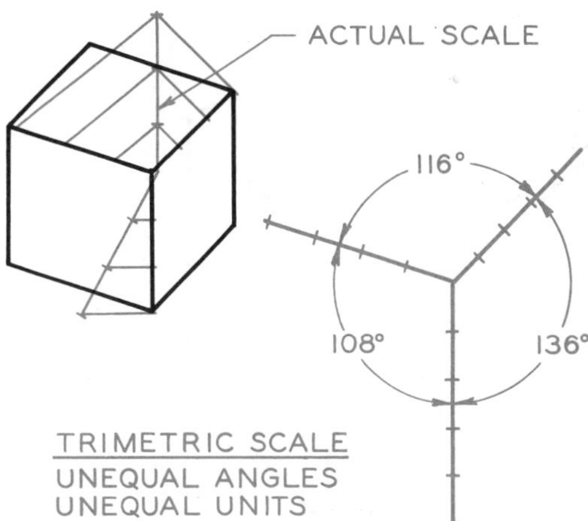

Step 3: All sides of a cube are equal; therefore divide each axis (or edge) into an equal number of units by proportional divisions as shown, even though the three axes in a trimetric have different lengths. The three axes can be extended and scaled into as many units as necessary and used for constructing trimetric pictorials at this particular angle.

FIGURE 17–51. ELLIPSE GUIDE ANGLES FOR A TRIMETRIC SCALE

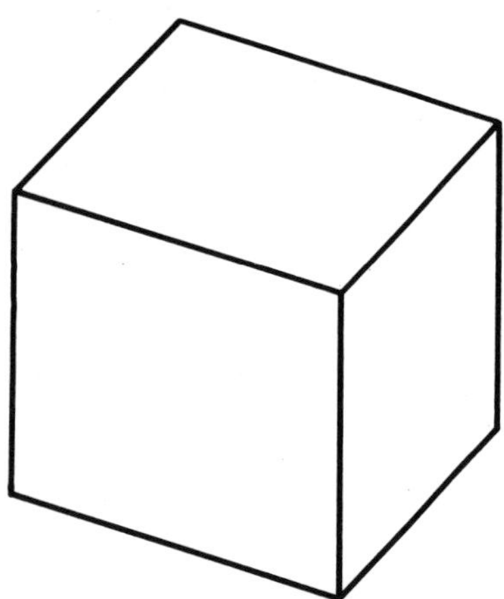

Given: A trimetric projection of the cube found in Fig. 17–50.
Required: Determine the ellipse guide for each plane and its position.
Reference: Article 17–22.

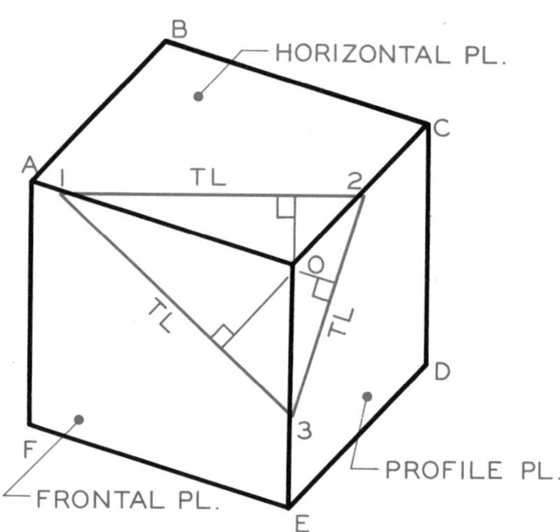

Step 1: The planes of a cube are mutually perpendicular; therefore line *OC* is perpendicular to plane *AOEF*, line *OA* is perpendicular to *OCDE*, and *OE* is perpendicular to plane *ABCO*. On each plane construct true-length lines, which are located perpendicular to the axis lines, *AO, CO,* and *EO.* The true-length lines are 1–2, 2–3, and 3–1. These lines will intersect at points on the axes forming a triangle 1–2–3.

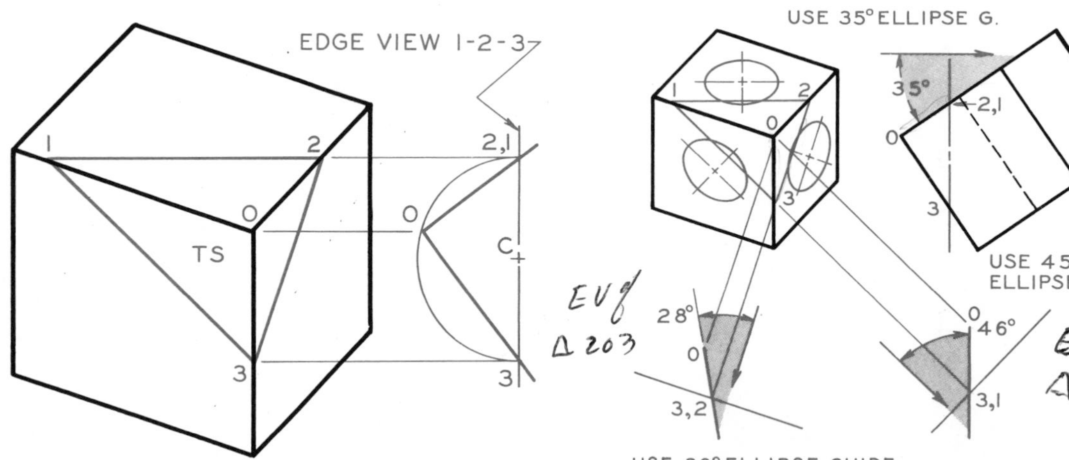

Step 2: Since the plane 1–2–3 is composed of true-length lines, it is true size in the trimetric projection. Determine the side view of the plane which is a frontal plane in the profile view by projection. Find the 90° angle of the cube in the side view by constructing a semicircle, using the edge view of 1–2–3 as the diameter. Project point *O* to the semicircle where the 90° angle is inscribed.

Step 3: Two views permit auxiliary views to be found. Determine the edge view of each principal plane by locating the point views of lines 1–2, 2–3, and 3–1. The ellipse guide angle is the angle between the edge views of 1–0–2, 2–0–3, and 1–0–3 and the line of sight. Position the ellipse guides on each plane so that the major diameter is parallel to the true-length lines on that plane.

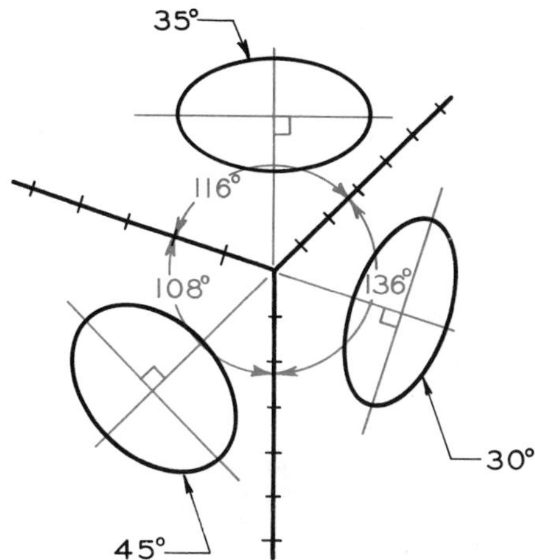

Fig. 17–52A. The complete trimetric scale.

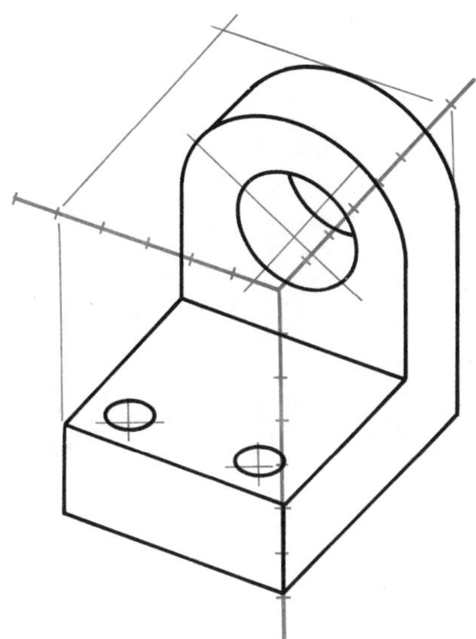

Fig. 17–52B. An application of the trimetric scale.

as shown in step 2 of Fig. 17–51. The edge view is bisected and a semicircle is drawn with its center at the midpoint and the edge view as the diameter. Point *O* is projected to the semicircle to locate the point at which the 90° angle of the cube will be inscribed. Two views are now available from which auxiliary views may be constructed to find the edge views of the three principal planes of the cube where the ellipse guide angles can be measured. We use planes 1–0–2, 1–0–3, and 2–0–3 as segments of the plane rather than projecting the entire plane in each auxiliary view. The ellipse guide for the horizontal plane can be read directly from the side view, where the plane, 1–0–2, appears as an edge and the line of sight true length.

The angles between the three planes were found to be 35°, 28°, and 46°. Ellipse guides are commonly available in increments of 5°; this makes it necessary to select the size nearest these angles, that is 35°, 30°, and 45°. The position of the ellipses with respect to the planes is important. The major diameters of an ellipse, which are always true length, will be parallel to the true-length lines on each plane that were previously constructed.

This construction is simplified into the form of a trimetric scale (Fig. 17–52A) which consists of three axes divided into the proper units, ellipse guide angles for each surface, and the direction of the major diameter of each ellipse. A pictorial can be drawn by placing tracing paper over this scale and constructing the trimetric in much the same manner as we would an isometric drawing, by drawing parallels to the three axes, as shown in Fig. 17–52B. Convenient units of measurement are assigned to the divisions of each scale. Circular arcs can be constructed using ellipse guides. A variety of trimetric and dimetric scales can be constructed in this fashion to be filed for use in future axonometric projections.

17–23 OBLIQUE PROJECTION

As previously mentioned, *oblique projection* is a method of constructing a pictorial with parallel projectors drawn oblique to a picture plane. Although these principles are applied generally in the three types of oblique drawings—cabinet, cavalier, and general—the true projection method is seldom used to construct an oblique pictorial. To provide a better understanding of the origin of oblique principles, we shall review the true oblique projection as shown in Fig. 17–53.

It can be seen that the line of sight is oblique to the projection planes of the cube given in the top and side views. The angle made by the line of sight with the projection planes is θ in the

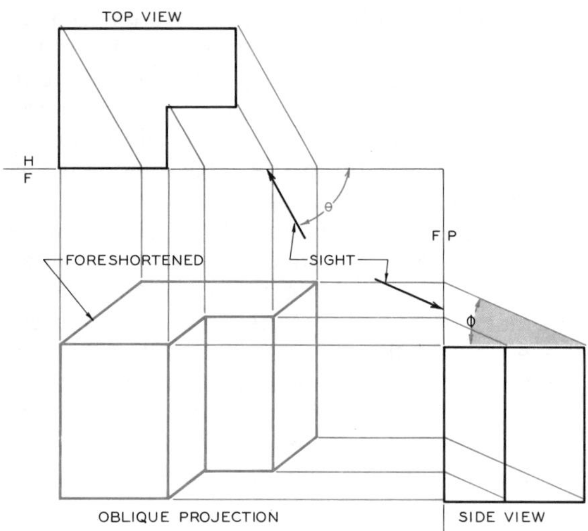

Fig. 17-53. An oblique projection.

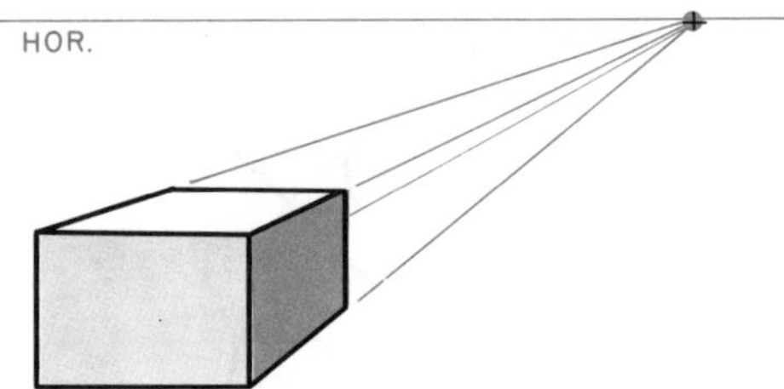

Fig. 17-54. A one-point perspective of a box.

Fig. 17-55. This photograph is a one-point perspective as proved by the construction. (Courtesy of Pan American Petroleum Corporation.)

top view and ϕ in the side view. Parallel projectors drawn from the object parallel to these lines of sight in both views establish points in the front view, resulting in an oblique projection. The cube face that is parallel to the projection plane appears in true size and shape in the front view, while the dimensions along the receding axes are less than true length when θ and ϕ are less than 45°. When one of these angles is greater than 45°, the measurement along the receding axis is greater than true length; this introduces an objectionable degree of distortion.

Oblique projection principles are used as the basis for the *oblique drawing* methods previously discussed. For most purposes, oblique drawings are more satisfactory than are the oblique projections discussed here.

17-24 PERSPECTIVE PROJECTION

Perspective drawing is the most realistic form of pictorial. A perspective is the view that is normally seen by the eye or camera. All parallel lines tend to converge as they recede from the observer or tend to vanish at infinite points. The observer's eye accepts this principle and expects its application when viewing a pictorial or photograph.

There are three basic types of perspectives: (1) one-point, (2) two-point, and (3) three-point, depending on the number of vanishing points required for the construction of each. An example of a *one-point perspective* is shown in Fig. 17-54, which shows a block on an infinite horizontal plane. The lines of the receding sides tend to vanish at an infinite point at the horizon. This point is called a *vanishing point*. One side of the block is parallel to the picture plane and

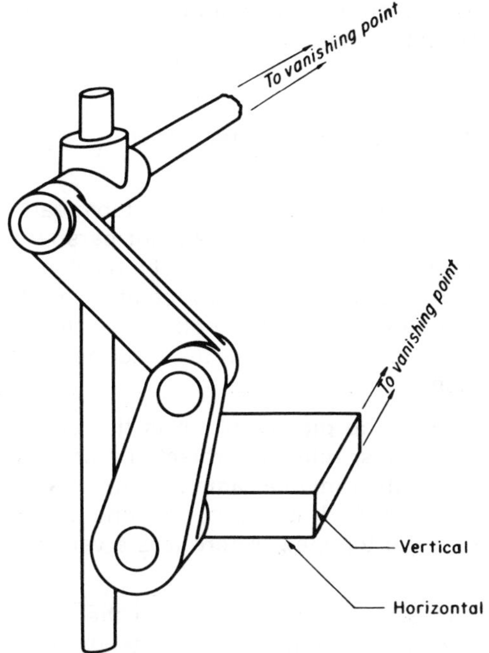

Fig. 17-56. A one-point perspective. (Courtesy of ANSI; Y14.4-1957.)

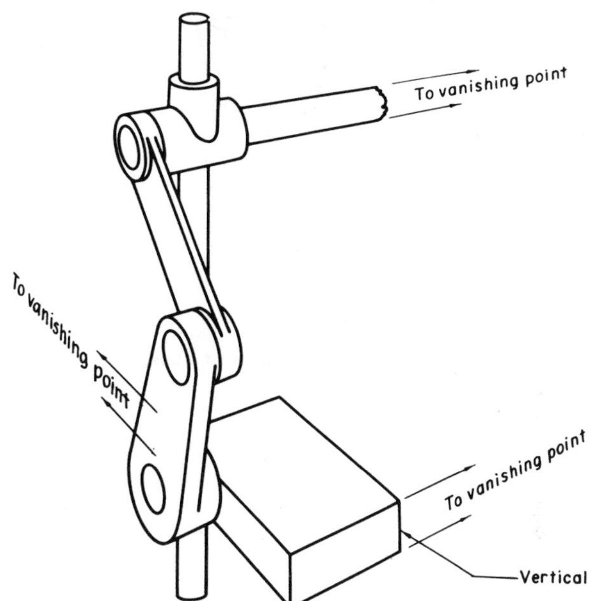

Fig. 17-58. A two-point perspective. (Courtesy of ANSI; Y14.4-1957.)

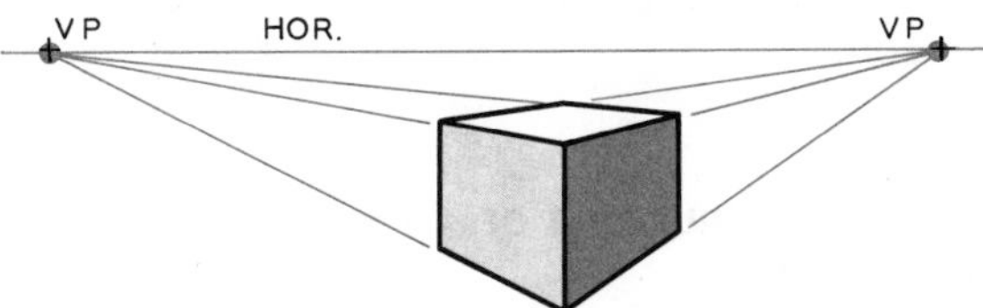

Fig. 17-57. A two-point perspective of a box.

consequently its lines do not vanish. A photographic example of a one-point perspective is shown in Fig. 17-55, where the vanishing point can be found by construction. A one-point perspective of the assembly previously drawn in various forms of pictorials is shown in Fig. 17-56. Lines of the object tend to converge to a single point. This type of perspective is effectively used to present the interior of a room or other interior features of various components.

The *two-point perspective* has two vanishing points, as illustrated in Fig. 17-57. Two of the prism's planes are inclined to the picture plane and hence appear foreshortened. All parallel lines in the two-point perspective converge at vanishing points; however, vertical lines do not. These remain vertical and with these lines distortion is the least noticeable. Another example of a two-point perspective is shown in Fig. 17-58.

The *three-point perspective* is drawn with three vanishing points that cause all principal lines to vanish to one of three points. Vertical lines, as well as horizontal lines, vanish to a point, as shown in Fig. 17-59. The horizontal lines vanish to points on the horizon at infinity. The vertical lines vanish to a point located over or under the horizon. This type of perspective is used for drawing large structures as viewed from a low vantage point or from a high vantage

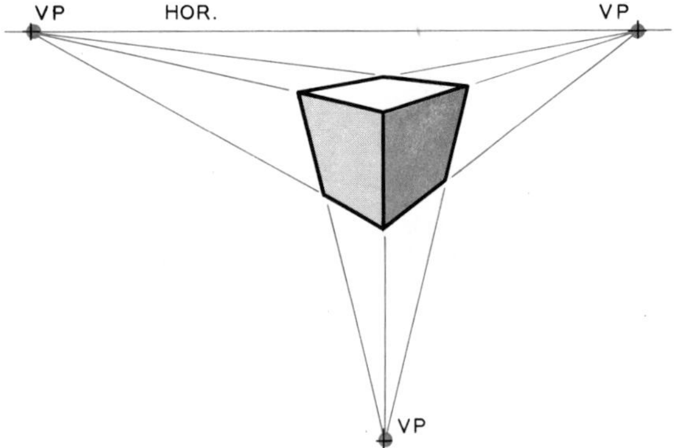

Fig. 17–59. A three-point perspective of a box.

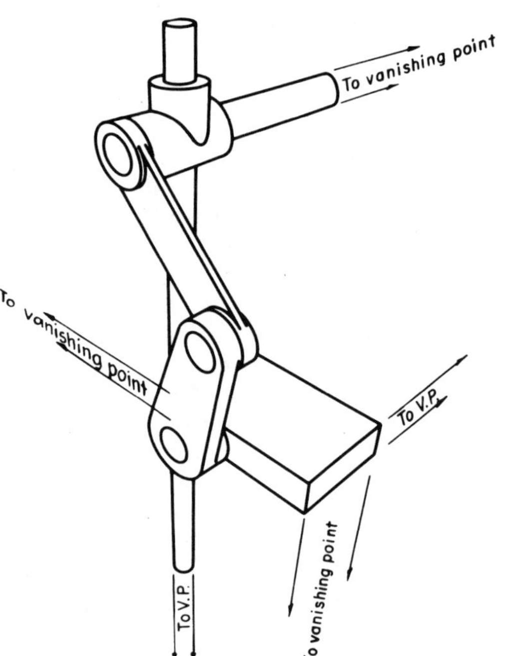

Fig. 17–60. A three-point perspective. (Courtesy of ANSI; Y14.4-1957.)

point near the object. An example of a three-point perspective is given in Fig. 17–60.

17–25 CONSTRUCTION OF A ONE-POINT PERSPECTIVE

Figure 17–61 shows the sequential steps leading to the construction of a one-point perspective. The top view and side views of a block are given, as are the horizon, station point, ground line, and picture plane. We shall define these terms, since they are used to describe the construction.

Picture Plane. The picture plane is the plane on which the perspective is projected much as though it were the film in a camera on which the image is projected. It is drawn horizontally on the sheet in the top view, where it is a vertical edge.

Horizon. This is a horizontal line in the front view, where the horizontal plane extends infinitely, just as the ocean extends to the horizon.

Vanishing Points. These are points on the horizon where horizontal lines will converge.

Station Point. This point marks the location of the observer's eye in the plan view. The front view of the station point will always lie on the horizon.

17–26 CONSTRUCTION OF A TWO-POINT PERSPECTIVE

In the two-point perspective, two planes of a block are inclined to the picture plane, resulting in two vanishing points on the horizon. Various perspective views can be obtained by the relationship of the ground line and horizon in a two-point perspective or any type of perspective. Three extremes are shown in Fig. 17–62. An *aerial view* is obtained when the height of the subject does not extend to the horizon (Fig. 17–62A). This effect will be exaggerated as the angle of vision approaches the vertical. A *ground view* is obtained when the ground line and the horizon coincide, as shown in Fig.

FIGURE 17-61. CONSTRUCTION OF A ONE-POINT PERSPECTIVE

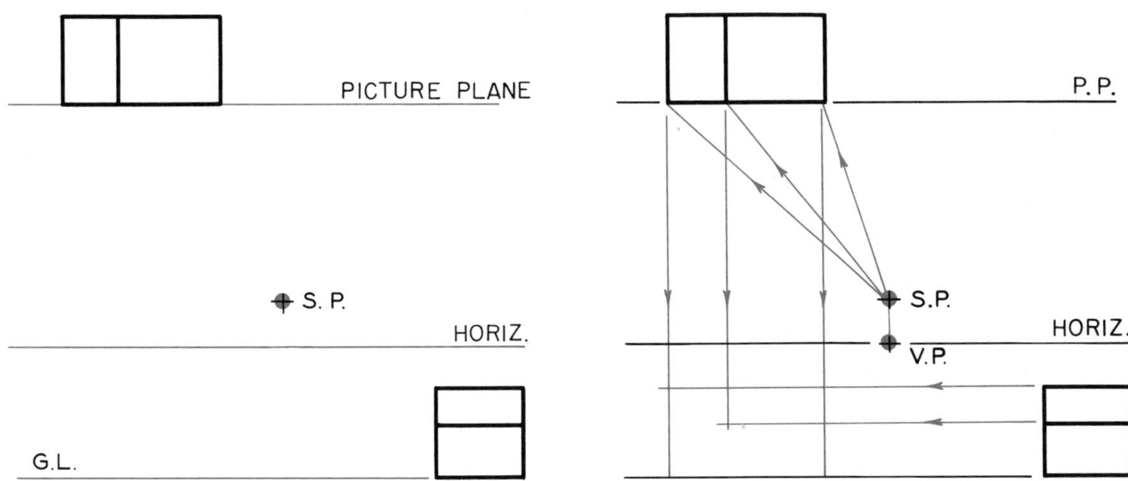

Given: The top and side views of an object, the station point, horizon, and ground line.
Required: Construct a perspective of the object.
Reference: Article 17-25.

Step 1: Since the object is parallel to the picture plane, there will be only one vanishing point, which will be located on the horizon below the station point. Projections from the top view and side view establish the front plane of the object. This surface is true size since it lies in the picture plane.

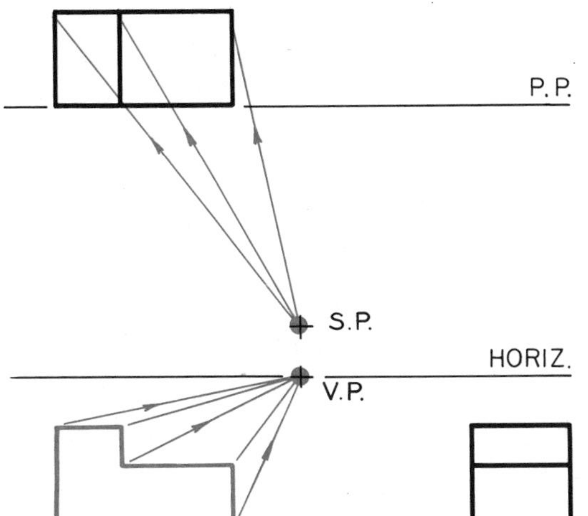

Step 2: Draw projectors from the station point to the rear points of the object in the top view and from the front view to the vanishing point on the horizon. In a one-point perspective the vanishing point is the front view of the station point.

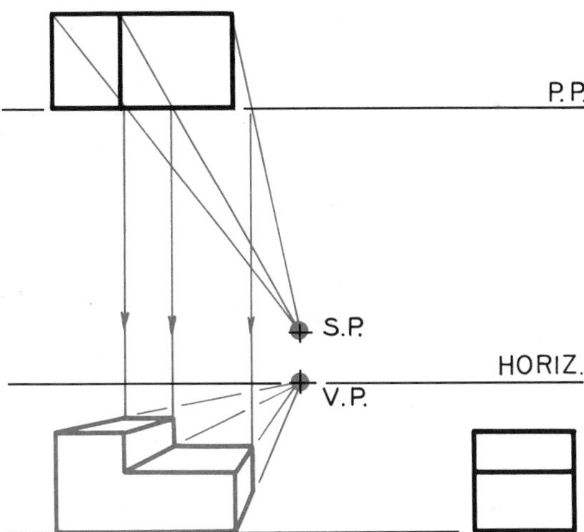

Step 3: Construct vertical projectors to the front view from the points where the projectors from the station point cross the picture plane. These projectors intersect the lines leading to the vanishing point to establish the complete perspective. This is called a one-point perspective since the lines converge at a single point.

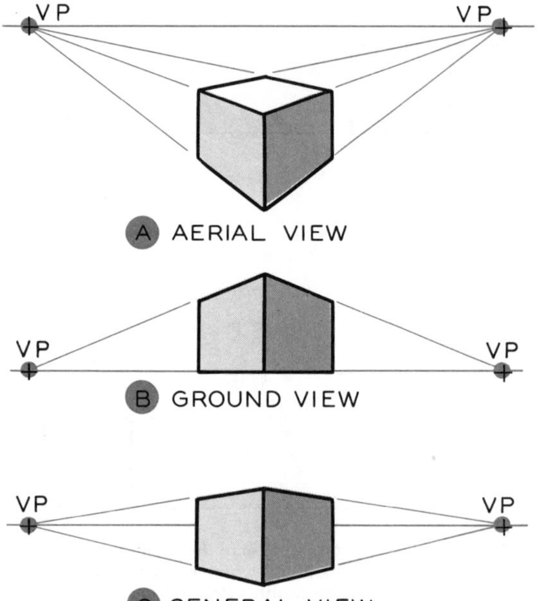

Fig. 17–62. Three types of views of a perspective.

17–62B. The viewer is assumed to be looking parallel to the edge view of the horizontal plane. The general type of perspective is seen in part C; a portion of the object extends above and below the horizon, giving a view which, for large objects, is a familiar one to viewers.

The construction of a two-point perspective is shown in sequential steps in Fig. 17–63. The horizon is located above the height of the object to give a slight aerial effect. The vanishing points are found by drawing lines parallel to the sides of the object in the top view through the station point.

Line *AB* in the top view lies in the picture plane; hence it will be true length in the perspective view (step 2). Lines are drawn from each end of the line *AB* to the vanishing points. These represent an extension of the surfaces of an object of infinite size. Projectors are drawn from the station point to the corners of the object in the top view. The intersections of these projectors with the picture plane are projected to the front view, where they intersect the infinite lines drawn to the vanishing points. These intersections establish the limits of the block being drawn.

The notch is removed from the perspective by locating point *C* on the true-length line *AB*, by projection from the side view (step 3). Lines are drawn from point *C* to the vanishing points.

In these examples, the objects were drawn to make contact with the picture plane in the top view. This approach is usually more convenient for perspective construction; however, the object can be drawn in perspective even if it does *not* contact the picture plane. A perspective of this type is illustrated in Fig. 17–64. The sides of the object are extended to the picture plane as though the object were infinite in size. Where the extension intersects the picture plane, heights will be true length in the perspective view or front view, thus establishing the height of an infinite plane that will vanish to the horizon. The perspective of the object that lies on a portion of this infinite plane can be found by projecting to the object from the station point to locate points on the picture plane. These points are projected vertically to the infinite plane to find object lines. Note that the other lines of the object in the top view (perpendicular to those that were extended) could have been extended to the picture plane and the same procedure could have been followed, using a different vanishing point.

17–27 MEASURING POINTS

The measuring-point system of drawing two-point perspectives is illustrated in Fig. 17–65. Measuring points eliminate the need for a top view after the vanishing points and measuring points have been located. This characteristic is very important when the top view is excessively large such as a house plan or similar layout. The designer using measuring points can mark with actual dimensions from the drawing rather than projecting to the top view from the station points as is customary in the usual perspective system.

FIGURE 17–63. CONSTRUCTION OF A TWO-POINT PERSPECTIVE

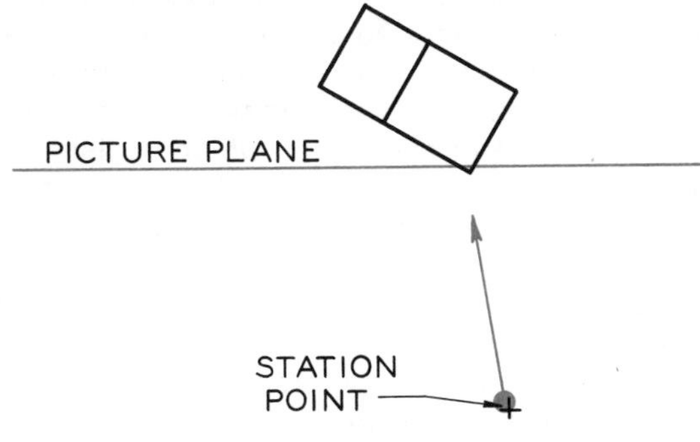

TOP VIEW
PP
S.P.
VP
HORIZON
VP
FRONT V.
G.L.

Given: The top view of an object and the station point (position of the observer's eye).
Required: Draw the perspective of the object.
Reference: Article 17–25.

Step 1: Construct projectors which extend from the top view of the station point to the picture plane parallel to the forward edges of the object. Project these points vertically to a horizontal line in the front view to locate vanishing points. Locate the horizon in a convenient position. Draw the ground line below the horizon and construct the known side view on the ground line.

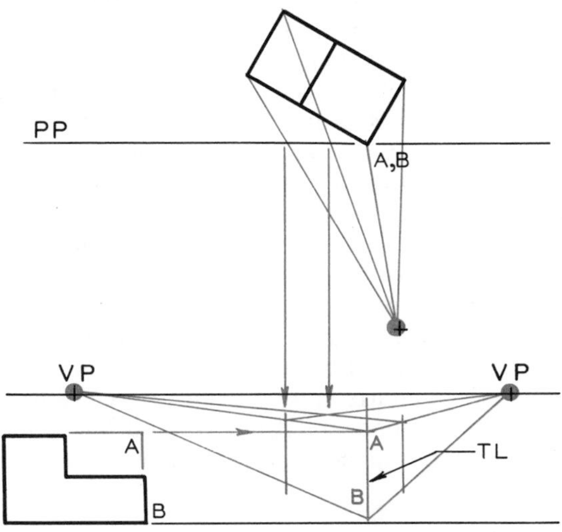
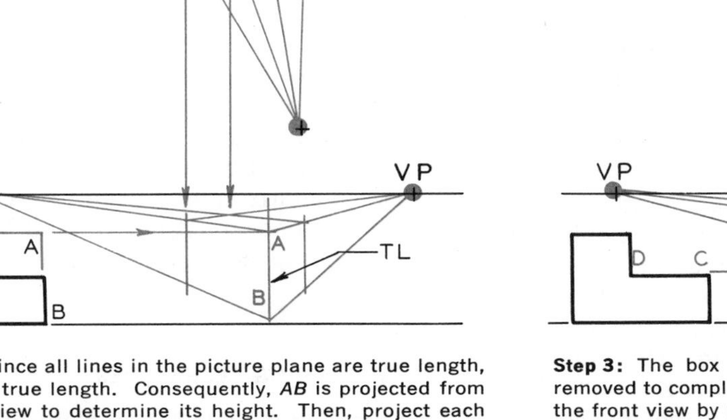

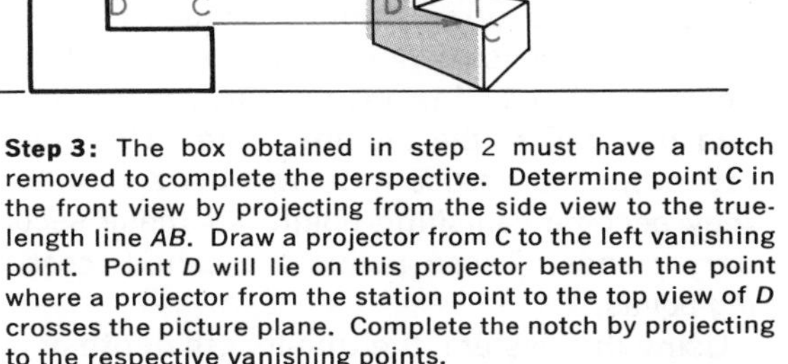

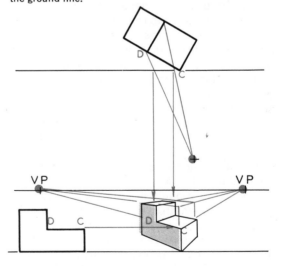

Step 2: Since all lines in the picture plane are true length, line *AB* is true length. Consequently, *AB* is projected from the side view to determine its height. Then, project each end of *AB* to the vanishing points to determine two perspective planes. Draw projectors from the station point to the exterior edges of the top view. Project the intersections of these projectors and the picture plane to the front view to determine the limits of the object.

Step 3: The box obtained in step 2 must have a notch removed to complete the perspective. Determine point *C* in the front view by projecting from the side view to the true-length line *AB*. Draw a projector from *C* to the left vanishing point. Point *D* will lie on this projector beneath the point where a projector from the station point to the top view of *D* crosses the picture plane. Complete the notch by projecting to the respective vanishing points.

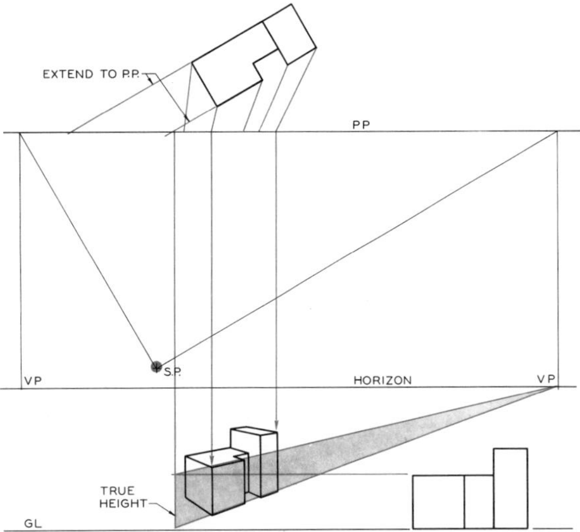

Fig. 17–64. The construction of a two-point perspective that is not in contact with the picture plane.

A measuring point is an alternative vanishing point used to locate dimensions along the receding lines that vanish to the horizon. The sequential steps of finding measuring points for a two-point perspective are shown in Fig. 17–65. The top view is positioned as desired, with the station point, vanishing points, ground line, and horizon located in the usual manner. In step 1, the two frontal edges of the top view are revolved into the picture plane, using point *B* as the center of revolution. Construction lines are drawn through both points *A* and points *C* as shown. Since lines *AB* and *BC* have been revolved into the picture plane, they can be projected to the ground line as true-length lines equal to their length in the top view of the object (step 2). Measuring points are found in step 2 by drawing construction lines from the station point parallel to the planes through points *A* and points *C* to the picture plane. The points are projected vertically to the horizon, where they become vanishing points for these secondary planes. These points are called *measuring points*.

Using this system, the true-length depth of an object, *AB*, can be measured along the ground line and projected to its respective measuring point, as shown in step 3. An imaginary plane can be drawn from this projector to the right measuring point, intersecting the infinite plane of the left side of the object, which vanishes to the left vanishing point, to establish the depth of the block. Similarly, the true length of the width, *BC*, can be measured along the ground line and projected to its measuring point to establish the width measurement in the perspective view. Following this procedure, we can draw the perspective without having to project from a large top view. Instead, dimensions can be taken directly from the top view and laid off on the ground line as true-length dimensions, provided these measurements are parallel to the principal lines established in the construction illustrated in step 1.

Perspective charts are time-saving devices that eliminate the need for the construction of vanishing points and other projections required in a perspective drawing. Charts are available in a number of forms for constructing perspectives from a variety of directions and angles. The grid is drawn to scale so that perspectives can be drawn by assigning a scale to the grid and measuring the pictorial directly on the chart. To permit repeated use, a sheet of tracing paper is usually placed over the chart on which the perspectives are drawn. An example of a two-point perspective on a grid is shown in Fig. 17–66. Perspective charts are excellent for preliminary sketches, since they give a general idea of the appearance of the finished perspective. The final perspective can be drawn with instruments in the same manner. Although perspective charts can be used to great advantage, the designer must understand the fundamentals of perspective projection to fully benefit from their use.

17–28 RENDERING TECHNIQUES

A line drawing is usually sufficient to convey a rough idea or to analyze a portion of a design. However, when a pictorial will be used for a formal presentation or as an illustration in a

FIGURE 17–65. CONSTRUCTION OF MEASURING POINTS

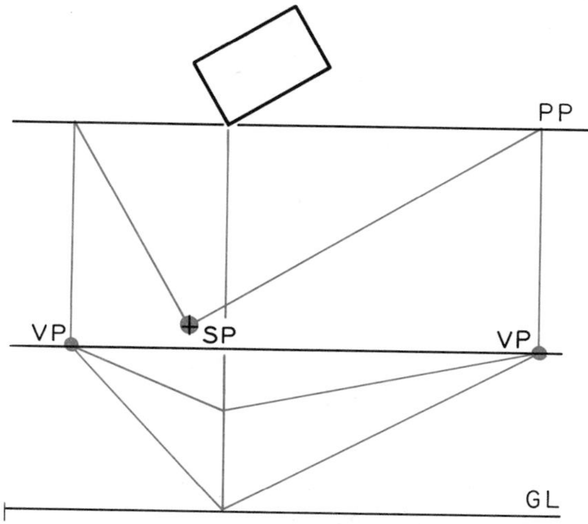

Given: The basic elements of a two-point perspective system.
Required: Find the measuring points to be used to eliminate the need for the top view of the perspective.
Reference: Article 17–27.

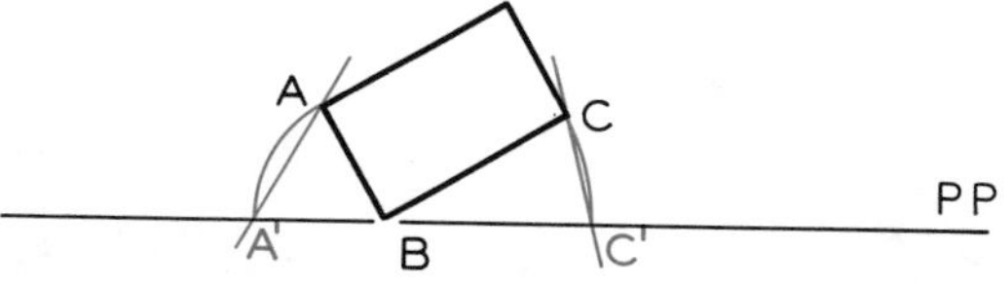

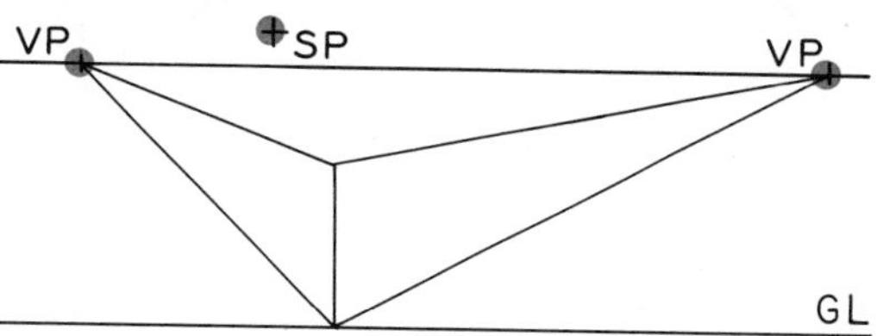

Step 1: In the top view, revolve lines *AB* and *BC* into the picture plane using point *B* as the center of revolution. Draw construction lines through points *A–A′* and points *C–C′*. These lines represent edge views of vertical planes passing through the corner points *A* and *C*.

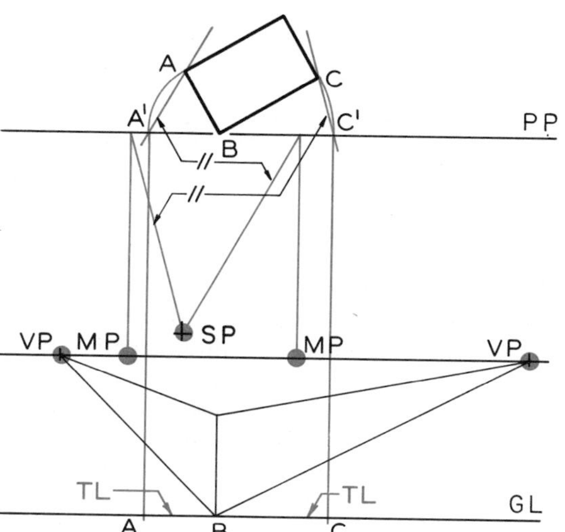

Step 2: Draw lines from the station point parallel to lines *A–A′* and *C–C′* to the picture plane. Project these points of intersection to the horizon to locate two measuring points. Distances *AB* and *BC* can be laid off true length on the ground line, since they have been revolved into the picture plane in the top view.

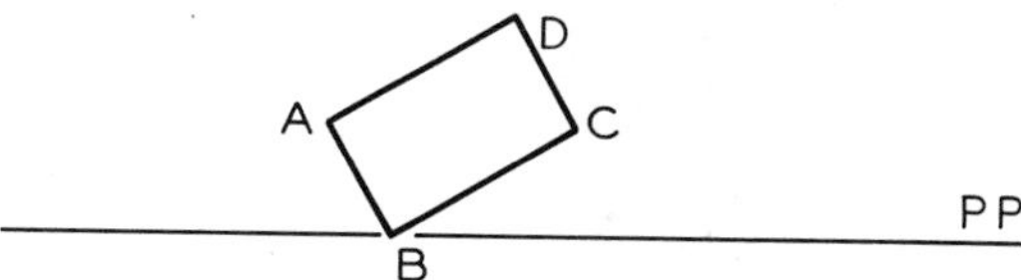

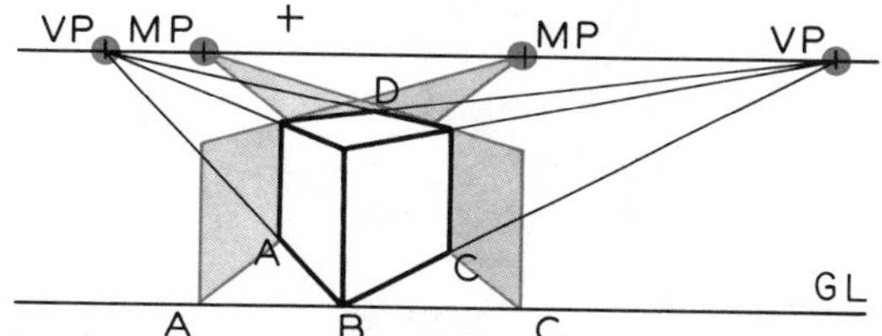

Step 3: Extend imaginary planes from points *A* and *C* on the GL to their respective measuring points. These planes intersect the infinite planes, which are extended to the vanishing points, to locate the two corners of the block. This method allows actual measurements to be laid off on the ground line and projected to measuring points to find corner points, rather than projecting points from the top view as in the conventional method.

Fig. 17-66. The use of a perspective grid. (Courtesy of Graphicraft.)

Fig. 17-67. A line drawing with a little shading applied. (Courtesy of the National Aeronautics and Space Administration.)

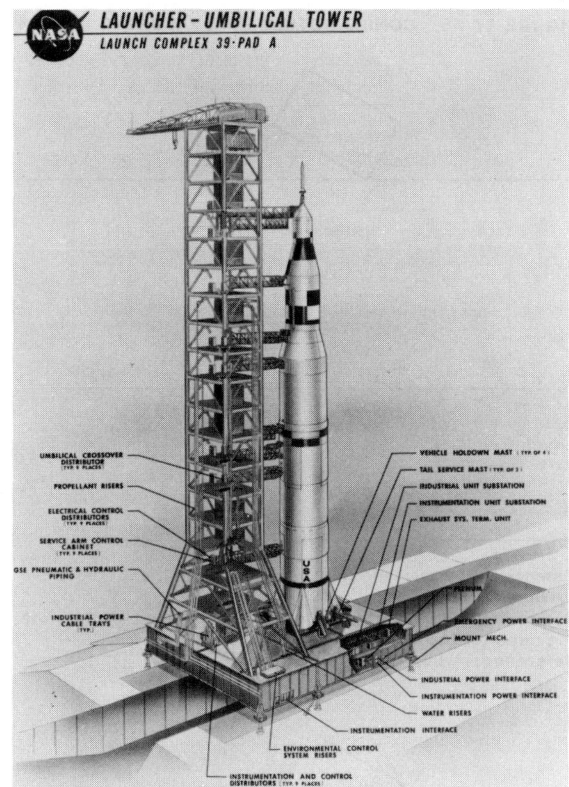

Fig. 17-68. A finished rendering of the outline drawing in Fig. 17-67. (Courtesy of the National Aeronautics and Space Administration.)

brochure or catalog, extra care should be taken to give the best effect possible. A line drawing can be greatly improved through the use of special materials and shading techniques. Shades and shadows give additional depth and realism to a drawing. This effect is emphasized in Figs. 17-67 and 17-68, where a drawing is presented first as a line drawing and then as a fully rendered illustration. Each form has its advantages in any given situation.

There are numerous techniques of rendering a pictorial, using many materials that are commercially available. The more basic forms of rendering will be covered in this chapter to give a general introduction to these methods, which are: (1) pencil, (2) ink, (3) overlay film, (4) scratch board, and (5) air brush.

Fig. 17–69. An example of a pencil sketch of an automobile. (Courtesy of Ford Motor Company.)

Pencil Shading. Pencil renderings are the most basic medium, since the designer does essentially all of his work with a pencil. He will make numerous sketches and pictorials from which he will develop his final design. Pencil shading can also be used effectively in his final, finished design sketch which is to be submitted for publication or exhibit.

Figure 17–69 is an example of a pencil rendering that is both realistic and attractive. This freehand sketch was drawn and shaded in a rather loose, casual, but effective style. Rather soft pencils, in the HB–3B range, are more appropriate for sketching. Tracing paper is often used as a sketching surface; however, a paper with a slight texture permits a greater variety of tones in line work and surface shading.

Two basic types of pencil shading are line shading and smudge shading. Line shading is accomplished by varying the pressure and shape of the pencil point on the paper. The strokes are usually visible in this type of shading. The smudge technique is the process of smoothing the graphite with fingertips or a piece of cotton to give a smudged tone appearance.

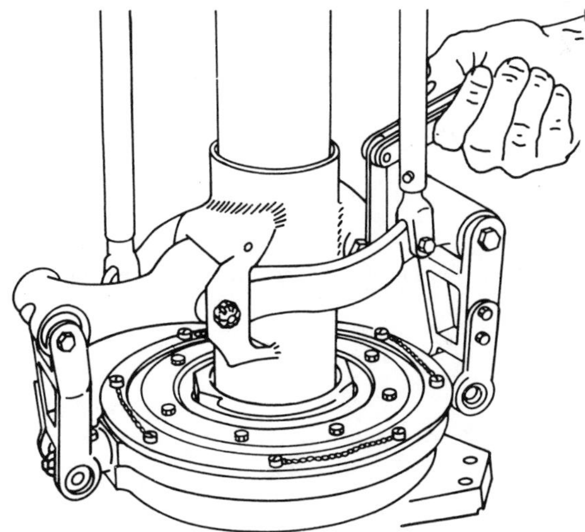

Fig. 17–70. An ink line drawing used to illustrate a technical manual. (Courtesy of Bell Helicopter Corporation.)

Ink Shading. Ink shading is a technique well suited for reproduction, since ink photographs and prints well to give reproductions of high quality. Ink illustrations can be produced by instruments, as in Fig. 17–67, or drawn freehand. Outline drawings illustrating specific parts of a mechanism are widely used in equipment catalogs and maintenance manuals, whenever the realism of a detailed rendering is not required. An example is the line drawing from the Bell Helicopter Corporation's overhaul instructions (Fig. 17–70).

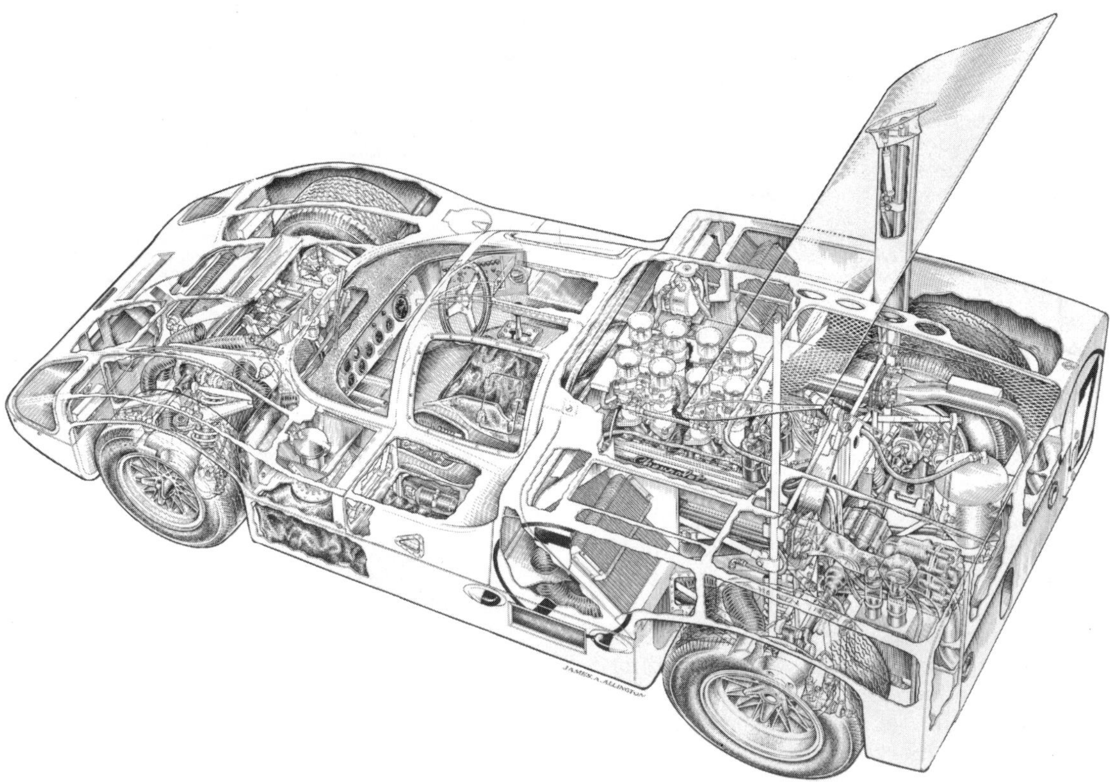

Fig. 17-71. Ink shading applied to an elaborate ink illustration. (Courtesy of Shell Oil Company.)

Fig. 17-72. An ink drawing made with a freehand technique.

Fig. 17-73. This photograph was used as a guide for the ink drawing in Fig. 17-72.

To give a more realistic appearance, surfaces can be crosshatched in ink and lines can be combined, both freehand and with instruments. Figure 17-71 is an ink-line orthographic view that is given more realism by the application of shading to its surfaces. In this case, the shading lines were drawn with instruments in a very precise uniform manner. On the other hand, the sketch of the building in Fig. 17-72 was drawn in pencil with instruments from the photograph in Fig. 17-73 and then rendered in a freehand ink technique. Crosshatching is used to give surface texture and shadowed areas. Sketches of this type can be easily outlined by overlaying an enlarged photograph with tracing paper or projecting the image from a photograph onto a drawing surface with an opaque projector. The illustrator can then establish major lines of the drawing to save construction time. A technique bolder than crosshatching in ink is shown in Fig. 17-74. More solids are used, and contoured surfaces are depicted by parallel lines drawn with instruments.

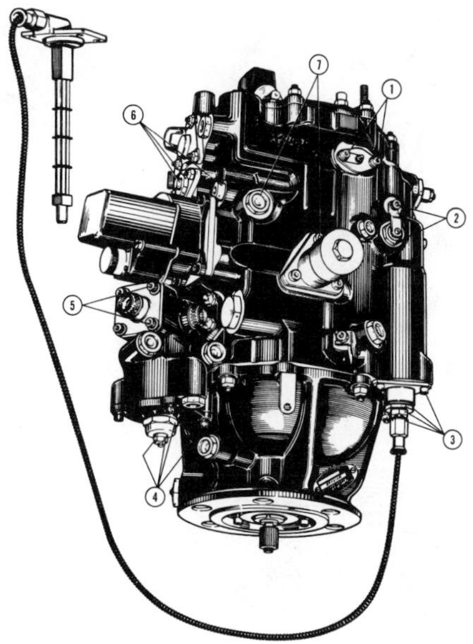

Fig. 17-74. An ink drawing using a bold technique. (Courtesy of Bendix Corporation.)

Overlay film. Overlay film is used to add realism and texture to surfaces (Fig. 17-75). This material, which comes in numerous patterns and colors, can be easily and rapidly applied to both pencil and ink drawings. The gray tone of the linkage system in Fig. 17-75 was achieved by placing overlay film over an ink line drawing. The film pattern consists of many small black dots that give the impression of a gray tone which has excellent reproduction qualities. The method of application is illustrated in Fig. 17-76. The desired pattern is selected and placed on the line drawing to be shaded (part A of the figure). The area to be shaded is lightly burnished with a smooth rounded instrument or stylus and then cut along the outline with a needle-pointed stylus or razor blade (part B). The unused portion of the film is then lifted from the drawing, and the shaded areas are burnished firmly into position.

Overlay films of this type are available from several commercial sources under different brand names. The film has an adhesive on one side and thus adheres to a paper surface when burnished. Films are available with special

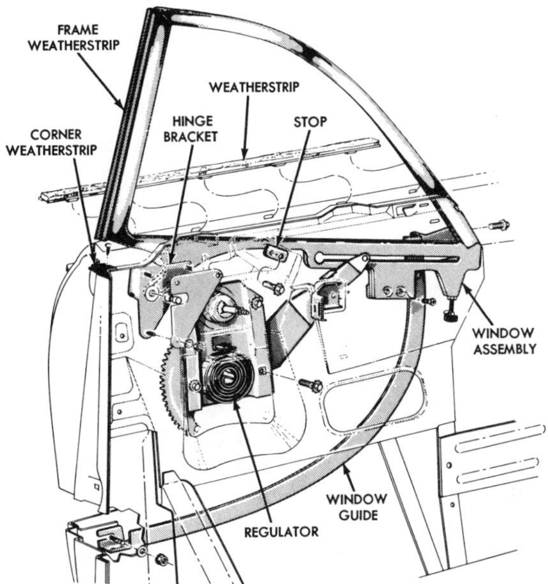

Fig. 17-75. An example of the application of overlay film to an ink line drawing. (Courtesy of Ford Motor Company.)

Fig. 17-76. The steps to follow in applying overlay film to shade an area. (Courtesy of Artype® Incorporated.)

Fig. 17-77. Example patterns available in 9″ × 12″ sheets of overlay film. (Courtesy of Artype® Incorporated.)

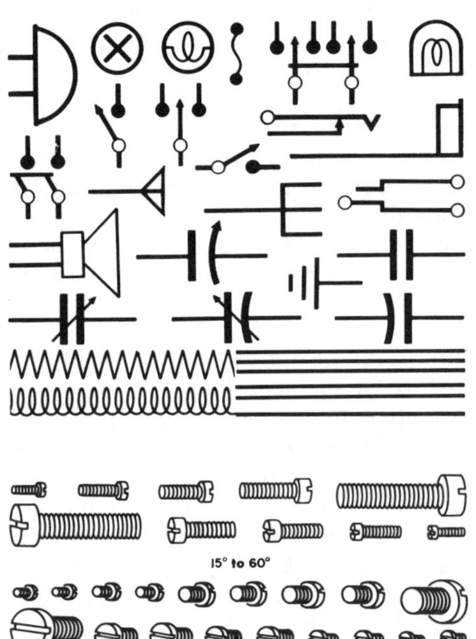

Fig. 17-78. A few of the many symbols available on an overlay film. (Courtesy of Artype® Incorporated.)

adhesives to withstand the heat of the diazo (blue line) reproduction process. Overlay film is available with a glossy or mat finish. The glossy finish is preferred for the artwork that is to be photographed and reproduced by offset methods. The mat finish is more advantageous for artwork that will be viewed in its original form, since the mat finish will appear to be produced by the illustrator. The glossy finish reflects light and thus is easily detected when applied on original work. Samples of a few of the many patterns available are shown in Fig. 17-77. When artwork is to be reduced in the reproduction process, one must select a dot pattern that will reduce without "closing up" (because the dot is too dense) or "dropout" (because the dot

Fig. 17–79. The steps to follow in applying leaders and numbers to an assembly drawing. (Courtesy of Artype® Incorporated.)

is too fine). Instructions are given by the manufacturers of overlay films to assist in this selection.

Symbols and schematics that are used repeatedly are also available commercially. Examples of electrical symbols and threaded fasteners are shown in Fig. 17–78. These are available at standard scales to adapt to most drawings. The application of a leader to a part drawing is illustrated in Fig. 17–79. The leader is applied in much the same manner as the overlay shading in Fig. 17–76. The numbers are taken from another overlay film sheet and attached to the leader as in the example. Symbols or patterns are also available in a different type of overlay film, which is applied in the same manner, but in which the line work transfers from the film to the paper when burnished, permitting the film to be completely removed. This film is well suited for artwork that will be used in its original form.

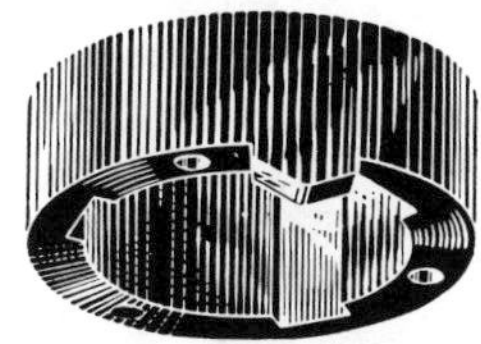

Fig. 17–80. Scratchboard drawing used to illustrate machine parts. (Courtesy of Carlyle Johnson Machine Company.)

Scratchboard. Scratchboard rendering is a negative technique: the surface is blacked in, and white lines are produced by etching through the inked areas with a stylus point. Available through commercial art suppliers, scratchboard is a specially prepared board with a chalky surface which is easily removed by scratching with a pointed instrument. The variety of lines formed is achieved through the use of different types of stylus points. Scratching points are available at a nominal cost to equip the standard pen staff for etching on scratchboard.

A scratchboard illustration is shown in Fig. 17–80. The white lines were made with a stylus. The illustrator blacked in the black areas in steps to preserve the guide lines rather than blacking in the entire area at one time. Note that the widths of the white lines vary to give a

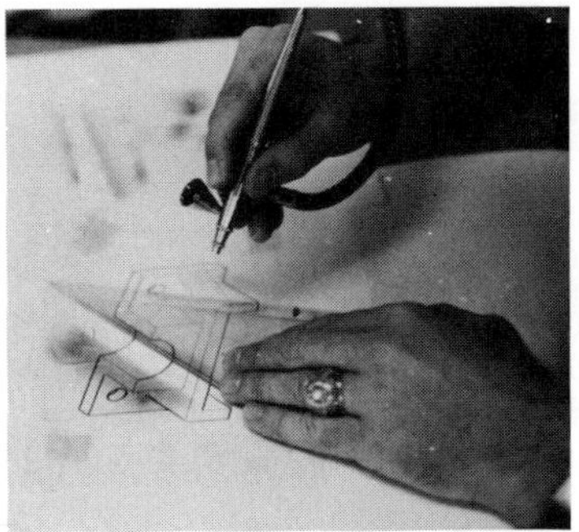

Fig. 17–81. An air brush being used to shade a drawing.

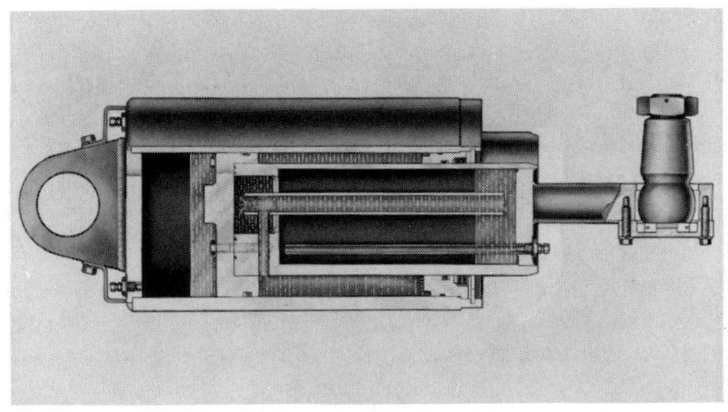

Fig. 17–82. An airbrush drawing of an orthographic view. (Courtesy of Aro, Inc., Arnold Engineering Center.)

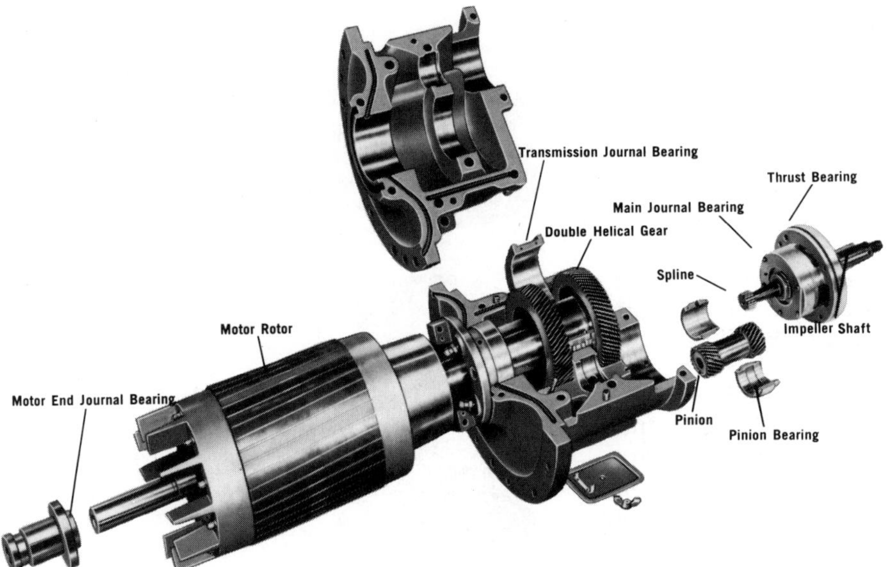

Fig. 17–83. A photograph that has been retouched with an airbrush. (Courtesy of Carrier Air Conditioning Corporation.)

natural representation of the parts. Although the scratchboard technique is a traditional method, it is not widely used in engineering illustrations.

Airbrush. An airbrush is a small spray gun that is used to spray a fine mist of diluted ink onto a drawing surface to give gradual variations in the tone (Fig. 17–81). A high degree of realism can be achieved with this delicate instrument. The realism is sufficient to be acceptable to the eye as an actual photograph. The airbrush was used to give added dimension and realism to the orthographic schematic in Fig. 17–82.

When working with an airbrush, the illustrator uses frisket paper or a mask to protect that portion of the drawing which is not being sprayed. Frisket is a specially prepared transparent paper treated with rubber cement on one side so it will adhere to the drawing surface while being used. Windows or openings are cut in the frisket to expose the area to be shaded. Air pressure (used to spray the diluted ink or tempera) is provided by a motor-driven compressor or carbon dioxide cylinders. This method of rendering is extensively used by commercial illustrators in the presentation of technical assemblies and details.

The airbrush is often used to retouch photographs for improved reproduction. An example is given in Fig. 17-83, in which a photograph of an assembly has been airbrushed to improve the representation of the parts. Many photographs may not clearly show significant details. Lines are added with white tempera and black ink in addition to the gray tones provided by the airbrush.

17-29 SUMMARY

The major types of pictorials discussed in this chapter were (1) isometric drawings, (2) oblique drawings, (3) axonometric projections, (4) oblique projections, and (5) perspective projections. Essentially all forms of pictorials are of these types or are modifications of these types. The designer must be familiar with these general types of pictorials in order to effectively use pictorials to communicate with himself and with others. Conventional multiview drawings may be difficult to interpret even though they are correctly and accurately drawn. This is especially true in the case of the layman or the nontechnical person unaccustomed to this form of representation. Pictorial drawings and sketches are effective in bridging this gap between expert and layman and in depicting the true configuration of the design that is being presented.

Technical reports are improved if pictorial methods are used to describe significant features of a design being discussed. Catalogs, maintenance instructions, and manuals are usually well illustrated with pictorials to explain important details and relationships between components. Oral reports are more effective when illustrated pictorially to supplement multiview drawings. The three-dimensional pictorial is the most universally understood language of graphics.

PROBLEMS

General

Problems should be presented on $8\frac{1}{2}'' \times 11''$ paper, grid or plain, using the format introduced in Article 1-19. All notes, sketches, drawings, and graphical work should be neatly prepared in keeping with good practices. Written matter should be legibly lettered using $\frac{1}{8}''$ guidelines. The grid on the given problems represents $\frac{1}{4}''$ squares at full size. Drawings and pictorials can be presented at a larger scale at the discretion of the student or as assigned by the instructor.

The objects shown in Figs. 17-84 through 17-87 can be drawn two per sheet if a $\frac{1}{4}''$ grid is used. They can be drawn one per page if a larger scale is used.

Isometric and Oblique Drawings

1. Prepare isometric drawings of the objects assigned from Figs. 17-84 through 17-87.

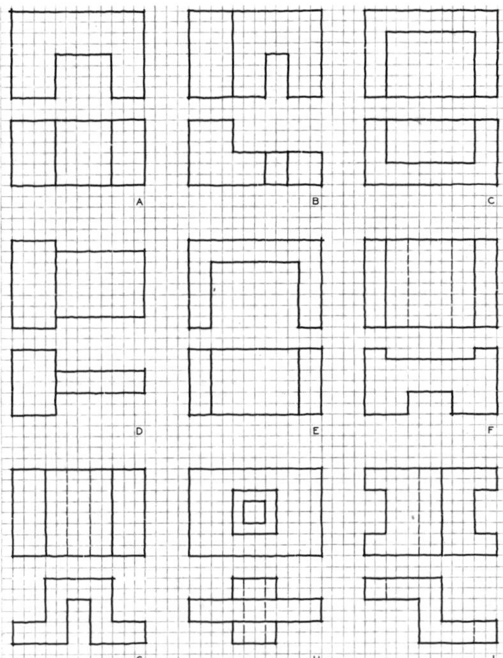

Fig. 17-84. Problems 1, 2, and 3.

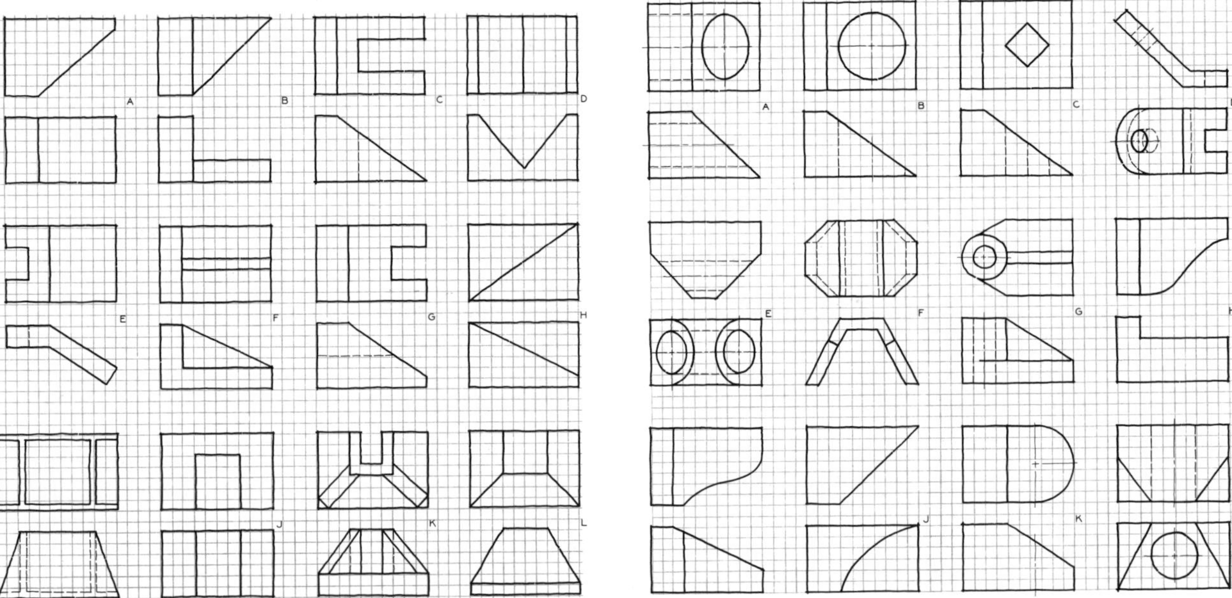

Fig. 17–85. Problems 1, 2, and 3.

Fig. 17–87. Problems 1, 2, and 3.

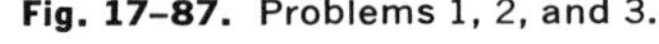

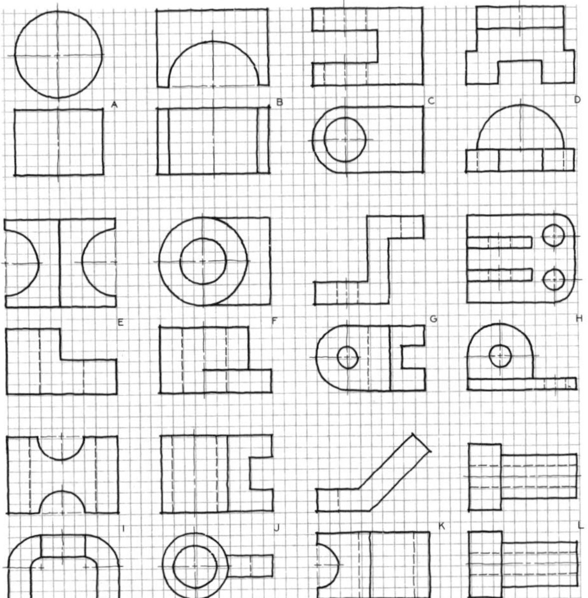

Fig. 17–86. Problems 1, 2, and 3.

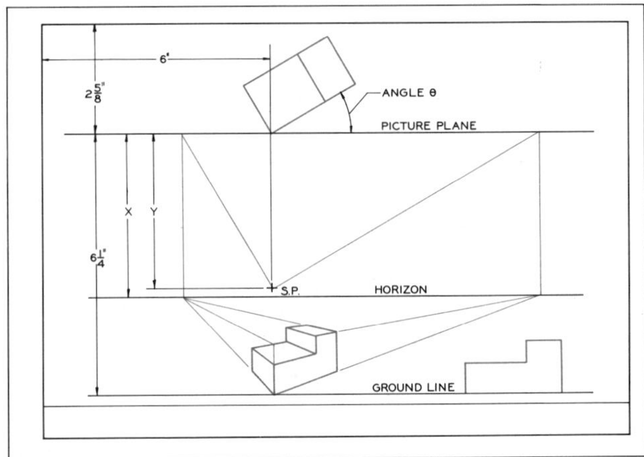

Fig. 17–88. The layout for perspective problems on Size B sheets.

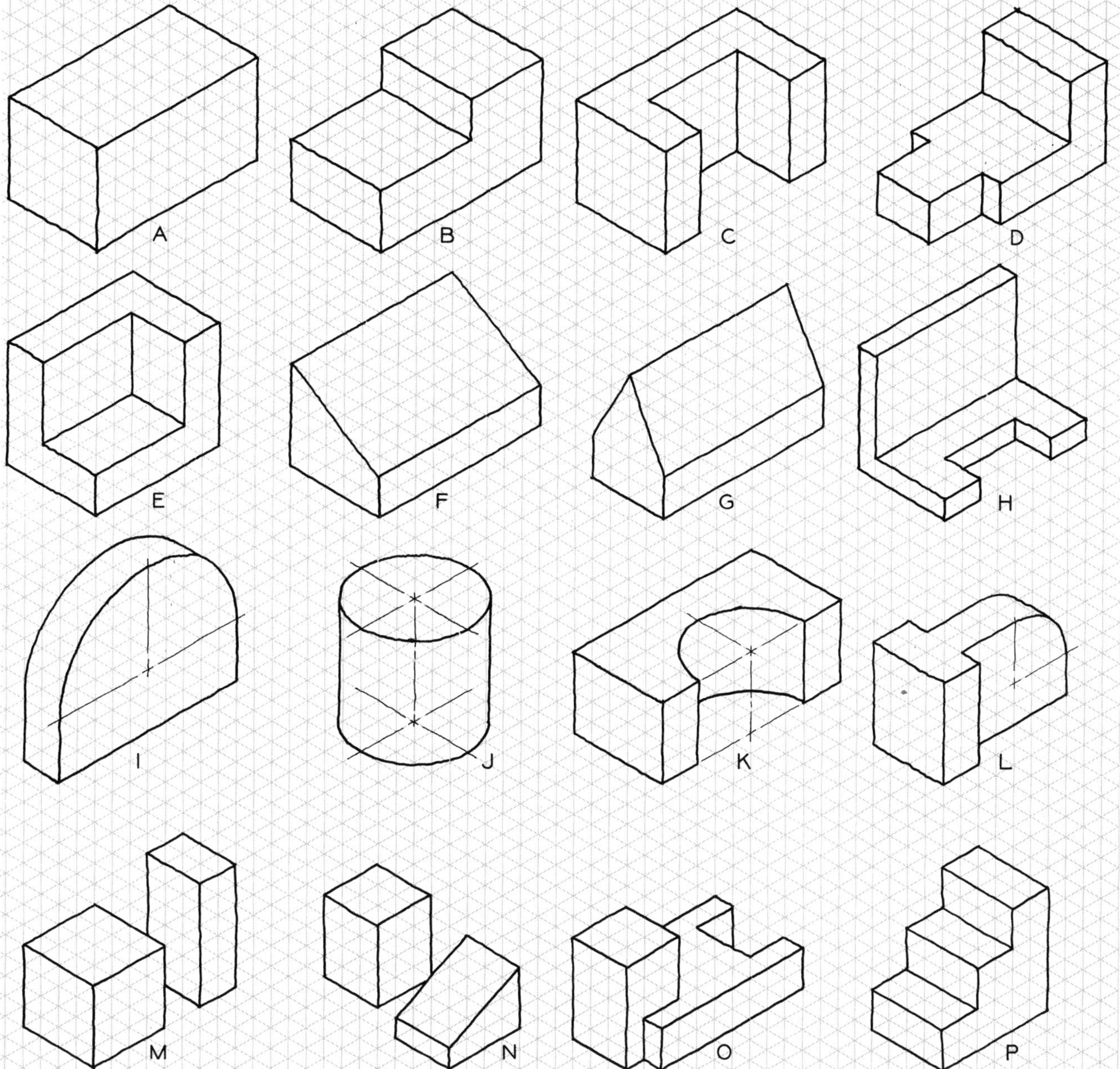

Fig. 17–89. Perspective problems.

2. Prepare cavalier obliques of the objects assigned from Figs. 17–84 through 17–87.

3. Prepare cabinet or general obliques of the objects assigned from Figs. 17–84 through 17–87.

4. Additional problems for isometric and oblique drawings can be selected from the problems at the end of Chapter 5.

Perspectives

Problems should be drawn on the size of paper specified for each series of problems.

One-Point Perspectives

5. Using the specifications given in Table 17–1 and Fig. 17–88, draw one-point perspectives of the objects assigned from Fig. 17–89. For example, you may be assigned to draw a perspective of object D using specifications C in Table 17–1. Specifications A through F may be assigned for any of these objects. Use Size B paper. Each grid in Fig. 17–89 is equal to $\frac{1}{4}''$.

Two-Point Perspectives

6. Using the specifications given in Table 17–1 and Fig. 17–88, draw two-point perspectives of the objects assigned from Fig. 17–89. Specifications A through F may be assigned for any of these objects. Use Size B paper. Each grid in Fig. 17–89 is equal to $\frac{1}{4}''$.

Renderings

7. Prepare finished illustrations using the shading techniques assigned by your instructor from those covered in this chapter. One of the outline drawings constructed in a previous problem can be used for the final presentation. Strive for a rendering of professional quality suitable for reproduction. The following techniques of illustration may be assigned: (1) pencil, (2) ink, (3) overlay film and ink, (4) scratchboard, and (5) airbrush.

Table 17–1

Dimensions in inches, Fig. 17–88

Specification	X	Y	θ
A	4	$3\frac{1}{2}$	25°
B	4	4	30°
C	$3\frac{1}{2}$	$4\frac{1}{2}$	30°
D	$3\frac{1}{2}$	$5\frac{1}{2}$	40°
E	4	$3\frac{1}{2}$	45°
F	4	$5\frac{1}{2}$	45°

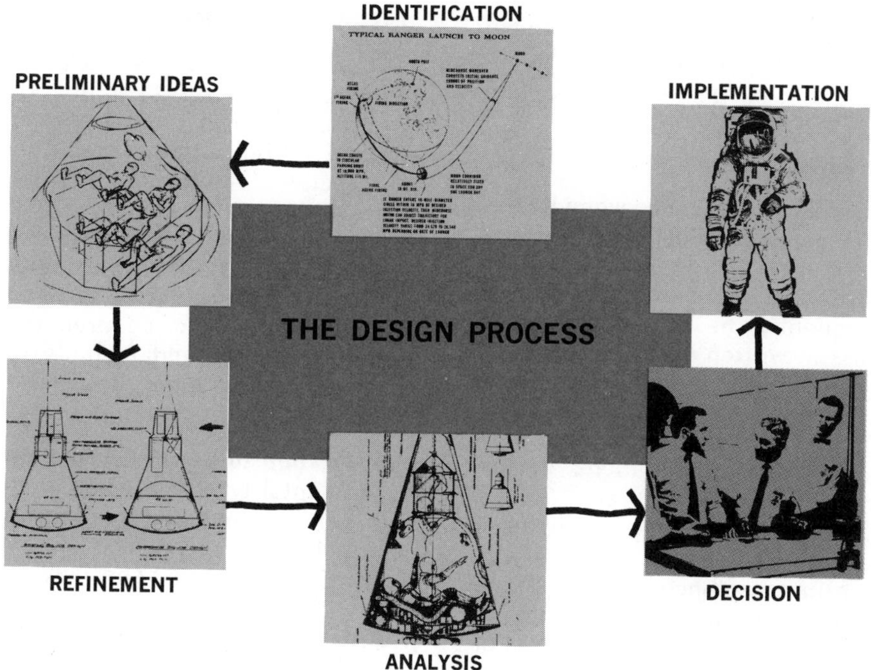

18 PRESENTATION FOR DECISION

18–1 GENERAL

The decision phase of the design process is a significant interval of the design sequence. The design has been conceived, developed, refined, analyzed; and now a decision must be made to determine which design is best and therefore worthy of implementation. The decision process is based to a great extent on facts and data; but at best, it is still a subjective decision that must be made by responsible individuals. The responsibility for making a decision cannot be relegated to a computer or a mechanical system. Individual judgment and intuitive evaluation will always remain as prominent deciding factors in approving a design for implementation.

This chapter discusses the details of organizing and planning an oral presentation on which a decision will be based. The presentation may be a discussion of alternative plans that will be decided upon, or it can be the presentation of a single design that the design team has selected as most feasible. A decision of this importance cannot be attempted unless a complete detailed review is presented of the background information, market surveys, analysis results, and cost analyses. The oral presentation is the means by which final decisions are determined following the review of the technical report, which was discussed in Chapter 16.

Chapter 17 will serve as a reference for the preparation of visual aids where pictorials are required. Formally prepared pictorials or rough freehand pictorials may be used to present design concepts for decision. In addition, the techniques of presentation and rendering a pictorial can be applied to the preparation of visuals that will be photographed as slides or presented on the overhead projector. These methods should be referred to as needed to supplement the preparation of visual aids covered in this chapter.

18-2 TYPES OF DECISIONS

The designer's work is not finished when he has completed his research and design. His efforts will be lost if he cannot gain acceptance for his design solution from his associates and administrators. Consequently, he must be able to express his ideas in written and oral presentations with conviction and clarity.

Several types of decisions are possible as an outcome of the oral presentation. *First*, the design solution or recommendations of the presentation may be rejected entirely. Such a rejection can be caused by changes in business climate or company policies; or it can result from failure to gain acceptance from the group responsible for the decision. It is obvious that a change in conditions during the development of a project may cause it to be rejected for natural economic reasons. An advanced device may not be developed to its final stages if in the meanwhile a superior device has been developed that would render the proposed design obsolete from the beginning. The design that is rejected when the need for it is present may be a result of inadequate design or a poor presentation that did not sell the idea.

Second, a design may be accepted in its entirety. This is a compliment to the designer on his efforts in researching his problem and solving it and in presenting his case. This decision clears his project for implementation and development to the final conclusion of the project.

The *third* type of decision is a compromise or modification of the recommendation of the presentation. As modifications of a particular design, better features may be suggested that would be more economical, more serviceable, or more appropriate under the existing conditions. Such modifications are not necessarily reflections on the design team; rather, they are natural suggestions that are expected during most decision presentations.

18-3 TYPES OF GROUPS

The presentation can be given to one or two individuals or to a large group. The groups can vary from a single project associate to laymen who are entirely unfamiliar with the project and its objectives. A presentation is usually made to a small group of associates or to a larger group (more than eight) who are less familiar with the project. An informal presentation would be sufficient for associates, whereas a more formal presentation should be prepared for the lay group. The basic fundamentals of the presentation remain the same, however, although different techniques must be used for each group.

Presentation to Several Associates. The most fundamental type of presentation is that given to a group of immediate associates on the project or to the supervisor. This presentation is very informal, without specially prepared visual aids that would be used for a large group. However, pictorials, schematics, sketches, and models should be used to convey a complete understanding of the design concept. As a result of this informal discussion, a decision can be made to change the approach to a design or even to discard the idea entirely. Consequently, every effort should be made to communicate the total idea through the use of every graphical means possible.

Ideas may be sketched and discussed when only a few people are involved (Fig. 18-1.). In a discussion that includes a few more individuals who may be working jointly on the project, ideas, schematics, and sketches can be drawn on a blackboard (Fig. 18-2). This type of presentation is less demanding than the formal group presentation to be discussed later, because the audience is composed of associates who are aware of the problem and its requirements. Informal presentations are usually preliminary presentations, made during the beginning stages of a design development; the same material will be formally presented in more detail at a later date. However, an informal presentation could be the full extent of a presentation in a small organization where the authority lies with the individuals involved.

Fig. 18-1. A decision may come from an informal presentation to a single individual, where ideas and designs are discussed and sketched. (Courtesy of Ford Motor Company.)

Fig. 18-2. An informal presentation may be given to professional associates by means of preliminary notes and blackboard sketches. (Courtesy of Esso Research of New Jersey.)

The Formal Presentation. The presentation of the formal type receives the most emphasis in this chapter, because it is usually more crucial than the informal presentation. The designer has completed his planning and preliminary designs; he has selected the best design and made his recommendations in a written report. He will now present his findings orally to a group who will decide on the acceptance or rejection of the design prior to production, construction, or implementation of the recommendations.

The group to whom the presentation is given may be composed exclusively of professional associates, administrators, laymen, or it may be mixed. A presentation to professional associates only will be more technically oriented than one given to the other groups or to a mixed group. Function and acceptability of the design from an engineering standpoint are the primary considerations of the engineering associates. Administrators will probably be concerned with the economic feasibility of a design and, in the final analysis, with its estimated profit return. The group of laymen could be the clients for whom the project is designed, stockholders, or members of the general public who may vote on the approval of a design. A formal presentation to a group requires a considerable amount of planning and organization to ensure that this vital stage of the design process is successful. All designs must go through the decision process before ideas and sketches can be converted to reality.

18-4 ORGANIZING THE PRESENTATION

Planning the sequence of the presentation and the types of visual aids that will be used is an important part of the preparation process. The presenter must consider the order of the presentation and the types of visual aids that will assist him in transmitting his thoughts. The entire presentation should be planned in complete form before any visual aids are prepared in order to prevent waste of effort because of changes in the later stages of organization.

An acceptable method that can be used to good advantage in planning a formal session is the use of 3″ × 5″ cards (Fig. 18-3). Separate ideas that could be illustrated graphically through drawings, schematics, or photographs are first written on separate cards in very rough fashion. A rough sketch is made to indicate the type of illustration required and the method of repro-

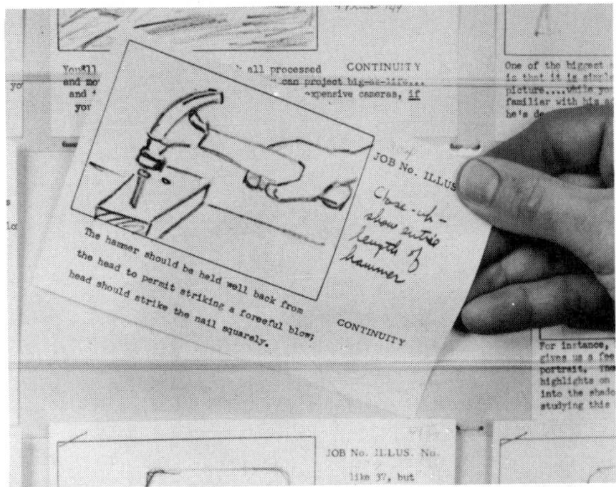

18–3

18–4

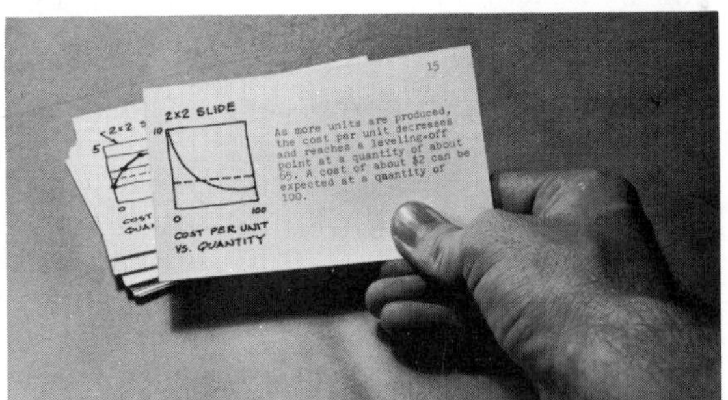

18–5

Fig. 18–3. A presentation should be planned by using a series of 3″ × 5″ cards on which the various topics and visual aids can be noted. (Courtesy of Kodak.)

Fig. 18–4. Planning cards can be used to prepare the sequence of the presentation by using a planning board (as shown here) or by merely arranging the cards on a table top. This method permits easy modification in the sequence by repositioning the cards. (Courtesy of Kodak.)

Fig. 18–5. An example layout of a 3″ × 5″ card for general purposes.

duction to be used, and brief notes are added to suggest a general outline of the discussion that will be given orally to accompany the visual aid. The entire presentation is organized in this manner, even though the ideas are still in a rough general form. The total sequence of the presentation can be easily reviewed by displaying the cards on a table, bulletin board, or planning board (Fig. 18–4).

The position or content of the cards can be changed easily at this point. Each card can be refined to be more descriptive of the information that must be presented. The completed cards (Fig. 18–5) should contain the following information.

1. *Number.* The card's position in the sequence of visual aids.
2. *Illustration.* A sketch of the illustration that must be prepared. Notes can be included to indicate special effects, types of visual aids, and other specifications that will be helpful in preparation.
3. *Text.* A general outline of the oral presentation that will be given with the visual aid.

If a variety of visual aids will be used during the presentation, such as flip charts, slides, transparencies, or combinations of these, the material should be divided into sections that will allow a smooth transition from one type of presentation to another. This organizational effort will reduce to a minimum any confusion caused by changes of position and projection equipment that would detract from the presentation.

After the 3″ × 5″ cards have been properly sequenced and related to the presentation, they should be grouped according to similarities in illustration or production. All graphs that are to be illustrated by transparencies should be grouped for preparation and production at the same time. Grouping of similar graphs and illustrations that will be photographed to make slides will facilitate production and reduce setup time and preliminary preparations that must be made for a particular process. The next step of preparing the presentation is the selection of the proper visual aid for the requirements of the presentation and the preparation of the artwork.

18–5 VISUAL AIDS FOR PRESENTATION

A presentation is organized and conducted in much the same manner for a small group as for a large one. The primary difference consists in the types of visual aids used to communicate the ideas being presented. Engineers, technicians, sales managers, and other professional people must often explain technical information to groups of associates or superiors at conferences or meetings. Communication of any type of information can be enhanced by the utilization of visual aids to ensure that a complete understanding of the presentation is being transmitted to the group.

Visual aids most commonly used are flip charts, photographic slides, overhead projector transparencies, and models. These visual aids can be developed as elaborate, expensive aids or they can be prepared rapidly and economically, using various shortcuts, to serve the purpose without sacrifice of effectiveness. General rules that will improve the effectiveness of any type of visual aid selected are:

1. Each slide or chart should convey one thought only.
2. Lengthy statements should be reduced to key phrases or words that will communicate the thought intended.
3. Tabular data should be presented in the form of a graph for easy comprehension.
4. Each slide or chart should be clearly readable by the group for whom the presentation is intended.
5. Illustrations, color, and attention-getting devices should be incorporated into the slides or charts for appropriate emphasis.
6. A sufficient number of slides or graphs should be prepared in order to ensure that only a few minutes of discussion will be required to convey the thought.

Fig. 18–6. The flip-chart presentation is an effective method of communicating with small groups.

18–6 FLIP CHARTS

A flip chart consists of a series of charts prepared on medium-weight paper and mounted on a backing board that can be placed on an easel for presentation before a group (Fig. 18–6). Each successive chart is flipped over the backing board to proceed to the next during the discussion. Although flip charts can be very suitable

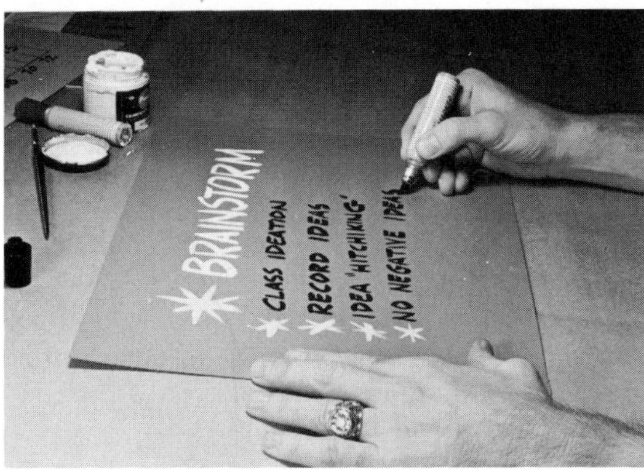

Fig. 18-7. Felt-tip markers are well suited for the preparation of flip charts and other visual presentation materials.

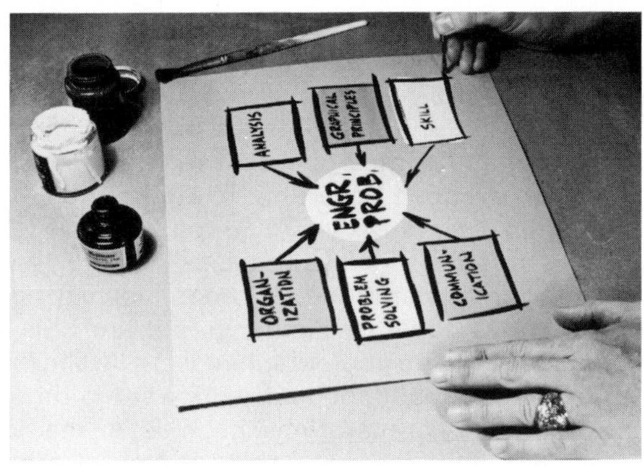

Fig. 18-8. Tempera and water-base paints are excellent for the preparation of visual aids with the use of color.

in some instances for rather sizable groups, they are more commonly used for small conferences or presentations in an area no larger than an average-sized classroom. The size of the audience and the seating arrangement will influence the size and composition of the charts. A common format for a flip chart is 30″ × 36″; smaller sizes tend to be too small for most groups.

Flip charts can be made on almost any quality of paper, using very inexpensive, time-saving materials. The important consideration is whether or not the flip charts communicate the ideas intended. A few methods of preparing flip charts are given in the following paragraphs.

Paper. Common brown or white wrapping paper is very suitable for a series of flip charts that will be used for a presentation to be given only once. A corrugated cardboard can be sized to serve as a backing board to which the flip charts can be attached. The sheets are cut to a size that will match the backing-board dimensions. The card sequence is used as a guide in laying out each chart. If very light pencil lines are made, they will not need to be erased after completion of the layout. Colored pencils that will leave less noticeable lines are often used. Light guidelines can be ruled with a straight edge to improve layout. It is advisable to lay out at one time all charts in a series in order to maintain uniformity of style and technique. The lettering and other artwork on the charts can also be developed in this way.

Lettering Materials. The final lettering can be done with felt-tip markers, chalk, ink, tempera or sign paints, or overlay film. Felt-tip markers, used extensively for fast bold lines in a variety of colors, give very sophisticated effects if properly used. Both freehand and straight-edge drawings can be made with them (Fig. 18-7). Colored chalks can be applied to flip charts for shading areas and for writing phrases. Chalk drawings must be handled carefully or sprayed with a fixative to prevent smearing. Ink is an effective medium for lettering and for adding emphasis to a chart. It can be applied freehand with a brush or by means of special lettering pens for bold lines. Ink can also be used to letter mechanically with commercial lettering guides. The designer should develop a freehand technique for lettering-in presentations, since it is faster than mechanical lettering and equally attractive. Tempera or sign paints are water-based, come in many colors, and can be applied with a brush for an attractive layout (Fig. 18-8).

Transfer Films. These commercially produced products save a great deal of time in the preparation of artwork of a repetitive nature while giving a highly professional appearance. The application of a specially produced sheet is shown in Fig. 18-9. The sheet is positioned as desired in step 1, and the insignia is carefully burnished in step 2 to transfer the design as if it were printed on the paper. Another useful application of this type of material is shown in Fig. 18-10. In this case, the letters are printed permanently on the film and cannot be transferred from it. Instead, the desired letters are removed from the sheet by cutting a portion of the film, as shown in step 1. A letter is removed (step 2) and the line printed under the letter on the film is aligned with the horizontal guideline (step 3). The letter is burnished to secure letter and film to the paper (step 4). The guideline is then cut away.

Sheets of this type may have a glossy surface or a mat finish that is hardly visible. They are available with dot patterns, symbols, letters, numbers, and in various colors for many applications to the presentation for decision, as covered in Chapter 17. Visuals prepared with these aids can be used on flip charts and transparencies, and they can be photographed for use on slides to give a finished appearance to the layout.

Color. A chart will be more attractive and effective if color is used to add variety. Any color selected should be readable from the audience and compatible with the other colors used. It is wise to check the visibility of a color by viewing it on a sample layout from the most extreme position in the room before proceeding with the entire series of flip charts.

Color can be added to a chart very fast and effectively through the use of construction paper and rubber cement. A graph or schematic can be laid out as in the initial steps of any layout. Instead of shading or painting areas to be colored, construction paper can be cut and pasted into position in a minimum of time. In general, a chart of this type should be rather bold and should present no tedious or time-consuming details. With a little practice, the

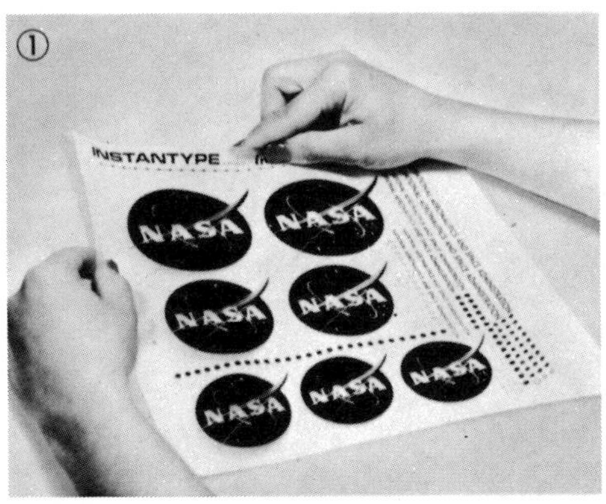

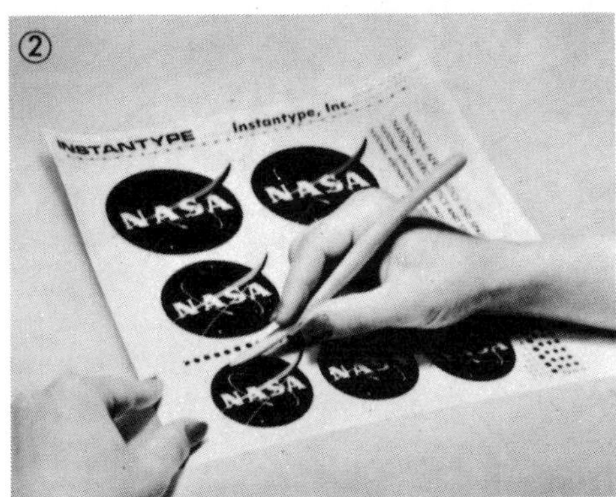

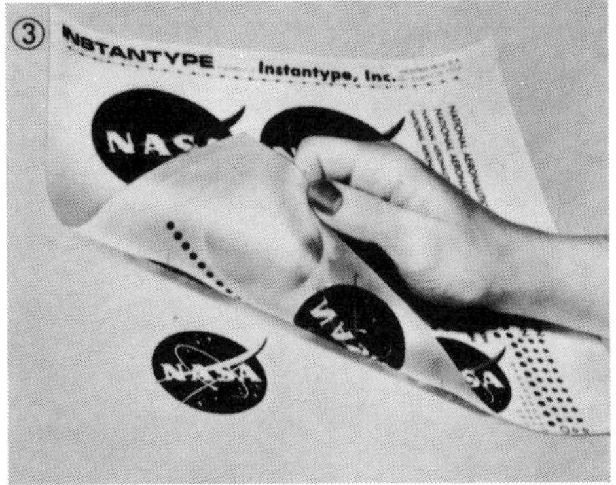

Fig. 18-9. Transfer films are available for the preparation of presentation materials. In this example, an emblem is being transferred onto the working surface. (Courtesy of Instantype® Incorporated.)

Fig. 18–10. Lettering can be applied through the use of overlay films to add professional appearance to a presentation. (Courtesy of Artype® Incorporated.)

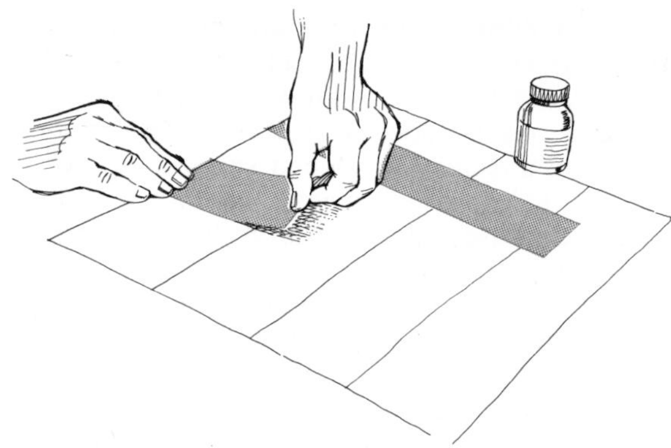

Fig. 18–11. Colored construction paper can be pasted on flip charts and other visuals to give an attractive appearance with the minimum of effort and expenditure of time.

designer can make good use of the bright colors of construction paper to give a degree of professionalism to a graph. This technique is especially useful for bar graphs, as illustrated in Fig. 18–11.

Assembly. The finished charts are assembled in order, with a title chart preceded by a blank sheet of paper covering it. These sheets are stapled or attached to the backing board. The blank cover sheet conceals the theme of the flip charts and delays any anticipation of the presentation until the time selected by the presenter. This lessens the possibility that the group will formulate an impression of the presentation before it has begun.

Presentation. In advance of the meeting, the flip charts should be mounted on an easel or secured in the most suitable position for viewing. At the beginning, it may be appropriate to give a few introductory remarks concerning the presentation before revealing the title page. The title page can be revealed with additional remarks that are more specific to the information to be covered. The charts are flipped in sequence and referred to with a pointer to ensure that the speaker is not blocking the view of the audience. Written notes can be kept to a minimum since the flip charts will serve as notes, but it may be helpful to write certain key points lightly on the charts in a convenient corner that will be visible only to the presenter. As in the technical report, there should be concluding charts that emphasize and review key points. A presentation should not require more than 20 to 30 minutes. It may be given in less than 20 minutes if effective visual aids are used.

18-7 PHOTOGRAPHIC SLIDES

In situations where flip charts are too small for good visibility, as in presentations to large groups, photographic slides are very effective. They are almost a necessity if photographs are required to depict actual scenes or examples. Photographic slides, usually 2″ × 2″ in size, can be easily filed and used in other presentations at relatively low cost. The remainder of this article will concern the preparation of graphic materials that will be photographed rather than general photographs of scenes, with which most are familiar.

Layout of Artwork for Photographic Slides. The film portion of the average 2″ × 2″ slide has a ratio of 3 : 2, and the same ratio can be used to lay out a conveniently sized surface on which to work. Figure 18-12 illustrates a method for sizing the layout in correct proportion for a 35 mm. slide. A format size of 8″ × 12″ is appropriate for most information that will be presented by slides. Colored backgrounds are much easier on the eyes than is a white background. A combination of different colors on each slide will add variety to the sequence and maintain a higher level of interest. Colored construction papers, mat board, and other poster materials can be used to good advantage in laying out the artwork for a slide. Light guide lines are drawn with a pencil that will not leave distracting traces on the finished slide. All slides of a similar format should be roughed in lightly at the same time to conserve time and reduce duplication of effort.

A margin of at least 1″ on all sides of a layout should be allowed to fill the slide with the illustration when it has been photographed. Colored chalk, ink, tempera, or other media used in the preparation of flip charts can be used for preparing photographic-slide layouts (Fig. 18-13). The use of mechanical devices is more feasible at an 8″ × 12″ size. Selection of the proper size for lettering is critical to ensure readability from any point in the audience. When a slide is to be projected on a 5′ wide screen and viewed from a distance of 30′ the letters on an original $5\frac{3}{4}$″ × $8\frac{1}{2}$″ layout should be no less than $\frac{1}{8}$″ high. Only capitals should be used, with space between lines equivalent to the height of the letters. The lettering specifications in the artwork in Fig.

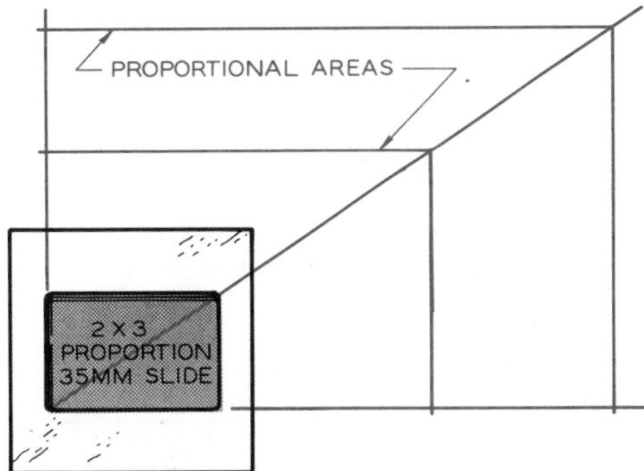

Fig. 18-12. A method of sizing artwork and charts to be proportional to the finished photographic slide.

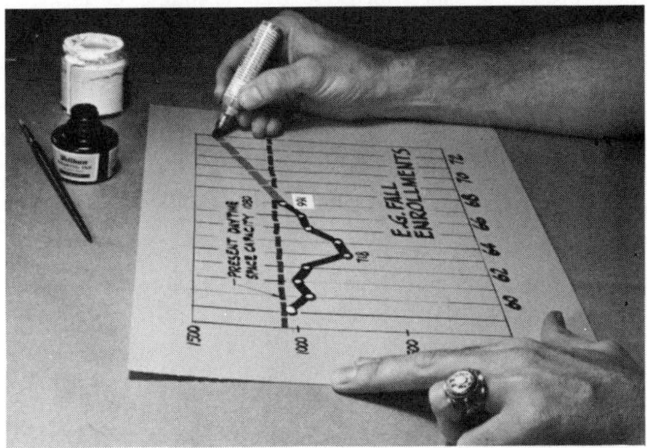

Fig. 18-13. Felt-tip markers, tempera, ink, and other techniques used in the preparation of flip charts, can be applied to the preparation of charts for photographic slides.

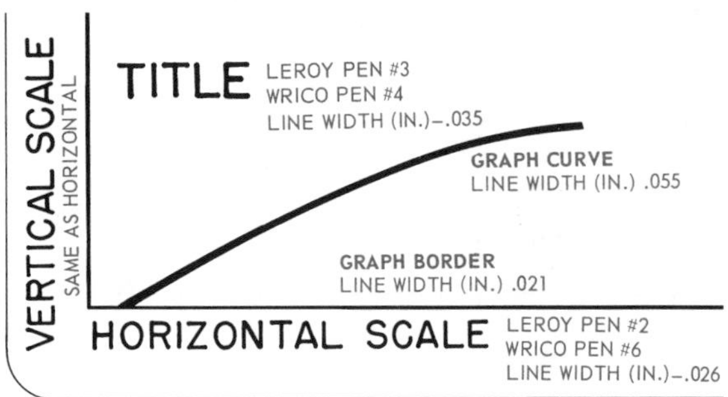

Fig. 18–14. The line weights here should be used as a guide when preparing charts for photographic slides. Lettering or lines should be at least this bold. (Courtesy of Kodak.)

Fig. 18–15. Three-dimensional letters are available for the preparation of photographic charts.

18–14 are suggested for an illustration of $5\frac{3}{4}'' \times 8\frac{1}{2}''$ for good projection.

Special effects can be achieved with three-dimensional letters or unusual backgrounds, and paper cutouts add color and interest to the slide. Three-dimensional letters are available commercially, as shown in Fig. 18–15. Photographs, schematics, and diagrams may be photographed directly from magazines, textbooks, and other references if details are bold enough to be legible when the slide is projected.

Copying the Layouts. Once the artwork and displays have been prepared the equipment needed for producing the slides consists of a camera and a copy stand, light meter and lights (Fig. 18–16). A 35 mm. reflex camera is recommended. Because the reflex camera has a through-the-lens viewfinder, the photographer can accurately focus and align each slide before photographing it. The copy stand holds the camera in the proper position during the photographing and thereby reduces problems of focusing and movement of the camera (Fig. 18–17). In many cases, however, the camera can be hand-held. If all layouts are drawn the same size, the camera can be left in the same position during the entire photographing process. If slides are made indoors, photographic lights that match the type of film being used are needed. Lighting intensity should be checked with a light meter. When weather permits, copy work can be photographed in natural sunlight without artificial lights. Book illustrations that are too small for regular copying can be photographed with a close-up lens that will fill the slide with the area being photographed.

The developed and mounted slides should be reviewed and sorted to determine their quality prior to the presentation (Fig. 18–18). If the information on a slide will be needed at more than one interval during the presentation, duplicate slides should be made rather than attempting to return to a previously shown slide. A poor slide should be discarded and a new one made to lessen the possibility of distractions during the presentation. The mounts of all slides should be numbered in their final sequence.

18-16

18-17

18-18

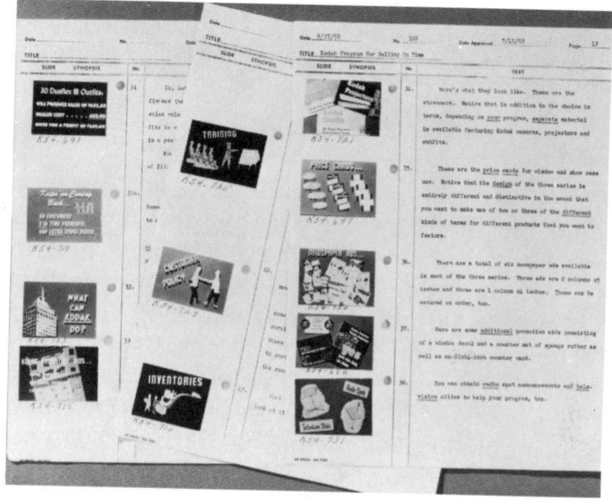

18-19

The Slide Script. A slide presentation that will remain on permanent file for repetitive use should have a script to serve not only in the presentation but also as a review guide. An example of a slide script is shown in Fig. 18-19.

A script can be prepared on standard $8\frac{1}{2}'' \times 11''$ paper and maintained in a binder or a notebook. The left-hand side of the script sheets contain black and white photographs of the slides used with the narration entered on the right-hand side. The narration is not intended to be read but to serve as a guide for the person

Fig. 18-16. A light meter and a 35 mm. reflex camera are required for the preparation of charts in the form of 2 × 2 slides.

Fig. 18-17. Charts and artwork can be reproduced easily with a 35 mm. camera mounted to a copy stand which facilitates positioning of the camera.

Fig. 18-18. Photographic slides should be sorted and arranged in proper sequence prior to loading in the slide tray.

Fig. 18-19. A slide manuscript for a slide presentation should be prepared for an important presentation or for presentations that will be given on a repetitive basis. (Courtesy of Kodak.)

Fig. 18-20. The overhead transparency, used on the overhead projector, is composed of an $8\frac{1}{2}'' \times 11''$ transparency mounted in a $10\frac{1}{2}'' \times 12''$ cardboard frame. The projection area of the transparency is $7\frac{1}{2}'' \times 9\frac{1}{2}''$.

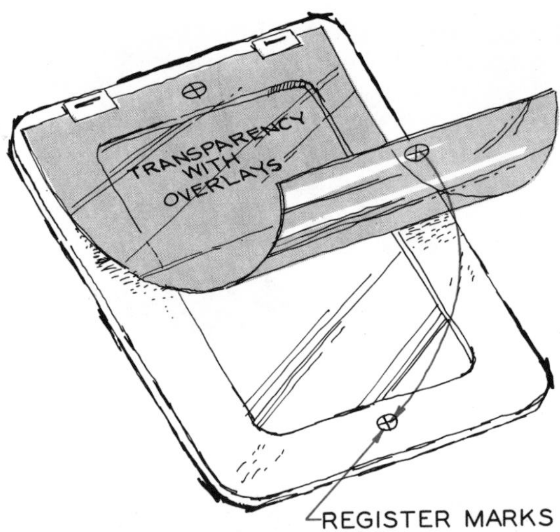

Fig. 18-21. Overlays of different colors can add interest to overhead transparencies.

who will give the presentation. The photographs allow the speaker to be aware of the slides that will be shown in sequence and enable him to key his narration to the slides without getting out of phase during the presentation.

The script can be filed with the slides and used again later with a minimum of planning and organization. The necessary information is available in a readily usable form and will require a minimum of review and research. Slide series of this type are good for instructional purposes to brief associates in certain areas.

18-8 OVERHEAD TRANSPARENCIES

Overhead transparencies are reproduced on clear transparent materials, $8\frac{1}{2}'' \times 11''$ by the heat-transfer process or the diazo process, and mounted in cardboard mounts (Fig. 18-20). Tracing paper is the most common material employed in the preparation of transparencies since it can be used in either process without special equipment. Diazo reproductions from books, photographs, or pages printed on both sides require supplementary equipment in addition to the basic diazo equipment.

Line work should be prepared in black India ink for best reproduction. Overlay materials and graphing tapes can be used to give a professional appearance. Lettering should be legible (at least $\frac{1}{4}''$ high) and brief for easy reading. The finished tracing-paper drawing is transferred to the transparencies in much the same way a diazo print is made. Both sheets are placed in contact and run through the duplicator. The completed transparency is then mounted for ease in handling and storage.

Color Overlays. Transparency materials are available in a variety of colors, and multicolor effects can be achieved on a single transparency. Several overlays of different colors can be hinged to the basic transparency for a sequential presentation that shows the development of an idea or problem. The artwork for overlays is prepared on tracing paper that has been positioned over the basic layout. Areas or lines that will be reproduced in a color during the duplicating process are darkened with black India ink. Register marks (Fig. 18-21) are used to align the transparencies with one another during the artwork presentation and mounting phase. This step in the preparation is very critical. Each overlay should be labeled for identification and numbered to serve as a guide in mounting the overlays properly.

Presentation with Transparencies. The overhead projector can be placed at the front of the room, much nearer the screen than a slide projector can be placed. The presenter can stand or sit near the projector in a semilighted room and refer to the transparencies while facing his audience (Fig. 18-22). With a small pointer he can indicate important points on the stage of the projector, and the image of the pointer will project on the screen. Just as several overlays can be hinged into position to develop an idea in sequential steps, opaque paper overlays can be hinged to the mount with tape to conceal portions of the overlay and focus audience attention on a single topic at a time. A transparency should not be left on the screen during any long period of time in which it is not germane to the presentation. Instead the projector should be turned off to direct audience attention to the speaker and turned on again only when attention should be redirected to the screen.

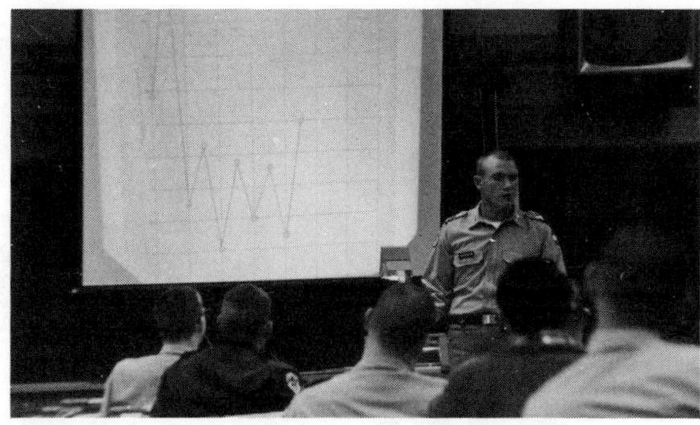

Fig. 18-22. Overhead projectors can be used in a semilighted room while the presenter faces his audience.

Fig. 18-23. The full-size prototype of a design is a highly effective aid in a presentation to small groups. (Courtesy of the Chrysler Corporation.)

18-9 MODELS

Models can be used to assist in the analysis of a design, as covered in Article 13-9, or to present the final solution for decision. A model is an excellent means of communicating the final design concept in its most realistic form. The general configuration of a design, as well as its major working parts, can be shown. Models are especially helpful in explaining a three-dimensional concept to a group composed primarily of laymen unfamiliar with the interpretation of drawings.

A model that is an actual-size prototype of the completed design (Fig. 18-23) gives the most accurate impression of the finished design. However, in many cases the model is consider-

Fig. 18-24. This scale model of an underwater observatory was used to present the structural system of the apparatus. (Official Photograph, U.S. Navy, Pacific Missile Range, Point Mugu, California.)

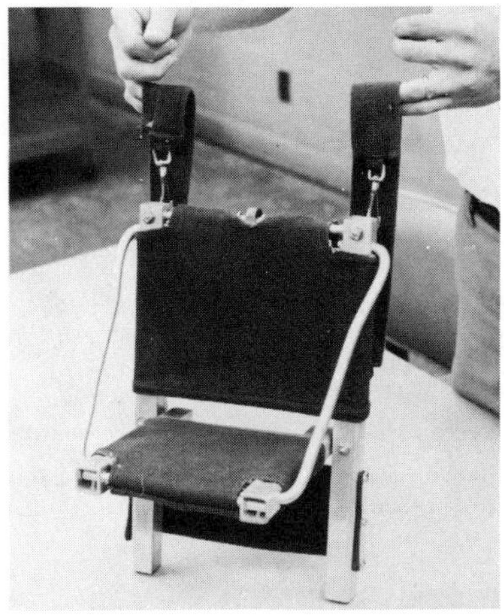

Fig. 18-25. This scale model was constructed to test the feasibility of an early design.

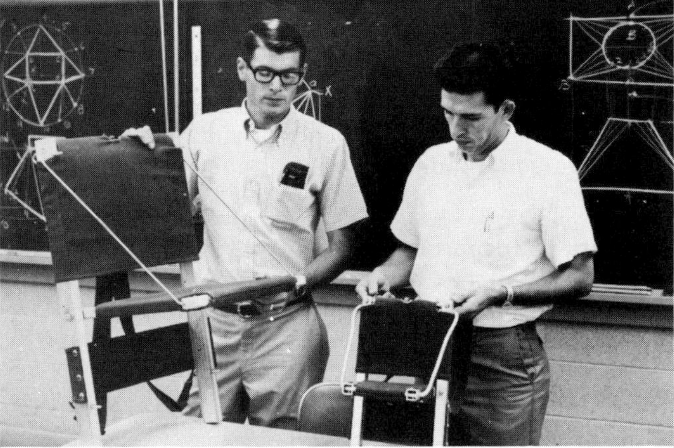

Fig. 18-26. A full-size model can be used to demonstrate the function of a design.

ably smaller. An example is the scale model of the Nemo underwater observatory, shown in Fig. 18-24. This model of the 10′ diameter observatory is constructed of plastic to afford a view of its internal parts and its structural system. Removable sections make possible the observation of internal parts of models that are not visible from a conventional view.

One of the more important considerations in construction of a model for presentation is the choice of a scale appropriate for the size of the group. Several individuals at a conference table can effectively study a rather small model, but a typical class group will require a considerably larger model. In general, to be seen from a distance of more than 12′, a model should be at least 12″ in size. Use of photographic slides can effectively supplement the model during a group presentation. A series of close-ups taken from appropriate angles can help to give each member of the audience a clear view of a relatively small model.

Models should be as similar to the final product as possible to prevent misleading or confusing the reviewing group. Materials can be painted to simulate their final treatment in the design. Model materials should closely approximate the general configuration of the total concept.

A model used to present a design for a hunting seat is shown in Fig. 18-25. It is made of the actual materials that will be used in the final design shown in Fig. 18-26. A full-size model can be used to demonstrate the function of the product and its more important design features. Additional pointers for model construction can be obtained from Chapter 13, where reference is made to the use of models for purposes of analysis.

18-10 THE GROUP PRESENTATION PREPARATION

When the presentation has been planned, the visual aids prepared, and the material organized, the design is ready for presentation. Planning for the presentation should be done in advance and should include consideration of seating arrangement, location of visual aid equipment, and facilities available in the room.

Seating Arrangements. Most conference rooms, classrooms, and auditoriums are arranged to afford good viewing when visual aids are used, but conditions should be checked by viewing the presentation materials from extreme locations in the audience area prior to the meeting. Figure 18–27 indicates the good viewing area for a slide presentation. For overhead transparencies, the viewing area is somewhat closer.

Room Facilities. The room where the presentation will be given should be checked for good ventilation, lighting, sound, and electrical control. Arrangements should be made for control of lights during the presentation by an assistant or by a remote control device. Sound amplification may be necessary if room and audience are large.

Location of Visual Aid Equipment. All projectors and other visual-aid equipment should be positioned and focused before the audience arrives. The screen or flip charts should be located where they afford the best view from all positions. Remote controls for slide projectors should be ready for use near the speaker's position.

Slide trays should be loaded and on the projector for immediate operation. Overhead transparencies should be grouped in sequence near the projector. Flip charts should be secured to the easel and a pointer provided for calling attention to specific points during the presentation.

The speaker should take care not to block the view of his audience when employing visual aids. A rehearsal with an assistant in the seating area to call attention to any blocking movements will help the speaker avoid them. Careful location and preparation of equipment prevents waste of time and enables the speaker to give his presentation in a professional manner.

18–11 THE PRESENTATION

The speaker should give his presentation at a moderate pace that is neither too rapid nor too slow. Proper timing can be gauged by rehearsal. Visual aids should be used only when they are directly related to the narration so that a close relationship may be maintained with the audience (Fig. 18–28).

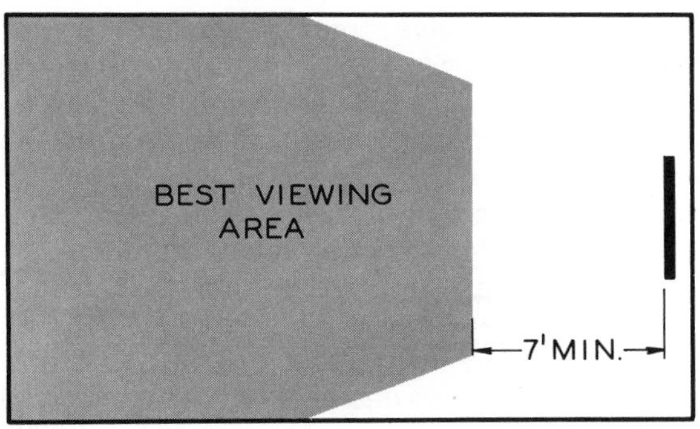

Fig. 18–27. The general viewing area for a slide presentation in a typical room.

Fig. 18–28. A presentation should make full use of graphical aids and models to assist the speaker in communicating his ideas. (Courtesy of the Bendix Corporation.)

Usually the speaker is better informed on the project being discussed than his audience is, since he has been intimately involved with it from the beginning. The speaker should thoroughly familiarize his audience with the objectives of his presentation in an introduction. The order of presentation should conform very closely to the technical report and in the discussion emphasis should be placed on significant points. The speaker must demonstrate sincere conviction in his ideas, which in many instances he must be trying to sell.

A positive approach in selling ideas should not be confused with high-pressure salesmanship that may be deceiving. The presenter should be the first to point out design weaknesses in his presentation, but these weaknesses should be offset by alternatives that compensate for them. No proposed design will be totally effective in all respects; the optimum design is one that has the best relationship of design factors. A presentation should not be given for decision unless the designer feels that he has a worthy solution to propose. Strong and weak points should be discussed in an objective manner. Conclusions and recommendations should be given in light of available research and analysis. If after thorough analysis a designer feels that he cannot recommend a design, he should state the reasons for his conclusion.

A period for questions and answers is usually provided at the end of the presentation to clarify technical points that may not be fully understood. If appropriate, the technical report should be available to members of the audience to accompany the oral presentation. In answering specific questions, the speaker may refer to the technical report where detailed supplementary data are available. A group cannot be responsive to a presentation unless the speaker is enthusiastic and well informed in all aspects of the material being presented.

18-12 SUMMARY

The decision phase can be the most important step of the design process, since this is the point at which previous effort is accepted or rejected. The designer must be able to provide a basis for the decision that will be made. Graphical methods are his best tools for presenting his concepts and recommendations. Tabular data are very difficult to interpret without intensive study; consequently charts and graphs are used to present significant data. Schematics, pictorials, diagrams, and photographs are natural supplements to presentations of this type.

Decision responsibility may rest with the designer, his immediate superior, or a group of people with a variety of backgrounds. When the designer is responsible, he must review his design worksheets and the preliminary designs that have been refined and base his decision on the information developed during the design process. In effect, he is communicating with himself. As the number of persons involved in the decision process increases, it becomes more necessary for the designer to prepare visual aids to improve communications.

Commonly used methods of presenting visual aids are flip charts, overhead projectors, slide projectors, and models. These should be selected to give the most effective results for the specific group. Visual aids can be economically prepared in a minimum of time, or they may be highly elaborate for a formal presentation to a large group. It is more desirable to accompany the presentation by an adequate number of visuals of an economical format than to have an insufficient number of formally prepared visuals.

The presentation should be as well organized as possible, with all visual aids closely integrated with the narration. The equipment and room facilities should be organized and readied for immediate use in order to keep confusion to a minimum. The presentation should be as concise and as brief as possible while covering the important points thoroughly. The acceptance of the design proposal at this point will lead to the final step of the design process—implementation—covered in Chapter 19, which deals with the preparation of the finished working drawings that will be used to produce the design in final form.

PROBLEMS

Class Simulation

The importance of a well-organized presentation to the decision stage of the design process can best be understood through an actual experience of giving a presentation. A good engineering project can be wasted effort unless the findings and ideas are presented in a form acceptable to those responsible for approving further development. Engineering does not end with the solution of the problem—the solution must be accepted before it can be carried out.

ORAL REPORT

EVALUATION SHEET FOR TEAM PROJECT PRESENTATIONS

Item Rating Scale: 5 (Thorough) 4 3 2 1 0 (omitted)

Team Designation: →	1	2	3	4		
Introduction to problem; specifications:	4	5	4	2.5		
Evidence of sufficient, pertinent data:	4.5	3	4	4		
Consideration of alternate designs:	5	4	3	4		
Selection of design from data and specifications:	4	4.5	4	5		
Conclusions and recommendations:	4	4	3	4		
Sequence of topics presented:	5	4	4	4		
Sufficiency, pertinence and quality of visual aids:	5	3	4.5	4		
Degree of participation of team members:	4	5	3	4		
Clarity of voice; poise and confidence:	4	4	5	3		
Use of time allotted for presentation:	5	4	4	5		
TOTALS:	44.5	40.5	38.5	39.5		
Multiply totals x 2						
OVERALL PRESENTATION GRADE:	89	81	77	79		

COMMENTS:

EVALUATOR'S NAME (OPTIONAL): R. L. SMITH

Fig. 18–29. A grading form for evaluating a team's oral presentation.

TEAM PARTICIPATION IN ORAL PRESENTATION

TEAM NO. 2 SECTION 165 TEACHER CLELAND

This evalution sheet should be submitted to your instructor after your team has prepared and given the oral presentation portion of your team project. The team as a group should evaluate each team member's contribution to the preparation of visual aids, flip charts, and the actual presentation.

Individual grades will be computed using the formula below. List team members and the percent of contribution of each in the space provided.

Project: HUNTING SEAT

Team Members: (N = 5)	% Contribution (C)	F=CN	Grade (G)
BROWN	20	100	
ROGERS	15	75	
SMITH	25	125	
ADAMS	20	100	
BROWN	20	100	

Individual grades to be computed from graph.

Summarize below any irregularities or circumstances that should be considered in arriving at a grade.

COMMENTS:

Fig. 18–30. A participation form that shows the percent contribution made by each team member to the preparation and presentation of the oral report. Individual grades can be determined from the chart in Appendix 29.

Classes can be divided into teams who will compete among themselves to develop the best solution to a given problem. Examples of suitable problems for class projects are given in Chapter 20. After the problems have been solved by the teams, each group will prepare a presentation to be given before the class. Presentations should utilize the visual-aid techniques covered in this chapter to illustrate the oral report. Each presentation should be organized to take no more than ten minutes, with approximately five minutes for a question and answer session at the end to permit discussion of specific points of the design being presented.

Class members should be asked to grade each presentation with a check list to indicate weaknesses and strengths as a means of offering constructive criticism to the presenting teams. A class will profit by sharing different approaches to solving the same idea and by observing the merits of different techniques for presenting information to a group.

An example of a grading form for evaluating an oral report presentation by members of a class is shown in Fig. 18–29. Class members can evaluate the presentations of other teams by filling in values from 5 through 0 for the topics listed. Note that the number of the team being graded is given at the head of each column. The average grade for each team can be found by averaging the scores given to each team. Figure 18–30 is a participation form that can be used to show the percent contribution of each individual on the team. This is multiplied by the number of team members in the second column to assist the teacher in arriving at the final grade of each student. The percent contribution of each team member should be decided by the team as a whole.

This type of presentation can be used for the presentation of a semester project for an entire class to a panel of visiting engineers, who would evaluate the oral reports from an engineering viewpoint. This experience will provide the student with a background in the preparation of an oral report and its presentation to a group for approval. Each team member should participate in the final presentation rather than selecting a single individual to represent the entire team.

1. Prepare a check list that could be used to evaluate an oral presentation of one of your classmates. List important items that should be considered and determine a point system that could be assigned to each. Keep the form simple, yet thorough enough to be of value to the presenter in improving his technique of presentation. Devise a means of tabulating the evaluation to arrive at an overall rating. Present this grading sheet in final form that can be used in an actual class presentation.

2. Prepare a series of 3″ × 5″ cards to plan a flip-chart presentation that will last no more than five minutes. The subject of your flip-chart presentation may be one of your choosing or one assigned by your teacher. Example topics: your career plans for the first two years after graduation; the role of this course in your total educational program; the importance of effective communications; the identification of a need for a design project that you are proposing; a comparison of the engineering profession with another profession of your choice.

3. Prepare graphical aids for an oral presentation, using the methods and materials indicated in this chapter to familiarize yourself with these techniques.

4. For a technique of your choice or one assigned by your instructor, prepare a five-minute briefing, using the planning cards developed in problem 2. Give this briefing to your class as assigned.

5. Assume that you are an engineer responsible for representing your firm in the presentation of a proposal for a sizable contract. Make a list of instructions that you could give to your assistants to coordinate the preparation of your presentation for a group of 20 persons ranging in background from bankers to engineers. The topic is not so important as the method of presentation, since most topics will require much the same preparation. Consequently, use a topic of your choice, one assigned by your teacher, or one suggested in problem 2. Your instructions should outline the materials you need, method of preparation of graphical aids, number required, method of projection or presentation, assistance needed in presenting materials, room seating arrangements, and other factors. Your outline should be sufficiently complete to cover the entire program of an ideal presentation within the time you think most desirable.

6. Prepare a model that can be used to effectively communicate an engineering graphics principle to your classmates and that might be used for instructional purposes, and demonstrate it in a class presentation.

7. Prepare a series of photographic slides of the model constructed in problem 6. Present these to your class for their evaluation.

8. Prepare a slide manuscript for the series of slides developed in problem 7. Insert these in a binder for permanent filing.

9. Prepare an overhead transparency to illustrate a descriptive-geometry principle, using hinged overlays to present the problem in sequential steps. Demonstrate the use of this transparency to your class.

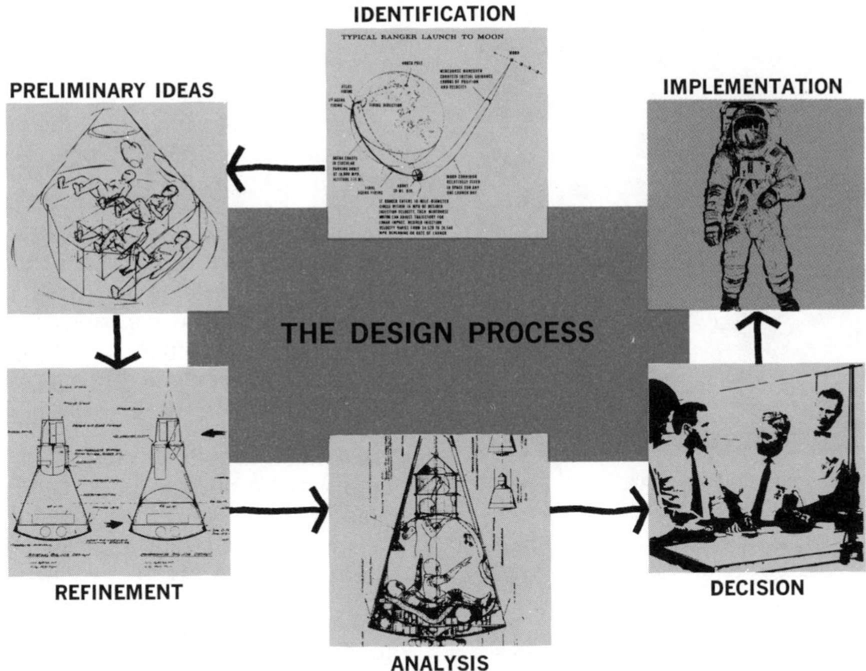

19 IMPLEMENTATION

19-1 GENERAL

After the design process has gone through each of the sequential steps covered in the previous chapters, the design is ready for implementation (Fig. 19-1). Implementation is that phase of the design process during which the design, whether for a single part, a mechanism, or a complicated system, becomes reality. The previous phases of the process dealt with identification, study, synthesis, analysis, and selection of the best solution. The total process represents a major portion of engineering activity, involving many disciplines and areas of study applied to the specific needs of the project. Graphical methods are essential to each step of the design process.

Graphical methods are particularly important during the initial steps of implementation, since all products or systems are constructed from *engineering drawings* or *working drawings*. Drawings of this type describe each part in detail, including all specifications and dimensions. Working drawings are usually quite extensive, consisting of many separate sheets containing notes and dimensions. A working drawing customarily uses orthographic projection, as discussed in Chapter 5.

For the most part, the working drawings in this chapter will be closely related to the presentation of machine parts, since the approach to these parts is fundamental and easily adapted to other products or systems. It is extremely important that working drawings and all details used for the implementation of a design conform to universally acceptable standards. Consequently, the techniques suggested for use in the preparation of working drawings in this volume have been adapted from the American National Standards Institute (ANSI). Many of the illustrations and examples are taken directly from *Dimensioning and Tolerancing for Engineering Drawings*, ANSI Y14.5-1966. Most engineer-

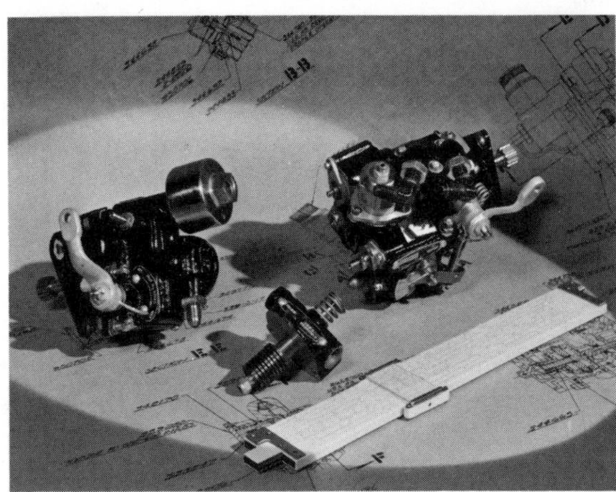

Fig. 19-1. Implementation from a drawing to product. (Courtesy of the Bendix Corporation.)

ing drawing standards developed by individual companies or other agencies are closely, if not entirely, related to these standards.

The preparation of working drawings for implementation is an almost totally graphical function. Finished working drawings can be produced by computer, assigned to draftsmen, or, in the case of simple drawings, sketched freehand. This stage of the design process is the least creative, since it is primarily concerned with clerical details to ensure that the final design is as complete as possible. Many people make the mistake of assuming that this form of graphics is the major application of graphical methods to the engineering function, probably because drawings are used extensively at this stage. However, we know from the preceding chapters that the creative steps of designing precede the preparation of the finished drawing.

This chapter will deal with the following areas of implementation: (1) dimensioning, (2) tolerancing, (3) fasteners and standard parts, (4) special applications. Reference will be made to additional standards and sources for a more detailed study of this broad field.

19-2 TERMINOLOGY OF DIMENSIONING

The following terms are used in dimensioning practice to improve communication. Refer to Fig. 19-2 to identify these terms.

Dimension lines are lines with numerals placed near their midpoints. The numerals give the length of the part being dimensioned. An arrowhead is placed at each end of the dimension line. Dimension lines are thin lines. Draw them with a hard pencil (2H-4H).

Extension lines are lines that extend from a view of an object for the purpose of dimensioning a measurement outside the area of the object. The arrowheads of dimension lines end at these lines. Extension lines do not touch the view from which they extend, but a gap is left between the object and the line. Use a 2H-4H pencil.

Center lines are thin lines used to locate the centers of cylindrical parts, such as cylindrical holes. Refer to Fig. 19-2 to see how center lines are applied to circular and rectangular views of cylinders. Use a 2H-4H pencil.

Leaders are lines drawn from a note to indicate the feature to which the note applies. An example is the $\frac{3}{4}$ DRILL note in Fig. 19-2. Leaders are thin lines of the same weight as dimension and extension lines. Use a 2H-4H pencil.

Arrowheads are used at the ends of dimension lines and leaders to indicate the endpoints of these lines. The length of an arrowhead is the same as the height of the numerals and letters used on a drawing. In most cases, this is $\frac{1}{8}''$. Methods of drawing arrowheads are shown in Fig. 19-3. The arrowhead at its widest point is one-third as wide as it is long; it is drawn with two strokes of an F or HB pencil. These strokes will tend to fill in and darken the arrowhead.

Dimension numerals are very important to the dimensioning of a drawing, since these numbers specify the dimensions of the parts. If the specifications are poorly lettered and difficult to interpret, the drawing is ineffective. Numerals should be made in accordance with the lettering practices discussed in Chapter 5.

Figure 19-2 illustrates general rules of dimensioning. Notes are given in this figure to show the placement and spacing of dimension lines.

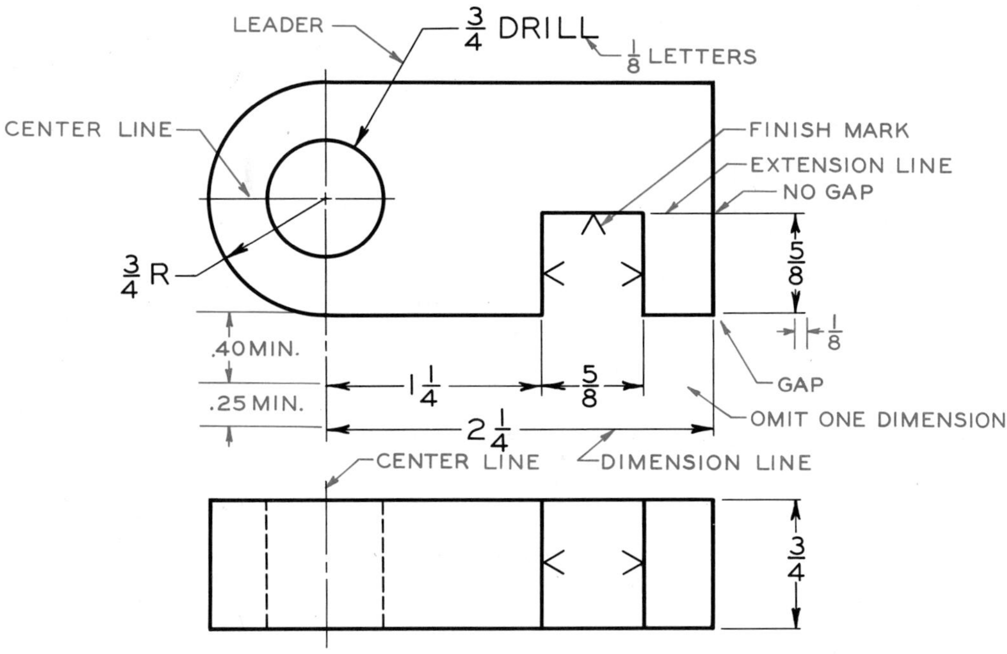

Fig. 19-2. A typical detail drawing with dimensions and notes.

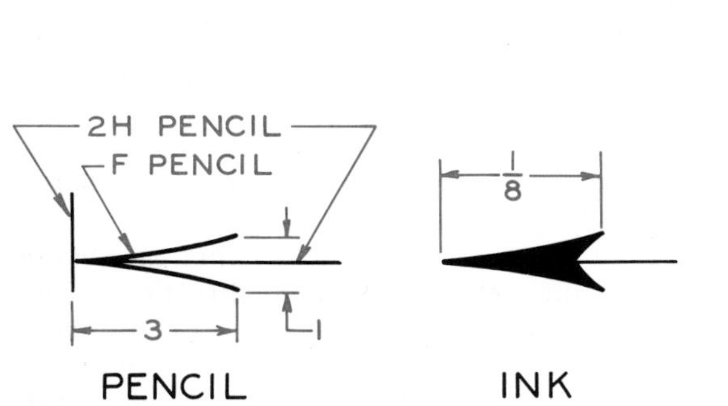

Fig. 19-3. The arrowhead.

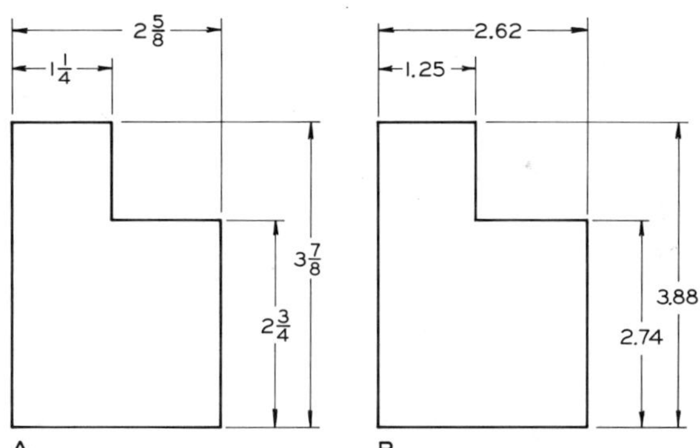

Fig. 19-4. Common fractions (A) or decimal fractions (B) can be used as units for dimensioning an object, but decimal fractions are preferred.

19-3 UNITS OF MEASUREMENT

English System. Current standards recommend that dimensioning units be decimals of an inch since decimals are easier to multiply, divide and add than are common fractions. However, common fractions may be used.

A comparison of common fractions and decimals is given in Fig. 19-4A and B, respectively. For values of less than one, zeros are not used before the decimal point. All decimal fractions should have the same number of

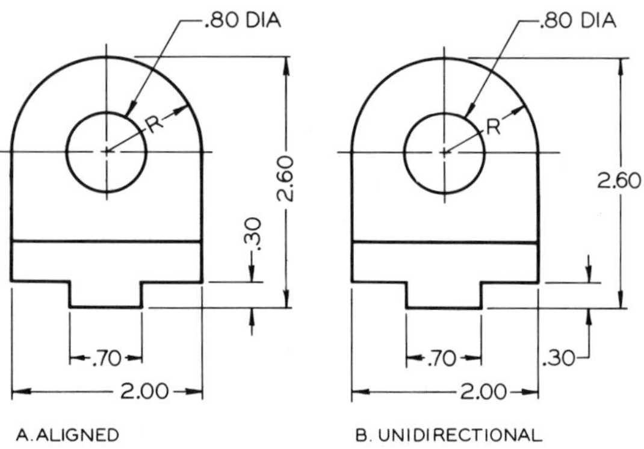

Fig. 19–5. A comparison of aligned and unidirectional dimensions on a drawing.

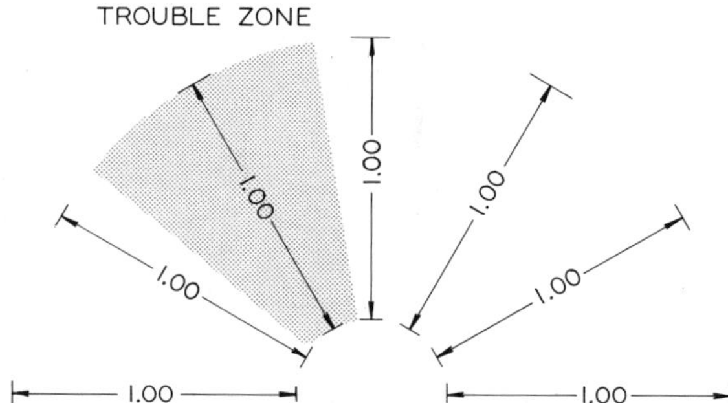

Fig. 19–6. Aligned dimension numerals should be positioned to be readable from the right or bottom side of the page. Avoid placement in the trouble zone.

decimal places to the right of the decimal point even if the last digits are zeros. Draw the decimal points dense and dark so they will not be overlooked.

All dimensions are given in inches unless the dimensions exceed six feet. Since it is understood that all dimensions under six feet are in inches, the inch marks are omitted. When dimensions exceed six feet, the foot marks are given, but the inch marks are still omitted. Example: 12′–5. Some industries use inches for all measurements, even for dimensions greater than six feet.

Metric System. The metric system is the most widely used measurement system in the world, with only the United States, England, and a few other countries using the English system of inches, feet, yards, etc. The English system is less functional than the metric system since it is difficult to convert inches to feet or feet to yards.

The present practice of using inches and decimal fractions of inches is a compromise to improve the mathematical manipulations of these units. However, it is likely that the metric system will be adopted as the universal system in the United States as well. Conversion tables for converting inches to millimeters, and millimeters to inches are given in Appendixes 3 and 4. One millimeter is equal to 0.03937 inch and one meter is equal to 39.370 inches.

19–4 ALIGNED AND UNIDIRECTIONAL NUMERALS

The two methods of positioning dimension numerals on a dimension line are *aligned* and *unidirectional.*

The unidirectional system has gained wider acceptance since it is easier to apply numerals to a drawing that read from the bottom of the page regardless of the direction of the dimension line (Fig. 19–5B). Guidelines are also easier to draw in this system than in the aligned system.

As its name implies, the aligned system places numerals in the same direction as the dimension lines (Fig. 19–5A). The numerals must always be read from the bottom or the right side of the page. When the aligned system is used, the numerals should not be placed in the area called the *trouble zone* in Fig. 19–6 since, in this area, they must be read from the left side rather than the right side of the page.

19–5 PLACEMENT OF DIMENSIONS

The following examples illustrate rules of good practice in dimensioning and contrast them with poor practices.

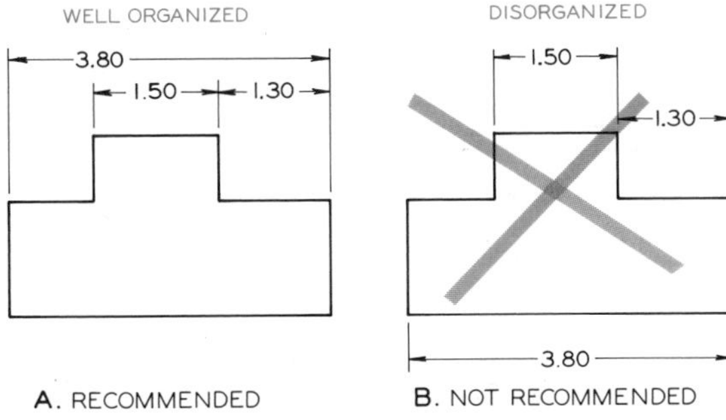

Fig. 19-7. Dimension lines should be logically grouped (A) to make the drawing more readable, rather than scattered as shown in B.

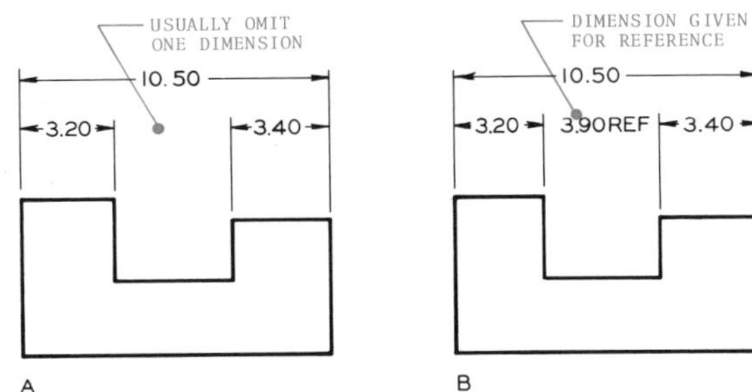

Fig. 19-8. One intermediate dimension is omitted; if all dimensions are given, one should be noted REF to show that it is for reference only.

The part in Fig. 19-7A is correctly dimensioned with one overall dimension and two intermediate dimensions. One dimension is omitted from a series of dimensions since the overall dimension determines the omitted dimension. It is good practice to place all the dimensions on the same side of the drawing for ease of reading. The intermediate dimensions should be placed in a single line rather than offset as shown in Fig. 19-7B.

Note that one intermediate dimension is omitted in Fig. 19-8A, since this dimension can be found by subtracting from the overall dimension. It is permissible to show the missing dimension if the abbreviation REF is placed after it to indicate that it is a *reference* dimension, that is, the least important dimension. Giving the reference dimension reduces the possibility of errors resulting from faulty arithmetic by shop personnel.

If at all possible, dimension lines should be placed outside the object. A dimension line should not be used as an extension line (see Fig. 19-9B). Also, in dimensioning angles, extension lines should be used to avoid placement of the dimension lines inside the angular feature (Fig. 19-9C and D).

Extension lines are drawn from the view being dimensioned, with a gap between the view and the extension line. Extension lines

FIGURE 19-9

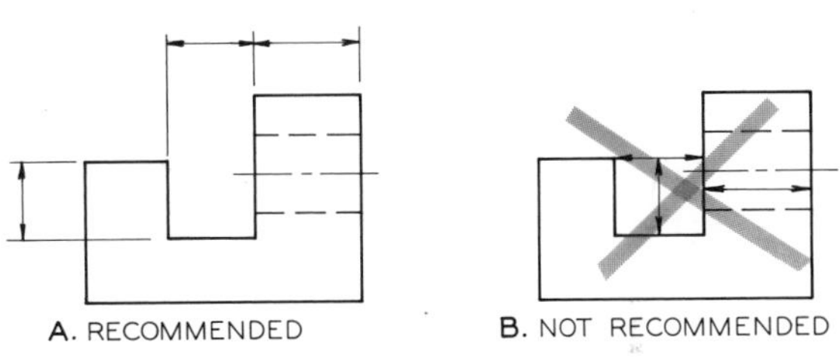

It is preferred practice to place the dimensions outside a part and not use other dimension lines as extension lines.

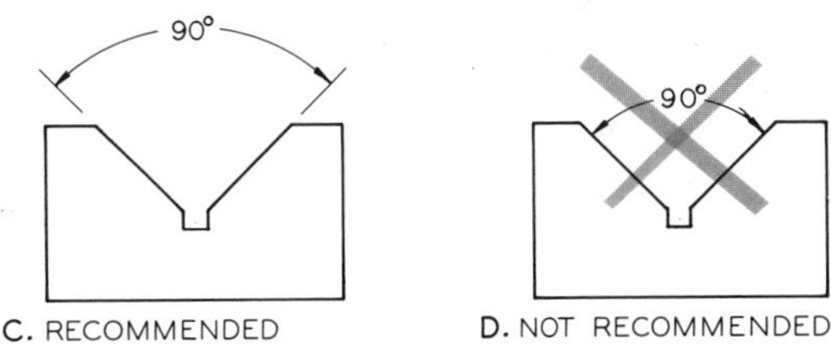

Place angular dimensions outside the angle being dimensioned as shown in C rather than on the inside as shown in D.

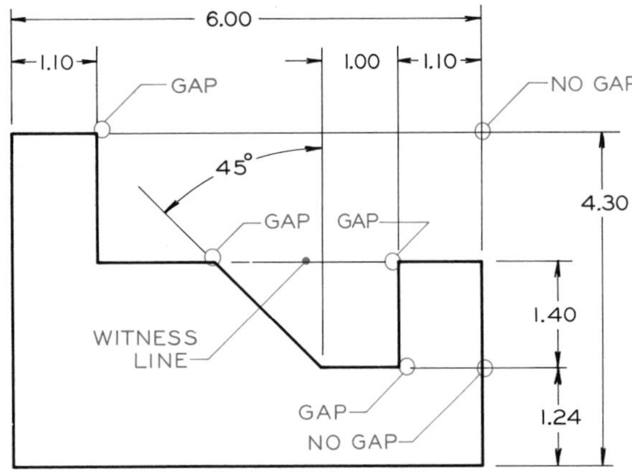

Fig. 19-10. Extension lines extend from the edge of an object leaving a small gap. They do not have gaps where they cross object lines and other extension lines. Note that a witness line is used to show that two planes of the part are aligned.

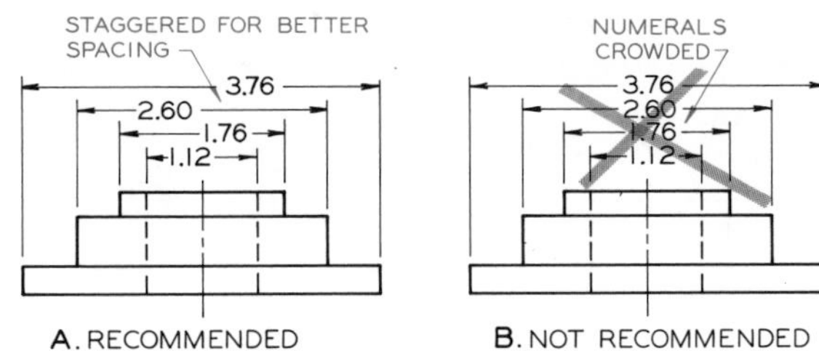

Fig. 19-13. Crowded numerals should be staggered to allow more space between them.

may cross other extension lines or object lines (Fig. 19-10); when this occurs, there are no gaps at the points of crossing.

Extension lines are also used to locate a theoretical point outside a curved surface (Fig. 19-11). This point is dimensioned and used to describe the shape of the object.

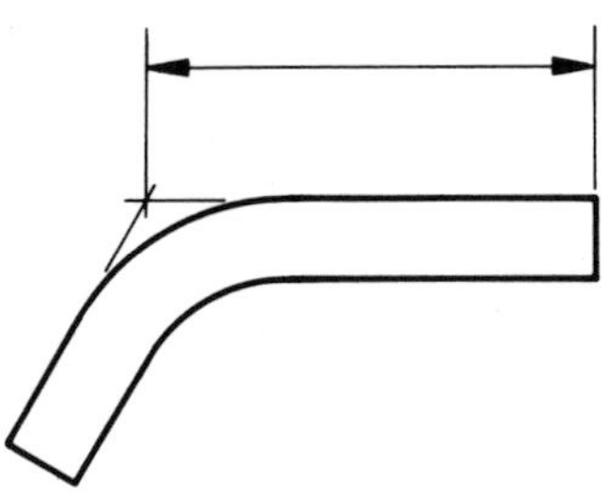

Fig. 19-11. Dimensioning a curved surface by locating a theoretical point with extension lines.

19-6 DIMENSIONING IN LIMITED SPACES

Many parts have very small features that do not provide much space for the placement of numerals or arrowheads. Several examples of dimensioning in limited spaces are shown in Fig. 19-12. Regardless of space limitations, the numerals should not be drawn smaller than the numerals used elsewhere in the drawing.

Often, rows of dimension lines are placed close together. In such a case (Fig. 19-13), it is good practice to stagger the numerals for the sake of readability.

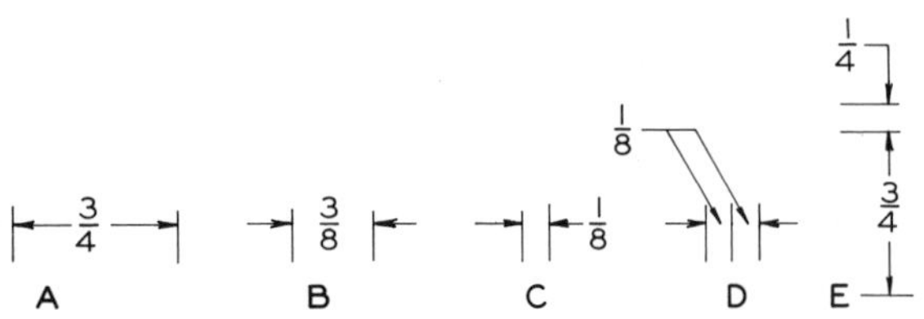

Fig. 19-12. Placement of dimensions in limited spaces.

19-7 DIMENSIONING PRISMS

The most basic design element is the prism, which when reduced to its simplest form is no more than a block. Various prisms are dimensioned in Fig. 19-14 to illustrate general rules of dimensioning. These rules apply to both freehand sketches and instrument drawings.

1. Dimensions should extend from the most descriptive view (Fig. 19-14A).
2. Dimensions which apply to two views should be placed between these two views (Fig. 19-14A).

FIGURE 19-14. DIMENSIONING PRISMS

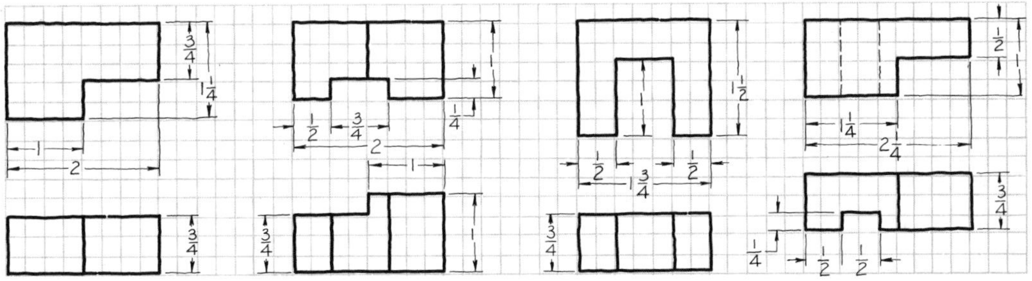

A. Dimensions should extend from the most descriptive view and be placed between the views to which they apply.

B. One intermediate dimension is not given. Extension lines may cross object lines.

C. It is permissible to dimension a notch inside the object if this improves clarity.

D. Whenever possible, dimensions should be placed on visible lines and not hidden lines.

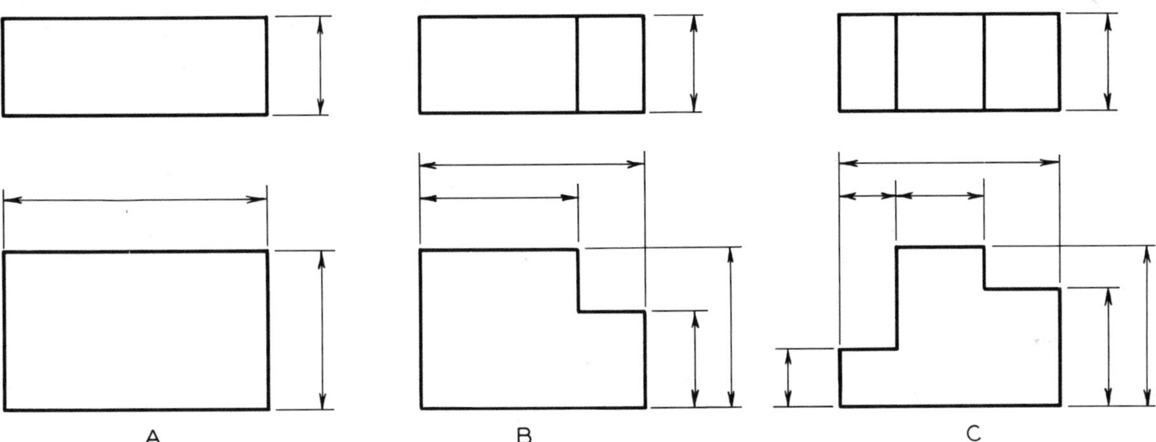

Fig. 19-15. Placement of dimensions on simple prisms with numerals omitted.

3. The first row of dimension lines should be placed a minimum of .40″ ($\frac{3}{8}$″) from the object. Successive rows are placed at least .25″ ($\frac{1}{4}$″) from one another (Fig. 19-14A).
4. Extension lines may cross, but dimension lines should not cross another line unless absolutely necessary.
5. In order to dimension each measurement in its most descriptive view, you may have to place dimensions in more than one view (Fig. 19-14B).
6. In the case of notches, clarity may be achieved more effectively by placing the dimension line inside the notch (Fig. 19-14C).
7. Whenever possible, dimensions should be applied to visible lines rather than hidden lines (Fig. 19-14D).
8. Dimensions should not be repeated nor should unnecessary information be given.

Examples of dimensioned prisms drawn with instruments are shown in Fig. 19-15. Numerals

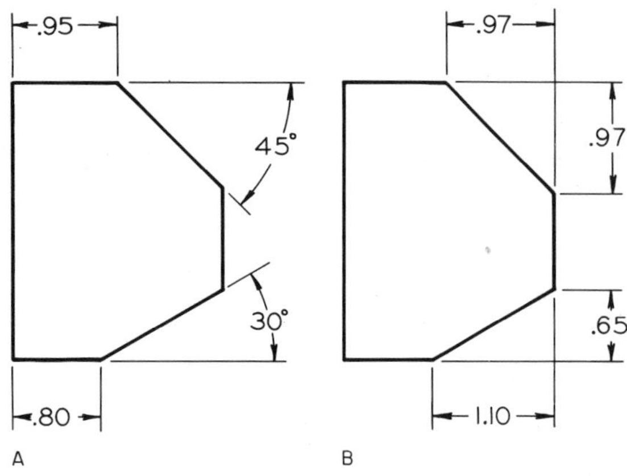

Fig. 19-16. Two acceptable methods of dimensioning angles: (A) angular measurements, and (B) coordinates.

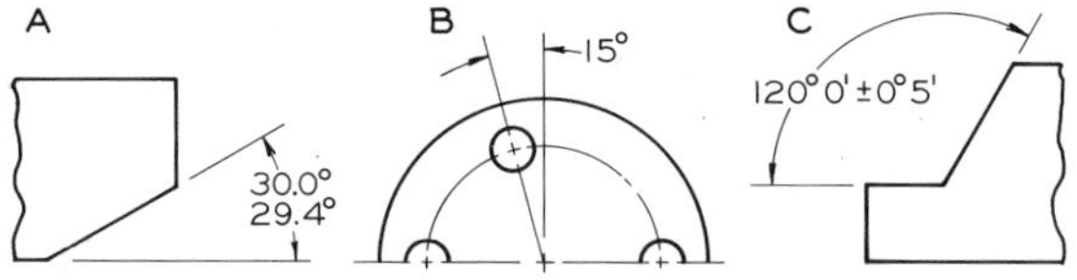

Fig. 19-17. Units of measuring angles are degrees and their decimal fractions (A), or degrees, minutes and seconds (C).

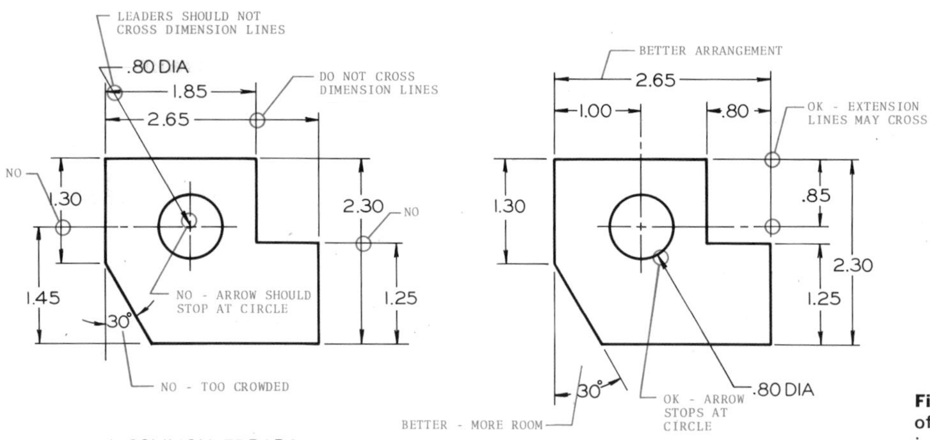

Fig. 19-18. A comparison of errors and good practices in dimensioning.

have been omitted, since the purpose of this figure is to illustrate the placement of the dimension lines.

19-8 DIMENSIONING ANGLES

Angles can be dimensioned by means of either angular measurements (degrees) or coordinates to locate the ends of the angular lines or planes. In Fig. 19-16A a part is dimensioned by means of angular measurements. When this method is used, it is necessary to locate the vertex of the angle with a dimension.

Coordinates are used in Fig. 19-16B to locate the two ends of each sloping plane. This method is more accurate than the use of angular measurements.

These two methods of dimensioning angles should not be mixed in the dimensioning of any single angle. Either one or the other method should be used to avoid conflicts in measurement.

Units for angular measurements are degrees, minutes, and seconds as shown in Fig. 19-17. Note that two angular measurements are shown in Fig. 19-17A to represent the maximum and minimum sizes allowed for tolerance. The angular measurements are given as decimal fractions. Whole degrees are used in Fig.

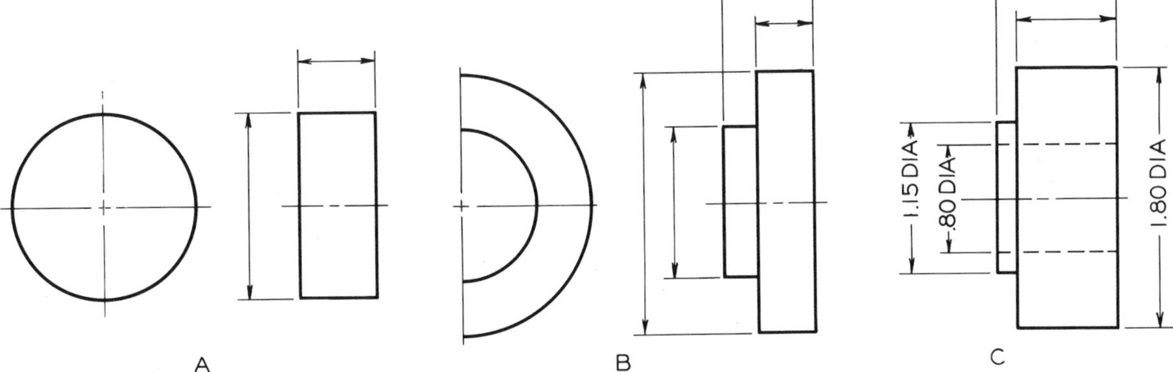

Fig. 19-19. Placement of dimensions on simple cylindrical shapes.

19-17B, and a measurement in degrees and minutes appears in Fig. 19-17C, where a tolerance of plus or minus 5 minutes (larger or smaller than 120°) is allowed.

19-9 COMMON ERRORS OF DIMENSIONING

Figure 19-18A illustrates a few of the most common mistakes made in dimensioning and the placement of dimensions. Remember: whenever possible, do *not* have dimension lines cross another line of any type. In addition, do *not* crowd notes and numerals. Figure 19-18B illustrates the proper way of applying dimensions to the object shown in part A of the figure. Be aware of the mistakes shown in part A in order to avoid them.

19-10 DIMENSIONING CYLINDERS

Most drawings contain cylinders, represented either as solids or as cylindrical holes. The simplest form of a cylinder is shown in Fig. 19-19A. The cylinder is dimensioned entirely in its rectangular view; note that the diameter is given, not the radius, since it is easier to measure a diameter than a radius. The dimensions are placed between the views for easy association with the two views.

When a part is composed of several concentric cylinders, each cylinder is dimensioned with a diameter, beginning with the smallest cylinder (Fig. 19-19B). These dimensions are placed on the rectangular view.

A cylindrical part may be dimensioned with only one view if the abbreviation DIA is placed after the dimensions of the diameters in the rectangular view (Fig. 19-19C).

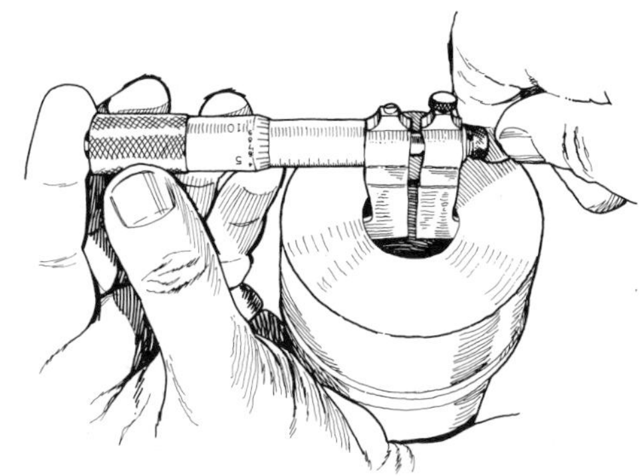

Fig. 19-20. A micrometer caliper is used for measuring internal cylindrical diameters.

19-11 MEASURING CYLINDRICAL PARTS

Cylindrical parts are dimensioned with diameters rather than radii because diameters are easier to measure. An internal cylindrical hole is measured with an internal *micrometer caliper* which has a built-in gauge permitting greater accuracy of measurement (Fig. 19-20).

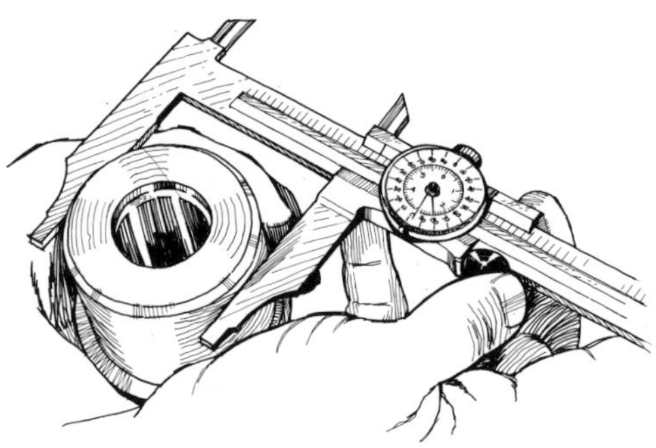

Fig. 19-21. An outside micrometer caliper with a built-in gauge for measuring the diameter of a cylinder.

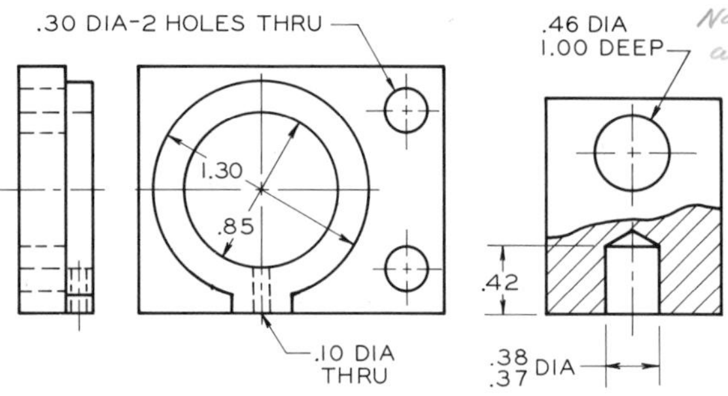

Fig. 19-22. Acceptable methods of dimensioning cylindrical holes and cylindrical shapes.

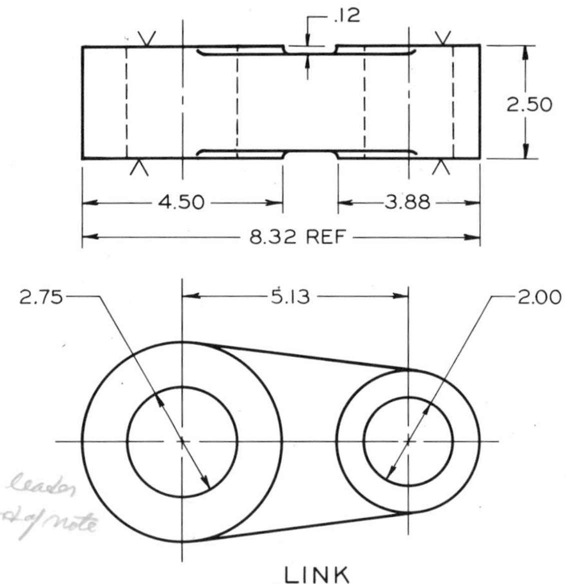

Fig. 19-23. An example of a dimensioned part composed of cylindrical shapes.

Likewise, an *external* micrometer caliper can be used for measuring the outside diameters of a part (Fig. 19-21). The choice of the diameter, rather than the radius, as the dimension makes it possible to measure diameters during machining when the part is being held between centers on a lathe.

19-12 CYLINDRICAL HOLES

Cylindrical holes may be dimensioned by one of the methods shown in Fig. 19-22, depending on the type of drawing and the space available. The diameter is always used when a full circle is being dimensioned. The preferred method is to draw a leader to the circular view, and then add the dimension followed by the abbreviation DIA to indicate the dimension is a diameter. Sometimes the note DRILL or BORE is added to specify the shop operation, but current standards suggest that DIA be used. When the dimension lines are drawn across the circular view so that it is obvious that the dimension is a diameter, we may omit the DIA note.

A part containing cylindrical features is dimensioned in Fig. 19-23 in both the circular and rectangular views to illustrate various methods of dimensioning.

19-13 DIMENSIONING CONES

Methods of dimensioning cones and truncated cones (cones with portions removed) are shown in Fig. 19-24. In parts A and B of the figure the height and diameter of the cones are dimensioned in the triangular and the trapezoidal view. The diameter of the base is placed at the

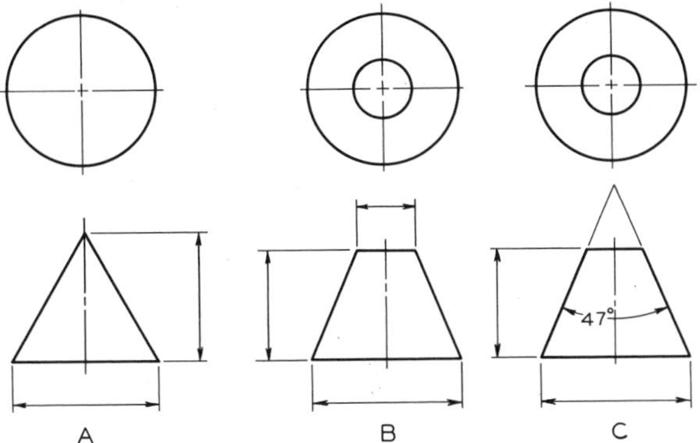

Fig. 19-24. Dimensioning conical shapes.

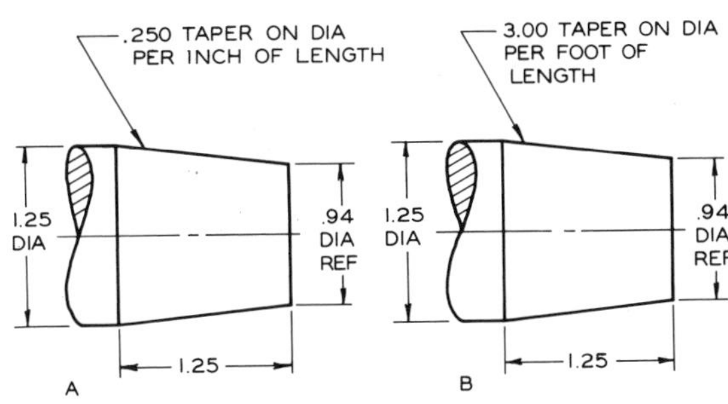

Fig. 19-25. Two acceptable methods of dimensioning tapers.

lower side of the front view, since this placement requires shorter extension lines and gives a more direct association with the view.

Another method of dimensioning cones, giving the base and the angular measurements of the cone, is shown in part C. All these methods are acceptable.

Tapers can be either conical surfaces or flat planes. Examples of tapered conical features are dimensioned in Fig. 19-25. The taper can be given in units of taper per inch or per foot.

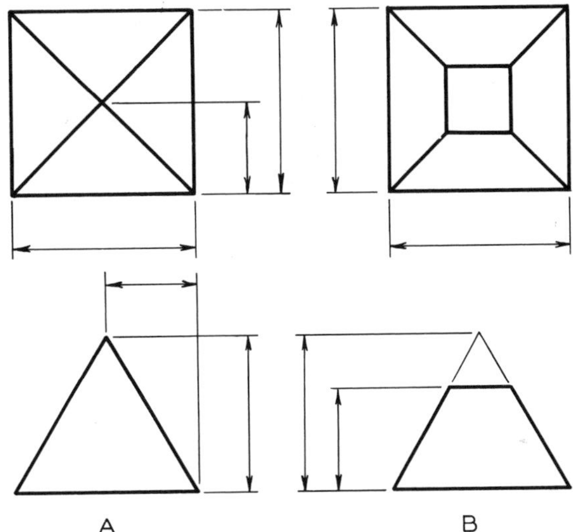

Fig. 19-26. Dimensioning pyramids.

19-14 DIMENSIONING PYRAMIDS

The pyramid in Fig. 19-26A is dimensioned to give the size of the base and the location of the apex in the top view. The height and the other location dimension of the apex are given in the front view. When the apex is located with dimensions, it is assumed that the pyramid is a right pyramid with its altitude perpendicular to the base at its midpoint.

An alternative method of dimensioning a truncated pyramid is shown in Fig. 19-26B.

19-15 DIMENSIONING SPHERES

The sphere is the simplest geometric element to dimension, since it appears as a circle in any view. Consequently, only one view is necessary, with a note placed outside the view as shown in Fig. 19-27A. When an object has a feature

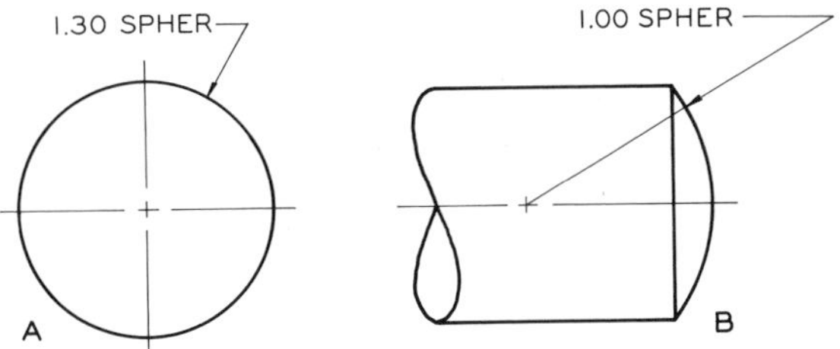

Fig. 19-27. Methods of dimensioning spheres and partial spheres.

Fig. 19-28. Finishing a surface by grinding. (Courtesy of Clausing Corporation.)

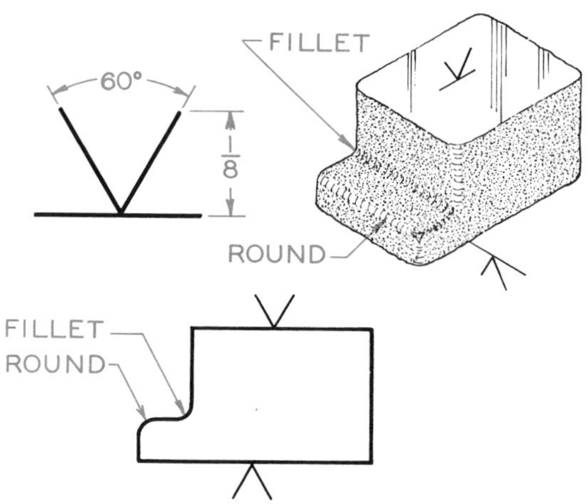

Fig. 19-29. Finish marks and fillets and rounds.

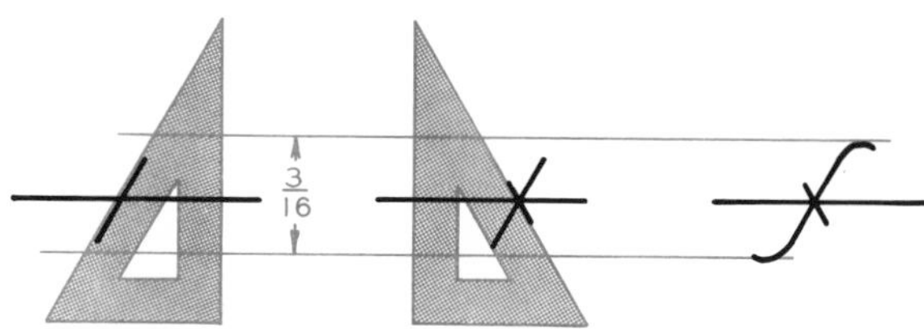

Fig. 19-30. An alternative method of drawing a finish mark.

that is a partial sphere, a radius and an abbreviation are used as shown in Fig. 19-27B.

19-16 FINISHED SURFACES

Many parts are formed as castings in a mold which gives their exterior surfaces a rough finish that must be machined by grinding, shaping, lapping, or a similar process if the part is designed to come into contact with another surface. Figure 19-28 shows a part being finished by grinding. This operation provides a smooth, uniform surface that permits accurate measurements.

To indicate that a surface is to be finished, *finish marks* are drawn on the edge of the view of that surface (Fig. 19-29). Finish marks should be repeated in every view where the surface appears as an edge, even if it is a hidden line.

Two methods of drawing finish marks are shown in Figs. 19-29 and 19-30. The simple V mark is preferred. When finish marks are applied to a pictorial, either of the methods shown in Fig. 19-29 is acceptable. The mark is drawn as if it were perpendicular to the plane of the surface.

When an object is finished on all surfaces, the note F.A.O. can be placed on the drawing to eliminate the need for finish marks. F.A.O. means "finished all over."

19-17 FILLETS AND ROUNDS

Fillets and rounds are rounded corners conventionally used on castings (Fig. 19-29). A *fillet* is an internal rounding, and a *round* is an external rounding. On any given drawing, the

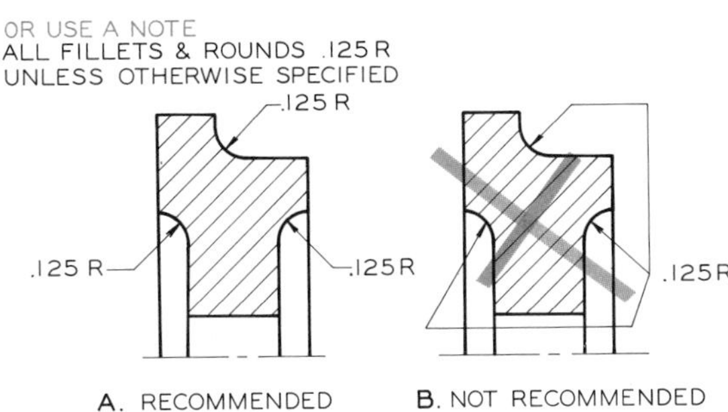

Fig. 19-31. Method of dimensioning fillets and rounds.

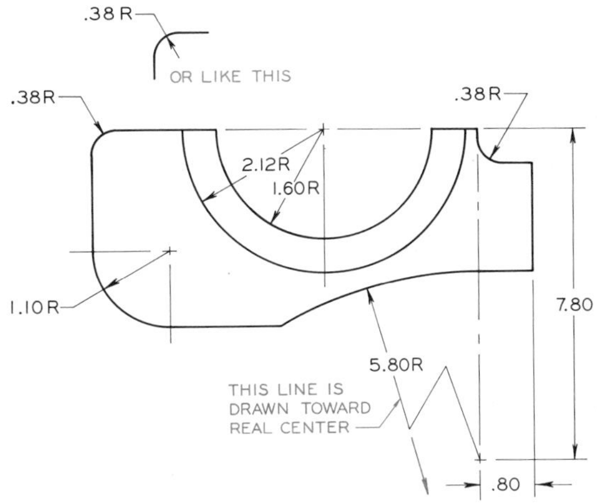

Fig. 19-32. Methods of dimensioning arcs.

same radius is usually applied to both fillets and rounds.

When fillets and rounds are of equal radii, a note may be added to the drawing to eliminate repetitive dimensioning. The note may read as follows: ALL FILLETS AND ROUNDS .125R. If most but not all of the fillets and rounds have equal radii, the following note may be used: ALL FILLETS AND ROUNDS .25R UNLESS OTHERWISE SPECIFIED. In this case, only the fillets and rounds of different radii are dimensioned, and it is understood that those not dimensioned are $\frac{1}{4}''$ in radius.

The correct method of dimensioning fillets is illustrated in Fig. 19-31A. Note that the letter R is placed after the dimensions to represent radius. It is preferable that leaders be close to the fillets and rounds to eliminate long, confusing leaders as shown in part B of the figure.

19-18 DIMENSIONING ARCS

When cylindrical or circular parts are less than a full circle, they are dimensioned with a radial dimension line extending from the center to the arc or with a note (Fig. 19-32). Where space permits, the numeral should be placed between the center and the arc, and the letter R should appear to the right of the numeral. When space does not allow this, the numeral can be placed in one of the other positions shown in the figure. However, in all cases, the arrowhead touches the arc being dimensioned either from the inside or outside.

When the radius of an arc is very long, the dimensioned drawing may show a radius that is less than the true radius, such as the 5.80R dimension in Fig. 19-32. To indicate that a radius is not a true measurement, the radius is drawn with a "zigzag." The portion of the radius nearest the arc should be drawn toward the arc's true center. The center of the arc should lie on the center line or the extension of the line on which the true center lies.

19-19 LEADERS

Leaders are used to relate notes and dimensions to the feature which they describe. A leader should be drawn as shown in Fig. 19-33. A standard triangle is used so the leader will pass through the center of the arc or circle if ex-

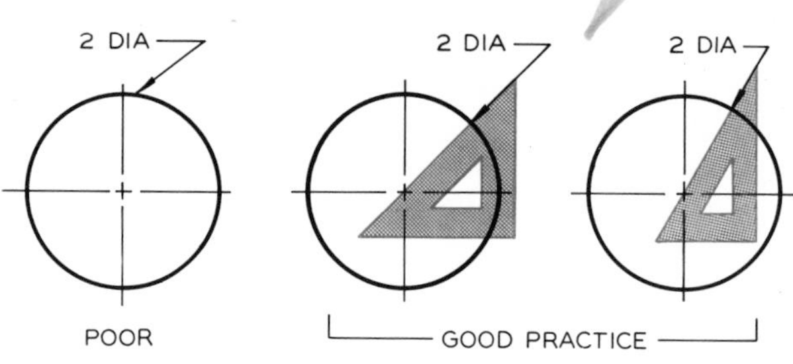

Fig. 19–33. Placement of leaders for dimensioning holes.

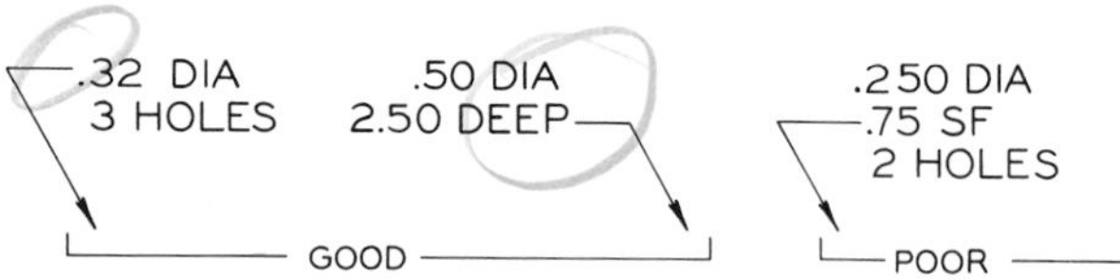

Fig. 19–34. Placement of notes with leaders. Leaders should begin with a horizontal segment at the left of the first word or the right of the last word.

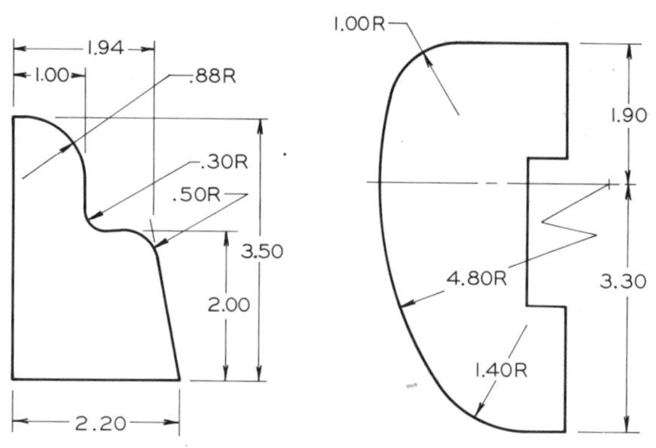

Fig. 19–35. Dimensioning shapes composed of arcs.

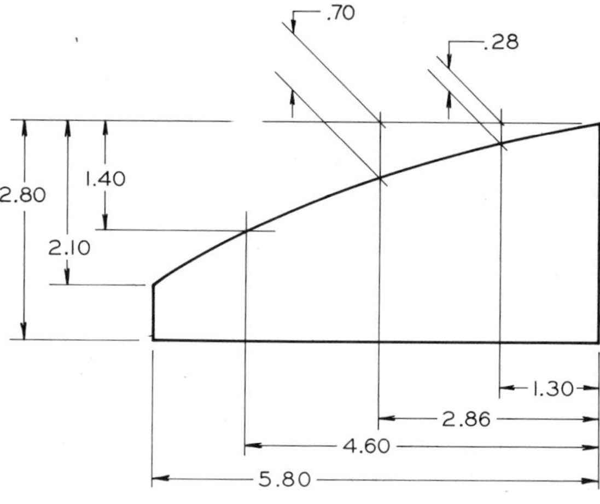

Fig. 19–36. Dimensioning an irregular curve from datum lines.

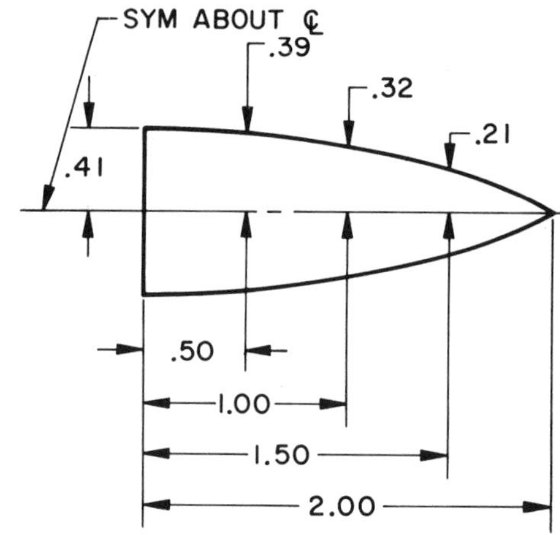

Fig. 19–37. Dimensioning a symmetrical curve about its center line and a datum line. (Courtesy of ANSI; Y14.5-1966.)

tended, but the arrow stops at the arc to which the leader applies.

Notes that are attached to leaders should be positioned so that the leader begins at either the first word or last word of the note (Fig. 19–34).

19–20 DIMENSIONING CURVED SURFACES

An irregular shape composed of a number of arcs of varying sizes (Fig. 19–35) can be dimensioned by using a series of radii. When these parts are laid out in the shop using these dimen-

FIGURE 19–38. LOCATION DIMENSIONS

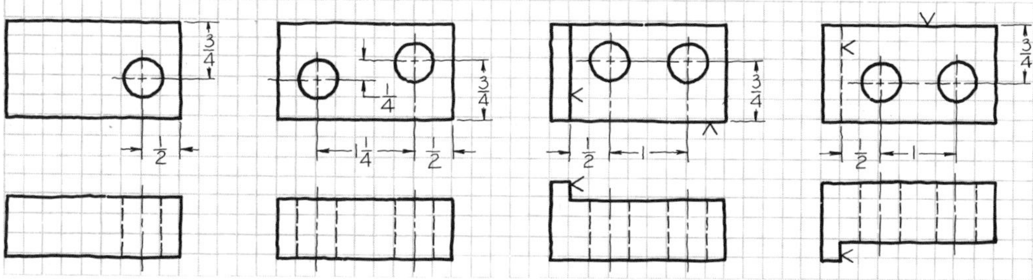

A. Cylindrical holes should be located in the circular view from two surfaces of the object.

B. When more than one hole is to be located, the other holes should be located in relation to the first from center to center.

C. A more accurate location is possible if holes are located from finished surfaces.

D. Holes should be located in the circular view and from finished surfaces, even if the finished surfaces are hidden.

sions, the principles of tangency construction covered in Chapter 5 must be applied.

When the curve is irregular rather than composed of arcs (Fig. 19–36), the coordinate method can be used to locate a series of points along the curve from two datum lines. The draftsman must use his judgment to determine the proper spacing for the points. Note that extension lines may be placed at an angle to provide additional space for showing dimensions.

A special case of an irregular curve is the symmetrical curve shown in Fig. 19–37. Note that dimension lines are used as extension lines in violation of a previously established rule.

19–21 LOCATION DIMENSIONS

Location dimensions are used to locate the positions of geometric elements, such as cylindrical holes. Figure 19–38 illustrates the basic rules of locating cylindrical holes. The size dimensions of the holes are omitted for clarity.

The cylindrical hole in A is located in the circular view with two dimensions that locate the center of the hole in the circular view. Any two visible surfaces of the prism can be used from which to draw extension lines to indicate the dimensions.

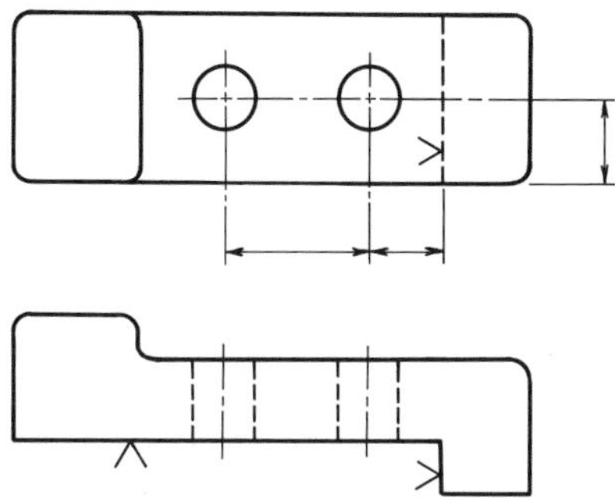

Fig. 19–39. Location of cylindrical holes from a finished surface.

The two holes in B are located with respect to each other from center to center. The hole at the right is located with respect to the surfaces of the prism, and the other hole is located from the center of the first hole.

The two holes in C are located with respect to a finished surface to achieve greater accuracy. Location dimensions should be related to finished surfaces whenever possible.

In part D, two holes are located with respect to a hidden surface, in violation of a previous rule; however, in this case, it is acceptable practice since the hidden surface is the only finished surface. The holes are located from

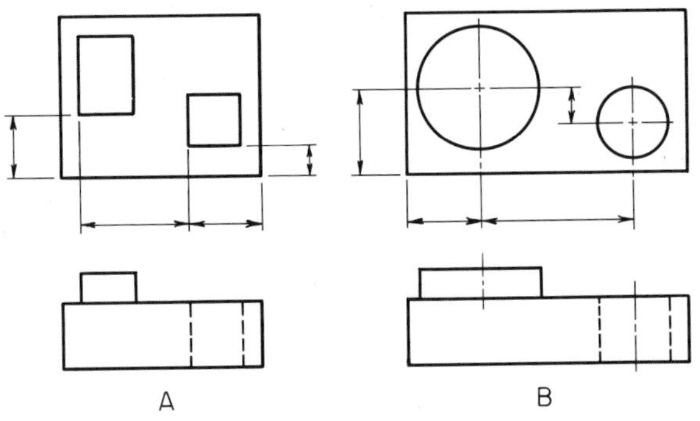

Fig. 19–40. Location of prism and cylinders.

center to center in the circular view. A similar example is the location of the holes in Fig. 19–39.

Prisms are located with respect to each other as shown in Fig. 19–40A. It is necessary to locate only a single corner of a prism with respect to another when the sides of each prism are parallel.

Location dimensions should be placed on that view which makes it possible to show both dimensions, the top view in this example. Cylinders are located in their circular views. This rule is illustrated in Fig. 19–41.

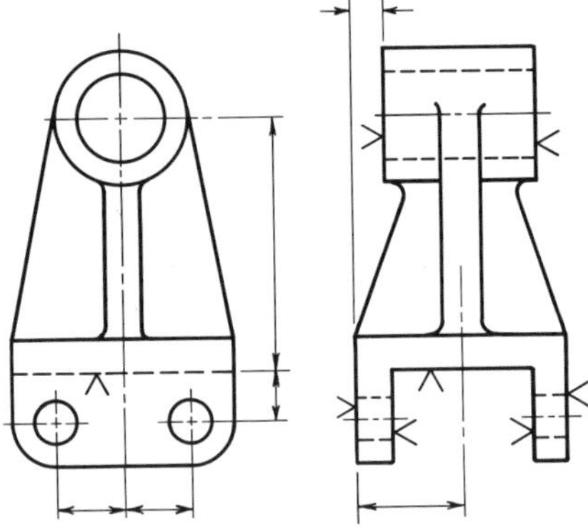

Fig. 19–41. Examples of location dimensions used to locate geometric elements.

19–22 LOCATION OF HOLES

When the location of holes must be very accurate, the dimensions should originate from a common reference plane on the part, to reduce the accumulation of errors in measurement as successive holes are located. Two examples of coordinate dimensions of this type are shown in Fig. 19–42A and B. When dimensions are located in this manner, the accumulation of errors will be minimal, especially if the reference surfaces are finished surfaces.

When several holes in a series are to be equally spaced, as in Fig. 19–42C, a note specifying that they are equally spaced can be used to locate the holes. The first and last holes of the series are determined by the usual location dimensions.

FIGURE 19–42. LOCATION OF HOLES

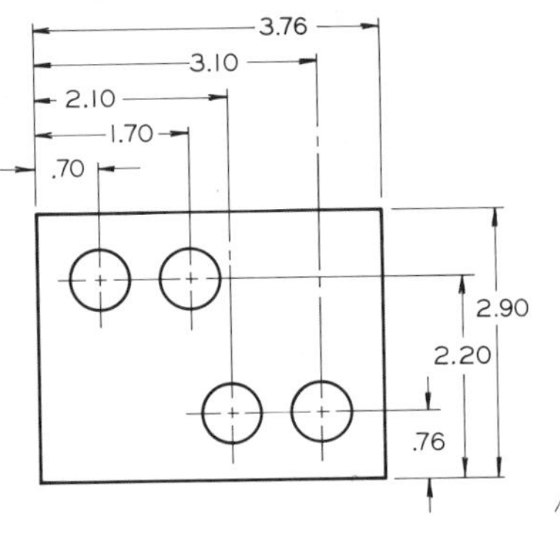

A. Holes can be more accurately located if common datum planes are used from which all measurements are made.

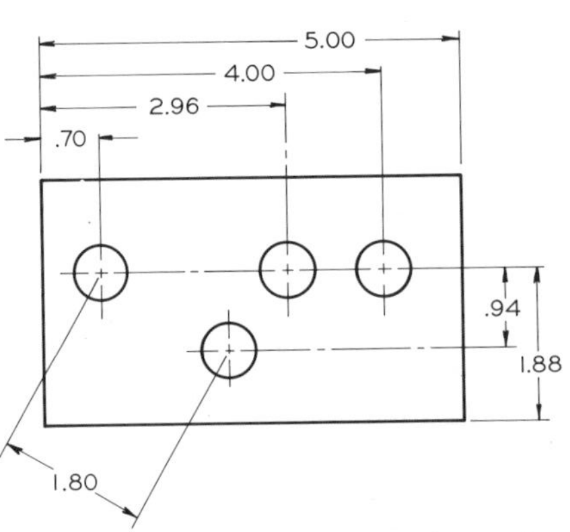

B. A diagonal dimension can be used to locate a hole of this type from another hole's center.

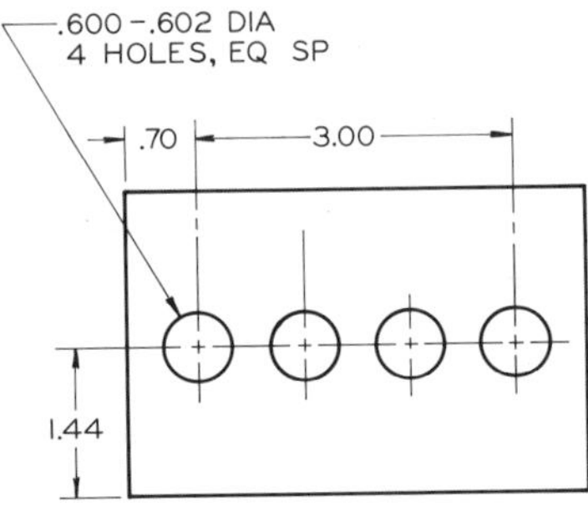

C. A note can be used to specify the spacing between the centers of holes in an equally spaced series.

Holes may be located on circular plates as shown in Fig. 19-43 by coordinates or by note. Greater accuracy is obtained when one uses coordinates measuring from the vertical and horizontal center lines as shown in Fig. 19-43A. When a note is used, the diameter of the circle passing through the centers of the hole must be given. The rest of the information appears in the note.

A similar method of locating holes is the polar system illustrated in Fig. 19-44A. The center of the arc that passes through the centers of the holes is used as the pole point. The radial distance from this point is given, together with the angular measurements (in degrees) between the holes. This method can be used to locate holes on a circular or a noncircular plate if the holes lie on a common circle (part B).

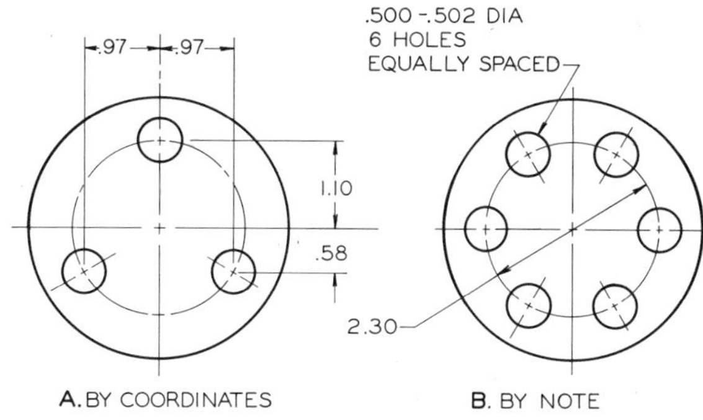

Fig. 19-43. Holes may be located in circular plates by coordinates (A) or by note (B).

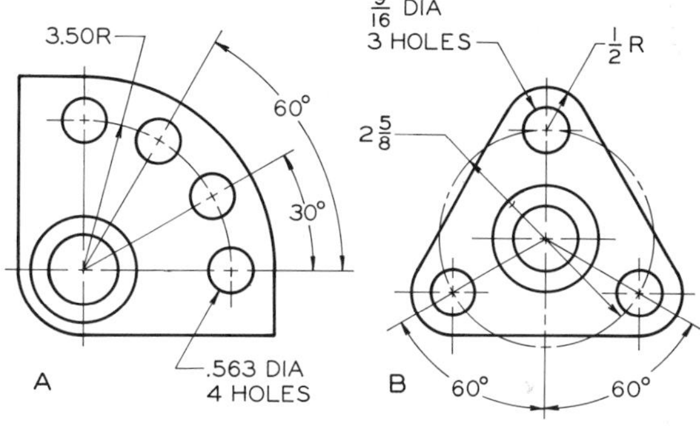

Fig. 19-44. Location of holes that lie on common arcs and circles.

19-23 DIMENSIONING OBJECTS WITH ROUNDED ENDS

Objects with rounded ends are dimensioned either from rounded end to rounded end or from center to center (Fig. 19-45). The method illustrated in part A is preferred since it provides the overall length of the piece without calculation. The radius is shown with the letter R without a dimension, since it is calculated to be half of the distance across the part.

If the object is dimensioned from center to center of the rounded ends, the overall dimension should be given as a reference dimension (REF) to eliminate the calculations required to determine the overall length. In this case (part B), the radius of the rounded ends is given.

A part with partially rounded ends is dimensioned as shown in Fig. 19-46A. The radii and their centers are given, since these data would not be known otherwise. The overall dimension is labeled as a reference dimension (REF) to serve as a check on the calculation of dimensions, but is itself of secondary importance.

When an object contains a rounded end that is less than a full semicircle (Fig. 19-46B), location dimensions must be used to locate the center of the arc. Location measurements are the first dimensions that are laid out in the con-

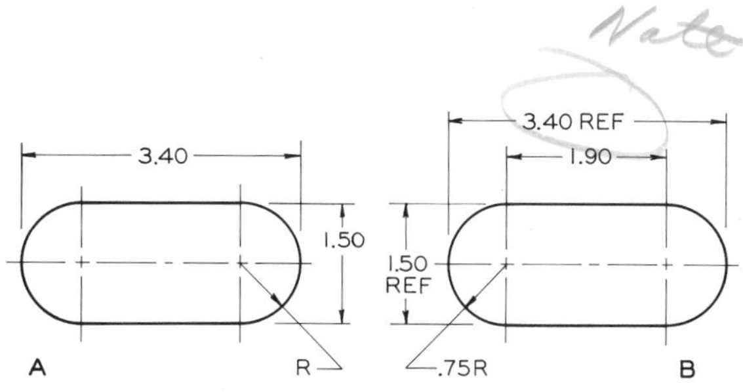

Fig. 19-45. Two acceptable methods of dimensioning objects with rounded ends.

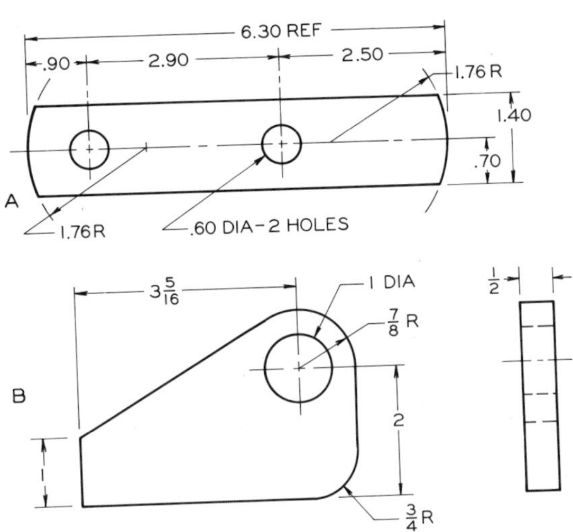

Fig. 19-46. Techniques of dimensioning parts with arcs and circular features.

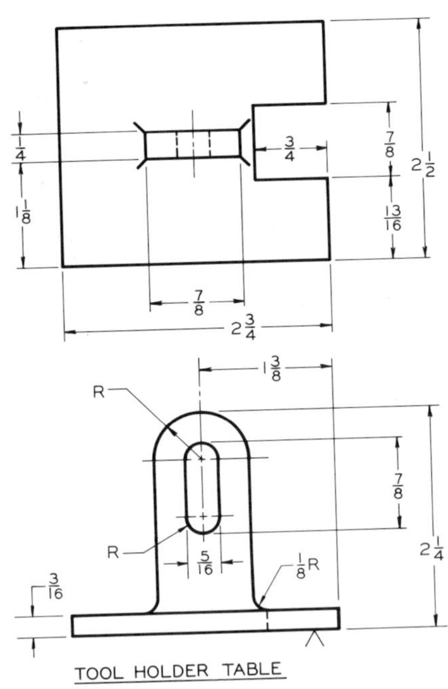

Fig. 19-48. An example of a part dimensioned in accordance with the principles discussed here.

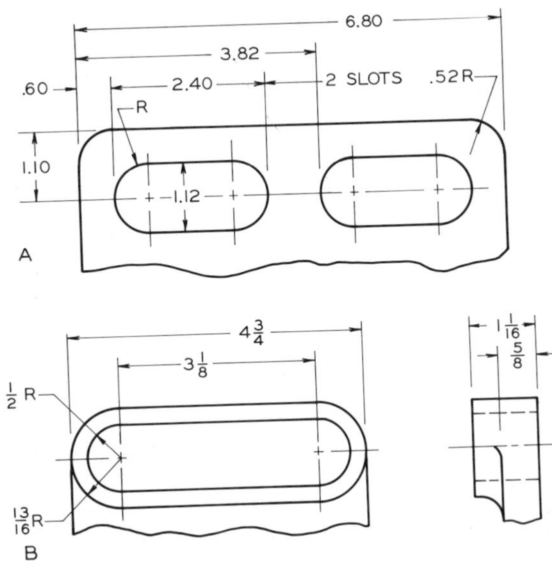

Fig. 19-47. Dimensioning slots.

struction of a drawing or a pattern. The arc is dimensioned and then used for constructing the contour of the object. To complete the drawing, lines are drawn from other established points tangent to the arc. A rounded 90° corner is dimensioned in the lower portion of Fig. 19-46.

Slots with rounded ends are dimensioned in Fig. 19-47. Note that the same general principles discussed earlier in this article apply to these shapes even though they are holes rather than solid objects. Only one slot is dimensioned in part A with a note indicating that there are two slots. The part in B is dimensioned (using common fractions) by locating the centers of the rounded ends.

The dimensioned drawing of a tool holder table in Fig. 19-48 shows examples of arcs and slots. To prevent the crossing of dimension lines, it is often necessary to place dimensions in a view that is not as descriptive of the features as might be desired.

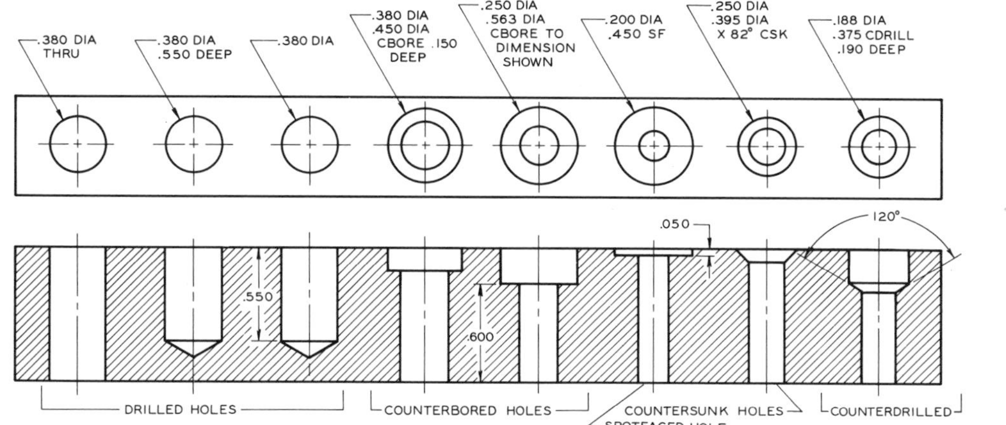

Fig. 19–49. Various types of machined holes and the proper notes to specify them.

Fig. 19–50. A cylindrical boss being spot-faced to provide a smooth bearing surface for a bolt. (Courtesy of Clausing Corporation.)

19–24 MACHINED HOLES

Machined holes are holes that are made or refined by a machine operation, such as drilling. Machined holes are specified by notes attached to leaders. The notes are positioned horizontally on the drawing regardless of the direction of the leader. Examples of machined holes and the proper notes to specify them are shown in Fig. 19–49.

It is preferable to give the diameter of the hole with the abbreviation DIA, with no reference to the method of making the hole. (Previously, we mentioned that it was common practice to give the machining operation in the note such as, $\frac{3}{4}''$ DRILL.)

Hole depths can be dimensioned in the rectangular views with a dimension or by a specification in the note. Where possible, hole notes should be on the circular view.

Drilled holes can be drilled through a part (through holes) or drilled to a specified depth. The specified depth of a drilled hole is the usable depth of the hole, not the depth to the point made by the drill. The drill point angle is 120°.

Counterbored holes are holes that have been enlarged by boring a hole with the same center as the original smaller hole (Fig. 19–49). One can add a note to indicate the diameter of the counterbore and its depth. An alternative method is to use a dimension in combination with a note.

Spot facing is a machining process used to finish the surface around the top of a hole, in order to provide a level seat for a washer or fastener head. The note in Fig. 19–49 gives the diameter of the spot face. The depth of the spot face can be indicated by means of a dimension or a note.

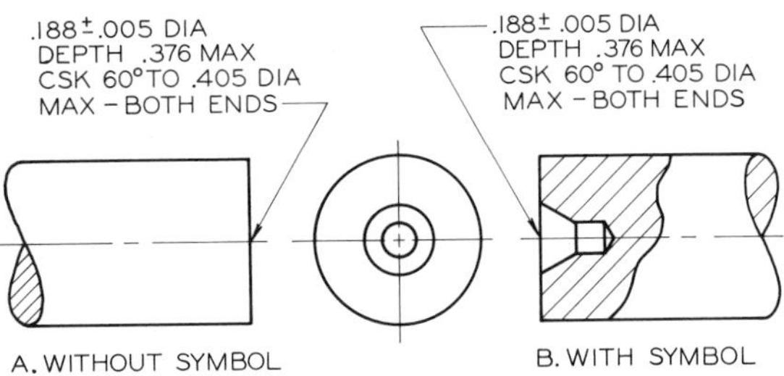

Fig. 19-51. Methods of indicating countersinking to receive machine centers during manufacture and inspection.

Fig. 19-52. Boring a large hole on a lathe with a boring bar. (Courtesy of Clausing Corporation.)

A spot-facing tool is shown in Fig. 19-50, where it has spot-faced a boss (a raised cylindrical element). This finished surface ensures that the part resting against it will be properly aligned.

Countersinking is the process of forming a conical enlargement at the top of a hole to receive a screw with a conical head (Fig. 19-49). The diameter of the countersunk hole (the maximum diameter at the surface) and the angle of the countersink are given in the note.

Countersinking is also used to provide center holes in shafts, spindles, and other cylindrical parts that will receive machine centers on which the work will be supported during manufacture or inspection. Two methods of noting the operation are illustrated in Fig. 19-51A.

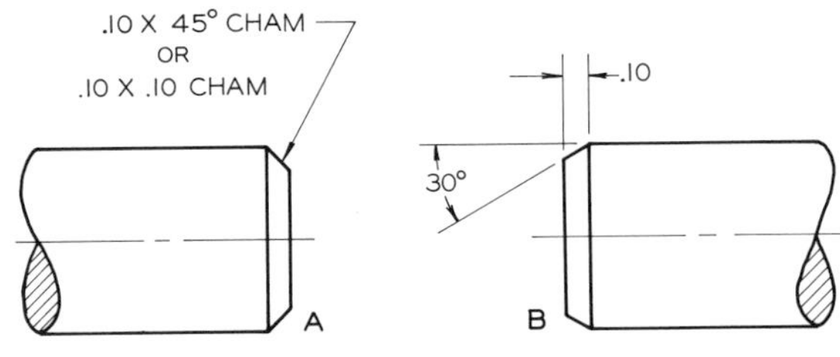

Fig. 19-53. Dimensioning chamfers.

Counterdrilled holes are holes that have been enlarged by drilling a hole with the same center as the smaller original hole (Fig. 19-49). The diameter of the counterdrill and its depth are given in the note. This recessed hole provides a concealed seat for a fastener to be inserted below the surface of the part.

Boring is a machine operation that is usually performed on a lathe with a boring bar (Fig. 19-52). Boring is used for larger holes that cannot be drilled.

Reamed holes are holes that have been "finished" or slightly enlarged after having been drilled or bored. This operation is done with a ream, which is similar to a drill bit.

19-25 CHAMFERS

Chamfers are beveled edges that are used on cylindrical parts such as shafts and threaded fasteners. They facilitate the assembly of these parts with other components and eliminate rough corners and edges.

When a chamfer is at an angle of 45°, a note can be used in either of the forms shown in Fig. 19-53A. When the chamfer is at an angle other than 45°, the angle and the length are given as shown in Fig. 19-53B.

Notes of this type can also be used for internal chamfers at the openings of holes. If the design of a part requires that the chamfer diameter be controlled, the chamfer should be dimensioned as in Fig. 19-54.

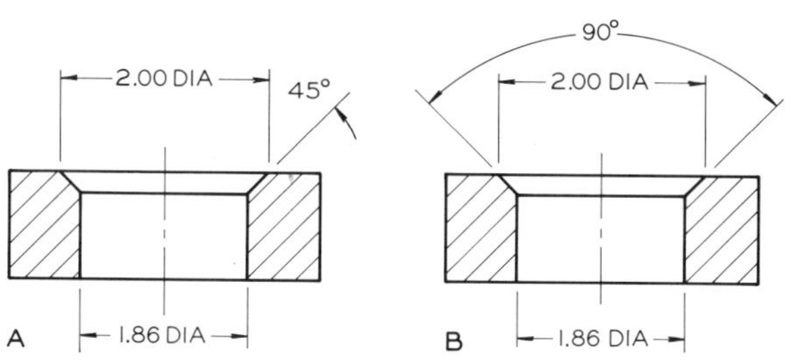

Fig. 19-54. Dimensioning internal chamfers.

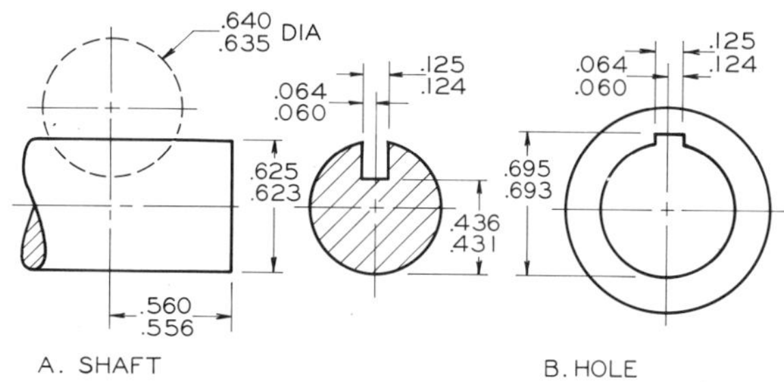

Fig. 19-55. Dimensioning keyseats.

19-26 KEYSEATS

A *keyseat* is a slot cut into a shaft for the purpose of aligning the shaft with a part mounted on it. This part may be a pulley or a collar. The proper method of dimensioning a key, keyway, and keyseat is shown in Fig. 19-55. Tolerances are shown in this example and will be discussed in more detail later in this chapter.

The milling machine shown in Fig. 19-56 is being used to cut a slot. This machine can also be used to cut keyseats in shafts.

Fig. 19-56. Cutting a slot with a milling machine. (Courtesy of Clausing Corporation.)

19-27 KNURLING

Knurling is the operation of cutting diamond shaped or parallel patterns on a cylindrical surface for gripping or for decoration, or for a press fit between two parts that will be permanently assembled as though welded. A diamond knurl and a straight knurl are dimensioned in Fig. 19-57.

Knurls are specified in terms of type, diametrical pitch (DP), and diameter before and after knurling if accuracy is important. The diameter can be omitted when control is not required, as in the case of a knurl used for gripping. In Fig. 19-58, a note is used to dimension a knurled surface. The knurled surface need not be drawn; a note is sufficient.

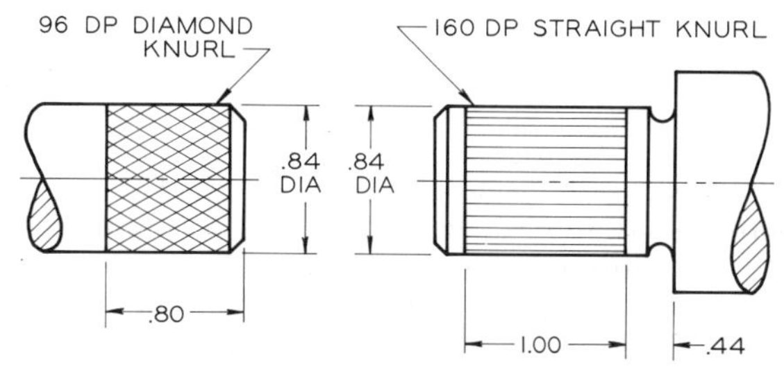

Fig. 19-57. Methods of dimensioning diamond and straight knurls.

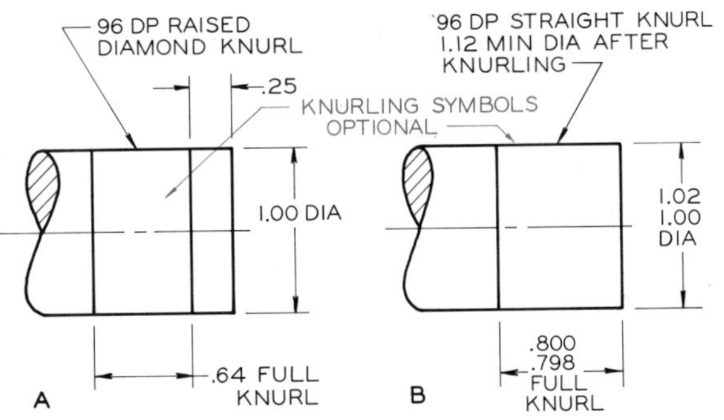

Fig. 19–58. Methods of dimensioning knurls and indicating size tolerances.

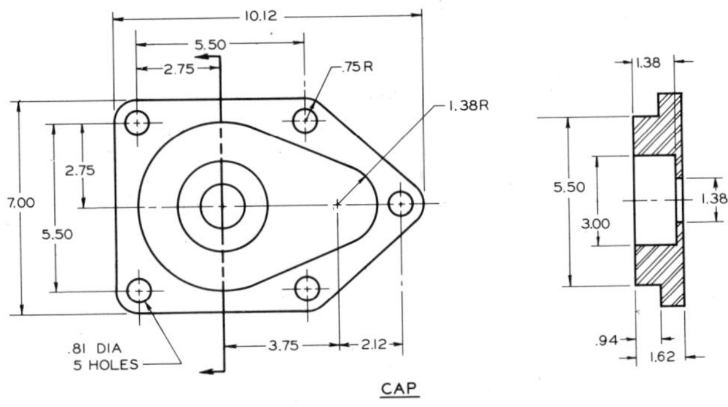

Fig. 19–61. A dimensioned section.

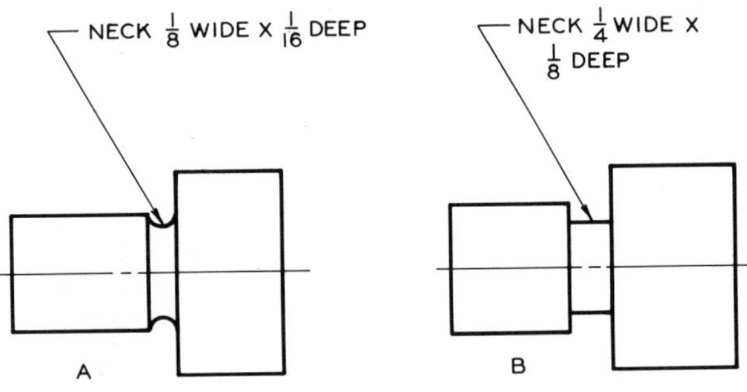

Fig. 19–59. Methods of dimensioning necks.

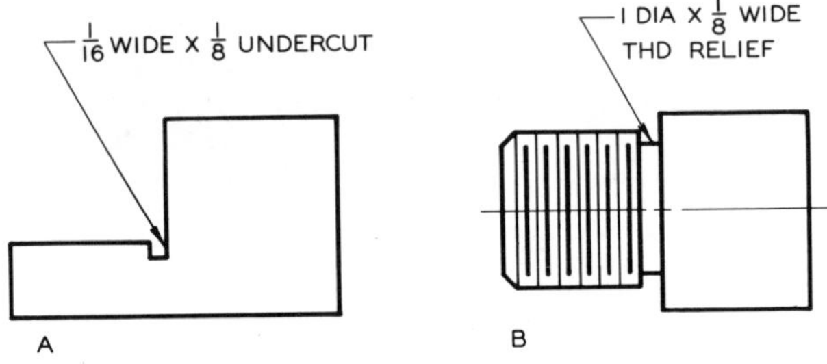

Fig. 19–60. Noting undercuts and thread reliefs.

When the knurled part is to be press-fitted with another part, the diameters before and after knurling must be given, as shown in Fig. 19–58A.

19–28 NECKS AND UNDERCUTS

A *neck* is a recess cut into a cylindrical part. This recess is commonly used at the point at which a cylinder changes from one diameter size to another (Fig. 19–59). The neck ensures that a pulley or a part that is assembled on the shaft can fit flush against the shoulder of the larger cylinder without binding.

Undercuts are somewhat similar to necks and serve much the same purpose. An undercut at the intersection between two perpendicular planes of a part is shown in Fig. 19–60A. It ensures that a mating part designed to fit this corner will fit flush against both surfaces. The undercut could also be a recessed neck on the inside of a cylindrical hole. In Fig. 19–60B, a *thread relief* is used, since it is difficult to cut threads to the very end of a cylinder that joins a larger cylinder.

19–29 DIMENSIONED SECTIONS

Sections are dimensioned in the same manner as regular views. Sections add clarity to a drawing that might otherwise be difficult to interpret.

A dimensioned section is shown in Fig. 19–61. The dimensioning principles discussed in this chapter have been applied to the cap shown in this figure.

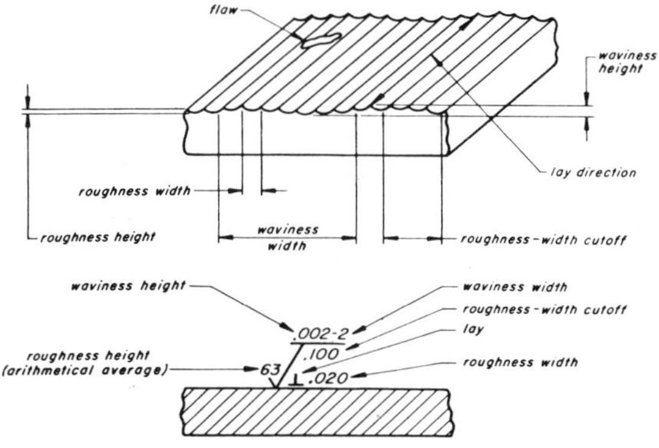

Fig. 19–62. Surface texture definitions. (Courtesy of ANSI; B46.1-1962.)

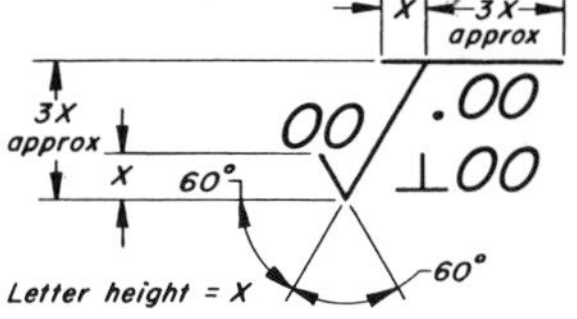

Fig. 19–63. The surface texture symbol. (Courtesy of ANSI; B46.1-1962.)

19–30 SURFACE TEXTURE

Many assemblies must operate within close tolerances requiring a special surface finish that needs to be more accurately specified than by the "V" customarily used to denote a finished surface. Since there are various degrees of finish, a single symbol is not a sufficient specification. Hence, in critical instances, the symbol is accompanied by notes that specify the degree of finish desired.

The meaning of notes and symbols must be understood before they can be used on drawings. For this purpose, refer to Fig. 19–62. The terms used in this figure are defined below.

Surface texture is the term used to indicate repetitive or random deviations from the nominal surface which form the pattern of the surface. These deviations include roughness, waviness, lay, and flaws.

Roughness describes the finer irregularities in surface texture usually caused by variations in the manufacturing and production processes.

Roughness height is the average (arithmetic) deviation from the mean plane of the surface. Roughness is measured in micro-inches or millionths of an inch, 0.000001″ (abbreviated as MU in.).

Roughness width (measured in micro-inches) is the width between successive peaks or ridges which constitute the predominant pattern of the roughness.

Roughness-width cutoff (measured in inches) is the largest spacing of repetitive surface irregularities to be included in the measurement of average roughness height.

Waviness (measured in inches) is a widely spaced component of surface texture, the spacing exceeding the roughness-width cutoff. Waviness may result from variations in machine operations, vibration, chatter, or warping. Roughness may be considered as superimposed on a wavy surface.

Waviness height (rated in inches) is the peak-to-valley distance between waves.

Waviness width (rated in inches) is the spacing of successive wave peaks or successive wave valleys.

Lay is the direction of the predominant surface pattern, ordinarily determined by the production method used.

Flaws are irregularities or defects that occur infrequently or at widely varying intervals on a surface. These include cracks, blow holes, checks, ridges, scratches, etc. Unless otherwise specified, the effect of flaws shall not be included in the roughness height measurements.

Contact area is the surface area that will make contact with its mating surface.

These features are specified on a drawing by the symbol shown in Fig. 19–63. The lettering

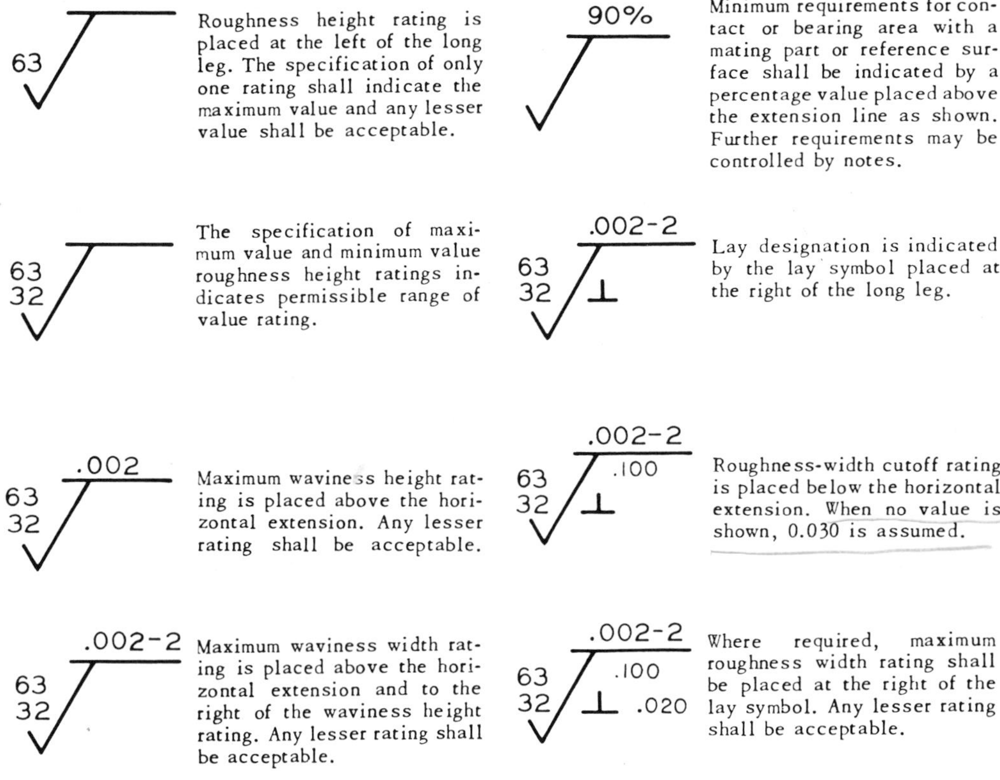

63
Roughness height rating is placed at the left of the long leg. The specification of only one rating shall indicate the maximum value and any lesser value shall be acceptable.
90%
Minimum requirements for contact or bearing area with a mating part or reference surface shall be indicated by a percentage value placed above the extension line as shown. Further requirements may be controlled by notes.
63
32
The specification of maximum value and minimum value roughness height ratings indicates permissible range of value rating.
.002-2
63
32
Lay designation is indicated by the lay symbol placed at the right of the long leg.
.002
63
32
Maximum waviness height rating is placed above the horizontal extension. Any lesser rating shall be acceptable.
.002-2
.100
63
32
Roughness-width cutoff rating is placed below the horizontal extension. When no value is shown, 0.030 is assumed.
.002-2
63
32
Maximum waviness width rating is placed above the horizontal extension and to the right of the waviness height rating. Any lesser rating shall be acceptable.
.002-2
.100
63
32
.020
Where required, maximum roughness width rating shall be placed at the right of the lay symbol. Any lesser rating shall be acceptable.

Fig. 19-64. Surface texture notes and their meanings. (Courtesy of ANSI; B46.1-1962.)

on the symbol should be of the same size as all other letters in the drawing. The top extension line can extend as far to the right as required. In some cases, the surface texture must be specified with a high degree of accuracy, while in other cases, general instructions are sufficient. Figure 19-64 shows how roughness, waviness and lay are specified by inserting the ratings in the appropriate portions of the symbol. Only the specifications that apply to a given surface should be included in the surface symbol, since special finishes increase production cost. Lay symbols and the manner in which they are combined with the surface symbol are illustrated in Fig. 19-65. Figure 19-66 shows surface symbols applied to a drawing to indicate the surface texture.

Common production methods result in roughness heights that are peculiar to the process used. The designer specifying a surface texture must know these characteristics and the machines available to him. Figure 19-67, giving the roughness of common production methods in micro-inches, can serve as a guide for selection of proper machining operations.

19-31 TOLERANCES

Engineering components produced today require more accurate dimensions than did those produced in the past, because today many parts are made by different companies in different geographical locations. Parts manufactured by

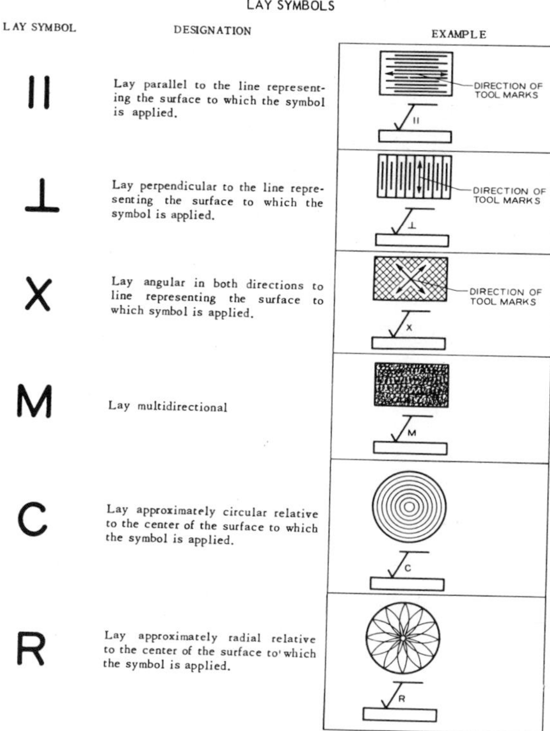

LAY SYMBOLS
LAY SYMBOL
DESIGNATION
EXAMPLE
Lay parallel to the line representing the surface to which the symbol is applied.
DIRECTION OF TOOL MARKS
Lay perpendicular to the line representing the surface to which the symbol is applied.
DIRECTION OF TOOL MARKS
Lay angular in both directions to line representing the surface to which symbol is applied.
DIRECTION OF TOOL MARKS
M
Lay multidirectional
C
Lay approximately circular relative to the center of the surface to which the symbol is applied.
R
Lay approximately radial relative to the center of the surface to which the symbol is applied.

Fig. 19–65. Lay notations used with surface texture symbols. (Courtesy of ANSI; B46.1-1962.)

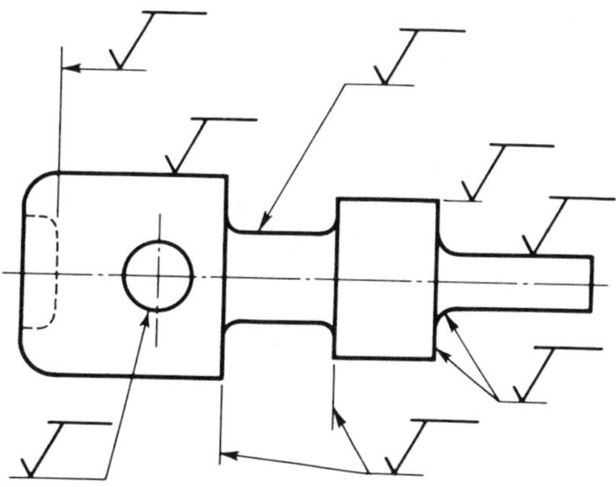

Fig. 19–66. The application of surface texture symbols to a drawing. (Courtesy of ANSI; B46.1-1962.)

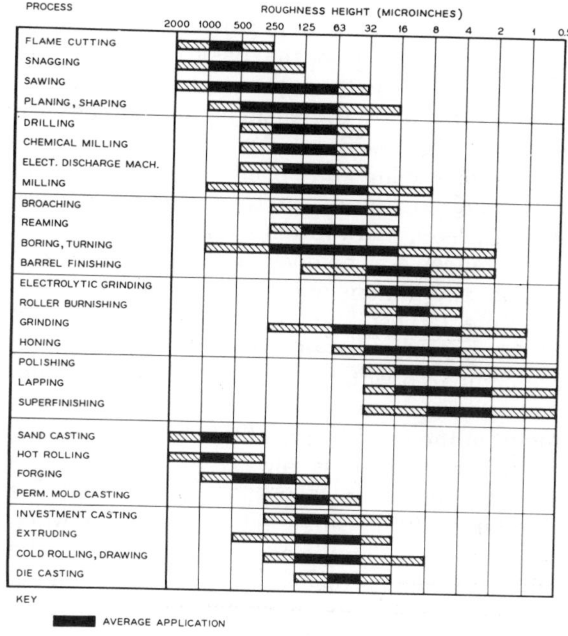

THE RANGES SHOWN ABOVE ARE TYPICAL OF THE PROCESSES LISTED.
HIGHER OR LOWER VALUES MAY BE OBTAINED UNDER SPECIAL CONDITIONS.

Fig. 19–67. Surface roughness produced by common production methods. (Courtesy of ANSI; B46.1-1962.)

any one company must be interchangeable with those made by other companies. If they are not, the parts must be modified to fit into the assembly—a very expensive process. Interchangeability of parts is also an important factor when replacement becomes necessary.

The technique of ensuring that manufactured parts are of proper size is called *tolerancing*. In tolerancing, each dimension is allowed a certain degree of variation within a specified zone, the range of permissible variation depending on the function of the part. It is not only very expensive, but most difficult to produce parts whose measurements are accurate to thousandths or ten-thousandths of an inch. Therefore, the manufacturer is given an allowable variation that will reduce costs while still controlling the size or position of the parts.

19-32 TOLERANCE NOTES

All dimensions of a part are toleranced to some degree either by the judgment of the manufacturer or by a note on the drawing. The usual practice is to supply a general tolerance note on a drawing or in specifications. Dimensions that are not critical because they do not involve mating parts may be toleranced by a general note such as TOLERANCE $\pm\frac{1}{64}$.

Other tolerances, for dimensions which involve mating parts, can be indicated more accurately by a note such as TOLERANCE $\pm$.001.

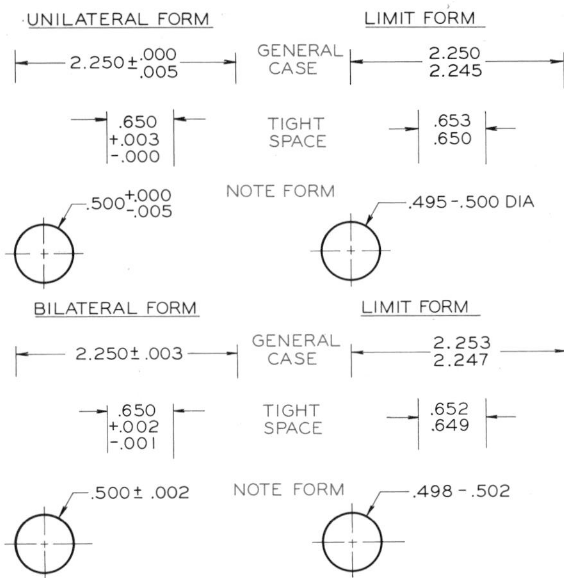

Fig. 19-68. Methods of noting tolerances in unilateral and limit forms.

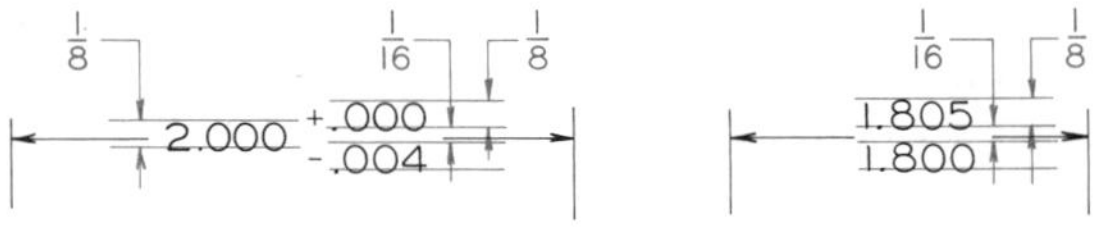

19-33 TOLERANCE DIMENSIONS

Several of the acceptable methods of specifying tolerances are shown in Fig. 19-68. When "plus-and-minus" tolerancing is used, tolerances are applied to a *basic diameter*. When the plus and minus dimensions allow variation in only one direction, the tolerancing is *unilateral*. Tolerancing that permits variation in either direction from the basic dimension is *bilateral*. The methods of applying these tolerances to both dimensions and notes are shown in Fig. 19-68.

The positioning and spacing of the numerals indicating the limits of tolerance are shown in Fig. 19-69. Both forms are acceptable.

Tolerances may be given in the form of *limits;* that is, two dimensions are given which represent the largest and smallest size permitted in the manufacture of the part. When limits are compared with their counterparts in "plus-and-minus" form, we see that both methods result in the same limits of tolerance.

The larger limit is always placed over the smaller limit in a toleranced dimension; the smaller limit precedes the larger limit when both are placed on the same line in a note. The plus dimension is placed over the minus dimension in the "plus-and-minus" system.

Fig. 19-69. Positioning and spacing of numerals used to specify tolerances.

19-34 MATING PARTS

Mating parts are parts that fit together with a reasonably high degree of accuracy. Figure 19-70A shows two mating parts, one of which is a block that is to fit into a rectangular notch. The upper piece is dimensioned with two measurements that indicate the upper and lower limits of the size. The tolerance dimensions for the notch are slightly larger than those for the block that fits into it. Note that undercuts are specified to allow dirt or obstructions to drop out when the parts are assembled.

The variation in size permitted in each part is shown in Fig. 19-70B. In all possible variations of size in the two parts, the notch will be larger than the block that fits into it. This form of

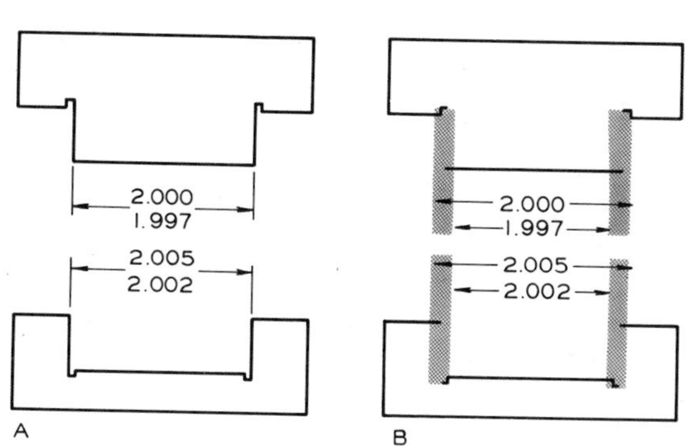

Fig. 19-70. Tolerances between two mating parts. Both parts have a tolerance of .003″ and an allowance of .002″.

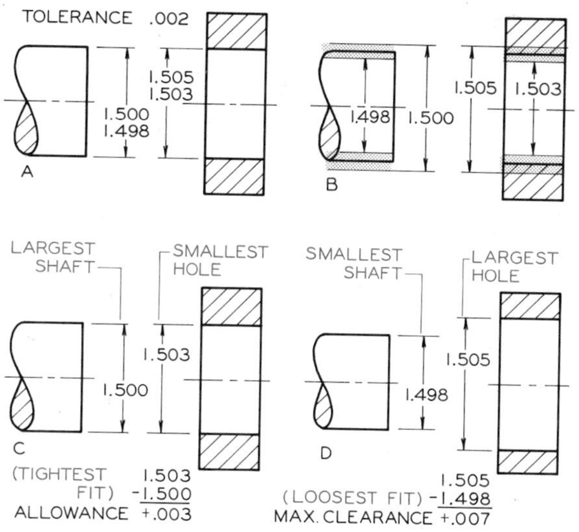

Fig. 19-71. Explanation of the terms of tolerancing as applied to cylindrical fits.

tolerancing ensures that the parts will assemble and function as desired. However, it is obvious that a few thousandths of an inch of variation could result in a notch too small for the block to fit into. Clearly, tolerances are important in situations of this type.

An example of mating cylindrical parts is shown in Fig. 19-71A. Part B of the figure illustrates the meaning of the tolerance dimensions given in part A; that is, it shows that the size of the shaft can vary in diameter from 1.500″ (its maximum size) to 1.498″ (its minimum size). The difference between these limits (on a single part) is called *tolerance*. In this case, the tolerance is .002. The dimensions of the hole in part A are given in limits of 1.505 and 1.503, for a tolerance of .002 (the difference between the limits as illustrated in part B).

19-35 TERMINOLOGY OF TOLERANCING

The meaning of most of these terms clearly emerges from Fig. 19-71. When the shaft and hole shown are assembled, the extreme conditions are the tightest and the loosest fits illustrated in parts C and D.

Allowance. The allowance is the tightest fit between two mating parts. In part C, the allowance between the shaft and the hole is +.003. (Negative for an interference fit.)

Nominal size. The nominal size is an approximate size. The nominal size of the shaft and the hole in Fig. 19-65 is 1.50 or $1\frac{1}{2}$.

Basic size is the exact, theoretical size from which limits are derived by the application of tolerances and allowances in "plus-and-minus" tolerancing (Fig. 19-68).

Actual size is the measured size of a finished part.

Limits of tolerance are the extreme measurements permitted by the tolerance or the maximum and minimum sizes of a part. The limits of tolerance of the shaft in Fig. 19-71A are 1.500 and 1.498.

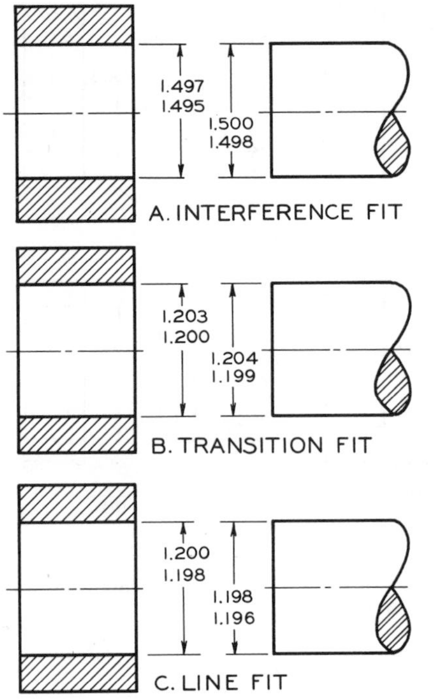

1.497
1.495
1.500
1.498
A. INTERFERENCE FIT
1.203
1.200
1.204
1.199
B. TRANSITION FIT
1.200
1.198
1.198
1.196
C. LINE FIT

Fig. 19-72. Types of fits between mating parts.

Tolerance is the difference between the limits prescribed for a single part. The tolerance of the shaft in Fig. 19-71A is .002.

Fit signifies the range of tightness between two parts which may result from a specific combination of allowances and tolerances in the design of mating parts. The four major general types of fits are: clearance, interference, transition, and line.

Clearance fit is the fit that gives clearance between two assembled mating parts. The fit between the shaft and the hole in Fig. 19-71 is a clearance fit, since it will provide an air space between the parts under the tightest conditions.

Interference fit is the fit that leads to interference between two assembled parts. The shaft in Fig. 19-72A is larger than the hole; this results in a *force fit* or *press fit* that has almost the same effect as a weld between two parts.

use gen'l note for this type of dim

1.000
MIN FULL THD

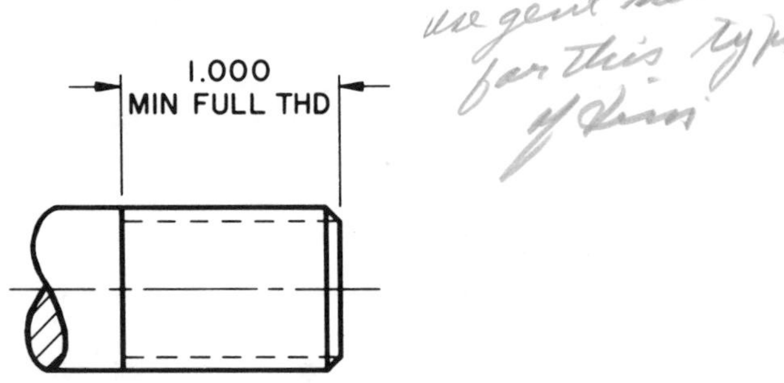

Fig. 19-73. Single tolerance dimensions. (Courtesy of ANSI; Y14.5-1966.)

Transition fit is a fit between two parts that can result in either interference or clearance. The shaft in Fig. 19-72B can be either smaller or larger than the hole and still be within the prescribed tolerances.

Line fit is a fit that can result in contact of surfaces between two parts or clearances. The shaft and the hole in Fig. 19-72C can have contact or clearance when the limits of tolerance are approached.

Selective assembly is a method of selecting and assembling parts by trial and error. Using this method, one can assemble parts with a larger tolerance and, consequently, at reduced cost. Parts can be toleranced with dimensions that may result in transition fits (both interference and clearance) and then assembled by selection to give the desired function. This method represents a compromise between a high degree of manufacturing accuracy and ease of assembly of interchangeable parts.

Single limits are dimensions that are designated by MIN *or* MAX (minimum or maximum) instead of being labeled by both. An example is given in Fig. 19-73. Depths of holes, lengths, threads, corner radii, chamfers, etc., are dimensioned in those measurements. In using this system caution should be exercised to prevent a substantial deviation from the single limit.

(use gen'l note)

Basic shaft or hole system is a system that uses the maximum size of a shaft or the minimum size of a hole as the *basic size* to which allowances and tolerances are applied. This system is used in industries that use great quantities of shafts of standard size.

19–36 BASIC HOLE SYSTEM

The *basic hole system* is a widely used system of dimensioning holes and shafts to give the required allowance between the two assembled parts. In this system, the smallest hole is taken as the basic diameter from which the limits of tolerance and allowance are applied.

The hole is used because many of the standard drills, reamers, and machine tools are designed to give standard hole sizes. Therefore, it is advantageous to use this diameter as the basic dimension.

If the smallest diameter of a hole is 1.500″, the allowance (.003, for example) can be subtracted from this diameter to find the diameter of the largest shaft (1.497″). The smallest limit for the shaft can then be found by subtracting the tolerance from 1.497″. The basic hole system is based on the assumption that it is easier to vary the size of the shaft than that of the hole.

19–37 BASIC SHAFT SYSTEM

Some industries use the *basic shaft system* of applying tolerances to dimensions, since many shafts come in standard sizes. In this case the largest diameter of the shaft is used as the basic dimension from which the tolerances and allowance are applied.

For example, if the largest permissible shaft is 1.500″, the allowance can be added to this dimension to yield the smallest possible diameter of the hole into which the shaft must fit. Therefore, if the parts are to have an allowance of .004″, the smallest hole would have a diameter of 1.504″.

19–38 STANDARD FITS

The ANSI B4.1-1955 standard specifies a series of fits between cylindrical parts that are based on the basic hole system. The tolerances placed on the holes are unilateral and positive.

The types of fit covered in this standard are:

RC Running and sliding fits
LC Clearance locational fits
LT Transition locational fits
LN Interference locational fits
FN Force and shrink fits

Each of these types of fit is listed in tables in the Appendix. There are several classes of fit under each of the types given above. For example RC 2 is a special type of running and sliding fit. The definition of each type of fit as given in the standards is listed below:

Running and sliding fits (*RC*) are fits for which limits of clearance are specified to provide a similar running performance, with suitable lubrication allowance, throughout the range of sizes. The clearance for the first two classes (RC 1 and RC 2), used chiefly as slide fits, increases more slowly with diameter than that of the other classes, so that accurate location is maintained even at the expense of free relative motion.

Locational fits (*LC*) are fits intended to determine only the location of the mating parts; they may provide rigid or accurate location (interference fits), or some freedom of location (clearance fits). They are divided into three groups: clearance fits (LC), transition fits (LT), and interference fits (LN).

Force fits (*FN*) are special types of interference fits, typically characterized by maintenance of constant bore pressures throughout the range of sizes. The interference therefore varies almost directly with diameter, and the difference between its minimum and maximum values is small, to maintain the resulting pressures within reasonable limits.

Figure 19–74 illustrates how one uses the values from these tables in the appendix. The

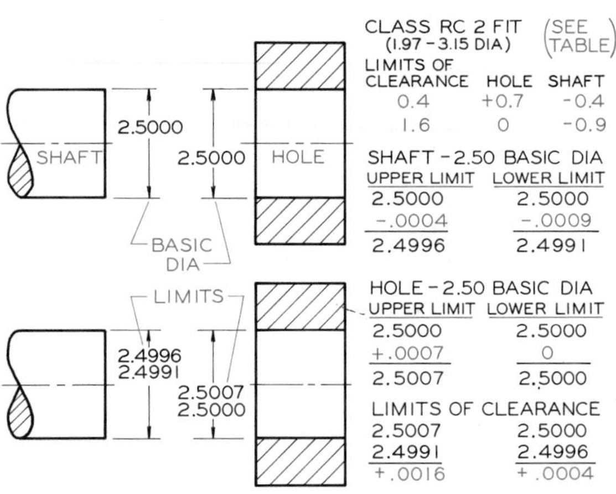

Fig. 19-74. The interpretation of a class RC 2 fit of cylindrical parts by using the specifications given in the Appendix.

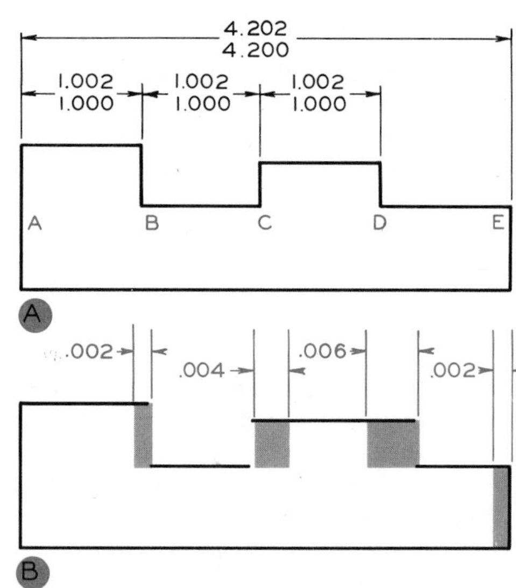

Fig. 19-75. Accumulation of tolerances resulting from chain dimensions.

example is an RC 2 fit. The basic diameter for the hole and the shaft is 2.5000″, which is between the range of 1.97 and 3.15 given in the first column of the table. Since all limits are given in thousandths, the values can be converted by moving the decimal point three places to the left. For example: +0.7 is +.0007″.

The upper and lower limits of the shaft (2.4996 and 2.4991) are found by subtracting the two limits (−.0004 and −.0009) from the basic diameter. The upper and lower limits of the hole (2.5007 and 2.5000) are found by adding the two limits (+.007 and .000) to the basic diameter.

When the two parts are assembled, the tightest fit (+.004) and the loosest fit (+.0016) are found by subtracting the maximum and minimum sizes of the holes and shafts. Note that these values are provided in the second column of the table as a check on the limits.

The same method (but different tables) is used for calculating the limits for all types of fits. Plus values of clearance indicate that there is clearance, and minus values indicate that there will be interference between the assembled parts.

19-39 CHAIN DIMENSIONS

When parts are dimensioned to locate surfaces or geometric features by a *chain of dimensions* as shown in Fig. 19-75A, variations may occur that exceed the tolerances specified. As successive measurements are made, with each new measurement based on the preceding one, the tolerances accumulate. The final tolerance may equal the sum of tolerances on the intermediate dimensions. For example, the tolerance between surface *A* and *B* is .002; between *A* and *C*, .004; between *A* and *D*, .006 (Fig. 19-75B). This accumulation of tolerances that could be significant if the number of chain

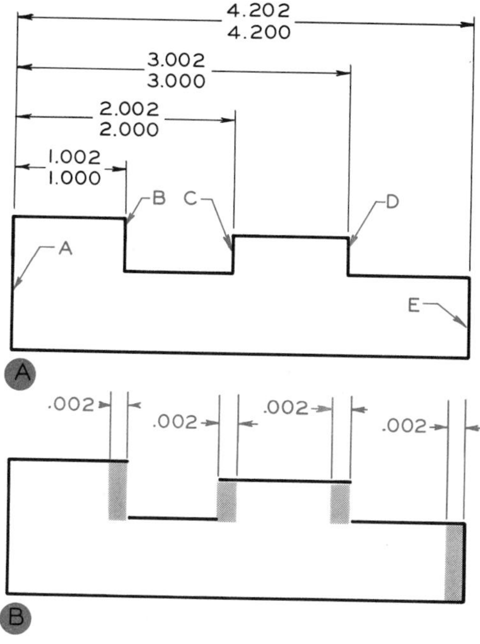

Fig. 19–76. Location of surfaces from a datum plane to reduce the accumulation of tolerances.

GEOMETRIC CHARACTERISTIC SYMBOLS			
		Characteristic	Symbol
Form Tolerances	For Single Feature	FLATNESS	▱
		STRAIGHTNESS	—
		ROUNDNESS (CIRCULARITY)	○
		CYLINDRICITY	⌭
		PROFILE OF ANY LINE	⌒
		PROFILE OF ANY SURFACE	⌓
	For Related Features	PARALLELISM	∥
		PERPENDICULARITY (SQUARENESS)	⊥
		ANGULARITY	∠
		RUNOUT	↗
Positional Tolerances		TRUE POSITION	⊕
		CONCENTRICITY	◎
		SYMMETRY	⌯

Fig. 19–77. Symbols of position and form. (Courtesy of ANSI; Y14.5-1966.)

measurements were great can be reduced by measuring from a single plane called a *datum plane*. A datum plane is usually a plane on the object, but it could be a plane on the machine used to make the part.

An example of tolerancing from a datum plane is shown in Fig. 19–76. Note that the tolerance between two intermediate points is equal to the tolerance between the two dimensions from the datum. In our examples this is .004, which represents the maximum tolerance when datum or baseline dimensions are used. The designer must thoroughly understand the function of each part in order to specify tolerances that will provide the condition required. In all cases, it is desirable to allow as much tolerance as feasible to reduce cost and simplify production.

19–40 SYMBOLS OF POSITIONAL AND FORM TOLERANCES

The specification of positional and form tolerances has become a rather complex procedure, since in many cases the geometric characteristics of a part must be given in great detail. For example, flatness, straightness, roundness, cylindricity, parallelism, perpendicularity, and other such characteristics may be toleranced on a drawing by note or by symbol. The notes and symbols introduced here are those suggested by the American National Standards Institute (ANSI) and are generally accepted by the Military Standards (Mil-Std) of the U.S. Department of Defense.

The two basic types of dimensions utilizing tolerances are: (1) form tolerances and (2)

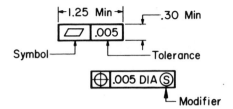

Fig. 19–78. Feature control symbols. (Courtesy of ANSI; Y14.5-1966.)

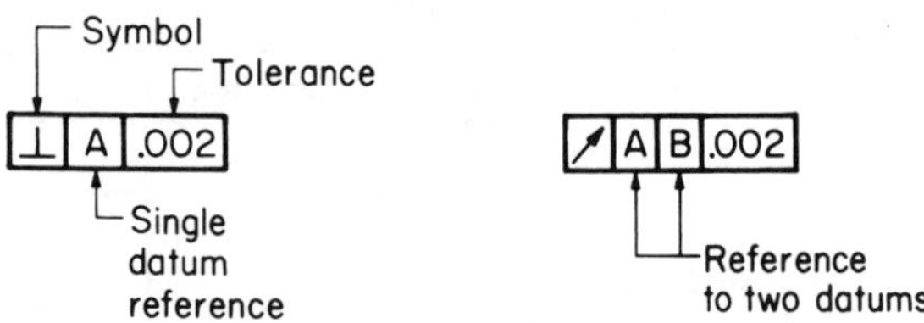

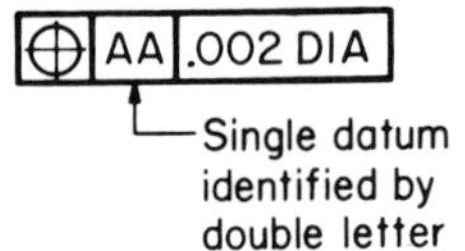

Fig. 19–79. Feature control symbols incorporating datum references. (Courtesy of ANSI; Y14.5-1966.)

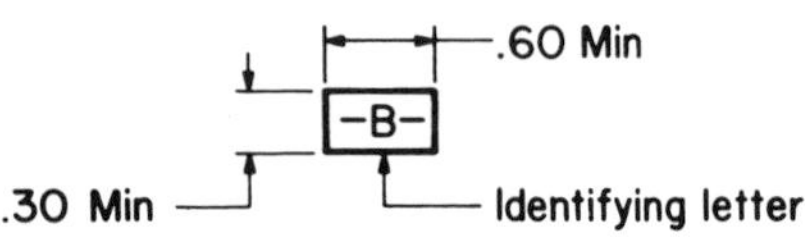

Fig. 19–80. Datum identifying symbol. (Courtesy of ANSI; Y14.5-1966.)

positional tolerances. Form tolerances can be applied to a single geometric shape. For instance, to specify flatness, only one surface has to be toleranced. Form may include the relationship between two or more features on the same part. Thus, for example, parallelism involves the relationship of one plane to another, the latter being used as a datum plane. Both planes are on the same part. Positional tolerances are applied to those dimensions that are used to locate or position geometric shapes with respect to specified datum planes.

The symbols shown in Fig. 19–77 specify the geometric characteristics being dimensioned; they can be used instead of a note that would state the same relationship in words. Other symbols not shown in this table are Ⓜ for "Maximum Material Condition," and Ⓢ for "Regardless of Feature Size." When tolerances are given as notes, the abbreviations MMC and RFS are used instead of the symbols. A feature is at maximum material condition at those points at which it contains the maximum amount of material. Thus a hole is at maximum material condition at the points at which its diameter is smallest. On the other hand, a shaft is at maximum material condition at those points at which its diameter is largest. Two mating parts will be most difficult to assemble when both are at maximum material condition. The symbols Ⓜ and Ⓢ are used as modifiers in feature control symbols (Fig. 19–78). The first symbol indicates the geometric characteristic. Next to it is the permissible tolerance. A vertical line separates the symbol from the tolerance. When a positional or form tolerance relates to one or more datums, the datum must appear in the symbol. As can be seen from Fig. 19–79, the letter representing the datum immediately follows the symbol describing the geometric characteristic. The datum plane should be indicated by an identifying letter, as shown in Fig. 19–80. This box is attached to the surface or its extension line. The placement of datum-identifying and feature-control symbols on a fully dimensioned

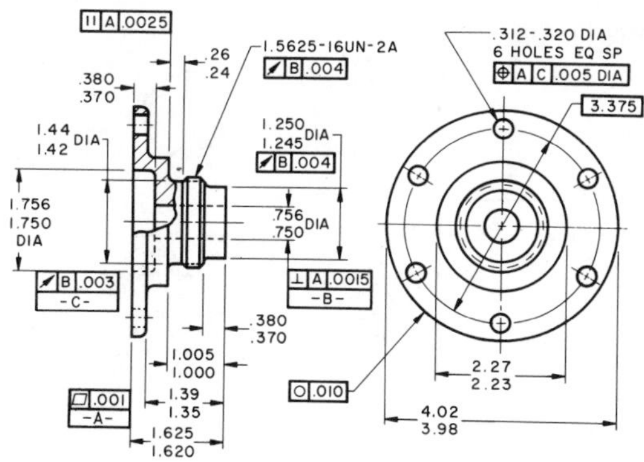

Fig. 19-81. Application of geometric characteristic symbols to a typical detail drawing. (Courtesy of ANSI; Y14.5-1966.)

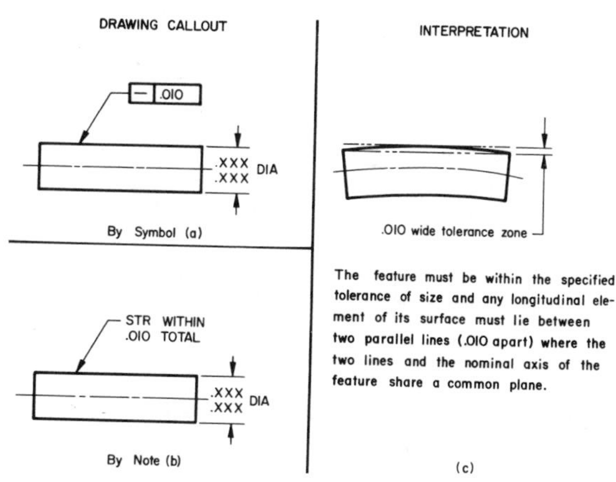

Fig. 19-82. Specifying straightness. (Courtesy of ANSI; Y14.5-1966.)

drawing is illustrated in Fig. 19-81. Additional symbols used in tolerancing will be introduced in succeeding articles.

19-41 TOLERANCES OF FORM

Variation in the geometry or the form of a part may not need to be dimensioned as fully as indicated in the following examples. Consideration should be given to established shop practices, which may provide sufficient accuracy. Whenever feasible, close tolerances for surface form dimensions should be avoided in order to reduce the effort and expense of production; however, in many instances, it will be imperative that the form of a part be controlled by tolerances to give the required flatness, straightness, roundness or other geometric characteristic.

Figures 19-82 through 19-87 give examples of form tolerances applied to typical geometric forms. Parts A and B of these figures show notes and feature control symbols applied to drawings. Parts C, labeled "interpretation," explain the meaning of the specified tolerances.

Straightness. A surface is straight when all its elements are straight lines. In Fig. 19-82 straightness is indicated by a note and symbol. In addition to the diameter, a tolerance is given for straightness; that is, a variation of .010 is allowed for the total length of the part. Note that the modifier, TOTAL, is used in the note, but not in the symbol.

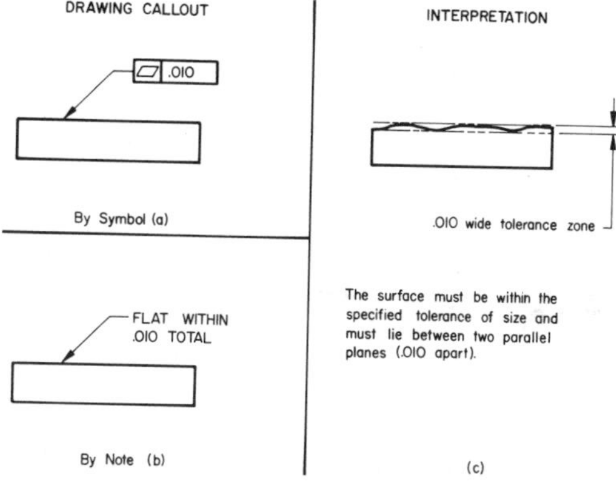

Fig. 19-83. Specifying flatness. (Courtesy of ANSI; Y14.5-1966.)

Flatness. A surface is flat when all its elements are in one plane. Flatness tolerance specifies a tolerance zone between two parallel planes (Fig. 19-83). Again, the modifier TOTAL is used in the note; this means that .010 is the total tolerance allowed for the length of the part.

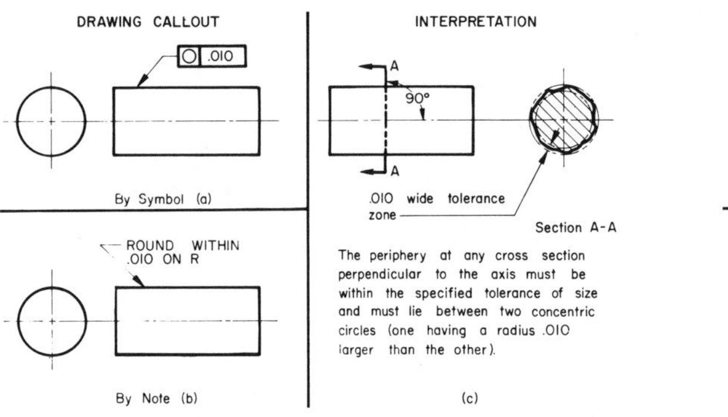

Fig. 19-84. Specifying roundness for a cylinder. (Courtesy of ANSI; Y14.5-1966.)

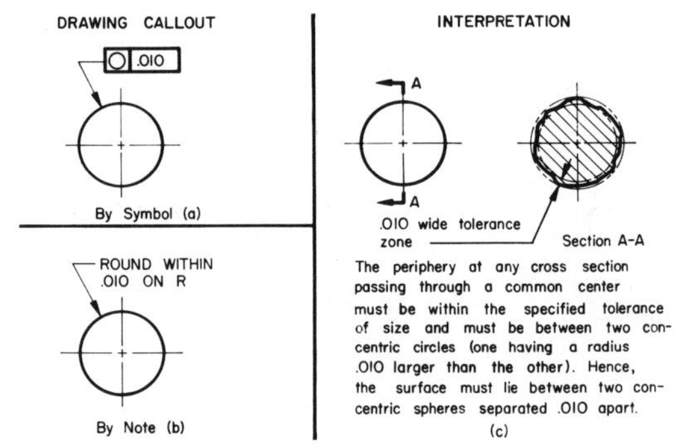

Fig. 19-86. Specifying roundness for a sphere. (Courtesy of ANSI; Y14.5-1966.)

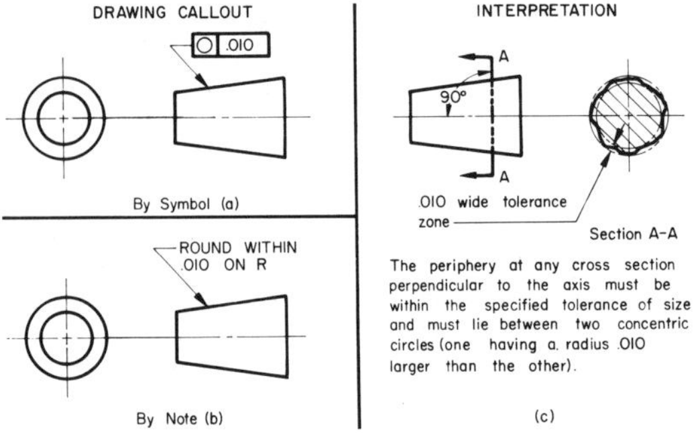

Fig. 19-85. Specifying roundness for a cone. (Courtesy of ANSI; Y14.5-1966.)

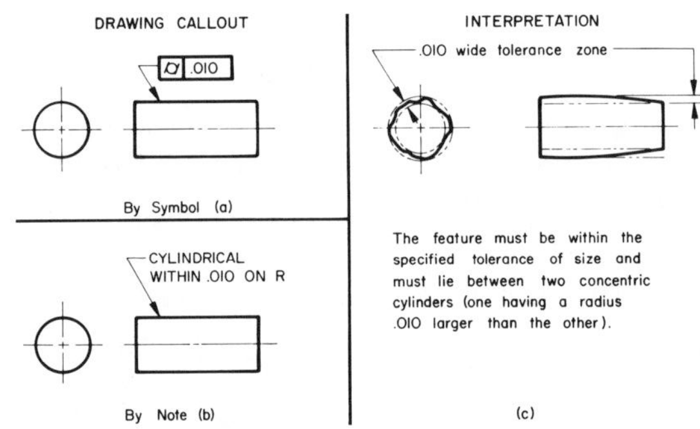

Fig. 19-87. Specifying cylindricity. (Courtesy of ANSI; Y14.5-1966.)

Roundness. A surface of revolution (cylinder, cone, or sphere) is round when all points of the surface intersected by a plane are equidistant from the axis. The intersecting plane may be (1) perpendicular to a common axis (cylinder or cone), or (2) passing through a common center (sphere). A roundness tolerance specifies a tolerance zone bounded by two concentric circles in the plane within which the surface must lie. Figure 19-84 illustrates the method of specifying the tolerance for the roundness of a cylinder. Note the modifier in the note, ON R. This means that the tolerance zone is established by a radial measurement.

The tolerance zone of roundness for a cone is shown in Fig. 19-85, and that for a sphere in Fig. 19-86. The tolerance zone for each of these is located by a radial measurement, as indicated by the modifier in the note.

Cylindricity. A surface of revolution is cylindrical when all its elements form a cylinder. A cylindricity tolerance zone is the zone between two concentric cylinders specified by the tolerance (Fig. 19-87). This zone is established by a radial measurement, ON R.

Profile. Profile tolerancing is a method of specifying tolerances for a contoured shape formed by irregular curves. Profile tolerancing can apply to a single line or a surface. A method of dimensioning an irregular curve is shown in

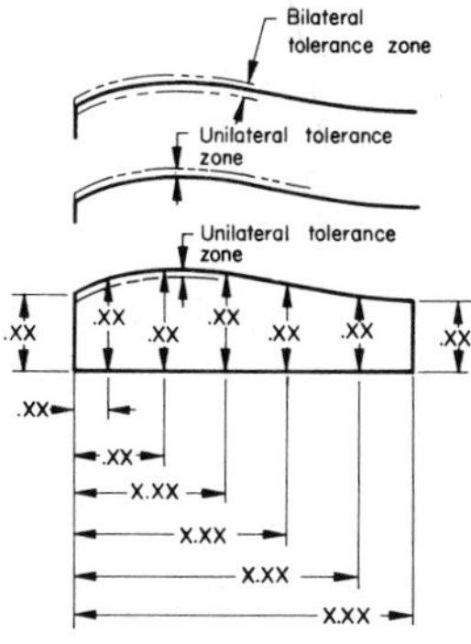

Fig. 19-88. Profile tolerance zones. (Courtesy of ANSI; Y14.5-1966.)

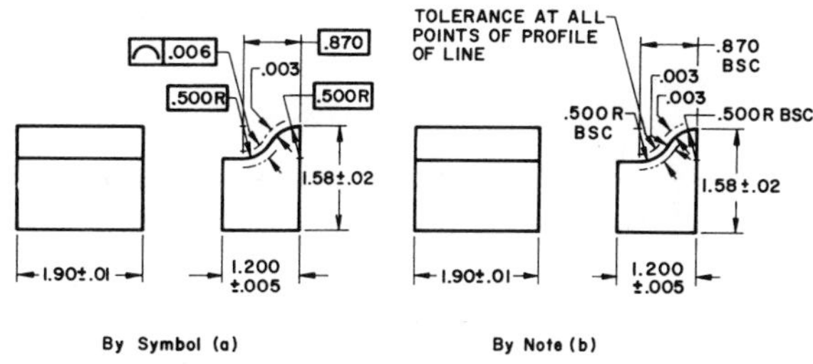

Fig. 19-90. Specifying the profile of a line. (Courtesy of ANSI; Y14.5-1966.)

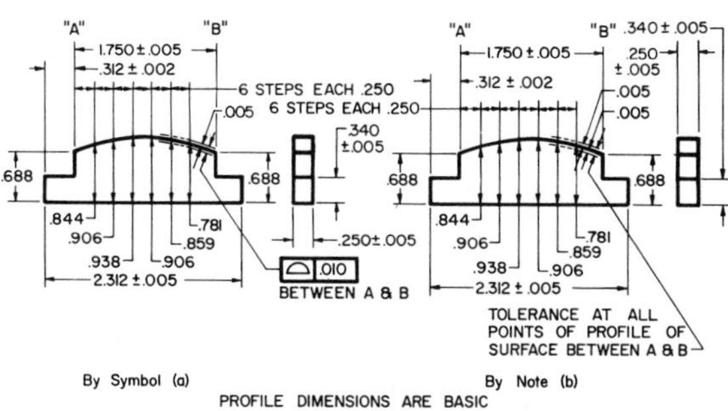

Fig. 19-89. Specifying the profile of a surface. (Courtesy of ANSI; Y14.5-1966.)

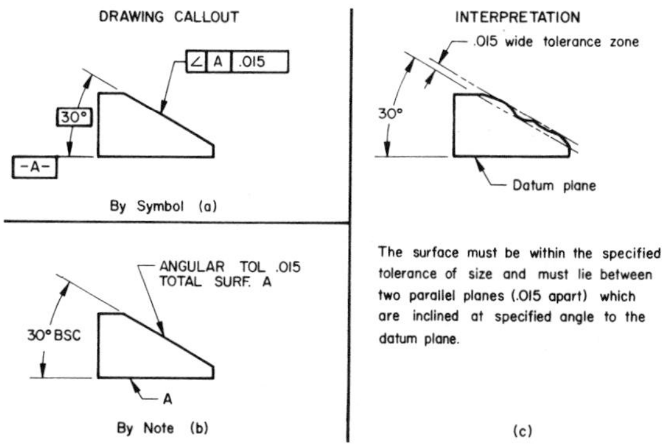

Fig. 19-91. Specifying angularity. (Courtesy of ANSI; Y14.5-1966.)

Fig. 19-88, where a series of coordinates are given to locate points along the contoured surface. The notes specify these dimensions as basic or as absolute theoretical dimensions from which tolerances are applied. Phantom lines are drawn at some conspicuous location along the profile, and the tolerance zone is indicated at an exaggerated scale to be clearly visible (Fig. 19-88). The tolerance can be bilateral or unilateral. This method of dimensioning is illustrated in Fig. 19-89. In part A of the figure, symbols are used; in part B, the tolerance is given in note form. The profile in this case gives the variation of the surface that appears as an edge in the toleranced view. On the other hand, the tolerance given in Fig. 19-90 applies only to the profile line and not to the plane. Since this curve is formed by arcs of a circle, the centers are located with untoleranced basic dimensions, with the tolerances applied to the radii.

Angularity. A surface or line is angular when it is at a specified angle (other than 90°) from a datum or axis. The tolerance zone for angularity lies between two parallel planes inclined at the specified angle and separated by the tolerance specified (Fig. 19-91).

Parallelism. A surface or line is considered parallel when all its points are equidistant from a datum plane or axis. There are two types of parallelism.

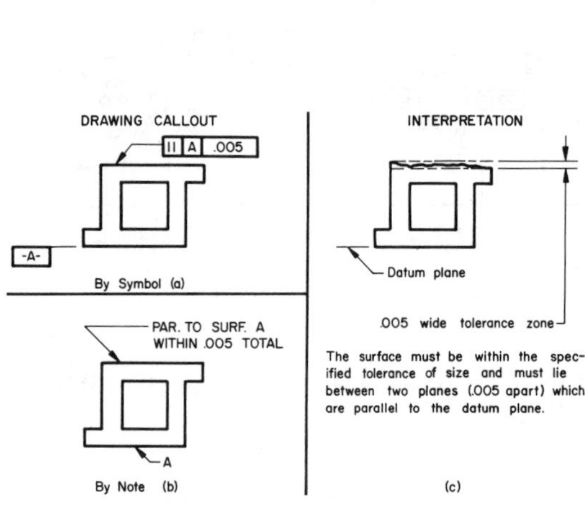

Fig. 19-92. Specifying parallelism. (Courtesy of ANSI; Y14.5-1966.)

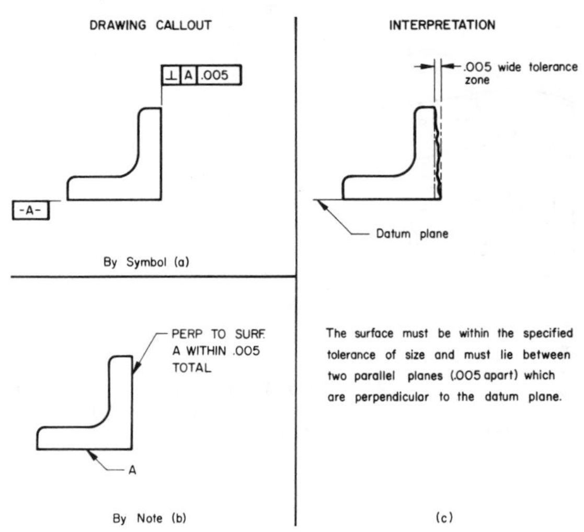

Fig. 19-94. Specifying perpendicularity. (Courtesy of ANSI; Y14.5-1966.)

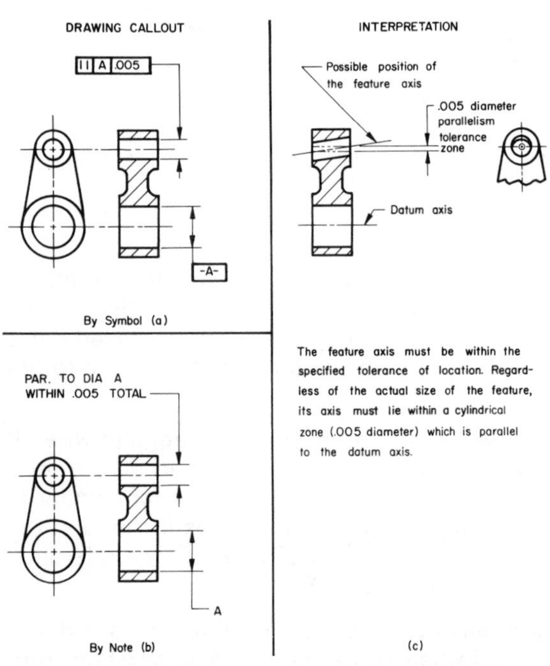

Fig. 19-93. Specifying parallelism. (Courtesy of ANSI; Y14.5-1966.)

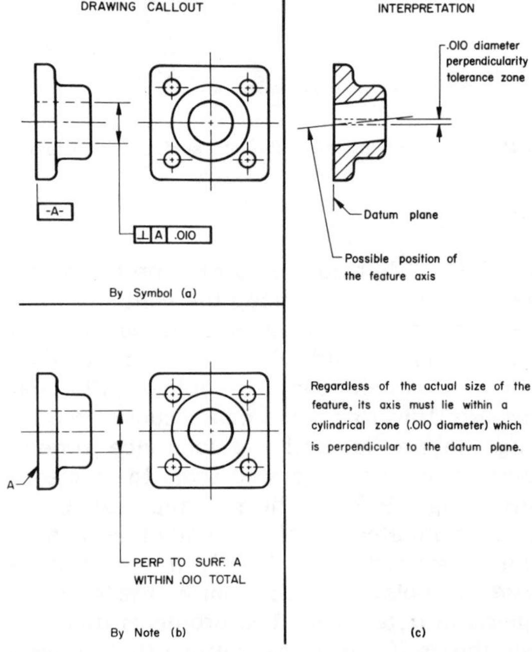

Fig. 19-95. Specifying perpendicularity. (Courtesy of ANSI; Y14.5-1966.)

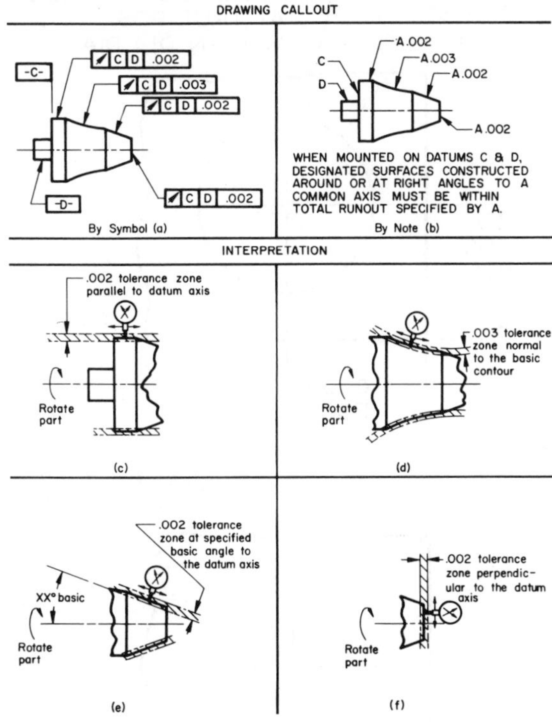

Fig. 19-96. Runout tolerance and its interpretation. (Courtesy of ANSI; Y14.5-1966.)

1) A tolerance zone between two planes parallel to a datum plane within which the axis or surface of the feature must lie (Fig. 19-92). This tolerance also controls flatness and a plane surface on which flatness tolerance is not given.

2) A cylindrical tolerance zone parallel to a datum feature within which the axis of a feature must lie (Fig. 19-93).

Perpendicularity. Surfaces, axes, or lines that are at right angles to each other are perpendicular. Two methods of expressing perpendicularity are illustrated in Figs. 19-94 and 19-95.

Runout. Runout tolerance is a means of controlling the functional relationship of two or more features of a part within the allowable errors of concentricity, perpendicularity, and alignment of features. It also takes into account variations in roundness, straightness, flatness, and parallelism of individual surfaces. In essence, it establishes a composite form of control of those features having a common axis. An example of this tolerance applied to a part is shown in Fig. 19-96. Parts C through F of the figure illustrate how an indicator is applied perpendicular to the surfaces being gauged as the part is revolved about its axis. This is one of the more complex types of tolerances that should be studied in greater detail than permitted in this volume. (See ANSI Y14.5-1966 standard.)

19-42 TOLERANCES OF POSITION

Positional tolerances apply to the location of features of a part with respect to other features. The three basic types of positional tolerances are:

1) *positional*—location of holes or slots with respect to surfaces;

2) *concentricity*—specification of the tolerance between diameters of a part, with several diameters sharing the same theoretical center line;

3) *symmetry*—the location of features about the axis of symmetry within a given tolerance.

Positional tolerances applying to a geometric shape (such as a hole) in a given part can be located by using coordinates, as shown in Fig. 19-97. The toleranced dimensions used to locate the position of the hole (part A of the figure) give a rectangular tolerance zone, which is enlarged in part B. The weakness of coordinate tolerances is that the diagonal of the maximum tolerance square is greater than the specified tolerance, .010, which would occur in extreme cases. This weakness has been overcome by a method called *true position tolerancing.* Using this method, the true center of the hole (or other feature) is located with a basic (untoleranced) dimension, with the tolerance specified by a diameter, DIA. Figure 19-98 shows that true position tolerancing gives a circular tolerance zone. All points on the same circle are at the same distance from the true center; there is no

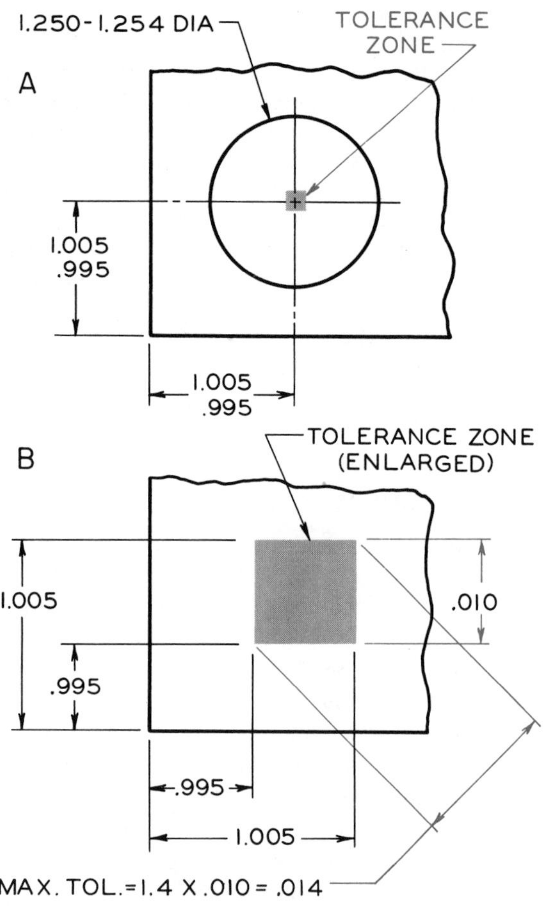

Fig. 19–97. The coordinate tolerance zone to locate a hole's center.

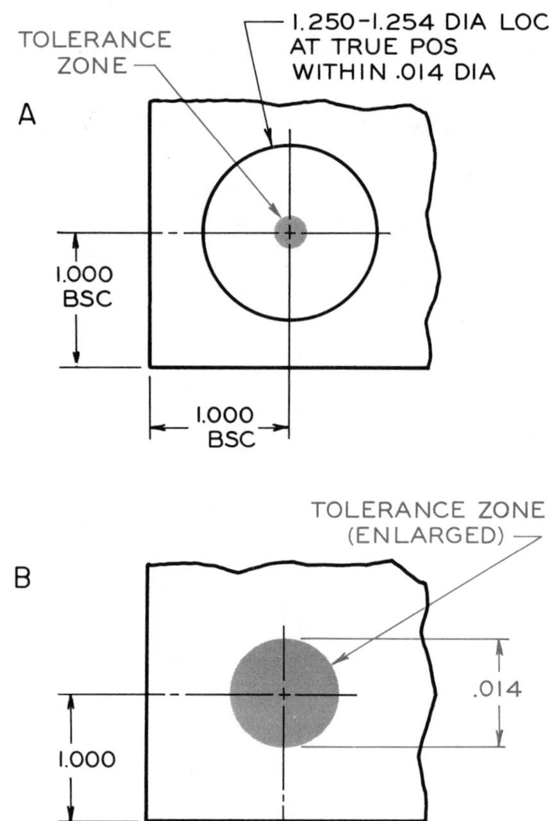

Fig. 19–98. True position tolerance zone.

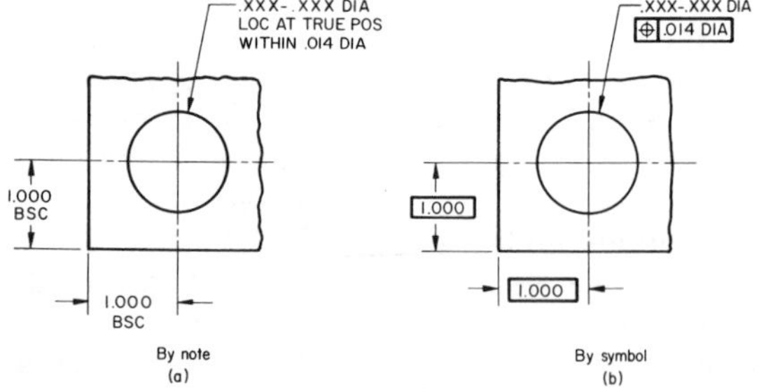

Fig. 19–99. True position tolerancing. (Courtesy of ANSI; Y14.5-1966.)

diagonal dimension to increase the tolerance. The true position tolerance will allow greater latitude in locating the position of the hole, a tolerance of .014 diameter, while maintaining the same degree of accuracy as the coordinate method. Or, if the same tolerance zone, namely 0.010, that was used for the coordinate method were applied to the true positional method (in the form of diameter tolerance), the hole would be located with a higher degree of accuracy, since the diagonal of the tolerance square would be eliminated. An example of the application

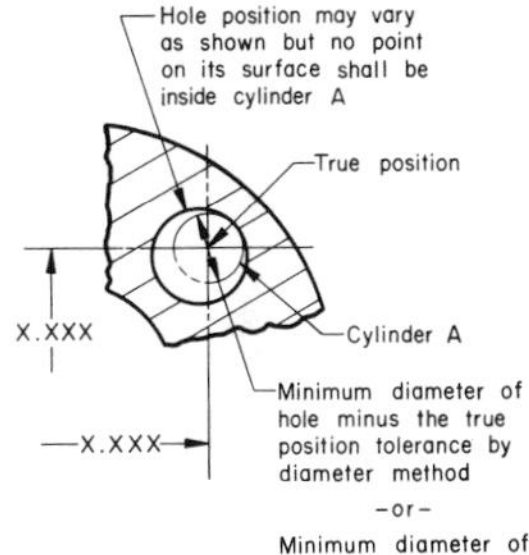

Fig. 19–100. Tolerance zone for the surface of a hole at MMC. (Courtesy of ANSI; Y14.5-1966.)

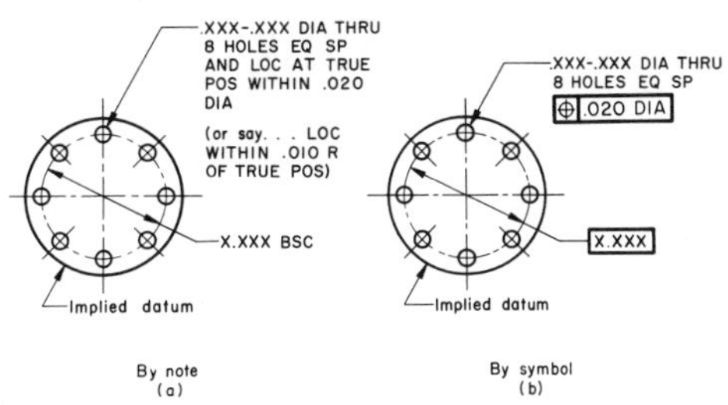

Fig. 19–101. True position location of holes. (Courtesy of ANSI; Y14.5-1966.)

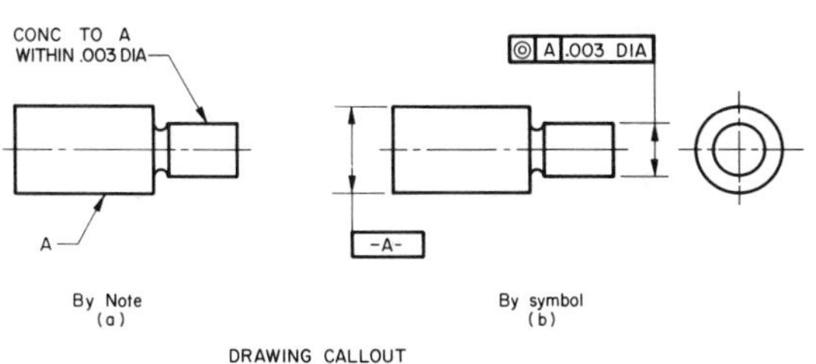

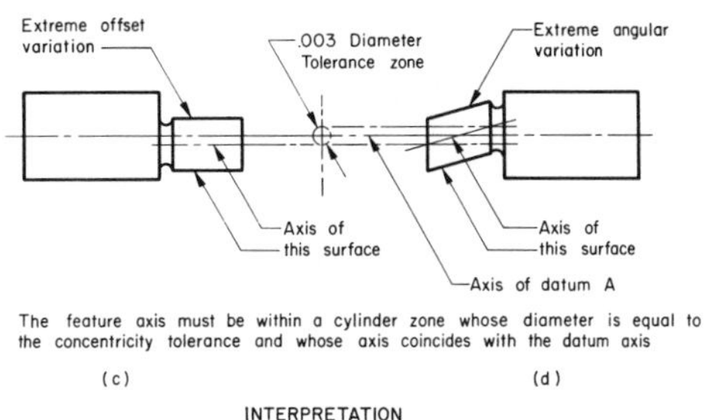

Fig. 19–102. Concentricity callout and interpretation. (Courtesy of ANSI; Y14.5-1966.)

of true position tolerancing to a hole is shown in Fig. 19–99. Note that true dimensions are labeled BSC or are enclosed in a box, indicating that these dimensions are exact with no tolerance. The tolerance zone can be expressed as a radius as well as a diameter. When a radius is used, the position of the hole in Fig. 19–99 will be noted as XXX-.XXX DIA LOCATED AT TRUE POSITION WITHIN .007R.

The circular tolerance zone is represented in the circular view and is assumed to extend the full depth of the hole. The axis of the hole can be located with its center at the extreme edge of the cylindrical zone or it can have an angular variation, provided the axis of the hole does not lie outside the cylinder of tolerance. The size of the hole *and* its position are also specified with tolerances; consequently, these two tolerances are applied to find cylinder *A* shown in Fig. 19–100. The circle is obtained by subtracting the true position tolerance, using the diameter method, from the hole at maximum material condition (the hole of smallest diameter). This zone represents the least favorable condition when the part is to be assembled with a mating part with a common datum plane. When the hole is not at MMC, it is, of course, larger, permitting a greater tolerance and an easier assembly. An example of true positioning applied to the location of equally spaced holes in a circular plate is shown in Fig. 19–101. The circle of centers is the basic dimension, with the hole located within .020 DIA of true position.

Concentricity. Surfaces of revolution are concentric when they have a common axis. Concentricity tolerances are specified as shown in Fig. 19–102. They are used to position coaxial features about a common axis of rotation. Unless there is a defined need for the control of axes, control should be specified as a runout instead of true position as illustrated.

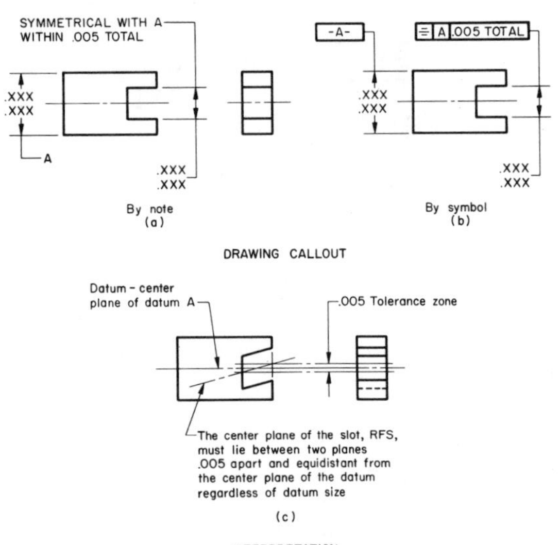

Fig. 19-103. Symmetry callout and interpretation. (Courtesy of ANSI; Y14.5-1966.)

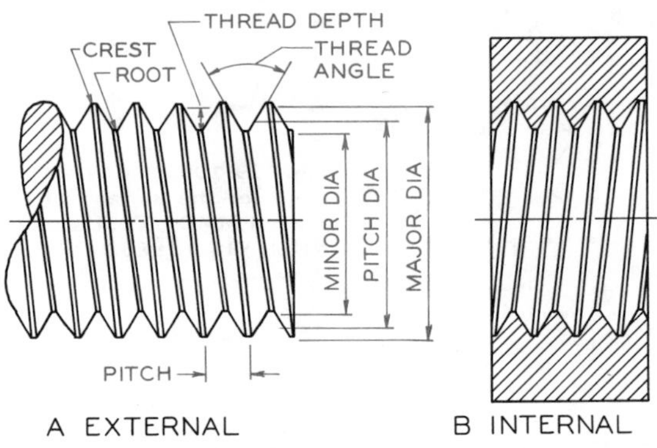

Fig. 19-104. Thread terminology.

Symmetry. A part or a feature is symmetric when it has the same contour and size on opposite sides of a central plane. In effect, a symmetry tolerance locates or positions features with respect to a datum plane. The method of specifying this tolerance by note and symbol is illustrated in Fig. 19-103. Concentricity and symmetry are closely related to form tolerances although they are considered primarily as positional tolerances.

19-43 THREADED FASTENERS

Threaded fasteners are used extensively in the manufacture of almost all engineering designs. Screw threads provide a relatively fast and easy method of fastening two parts together and of exerting a force that can be used for adjustment of movable parts. For a screw thread to function, there must be two parts—an internal thread and an external thread. The internal threads may be tapped inside a part such as a motor block, or more commonly, they may be tapped inside a nut. Whenever possible, the threaded fasteners, nuts, and bolts used in industrial projects are stock parts that can be obtained from many sources. The use of stock parts reduces manufacturing expenses and improves the interchangeability of parts. Interchangeability is very important for repair work or replacement of damaged fasteners.

Threaded fasteners made in different countries or by different manufacturers in the same country may have threads of different specifications that will not match. This problem has not been completely resolved; however, progress has been made toward establishing standards that will unify threads both in this country and abroad. These efforts have led to the adoption of the *Unified Screw Thread* by the United States, Britain, and Canada (ABC Standards), which is a modification of both the American Standard thread and the Whitworth thread.

19-44 DEFINITIONS OF THREAD TERMINOLOGY

Succeeding articles will discuss the uses and methods of representing screw threads. The terms used and defined below are illustrated in Fig. 19-104.

External thread is a thread on the outside of a cylinder, such as a bolt (Fig. 19-105).

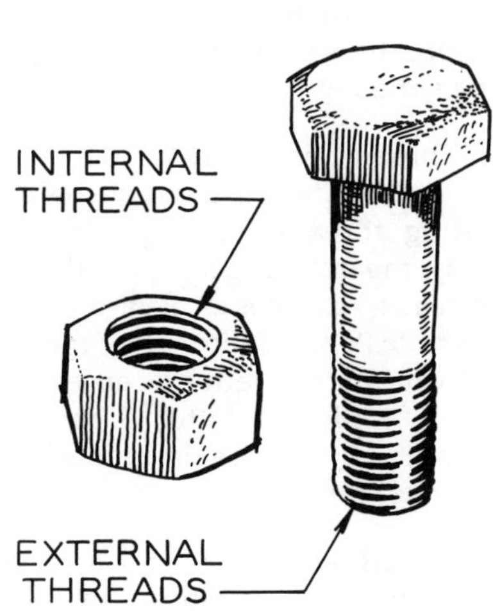

Fig. 19–105. A nut and a bolt represent internal and external threads respectively.

Internal thread is a thread cut on the inside of a part, such as a nut (Fig. 19–105).

Major diameter is the largest diameter on an internal or external thread.

Minor diameter is the smallest diameter that can be measured on a screw thread.

Pitch diameter is the diameter of an imaginary cylinder passing through the threads at the points at which the thread width is equal to the space between the threads.

Pitch is the distance between crests of threads. Pitch is found mathematically by dividing one inch by the number of threads per inch of a particular thread.

Crest is the peak edge of a screw thread.

Thread angle is the angle between threads cut by the cutting tool.

Root is the bottom of the thread cut into a cylinder.

Thread form is the shape of the thread cut into a threaded part.

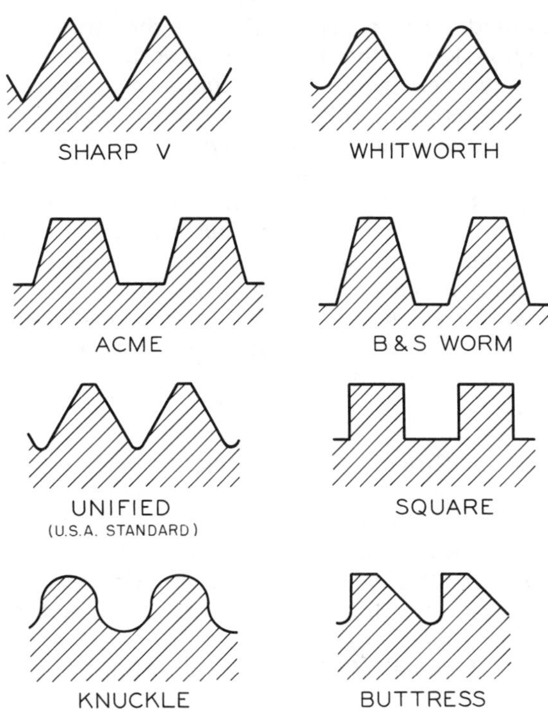

Fig. 19–106. Standard thread forms.

Thread series is the number of threads per inch for a particular diameter.

Thread class is closeness of fit between two mating thread parts. Class 1 represents a loose fit, and Class 3, a tight fit.

Right-hand thread is a thread that will assemble when turned clockwise. A right-hand thread will slope downward to the right on an external thread when the axis is horizontal, and in the opposite direction on an internal thread.

Left-hand thread is a thread that will assemble when turned counterclockwise. A left-hand thread slopes downward to the left on an external thread when the axis is horizontal, and in the opposite direction on an internal thread.

19–45 THREAD SPECIFICATIONS

Form. A thread form is the shape of the thread cut into a part as illustrated in Fig. 19–106. The

Unified form, a combination of the American National and the British Whitworth, is most widely used, since it is a standard in several countries. It is referred to as UN in abbreviations and thread notes. The American National is signified by the letter N.

The transmission of power is achieved by the use of the *Acme, square, buttress,* and *worm* threads. These are commonly used in gearing and other pieces of machinery. The *sharp V* is used for set screws and in applications where friction in assembly is desired. The *knuckle* form is a fast-assembling thread used for light assemblies such as light bulbs and bottle caps.

Series. Thread series is closely related to thread form. It designates the type of thread specified for a given application.

There are six series of threads listed under the American National form and the Unified National form. These six series and their abbreviations are: coarse (C), fine (F), extra-fine (EF), 8 thread (8), 12 thread (12), and 16 thread (16).

A Unified National form for a coarse-series thread is specified as UNC, which is a combination of form and series in a single note. Similarly, an American National form for a coarse thread is written NC. The coarse-thread series (UNC or NC) is suitable for bolts, screws, nuts, and general use with cast iron, soft metals, or plastics when rapid assembly is desired. The *fine* thread series (NF or UNF) is suitable for bolts, nuts, or screws when a high degree of tightening is required. The *extra fine* series (UNEF or NEF) is used for applications that will have to withstand high stresses. This series is suitable for sheet metal, thin nuts, ferrules, or couplings when length of engagement is limited.

The 8 thread series (8 N), 12 thread series, (12 N or 12 UN), and 16 thread series (16 N or 16 UN) are threads with a uniform pitch for large diameters. The 8 N is used as a substitute for the coarse thread series, on diameters larger than 1″ when a medium pitch thread is required. The 12 N is used on diameters larger than $1\frac{1}{2}$″, with a thread of a medium fine pitch as a continuation of the fine thread series. The 16 N series is used on diameters larger than 2″, with threads of a fine pitch as a continuation of the extra-fine series.

Class of Fit. Thread classes are used to indicate the tightness of fit between a nut and a bolt or any two mating threaded parts. This fit is determined by the tolerances and allowances applied to threads. Classes of fit are indicated by the numbers 1, 2, or 3 followed by the letters A or B. For UN forms, the letter A represents an external thread, while the letter B represents an internal thread. These are omitted when the American National form is used.

Classes 1*A and* 1*B* are used on parts which require assembly with a minimum of binding.

Classes 2*A and* 2*B* are general purpose threads for bolts, nuts, screws, and nominal applications in the mechanical field and are widely used in the mass production industries.

Classes 3*A and* 3*B* are used in precision assemblies where a close fit is desired to withstand stresses and vibration.

Single and Multiple Threads. A *single thread* (Fig. 19–107A) is a thread that will advance the distance of its pitch in one full revolution of 360°. In other words, its pitch is equal to its lead. In the drawing of a single thread, the crest line of the thread will slope $\frac{1}{2}$P, since only 180° of the revolution is visible in a single view. A double thread is composed of two threads resulting in a lead equal to 2P, meaning that the threaded part will advance a distance of 2P in a single revolution of 360° (Fig. 19–107B). The crest line of a double thread will slope a distance equal to P in the view in which 180° can be seen. Similarly, a triple thread will advance 3P in 360° with a crest line slope of $1\frac{1}{2}$P in the view in which 180° of the cylinder is visible (Fig. 19–107C). The lead of a double thread is 2P; that of a triple thread, 3P. Although power on multiple threads is somewhat limited, they are used wherever quick motion is required.

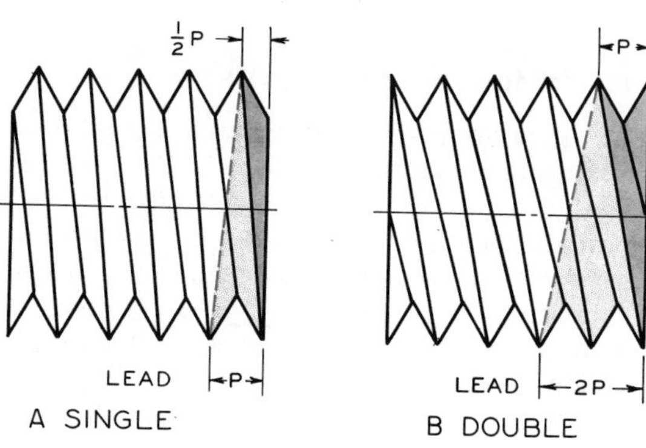

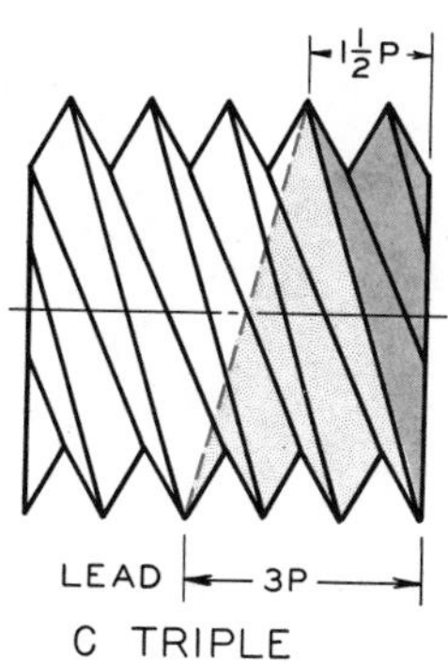

Fig. 19-107. Single and multiple threads.

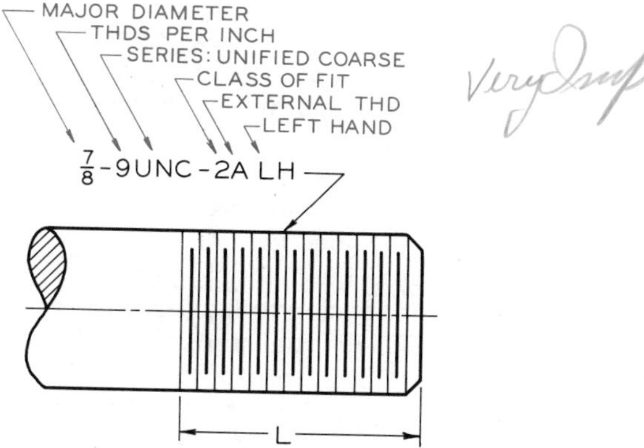

Fig. 19-108. The parts of a thread note.

Thread Notes. Threads can be approximated in graphical illustrations or shown in photographs, but the most important aspect of thread representation is the thread note, which gives specifications. This is the information used in manufacturing the thread or in selecting a threaded part from available stock fasteners. It would be impractical and almost impossible to graphically represent threads to the necessary specifications required. A typical thread note is shown in Fig. 19-108, where it is applied to an external thread. The most important part of the note, the major diameter, is given first. It is followed by the number of threads per inch, from which the pitch is determined, and the form and series (UNC). For a single right-hand thread the class of fit completes the note. However, if the thread is left-hand or double, this information must be added to the note. The words DOUBLE or TRIPLE are included after LH for multiple threads.

These notes must be placed on *all* threads that appear on a working drawing since this is the information used in manufacture. They should be applied to internal threads as well in the circular view (by means of a leader) when possible.

19-46 THREAD REPRESENTATION

If threads were shown by true projections, they would have to be drawn as a series of helical curves. Since this procedure would require considerable construction time, the methods actually used to depict threads on a working drawing are approximations or thread symbols. The three major types of thread representations are (1) detailed, (2) schematic, and (3) simplified (Fig. 19-109). The detailed representation is the most realistic approximation of the true appearance of a thread, while the simplified representation is the most symbolic.

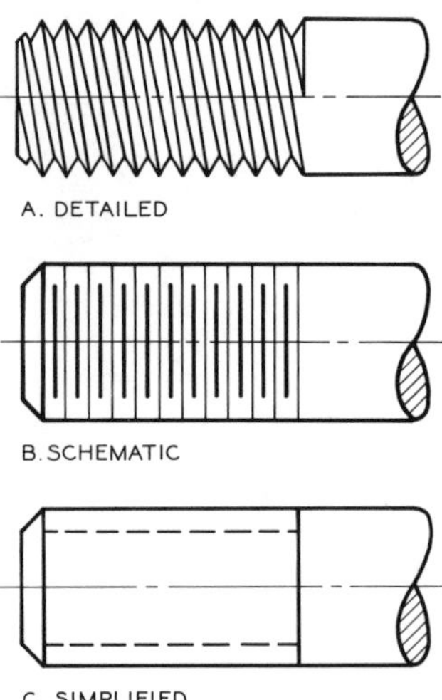

Fig. 19–109. Three types of thread representation.

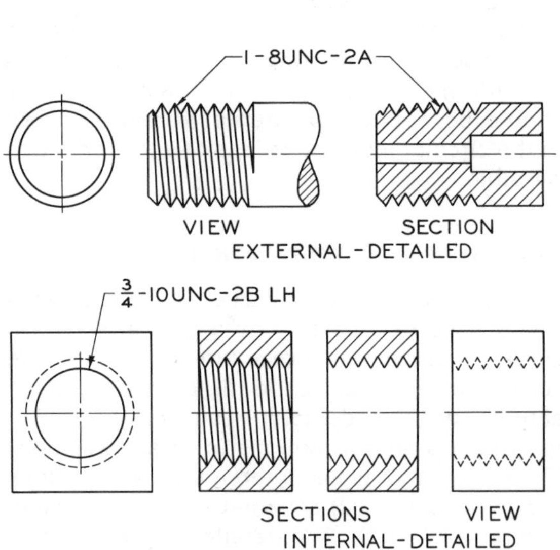

Fig. 19–110. Detailed thread representations.

19–47 DETAILED UN AND UNC THREADS

Examples of detailed representations of internal and external threads are shown in Fig. 19–110. Instead of helical curves, straight lines are used to indicate crest and root lines. In this form of representation, internal threads in section can be indicated in two ways. Thread notes are applied in all cases, regardless of the representation used.

The construction of a detailed representation is shown in Fig. 19–111. The pitch is found by dividing 1″ by the number of threads per inch. This can be done graphically as shown in step 1. However, in most cases, this construction is unnecessary, since the pitch can be approximated by using a calibration close to the true pitch taken directly from an existing scale or by using dividers for spacing. The representation is no more than a symbol used to represent a thread; this eliminates the need for a high degree of time-consuming construction that would be necessary if the threads were to be reproduced to rigid specifications. Also, where threads are close, they should purposely be drawn at a larger spacing to facilitate the drawing process. The sequential steps of Fig. 19–111 illustrate the detailed representation of an external thread. Note in Step 4 that a 45° chamfer is used to indicate a bevel of the threaded end to improve ease of assembly of the thread parts. The chamfer is begun at the minor diameter and drawn at 45°.

19–48 DETAILED SQUARE THREADS

The method of drawing a detailed representation of a square thread is shown in four steps in Fig. 19–112. This method gives an approximation of the true projection of a square thread.

Step 1. The *major* diameter is laid off. The number of threads per inch is taken from the table in Appendix 14 for this size of thread. The pitch (P) is found by dividing 1″ by the number of threads per inch. Distances of $P/2$ are marked off with dividers.

FIGURE 19-111. CONSTRUCTION OF DETAILED THREADS

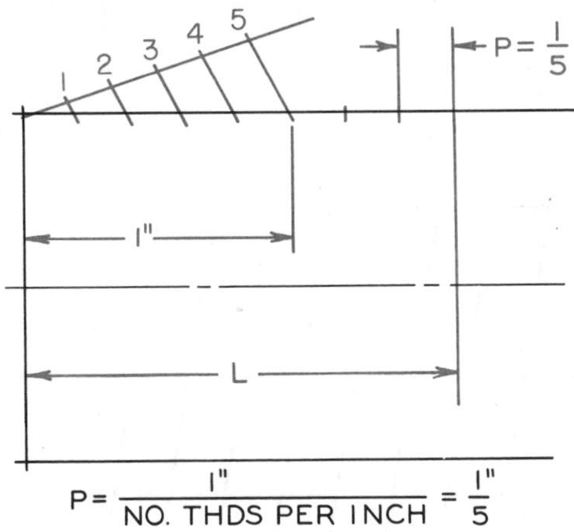

Required: Construct a detailed representation of a thread specified by the note $1\frac{3}{4}$-5UNC-2A.

Step 1: The major diameter is constructed. The pitch is determined by dividing 1″ by the number of threads per inch (found in the table in Appendix 12). The pitch is laid off for the full length of the thread, *L*, using dividers.

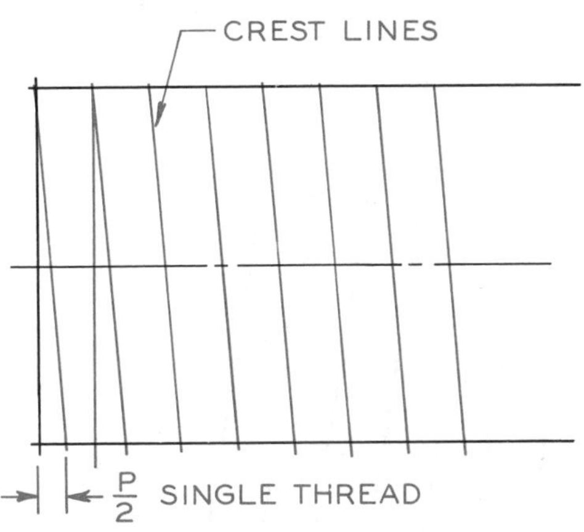

Step 2: Since this is to be a right-nand thread, the crest lines slope downward to the right. The amount of slope will be $\frac{1}{2}P$, since the thread is a single thread. The crest lines are drawn parallel as shown. These will be final lines drawn with a medium weight pencil (H-F).

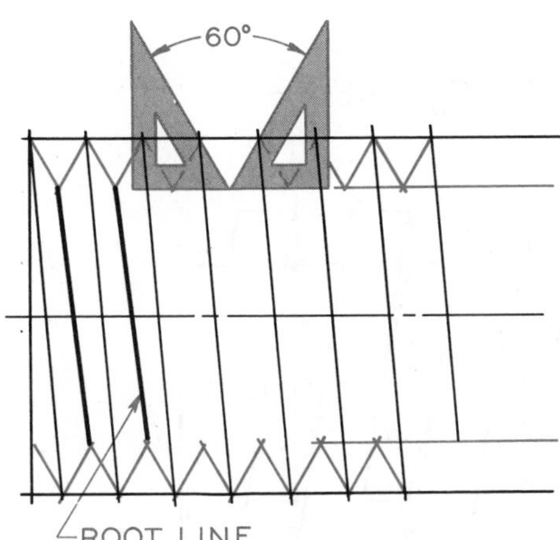

Step 3: Angles of 60° are drawn between the crest lines to establish the root lines. These are lines that are parallel to each other, but are not parallel to crest lines. These can be drawn as finished lines in this step the same weight as the crest lines.

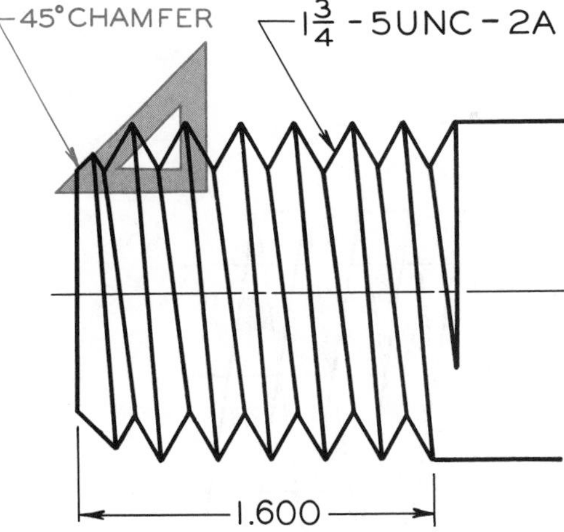

Step 4: A 45° chamfer is constructed at the end of the thread from the minor diameter. All lines are strengthened to an acceptable degree. The thread note is added to provide the specifications of the thread.

FIGURE 19-112. DRAWING THE SQUARE THREAD

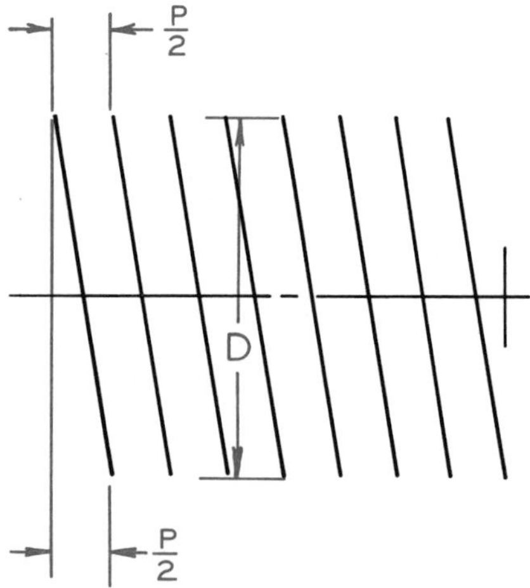

Step 1: Lay out the major diameter. Space the crest lines $\frac{1}{2}P$ apart. Slope them downward to the right for right-hand threads.

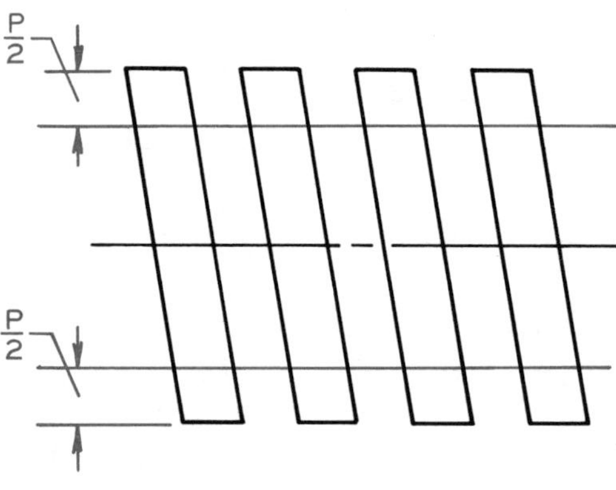

Step 2: Connect every other pair of crest lines. Find the minor diameter by measuring $\frac{1}{2}P$ inward from the major diameter.

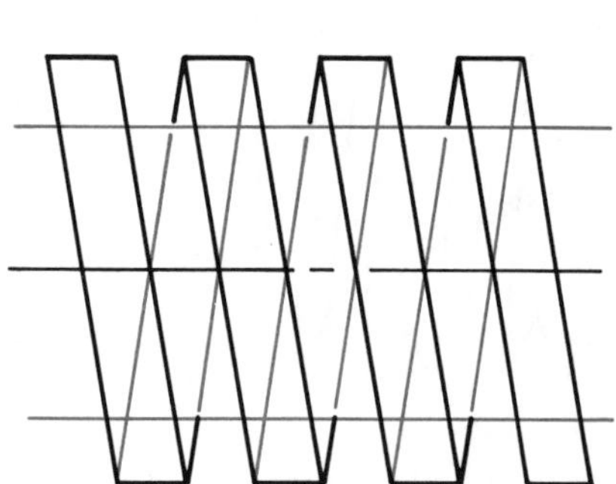

Step 3: Connect the opposite crest lines with light construction lines. This will establish the profile of the thread form.

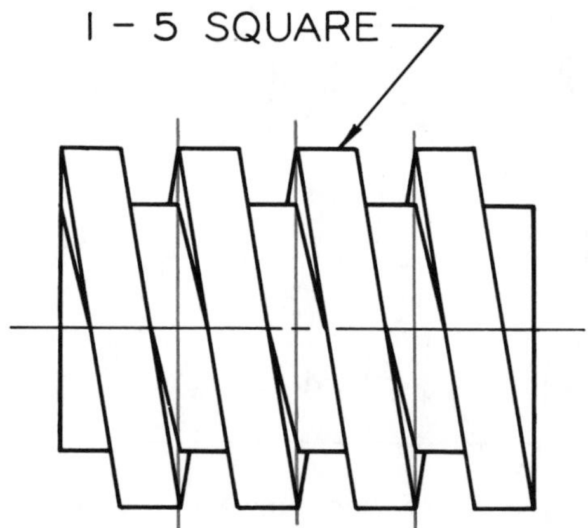

Step 4: Connect the inside crest lines with light construction lines to locate the points on the minor diameter where the thread wraps around the minor diameter. Supply the thread note.

Step 2. The *minor* diameter is found by measuring a distance $P/2$ from the major diameter. The tops of the threads are drawn in.

Step 3. Connect the tops of the threads with diagonal construction lines. Visible lines are drawn to represent the visible parts of the threads on the back side, between the major and the minor diameter.

Step 4. The inside of each thread is connected with the inside of the opposite thread by a light construction line. This gives the points on the minor diameter that are to be used for drawing visible root lines. After the root lines are drawn, the thread note is added to complete the drawing.

Square internal threads are drawn in the same manner, as shown in Fig. 19–113. Note that the threads in the section view are drawn in a slightly different way. The thread note for an internal thread is placed in the circular view whenever possible, with the leader pointing toward the center.

When a square thread is rather long, it need not be drawn continuously, but can be represented using the symbol shown in Fig. 19–114.

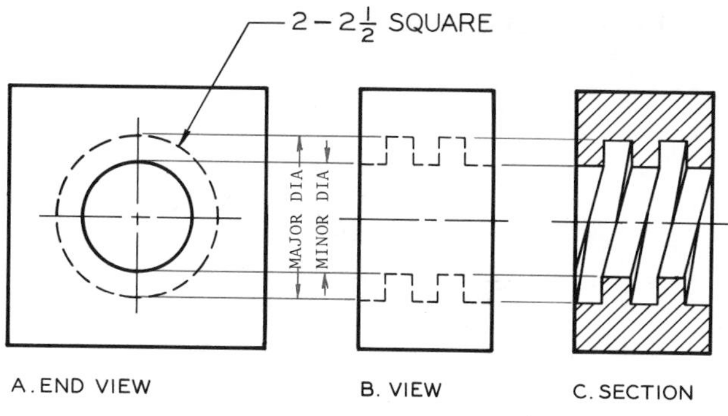

Fig. 19–113. Internal square threads.

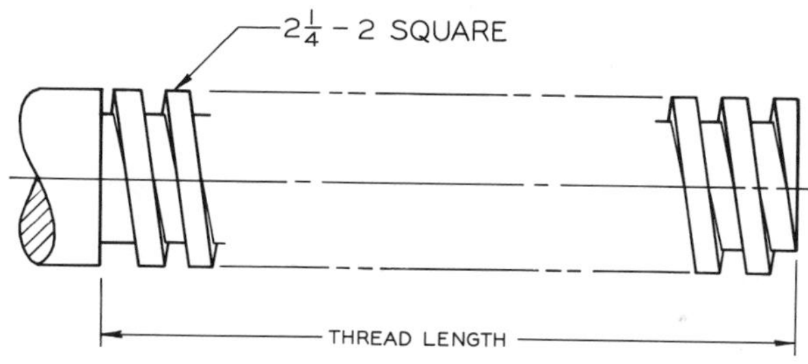

Fig. 19–114. Conventional method of showing square threads without drawing each thread.

19–49 DETAILED ACME THREADS

The four steps involved in preparing detailed drawings of Acme threads are shown in Fig. 19–115.

Step 1. Lay off the length and the major diameter with light construction lines. From the table in Appendix 14, find the pitch by dividing the number of threads per inch into 1″. Using light construction lines, mark off a series of divisions $\frac{1}{2}P$ apart.

Step 2. Locate the minor diameter by measuring a distance $\frac{1}{2}P$ from each side of the major diameter. Locate a line between the major and minor diameters that has a depth of $\frac{1}{4}P$.

Step 3. Construct the sides of the threads by drawing lines at an angle of 15° with the vertical through the points marked off on the middle line, the pitch diameter. The total angle between the crests is 30°. For right-hand threads connect the crests with parallel lines that slope $\frac{1}{2}P$ downward to the right.

Step 4. Construct the root lines to complete the drawing. Add a thread note to complete the specifications.

FIGURE 19-115. DRAWING THE ACME THREAD

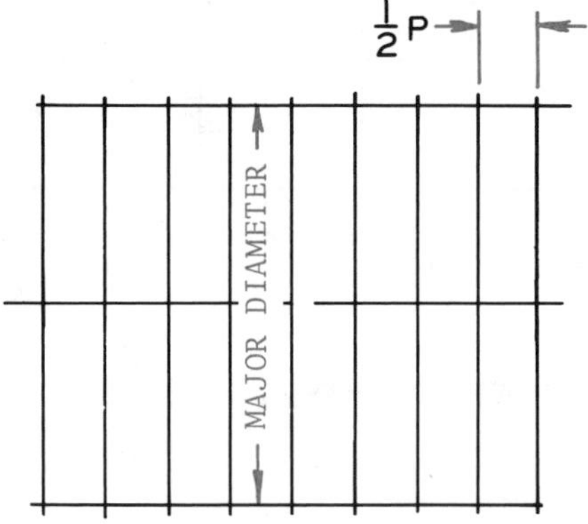

Step 1: Lay out the major diameter and divide the shaft into equal divisions $\frac{1}{2}P$ apart.

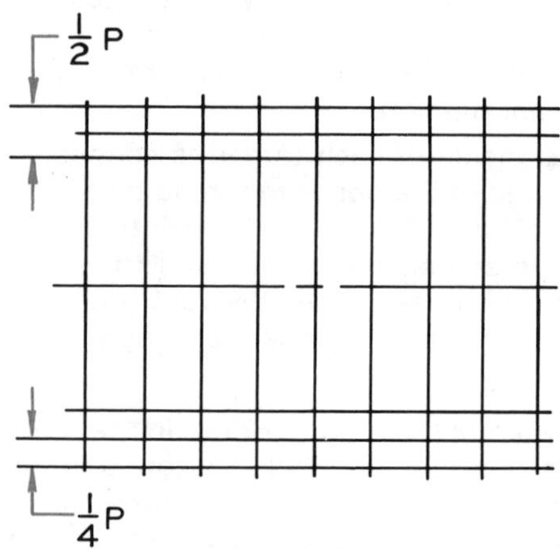

Step 2: Locate the minor diameter a distance of $\frac{1}{2}P$ inside the major diameter. Locate the pitch diameter between the major and minor diameters.

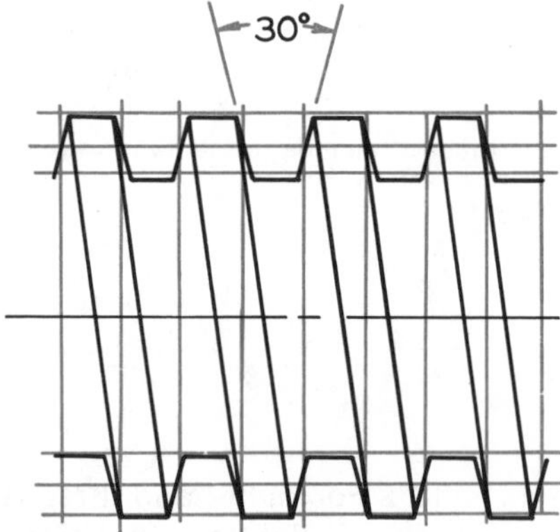

Step 3: Draw lines through the points at which the vertical lines intersect the pitch diameter to make an angle of 30° (15° on each side). Draw the crests and the thread profile.

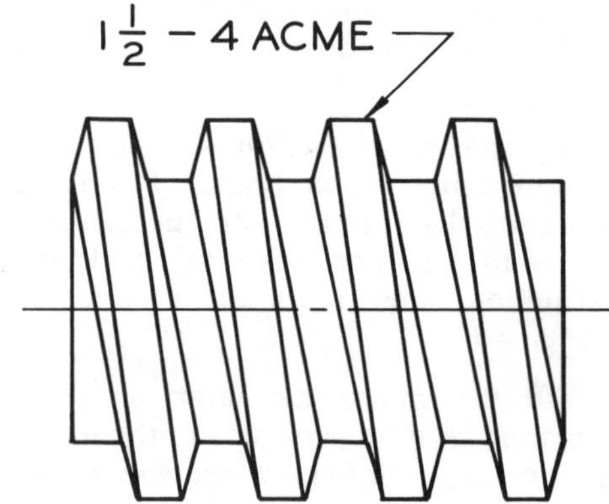

Step 4: Darken the lines and add the thread note to complete the drawing of the Acme thread.

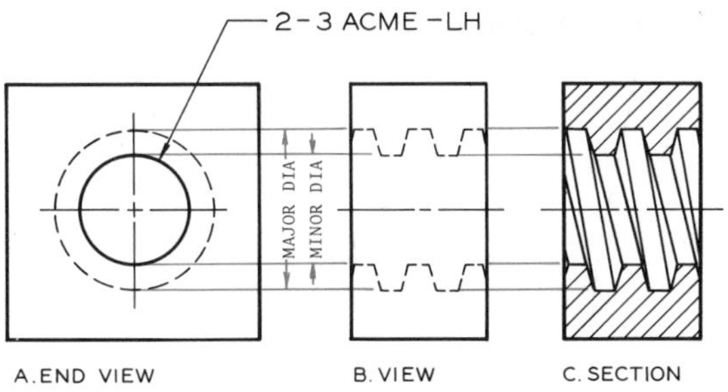

Fig. **19–116.** Internal Acme threads.

2-3 ACME-LH

MAJOR DIA MINOR DIA

A. END VIEW B. VIEW C. SECTION

Internal Acme threads are shown in Fig. 19–116. Note that in the section view, left-hand internal threads are sloped so that they look the same as right-hand external threads.

Figure 19–117 shows a shaft that is being threaded on a lathe. These Acme threads are being cut as the tool travels the length of the shaft.

Fig. 19–117. Cutting an Acme thread on a lathe. (Courtesy of Clausing Corporation.)

19–50 SCHEMATIC REPRESENTATION

Examples of schematic representations of internal and external threads are shown in Fig. 19–118. Note that the threads are indicated by parallel, nonsloping lines which do not show whether the threads are right-hand or left-hand. This information is given in the thread note. Since this representation is easy to construct and gives a good symbolic representation of threads, it is the most generally used thread symbol.

The method of constructing schematic threads is illustrated in Fig. 19–119 in four steps.

Step 1. The major diameter of the thread is drawn with light construction lines. The pitch is laid off by graphical construction or by estimation, since accuracy is not important. Thin lines are drawn as crest lines across the diameter.

Step 2. The minor diameter of the thread is found by constructing a 60° angle between the crest lines. The minor diameter is drawn with light construction lines.

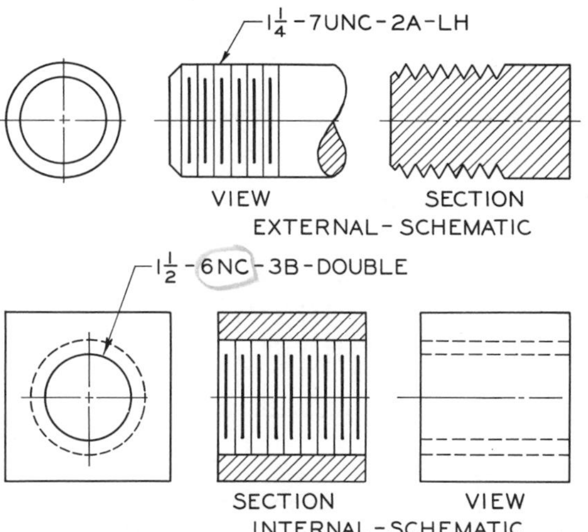

Fig. 19–118. Schematic representation of threads.

FIGURE 19–119. DRAWING SCHEMATIC THREADS

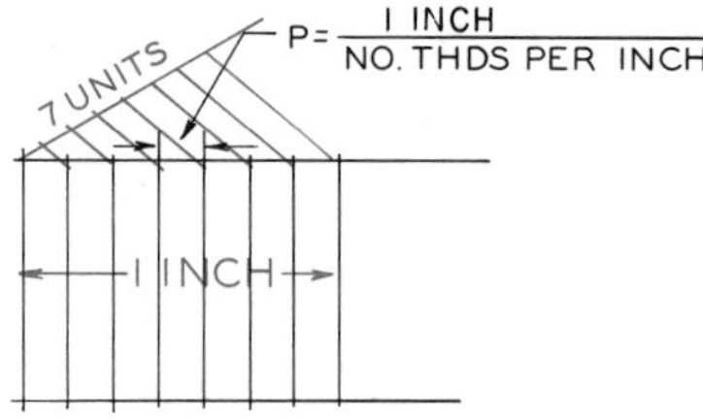

Step 1: Lay out the major diameter and divide the shaft into equal divisions a distance *P* apart. These division lines will be the crest lines; they should be drawn as thin lines.

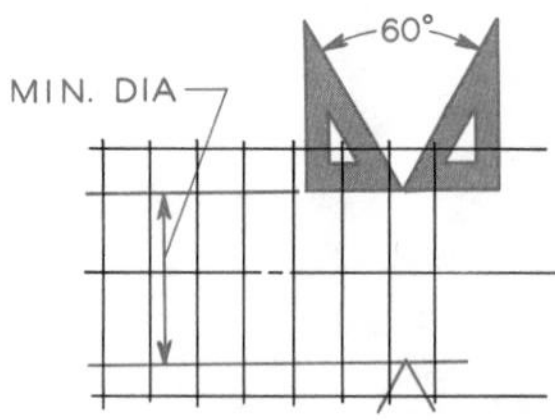

Step 2: Find the minor diameter by drawing a 60° angle between two crest lines.

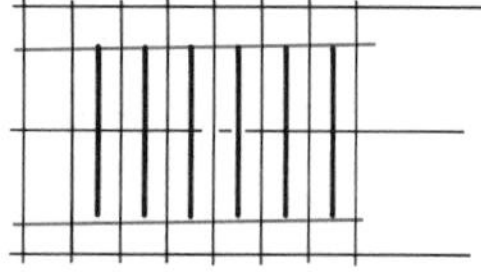

Step 3: Draw heavy root lines between the crest lines.

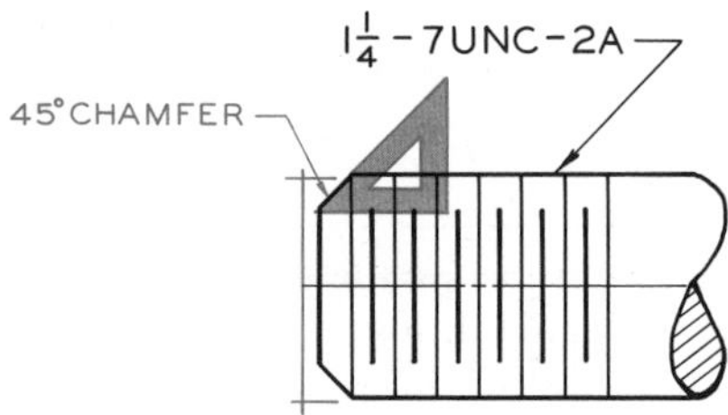

Step 4: Chamfer the end of the thread and give a thread note.

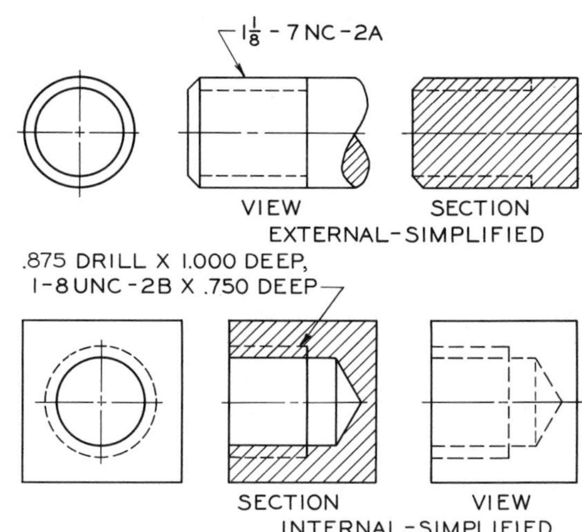

Fig. 19–120. Simplified thread representations.

Step 3. Heavy root lines are drawn across the minor diameter.

Step 4. A 45° chamfer is drawn from the last full thread to the minor diameter. The lines are strengthened and a thread note is added to complete the drawing.

19–51 SIMPLIFIED THREADS

Figure 19–120 illustrates the use of simplified representations with notes to specify thread details. Of the three types of thread representation covered here, this is the easiest to draw. Hidden lines are used to represent the minor diameter. These can be positioned by eye to approximate the minor diameter.

The steps involved in constructing a simplified thread drawing are shown in Fig. 19–121.

Step 1. The major diameter is laid off with dark visible lines. The pitch is determined to establish the distance between the crest lines.

Step 2. A 60° angle is drawn between these crest lines on each side of the shaft to locate the minor diameter. The minor diameter is drawn with light construction lines.

FIGURE 19-121. DRAWING SIMPLIFIED THREADS

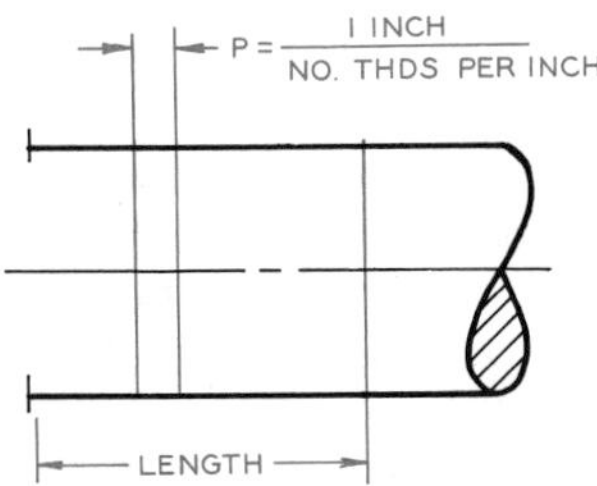

Step 1: Lay out the major diameter. Find the pitch (*P*) and lay out two lines a distance *P* apart.

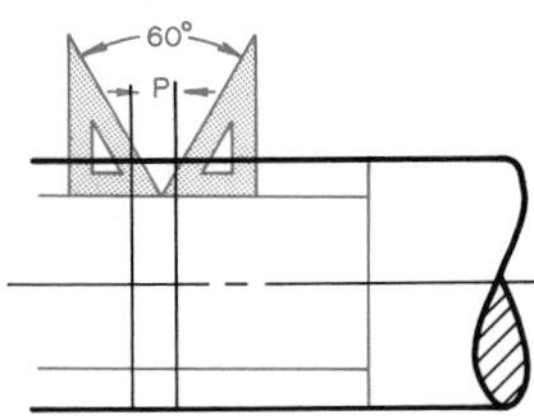

Step 2: Find the minor diameter by constructing a 60° angle between the two lines.

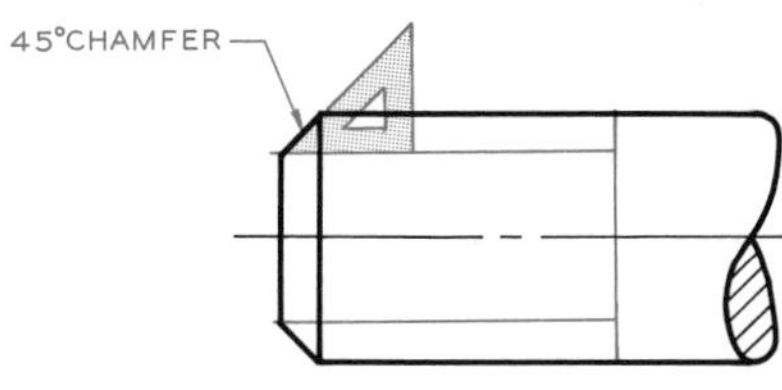

Step 3: Draw a 45° chamfer from the minor diameter to the major diameter.

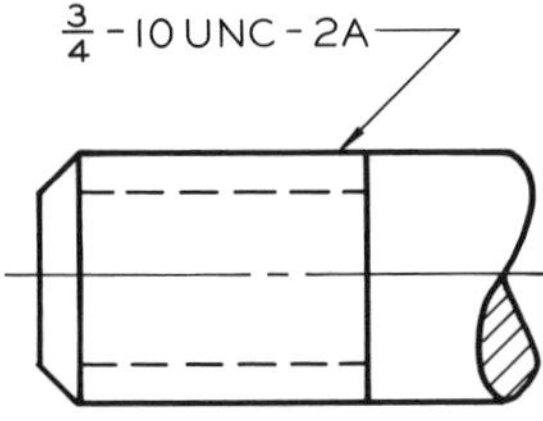

Step 4: Show the minor diameter as a dashed line. Add a thread note.

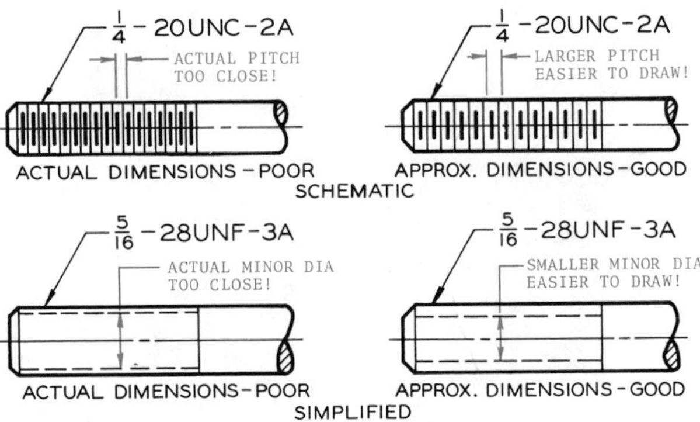

Fig. 19-122. Simplified threads should be drawn using approximate dimensions if the actual dimensions would result in lines drawn too close together.

Step 3. A 45° chamfer is drawn from the minor diameter to the major diameter.

Step 4. Dashed lines are drawn to represent the minor diameter.

19-52 DRAWING SMALL THREADS

Very small threads may be impossible to draw to their true dimensions without crest and root lines that touch. This is true of both simplified and schematic thread drawings.

Instead of using exact measurements to draw small threads, minor diameters can be drawn smaller by eye in order to separate the root and crest lines, as illustrated in Fig. 19-122. This procedure makes the drawing more readable and easier to draw. Accuracy is unnecessary, since the drawing is only a symbolic representation of a thread. The draftsman should develop his ability to represent threads symbolically by eye, thereby saving drafting time.

For both internal and external threads, a thread note is added to the symbolic drawing to give the necessary specifications and to complete the description of the threaded part.

Fig. 19-123. Examples of nuts and bolts. (Courtesy of Russell, Burdsall & Ward Bolt and Nut Company.)

19-53 NUTS AND BOLTS

Nuts and bolts come in many forms and sizes for different applications (Fig. 19-123). Drawings of the more common types of threaded fasteners are shown in Fig. 19-124. A *bolt* is a threaded cylinder with a head and a nut for holding two parts together (Fig. 19-124A). A *stud* does not have a head, but is screwed into one part with a nut attached to the other end (Fig. 19-124B). A *cap screw* is similar to a bolt, but it does not have a nut; instead it is screwed into a member with internal threads for greater strength (Fig. 19-124C). A *machine screw* is similar to a cap screw, but it is smaller. A *set screw* is used to adjust one member with respect to another, usually to prevent a rotational movement.

The types of heads used on standard bolts and nuts are illustrated in Fig. 19-125. These heads are used on all three series of bolts:

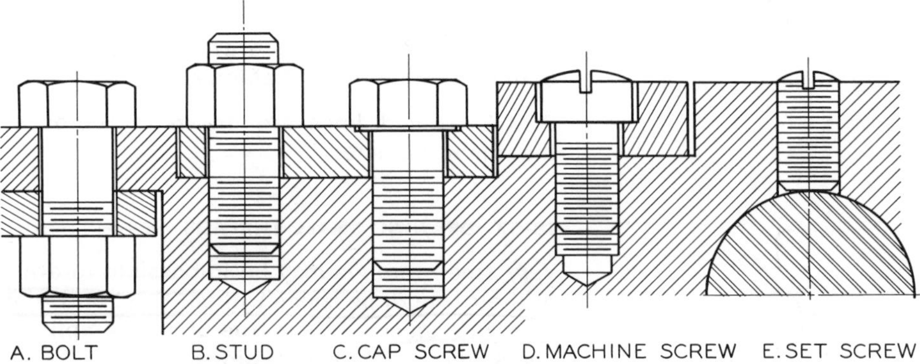

Fig. 19-124. Types of threaded bolts and screws.

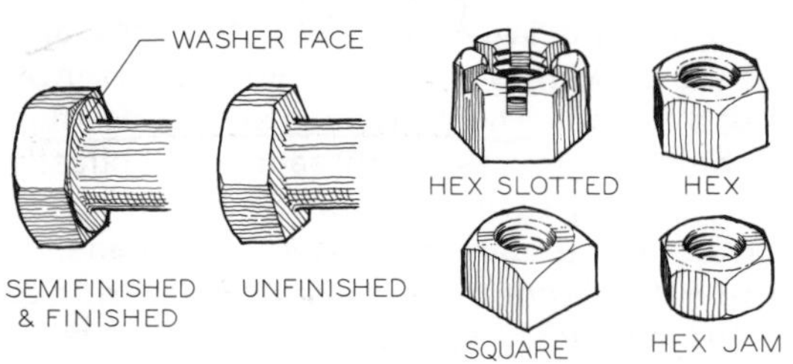

Fig. 19-125. Types of finish for bolt heads and types of nuts.

regular, light, and *heavy.* The thickness of the head is the primary difference among the three series. Heavy-series bolts have the thickest heads and are used at points where bearing loads are heaviest. Bolts and nuts are classified as *finished, semifinished,* and *unfinished.* Figure 19-125 shows an unfinished head; that is, none of the surfaces of the head are machined. The semifinished head has a washer face that is $\frac{1}{64}''$ thick to provide a circular boss on the bearing surface of the bolt head or the nut. The finished bolt looks like the semifinished one, but it has been machined to conform to prescribed tolerances.

Other standard forms of bolt and screw heads are shown in Fig. 19-126. These heads are used primarily on cap screws and machine screws. Many tables and standards are available for use in selecting the proper head for an application. Standard types of nuts are illustrated in Fig. 19-125. These can be machined to give a washer face for the finished and semifinished series. A hexagon jam nut does not have a washer face, but it is chamfered on both sides.

A photograph of several types of nuts is shown in Fig. 19-127. Many more specialized heads and nuts are available for less common applications.

19-54 DRAWING THE SQUARE BOLT HEAD

Detailed tables are available in the Appendix and in published standards for various types of threaded parts. In most cases it is sufficient to draw nuts and bolts using only general proportions. This method will be described here.

The first step in drawing a bolt head or a nut is to determine whether it is to be *across corners* or *across flats.* In other words, are the outlines at either side of the view going to represent corners, or are they going to be edge views of flat surfaces of the part? The head in Fig. 19-128 is drawn across corners. Nuts and bolts should be drawn across corners whenever possible; this type of drawing gives a better representation than drawing across flats.

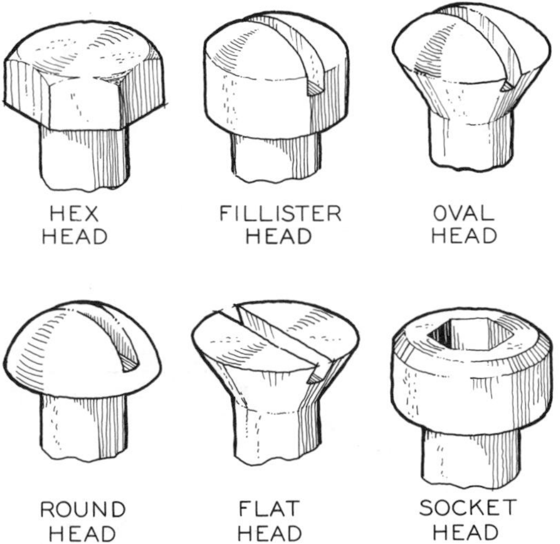

Fig. 19-126. Common types of bolt and screw heads.

Fig. 19-127. Examples of a variety of nuts that are available for special applications. (Courtesy of Russell, Burdsall & Ward Bolt and Nut Company.)

FIGURE 19–128. DRAWING THE SQUARE HEAD

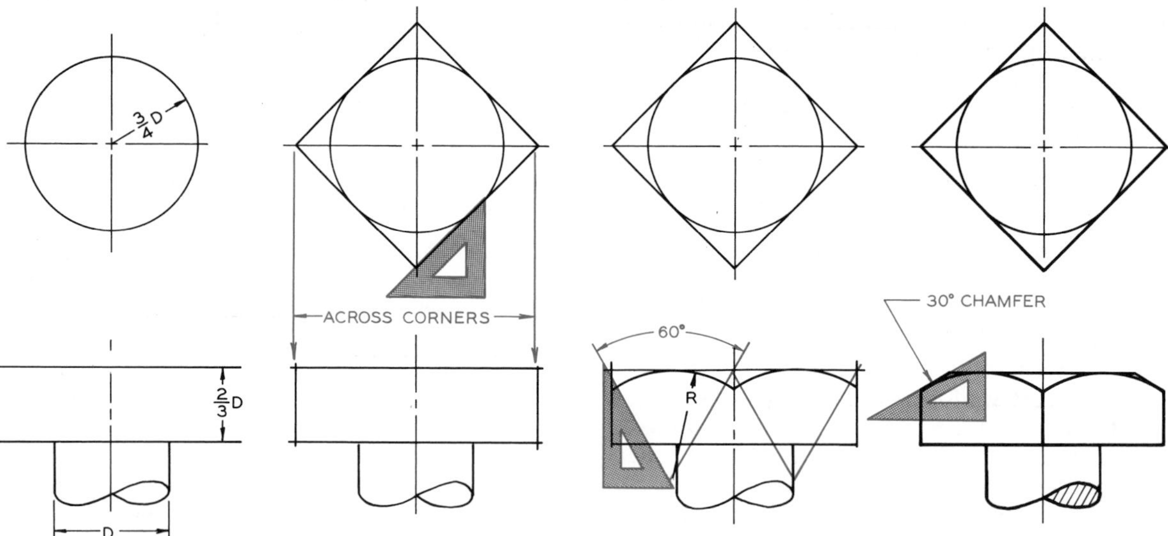

Step 1: Draw the diameter of the bolt. Use this to establish the head diameter and thickness.

Step 2: Draw the top view of the square head with a 45° triangle to give an across-corners view.

Step 3: Show the chamfer in the front view by using a 30°-60° triangle to find the centers for the radii.

Step 4: Draw a 30° chamfer that is tangent to the arcs in the front view. Strengthen the lines.

FIGURE 19–129. DRAWING THE HEXAGON HEAD

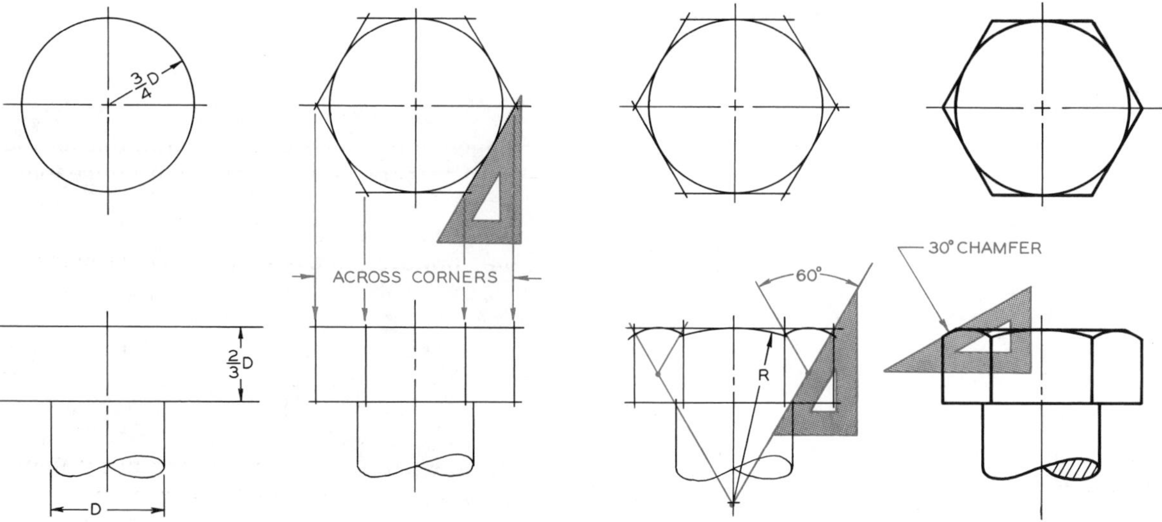

Step 1: Draw the diameter of the bolt. Use this to establish the head diameter and thickness.

Step 2: Construct a hexagon with a 30°-60° triangle to give an across-corners view.

Step 3: Find arcs in the front view to show the chamfer of the head.

Step 4: Show a 30° chamfer tangent to the arcs in the front view. Strengthen the lines.

Step 1. The diameter of the bolt is used as the basis for most of the construction involved in drawing the bolt head. The thickness of a regular bolt head is equal to two-thirds the diameter of the bolt. The distance from one flat surface on the head to the opposite flat surface is equal to $1\frac{1}{2}$ times the diameter. Therefore, a circle with a radius of $\frac{3}{4}D$ is drawn in the top view.

Step 2. Since the head is to be drawn across corners, the top view of the square head is drawn with a 45° triangle. This will give a view across corners in the front view.

Step 3. To show a 30° chamfer of the head, use a 60° triangle to locate the centers for radius *R*. Use these centers to draw two arcs in the front view.

Step 4. Use a 30° triangle to draw the chamfer at the two corners. Strengthen the lines to complete the drawing. Square heads are unfinished and have no washer face.

19–55 DRAWING THE HEXAGON BOLT HEAD

As previously mentioned, it is desirable that nuts and bolts be drawn across corners since this gives a better impression of the parts. An example of constructing the head of a bolt is shown in Fig. 19–129.

Step 1. The diameter of the bolt is *D*. The thickness of the head is drawn equal to $\frac{2}{3}D$. The top view of the head is drawn as a circle with a radius of $\frac{3}{4}D$.

Step 2. A hexagon is drawn tangent to the circle with the aid of a 60° triangle. The corner edges are projected to the front view.

Step 3. The radii for drawing the arcs formed by chamfering the head in the manufacturing process are located with a 30°-60° triangle.

Step 4. A 30° chamfer is drawn at each corner with a 30° triangle. The lines are strengthened to complete the drawing.

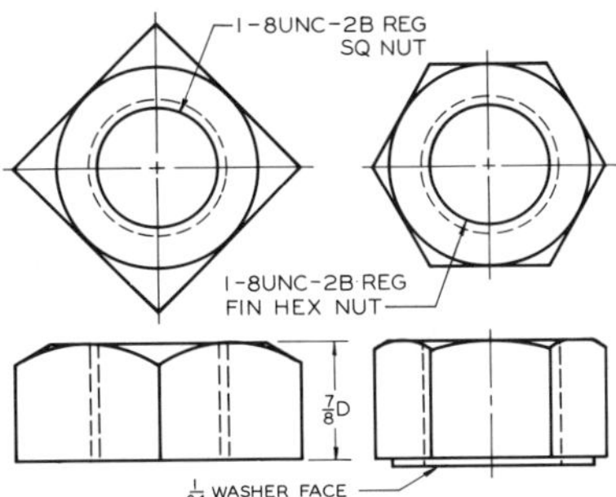

Fig. 19–130. Drawings of hexagon and square nuts are constructed in the same manner as drawings of bolt heads. Standard notes are added to give nut specifications.

19–56 DRAWING NUTS

The construction of a drawing of a square nut or a hexagon nut across corners is exactly the same as the construction of a drawing of a bolt head across corners. The only variation is the thickness of the nut. The regular nut thickness is $\frac{7}{8}D$, and for the heavy nut the thickness is equal to the diameter (*D*).

Examples of square and hexagon nuts drawn across corners are shown in Fig. 19–130. Hidden lines are shown in the front view to indicate threads. Since it is understood that nuts are threaded, these hidden lines may be omitted in general applications.

Note that a $\frac{1}{64}''$ washer face is shown on the hexagon nut. This is usually drawn thicker than $\frac{1}{64}''$ so that the face will be more noticeable in the drawing. Thread notes are placed in the top views rather than the front views where possible; however, these notes may be placed in front views if necessary. These are standard notes. In the case of the square nut, the note tells us that the major diameter of the thread is 1″, that the nut has 8 threads per inch, that the thread is of the Unified National form and coarse series, with a fit of 2, and that the nut is a regular square nut. The hexagon nut is similar except that it is a finished hexagon nut.

The leader from the note is directed toward the center of the circular view, but the arrow stops at the first visible circle it makes contact with.

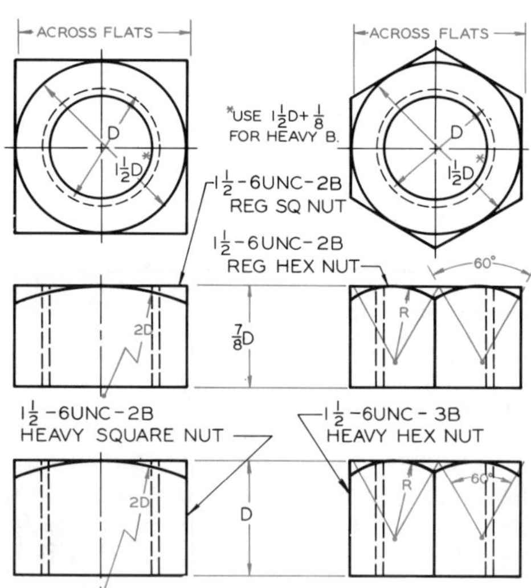

Fig. 19-131. Examples of hexagon and square nuts drawn across flats. Notes are added to give nut specifications.

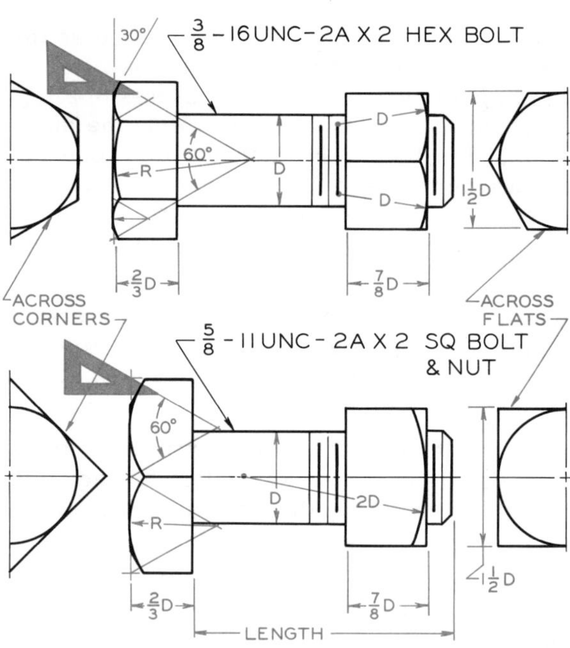

Fig. 19-132. Construction of nuts and bolts in assembly.

Nuts can be drawn across flats in situations where doing so improves the drawing. Examples of nuts drawn across flats are shown in Fig. 19-131.

For regular nuts, the distance across flats is $1\frac{1}{2} \times D$ (D is the major diameter of the thread). For heavy nuts this distance is increased by $\frac{1}{8}''$. The top views are drawn in the same manner as in across-corners drawings except that they are positioned to give different front views.

In the case of the square nut (Fig. 19-131), the front view is a simple rectangle, with only the arc formed by the chamfer giving a hint that the object is a nut. This is one of the disadvantages of drawing nuts across flats. The arc is drawn with a radius of $2D$, with the center located on the centerline of the nut. The heavy nut has a thickness equal to the major diameter of the threads.

The hexagon nut drawn across flats looks more like a nut in the front view than does the square nut. Still, the hexagon nut drawn across corners is a better representation. The method of drawing a nut across flats is shown in Fig. 19-131. The centers for the arcs used to show the chamfer are found with a 30°-60° triangle. Notes are added with leaders to complete the representation of the nuts. A washer face should be added to a nut if it is finished or semifinished, except in the case of the square nut. Square nuts are always unfinished.

19-57 DRAWING NUTS AND BOLTS IN COMBINATION

It is often necessary to draw a nut and bolt assembled. The same rules followed in drawing nuts and bolts separately apply. Examples are shown in Fig. 19-132.

The construction illustrated here is the same as that covered earlier. The diameter of the bolt is used as the basis for other dimensions. The note is added to give the specifications of the nut and bolt. In the figure, the bolt heads are drawn across corners and the nuts across flats.

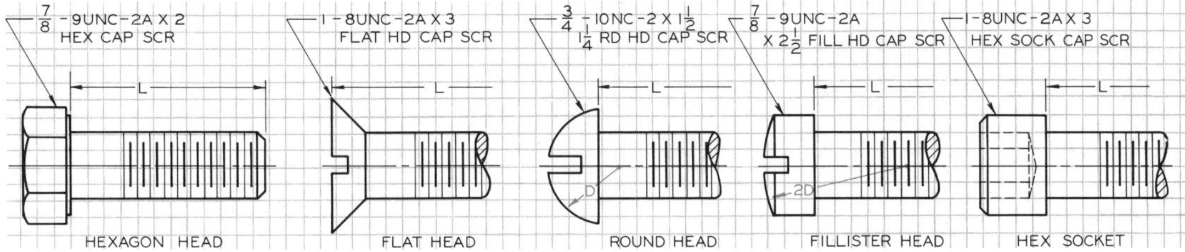

Fig. 19-133. Standard types of cap screws. The proportions shown here can be used for drawing cap screws of all sizes.

The end views have been included to show how the front views were found by projection. These may not be necessary in a finished drawing if only one view of the nut is needed. Again the bolt diameter is used as the basis for this construction.

19-58 CAP SCREWS

Cap screws are used to hold two parts together without the use of a nut. One of these two parts has a threaded cylindrical hole and thus serves the same function as the nut. The other part is drilled with an oversize hole so that the cap screw will pass through it freely. When the cap screw is tightened, the two parts are held securely together.

The standard types of cap screws are illustrated in Fig. 19-133. The standard types are defined by the type of head used. Tables are available in the Appendix to give the dimensions of several of these types of cap screw.

The cap screws in Fig. 19-133 are drawn on a grid in order to show the proportions of each type. The proportions shown here can be used for drawing cap screws of all sizes. These types of cap screws range in diameter from No. 0 (0.060″) to $1\frac{1}{2}$″. Standard thread notes are given on each type to show the correct form for specifying cap screws.

19-59 MACHINE SCREWS

Machine screws are smaller than most cap screws, usually less than 1″ in diameter. The machine screw is used to attach parts together; it is screwed either into another part or into a nut. Machine screws are threaded their full length when they are 2″ long or shorter. Several types of slotted and Phillips recessed machine screws are shown in Fig. 19-134.

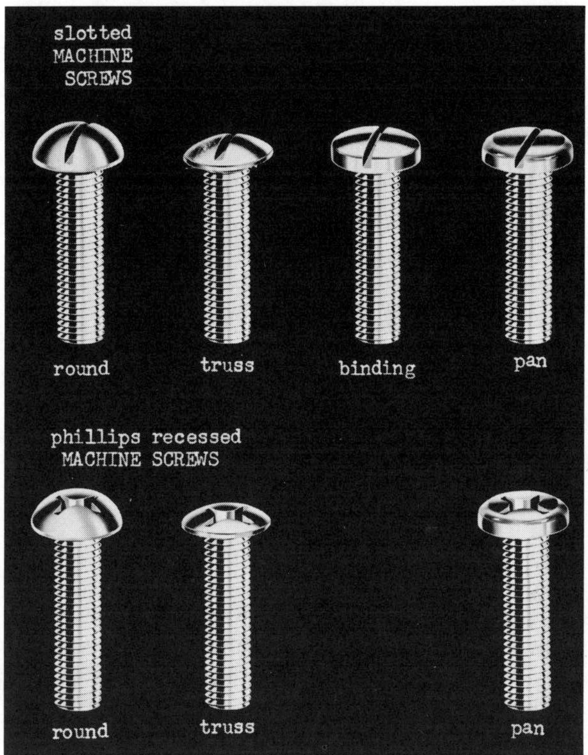

Fig. 19-134. Examples of the different types of machine screws. (Courtesy of the H. M. Harper Company.)

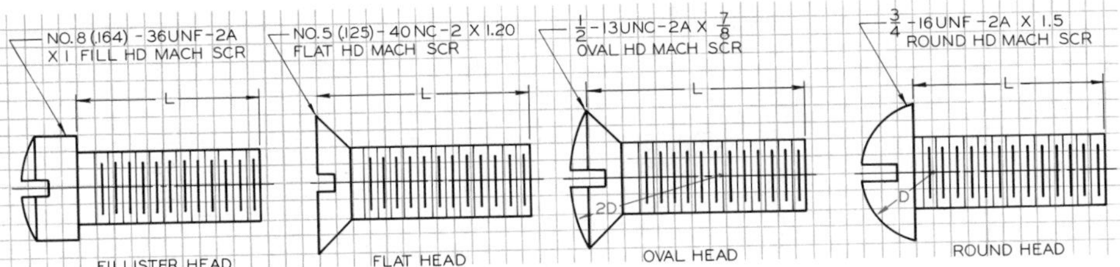

Fig. 19–135. Drawings of the standard types of machine screws. The proportions shown here can be used for drawing machine screws of all sizes.

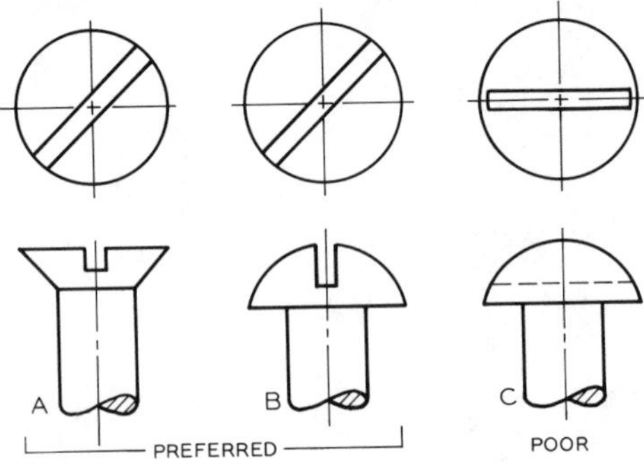

Fig. 19–136. Slotted-head screws should be drawn with the slot at 45° in the top view and with the notch shown in the front view.

Drawings of common machine screws are given in Fig. 19–135. Many other types are available in addition to these types. The dimensions of round-head machine screws are given in the Appendix. Typical notes are shown with these basic types of machine screws.

The four types of machine screws in Fig. 19–135 are drawn on a grid to give the proportions of the head in relation to the major diameter of the screw. The proportions shown here can be used for drawing these screws regardless of their size or scale. Machine screws range in size from No. 0 (0.060″ in diameter) to a diameter of $\frac{3}{4}$″.

When slotted-head screws are drawn, it is conventional practice to show the slots positioned at a 45° angle in the circular view as illustrated in Fig. 19–136. Even though the slot is turned at this angle in the top view, the front view of the slot is drawn to show the width and depth of the slot, as in Fig. 19–136A and B. By inspection, you can see that this gives a better representation of the screw head than does the example in Fig. 19–136C. This practice applies to all types of slotted fasteners.

19–60 SET SCREWS

Parts such as wheels or pulleys are commonly attached to shafts. To attach these parts to a shaft, set screws or keys are used. Examples of various types of set screws are shown in Fig. 19–137.

Table 19–1 shows the dimensions of the various features of the set screws shown in Fig. 19–137. This table is useful in selecting the appropriate standard size of set screw for the application at hand. Drawings of set screws need not employ these dimensions precisely; like the other fasteners discussed in this chapter, set screws can be drawn as approximations.

Note that the points and the heads of these set screws are of different types. Set screws are available in any desired combination of point and head. The shaft against which the set screw is tightened may have a flat surface machined to give a good bearing surface for the set screw point. In this case a dog point or a flat point would be most effective to press against the flat surface. The cup point gives good friction when

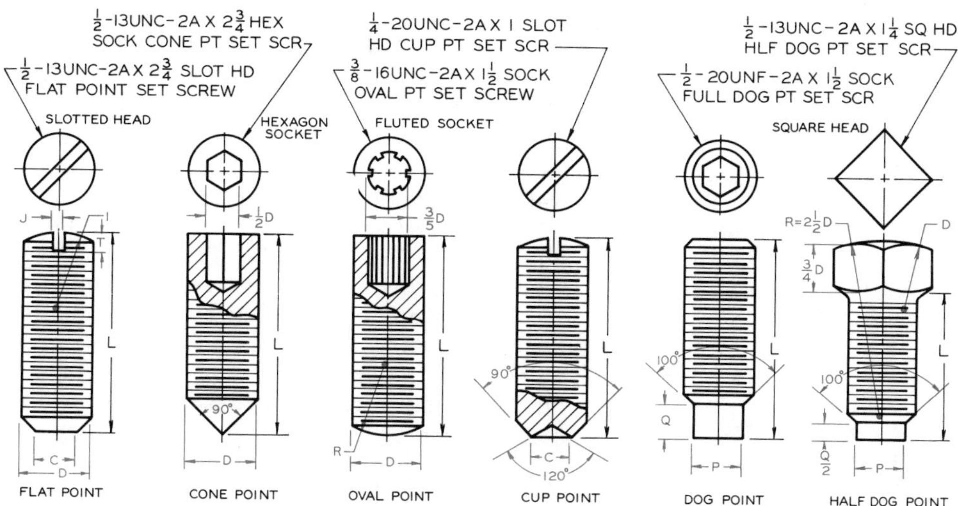

Fig. 19-137. Types of set screws. Set screws are available with various combinations of heads and points. Notes give their specifications. Dimensions are given in Table 19-1.

Table 19-1

Dimensions for the set screws shown in Fig. 19-137 (all dimensions given in inches)

D	I	J	T	R	C		P		Q	q
Nominal size	Radius of headless crown	Width of slot	Depth of slot	Oval point radius	Diameter of cup and flat points		Diameter of dog point		Length of dog point	
					Max	Min	Max	Min	Full	Half
5 0.125	0.125	0.023	0.031	0.094	0.067	0.057	0.083	0.078	0.060	0.030
6 0.138	0.138	0.025	0.035	0.109	0.074	0.064	0.092	0.087	0.070	0.035
8 0.164	0.164	0.029	0.041	0.125	0.087	0.076	0.109	0.103	0.080	0.040
10 0.190	0.190	0.032	0.048	0.141	0.102	0.088	0.127	0.120	0.090	0.045
12 0.216	0.216	0.036	0.054	0.156	0.115	0.101	0.144	0.137	0.110	0.055
1/4 0.250	0.250	0.045	0.063	0.188	0.132	0.118	0.156	0.149	0.125	0.063
5/16 0.3125	0.313	0.051	0.078	0.234	0.172	0.156	0.203	0.195	0.156	0.078
3/8 0.375	0.375	0.064	0.094	0.281	0.212	0.194	0.250	0.241	0.188	0.094
7/16 0.4375	0.438	0.072	0.109	0.328	0.252	0.232	0.297	0.287	0.219	0.109
1/2 0.500	0.500	0.081	0.125	0.375	0.291	0.270	0.344	0.344	0.250	0.125
9/16 0.5625	0.563	0.091	0.141	0.422	0.332	0.309	0.391	0.379	0.281	0.140
5/8 0.625	0.625	0.102	0.156	0.469	0.371	0.347	0.469	0.456	0.313	0.156
3/4 0.750	0.750	0.129	0.188	0.563	0.450	0.425	0.563	0.549	0.375	0.188

Courtesy of ANSI; B18.6.2-1956.

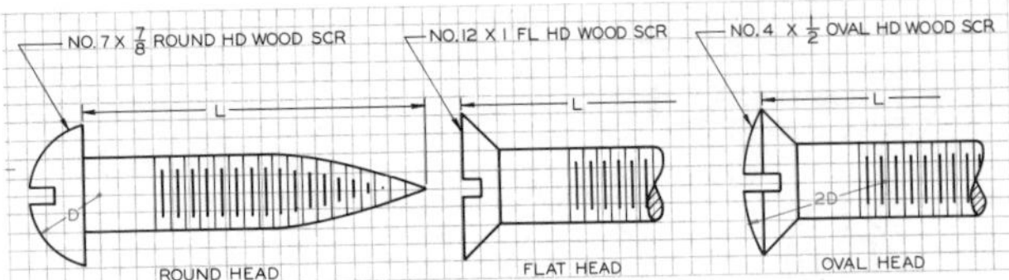

Fig. 19-138. Drawings of the standard types of wood screws. The proportions shown here can be used for drawing wood screws of all sizes.

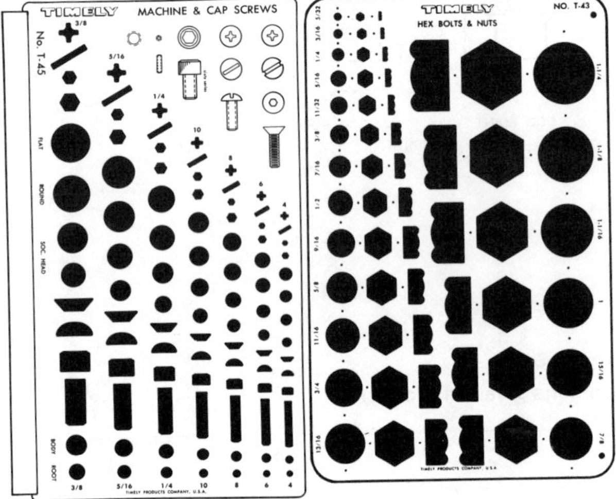

Fig. 19-139. Examples of templates that can be used for drawing threaded fasteners. (Courtesy of Timely Products Company.)

applied to a round shaft where there is no flat surface.

Study the types of notes and abbreviations used to specify the set screws. As with all threaded fasteners, the use of such notes is essential.

19-61 WOOD SCREWS

A wood screw is a pointed screw having a sharp thread of coarse pitch for insertion in wood. The three most common types of wood screws are shown in Fig. 19-138. These are drawn on a grid to show the proportions of the various heads in relation to the major diameter of the screw. The same proportions can be used for all sizes of wood screws in practical applications. Many of the detailed dimensions for wood screws are given in tables published by the American National Standards Institute.

Sizes of wood screws are specified by single numbers such as 0, 6, or 16. From 0 to 10 each digit represents a different size. Beginning at 10, only even-numbered sizes are standard, i.e., 10, 12, 14, 16, 18, 20, 22, and 24. The following formula can be used to relate these numbered sizes to the actual diameter of the screws:

$$\text{Actual Dia.} = 0.060 + \text{Screw Number} \times 0.013.$$

For example, the actual diameter of a No. 5 screw is

$$0.060 + 5(0.013) = 0.125.$$

Standard notes are given to specify the wood screws illustrated in Fig. 19-138. These should be added in all cases to explain the symbolic drawing of the wood screw.

19-62 USE OF TEMPLATES

Templates are available for drawing threads, nuts, and threaded fasteners. They are available for a range of sizes that is satisfactory for most applications, since thread representations are approximations at best.

Two typical templates are shown in Fig. 19-139. The black areas represent the holes cut into the thin plastic templates. The template is laid on the drawing and the threaded features are drawn using the template as a guide. Templates are also available for drawing nuts and bolts in pictorial. These are used primarily by the technical illustrator.

19-63 KEYS

Keys are used to attach parts to shafts in order to transmit power to pulleys, gears, or cranks. Several types of keys are shown pictorially and orthographically in Fig. 19-140. The four types

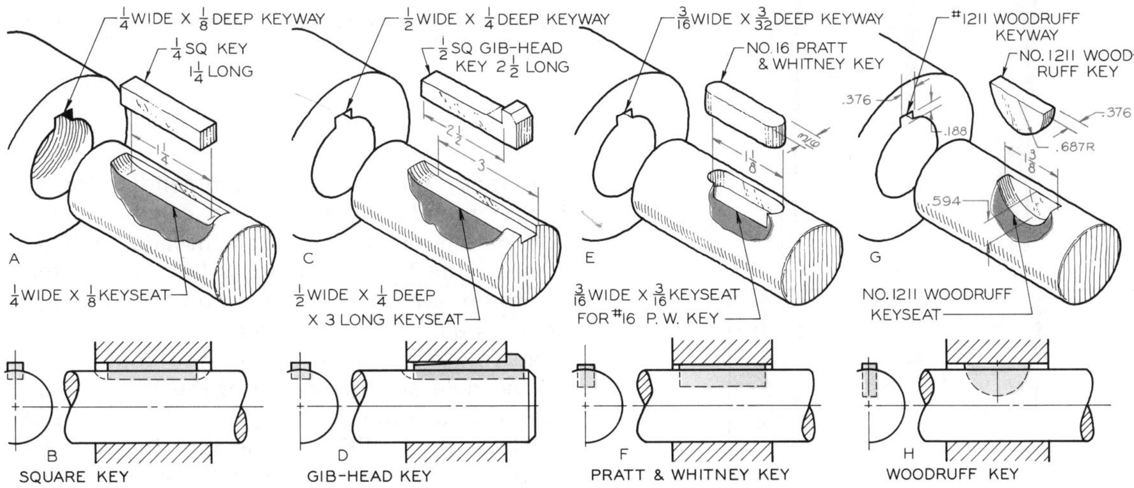

Fig. 19–140. Standard keys used for holding parts on a shaft.

illustrated here are the most commonly used keys. To specify a key, notes must be given for the keyway, the key, and the keyseat, as shown in Fig. 19–140A, C, E, and G. The notes given in Fig. 19–140 are typical of the notes used to give key specifications.

19–64 THREAD REPRESENTATIONS IN COMBINATION

It is good practice to use the same type of thread representation—simplified, schematic, or detailed—throughout a single drawing. However, there are cases where using these representations in combination adds clarity to the drawing. Such a case is shown in Fig. 19–141. In this example, all three representations are used—simplified, schematic, and detailed. This is permissible for the sake of clarity.

19–65 TAPPING A HOLE

A threaded hole is called a *tapped hole,* since the tool used to cut the threads is called a tap. The types of taps available for threading small holes by hand are shown in Fig. 19–142.

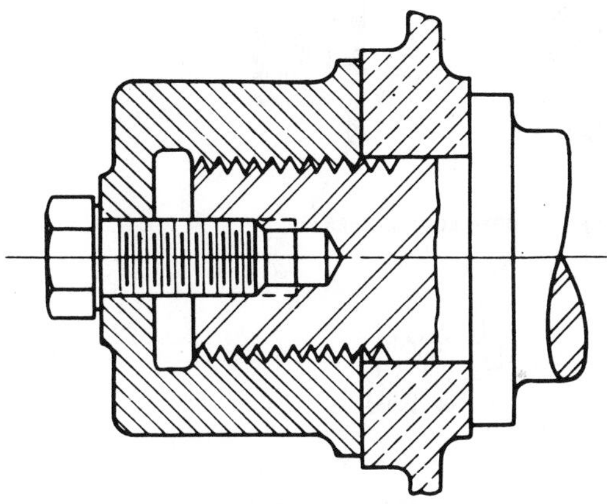

Fig. 19–141. Three types of thread representations used on the same drawing for clarity.

The taper, plug, and bottoming hand taps are identical in size, length, and measurements, their only difference being the chamfered portion of their ends. The taper tap has a long chamfer (8 to 10 threads), the plug tap has a chamfer of 3 to 5 threads, and the bottoming tap has a short chamfer of only 1 to $1\frac{1}{2}$ threads.

When tapping by hand in open or "through" holes, the taper should be used for coarse threads, since it ensures straighter starting.

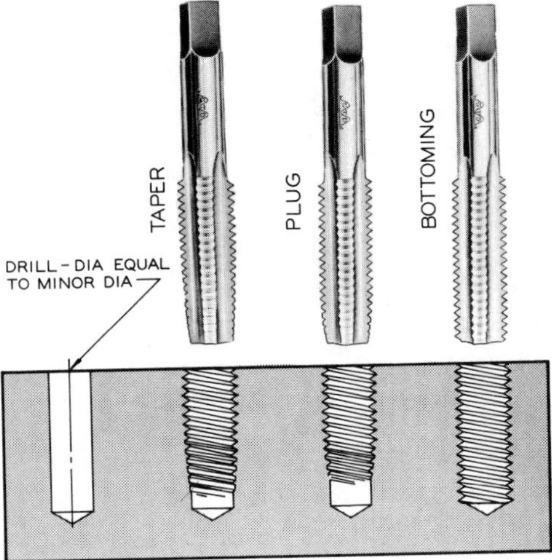

Fig. 19-142. Three types of taps for threading internal holes. (Courtesy of Greenfield Tap and Die Corporation.)

The taper tap is also recommended for the harder metals. The plug tap can be used in soft metals or for fine-pitch threads. When it is desirable to tap a hole to the very bottom, all three taps—taper, plug, and bottoming—should be used in this order.

Notes are added to specify the depth of the drilled hole and the depth of the threads. For example, a note reading $\frac{7}{8}$ DRILL, 3 DEEP, 1-8UNC-2A, 2 DEEP means that the hole will be drilled deeper than it is threaded and the last usable thread will be 2″ deep in the hole. Note that the drill point has an angle of 120°.

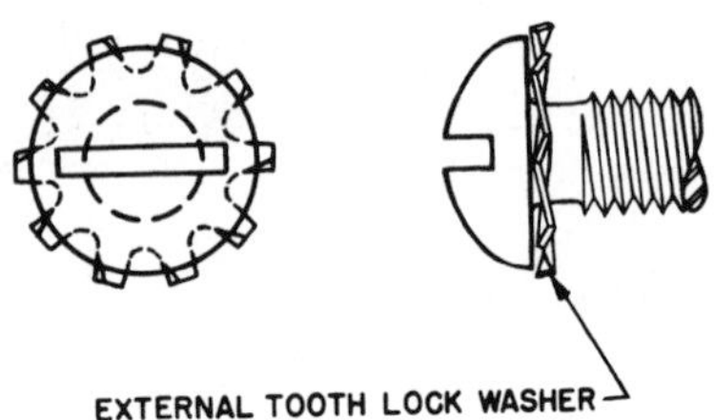

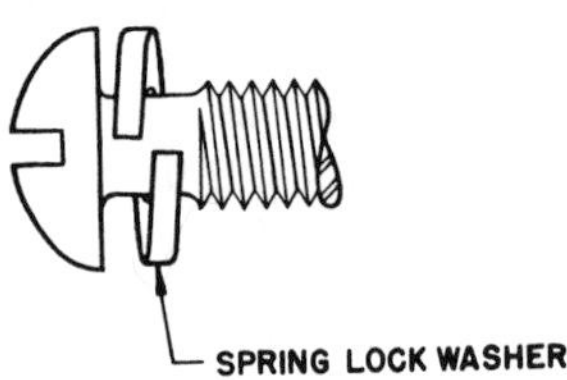

Fig. 19-143. Two types of lock washers for preventing a bolt from unscrewing.

19-66 LOCK WASHERS

A lock washer is a device that is used to prevent a nut or a cap screw from loosening as a result of vibration or movement. These washers may take many forms, but two of the most common types are shown in Fig. 19-143.

The external-tooth lock washer has a series of teeth around the circumference of the washer. These teeth are angled to resist unscrewing after tightening. The spring lock washer is the more common type. This is simply a washer that has a cut and has been sprung so that it will resist unscrewing once tightened. Photographs of lock washers are shown in Fig. 19-144.

Other locking devices of this type are cotter pins and specially designed nuts such as the castle nut and the jam nut (Fig. 19-145). Some locking devices have inserts of plastic that fuse the threads together when tightened. Many manufacturers specialize in making locking nuts and fasteners that resist heavy vibrations without unscrewing.

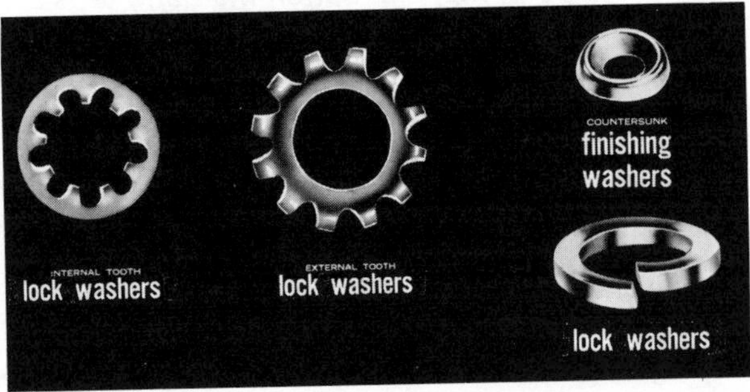

Fig. 19-144. Types of lock washers. (Courtesy of the H. M. Harper Company.)

Fig. 19–145. Other types of locking devices. (Courtesy of the H. M. Harper Company.)

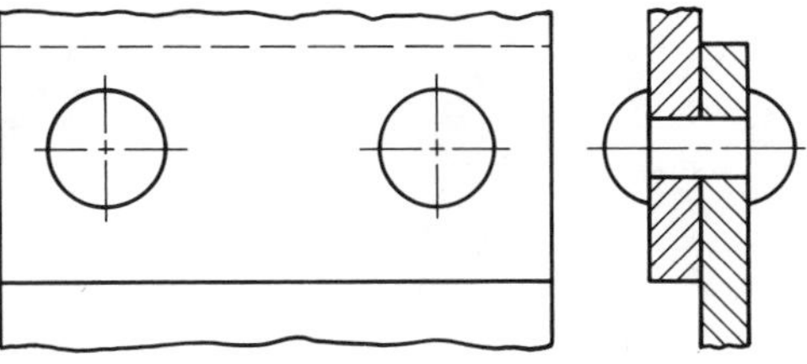

Fig. 19–147. Representation of a lap joint fastened with two rivets.

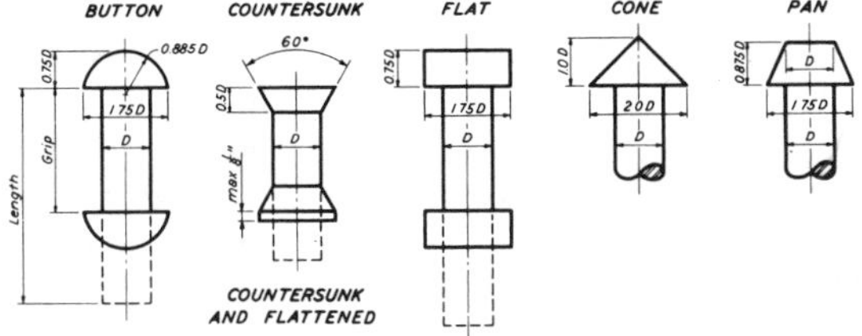

Fig. 19–146. Rivet forms. (Courtesy of the Tennessee Valley Authority.)

Fig. 19–148. A system of gears and linkages in the main drive of a multiple spindle bar machine. (Courtesy of the National Acme Company.)

19–67 RIVETS

Rivets are a type of fastener used to join thin materials in a permanent joint. Rivets are designed to fit into holes that are slightly larger than the diameter of the rivet. The rivet is inserted in the hole and the headless end is formed into the specified shape by applying extreme pressure to the projecting end. This forming operation is done when the rivets are either hot or cold, depending on the application.

Typical shapes and proportions of rivets are shown in Fig. 19–146. These rivets vary in diameter from $\frac{1}{16}''$ to $1\frac{3}{4}''$. Rivets are used extensively in pressure-vessel fabrication and in heavy structures such as bridges and buildings. They are also used in construction with sheet metal.

A simple lap joint is illustrated in Fig. 19–147 where two button-head rivets are applied. The rivets are shown with circles to represent their heads. The diameter of the rivet passing through the hole is not shown as a hidden circle. A more detailed set of riveting symbols is used by industries specializing in fabrication that uses this type of fastening.

19–68 GEARS

Gears are toothed wheels that mesh together to transmit force and motion from one gear to the next. A complicated system of gears is shown in Fig. 19–148. This system of gears can give a variety of speeds and power ratios as different gears are engaged.

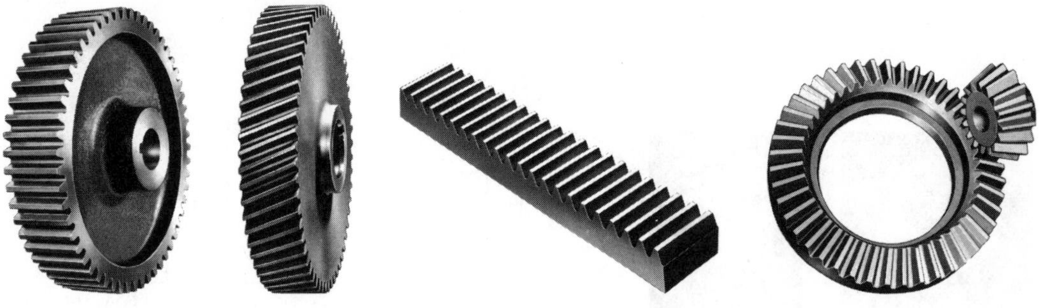

Fig. 19-149. Left to right: a straight spur gear, a helical spur gear, a rack, and bevel gears. (Courtesy of Philadelphia Gear Corporation.)

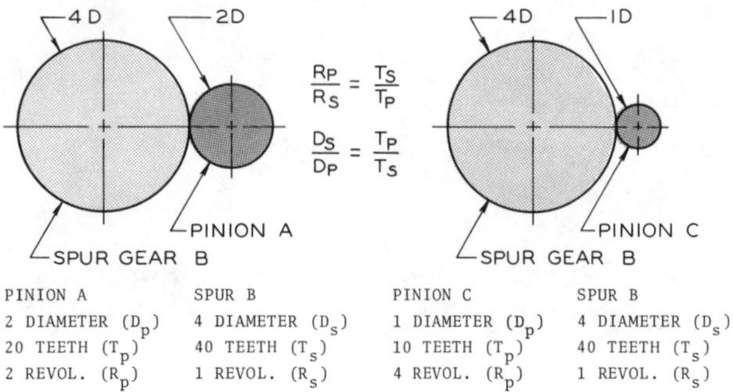

Fig. 19-150. The difference in size between gears and pinions affects the speed and power ratios.

Gears are linked together by teeth cut into the surfaces which make contact with each other. The ratio of the number of teeth on one gear to the number on the matching gear determines the rate of variation in speed and power between the two.

19-69 TYPES OF GEARS

The more common types of gears are shown in Fig. 19-149. These are (a) the spur gear (straight and helical), (b) the rack, and (c) the bevel gear.

The *spur gear* is a circular gear with teeth cut around the circumference. Two spur gears can transmit power from a shaft to a parallel shaft. When the two meshing gears are unequal in size, the smaller gear is called the *pinion* and the larger one is called the *gear.*

The *rack* is a series of teeth in a straight line on which a spur gear can travel. The axes of the two are perpendicular but do not intersect.

The *bevel gear* is a gear mounted on an axis whose centerline intersects the centerline of the axis of another gear at some angle, usually 90°. An example of a pinion and bevel gear is shown in Fig. 19-149. When two bevel gears with the same number of teeth intersect at 90°, they are called *miter* gears.

19-70 GEAR RELATIONSHIPS

The sizes of two meshing spur gears or bevel gears establish ratios that are important to the engineer. Examples are given in Fig. 19-150 to illustrate these ratios. If the radius of a gear is twice that of its pinion, then the gear's diameter and circumference are twice those of the pinion. Also, the gear must have twice as many teeth as the pinion. The pinion, in this case, must make two turns to a single turn of the gear. This means that the number of revolutions of the pinion per minute is equal to twice the number of revolutions of the gear.

When the diameter of the gear is four times the diameter of the pinion, there must be four times as many teeth on the gear as on the pinion. The number of revolutions of the pinion per

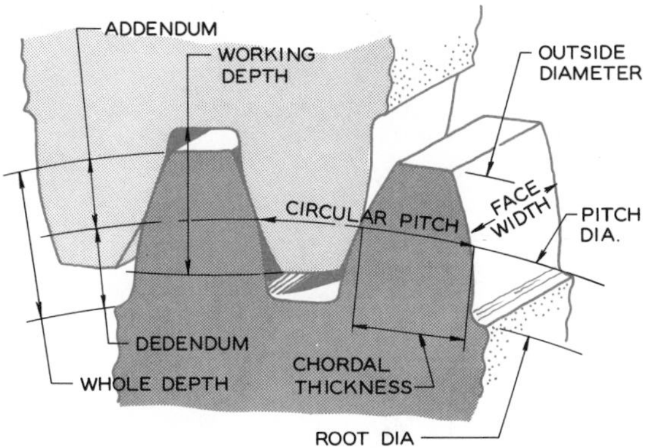

Fig. 19-151. Gear terminology.

minute will be four times the number of revolutions of the gear.

These ratios and formulas can be applied to many combinations of sizes of gears. The primary application of a gear is to regulate the speeds of various components of a machine so that they conform to certain predetermined ratios.

19-71 GEAR TERMINOLOGY

A number of terms are used to describe the parts of a gear and the features of gear teeth (Fig. 19-151). Each of the features has different dimensions with each size of gear. These dimensions can be found in tables of values or calculated from formulas.

Pitch diameter is the diameter that would establish the same ratio of speeds between two components if friction wheels without teeth were used to link them in place of two meshing gears.

Outside diameter is the diameter of a gear measured from the outside of the gear teeth.

Root diameter is the diameter of a gear measured from the bottom of the gear teeth.

Addendum is the height of the gear tooth above the pitch diameter.

Dedendum is the height of the gear tooth below the pitch diameter.

Whole depth is the total depth of a gear tooth: the addendum plus the dedendum.

Working depth is the depth to which a tooth fits into the meshing gear.

Circular pitch is the circular measurement from one point on a tooth to the corresponding point on the next tooth along the pitch diameter.

Chordal thickness is the straight-line distance across a tooth at the pitch diameter.

Circular thickness is the circular distance across a tooth along the pitch diameter.

Face width is the distance across a gear tooth measured perpendicular to the axis of a gear.

Diametral pitch is the ratio between the number of teeth on a gear and its pitch diameter. For example, a gear with 20 teeth and a 4″ pitch diameter will have a diametral pitch of 5, which means 5 teeth per inch of pitch diameter.

Formulas for some of the more important gear measurements are as follows:

$$N = \text{number of teeth},$$

$$\text{PD} = \text{pitch diameter} = \frac{N}{\text{DP}},$$

$$\text{DP} = \text{diametral pitch} = \frac{N}{\text{PD}},$$

$$\text{RD} = \text{root diameter} = \text{PD} - 2D,$$

$$\text{OD} = \text{outside diameter} = \frac{N+2}{\text{DP}},$$

$$A = \text{addendum} = \frac{1}{\text{DP}},$$

$$D = \text{dedendum} = \frac{1.157}{\text{DP}},$$

$$\text{CP} = \text{circular pitch} = \frac{\pi \times \text{DP}}{N},$$

$$\text{WD} = \text{whole depth} = A + D,$$

$$\text{CT} = \text{circular thickness} = \frac{\text{CP}}{2}.$$

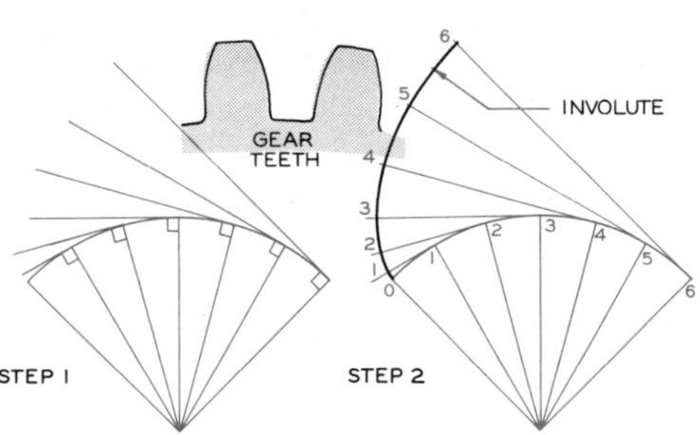

Fig. 19–152. Construction of an involute that represents the geometric shape of gear teeth.

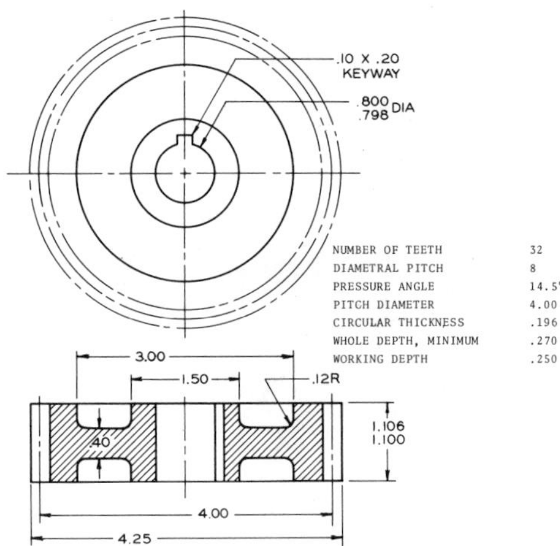

Fig. 19–153. A typical detail drawing of a spur gear with a table of values to give the gear specifications.

19–72 TOOTH FORMS

The most common gear tooth is an involute tooth with a $14\frac{1}{2}°$ pressure angle. The $14\frac{1}{2}°$ pressure angle is the angle of contact between two gears when the tangents of both gears pass through the point of contact. Gears with 20° and 25° pressure angles are also used. The gear teeth with larger pressure angles are wider at the base and thus are stronger than the standard $14\frac{1}{2}°$ teeth.

The standard gear face is an involute that keeps the meshing gears in contact as the gear teeth are revolved past one another.

The method of constructing an involute is shown in Fig. 19–152.

Step 1. An arc, called the base arc, is drawn and divided into equal divisions with radial lines from the center of the arc. Tangents are drawn perpendicular to these radial lines at the points where they intersect the base arc.

Step 2. The chordal distance from point 1 to point 0 is used as a radius with point 1 as the center. This distance is revolved to find point 1 on the involute. Then the distance from point 2 to the newly found point 1 is revolved to the line tangent to the arc through point 2, to give point 2 on the involute. This procedure is followed until the complete involute curve is found.

The involute curve thus found is an approximation of the path followed by the end of a string that is kept taut as it is unwound from the base arc. Instead of an arc, a full circle could be used as the base to find a full involute that would look like a spiral when completed.

It is unnecessary to use this procedure to draw gear teeth, since most detail drawings employ approximations of gear teeth. Gear teeth are, in fact, seldom shown on drawings; instead, conventional methods of specifying them are used with appropriate notes and tables.

19–73 DRAWING A SPUR GEAR

The detail drawing of the spur gear in Fig. 19–153 shows the conventional method of drawing this type of gear. The circular view is often omitted since the sectional view is adequate for most applications. When the circular view is shown, circular center lines are drawn to represent the root diameter, pitch diameter,

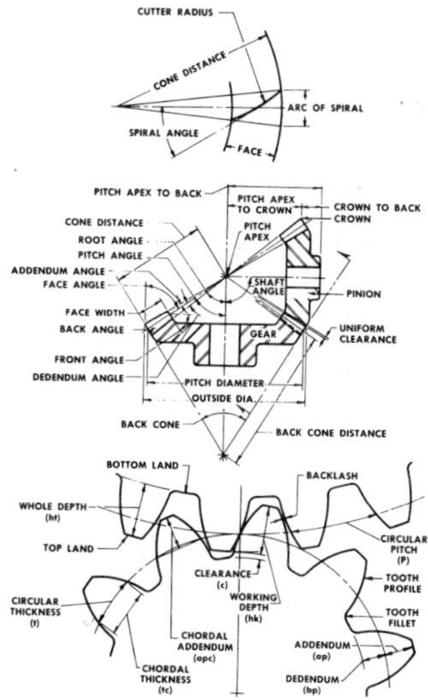

Fig. 19–154. Terminology of bevel gearing. (Courtesy of Philadelphia Gear Corporation.)

and outside diameter of the gear teeth.

Note that a table of values is given to describe the gear. These values can be computed using the formulas given in Article 19–71. Other information must be taken from standard gear tables. Some industries require much more information in gear specifications. Individual teeth should not be drawn unless required for a special application.

19–74 DRAWING BEVEL GEARS

Bevel gears are gears with axes that intersect at angles. This angle is usually 90°, but other angles are sometimes used. The smaller of the two bevel gears is called the pinion.

The terminology of bevel gearing is shown in Fig. 19–154. Many of these terms are common to all types of gears.

The method of constructing two bevel gears whose axes intersect at 90° is illustrated in Fig. 19–155.

Step 1. The pitch diameters of the two gears are measured along two perpendicular intersecting lines. Intersecting centerlines are then drawn with their construction lines to represent the axes of the two gears. Points are connected to form two adjacent isosceles triangles having the pitch diameters as their bases.

Step 2. Perpendiculars to the sides of the two triangles are drawn through the corner points. The addendum and dedendum are located on these lines on either side of each of the corner points. Radial lines are drawn from these addendum and dedendum points to the point of intersection of the axes of two gears.

Step 3. The gears are drawn to standard dimensions taken from bevel-gear tables.

Step 4. Each gear is drawn separately in a working drawing and dimensioned. A table of specifications is also given. The circular views may be omitted since the sectional views are sufficient to explain the details of each gear.

19–75 WORM GEARS

A worm gear is illustrated in Fig. 19–156. The threaded shaft is called the *worm* and the circular gear is sometimes called the *spider.* The worm is revolved in a continuous motion which causes the spider to revolve about its axis.

Typical drawings of worms and gears are shown in Fig. 19–157 with tables of values for various sizes. Letters are used to specify certain dimensions that must be taken from the tables.

19–76 THE WORKING DRAWING

The working drawing is the document from which the design is implemented. Supplemental information and written specifications may be prepared separately or included on the working drawing. In almost all cases, the engineer must direct the preparation of working drawings and specify the critical dimensions and tolerances. Much of the work is routine and can be prepared by draftsmen with the minimum of supervision. The final drawings will be closely reviewed by his staff, but the engineer is responsible for their correctness.

FIGURE 19–155. CONSTRUCTION OF BEVEL GEARS

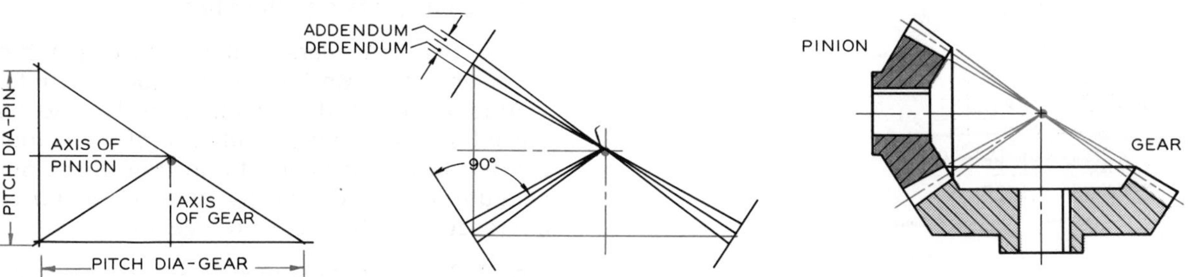

Step 1: Lay out the pitch diameters and axes of the two bevel gears.

Step 2: Draw construction lines to establish the limits of the teeth by using the addendum and dedendum as shown.

Step 3: Draw the pinion and the gear using specified dimensions or dimensions taken from gear tables.

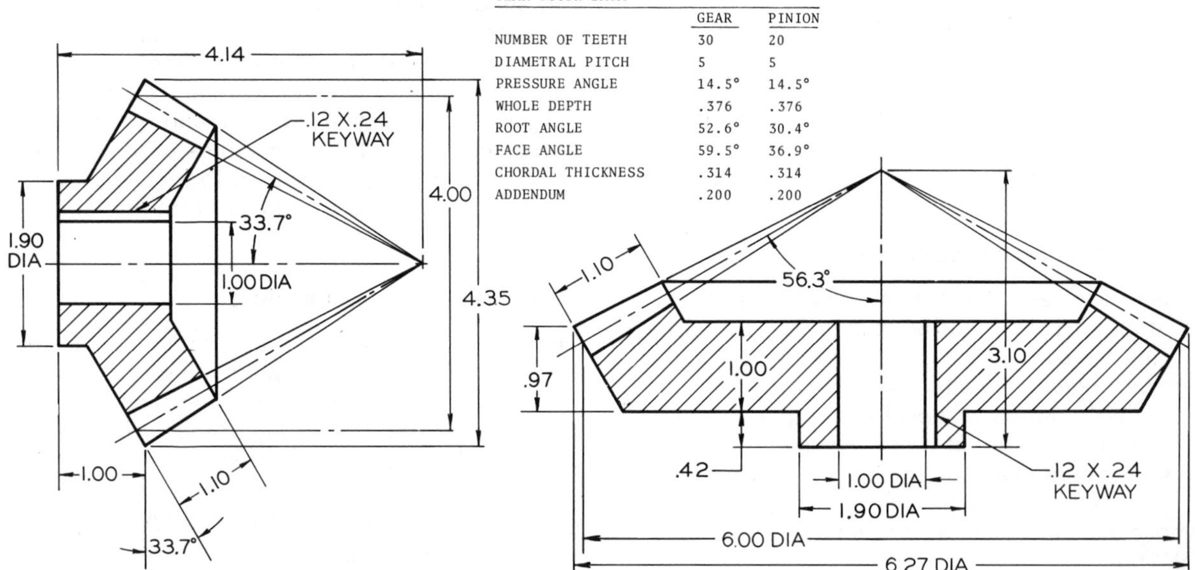

GEAR TOOTH DATA

	GEAR	PINION
NUMBER OF TEETH	30	20
DIAMETRAL PITCH	5	5
PRESSURE ANGLE	14.5°	14.5°
WHOLE DEPTH	.376	.376
ROOT ANGLE	52.6°	30.4°
FACE ANGLE	59.5°	36.9°
CHORDAL THICKNESS	.314	.314
ADDENDUM	.200	.200

Step 4: Complete the detail drawings of both gears. The table of gear tooth data applies to both the pinion and the gear.

Fig. 19–156. A worm gear. (Courtesy of Ex-Cell-O Corporation.)

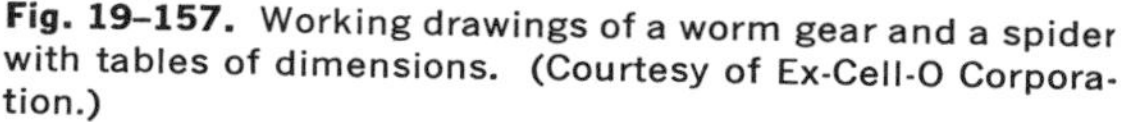

Fig. 19–157. Working drawings of a worm gear and a spider with tables of dimensions. (Courtesy of Ex-Cell-O Corporation.)

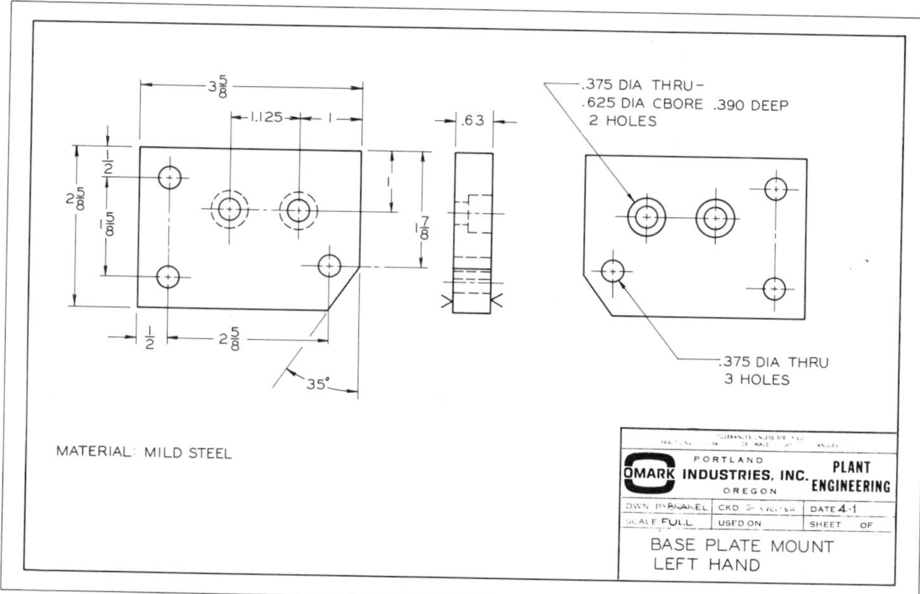

Fig. 19–158. A working drawing of a simple part. (Courtesy of Omark Industries, Inc.)

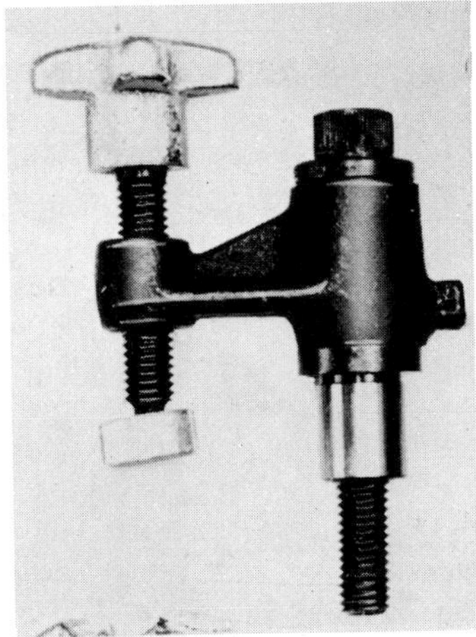

Fig. 19–159. A revolving clamp assembly manufactured to hold parts stationary while they are being machined. (Courtesy of Jergens, Inc.)

A working drawing is often called a *detail drawing* because it describes the features and dimensions of the details of the various parts of a design. All the techniques and principles of graphics must be used in the working drawing because its purpose is to describe the parts of a design with as much clarity as possible.

A detail drawing of a base plate mount is shown in Fig. 19–158. Three orthographic

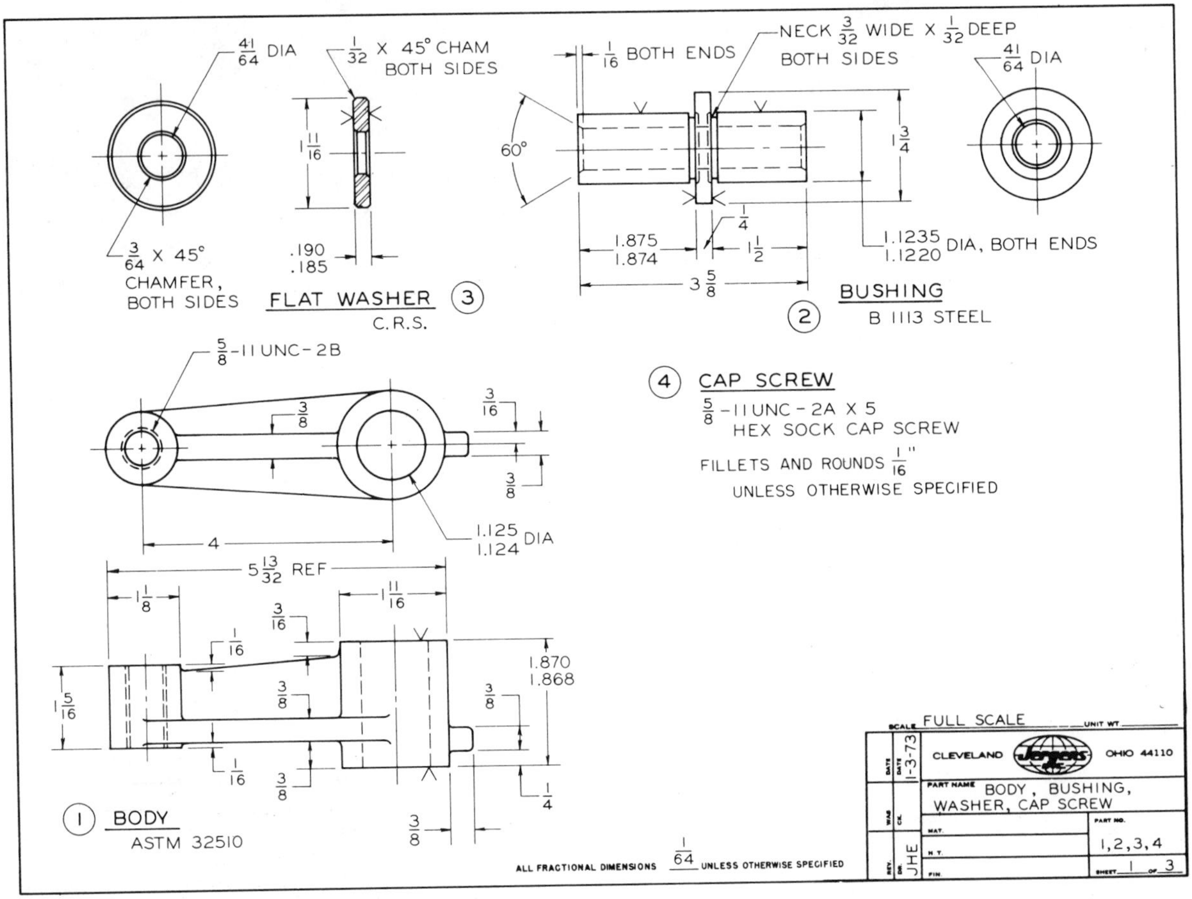

$\frac{41}{64}$ DIA

$\frac{1}{32}$ X 45° CHAM BOTH SIDES

$1\frac{11}{16}$

$\frac{3}{64}$ X 45° CHAMFER, BOTH SIDES

.190
.185

FLAT WASHER (3)
C.R.S.

$\frac{1}{16}$ BOTH ENDS

NECK $\frac{3}{32}$ WIDE X $\frac{1}{32}$ DEEP BOTH SIDES

$\frac{41}{64}$ DIA

60°

$1\frac{3}{4}$

$\frac{1}{4}$

1.875
1.874

$1\frac{1}{2}$

$3\frac{5}{8}$

1.1235
1.1220 DIA, BOTH ENDS

(2) BUSHING
B 1113 STEEL

$\frac{5}{8}$-11 UNC-2B

$\frac{3}{8}$ $\frac{3}{16}$ $\frac{3}{8}$

4

1.125
1.124 DIA

(4) CAP SCREW
$\frac{5}{8}$-11 UNC-2A X 5
HEX SOCK CAP SCREW

FILLETS AND ROUNDS $\frac{1}{16}$"
UNLESS OTHERWISE SPECIFIED

$5\frac{13}{32}$ REF

$1\frac{1}{8}$ $1\frac{11}{16}$ $\frac{3}{16}$ $\frac{1}{16}$

$1\frac{5}{16}$

$\frac{3}{8}$ $\frac{1}{16}$ $\frac{3}{8}$

1.870
1.868

$\frac{3}{8}$ $\frac{1}{4}$ $\frac{3}{8}$

(1) BODY
ASTM 32510

ALL FRACTIONAL DIMENSIONS $\frac{1}{64}$ UNLESS OTHERWISE SPECIFIED

SCALE FULL SCALE UNIT WT

DATE 1-3-73 CLEVELAND Jergens Inc. OHIO 44110

PART NAME BODY, BUSHING, WASHER, CAP SCREW

MAT. H.T. FIN. PART NO. 1,2,3,4

DR. JHE SHEET 1 OF 3

Fig. 19–160. A detail drawing showing parts of the clamp assembly. Abbreviations: C.R.S.—cold rolled steel, ASTM 32510 and B 1113—types of steel. (Courtesy of Jergens, Inc.)

views describe the part, and dimensions are added to give its measurements. Notes specify the material and the sizes of the holes. If you built this part in the shop, the end product would be the same as the part made by anyone else using the same drawing.

A revolving clamp assembly (Fig. 19-159) is manufactured to clamp parts in a stationary position while they are machined. The detail drawings of the parts of the assembly are given in Figs. 19-160 through 19-162. Note that several parts can be drawn on a single sheet. Each part is drawn with the necessary orthographic views and notes to explain it fully. The name of the part, the identifying number, and the material are given near the views. No attempt is made to align the parts with one another to indicate their order of assembly. Instead, the parts are located to make the best use of the available space.

Each sheet is numbered in the title block with respect to the total number of sheets in the set of drawings. For example, Fig. 19-160 is numbered as sheet 1 of 3 sheets.

An orthographic *assembly drawing* is given in Fig. 19-162 to show how the parts fit together. The identifying number of each part is attached to the assembly with a leader. These numbers can be cross-checked with the details of each part for specific information.

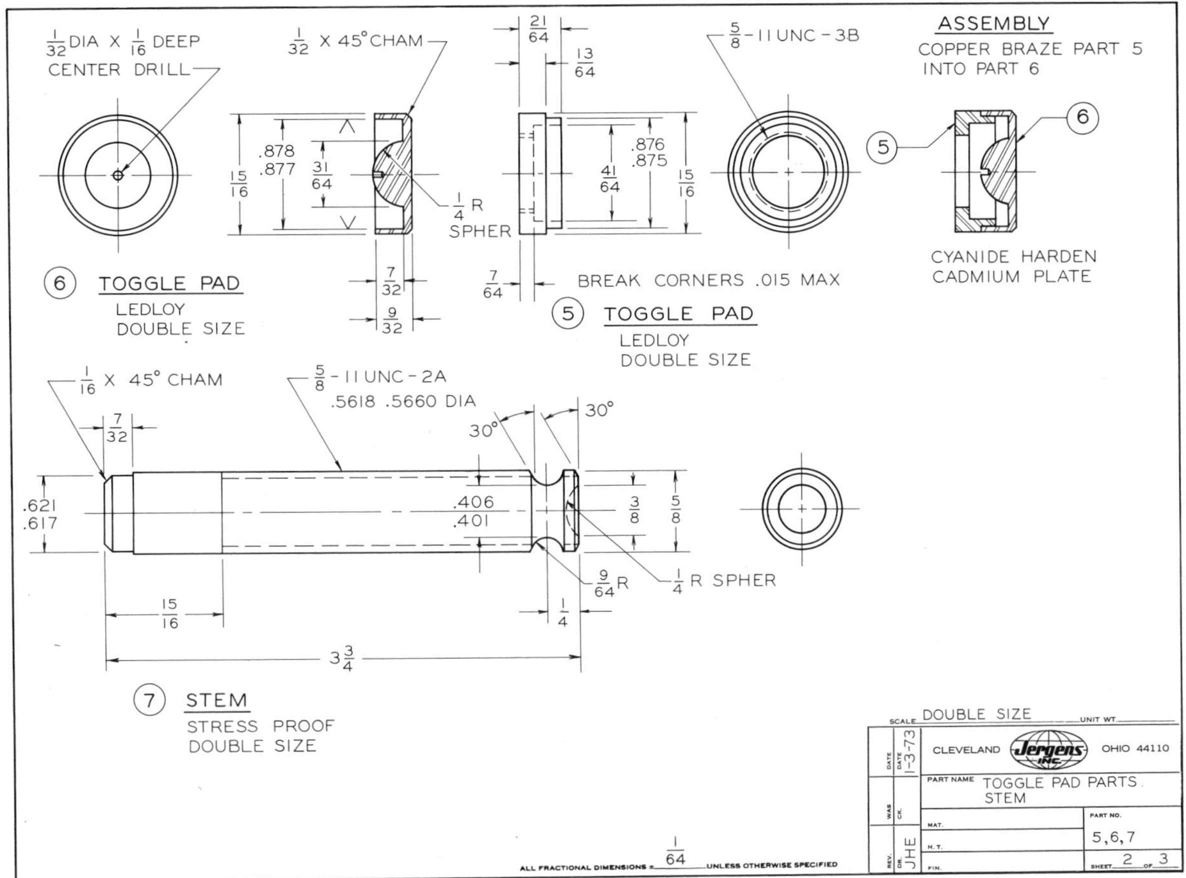

Fig. 19-161. A detail drawing showing parts of the clamp assembly. (Courtesy of Jergens, Inc.)

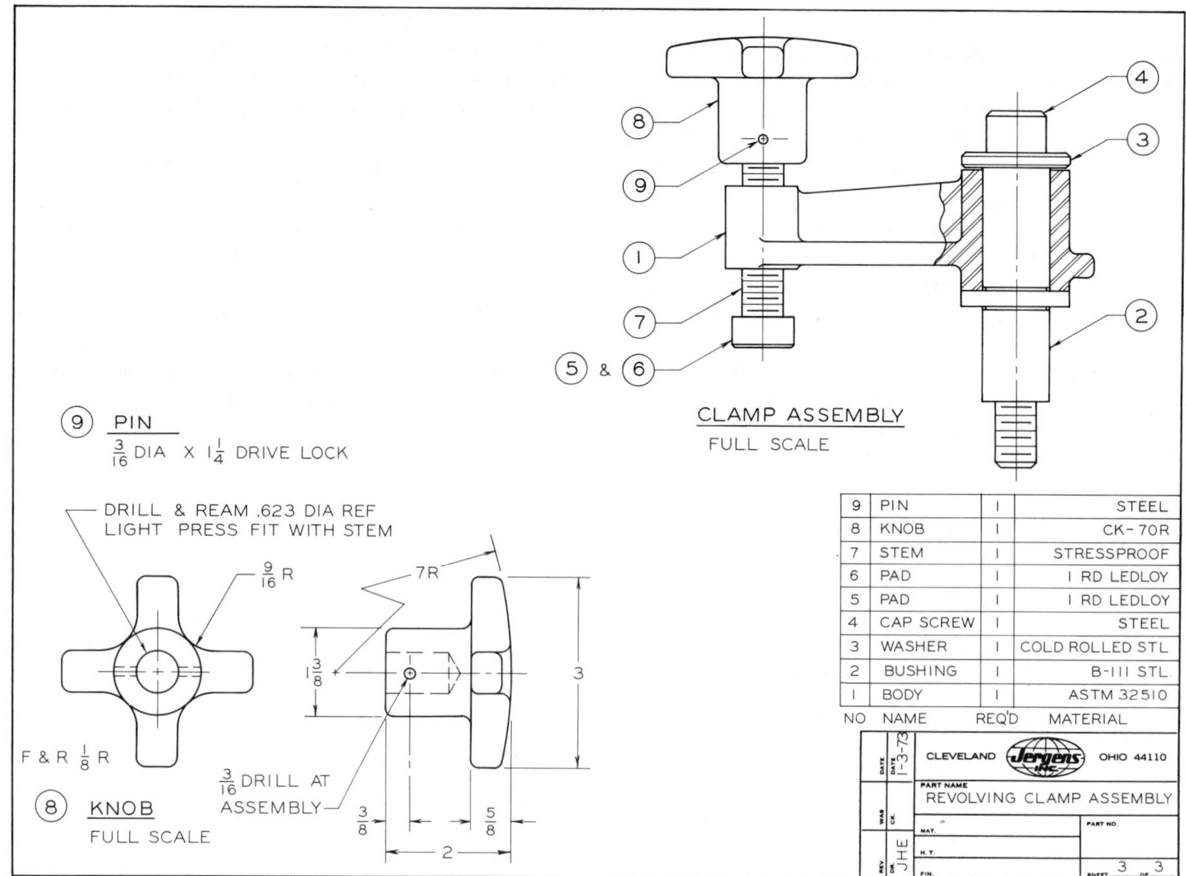

Fig. 19-162. A detail drawing and an orthographic assembly of the clamp assembly. (Courtesy of Jergens, Inc.)

19-77 TYPES OF DETAIL DRAWINGS

Some companies prepare working drawings with only one part to a sheet regardless of how small the part may be. This procedure makes it possible to assign various parts to the shop without using bulky drawings that contain more parts and information than some of the workmen need. In addition, more copies may be needed of the drawings of some parts than of others, and it is more convenient to obtain the required numbers of copies if there is only one part per sheet. Figure 19-158 is an example of this sort.

Tabulated drawings are used to dimension parts that are similar except for variations in dimensions. The part in Fig. 19-163 is a drawing of this type. The part is drawn and referenced with letters that correspond to a table of dimensions placed on the drawing. The sizes can be selected from the table to correspond to the letters on the drawing. This procedure makes it possible for one drawing to serve several parts.

The two parts shown in Fig. 19-164 illustrate the difference between a forged part and a

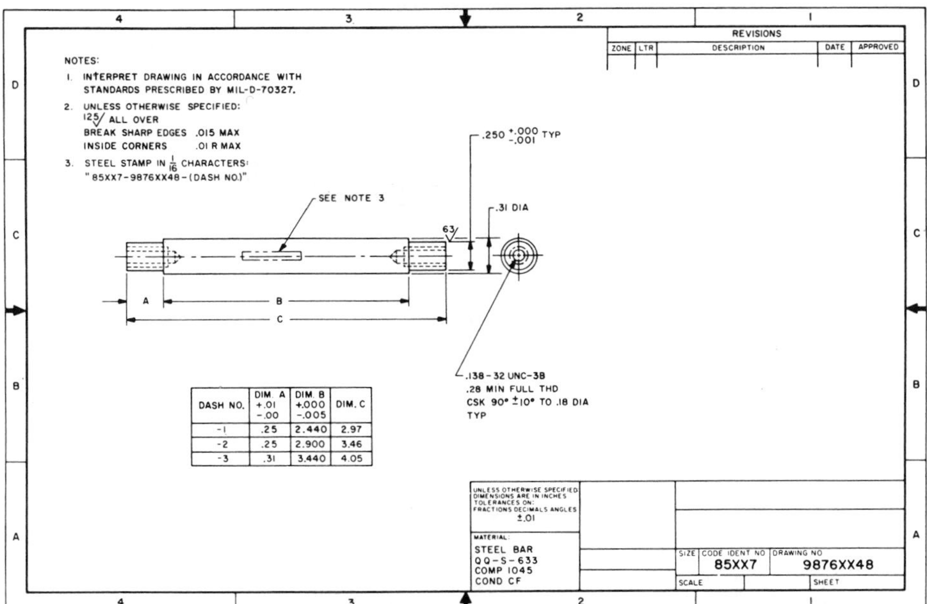

DASH NO.	DIM A +.01 -.00	DIM B +.000 -.005	DIM. C
-1	.25	2.440	2.97
-2	.25	2.900	3.46
-3	.31	3.440	4.05

Fig. 19–163. A tabulated drawing with a table of values for parts that vary in size. (Courtesy of Department of Defense.)

machined part. The unfinished forging at the top was produced by a die casting process in which force is applied to form a piece of material in a mold. The forged piece is then machined to its finished form as shown in the lower portion of the figure.

The drawings that give the dimensions and details for making the forging are called *forging drawings*. The drawing that specifies the machining operations is called a *machining drawing*. These drawings are often combined into one drawing, with the understanding that the forgings must be made with additional material in order to allow for the removal of excess by machining to meet the final design specifications.

The machining drawing in Fig. 19–165 uses orthographic views and sections to describe the features of a body-wheel cylinder. Notes

Fig. 19–164. An unfinished forging and the same part after machining. A drawing is needed to give the specifications of the forging and the details of the machining operations required to complete the part. (Courtesy of Lycoming Division of Avco.)

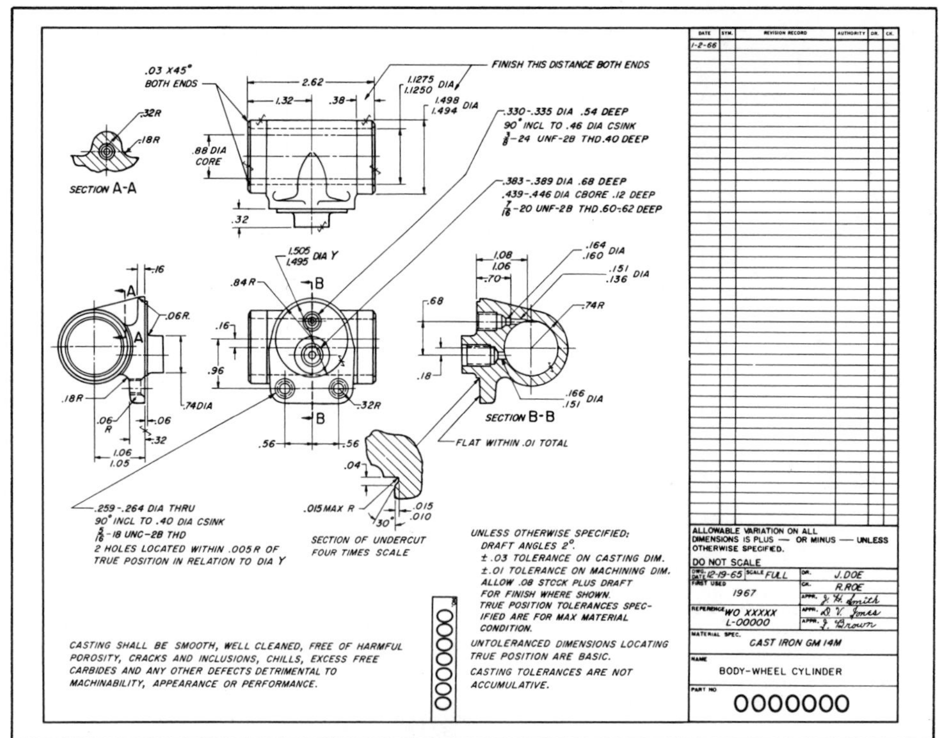

Fig. 19–165. A machining drawing of a body-wheel cylinder. (Courtesy of General Motors.)

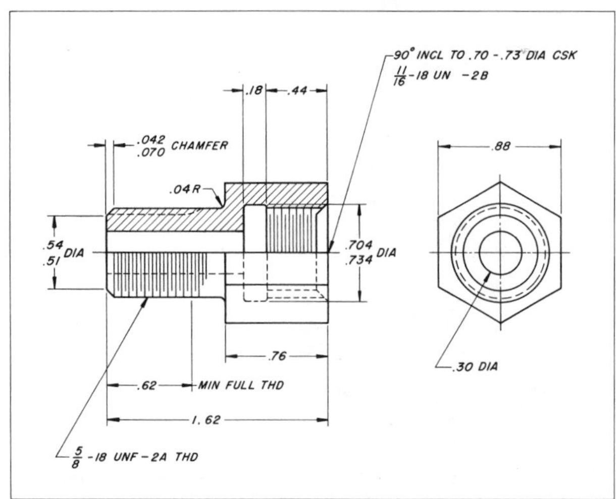

Fig. 19–166. A detail drawing that indicates machining specifications. (Courtesy of General Motors.)

and finish marks are used with tolerance dimensions to give the final measurements of the part. The detail drawing in Fig. 19–166 gives the specifications for a threaded component.

19–78 LAYOUT OF A WORKING DRAWING

The standard sizes of working drawings are shown in Fig. 19–167. The diagram shown here indicates the layout of the sheet and the position of the borders for each size. Tracing paper or film is used for the preparation of working drawings because it permits the draftsman to trace rough pencil layouts by placing transparent tracing paper over the layout. In addition, tracing paper (or film) must be used in order to make diazo (blue-line) prints.

FLAT SIZES				ROLL SIZES				
SIZE DES LTR	X WIDTH	Y LENGTH	Z MARGIN	SIZE DES LTR	X WIDTH	Y MIN LENGTH	Y MAX LENGTH	Z MARGIN
A(HORIZ)	8.50	11	.25&.38*	G	11	42	144	.38
A(VERT)	11	8.50	.25&.38*	H	28	48	144	.50
B	11	17	.38	J	34	48	144	.50
C	17	22	.50	K	40	48	144	.50
D	22	34	.50					
E	34	44	.50					
F	28	40	.50					

*HORIZONTAL MARGINS .38-INCH; VERTICAL MARGIN .25-INCH

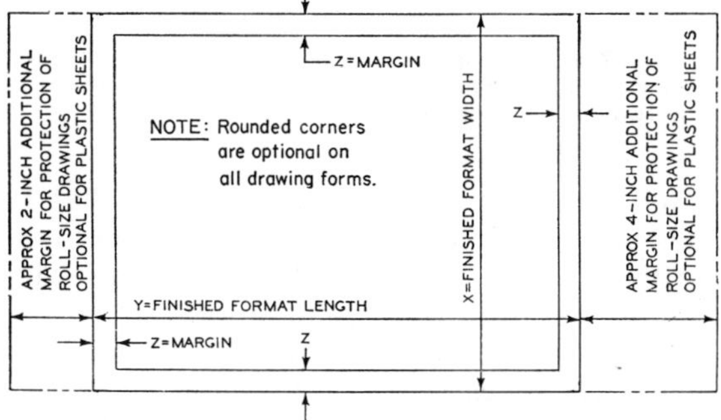

Fig. 19–167. Standard sizes of working drawings. (Courtesy of Department of Defense.)

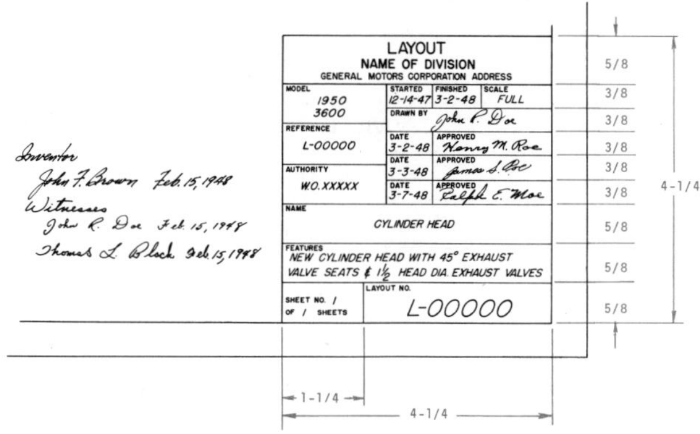

Fig. 19–168. A typical title block used on working drawings in industry. (Courtesy of General Motors.)

5 APPROX.

3	SIDE BRACE	2	C.I.
2	SHAFT	2	STEEL
1	BASE	1	C.I.
NO	PART NAME	REQ'D	MATERIAL

$\frac{1}{4}$ $\frac{1}{4}$ — $\frac{1}{8}$ LETTERS

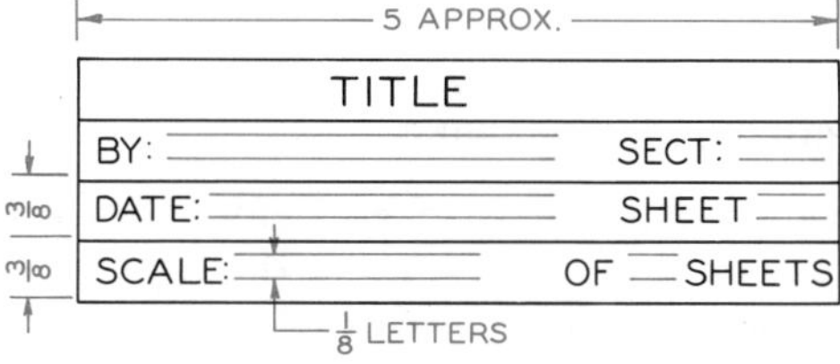

Fig. 19–169. A title strip and parts list satisfactory for most student assignments.

Most drafting offices have title blocks and borders printed on the drawing sheets. This reduces the amount of valuable drafting time that has to be spent on this part of a drawing.

The title block can take many forms. All companies use title blocks. These usually contain the same information, but differ in layout. A title block used by the General Motors Corporation is shown in Fig. 19–168. All title blocks include the name of the draftsman, the scale, the sheet number, and the name of the company. Many companies give a layout number to each drawing sheet; this number may also be the number of the part drawn.

When a design that is presented on a working drawing is unique enough to be considered for a patent as a new invention, additional information should be given near the title block. The inventor should sign and date his work and have it witnessed by at least two people to establish ownership of the ideas (Fig. 19–168). Even though the idea must be patented in the name of the inventor, the rights to the design may, by previous agreement, be the property of the company for which he works.

Student drawings prepared as class assignments are usually simpler than those prepared by large industrial concerns. An example of a title block and a parts list is shown in Fig. 19–169. The title block should be placed against the border in the lower right corner of the

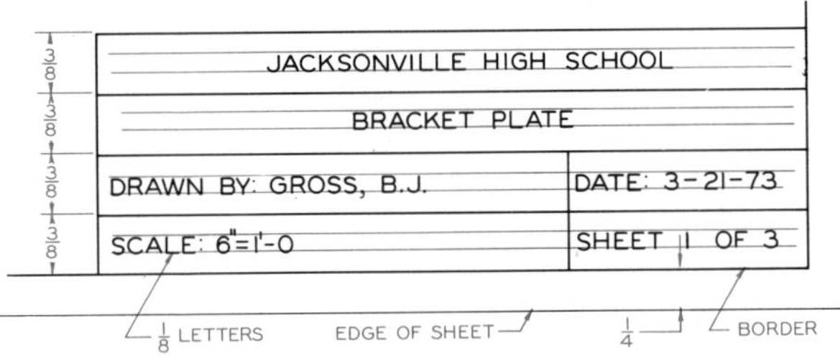

Fig. 19-170. A title block layout for class assignments.

Fig. 19-171. An engineering department is required to check working drawings before they are released for production. (Courtesy of The Austin Company.)

drawing. The parts list should be above the title block, in contact with it.

An alternative title block that can be used for class assignments is shown in Fig. 19-170. The spacing between the lines should not be changed, but the width of the block can vary to provide adequate space for all titles and names. Each title block on a set of drawings should be the same size. Each sheet should also be the same size so that the set can be bound with staples and the pages will turn like those of a book for easy reference.

19-79 CHECKING A DRAWING

All drawings must be checked before they are released for production, since a slight mistake could prove very expensive when many parts are made. The people who check drawings have special qualifications that enable them to suggest revisions and modifications that will result in a better product at less cost (Fig. 19-171). The checker may be a chief draftsman who is experienced in this type of work, or the engineer or designer who originated the project. In larger companies the drawings are reviewed by the various shops involved to determine whether the most efficient methods of production are specified for each particular part.

The checker never checks an original drawing, but instead he checks a diazo print (a blueline print). He marks the print with a colored pencil, making notes and corrections that he feels are desirable. The print is returned to the draftsman for revision of the original drawing and another print is made for approval.

In Fig. 19-172 a detail drawing of a special bushing is shown. In this drawing the various modifications made by checkers are labeled with letters which are circled and placed near the revisions. The changes are listed and dated in the revision record by the draftsman. Note that the change numbers are placed in a row along the lower border approximately below the revisions. This procedure serves as a check on the various revisions to prevent one from being overlooked.

Note that several draftsmen and checkers were involved in the approval and preparation of the drawing. Tolerances and general information are printed in the title block to ensure uniformity in the production of similar parts.

The checker is responsible for the soundness of the design and its functional characteristics. He is also responsible for the completeness of the drawing, the quality of the drawing, its readability, lettering, drafting techniques, and clarity. A poorly drawn view must be redrawn to meet company requirements so that it will reproduce well and be clearly understood by those using it. Quality of lettering is very important. Since working drawings should not be scaled, the craftsmen in the shop must rely on lettered notes and dimensions for their information. The best method for the student

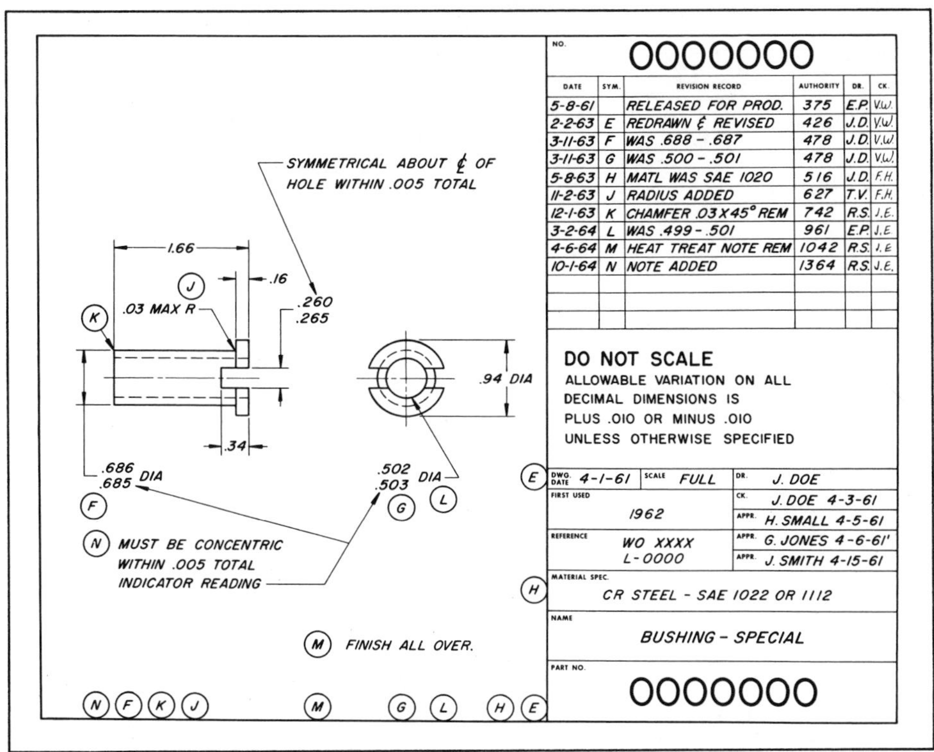

Fig. 19-172. A detail drawing showing various revisions that were made and listed in the table. (Courtesy of General Motors.)

to check his drawing is to make a scale drawing of the part from his working drawings when they are complete. It is often easier for someone to find another's mistakes than his own. It is good exercise to exchange drawings with a classmate and check each other's drawing.

19-80 DRAFTSMAN'S LOG

The draftsman will find that many changes and revisions must be made before a final drawing is approved. He should keep a record called a *log* to show all changes and modifications and decisions that were made during the project. Changes, dates, and the people involved should be recorded for reference as the project progresses, and as a review of the finished project.

An example of a draftsman's log is shown in Fig. 19-173. The description of the project and its objectives are given first. Each change and the reason for it are tabulated under "Progress, Decisions and Authority." The people responsible for the changes are mentioned by name.

These notes serve to refresh the memory of anyone who wishes to review the project. Calculations are often made during the process of preparing a drawing. If they are lost or if they are poorly done, it may be necessary to make them again. Consequently, they should be made a permanent part of the log and attached to the log. This will reduce lost time and repetition of effort. All notes should be complete enough to be understood by anyone who may read the log.

DRAFTSMAN'S DESIGN LOG

Sheet No. 1 of 1 Sheet

Detailed Description: Layout and details of new transmission low speed gear and mainshaft combination. Low speed gear to have I.D. of splines accurately ground with respect to gear teeth, and mainshaft to have three ground lands for mounting low speed gear on these surfaces.	Job no. 9344-97 Job name Trans. Mainshaft First and Reverse Gear Models 1950 Engineer Poe Job started 3-25-48 Job finished 4-7-48 Layout numbers L-36042

Job Objective: To eliminate selective fit on mating parts.

References: L-33827

Progress, Decisions and Authority:

3-30-48 - Messrs. Roe and Poe decided to change from a 22 tooth basic spline with 3 unevenly spaced lands to both a 24 tooth basic spline with 6 evenly spaced lands and a 24 tooth basic spline with 8 evenly spaced lands.

Engineers also requested study of a longer hub for 1st reverse gear to reduce runout.

4-6-48 After preliminary investigation Messrs. Roe and Poe decided to cancel the 8 lands construction and the elongated hub.

4-7-48 Mr. Poe decided to have an additional layout made of a 22 tooth basic spline with alternating teeth and lands.

Calculations and sketches to be dated and attached.

R. Doe
Signature

Fig. 19–173. A draftsman's log should be kept as a record of the project to explain the actions taken that might otherwise be forgotten. (Courtesy of General Motors.)

Fig. 19–174. An assembly drawing is used to explain how the parts of a product such as this Ford tractor are assembled. (Courtesy of Ford Motor Company.)

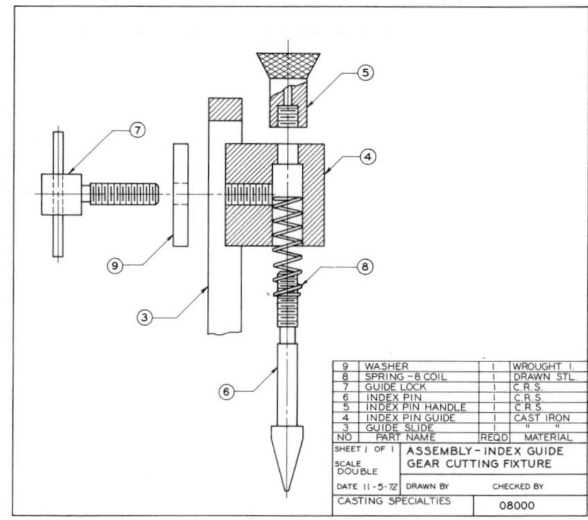

5
7
4
9
8
3
6
9 WASHER 1 WROUGHT I.
8 SPRING - 8 COIL 1 DRAWN STL.
7 GUIDE LOCK 1 C.R.S.
6 INDEX PIN 1 C.R.S.
5 INDEX PIN HANDLE 1 C.R.S.
4 INDEX PIN GUIDE 1 CAST IRON
3 GUIDE SLIDE 1 " "
NO PART NAME REQD MATERIAL
SHEET 1 OF 1
SCALE DOUBLE
DATE 11-5-72
ASSEMBLY - INDEX GUIDE
GEAR CUTTING FIXTURE
DRAWN BY
CHECKED BY
CASTING SPECIALTIES
08000

Fig. 19–175. A partially exploded orthographic assembly drawing of an index guide of a cutting tool.

19–81 ASSEMBLY DRAWINGS

Most designs are composed of a number of parts that fit together in a particular manner to perform the desired function. Most parts are made independently and perhaps in separate geographical locations by different people. When the parts are completed and ready for assembly, a drawing is needed to explain how they should be put together. For example, the parts of the tractor engine and transmission shown in Fig. 19–174 fit together in the order specified by an assembly drawing.

An assembly drawing can be either an orthographic or a pictorial drawing. In addition, it may show the parts actually assembled or it may show them in an exploded assembly, whichever gives the greater clarity.

A subassembly of an index guide for a gear cutting fixture is shown in Fig. 19–175. Several of the parts are exploded for clarity, and the index pin and spring are partially exploded. Only the part numbers are given to identify each of the parts, since the parts have been fully dimensioned and described in the working drawings. A parts list is provided as a cross

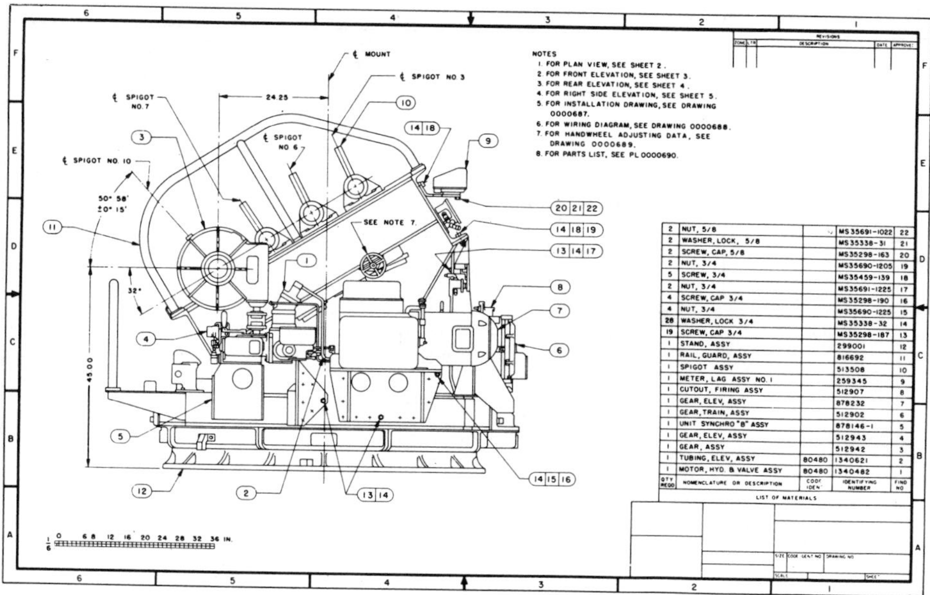

Fig. 19-176. An outline assembly drawing showing the general relationships of the parts of an assembly. (Courtesy of Department of Defense.)

reference for listing the parts of the assembly. Sections are used to clarify details of the assembly. Another assembly of this type can be seen in Fig. 19-162.

Assembly drawings make it possible for the shop to assemble the parts in the desired arrangement. Dimensions are unnecessary on an assembly drawing of this type.

An *outline assembly* is shown in Fig. 19-176. This represents the assembly of various components, several of which have their own assembly of parts. Only a few essential dimensions are given to locate important components in relation to others. Each component of the assembly is listed by number in the list of materials. The materials list also gives the identifying number of each part required to complete the assembly.

A more detailed assembly drawing is shown in Fig. 19-177. This drawing describes how a vertical instrument panel will be supported. In addition to showing the method of assembly, this drawing gives the complete dimensions of the support.

19-82 PICTORIAL ASSEMBLIES

It is advantageous in many cases to illustrate assemblies pictorially to make them more easily understood. A typical example of a pictorial assembly is shown in Fig. 19-178. All the parts of the lathe assembly are exploded, and each component is positioned to make it clear how the parts fit together. The parts are numbered to correspond to a parts list (not shown).

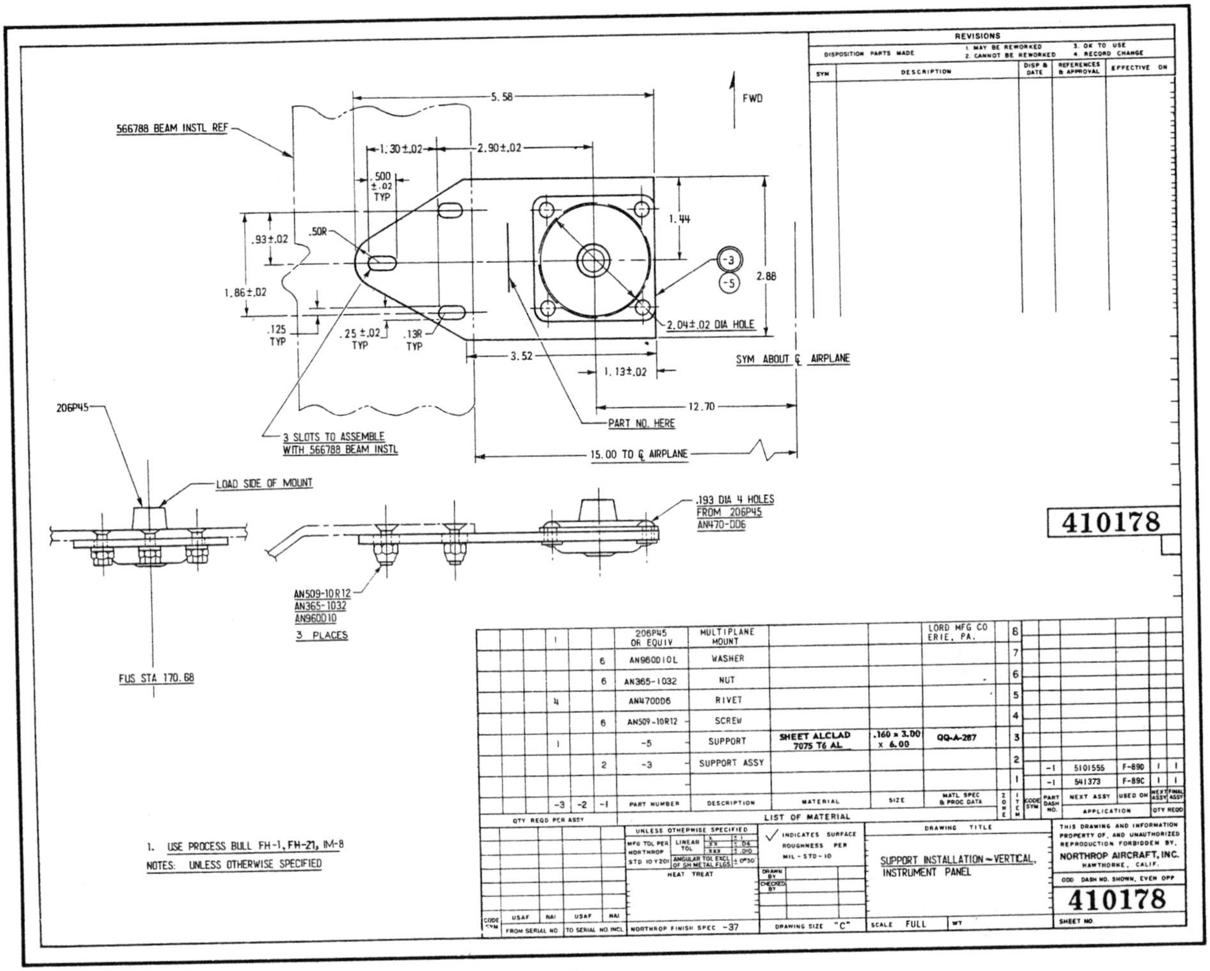

Fig. 19-177. An assembly-detail drawing. (Courtesy of Northrop Corporation.)

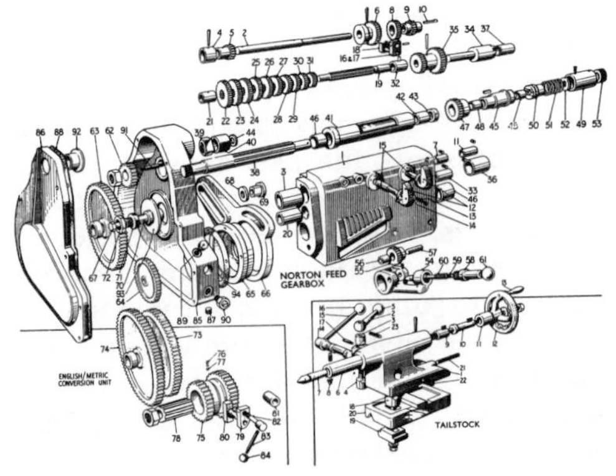

Fig. 19-178. A pictorial exploded assembly of the parts of the gearbox and tailstock of a lathe. (Courtesy of T. S. Harrison & Sons Limited.)

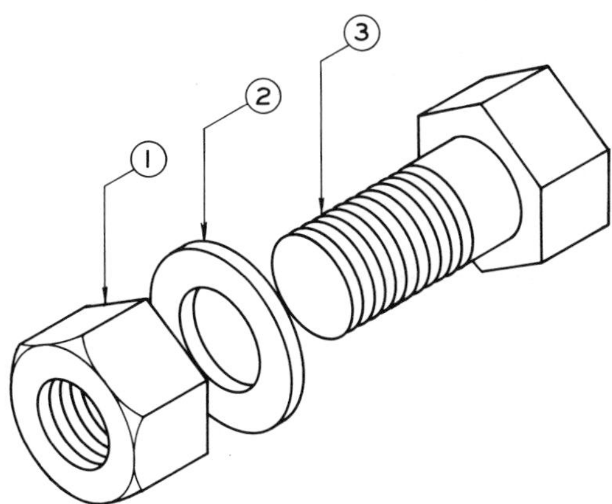

Fig. 19–179. An exploded isometric assembly of three parts.

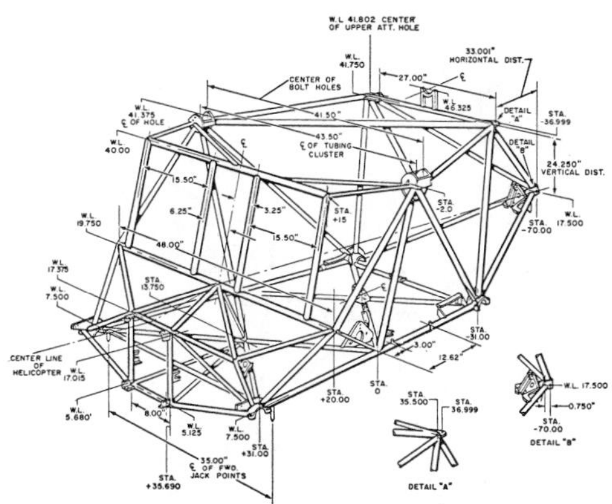

Fig. 19–180. A dimensioned pictorial assembly drawing of a helicopter frame. (Courtesy of Bell Helicopter Corporation.)

A simpler assembly is shown in Fig. 19–179. Use of pictorial principles makes these assemblies very easy to understand.

Since pictorials are more easily understood by the nontechnical person than are orthographic views, many drawings are dimensioned in their pictorial views for greater clarity. Such an example is the frame of a helicopter in Fig. 19–180. This illustration shows the details and dimensions of the assembly more clearly than would any other type of drawing.

19–83 LAYOUT DRAWINGS

A *layout drawing* is a preliminary drawing which shows a part or several parts and their relationship to one another. A layout may be one of the first steps of developing a new design. It can be useful in determining how several parts should be assembled and what their clearances should be. It is also useful in the study of the geometric relationships between moving parts.

The layout drawing in Fig. 19–181 was used to analyze the clearance between the connecting rod path and the crankcase walls and the camshaft. The clearance between the connecting rod path and the crankcase walls must necessarily be greater, since the connecting rod forging and the rough crankcase walls are involved. Allowances must be given on both sides for the connecting rod as shown at the left.

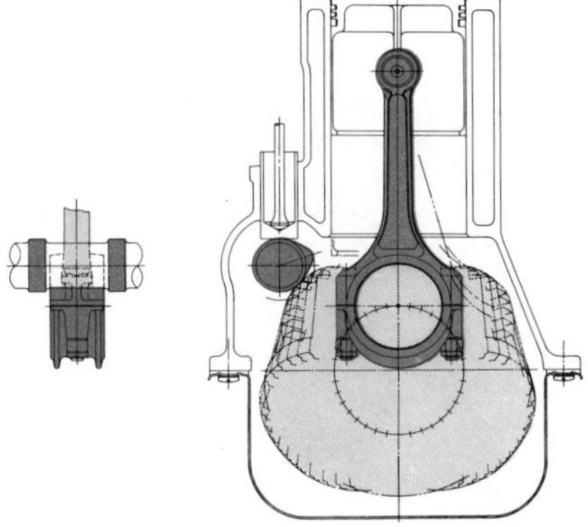

Fig. 19–181. A layout drawing is used to analyze the clearances between the connecting rod and crankcase walls. (Courtesy of General Motors.)

19–84 PIPING LAYOUTS

A piping drawing gives the layout of a piping system, specifying the lengths of pipe and the standard components of the system. A piping layout may be represented in an orthographic

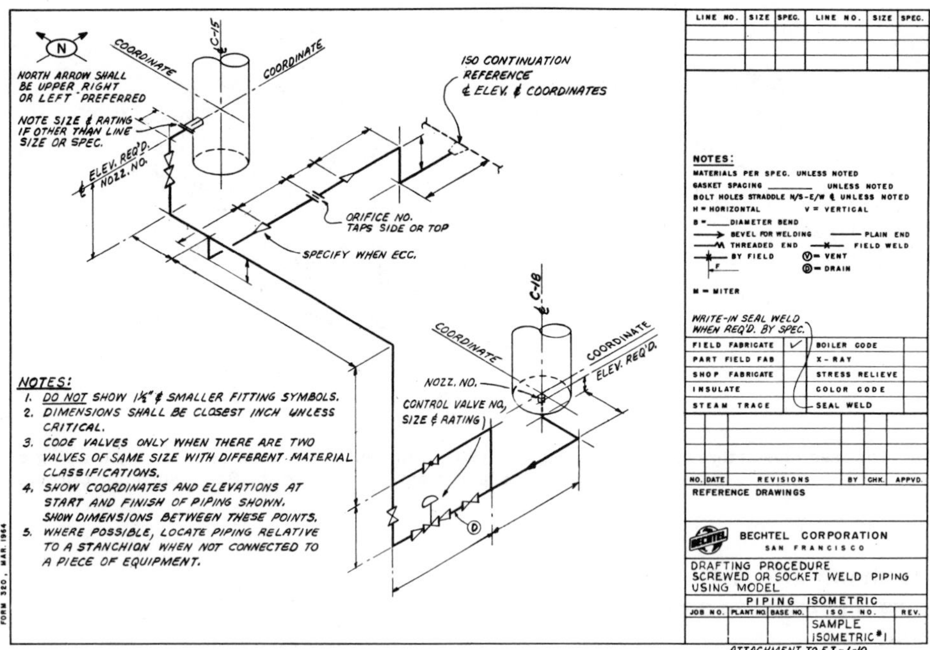

Fig. 19–182. A piping layout using single-line symbols. (Courtesy of Bechtel Corporation.)

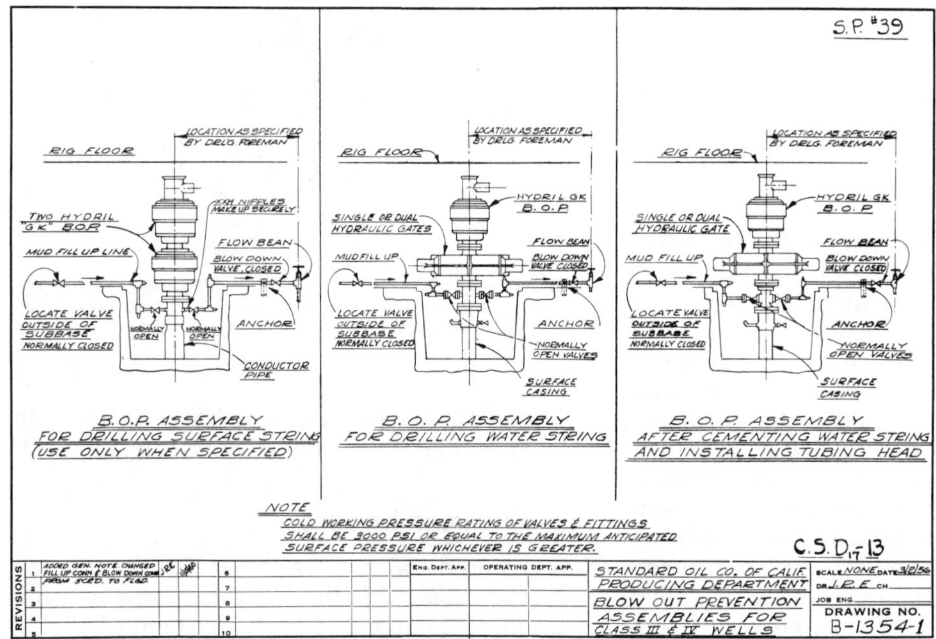

Fig. 19–183. A double-line piping drawing. (Courtesy of Standard Oil Corporation of California.)

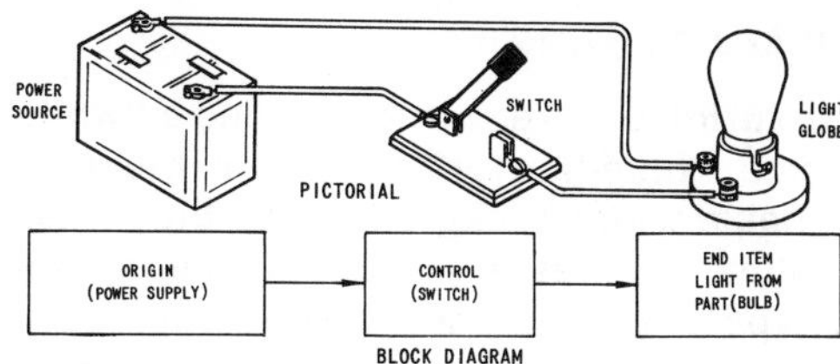

Fig. 19-184. A block diagram of an electrical circuit compared with a pictorial drawing of the circuit. (Courtesy of Boeing Company.)

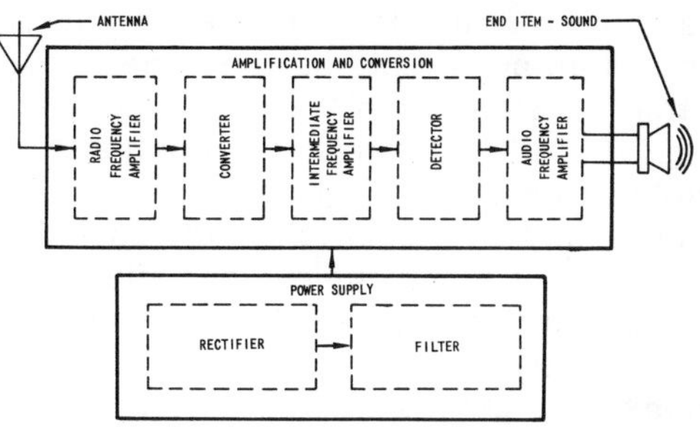

Fig. 19-185. A block diagram combines parts of an electronic system into functional blocks. (Courtesy of Boeing Company.)

drawing or in a pictorial. The example in Fig. 19-182 is a *single-line* isometric drawing. Single lines and symbols are used to represent the pipe. These symbols are explained in Appendix 8 both as single-line and double-line symbols.

A *double-line* drawing uses two lines to represent the pipe; it is thus more realistic than a single-line drawing. Both are equally effective in practice; however, the single-line drawing has the advantage of being easier to prepare. An example of a double-line drawing is shown in Fig. 19-183.

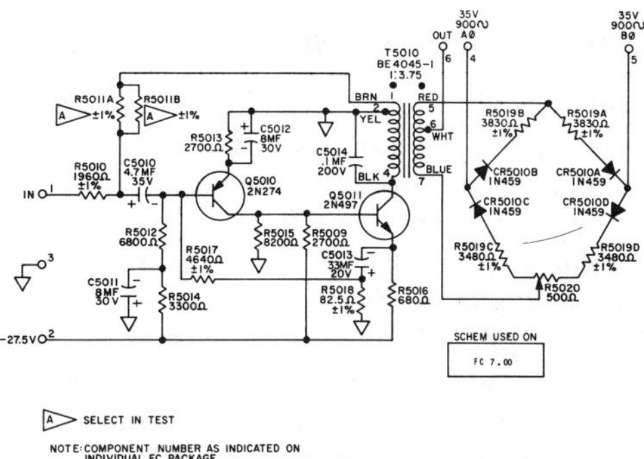

Fig. 19-186. A schematic diagram of an electronic circuit. (Courtesy of Boeing Company.)

19-85 ELECTRONIC DRAWINGS

Electrical and electronic drawings are more closely related to schematics than to actual dimensioned working drawings as discussed in this chapter. Components can be represented in a block diagram instead of being drawn pictorially, as shown in Fig. 19-184. A simple block diagram is composed of blocks that are labeled and connected in sequence; the end block represents the desired function of the system.

Block diagrams can be used to combine parts of an electrical or electronic system into functional units beginning with the power supply, the input, and ending with the output function (Fig. 19-185); the output of a radio, for example, would be sound. Block diagrams cannot be used for assembling electronic circuits. For this a *schematic drawing* is required.

Figure 19-186 is a schematic diagram showing the various parts of a circuit. Each symbol is drawn and a note is supplied to specify each

Fig. 19-187. An electronic schematic drawing is necessary to check out a faulty circuit. (Courtesy of U.S. Air Force.)

part that will be connected into the circuit. A schematic drawing is also used to check out an electronic system when there is a malfunction (Fig. 19-187). There is no relationship between the sizes of the symbols or the lengths of the lines and actual physical dimensions. The schematic drawing simply specifies the sequence in which the parts are connected to complete the circuit.

Templates and guides are available to assist the draftsman in preparing schematic drawings. The table in Appendix 7 gives the relative sizes of the symbols used in schematic drawings.

19-86 REPRODUCTION OF WORKING DRAWINGS

A drawing made by a draftsman is of little use in its original form. It would be impractical for the original to be handled by checkers and, even more so, by workmen in the field or in the shop. The drawing would quickly be damaged or soiled and no copy would be available as a permanent record of the job. Consequently, reproduction of drawings is necessary so that copies can be available for use by the various people concerned. A checker can mark corrections on a work copy without damaging the original drawing. The draftsman in turn can make the corrections on the original from the work copy.

Copies of the original drawing must be made for the people who will bid on a job or for the workman who will build according to the specifications of the drawing. Several methods of reproduction are used for making the copies that have traditionally been called "blueprints." This term comes from the original reproduction process which gives a blue background with white lines. The term blueprint is still used, although incorrectly, to describe almost all reproduced working drawings regardless of the process. However, you should become familiar with the various processes so that you can refer to them properly.

The processes discussed here are (1) diazo printing, (2) blueprinting, (3) microfilming, and (4) xerography. These are the most often used processes of reproducing engineering drawings.

19-87 DIAZO PRINTING

The diazo print is more correctly called a "whiteprint" or a "blue-line print" than a blueprint since it has a white background and blue lines. Other colors of lines are available depending on the type of paper used. The white background makes notes and corrections drawn on the drawing more clearly visible than does the blue background of the blueprint.

Both blueprinting and diazo printing require that the original drawing be made on semitransparent tracing paper, cloth, or film that will allow light to pass through the drawing. The paper on which the copy is made, the diazo paper, is chemically treated so that it has a yellow tint on one side. This paper must be stored away from heat and light to prevent spoilage.

The tracing-paper drawing is placed face up on the yellow side of the diazo paper and is run through the diazo-process machine, which exposes the drawing to a built-in light. The light passes through the tracing paper and burns out the yellow chemical on the paper except where the drawing lines have shielded the paper from the light. After exposure to light, the diazo paper is a duplicate of the original drawing except that the lines are light yellow and are not permanent. The diazo paper is then passed through the developing unit of the diazo machine where the yellow lines are developed into permanent blue lines by exposure to ammonia fumes. Diazo printing is a completely dry process.

A typical diazo printer-developer, sometimes called a whiteprinter, is shown in Fig. 19-188. This machine will take sheets up to 42″ wide.

The speed at which the drawing passes under the light determines the darkness of the copy. A slow speed burns out more of the yellow and produces a clear white background; however, some of the lighter lines of the drawing may be lost. Most diazo copies are made at a somewhat slower speed to give a light tint of blue in the background and stronger lines in the copy. Ink drawings give the best reproductions since the lines are uniform in quality.

It is important to remember that the quality

Fig. 19-188. The Bruning 450 whiteprinter for making diazo prints of drawings up to 42" wide. (Courtesy of Bruning Company.)

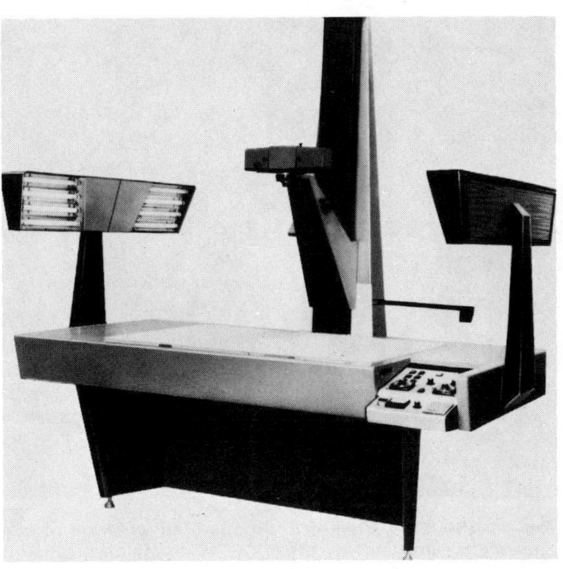

Fig. 19-189. The Micro-Master® 35mm camera and copy table for microfilming engineering drawings. (Courtesy of Keuffel & Esser Company.)

of the diazo print is determined by the quality of the original drawing. A print will not be clear and readable unless the lines of the drawing are dark and dense. Light will pass through gray lines and the result will be a fuzzy print that will not be satisfactory.

19-88 BLUEPRINTING

Blueprints are made with paper that is chemically treated on one side. As in the diazo process, the tracing-paper drawing is placed in contact with the chemically treated side of the paper and exposed to light. The exposed blueprint paper is washed in clear water for a few seconds and is coated with a solution of potassium dichromate. The print is washed again and dried. The wet sheets can be hung on a line to dry or dried by special equipment made for this purpose.

This process is still used but to a lesser degree than in the past. Being a wet process, more time is required for it than for the diazo process.

19-89 MICROFILMING

Microfilming is a photographic process that converts large drawings into film copies—either aperture cards or roll film. Drawings must be photographed on either 16 mm or 35 mm film. A camera and copy table are shown in Fig. 19-189.

The roll film or aperture cards can be placed in a microfilm enlarger-printer (Fig. 19-190) where the individual drawings can be viewed on a built-in screen. The selected drawings can then be printed from the film to give standard size drawings. The range of enlargement varies with the equipment used. Microfilm copies are usually smaller than the original drawings; this saves paper and makes the drawings more manageable and easier to use.

Microfilming makes it possible to eliminate large, bulky files of drawings, since hundreds of drawings can be stored in miniature size on a small amount of film. The aperture cards shown in Fig. 19-190 are data processing cards

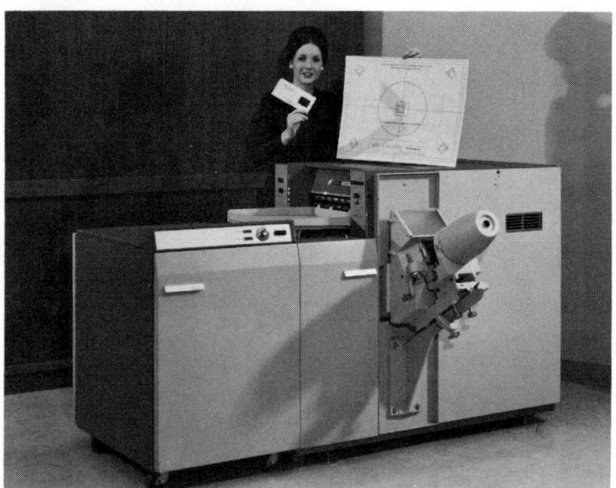

Fig. 19–190. The Bruning 1200 microfilm enlarger-printer that makes drawings up to 18″ × 24″ from aperture cards and roll film. (Courtesy of Bruning Company.)

Fig. 19–192. The Xerox 840 reduces drawings as large as 24″ × 36″ to sizes as small as 8″ × 10″. Forty prints per minute can be made by this machine, which uses the xerographic reproduction process. (Courtesy of Xerox Corporation.)

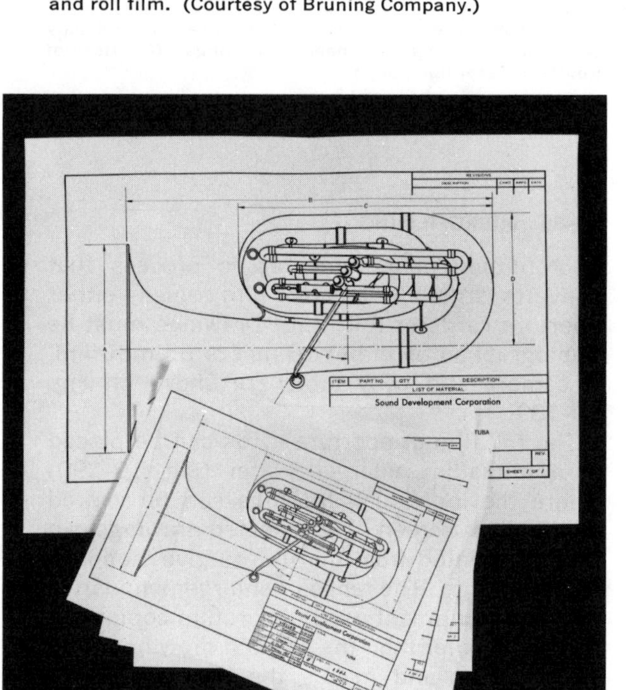

Fig. 19–191. Xerography is an electrostatic process of making dry copies on unsensitized paper. Copies can be reduced to more convenient sizes. (Courtesy of Xerox Corporation.)

that can be catalogued and recalled by a computer to make them accessible with a minimum of effort. The main advantage of microfilming is the saving in time and space.

19-90 XEROGRAPHIC REPRODUCTION

Xerography is an electrostatic process of duplicating drawings on ordinary, unsensitized paper. This process was developed originally for office duplication uses, but has recently been used for the reproduction of engineering drawings.

An advantage of the xerographic process is the possibility of making copies of drawings at a reduced size (Fig. 19–191). The new Xerox 840 reduces drawings as large as 24″ × 36″ directly from the original to paper sizes ranging from 8″ × 10″ to 14″ × 18″ (Fig. 19–192). This machine can make 40 copies per minute.

A sorter and folder can handle up to 50 sets of drawings and specifications automatically. Thirty sets of 15 drawings each (450 documents in all) can be reproduced, folded, and sorted in less than 30 minutes. Other processes of this type will be developed in the future to save time and effort.

19–91 SUMMARY

The first step of implementation of a conceived design is an almost completely graphical process that is required in all fields of engineering and technology. The engineer must understand the details of preparing a drawing regardless of whether he makes the drawing or supervises its preparation, for he is responsible for the correctness of the finished drawings. Working drawings are usually dimensioned orthographic drawings, but there are no limitations as to which types of drawings should be used. The primary objective is to communicate specific ideas, utilizing any graphical process available. Drawings can vary from pictorials to schematics.

Dimensions and notes must be checked for accuracy to ensure that they do not contain errors or conflicting information. It is more important that the dimensions and notes be correct than that the drawing be prepared with a high degree of detail. Some industries have developed a simplified form of symbolism that has reduced drawing time and the need for elaborate detail. The burden of clarifying the details of the drawing is borne by the notes used to supplement the drawing in much the same manner as thread notes are used on thread symbols.

Without the use of graphical processes at all stages of the design process, a design would never become a reality in modern technology. Graphical methods are less creative and more routine at the working drawing stage of the design process than during the preliminary stages of conceptualization. However, these methods are as essential at one stage as at the next. Graphics is the cornerstone of the design process.

PROBLEMS

General

Problems should be presented on $8\frac{1}{2}'' \times 11''$ paper, grid or plain, using the format introduced in Article 1–19. Fully dimensioned drawings should be drawn at an enlarged scale on lager paper—size B or size C—as assigned by your instructor. Use $\frac{1}{8}''$ letters with guidelines. When problems are drawn on a grid, the squares represent $\frac{1}{4}''$ when drawn full size.

Dimensioning

1 through 16. Refer to Figs. 19–193 through 19–208. Use size A paper. Using instruments, draw the orthographic views of the parts to be dimensioned on detail paper or tracing paper. Complete the views if lines are missing. Dimension each part, using the principles discussed in this chapter. Each square on the grid represents $\frac{1}{4}''$ (.25″). Concentrate on placement of dimensions and neatness in lettering and construction.

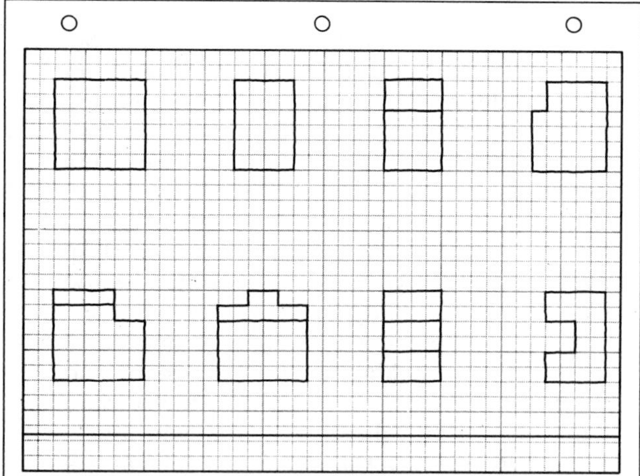

Fig. 19–193. Problem 1: Prisms.

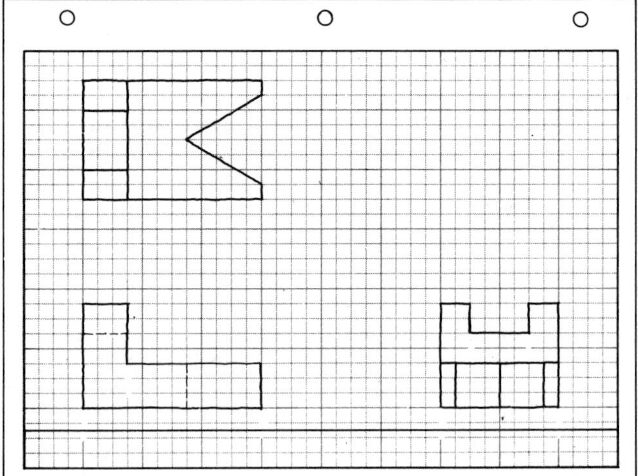

Fig. 19–195. Problem 3.

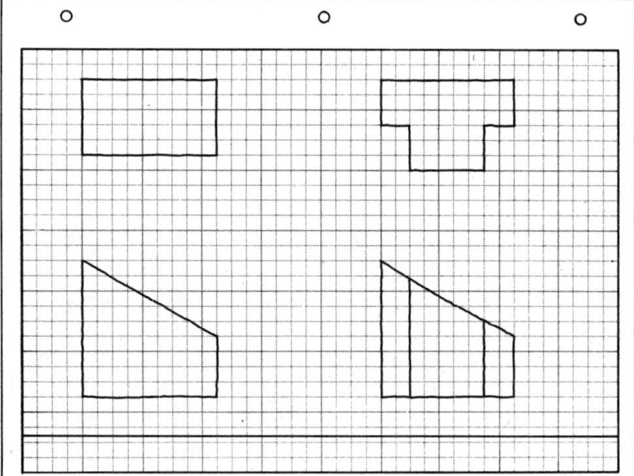

Fig. 19–194. Problem 2: Dimensioning angles.

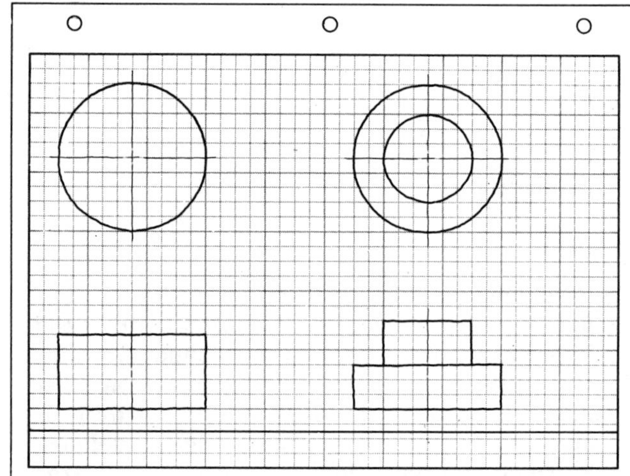

Fig. 19–196. Problem 4: Cylinders.

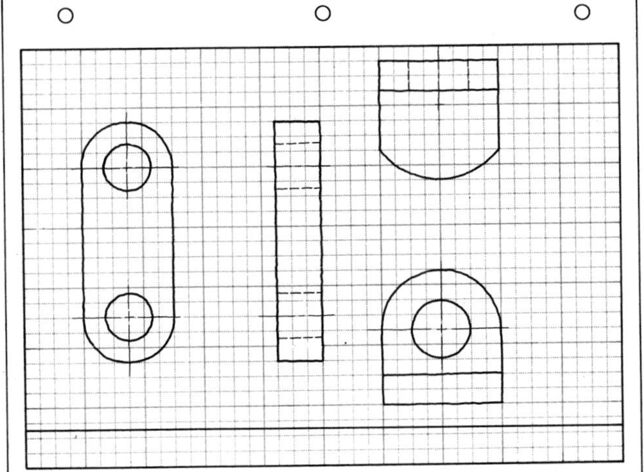

Fig. 19–197. Problem 5: Objects with rounded ends.

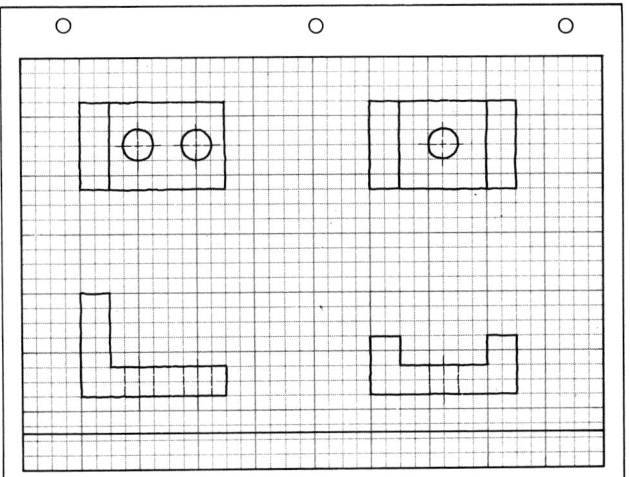

Fig. 19–199. Problem 7: Prisms.

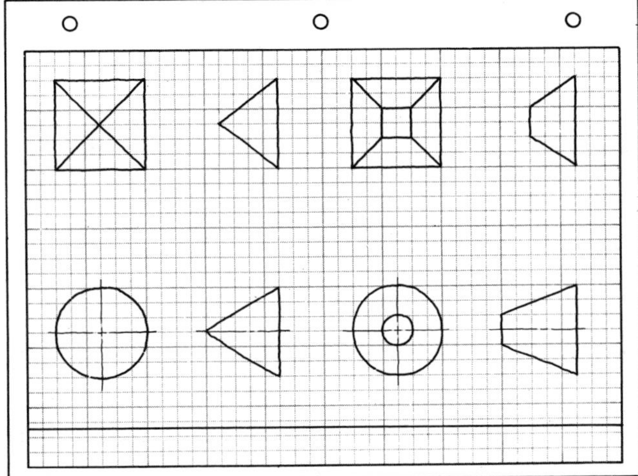

Fig. 19–198. Problem 6: Pyramids and cones.

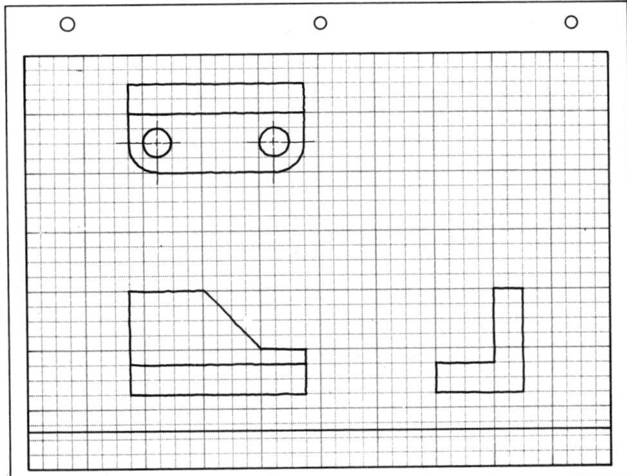

Fig. 19–200. Problem 8: Guide block.

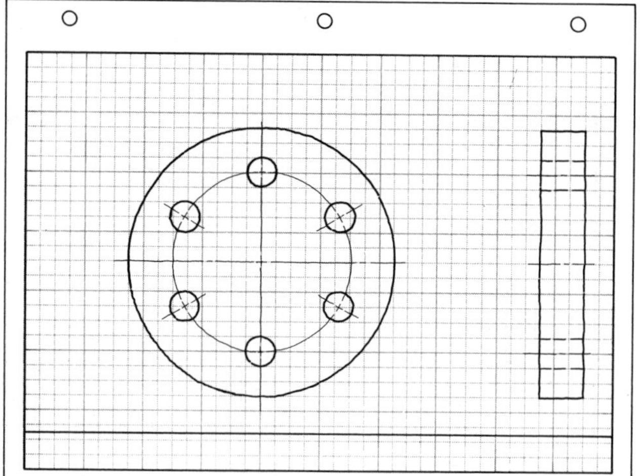

Fig. 19–201. Problem 9: End plate.

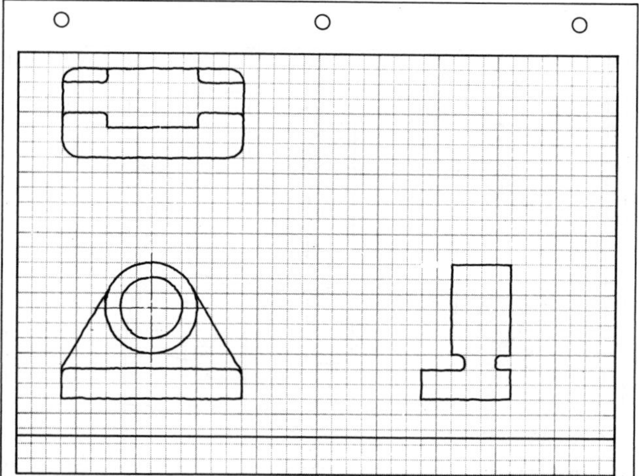

Fig. 19–203. Problem 11: Journal support.

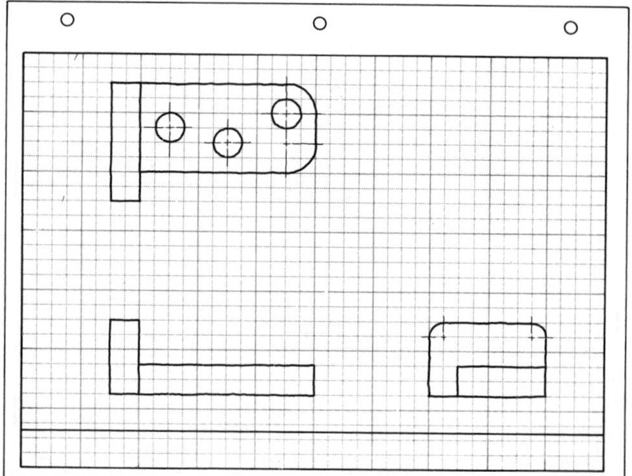

Fig. 19–202. Problem 10: Thrust block.

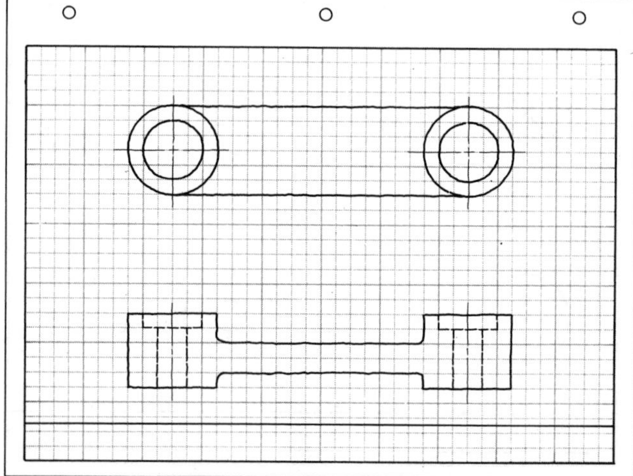

Fig. 19–204. Problem 12: Crank arm.

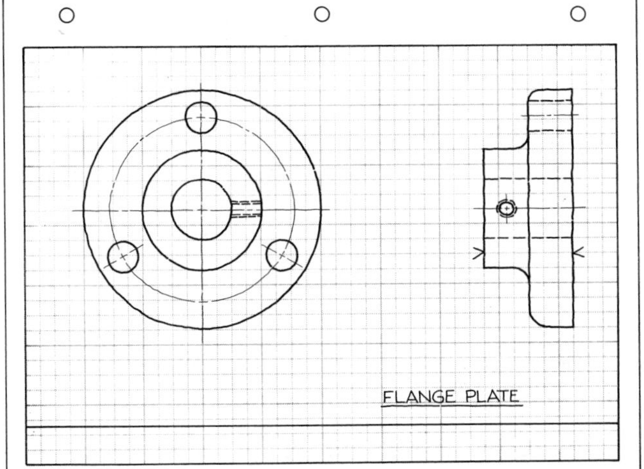

Fig. 19–205. Problem 13: Flange plate.

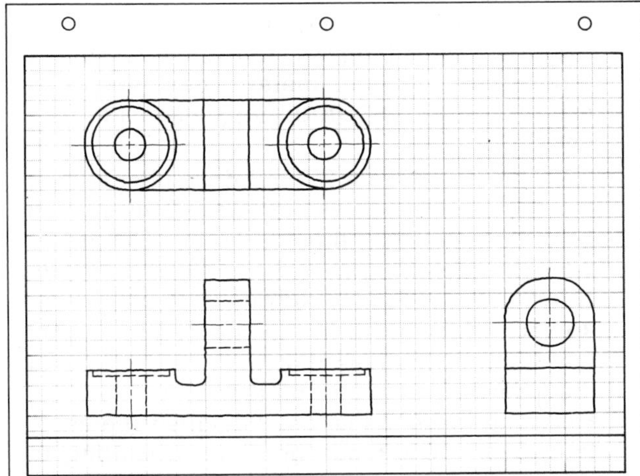

Fig. 19–206. Problem 14: Shaft guide.

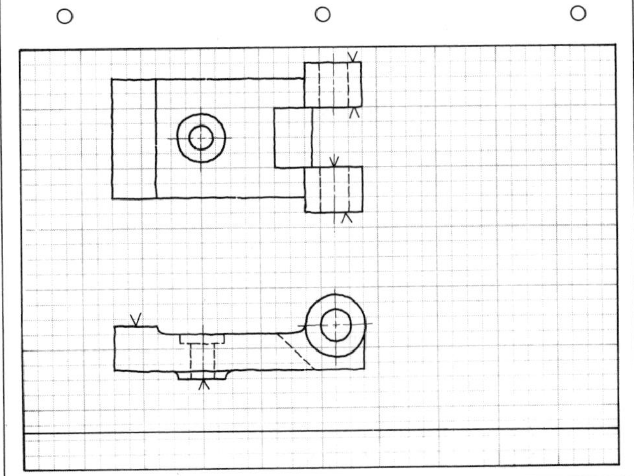

Fig. 19–207. Problem 15: Hinge plate.

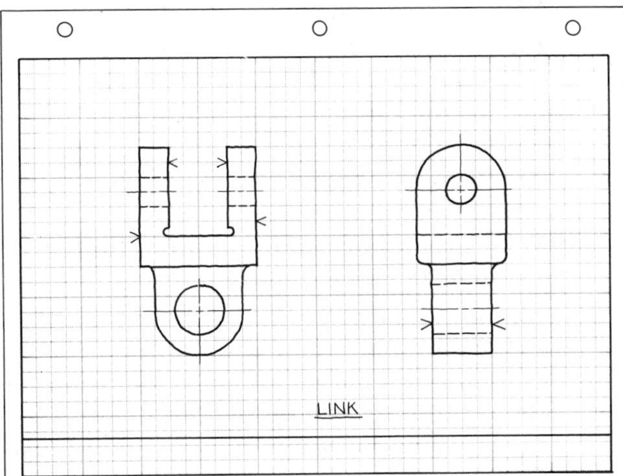

Fig. 19–208. Problem 16: Link.

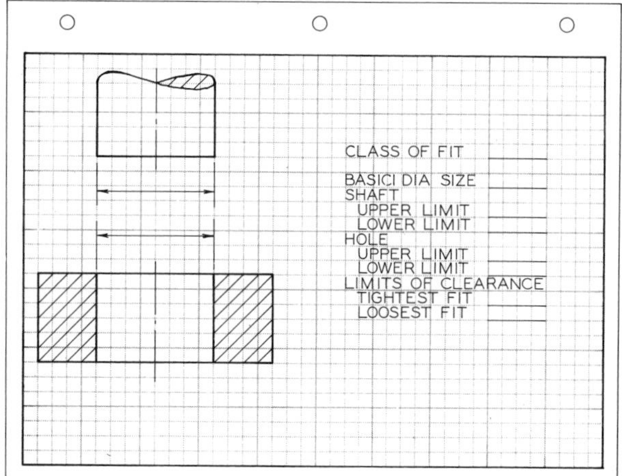

Fig. 19–209. Problems 17 through 26.

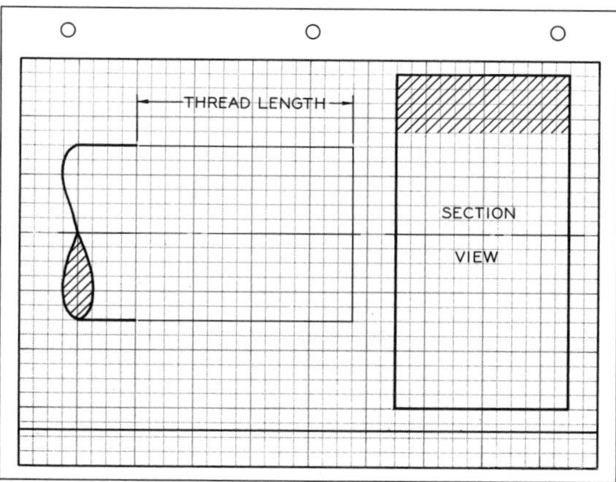

Fig. 19–210. Problems 27, 28, and 29: Construction of thread symbols.

Tolerances—Cylindrical Fits

For Problems 17 through 26, refer to Fig. 19–209 for the format. A single drawing is to be made for each set of specifications given in these problems. Complete the table of values by converting the values from the Appendix to whole decimal values.

17. Complete the dimensions and table of values in Fig. 19–206 using a basic diameter of 4.50″ and class RC 3 fit.

18. Same as Problem 17, but use a basic diameter of 1.50″ and class RC 1 fit.

19. Same as Problem 17, but use a basic diameter of 3.00″ and a class LC 1 fit.

20. Same as Problem 17, but use a basic diameter of 5.00″ and a class LC 4 fit.

21. Same as Problem 17, but use a basic diameter of 4.00″ and a class LT 2 fit.

22. Same as Problem 17, but use a basic diameter of .50″ and a class LT 6 fit.

23. Same as Problem 17, but use a basic diameter of 8.50″ and a class LN 1 fit.

24. Same as Problem 17, but use a basic diameter of 1.80″ and a class LN 3 fit.

25. Same as Problem 17, but use a basic diameter of .75″ and a class FN 2 fit.

26. Same as Problem 17, but use a basic diameter of 6.50″ and a class FN 4 fit.

Fasteners

27. The layout in Fig. 19–210 is to be used for constructing a detailed representation of an Acme thread with a major diameter of 3″. The thread note specifications are 3–1$\frac{1}{2}$ ACME. Show both external and internal thread representations. Show the thread note.

28. Repeat Problem 27, but draw internal and external detailed representations of a square thread that is 3″ in diameter. The note specifications are 3–1$\frac{1}{2}$ SQUARE. Apply notes to both parts.

29. Repeat Problem 27, but draw internal and external detailed thread representations of an American National thread form. The major diameter of each part is 3″. The note specifications are 3–4NC–2. Apply notes to both parts.

30. Notes are given in Fig. 19–211 to specify the depth of the hole that is to be drilled and the threads that are to be tapped in the hole. Following these notes, draw detailed representations of the threads as views according to specifications.

31. Repeat Problem 30, but use schematic representations.

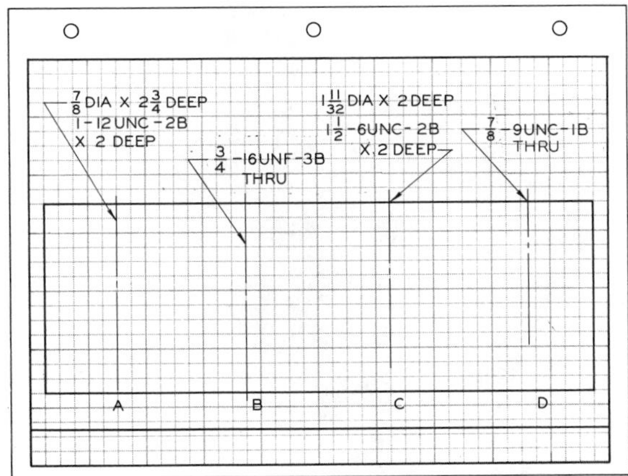

Fig. 19-211. Problems 30, 31, and 32: Internal threads.

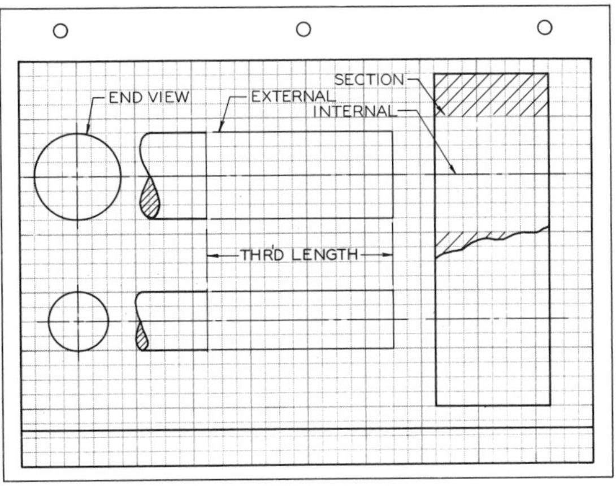

Fig. 19-212. Problems 33, 34, and 35: Internal and external threads.

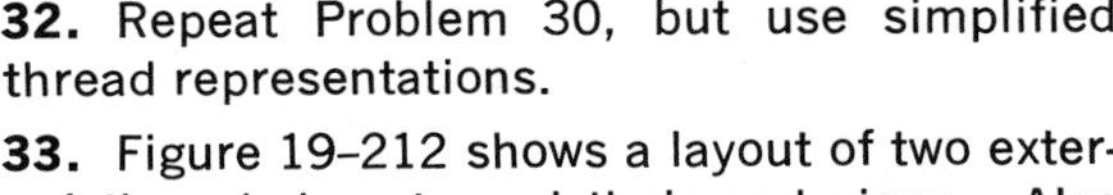

32. Repeat Problem 30, but use simplified thread representations.

33. Figure 19-212 shows a layout of two external threaded parts and their end views. Also shown is a piece into which the external threads will be screwed. Complete all three views of each of the parts. Use detailed threads and apply notes to the internal and external threads. Use the table in Appendix 12 for thread specifications. Use UNC threads.

34. Repeat Problem 33, but use schematic thread representations.

35. Repeat Problem 33, but use simplified thread representations.

36. Referring to Fig. 19-213, complete the drawing with instruments as a semifinished hexagon bolt and nut. The bolt head is to be drawn across corners. The nut is a heavy nut drawn across corners. Use detailed thread representations. Show notes to specify the parts of the assembly. Thread specifications are $1\frac{1}{2}$-6UNC-3.

37. Referring to Fig. 19-213, complete the drawing with instruments as an unfinished square-head bolt and nut. The bolt head is drawn across corners. The regular nut is to be drawn across corners. Use schematic thread representations. Show notes to specify the parts. Use the table in Appendix 12 for thread specifications.

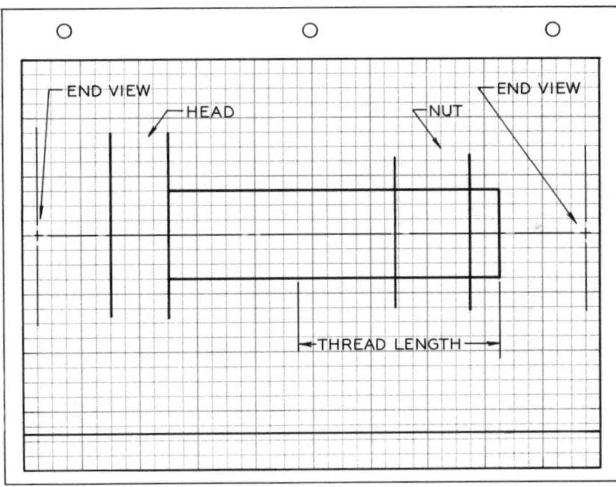

Fig. 19-213. Problems 36, 37, and 38: Nuts and bolts in assembly.

38. Referring to Fig. 19-213, complete the drawing with instruments as a finished hexagon nut and bolt. The regular bolt and nut are to be

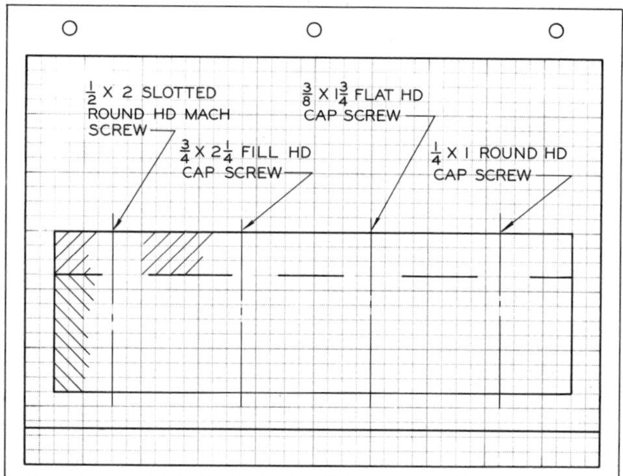

Fig. 19–214. Problems 39, 40, and 41: Cap screws and machine screws.

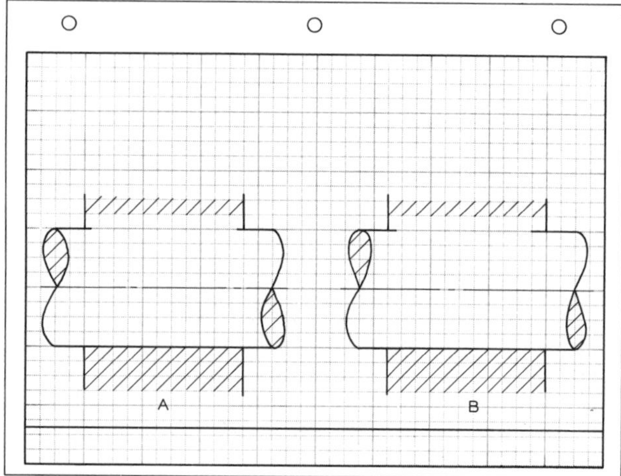

Fig. 19–215. Problems 42 and 43.

drawn across flats. Use simplified thread representations. Show notes to specify the parts. Use the table in Appendix 12 for specifications.

39. The notes in Fig. 19–214 apply to machine and cap screws that are to be drawn in the section view of the two parts. The holes in which the screws are to be drawn should be considered as through holes. Complete the drawings and show the notes as given. Show the remaining section lines. Use detailed thread symbols.

Fig. 19–216. Problems 44 and 45: A design involving threaded parts. (Courtesy of Koh-I-Noor Corporation.)

40. Repeat Problem 39, but use schematic thread symbols.

41. Repeat Problem 39, but use simplified thread symbols.

42. Figure 19–215 shows two parts assembled on a cylindrical shaft. These parts are to be held in position by a square key in A and a gib-head key in B. Show the necessary notes to specify the key, keyway, and keyseat.

43. Repeat Problem 42, but use a No. 16 Pratt & Whitney key in A and a No. 1211 Woodruff key in B. Show the necessary notes to specify the key, the keyway, and the keyseat.

44. *Design.* The pencil pointer shown in Fig. 19–216 has a shaft of $\frac{1}{4}''$ that fits into a bracket designed to clamp onto a desk top. A set screw holds the shaft in position. Make a drawing of the bracket, estimating its dimensions. Show the details and the method of using the set screw to hold the shaft. Give the specifications for the set screw.

45. Referring to Fig. 19–216, make the necessary drawings to illustrate the threaded screw that is used to clamp the bracket to the table. Give the necessary specifications in a note.

Gears

Use size A ($8\frac{1}{2}'' \times 11''$) sheets for the following gear problems.

46. Make a drawing of a spur gear similar to the one shown in Fig. 19–153. Compute the values for the table and show the necessary dimensions on the drawing. The gear is to have 25 teeth and a diametrical pitch of 5.

47. Repeat Problem 46 for a gear that has 36 teeth and a diametrical pitch of 8.

48. Construct an involute using a 60° arc drawn with a radius of 4″. Use 10° intervals and show the entire construction.

49. Construct an assembly drawing of a spur gear and pinion that are assembled. The pinion is to have 10 teeth and a diametrical pitch of 4. The gear is to have 15 teeth and a diametrical pitch of 4.

50. Make a layout of a size B sheet ($11'' \times 17''$) showing a pinion and a bevel gear assembled at 90° to give a miter fit. On the same sheet show a separate detail drawing of each gear.

51. Make detail drawings of the gears shown in Fig. 19–155.

Working Drawings

52 through 83. These problems are to be drawn as detail drawings and should follow the specifications of Article 19–77 and the examples covered in this chapter. Tracing paper or film is suggested as the drawing surface so that it will be possible to make diazo prints from the finished drawings. Show all notes and dimensions necessary to make the drawings ready for release to production.

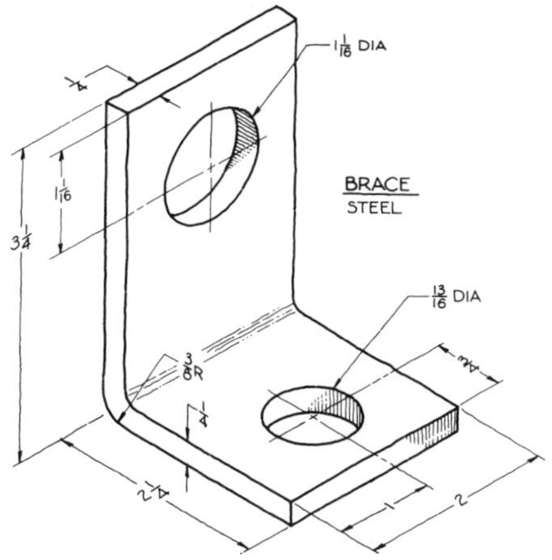

Fig. 19–217. Problem 52: Size A sheet.

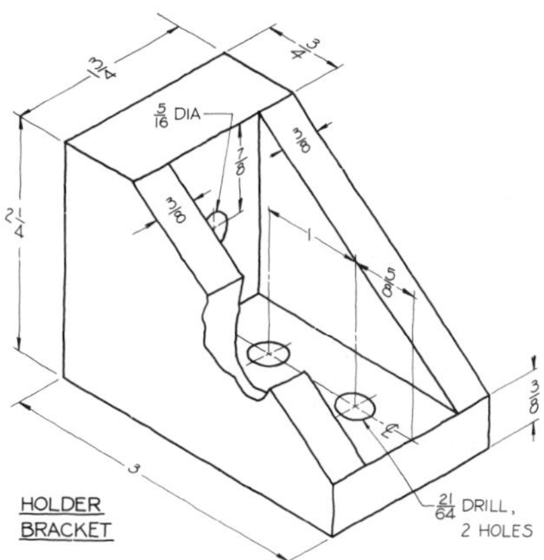

Fig. 19–218. Problem 53: Size A sheet.

52. Refer to Fig. 19–217. Make a detail drawing of the brace on a Size A sheet. Show all notes and dimensions necessary to describe the part.

53. Refer to Fig. 19–218. Make a detail drawing of the part on a Size A sheet. Show all notes and dimensions necessary to describe the part.

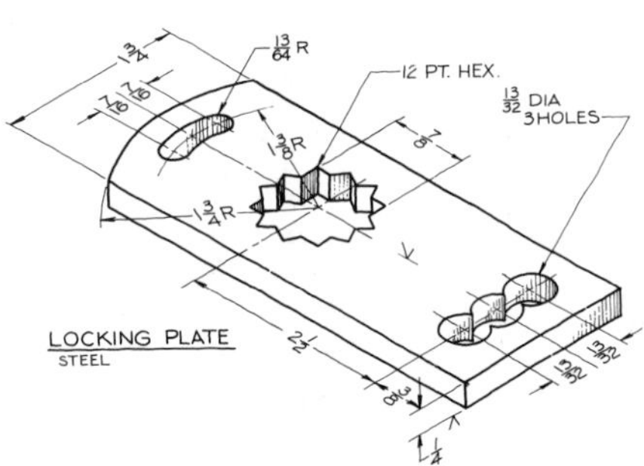

Fig. 19–219. Problem 54: Size A sheet.

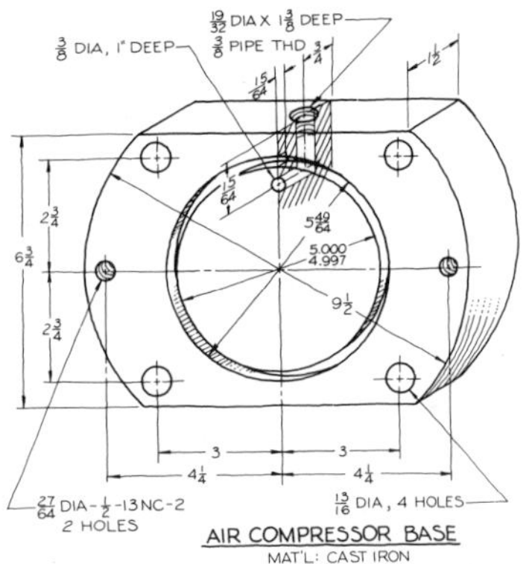

Fig. 19–220. Problem 55: Size A sheet.

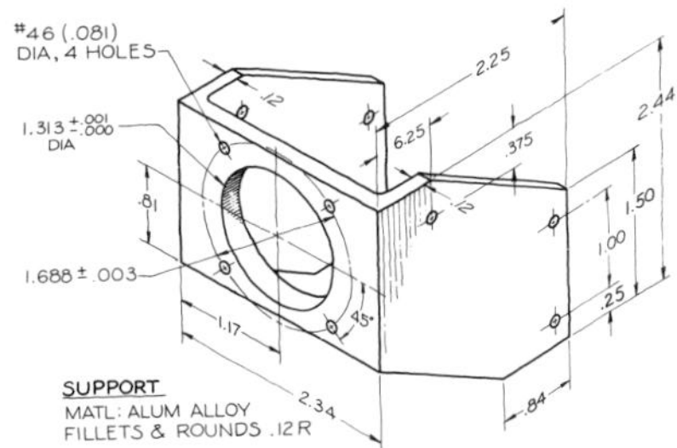

Fig. 19–221. Problem 56: Size A sheet.

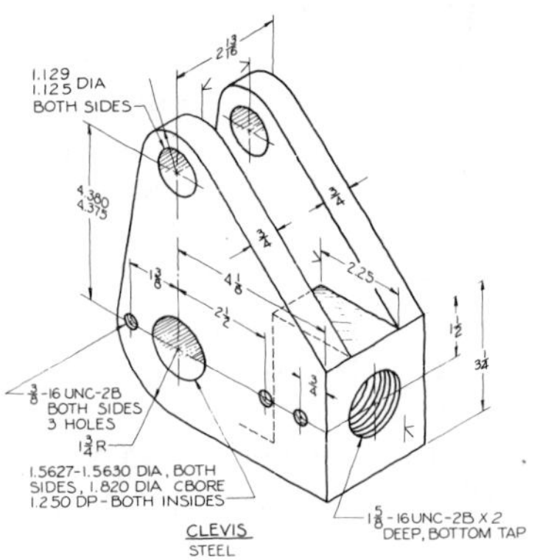

Fig. 19–222. Problem 57: Size B sheet.

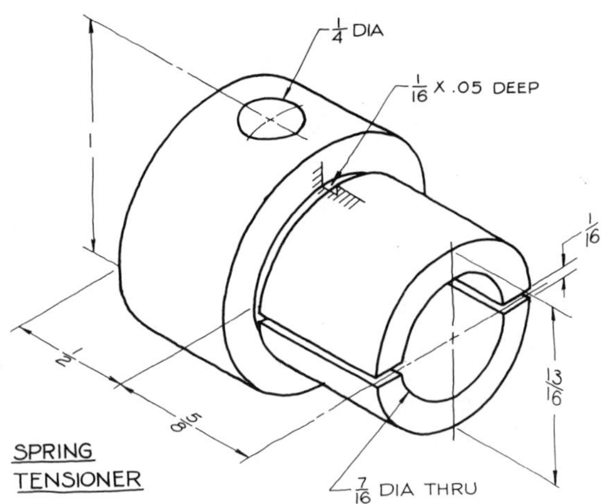

Fig. 19–223. Problem 58: Size B sheet.

54. Refer to Fig. 19–219. Make a detail drawing of the locking plate on a Size A sheet.

55. Refer to Fig. 19–220. Make a detail drawing of the air compressor base on a Size A sheet.

56. Refer to Fig. 19–221. Make a detail drawing of the support on a Size A sheet.

57. Refer to Fig. 19–222. Make a detail drawing of the clevis on a Size B sheet.

58. Refer to Fig. 19–223. Make a detail drawing of the spring tensioner on a Size B sheet.

59. Refer to Fig. 19–224. Make a detail drawing of the pedal crank on a Size B sheet.

60. Refer to Fig. 19–225. Make a detail drawing of the brake chamber clevis on a Size B sheet.

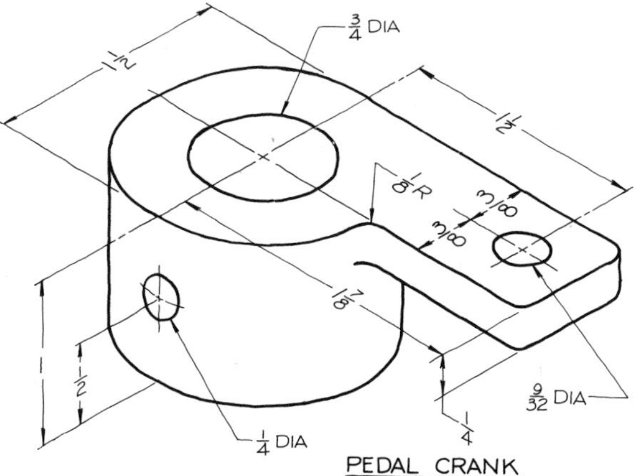

Fig. 19–224. Problem 59: Size B sheet.

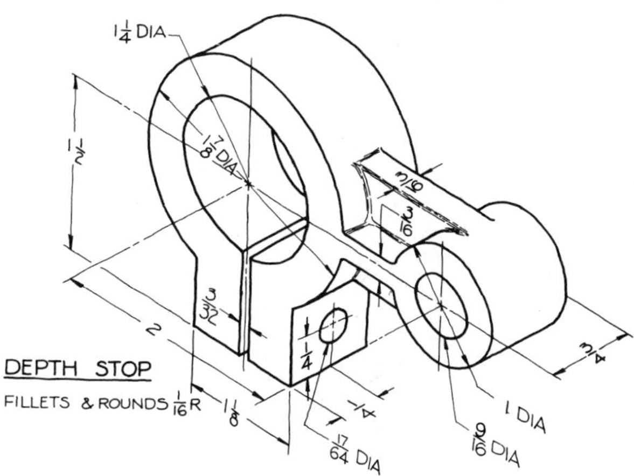

Fig. 19–226. Problem 61: Size B sheet.

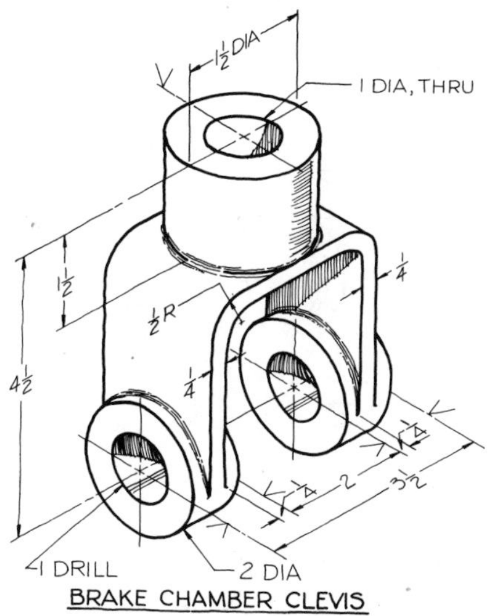

Fig. 19–225. Problem 60: Size B sheet.

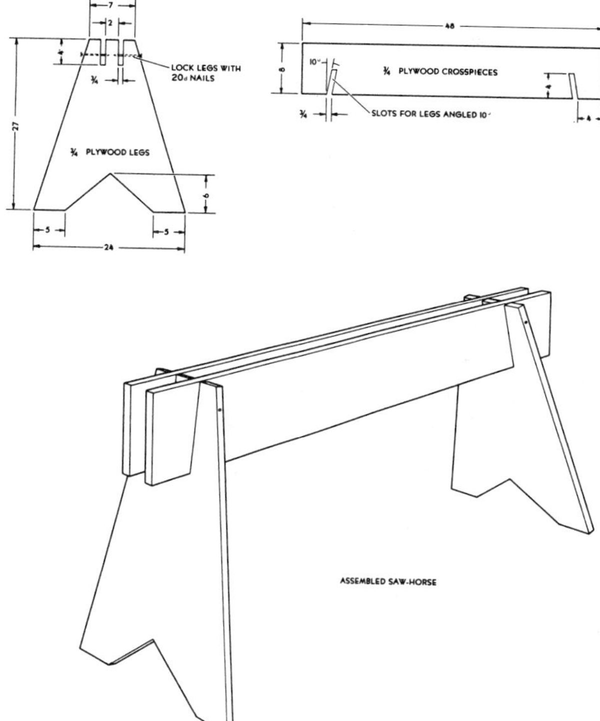

Fig. 19–227. Problem 62: Size B sheet.

61. Refer to Fig. 19–226. Make a detail drawing of the depth stop on a Size B sheet.

62. Refer to Fig. 19–227. Make a detail drawing of the saw-horse on a Size B sheet.

63. Refer to Fig. 19–228. Make a detail drawing of the slider on a Size B sheet.

64. Refer to Fig. 19–229. Make a detail drawing of the wedge lift on a Size B sheet.

65. Refer to Fig. 19–230. Make a detail drawing of the bearing on a Size B sheet.

66. Refer to Fig. 19–231. Make a detail drawing of the column base on a Size B sheet.

67. Refer to Fig. 19–232. Make a detail drawing of the solenoid connection on a Size A sheet.

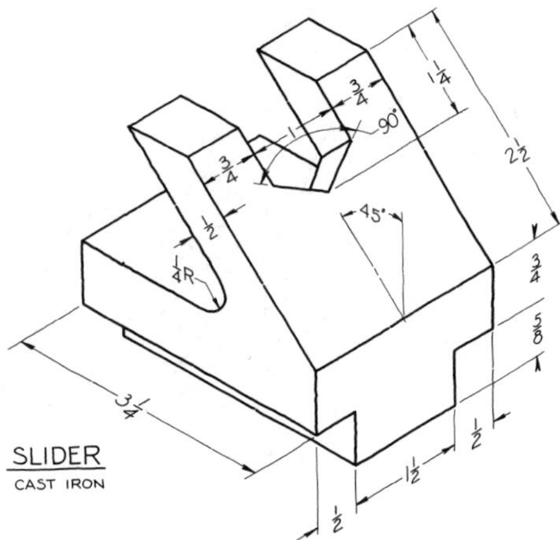

Fig. 19–228. Problem 63: Size B sheet.

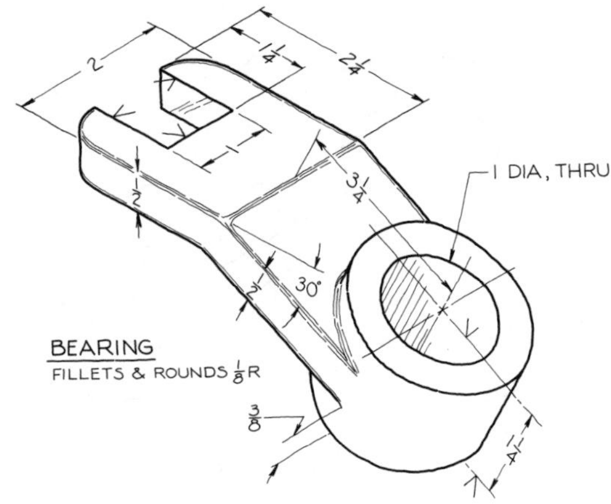

Fig. 19–230. Problem 65: Size B sheet.

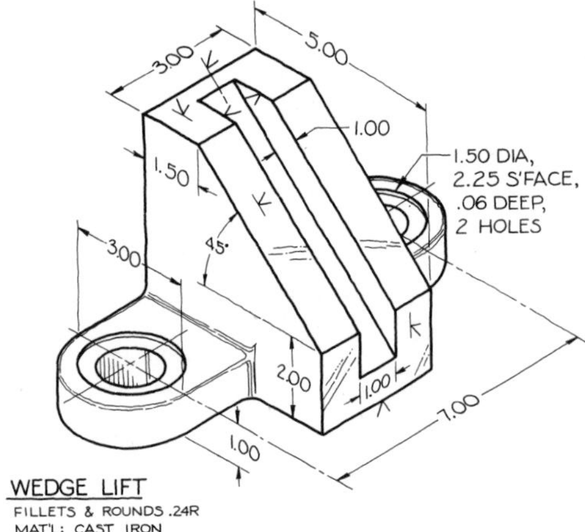

Fig. 19–229. Problem 64: Size B sheet.

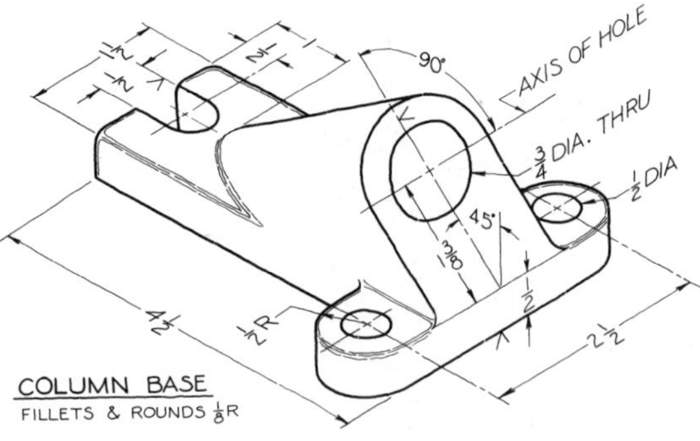

Fig. 19–231. Problem 66: Size B sheet.

68. Refer to Fig. 19–233. Make a detail drawing of the support arm on a Size A sheet.

69. Refer to Fig. 19–234. Make a detail drawing from the freehand sketch of the link on a Size B sheet. Add views that will clarify the drawing. Use instruments.

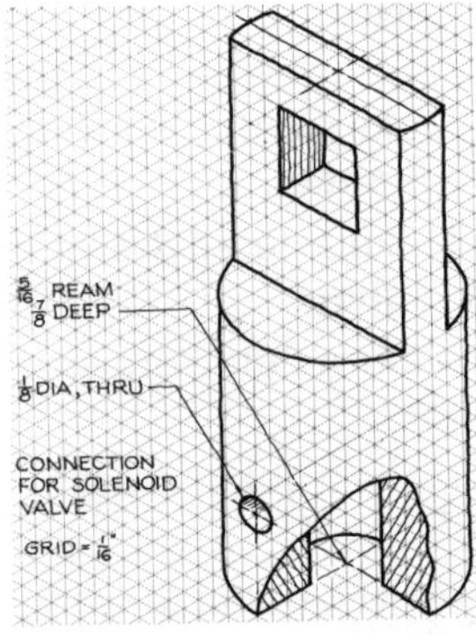

Fig. 19–232. Problem 67: Size A sheet.

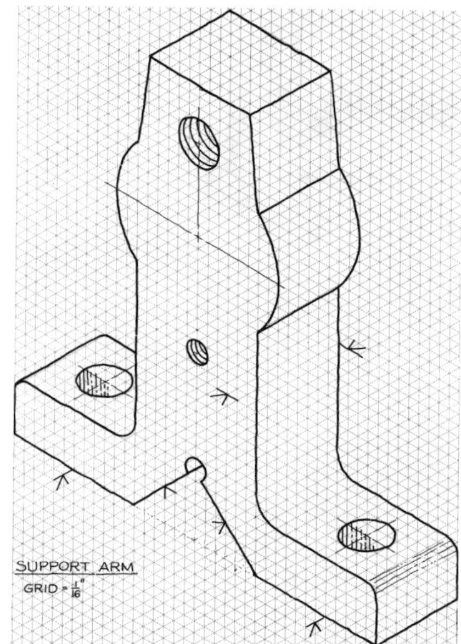

Fig. 19–233. Problem 68: Size A sheet.

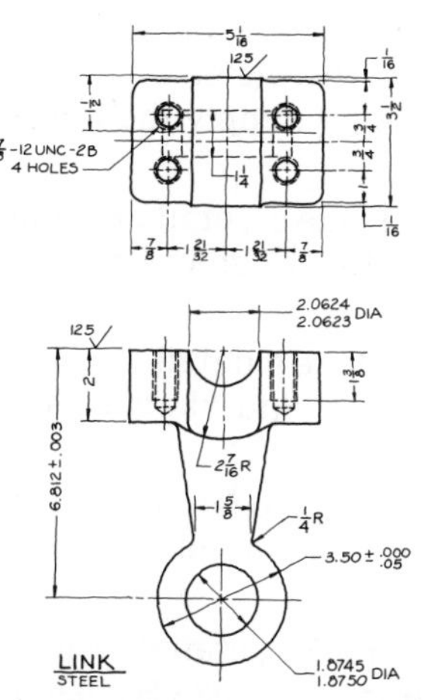

Fig. 19–234. Problem 69: Size B sheet.

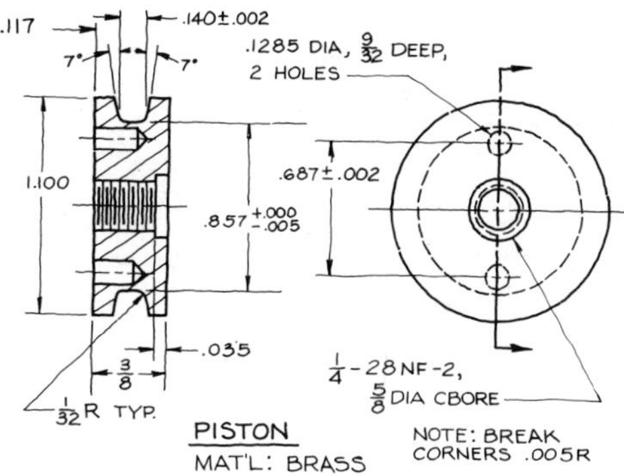

Fig. 19–235. Problem 70: Size A sheet.

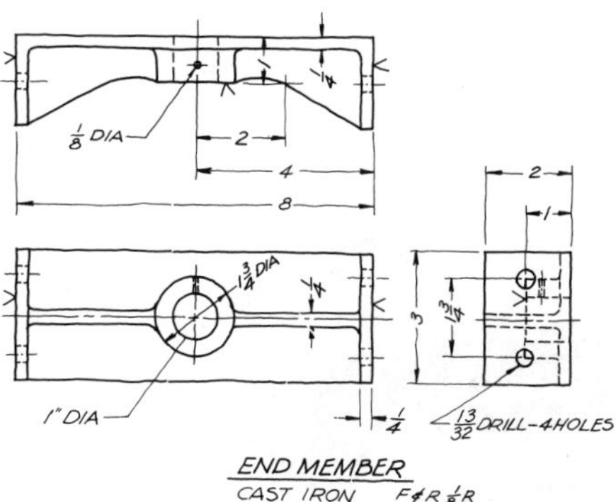

Fig. 19–236. Problem 71: Size B sheet.

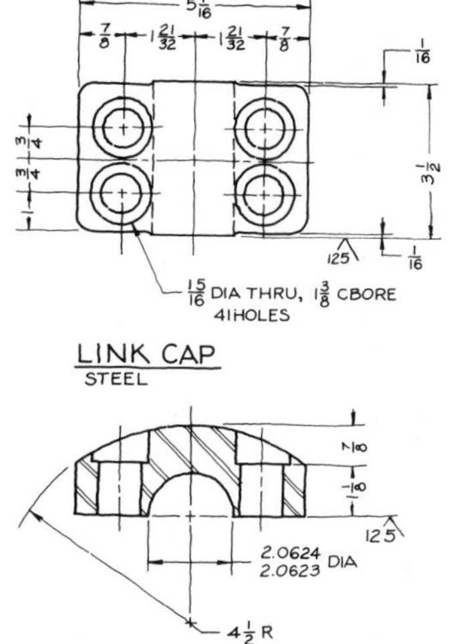

Fig. 19–237. Problem 72: Size B sheet.

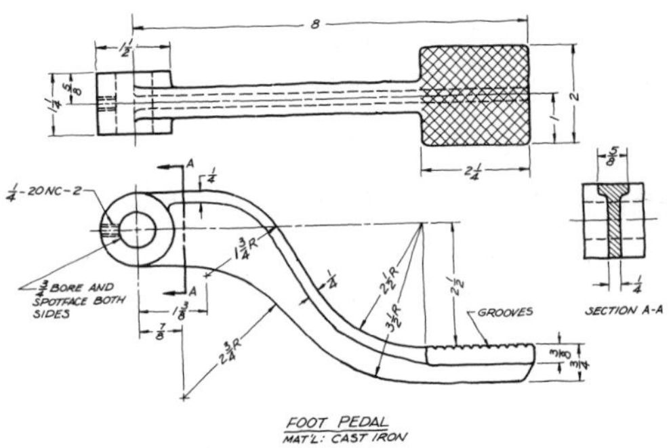

Fig. 19–238. Problem 73: Size C sheet.

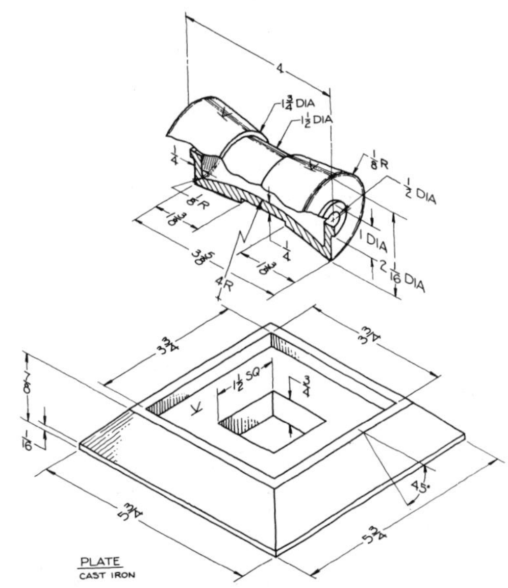

Fig. 19–239. Problem 74: Size B sheets.

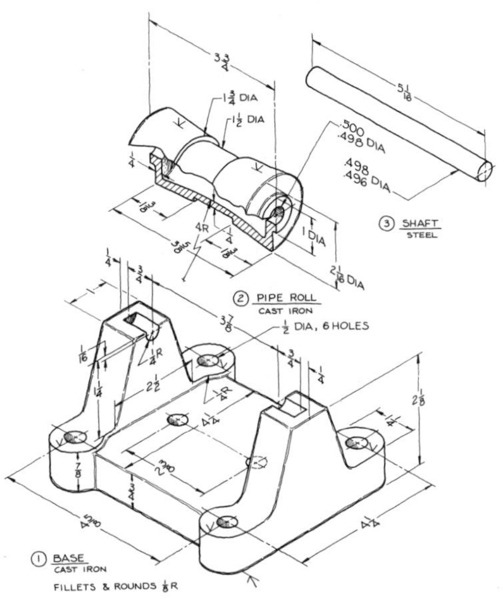

Fig. 19–240. Problem 76: Size B sheets.

70. Refer to Fig. 19–235. Make a detail drawing from the freehand sketch of the piston on a Size A sheet. Use instruments and supply the missing dimensions.

71. Refer to Fig. 19–236. Make a detail drawing of the end member from the freehand sketch on a Size B sheet.

72. Refer to Fig. 19–237. Make a detail drawing of the link cap from the freehand sketch on a Size B sheet.

73. Refer to Fig. 19–238. Make a detail drawing of the foot pedal from the freehand sketch on a Size C sheet.

74. Refer to Fig. 19–239. Make detail drawings of the parts of the pipe support on Size B sheets. Give a parts list.

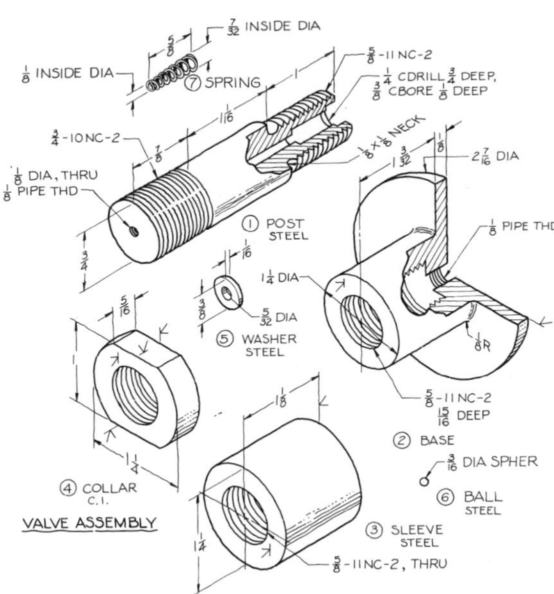

Fig. 19–241. Problem 78: Size B sheets.

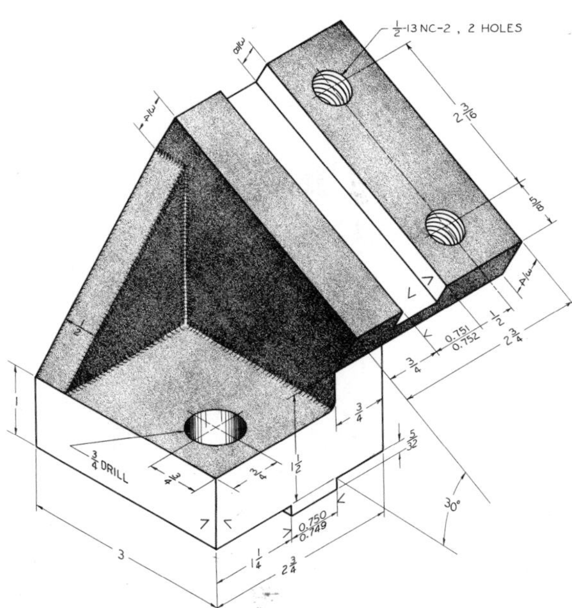

Fig. 19–242. Problem 80: Size B sheet.

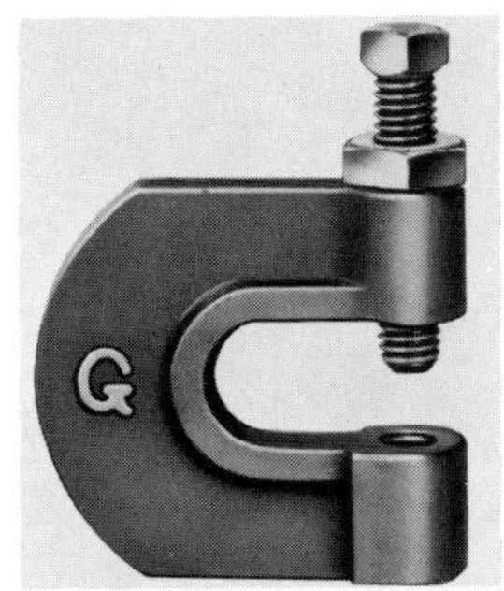

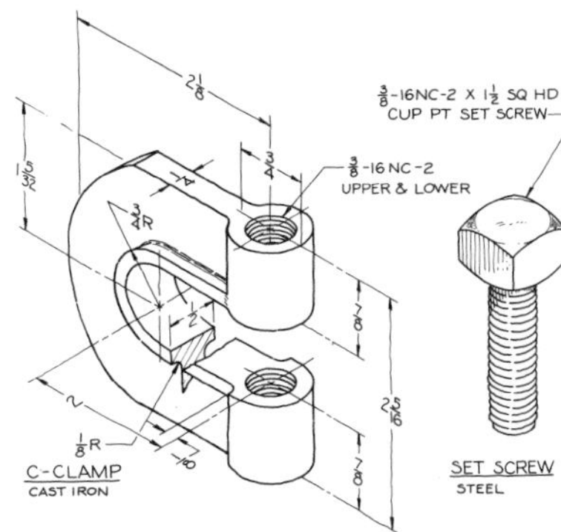

Fig. 19–243. Problem 81: Size B sheet.

75. Refer to Fig. 19–239. Make an assembly drawing, either orthographic or pictorial, of the pipe support.

76. Refer to Fig. 19–240. Make a detail drawing of the parts of the pipe support. Give a parts list.

77. Refer to Fig. 19–240. Make an assembly drawing, either orthographic or pictorial, of the pipe support.

78. Refer to Fig. 19–241. Make detail drawings of the parts of the valve assembly. Give a parts list.

79. Refer to Fig. 19–241. Make an assembly drawing, either orthographic or pictorial, of the valve assembly on a Size B sheet.

80. Refer to Fig. 19–242. Make a detail drawing of the guide on a Size B sheet.

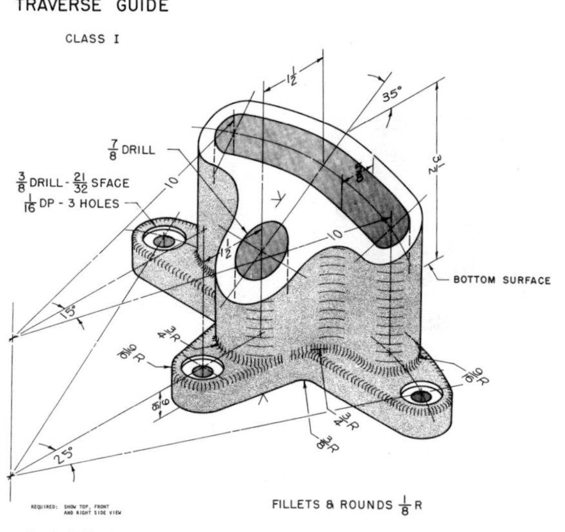

Fig. 19–244. Problem 83: Size B sheet.

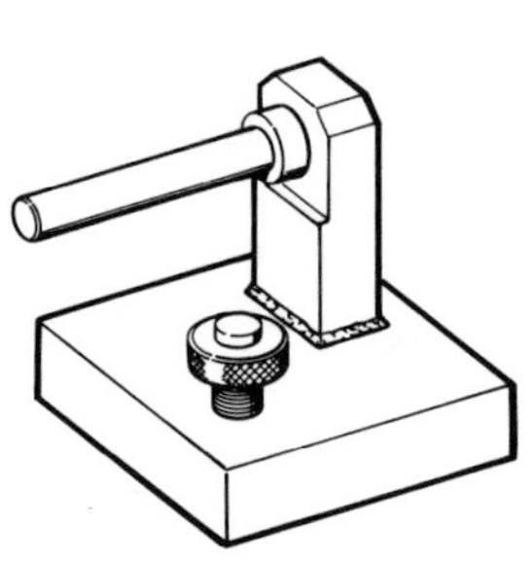

Fig. 19–245. Problem 84: Size B sheet. (Courtesy of Bendix Corporation.)

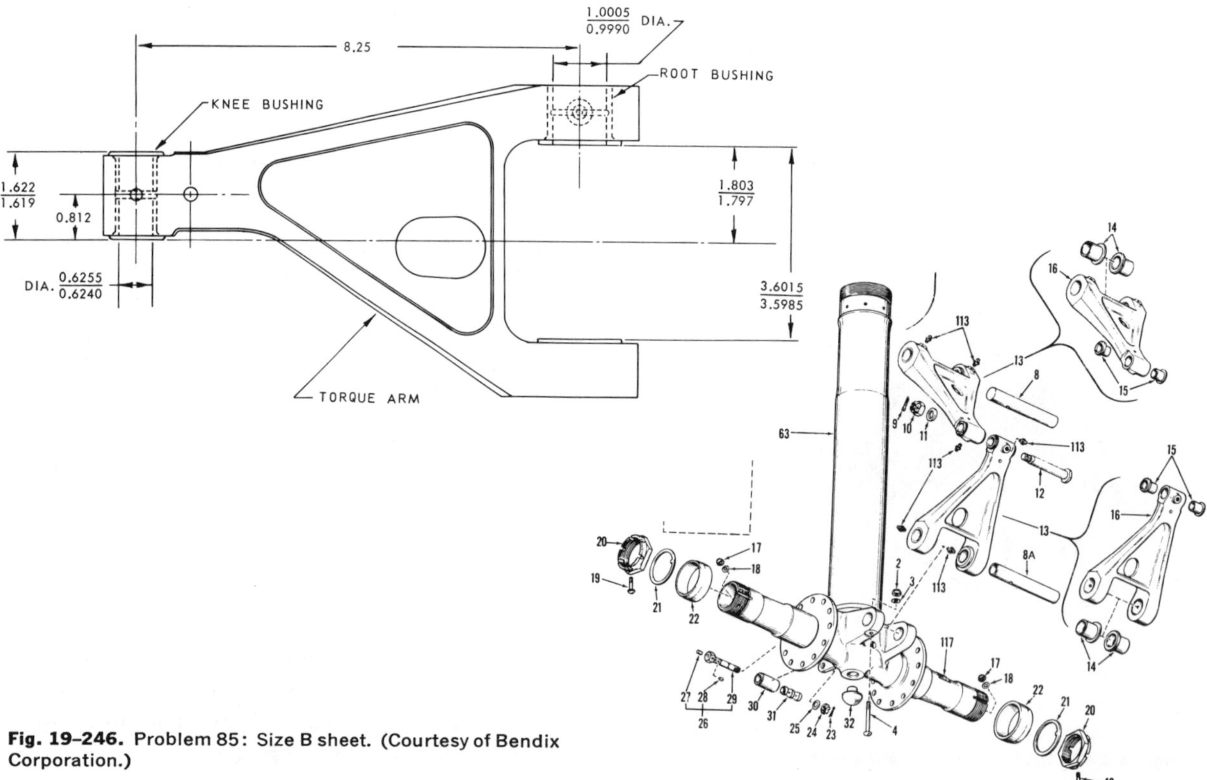

Fig. 19–246. Problem 85: Size B sheet. (Courtesy of Bendix Corporation.)

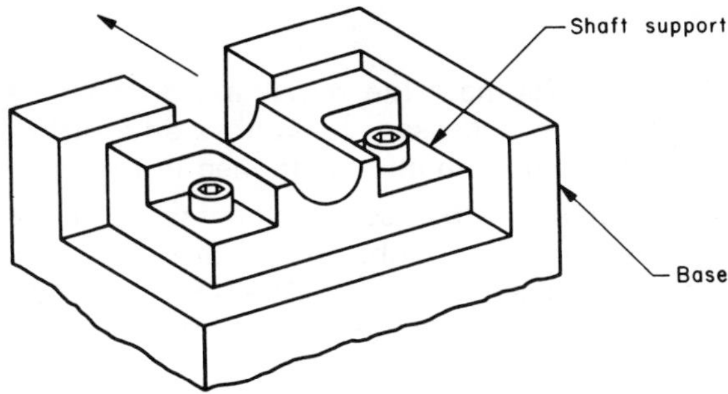

Fig. 19–247. Problem 86: Size B sheet. (Courtesy of ANSI; Y14.5-1966.)

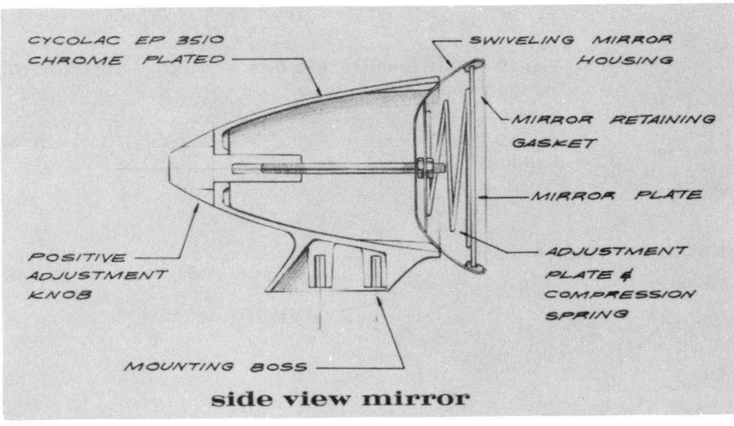

Fig. 19–248. Problem 87: Size B sheets. (Courtesy of Borg-Warner Corporation.)

81. Refer to Fig. 19–243. Make detail drawings of the parts of the C-clamp. Give a parts list and supply any missing dimensions.

82. Refer to Fig. 19–243. Make an assembly drawing, either orthographic or pictorial, of the C-clamp on a Size B sheet.

83. Refer to Fig. 19–244. Make a detail drawing of the traverse guide on a Size B sheet.

84. Prepare a finished working drawing of the pressing fixture shown in Fig. 19–245, in accordance with the following specifications. The shaft is $\frac{3}{4}''$ in diameter, with the 1″ diameter end press fitted into the upright piece. This should be an interference fit of .010 allowance with a tolerance of .002. The center line of the shaft is 3″ above the 7″ × 7″ base. The knurled thumb screw has a major diameter of $\frac{3}{4}''$ and is screwed into a threaded hole that passes completely through the base. Estimate the other dimensions by eye.

85. A partially dimensioned view of a torque arm is given in Fig. 19–246, which also shows the pictorial assembly of the parts. Using the given dimensions and estimating the remaining ones, prepare a finished working drawing of the part. Construct additional orthographic views as required.

86. Prepare a finished working drawing of the assembly shown in Fig. 19–247. The shaft support has a semicylinder $1\frac{1}{4}''$ in diameter and

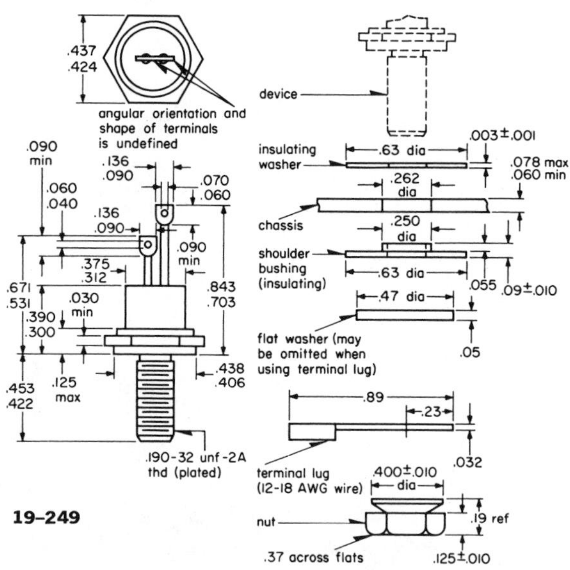

19–249

3″ long. Estimate the remaining dimensions. Indicate the necessary tolerances and surface treatments that should be applied in this case.

87. Prepare an exploded orthographic or pictorial exploded assembly of the parts of the side view mirror shown in Fig. 19–248. Include a parts list to indicate the various parts.

Fig. 19–249. Problem 88: Size A sheets. (Courtesy of Westinghouse Corporation.)

Fig. 19–250. Problem 89: Size B sheets. (Courtesy of Randolph Company.)

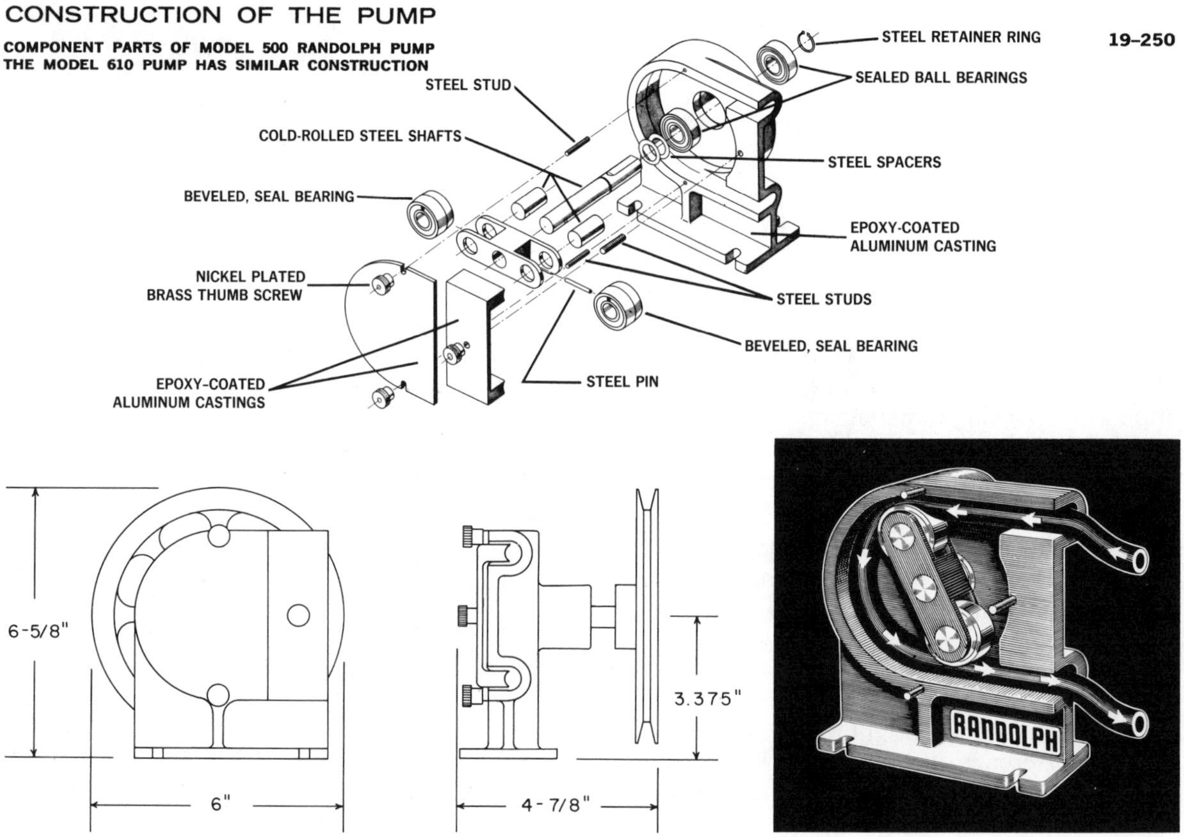

CONSTRUCTION OF THE PUMP

COMPONENT PARTS OF MODEL 500 RANDOLPH PUMP
THE MODEL 610 PUMP HAS SIMILAR CONSTRUCTION

STEEL RETAINER RING
SEALED BALL BEARINGS
STEEL STUD
COLD-ROLLED STEEL SHAFTS
STEEL SPACERS
BEVELED, SEAL BEARING
EPOXY-COATED ALUMINUM CASTING
NICKEL PLATED BRASS THUMB SCREW
STEEL STUDS
BEVELED, SEAL BEARING
EPOXY-COATED ALUMINUM CASTINGS
STEEL PIN

19–250

6-5/8"
6"
3.375"
4-7/8"
RANDOLPH

88. A dimensioned drawing of a silicon-controlled rectifier is shown in Fig. 19–249. Prepare an exploded pictorial assembly of the rectifier and the parts that assemble with it. Include a parts list with the assembly.

Design Problems

The following problems require you to perform more of the function of a design draftsman, using your judgment to supply information that is not given. You may also need to make changes in various details of the parts if errors are apparent. These problems will have more than one answer, since you will be applying your imagination and judgment to their solution. More analysis will be required than in the previous problems.

89. A rotary pump is illustrated in Fig. 19–250 with several drawings and sketches. Using the general dimensions given, make a complete working drawing of each of the parts, including the information necessary for its construction and assembly. Indicate dimensions, notes, and tolerances.

90. An orthographic sketch of a pipe hanger bracket is shown in Fig. 19–251. This bracket, which is attached to a wall to support steam pipes, has been redesigned as shown in the photograph, utilizing the same general dimensions. Prepare a working drawing of the modified design.

91. Prepare a working drawing to fully detail the parts of the pawl fastener in Fig. 19–252. Indicate tolerances, allowances, and surface textures.

92. Prepare an exploded or assembled orthographic assembly of the pawl (Fig. 19–252), including a parts list.

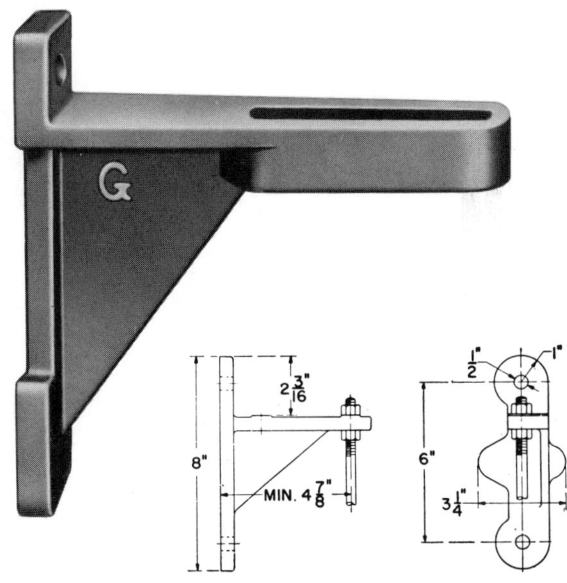

Fig. 19–251. Problem 90: Size A sheet. (Courtesy of Grinnell Corporation.)

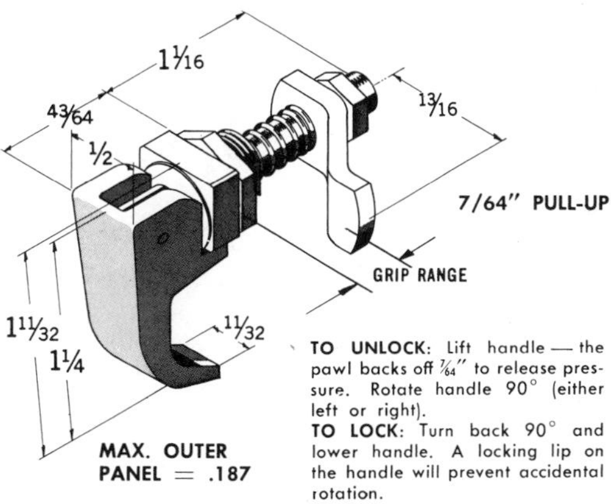

Fig. 19–252. Problem 91: Size B sheet. (Courtesy of Southco Corporation.)

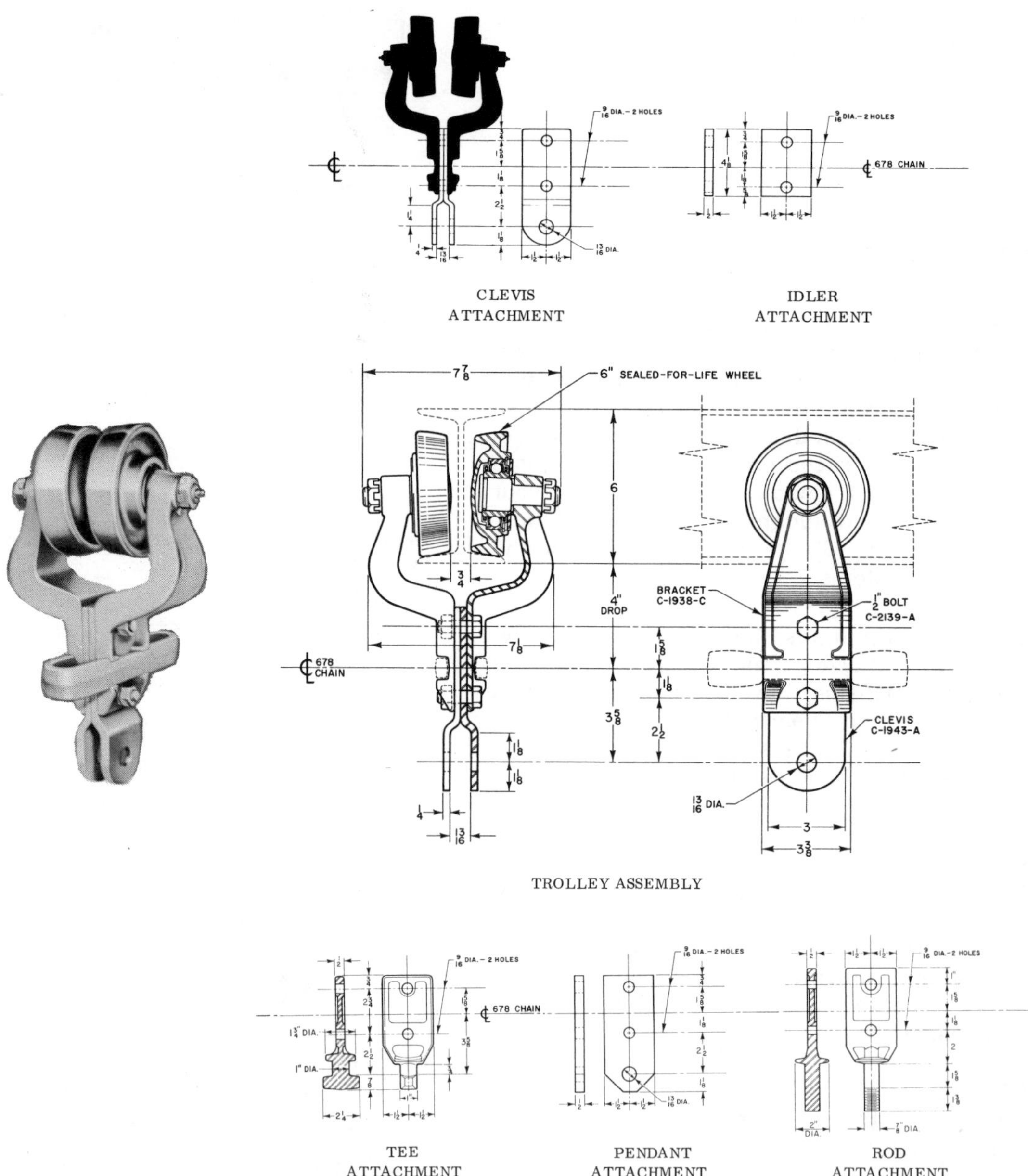

Fig. 19–253. Problem 93. (Courtesy Mechanical Handling Systems, Incorporated.)

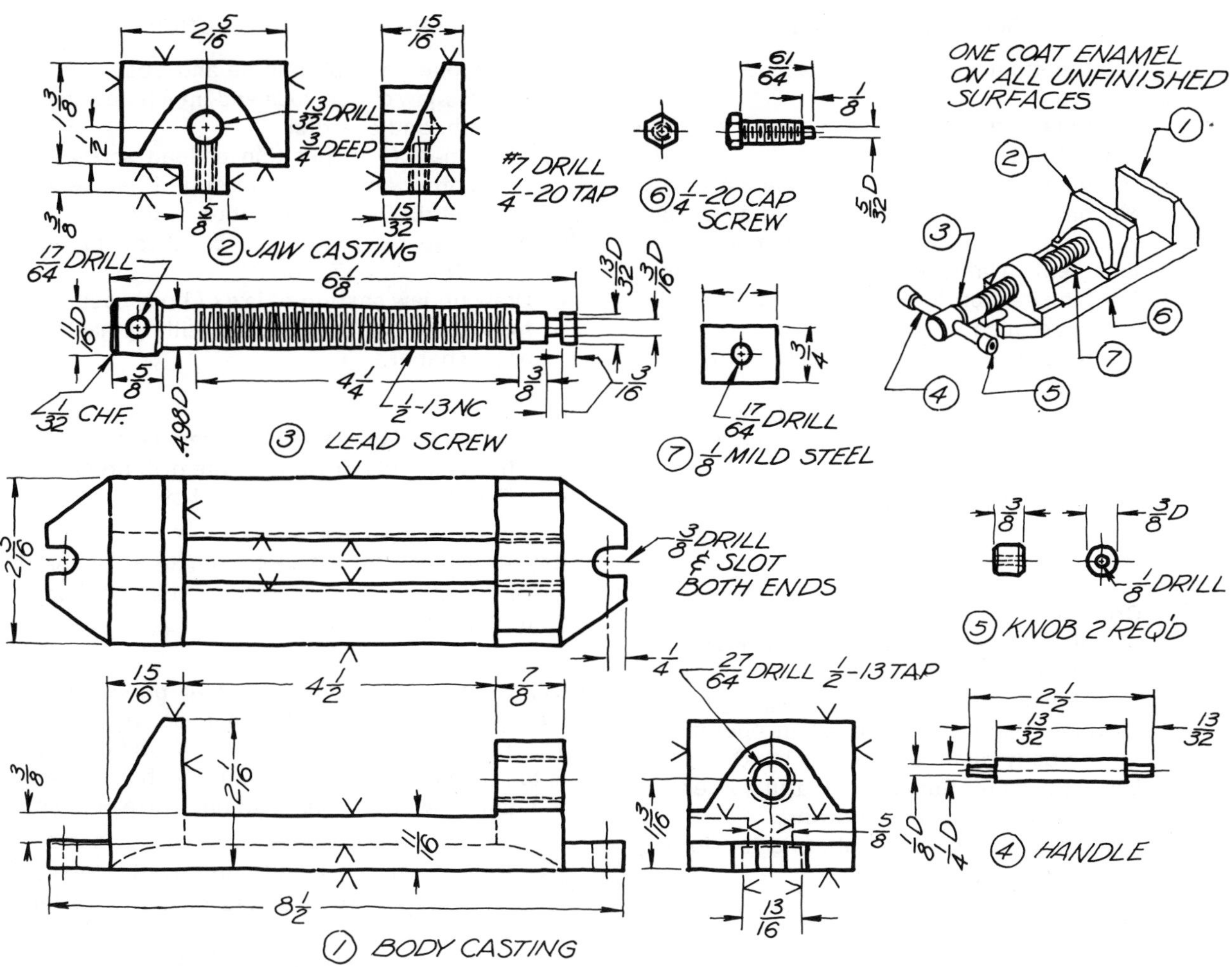

Fig. 19-254. Problems 94, 95, and 96: Size B sheets. (Courtesy of C. F. Struck Corporation. Ready-made castings of this project and others are available from this company in Cedarburg, Wisconsin 53012.)

93. Refer to Fig. 19-253. Make a detail drawing of the parts assigned. Draw each part on a single Size A or B sheet. Additional views, notes, and dimensions may be needed to explain the parts.

94. Refer to Fig. 19-254. A designer has made a freehand layout of the various parts of a drill press vise and has given the major dimensions of each part. As the design draftsman, you are required to make a complete detail drawing of all the parts, adding any views or notes that would make the drawing easier to understand. Other dimensions must be added also. Show a parts list.

Machining Operations

The following machining operations are given to describe the steps that will be performed by the machine shop in finishing the rough casting of the parts of this assembly.

BODY CASTING (No. 1)

1. Grind bottom, sides, jaw surface, and sliding surface.
2. Machine bottom in four-jaw chuck on lathe or by shaper.
3. Machine one side as in operation 2 above.
4. Machine surface of jaw and sliding surface with milling machine, milling machine attachment on lathe with end mill, or by shaper.
5. Machine section for Part No. 7. Same setup as in operation 4.
6. Machine opening for sliding jaw. Same setup as in operation 4.
7. Lay out, drill, and slot both ends for bolting.
8. Lay out and center-punch location for lead screw.
9. Drill and tap for lead screw.

JAW CASTING (No. 2)

1. Grind both surfaces, sides, and bottom.
2. Machine surfaces in four-jaw chuck on lathe or by shaper.
3. Machine bottom section to fit opening in body casting. Use same setup as in operation 4 for the body casting, or file by hand.
4. Lay out, center-punch, and drill for end of lead screw as shown in drawing.
5. Lay out, center-punch, drill, and tap for cap screw as shown in drawing.

LEAD SCREW (No. 3)

1. Select and machine stock in preparation for threading.
2. Prepare lathe for threading. Check lead screw with threads in body casting. Machine for perfect thread fit.

HANDLE (No. 4)

1. Select and machine stock as shown on drawing.

KNOBS (No. 5)

1. Select and machine stock as shown on drawing.

ASSEMBLING INSTRUCTIONS

1. Place one knob on handle and upset. Place in three-jaw chuck, face end, machine surface of knob, and chamfer.
2. Place handle in position of lead screw and place other knob on other end of handle and upset end. Repeat operation 1 above.
3. Assemble jaw casting to body casting with Parts Nos. 3, 6, 7, and 8.
4. Draw up jaw casting to jaw of body casting in four-jaw chuck on lathe, by milling machine, or by shaper.

95. Refer to Fig. 19–254. Prepare an orthographic assembly drawing of the drill press vise on a Size B sheet. Give a parts list.

96. Refer to Fig. 19–254. Make a pictorial assembly drawing of the drill press vise on a Size B sheet. Give a parts list.

97. Refer to Fig. 19–255. Two photographic views of the same cast iron base are shown. The overall height of the part is $7\frac{3}{4}''$ and the base is to be held in position by four $\frac{3}{16}''$ bolts. Make a detail drawing of the base on a Size B sheet.

98. Refer to Figs. 19–256 and 19–257. A testing device is shown that was designed to test the quality of bonds in metal-to-metal constructions. This device applies a "peeling" action to determine the resistance of test samples. Prepare a detail drawing to describe each part of this apparatus, including the upper and lower clevises shown in the photograph and the cylindrical base pieces.

99. Refer to Figs. 19–256 and 19–257. Prepare an assembly drawing, either orthographic or pictorial, of the parts of the testing apparatus.

100. Refer to Figs. 19–258 and 19–259. A designer has made a preliminary detail drawing of a machinist's bench vise as a freehand layout on grid paper. The drawing is made generally to scale with each grid equal to $\frac{1}{4}''$. The more important dimensions have been given, but many will have to be supplied by the draftsman. Some of the parts need additional views or sections to explain them more clearly to the craftsman in the shop.

Prepare a complete working drawing of the parts of the bench vise on Size C sheets. Give all dimensions and views that are necessary to explain the design. Give a parts list. Estimate the dimensions that are not given. Study the assembly of the parts to make sure that mating parts are properly dimensioned to fit.

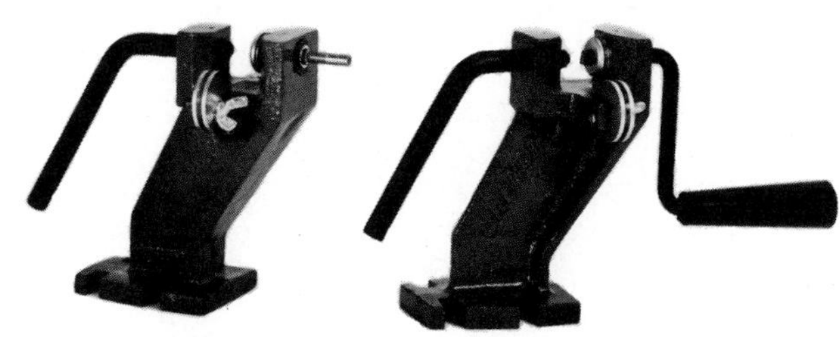

Fig. 19–255. Problem 97: Size B sheet. (Courtesy of Omark Industries.)

Fig. 19–256. Problems 98 and 99. (Courtesy of U.S. Department of Agriculture, Forest Service.)

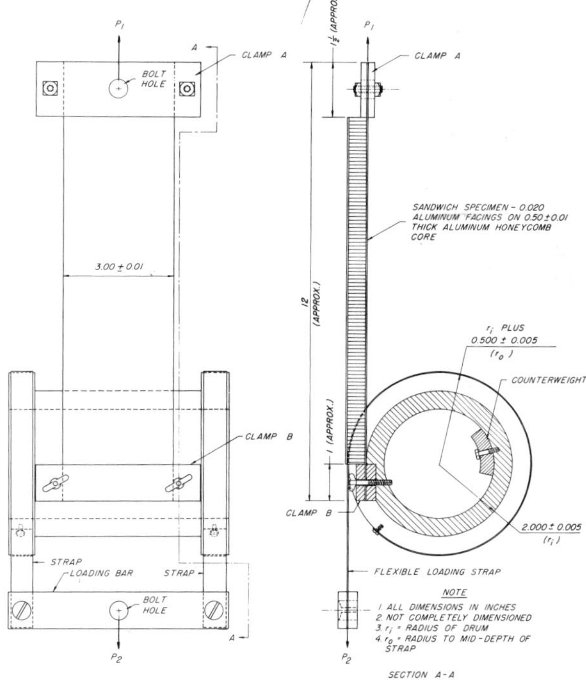

Fig. 19–257. Problems 98 and 99. (Courtesy of U.S. Department of Agriculture, Forest Service.)

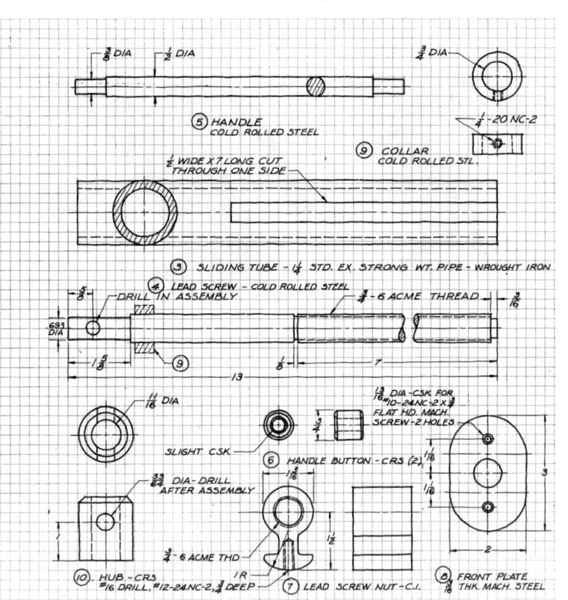

Fig. 19–258. Problems 100 and 101. (Courtesy of C. F. Struck Corporation.)

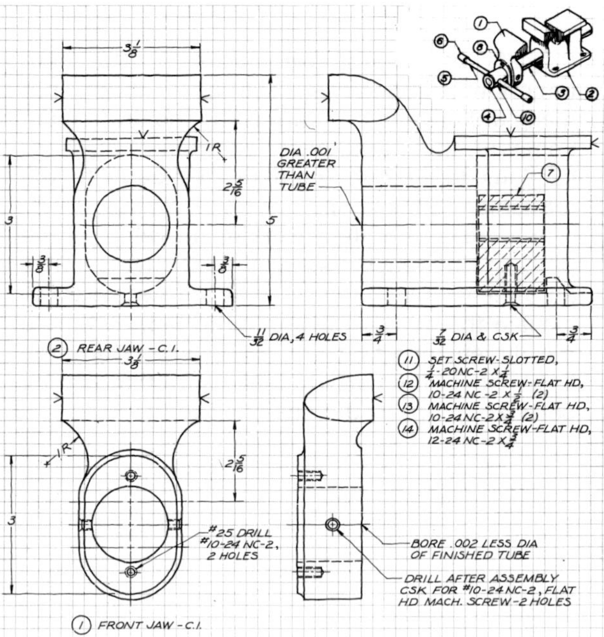

Fig. 19–259. Problems 100 and 101. (Courtesy of C. F. Struck Corporation.)

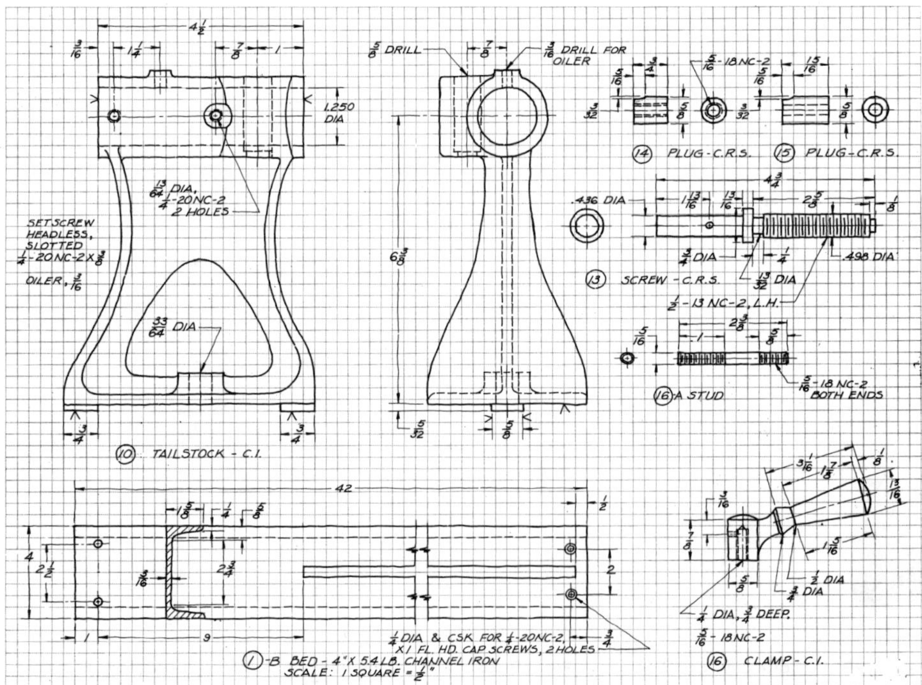

Fig. 19–260. Problems 102 and 103. (Courtesy of C. F. Struck Corporation.)

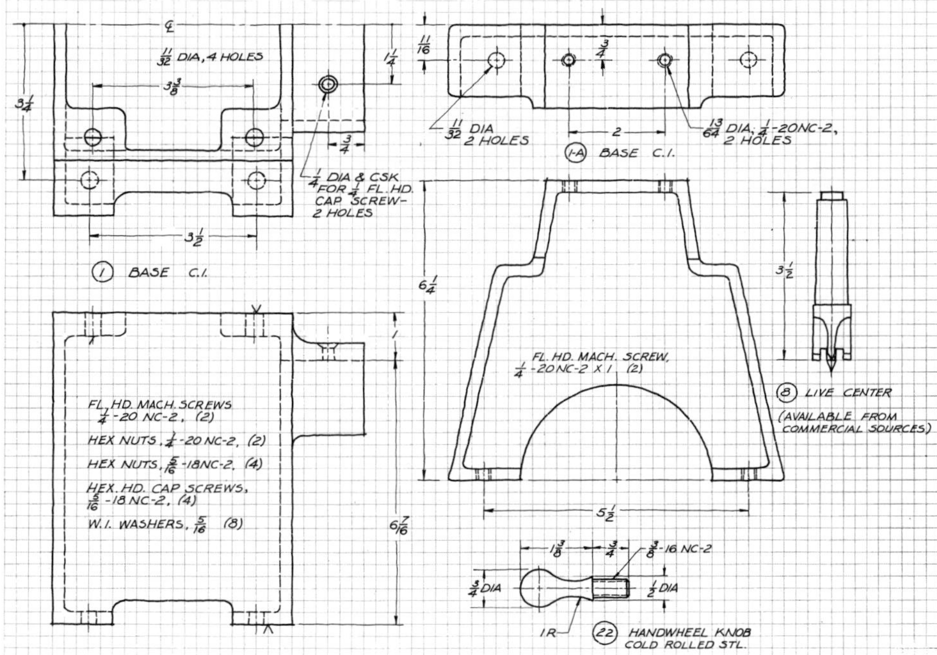

Fig. 19–261. Problems 102 and 103. (Courtesy of C. F. Struck Corporation.)

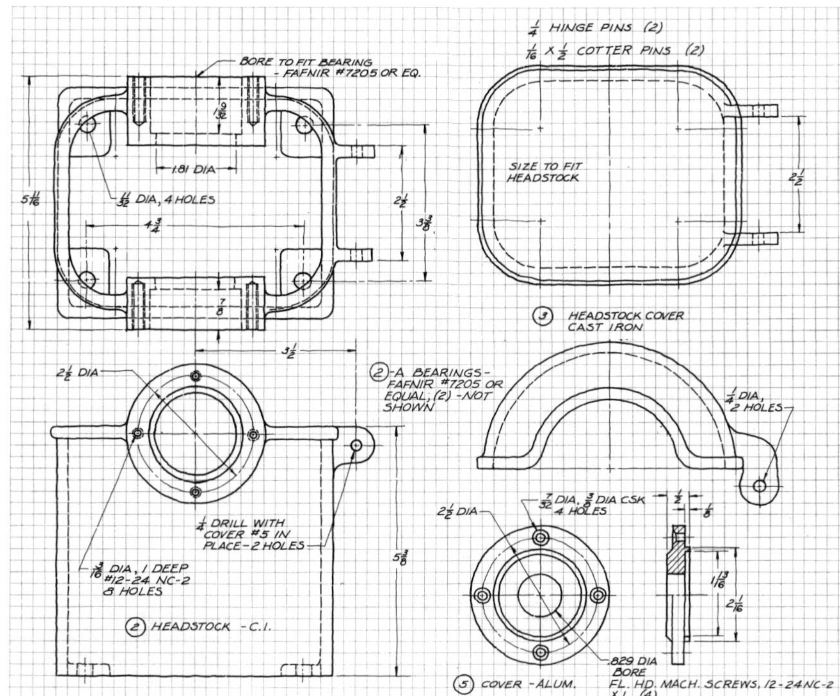

Fig. 19–262. Problems 102 and 103. (Courtesy of C. F. Struck Corporation.)

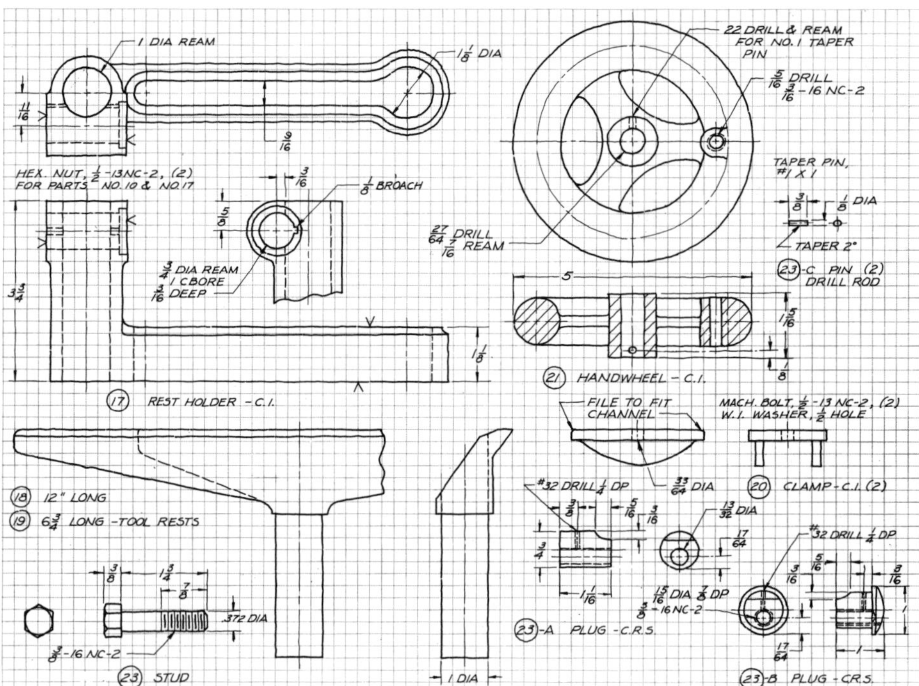

Fig. 19-263. Problems 102 and 103. (Courtesy of C. F. Struck Corporation.)

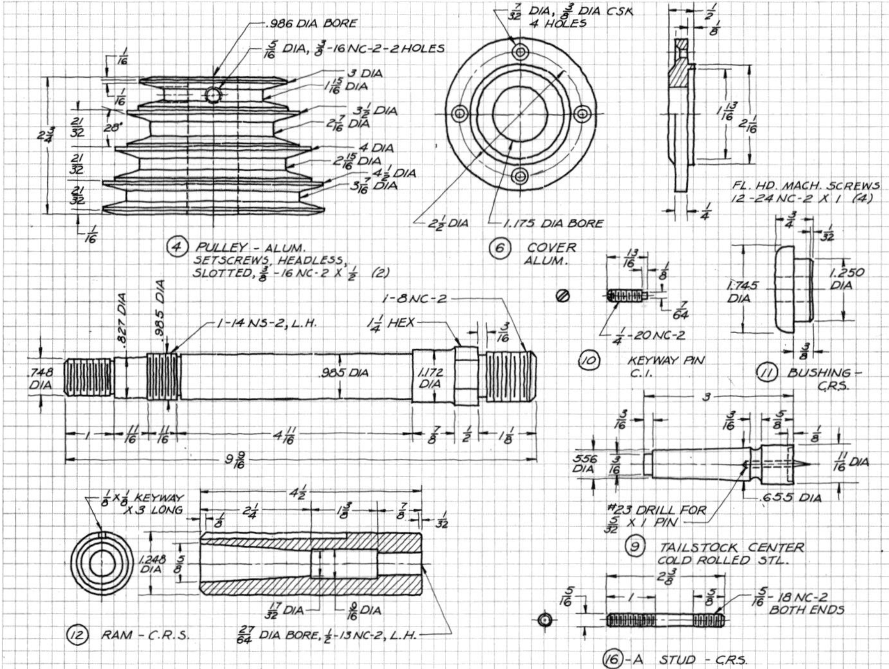

Fig. 19-264. Problems 102 and 103. (Courtesy of C. F. Struck Corporation.)

101. Refer to Figs. 19–258 and 19–259. Prepare an assembly drawing, either orthographic or pictorial, of the bench vise. Give a parts list.

102. Refer to Figs. 19–260 through 19–265. A designer has made a partial freehand detail drawing of the parts of a wood lathe. Each grid on the layout represents $\frac{1}{4}''$. As a design draftsman, you are required to make a complete working drawing of these parts on Size C sheets for the approval of the engineer. It will be necessary to study each view in order to decide on additional views and methods of drawing that will make the completed drawing easier to understand. Many dimensions must be determined by your judgment and your analysis of the parts and their relation to one another.

The assembly drawing (Fig. 19–265) will assist you in understanding how the parts fit together. Give a parts list.

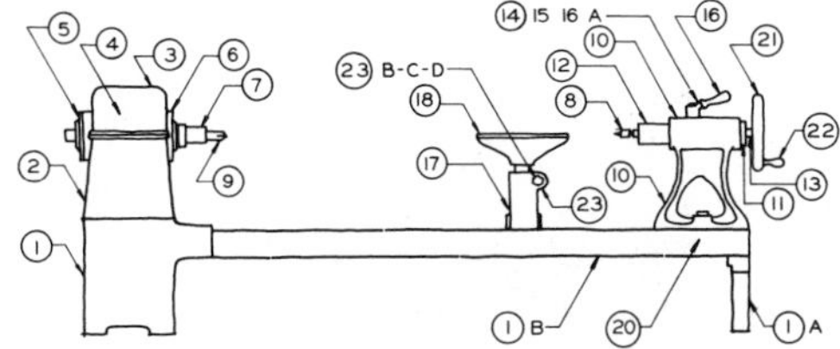

Fig. 19–265. Problems 102 and 103. (Courtesy of C. F. Struck Corporation.)

103. Refer to Figs. 19–260 through 19–265. Prepare assembly drawings of (A) the headstock assembly, (B) the tailstock assembly, and (C) the tool rest assembly in Size C sheets. Give a parts list for each assembly. These assembly drawings may be either orthographic or pictorial.

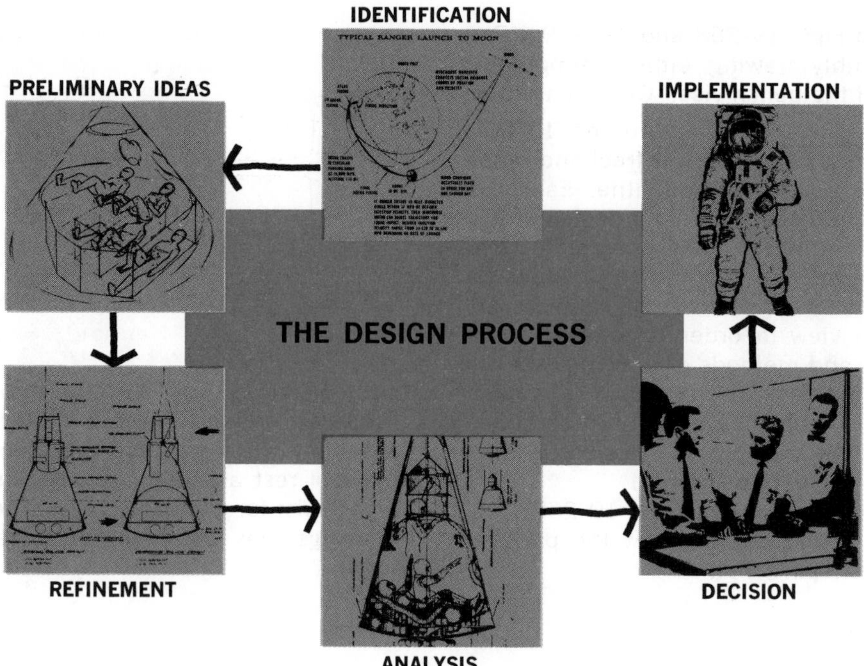

20 DESIGN PROBLEMS

20-1 GENERAL

Most engineering problems are relatively unstructured and require a considerable degree of analysis to identify the actual needs and to determine whether or not the problem does exist and is worthy of solution. Many academic engineering problems are more easily understood than are design problems since the former involve fewer variables and are more clearly defined. This simplification is necessary in presenting important techniques and principles of problem solving. In reality, engineering problems are seldom compartmentalized by subject area in a clearly defined structure that suggests a single solution. It is more common for problems to contain a blend of several areas, ranging from psychological and social factors to different fields of engineering. Consequently, the engineer and technician must work as members of a team composed of specialists in as many areas as may be involved in the problem. Each must play a significant role in attaining an optimum result that will satisfactorily meet the design criteria.

This chapter will introduce problems that can be used for class assignments, team projects, and other combinations of approaches to provide an experience in applying all of the previously covered principles and techniques of this volume. Specifications for these assignments are given to suggest problems that can be used as short, one-period projects or as comprehensive semester projects.

20-2 THE INDIVIDUAL APPROACH

The short problem—requiring one or two hours—will probably be assigned for solution by students working individually with responsibility for each step of the design process and the solution of the problem. A series of short problems that familiarize the student with an orderly approach to a typical design problem is the keystone to design. The individual approach is introduced in Article 4–2.

An advantage to the individual approach is unity of control with the authority to make decisions without consulting associates. No time or effort need be expended in the management or coordination of the work of team members. This advantage is most apparent when a design problem is of limited scope and well within the abilities of a single designer. A more complex problem that is beyond the competence of a single designer requires specialists to provide assistance in unfamiliar areas. The designer who works individually, whether on a class project in school or on an engineering project in actual practice, may easily overlook an important consideration in solution when his ideas are not discussed with his associates. Such an oversight may not be due to his inability, but rather to the human tendency to become too closely involved in a problem to recognize all of its aspects.

The procedure for solving a design problem is the same for all types of problems. A simple design problem may involve fewer details and less depth in each step, but all design steps are applied as in the more sophisticated, comprehensive problem.

20–3 TEAM APPROACH

The complexity of today's technology necessitates the team approach to most problems of any significance because most problems are too comprehensive for a single designer's capabilities. Consequently, the team approach to design will introduce the student to the interaction of team dynamics that will be an integral part of his professional practice. Specialists with widely varying background will work together toward common design objectives. These specialists may have different backgrounds in engineering and in other professions.

The team approach requires that more effort be devoted to the organization and coordination of group effort. An effectively organized team working on a single problem has access to more talent than does the typical individual who devotes the same number of man-hours to the project. The application of this talent will be a problem if the team is not properly organized toward a unified effort. Team management and working effectively with others are valuable traits that should be developed by the student; they are requirements in professional practice.

Team Size. The design team can be too large to effectively utilize the varying talents of the team members. It is obvious that the larger a team becomes, the more difficult the management process will be. There are many examples of weaknesses in organization and communication in large corporations, because the involvement of thousands of people introduces severe management difficulties.

A student design team should have from three to seven members. Three is considered a minimum number for a valid team experience in the group approach. The optimum size, four, lessens the possibility of domination by one or more members. Teams larger than five approach the unmanageable size because the possibility of dissension among the members may be increased by ineffective organization and wide differences of opinion. Such dissension is more likely in class situations than in professional practice, where authority and supervision are more easily applied to direct the activity.

Team Composition. Teams need not be composed of close friends or persons with particular relationships. In actual practice, the engineering team may be composed of professionals from different firms who may be total strangers. This arrangement can be advantageous, in that it reduces the impact of personalities and individual traits that may affect an association of close friends. The members of such a team are likely to be concerned more with the project and the merits of each idea than with the person presenting it. The solution of a typical engineering team project by a student team composed of randomly selected members will provide experience in team dynamics.

20-4 THE SELECTION OF A PROBLEM

The design team, once assigned by the instructor, will work on a problem selected from any of several sources to be solved within the allotted time. They may select a problem of the system or product variety that interests the team, or the instructor may assign a specific problem. Assignment by the instructor would of course approximate the industrial situation, where an engineering problem is assigned for solution by an engineering group without the group's involvement in selection. As a third source, the team may select a problem, or a modification of a problem, from those given in this chapter as their project.

If the team is to select its own problem and submit it as a proposal, consideration should be given to the requirements stipulated by the instructor—available time and the abilities of the team. Guidelines for problem assignment are given later in this chapter. A team may obtain a list of possible problems by means of a "brainstorming session" (Article 4-6). If possible, problems should relate to real situations at the local level, where the team can observe the needs and conditions firsthand. The problem selected should provide a challenge without being so complex that it causes frustration or requires more time than is available. Consequently, problems should be investigated and discussed by the team members to evaluate their appropriateness and interest to the group.

The best problem for a student design project is one that involves familiar and, if possible, accessible areas. This requirement is especially important in the systems problem, for which the student must gather field data. Evaluation of the situation by means of firsthand observation is always preferable. The design of the parking lot, introduced in Chapter 2, is a specific and realistic problem to which the student can relate. Consequently, it is more effective than a hypothetical problem for which design criteria are unavailable. A design for a product to fill a need with which the student is familiar requires less time than does the investigation of an unfamiliar assignment. A design for a water ski rack for an automobile is more feasible than one for a support bracket for an airplane, since the average student is familiar with water skis and has access to an automobile to establish the limiting factors of the design problem.

20-5 PROBLEM PROPOSAL

The best design problem is one that has been recognized and proposed by the student who will be working toward its solution. The mere ability to recognize the need for a new design or a modification of an existing design is the first step toward the development of a creative attitude. An awareness of surroundings, environment, and factors affecting everyday activities can provide many problems in need of solution. It is not unusual to find that several suggestions for the improvement of a newly purchased product can be made after its first use. Furthermore, many relatively simple new products gain acceptance on the wide scale market because they fulfill definite needs. The average person can develop an awareness of the need for patentable ideas and, with a positive attitude, propose solutions that can actually be patented.

When the members of a design team decide on a design project they would like to pursue, they should prepare a written proposal to identify the problem and to outline its limits. The format for the proposal and a description of its contents are given in Article 16-5. A proposal need not be lengthy, but it should reflect sufficient thought and planning to indicate an adequate grasp of the problem. A brief schedule of time and the sequence of activities to be followed during the project can help in indicating the method of approach. Suggested forms for scheduling that can be included in the proposal are given in Article 3-7.

Instructor-Assigned Problems. Three or four problems may be assigned by the instructor to teams of equal size. Assigned problems are appropriate for class competitions, in which the best designs will be selected from those presented. Competition, a natural source of stimulation, demonstrates at the same time the wide variety of possible solutions to the same problem. Assigned problems are more likely to be structured to comply with the available time than are student-proposed projects, which often tend to be overambitious.

20–6 TEAM ORGANIZATION

During the problem selection and proposal stage of the project, the team can function as a group with little organization, but once the problem has been approved, a higher level of organization will be advantageous. The most generally accepted method of organization is the selection of a *chief designer* or *project chief,* who will be in charge of the assignments and their implementation. His function is not that of a dictator; rather, he is the final arbitrator of differences of opinions or stalemates that may arise during the project. In addition to coordinating the total effort and recognizing needed corrections, the chief designer will be expected to carry a work load equal to that of each team member on the project.

Organizational Suggestions. The following suggestions can be used by a team as guidelines to assist its members in working toward the completion of their project. (In addition, references are provided to those portions of the text where more detailed instructions may be found.)

A progress report should be prepared after each project period; Fig. 16–8 is an example of a progress report format. The periods of this team project assignment are spread over fourteen weeks, beginning with the second week of the semester and ending with the fifteenth week. The instructor may choose to have the team work on their team assignments during regular class periods throughout the semester or, else, he may ask the students to meet as a team outside of class periods. In either case, the team should meet for at least one hour per week during the semester to work on the project.

Week 1: Team Organization. Each team should discuss each part of the project as a group, but it will probably be necessary to appoint a project chief. This assignment can be for the duration of the project or it can be rotated among other team members.

Week 2: First Meeting. The following activities should be discussed and assigned to specific team members.

A. After the project has been selected, each team member should review these text references before the first group meeting: Chapters 2, 3, 4, and the first part of Chapter 20.
B. Do not attempt to solve the problems confronting you during the first meeting. Instead, try to identify the problems and the factors affecting them. Use worksheets (Article 3–2) to list all facts and information as a permanent record. See Figs. 3–5 and 3–6.
C. Consider writing letters to manufacturers and suppliers for technical information (Article 4–4). Search library materials. These tasks should be assigned early in the project.
D. Determine the data that must be gathered to identify your problems—dimensions, trends, surveys, and similar information (Articles 3–3 through 3–6).

Week 3: Second Meeting. Problem Identification

A. List jobs that must be performed on the D.S. & P.R. form (Articles 3–7 and 3–10).
B. Prepare an activities network (Article 3–8) to determine the sequence of activities necessary to complete the project.
C. List the activities on an Activity Sequence Chart (ASC) (Fig. 3–20) and assign each job to a team member.
D. Each team member should make a copy of the ASC for reference.
E. Prepare a progress report to cover this period's effort (Fig. 16–8).

Week 4: Third Meeting. Preliminary Ideas

A. Team members may make more progress if, at the beginning of each meeting, they work individually to develop as many ideas as possible. Notes and sketches should be prepared legibly and kept for group discussion (Article 4–2).
B. Review individual ideas as a group (Article 4–3).

C. Conduct a brainstorming session (Article 4-6). List all ideas.
D. Make assignments to team members.
E. Discuss the need for a survey (Article 4-5).
F. Prepare a progress report for your instructor (Fig. 16-8).

Week 5: Visiting Engineers
A. Invite engineers from industry or representatives from other departments on your campus to serve as consultants to your class during one class period. These consultants can discuss your problems with you and offer advice that may be of help to you.
B. The consultants cannot be expected to solve your problems, but instead, they will serve as counselors and as coaches to guide each team.
C. Each team should make a brief progress report to each consultant at the outset of the meeting.
D. Questions can be asked each consultant concerning his job, company, or any other aspect of his profession that might improve your understanding of career opportunities.

Week 6: Fourth Meeting. Preliminary Ideas
A. Continue collecting ideas. Keep all worksheets and notes for inclusion in the appendix of your written report (Articles 3-2 and 4-8 through 4-10).
B. Prepare a progress report for your instructor.

Week 7: Fifth Meeting. Design Refinement
A. Begin making scale drawings and determining specific characteristics of your project (Chapter 6).
B. Prepare graphs, diagrams, and schematics that can be used in your report and also as visual aids in the oral presentation (Chapters 16 and 17).
C. Apply more critical judgment at this stage than in the previous examples.

Week 8: Sixth Meeting. Analysis
A. Review all collected data, preliminary ideas, and refined designs. Consider weights of materials, strength, economy, market prospects, and human factors as they might affect your design (Chapter 13).
B. Apply engineering fundamentals learned in other courses.
C. Prepare a progress report for your instructor.

Week 9: Seventh Meeting. Decision and Implementation
A. Your team must select or reject the best solution at this point. If a solution is not feasible, your report should clearly state why this is the case. Lack of a solution is not considered a team failure if you have carefully studied the problem.
B. Implementation is the final step of the design project. All findings will be presented in a technical report; a model may be required for product designs.
C. If your team has kept data, sketches, and graphs, and has accumulated a record of all activities, a great portion of the report will be completed except for editing (Chapter 16).
D. Assign responsibilities for the preparation of the final drawings and the text of the report.
E. Prepare a progress report.

Week 10: Eighth Meeting. Implementation and Report
A. Make individual assignments and continue with the various parts of the written report.
B. Refine final figures and illustrations. Prepare a letter of transmittal.
C. Prepare a progress report.

Week 11: Ninth Meeting. Complete Report
A. Prepare an evaluation form that reports the contribution of each team member (Fig. 16-10A).
B. Complete the first draft of final report.

Week 12: Tenth Meeting. Preparation for Presentation
A. Organize your presentation (Article 18-4). Determine the types of visuals that are needed (Articles 18-5 and 18-9).
B. Prepare 3 × 5 cards for each visual (Article 18-4).
C. Assign responsibilities for the preparation of visuals.
D. Refer to Chapter 15 for good practices of preparing graphs and visuals.

Week 12: Eleventh Meeting. Preparation for Presentation

A. Continue with assignments to complete presentations for the final presentation.

Week 12: Twelfth Meeting. Preparation for Presentation

A. Complete preparation of visual aids for final presentation.

Week 13: Thirteenth Meeting. Practice Presentation

A. Conduct a practice presentation (Articles 18–10 and 18–11).
B. Use the same techniques of presentation that will be used in the final presentation.
C. Refer to oral report evaluation forms (Fig. 18–29).
D. Have as many team members share in the presentation as possible.

Week 14: Fourteenth Meeting. Final Presentation

A. Give final presentation to the returning consultants.
B. Complete evaluation forms for oral presentation. Include percentage contributed by each team member to the oral presentation (Fig. 18–30).
C. Classes will evaluate each team presentation using the forms provided. Teams will not grade their own.

20–7 DESIGN PROBLEM SPECIFICATIONS

The following specifications are those an individual or design team must consider when preparing a design proposal or outlining their assignments. The specifications, or part of them, may be minimum requirements, as assigned by the instructor or as agreed to by the team. The usual steps of the design process should be followed: identification, preliminary ideas, refinement, analysis, decision, and implementation. This process applies to the short problem requiring one to four man-hours, as well as to the comprehensive problem involving more time.

The Short Problem. The typical short problem can be completed during one class period or as an outside assignment by a single student. A problem of this type will be solved as indicated in Article 2–13. The short problem, usually simple, requires the application of all steps of the process, but in considerably less time than does the comprehensive problem. The specifications for a short problem could include all or part of the following:

1. Completed work sheets illustrating the development of the design process (Chapter 2).
2. A freehand sketch of the design for implementation (Chapters 4 and 19).
3. An instrument drawing of the proposed design (Chapter 19).
4. A dimensioned instrument drawing of the proposed design (Chapter 19).
5. A pictorial sketch (or one made with instruments) illustrating the design (Chapters 4 and 17).
6. Visual aids, flip charts, or other media to present the design to a group (Chapter 18).

The short problem may be presented entirely by means of freehand sketching, which reduces time but requires a high degree of imagination and creativity on the part of the designer. When time permits, instrument drawings can be assigned or used at the option of the student.

The Comprehensive Problem. Comprehensive problems can vary in time, but a typical one takes an average of 80 man-hours. More complex problems can require 120 man-hours, or about 20 hours per man when solved by a team of six. The comprehensive problem can be solved by a designer working alone, but the team approach introduces the student to the problems and advantages of team dynamics. In actual practice, the engineer must perform his duties as a member of a team because of the complexity of engineering.

The following specifications will apply in total or in part to a comprehensive problem of the systems- or product-development type. It will be apparent which apply to the one type and not to the other. For example, a market survey would not be appropriate for a systems problem involving the design of a parking lot.

1. A proposal outlining the problem, the method of approach, and the specifications used in solving the problem (Chapter 16).
2. Completed work sheets illustrating the development of the design process (Chapter 2).
3. Schematic diagrams, flow charts, or other symbolic methods of illustrating the design and its function (Chapter 15).
4. An opinion survey determining interest for the proposed design (Chapter 4).
5. A market survey evaluating the product's possible acceptance and estimated profit (Chapter 13).
6. A model or prototype for analysis or presentation (Chapter 13).
7. Pictorials explaining features of the final design solution that are not clearly shown in other drawings (Chapter 17).
8. Dimensioned engineering drawings giving details and specifications of the design (Chapter 19).
9. A technical report, fully illustrated with charts and graphs, explaining the activities leading to the solution and ending with conclusions and recommendations (Chapter 16).
10. An oral presentation of the design solution (Chapter 18).

20-8 SHORT DESIGN PROBLEMS

The following are short problems that can be completed in less than two periods. They are usually assigned as individual assignments.

Problem 1: Lamp bracket. Design a simple bracket to attach a desk lamp to a vertical wall for reading in bed. The lamp should be easily removable so that it can be used as a conventional desk lamp. The bracket can be left on the wall as a permanent fixture.

Problem 2: Towel bar. Design a towel bar for a kitchen or bathroom. Determine optimum size, and consider styling, ease of use, and method of attachment. This design will be a modification of those already available on the market.

Problem 3: Luggage wheels. The traveling executive or businessman may have to carry his luggage considerable distances in terminals and other places. Design a built-in wheel system or some other system as an integral part of a suitcase to reduce the necessity of carrying it. The finished product should enable the traveler to tow, push, or guide his luggage in some fashion. It should be durable, economical, quiet, and lightweight.

Problem 4: Pipe aligner for welding. Pipes are often welded together in sections for various engineering needs. The initial problem of joining pipes with a butt weld is the alignment of the pipes in the desired position. Design a device with which to align pipes for this purpose for on-the-job welding. For ease of operation, a hand-held device would be desirable. Assume that the pipes will vary in diameter from 2″ to 4″.

Problem 5: Conduit bender. Conduit (steel tubing used to contain utility wiring) is difficult to bend without causing the tubing to collapse, thus making insertion of the wiring impossible. Bending must be on a gradual curve to overcome this problem. Design a device that will permit the bending of 1′ thin-wall conduit to a $6\frac{1}{2}''$ inside radius at the bends. The device should be sufficiently simple for on-the-job application.

Problem 6: Work-load lift stabilizer. A work-load lift used for elevating loads and providing a work platform for repairs on above ground installations is shown in Fig. 20-1. Given that the maximum extended height of a particular lift is 15′-6″, design a device to stablize the platform to prevent it from overturning. The stabilizer should be easy to install and adjust while providing the necessary stability for the maximum situation that could be expected.

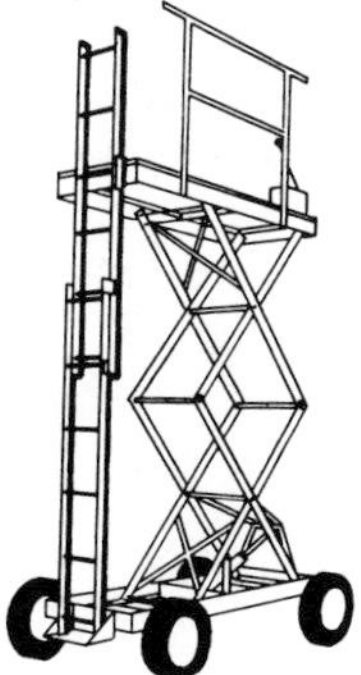

Fig. 20–1. A work-load lift.

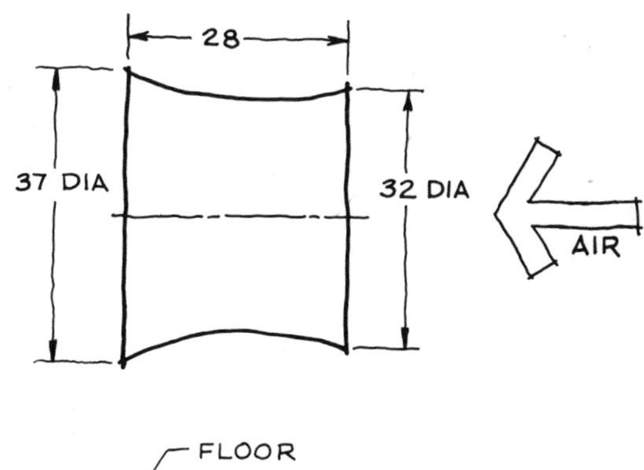

Fig. 20–2. An industrial fan profile.

Problem 7: Fan support. Design a fan base for the fan shown in Fig. 20–2. The fan is to be used in plants and shops where heat is a handicap to the workmen. The stand should be portable so that the fan can be moved to various locations. Consider the possibility of providing a tilt adjustment for pointing the fan into various directions. Your design should be as economical and light as possible.

Problem 8: Troughed belt idler. A conveyor commonly used for handling lightweight materials employs a troughed rubber belt of about 20″ width that is supported, at intervals, by a series of idlers. These consist of three drums that are positioned as shown in Fig. 20–3. Using these specifications, design the hardware to support the drums in the position shown to complete the design for an idler. A one-piece assembly might be preferable.

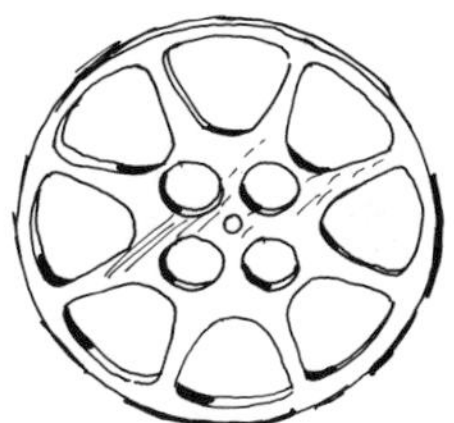

Fig. 20–4. A typical movie projector reel.

Problem 9: Film reel design. The film reel used on projectors is often difficult to thread due to the limited working space. A typical 12″ diameter movie reel is shown in Fig. 20–4. Redesign this type of reel to allow more space for threading. Your design should also be attractive, since the reel is a consumer product that must compete against other designs.

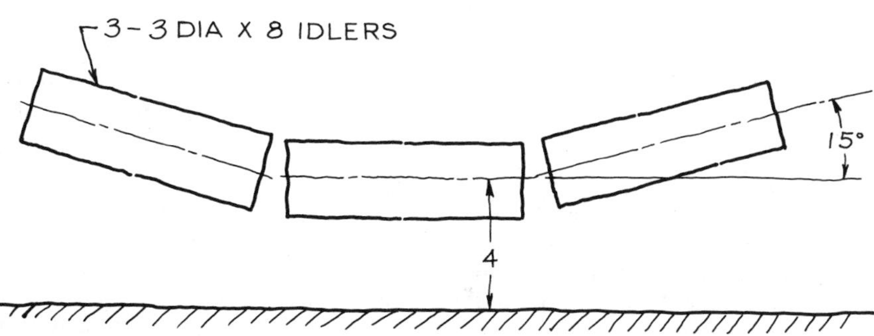

Fig. 20–3. Three idler rollers used for a conveyor belt.

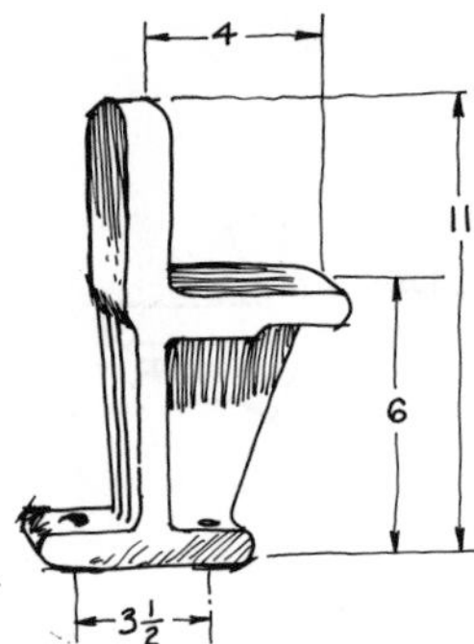

Fig. 20–5. A motor mount bracket.

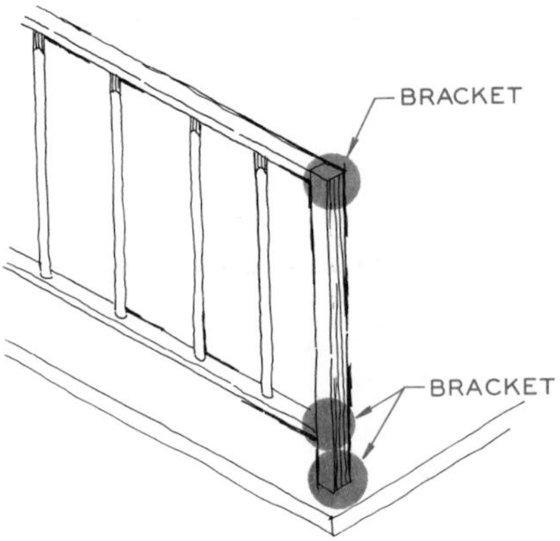

Fig. 20–6. A porch railing system.

Problem 10: Redesign a motor mount bracket. Older machine tools were heavy and often poorly balanced by today's standards. Considerable savings have been made by reducing the material and labor required in the production of parts while maintaining the same function, strength, and stability. Using common sense and analysis, redesign the bracket illustrated in Fig. 20–5 to make it lighter and easier to fabricate.

Problem 11: Side-view mirror. In most cars, rear-view mirrors are attached to the side of the automobile to improve the driver's view of the road. Analyze the requirements this mirror will have to satisfy and its optimum location on the typical automobile. Design a side-view mirror that is an improvement over those with which you are familiar. Develop its design to permit adjustment and tilting of the mirror. Consider the aerodynamics of your design, protection from inclement weather, and other factors that would affect the function of the mirror.

Problem 12: Railing post mount. An ornamental iron railing is to be attached to a wooden porch surface supported by several 1″ square tubular posts. Design the mounting piece that will attach the post to the surface. Figure 20–6 shows typical railing to clarify the problem requirements. Consider the production methods that will be used.

A second attachment is needed to assemble the railing with the support post at each end. Given that two screw holes are to be used, design the part that can be used to secure the two perpendicular members.

Problem 13: Nail feeder. A workman loses time in covering a roof with shingles if he has to fumble for nails. Design a device that can be attached to a workman's chest and will hold nails in such a way that these will be fed in a lined-up position ready for driving. Determine the number of nails that should be held in this device at any one time.

Problem 14: Cupboard door closer. Kitchen cupboard and cabinet doors are usually not self-closing and thus cause safety hazards and an unsightly appearance. Design a device that will close doors left partially open. It would be advantageous to provide a means for disengaging the closer when desired. To have sales appeal, the device should be very simple and economical. The fewer parts used, the better.

Problem 15: Paint can holder. Paint cans are designed with a simple wire bail that, when held, makes it difficult to get a paint brush in the can. Wire bails are also painful to hold for any length of time. Design a holding device that can be easily attached and removed from a gallon paint can (6.5″ diameter × 7.5″ height). Consider the human factors such as comfort, grip, balance, and function.

Problem 16: Self-closing or opening hinge. Interior doors of residential dwellings tend to remain partially open instead of staying in a completely open position against the wall. This introduces a problem when a door opens into the end of a hall, since the edge of the door which is ajar in the middle of the hall can be a hazard to the occupants.

Design a hinge that will hold the door in a completely open position. This can be used to replace door stops and other devices used to hold doors. Your design should be as simple as possible.

Problem 17: Tape recorder cartridge storage unit. Tape recorders are used frequently in automobiles. A cartridge of recorded music, etc., is inserted into the amplifier system. Design a storage unit that will hold a number of these cartridges in an orderly fashion, so that the driver can select and insert them with a minimum of motion and distraction. Determine the best location for this unit and the method of attachment to an automobile. Provision should be made to protect the cartridges from theft.

Problem 18: A better mousetrap. It is said that the world will beat a path to the door of the designer of a better mousetrap. Consider the mechanics of trapping mice and design a trap that would be an improvement over existing designs. Determine the market value of the trap and its acceptability as a production item for the general market.

Problem 19: Slide projector elevator. Most commercial slide and movie projectors have adjustment feet used to raise the projector to the proper position for casting an image on a screen (Fig. 20–7). The range of variation of this adjustment is usually less than 2″. Since this is a relatively small range, projectors must often be propped on books or other objects to reach the desired height. Study a slide projector available to you, to determine the specific needs and the limitations of an adjustment that would provide a greater variation in elevation. Design a device to serve this purpose as part of the original design or as an accessory that could be used on existing projectors.

Fig. 20–7. A movie projector. (Courtesy of Kodak.)

Problem 20: Bookholder for reading in bed. As a student, you may often desire to read while lying in bed. It becomes uncomfortable to hold a book for a period of time in a position that will offer good vision. Design a holder that can be used for supporting a book in the desired position while providing comfortable conditions. Prepare drawings and schematics to explain your design and its construction.

Problem 21: Table leg design. Do-it-yourselfers build a variety of tables using slab doors, plywood, and commerically available legs. Table tops come in a number of sizes, but table heights are fairly standard. Determine what the standard table heights are and design a family of legs that can be attached to table tops with screws. For improved appearance, the legs should not be vertical but should slant from the table top. Design your legs, indicating the method of manufacture, size, cost, and method of attachment.

Problem 22: Canoe mounting system. Canoes and light boats are often transported on the top of automobiles on a luggage rack or similar attachment. It is quite difficult for one person to load and unload a boat in this position without assistance. Design an accessory that will enable a person to remove and load a boat on top of an automobile without additional help from a second party. This accessory should be as simple as possible to be economical and maintenance free. Assume that this attachment will accommodate aluminum boats varying from 14′ to 17′ in length and 100 lbs to 200 lbs in weight. Make drawings explaining your design and its operation. Give specifications for a method of securing the boat after it is in its final position on top of the automobile.

Problem 23: Anchor clamp. Anchors are used on small fishing boats to prevent drifting. Design a clamp or some attachment that can be used to secure the anchor to the side of the boat with the minimum of effort. The clamp should be self-locking when pressure is applied to the anchor line from the anchor's end of the line.

20-9 SYSTEMS DESIGN PROBLEMS

The systems design problem is a broad engineering problem that requires the study of the interrelationships of various components—social, economic, physical, and management considerations. The end result of a systems problem may be a plan, a conclusion, or a recommendation—as opposed to a hardware design for product development. Five types of systems design problems will be presented and defined: (1) feasibility studies, (2) experimental systems, (3) planning for the future, (4) modification of a system, and (5) production management.

Feasibility Study. Much engineering effort is devoted to the study of a particular problem to determine if a solution to a systems problem is feasible or if a problem does in fact exist. An example is the engineering-management problem of locating an industrial plant in a given area. The engineer must analyze the requirements of both company and community, and the benefits to be derived by each. Engineering problems are studied concurrently with management needs. Predictions are based on the available information, obtained from like situations previously tried or from entirely unproven criteria. A feasibility study that results in a negative recommendation may be as valuable to a company as one conducted on another location that produces a positive recommendation. A negative report can save a corporation millions of dollars that might be lost if invested unwisely. A feasibility study means exactly what its name implies—it is a study of a given situation to ascertain whether or not a particular solution is feasible.

Problem 24: A multi-purpose utility meter. Today's residential units have separate meters for electricity, water, and gas that are checked each month by separate companies. Hence there is considerable duplication of effort and expense. Consider the feasibility of combining all meters into a single unit which could be read by a meter-reading service. A unit of this type would reduce the number of meter readers to one-third. Outline how such a system could be organized and implemented.

Problem 25: Portable bleachers. Portable bleachers are required for some outdoor and indoor activities which attract only small crowds of 100 or less. When conventional chairs are used, seating becomes a problem, since the view from all rows except the first few is limited. Design a portable bleachers system that can be assembled and disassembled with minimum of effort, and which can be stored for continuous use. Consider the structure, size, materials, and method of construction. Determine the weight, size, and storage space needed. Can you identify a variety of uses for these bleachers that would justify their production for the general market?

Problem 26: Archery range. With the increase in leisure time, the manufacture of entertainment and recreation equipment has become an important industry. Skeet ranges, golf ranges, drag strips, and other facilities are being successfully operated with profitable returns. Your assignment is to determine the feasibility of providing an archery range for beginning and experienced archers that can be operated at a sound profit. Your problem is to investigate the need for such a facility, its potential market, its location, the equipment needed, method of operation, costs and fees, and other factors that would bear upon your decision regarding the feasibility of the project. Consider all engineering aspects of site preparation, utilities, concessions, and parking.

Problem 27: Car rental system. Many college students cannot afford automobiles because of expense, or perhaps their colleges do not allow them to own cars. However, most students would like to have access to an automobile for weekends and other student activities. Investigate the possibilities and feasibility of a student-operated rental car system. Data must be collected to determine student interest, cost factors, number of cars needed, rates, personal needs, storage, maintenance, and other factors affecting the feasibility of the operation. Evaluate the total system, so that you can make recommendations based on pertinent data. Specify the details of your system, including the location, the cost of operation, and the expected level of income.

Problem 28: Model airplane field. Model airplane hobbyists who build and fly gasoline engine models often have inadequate facilities for pursuing their hobby. You are commissioned to investigate the need for a facility which will provide these hobbyists with a place for flying their models. You must analyze their needs, the space required, the type of surfaces, control of sound, safety factors, method of operation, and come up with a total evaluation of the system. Select a site on or near your campus which you feel is adequate for this facility. Evaluate the equipment, utilities, and site preparation that would be required. Determine the degree to which a facility of this sort would be utilized and the income, if any, that could be expected from it. Your final solution should explain your approach to the problem, your suggested plan, and recommendations.

An Experimental System. The experimental system, a design related to a totally unproven area, may be considered as radical since it may not have been tried before. Usually, the experimental system concerns the frontiers of engineering where new principles are developed through experience. The entire space program is an offspring of the experimental system designed for use in an atmosphere where conditions are unknown. Aircraft and automobile manufacturers employ teams of engineers to develop futuristic models propelled and guided by highly unconventional systems. Undersea exploration is another engineering area that is probed through the use of experimental systems and techniques. In a sense, all new products are experimental since they are new and untested. Consequently, product designs tend to evolve and change with experience and data obtained through use and application.

Problem 29: Outdoor shower. You are the owner of a weekend cottage. For economy reasons, you do not have a hot and cold water system—you have only cold water. Design a system that can take advantage of the sun's heat in the summer to heat the water used for bathing and kitchen purposes. Devise a means of using the same system in the winter with heat provided from some other source (a wood fire, kerosene, or other method). Explain your design, the operating temperature, and the cost of operating the system when heated artificially in the winter. Can you design a totally portable shower that can be used on camping trips? Consider the possibilities of this product on the general market.

Problem 30: Exercising apparatus. Emphasis is placed on the lack of physical fitness among adults who hold office jobs and do little exercising. Consider the body needs and exercises that are most beneficial to maintaining the body tone necessary for good health. Design a product or an exercising system that can be used as a home exerciser. Explain how your design is to be used and what benefits the user can expect from it.

Problem 31: Overhead skylift. Many campuses are confined to rather small areas, making it impossible for visitors to drive through in an automobile. A visitor who would like to get to know a campus would have to wander about and discover various areas much by chance. It would therefore be helpful to provide a system which would give a visitor an overall view of the campus. One possibility would be an overhead skylift which transports passenger cabs over the campus on a cable. A system of this type could be adapted to give visitors a view of the major sections of the campus, its general layout, and its major buildings. Consider the development of this or a similar system for your campus. Additional accessories could include a sound system that would describe the various buildings during the tour. Determine the route of the cable transport, its method of structure, safety factors, expense of operation, passenger fees, and the anticipated number of customers that could be expected.

Problem 32: Accident recorder. Many accidents occur at intersections with stop lights where traffic is heavy. A great deal of paper work and police effort is required to record the details of an accident from reports of the parties involved and witnesses at the site. What is needed is a system capable of recording the accident on film or TV tape. This idea is very broad and general, requiring detailed study and investigation. Since cost of such a system could be rather high, installations should be restricted to areas where accidents are more likely to occur. One aspect of this problem is to suggest a method of selecting these areas. The design of the system and the description of its mode of operation represent a comprehensive problem which requires, among others, a thorough review of available recording devices. Estimate the cost of operation of your design and its feasibility.

Problem 33: Golf driving range ball return system. Golf driving ranges are usually designed in such a way that the balls must be retrieved by hand or by means of a specially designed vehicle that collects them from the range. This causes a delay in operation, expenditure of labor, and expense. Design a system capable of automatically returning the balls to the driving area. Consider all possibilities of this system from site modification to selection of a special site. If you come up with a feasible system, evaluate the market potential of your design.

Problem 34: Instructional systems. Classroom instruction could be improved by providing two-way communication between the teacher and his students. For example, the teacher could proceed at a more efficient rate if he had some idea as to whether or not his class was understanding the points he was making. Study this problem to determine whether a system could be developed that would give the student some means of signaling his understanding, or lack of understanding, of the lecture without having to ask questions that cause a loss of time. If a system could be devised that would inform the teacher of the effectiveness of his lecture, he could increase or reduce the pace of his presentation, in accordance with the level of comprehension of his class.

Problem 35: Pedestrian transport system. Your campus has considerably more pedestrian traffic in some areas than in others, causing traffic congestion. The flow of traffic may be hampered during rush hours, with the result that students are late to class. Consider the possibility of developing a system that would provide a more even flow of pedestrian traffic during these rush periods. Much time is lost between classes when a student must leave the upper floor of a building, descend to ground level with many other students, travel to another building at ground level, and climb a series of stairs to an upper story of the building. Consider a solution to this problem of pedestrian traffic. Even though your ideas may be experimental and appear to be impractical at first glance, seek a solution to the problem that might introduce an entirely new traffic concept.

Planning for the Future. Essentially all engineering systems problems are designed for the needs of tomorrow as well as today. It would be very costly to design a highway system for present traffic loads without consideration of future needs. The economic survival of entire communities and cities will be determined to a great extent by today's designs. Lack of foresight can result in inadequacy of facilities and systems necessary for normal modifications, expansion, and development. The designer must utilize historical data as a basis for extrapolation of future needs prior to the employment of the more conventional engineering sciences.

Problem 36: Helicopter service. You have been assigned the responsibility of planning a helicopter passenger service that will connect with the local airlines in your community. Helicopters will transport passengers from terminals to your campus on a regular schedule to reduce time loss due to excessive automobile traffic. Analyze the needs of your campus to determine when such a system could be feasible and self-supporting. Determine the helicopter landing area on your campus and the flight schedule. Estimate the number of passengers necessary to justify installation of such a system and the cost per passenger.

Problem 37: Fallout shelters. Recent emphasis has been placed on the importance of shelters for protection against nuclear fallout. Many new urban buildings have been constructed to include shelters as an integral part of the structure. Referring to available data from local and governmental agencies concerning the need for nuclear protection, determine the general needs of your campus for fallout protection ten years from now. As a first step, project the campus population to estimate the number of people who will be involved ten years hence. Estimate the basic needs, length of protection, provisions, etc., as a means of arriving at the space requirements for protection. Your investigation should recommend methods of achieving the desired level of protection in light of the existing protection available.

Problem 38: Campus planning. Assume that your college campus was to begin planning for full-capacity utilization. Full utilization means the total use of your present facilities on a 12-month, 24-hour basis. Determine how many students could be accommodated in your classrooms, dormitories, and in other facilities without adding new buildings. Analysis of teaching schedules, faculty, and service personnel needed should be studied to identify possible problems. Evaluate the changes that will occur in parking systems, pedestrian traffic, and the management of the total system. A considerable portion of this problem is the identification of the critical areas that must be studied. Data should be gathered to support your findings.

Problem 39: Diazo machine operation. Blue-line prints (often called blueprints) are made on a diazo machine by putting the tracing paper drawing in contact with the diazo paper and feeding it through the diazo machine. A reproduction department in a sizable company will have to reproduce many prints; hence a full-time operator will be required. Assume that you have been given the assignment of establishing a system to provide the most efficient utilization of the equipment and the operator's time to meet the specifications outlined below.

The machine will accept individual drawings or groups of drawings along its 40″ belt at a rate of 10′ per second. The drawing size used most frequently by your company is 11″ × 17″. The diazo paper must be run through the developing chamber of the machine directly above the intake at a speed of 10′/second. The machine is 60″ long, 24″ deep, and 48″ high. Determine the equipment and tables and their optimum arrangement for most efficient operation. Analyze the working space required and the sequence of activities. Assuming that the system is designed to your specifications, what is the cost per drawing of the operator working at peak efficiency? Consider the other duties of the operator, such as stapling sets of drawings together and gathering original drawings to be returned with their prints. Make the necessary drawings and schematics to explain your design.

Problem 40: Drive-in theater. You have been commissioned to develop an area for a drive-in motion picture theater. As the chief designer you must determine the optimum size of the drive-in to provide adequate parking and viewing from the audience, as well as an adequate profit. Consideration must be given to traffic flow, screen size, and position, electrical problems, drainage, utilities, concessions, and other facilities commonly found in a theater of this type. Consider the various disciplines of engineering that must be involved in a problem of this complexity. Outline as many as possible of the basic requirements that you will have to provide for. Determine the overall layout of the drive-in, its traffic system, and major components. Detail a typical parking space for a single car, indicating the contour of the surface to provide the proper car angle.

List the areas that would require specialists such as electrical engineers, civil engineers, etc. Outline your plan for involving consultants who could assist you in preparing your final design. Refer to the yellow pages of a telephone directory for names of individuals or firms that could help you.

Problem 41: Boat launching facility. Assume that your community was planning the construction of a lake that would be used as a water sports center. You are to design a boat launching area where boat trailers could be positioned. Assume that as many as 500 boats may be unloaded during the peak hours of a day. Analyze the requirements of a workable system that will control this traffic with a minimum of confusion. Thought must be given to the unloading area, the space required, the parking area, and the type of terrain required for the facility. Determine the charges required to maintain this facility and pay for help if any is needed.

Modification of an Existing Facility. An existing system may prove to be inadequate because of unforeseen technological advancements and the introduction of additional factors to a given situation. The need to enlarge a campus would affect the traffic system, assignment of classes, type of facilities needed, and other related factors. Banks have modified their operational and physical systems to accommodate the drive-in customer. Zoning ordinances are modified to enable a community to keep abreast of changes affecting it. The designer is responsible for introducing innovations within the framework of the existing system while applying the benefits of each to the most productive result.

Problem 42: Shopping checkout system. An acute problem of the shopping center and grocery market is that of checking out goods, payment, and delivery of purchases to the customers' automobiles. Your project is to develop a system for expediting the transfer of goods selected by the customer, from the shelf to the customer's car. This includes the process of packaging and payment. Under the present method, a number of sackers and delivery boys are required to package the groceries and cart them to each customer's car. A more efficient and economical method may be warranted. Consider a solution that will speed up the flow of customers, reduce congestion, reduce cost, and add convenience to as many aspects of the grocery checkout operation as possible.

Problem 43: Automobile interior. The interiors of most automobiles have the same layout, that is, two parallel seats facing the front of the automobile. Interiors of station wagons show some but very minor variations. Analyze the interior of a typical automobile to devise a system that would permit flexibility and increased comfort in seating arrangements. Perhaps seats could be of a modular design, permitting flexible positioning to provide a more comfortable arrangement for watching TV in the back seat or for facilitating conversation among the passengers. Other units could be considered for inclusion in the interior—tape recorders, coolers, couches, reading lights, individual air-conditioning outlets for each passenger. Completely analyze a car's interior, taking into account the human factors and the interrelated systems.

Problem 44: Loading dock system. The trucking industry provides a sizable portion of the trans-

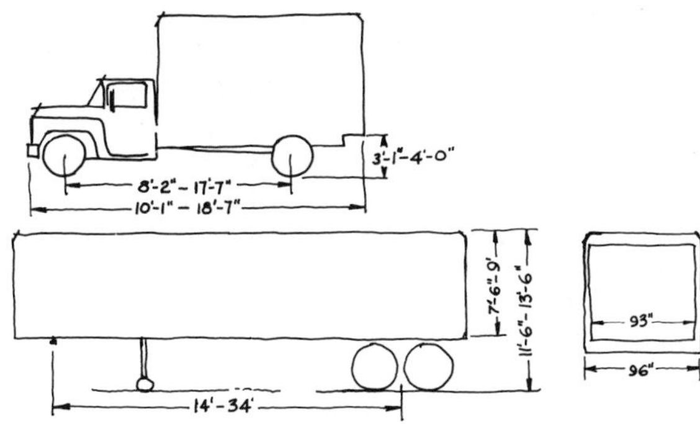

Fig. 20–8. Standard sizes of freight trucks.

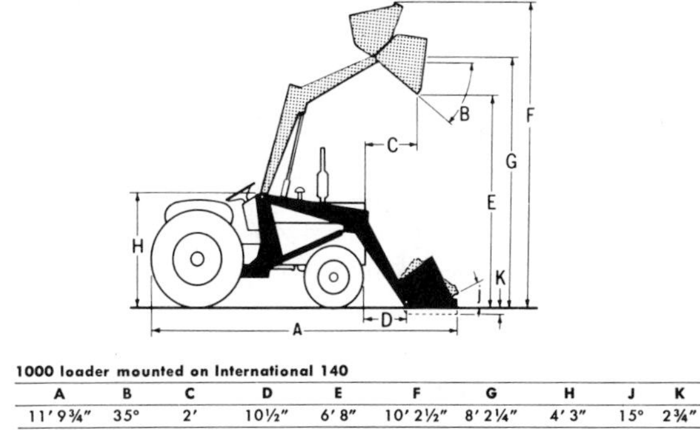

1000 loader mounted on International 140

A	B	C	D	E	F	G	H	J	K
11′ 9¾″	35°	2′	10½″	6′ 8″	10′ 2½″	8′ 2¼″	4′ 3″	15°	2¾″

Fig. 20–9. General dimensions of a farm tractor with a scoop attachment. (Courtesy of the International Harvester Company.)

portation of goods and supplies. It is important that these materials be unloaded and stored as efficiently as possible to keep the trucks en route with the minimum of layover. Unloading is usually performed by a fork lift truck at a loading dock that is level with the truck's floor. Design a method ensuring that the dock can be adjusted to level with the truck's floor. The height of trucks may vary; consequently, an adjustment may be needed to position the floor.

In the winter, dock workers may have to work in extremely cold weather, which reduces their efficiency. Design a system that will allow the truck to be enclosed or protected from the weather during its loading or unloading while taking advantage of the warehouse's heating. The dimensions of average trucks are given in Fig. 20–8 to serve as a guide. In addition to the dock design make a layout of the plan of your design.

Problem 45: Tractor safety device. It is not uncommon for a tractor driver to be killed because the tractor overturned on irregular terrain. A design protecting the driver is therefore worthy of investigation. Consider the types of device or attachment that could be designed to protect tractor drivers. Visit your local farm machinery dealer to obtain the dimensions and specifications that pertain to your solution. The general dimensions of the type of tractor you are to consider are given in Fig. 20–9.

Problem 46: Modification of an existing facility. Isolate an area on your campus or in your community that is inadequate for the present demands made on it. This could be a traffic intersection, parking lot, recreational area, or a classroom. Identify the problem and the deficiencies that should be corrected. Propose modifications that would improve the existing facility. Design a total system that would update this obsolete facility or system.

Problem 47: Tape recording system. In the majority of classes, the student must spend most of his time taking notes; this activity interferes with his concentration on the concepts being presented. In addition, the notes taken may be difficult to read and hence may be ineffective. This note-taking procedure is still predominant although many advanced technological achievements exist that are far superior to the taking of notes. Design a system that would provide a student with a tape recording of class lectures which he could take to his room and play for review purposes. Consider the possibility of providing an automatic system that would record illustrations and diagrams presented by the instructor in class, eliminating manual copying. Estimate the cost of such a system and determine its value to the educational program. Approach this design as though your company were planning to produce an experimental system of this type for the educational market. List applications and needs for such a system outside the educational market.

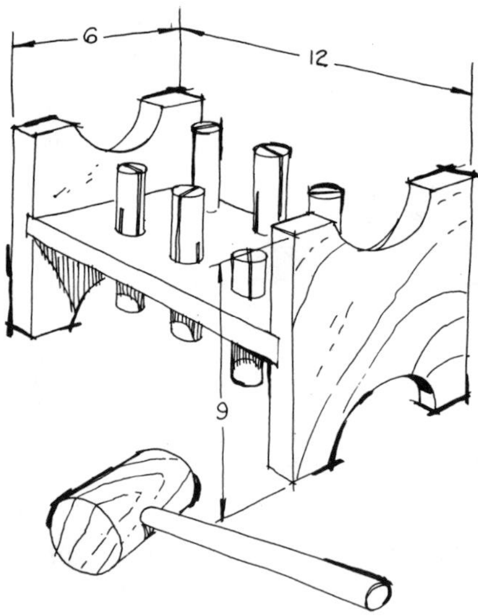

Fig. 20-10. An educational toy to be manufactured in quantities.

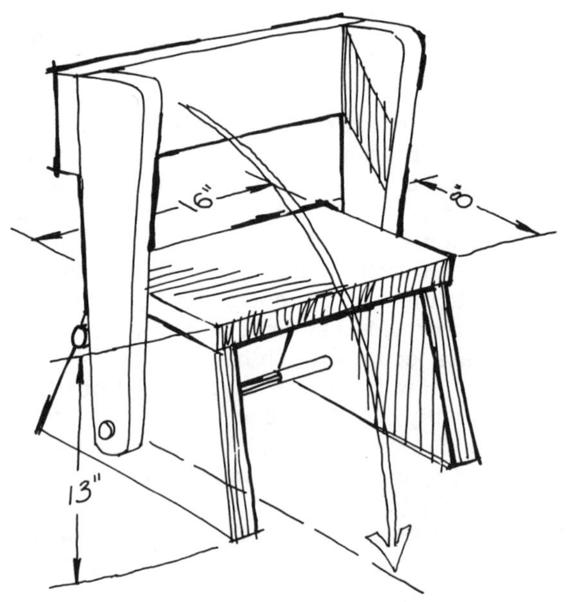

Fig. 20-11. Problem 50: A child's seat.

Problem 48: Service station modification. The service station system used today differs little in arrangement and function from the first filling stations to come into existence. One major change, however, is the conversion to the credit card system, which has slightly complicated the duties of the attendants. A ticket must be prepared and signed by the customer; this requires more effort than the cash payment does. The customary procedure is for the attendant to take the credit card to the office, fill out the ticket, and return to the customer's car. These steps represent lost motion and expenditure of time. The method of servicing automobiles—cleaning windshields, checking oil, and other routine chores—is approached in the same manner, with little improvement in technique.

Consider the usual operations performed in servicing an automobile to develop a more efficient system. This may involve a new layout for the station and the utilities used in servicing cars. Perhaps stations should be designed to quickly accommodate the customer who needs only gasoline and does not need to have his car checked thoroughly. Modify the system so that it will be an improvement over the present one.

Production Management. Engineers must be concerned with methods of economically establishing production systems, routing products, and managing people and machines necessary for an efficient operation. They must consider a wide range of areas, including the availability of alternative systems to augment capacity in case of emergencies. Production problems include the improvement of manufacturing processes, automation of production flow, or even the revision of an entire industry. This is an area requiring the engineer to be aware of cost analysis, organization or machinery, personnel management, and flow of materials.

Problem 49: Educational toy. Assume that you are assigned the responsibility for establishing the production system for manufacturing the educational toy shown in Fig. 20-10 at a rate of 5000 per month. You must determine the square footage needed, types of machines required, space for raw materials, office facilities, and warehousing necessary to sustain this operation. Determine the number of employees needed, their rate of pay, and the number of work stations required. Compute the expense to produce the item and the selling price necessary to provide the required profit margin.

Problem 50: Child's furniture. Proceed as in Problem 49 but assume that the child's furniture shown in Fig. 20-11 is the product to be produced. Determine the number to be manufactured per month to break even and establish the selling price. Establish scales for selling prices in quantities in excess of the break-even level.

Problem 51: Simple product. Select a simple product and establish the production system and requirements for its manufacture, proceeding as in Problem 49. Have the product approved by your instructor before going ahead.

Product Design

Problem 52: Hunting blind. Hunters of geese and ducks must remain concealed while hunting. Design a portable hunting blind to house two hunters. This blind should be completely portable so that it can be carried in separate sections by each of the hunters. Specify its details and how it is to be assembled and used.

Problem 53: Convertible drafting table. Many laboratories are equipped with drawing tables that have drafting machines attached to them. This arrangement clutters the table top surface when the tables are used for classes that do not require drafting machines. Design a drafting table that can enclose a drafting machine, thereby concealing it and protecting it when it is not needed. The table should be easily convertible from a drafting table to a student desk with an uncluttered top.

Problem 54: Football helmet face guard. A great number of injuries in football are face injuries caused by impact from opposing players' helmets and the lack of protection afforded by the helmet used at present (Fig. 20-12). Evaluate this problem and the needs for improvement. Design a better face mask or consider totally redesigning the existing football helmet to provide a greater degree of safety.

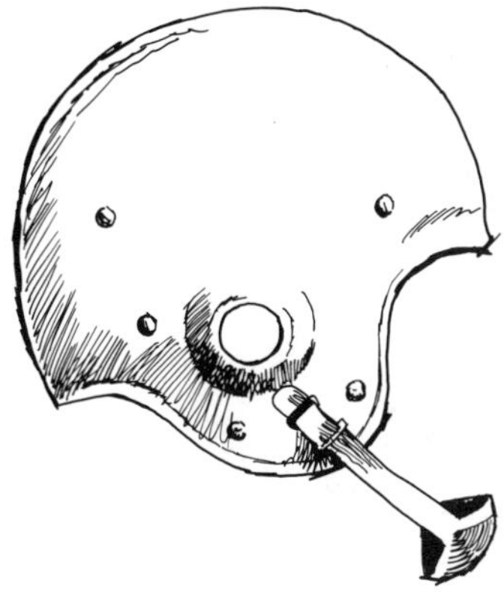

Fig. 20-12. The configuration of the presently used football helmet.

Fig. 20-13. A folding chair with a writing tablet attachment.

Problem 55: Writing tablet for a folding chair. **Design a writing tablet arm for a folding chair** that could be used in an emergency or when a class needs more seating. To allow easy storage, the tablet arm must fold with the chair. (Fig. 20-13). Use a folding chair available to you for your dimensions and specifications.

Fig. 20-14. A delivery ramp for unloading goods.

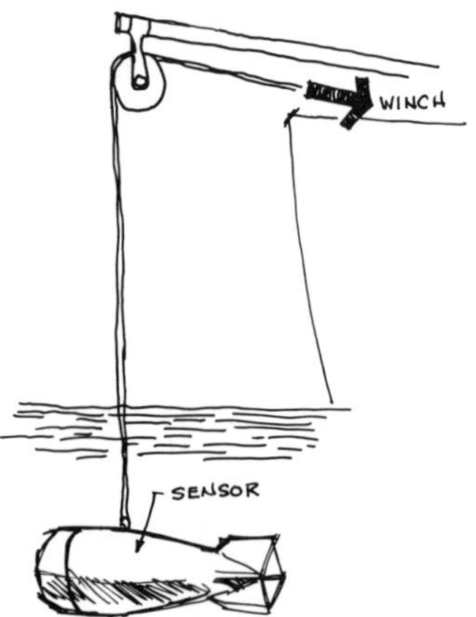

Fig. 20-15. An underwater sensor.

Fig. 20-16. A military vehicle requiring a flexible trailer hitch. (Courtesy of General Dynamics.)

Problem 56: Baby sleigh. A manufacturer of snow sleds would like to expand his present market to include baby products. Design a sleigh that could be used to take a baby for a stroll in the snow while providing the necessary comfort and safety. It should have a sturdy back support for the child, be economical, and lightweight. Consider the possibility of designing it so it can be used on a clear sidewalk or in the snow during the same stroll without requiring difficult or complicated adjustments.

Problem 57: Portable truck ramp. Delivery trucks need ramps to load and unload supplies and materials at their destinations. Consider, for example, a local dealer who deals in heavy items such as paints or beverages, which are difficult to lift (Fig. 20-14). Assume that the bed of the truck is 20″ from ground level. Design a portable ramp that would permit the unloading of goods with the use of a hand dolly and reduce manual lifting.

Problem 58: Sensor retaining device. The Instrumentation Department of the Naval Oceanographic Office uses underwater sensors to learn more about the ocean. These sensors are submerged on cables from a boat on the surface. The winch used to retrieve the sensor frequently overruns (continues pulling when it has been retrieved), causing the cable to break and the sensor to be lost. Design a safety device that will retain the sensor if the cable is broken when the sensor reaches a pulley. The problem is illustrated in Fig. 20-15. Assume that the sensor weighs 75 lb when submerged under water.

Problem 59: Flexible trailer hitch. The vehicle towing the trailer (Fig. 20-16) is designed for use in combat zones where terrain may be very uneven and hazardous. You are to design a trailer hitch that will provide for the most extreme conditions possible. Study the problem requirements and limitations to identify the parameters within which your design must function. Design your hitch to be dependable, functional, and easy to hitch and unhitch.

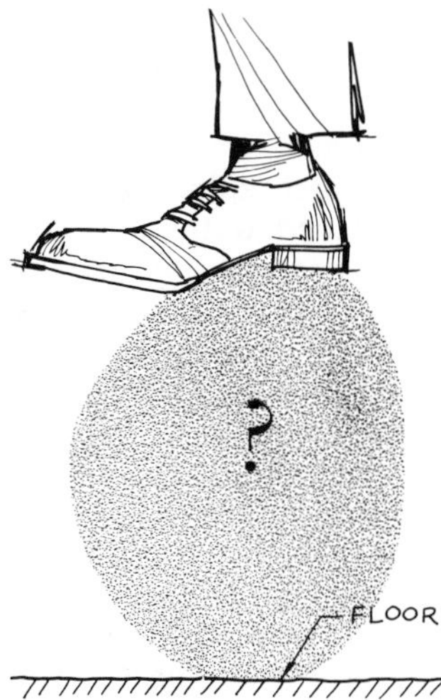

Fig. 20–17. The need for a stilt design.

Problem 60: Tubing and utility layer. Copper tubing, flexible pipe, and insulated electrical lines can be laid under ground by digging a ditch, but this is an expensive and time-consuming chore. Design a device that can be used to plow a trench in the ground and lay these utilities simultaneously in a more economical fashion. Assume that the device will be powered by a truck that would winch or pull it through the ground. The plowing should not damage a lawn or terrain to any great extent. The utilities should be placed 18″ underground. The maximum size cable or pipe for this device is 1″ in diameter. Examine the market potential for a device of this type.

Problem 61: Workman's stilts—human engineering. Workmen who apply gypsum board and other types of wallboards to the interiors of buildings and homes must work on scaffolds or wear some type of stilts to be able to reach the ceiling to nail the boards into position (Fig. 20–17). Stilts are more efficient than a scaffold or a ladder, since the workman does not have to get down to move the equipment. The typical wall board is 4′ × 8′ in size.

Design stilts that will provide the workman with access to a ceiling 8′ high while permitting him to perform his job of nailing ceiling panels with comfort. The stilts should be adjustable to accommodate workmen of various weights, sizes, and heights. Analyze the needs of the workmen and the requirements for stilts that will provide comfort, traction, safety, and adapt to the human body. Consider how the boards should be placed to be accessible to the workman while he is on stilts.

Problem 62: Pole vault standards. Many pole vaulters are exceeding the seventeen foot height in track meets which introduces a serious problem for the officials of this event. The pole vault uprights must be adjusted for each vaulter by moving them forward or backward plus or minus 18″. Also, the crossbar must be replaced with great difficulty at these heights by using forked sticks and ladders which is a crude and inefficient method. Develop a more efficient set of uprights that can be easily repositioned and will allow the crossbar to be replaced with greater ease. Investigate the market for a device of this type.

Problem 63: Sportsman's chair. Analyze the need for a sportsman's chair that could be used for camping, fishing from a bank or boat, at sport events, and for as many other purposes as you can think of. The need is not for a special-purpose chair, but for a chair that is suitable for a wide variety of uses to fully justify it as a marketable item. Make a list of as many applications as possible and use this as a basis for your design. Evaluate the market potential of your design.

Problem 64: Portable toilet. Design a portable toilet unit for the camper and outdoorsman. This unit should be highly portable, with consideration given to the method of waste disposal. Evaluate the market potential for this product.

Problem 65: Child carrier for a bicycle. Design a seat that can be used to carry a small child as a passenger on a bicycle. Assume that the bicycle will be ridden by an older youth or an adult. Determine the age of the child who would probably be carried as a passenger. Design the seat for safety and comfort. Determine the most satisfactory method of attaching the seat to and removing it from the bicycle.

Problem 66: Lawn sprinkler control. Design a sprinkler that can be used to water irregularly shaped yards while giving a uniform coverage. This sprinkler should be adjustable so that it can be adapted, within its range, to yards of any shape. Also consider a method of cutting the water off at certain sprinkler positions to prevent the watering of patios or other areas that are to remain dry.

Problem 67: Automatic cutoff for a water sprinkler. A lawn sprinkler that is not periodically checked may flood and ruin a lawn or waste water. Design an automatic cutoff that will relieve the homeowner from the task of periodically checking his sprinkler. Perhaps you can devise a sprinkler cutoff that can be set to a specified time. Another possibility is a gauge that will measure the amount of water that has fallen on a given surface and, when the limit is reached, will automatically cut off the sprinkler. Develop this idea as far as possible.

Problem 68: Power lawn fertilizer attachment. The rotary power lawn mower emits a force through its outlet caused by the air pressure from the rotating blades. This force might be used to distribute fertilizer while the lawn is being mowed. Design an attachment for a power mower that could spread fertilizer while the mower is performing its usual cutting operation. Analyze how this attachment operates, how it is fastened to the mower, and determine its range of operation.

Problem 69: Car and window washer. The force of water coming from a hose provides a source of power that could operate a mechanism which could be used to wash windows or cars. Design an attachment for the typical garden hose that would apply water and agitation (for optimum action) to the surface being cleaned. Consider other applications of the force exerted by water pressure in the performance of yard and household chores which involve water and require agitation that could be provided by the water force.

Problem 70: Projector cabinet. Many homes have slide projectors, but each showing of the family slides must be preceded by the very time-consuming operation of setting up the equipment. Design a cabinet that could serve as an end table or some other function while also housing a slide projector ready for use at any time. The cabinet might also serve as storage for slide trays. It should have electrical power for the projector. Evaluate the market for a multipurpose cabinet of this type.

Problem 71: Heavy appliance mover. Design a device that can be used for moving large appliances such as stoves, refrigerators, and washers, about the house. This product would not be used often—only for rearrangement, cleaning, and for servicing of the equipment. Consequently, to be acceptable, the item should be as economical as possible. Analyze your design from the standpoint of its use, advantages, and limitations.

Problem 72: Car jack. The conventional car jack is a somewhat dangerous means of changing tires on any surface other than a horizontal one. The average jack does not attach itself adequately to the automobile's frame or bumper, introducing a severe safety problem. Design a jack that would be an improvement over existing jacks and possibly employ a different method of applying a lifting force to a car. Consider the various types of terrain for which the device must serve. Analyze the function of your design, the method of applying power, method of attachment to a car for lifting, storage required in a trunk, and market potential.

Problem 73: Map holder. The driver of an automobile who is traveling alone in an unfamiliar part of the country must frequently refer to a map. This is especially critical in large cities, where traffic routes must be followed very closely to avoid complicated, time-consuming detours. Design a system that will give the driver a ready view of his map in a convenient location in the car. Provide a means of lighting the map during night driving that will not distract the driver. Consider all possibilities of making the map's information more available to the driver.

Problem 74: Vacation trailer. A typical family taking a vacation will often find that their automobile has inadequate storage space. Evaluate the needs of the typical family, the items that are needed on a vacation, the average miles traveled, the length of time on the road, and similar data. Using this information, design a trailer that could be attached to the automobile to provide supplemental storage for luggage and equipment. In your design, use stock components and assemblies available from catalogs and suppliers to eliminate the cost of manufacturing special parts. Provisions should be made for protection from weather and ease of access to the luggage. Consider the possibility of providing storage by means other than a trailer.

Problem 75: Bicycle-for-two adapter. Design the parts and assembly required to convert the typical bicycle into a bicycle built for two (tandem) when mated with another bicycle of the same make and size. Work from an existing bicycle, and consider, among other things, how each rider can equally share in the pedaling. Determine the cost of your assembly and its method of attachment to the average bicycle. Use existing stock parts when possible to reduce special machining.

Problem 76: Automobile unsticker. All drivers have had the experience of getting their car stuck in soft sand, mud, or snow and are familiar with the lack of traction and the sound of spinning wheels. It is difficult for one person to successfully push a car out of a situation of this type. Design a kit to be carried in the car trunk in a minimum of space that will contain the items required by the driver who must get his car "unstuck" when no other help is available. This kit can be composed of one or several items. Investigate the need for such a kit and the main factors that lead to the loss of traction. Explain and illustrate how your design will work and specify its limitations as well as its advantages.

Problem 77: Windshield de-icer. Freezing rain is a menace to safe driving and critically reduces visibility since it covers the windshields with ice. The process of de-icing a frozen windshield takes quite a long time (15 to 25 minutes). One must wait for the heating system of the car to produce the heat necessary to melt the ice on the windshield.

Design a device, system, or other means that will de-ice a frozen windshield in minimum time while not damaging the car's finish or exterior. Your solution to the problem should work fast, be easy to implement, and thorough. Not only the front windshield should be considered, but all windows essential to safety and good vision. Your design should be as economical and simple as possible.

Problem 78: Electric drill mount. The typical electric drill is a versatile tool with a power source that can be used for purposes other than the drilling of holes, which is its primary function. Its versatility would be even broader if it could be mounted on a stationary mount or stand, so that it could be used as a drill press or for other operations that cannot be performed as well when the drill is hand-held. Analyze the various operations that require a stationary mounting as well as other uses for the drill, such as powering a small circle saw or similar device, and list the advantages of such a mount. Design a mount or holder to enhance the versatility of a hand drill that could be produced and sold economically. Refer to various catalogs and other sources to select the drill for which your mount will be designed.

Problem 79: Distress signal for an automobile. All drivers of automobiles have, at one time or another, been temporarily stranded on the highway. This problem is more acute at night when visibility is poor. Investigate an accessory to be attached to the automobile that could serve as a signaling device for a disabled car.

The accessory should clearly indicate that the car is in need of help and warn on-coming drivers of the presence of the vehicle, especially when it partially or completely blocks the path of traffic.

It would probably be desirable if the device were electrical to provide lighting, but other methods should be considered. Determine how the device would be controlled and where it should be located. Make an estimate of the cost of your design and its market value.

Problem 80: Paint mixer. Paint purchased from the shelf of a paint store must be mixed by stirring or some other form of agitation that will bring it to a consistent mixture. Stirring by hand is a time-consuming, inefficient procedure. Design a product that could be used by the paint store or the paint contractor to quickly mix paint in the store and on the job. Determine the standard size paint cans for which your mixer will be designed. Consider all possibilities and methods available for this operation. Evaluate the market potential for this product.

Problem 81: Mounting for an outboard motor on a canoe. Unlike a square-end boat, the pointed-end canoe does not provide a suitable surface for attaching an outboard motor. Design an attachment that will adapt an outboard motor to a canoe. Indicate how the motor will be controlled by the operator in the canoe. Your design should be as simple and economical as possible.

Problem 82: Automobile coffee maker. More and more accessories and conveniences are being incorporated into the design of automobiles. However, essentially no provision has been made for the coffee drinker who would like to enjoy a cup of coffee while driving to work. Adequate heat is available in the automobile's power system to prepare coffee in minimum time. Design an attachment as an integral system of an automobile that will serve coffee in the dashboard area. Consider the type of coffee to be used, instant or regular, method of changing or adding water, the spigot system, and similar details. Prepare the necessary notes, drawings, pictorials, and specifications to explain your design.

Problem 83: Baby seat (cantilever). The most common method of elevating a small child to table height is by means of a high chair of a fixed height. However, the majority of high chairs are designed in such a way that they do not give the child access to the table top. Design a child's chair that can be attached to a standard table top and will support the child at the required height. The chair should be designed to ensure that the child cannot crawl out or detach it from the table top. A possible solution could be a design that would cantilever from the table top, using the child's body as a means of applying the force necessary to grip the table top. The design would be further improved if the chair were collapsible or suitable for other purposes. In other words, make your design as versatile as possible. Determine the age group that would be most in need of the chair and base your design on the dimensions of a child of this age.

Problem 84: Miniature TV set support. Miniature television sets for close viewing are available with a screen size of 5″ × 5″. An attachment is needed that would support sets ranging in size from 6″ × 6″ to 7″ × 7″ for viewing from a bed. Determine the placement of the set with respect to a viewer for best results. Provide adjustments on the support that will be used to position the set properly. Analyze the method of concealing electrical wires within the apparatus. Evaluate your design with respect to its market potential.

Problem 85: Panel applicator. A workman who applies 4′ × 8′ gypsum board or paneling must be assisted by a helper who holds the panel in position while it is being nailed to the ceiling. This helper is only partially efficient but adds to the cost of labor. Contractors would therefore welcome a device that would enable a single workman to apply the gypsum board to walls and especially ceilings. Such a device would pay for itself almost immediately through the saving of helpers' wages.

Design a device that could be used in this capacity; it should be collapsible for easy transportation, economical, and versatile. Consider the most efficient way in which the operator could control the mechanism and list the features that would be advantageous to the marketing of the device. The average ceiling height is 8′, but provide adjustments that would adapt the device to lower or higher ceilings.

Problem 86: Backpack. Design a backpack that can be used by the outdoorsman who must carry his supplies while hiking. Your design should be based on the analysis of the supplies that would be carried by the average outdoorsman. A major portion of your design effort should be devoted to adapting the backpack to the human body for maximum comfort and the best leverage for carrying a load over an extended period of time. Can other uses be made of your design?

Problem 87: Bilge pump. Design a manually operated pump that can be used to pump water out of the bottom of a boat. This should be a simple, trouble-free design requiring the minimum of storage space while serving the needs of the boatsman.

Problem 88: Knee support for an athlete. A number of sports have a high knee-injury rate. This is particularly true of football, soccer, and other sports involving running and bodily contact. Determine the possibilities of designing a support that could be attached to knees to prevent wrenching or twisting injuries. Consider all aspects of the problem in your attempt to provide this protection.

APPENDIXES

CONTENTS

APPENDIX 1. LOGARITHMS OF NUMBERS

N	0	1	2	3	4	5	6	7	8	9
1.0	.0000	.0043	.0086	.0128	.0170	.0212	.0253	.0294	.0334	.0374
1.1	.0414	.0453	.0492	.0531	.0569	.0607	.0645	.0682	.0719	.0755
1.2	.0792	.0828	.0864	.0899	.0934	.0969	.1004	.1038	.1072	.1106
1.3	.1139	.1173	.1206	.1239	.1271	.1303	.1335	.1367	.1399	.1430
1.4	.1461	.1492	.1523	.1553	.1584	.1614	.1644	.1673	.1703	.1732
1.5	.1761	.1790	.1818	.1847	.1875	.1903	.1931	.1959	.1987	.2014
1.6	.2041	.2068	.2095	.2122	.2148	.2175	.2201	.2227	.2253	.2279
1.7	.2304	.2330	.2355	.2380	.2405	.2430	.2455	.2480	.2504	.2529
1.8	.2553	.2577	.2601	.2625	.2648	.2672	.2695	.2718	.2742	.2765
1.9	.2788	.2810	.2833	.2856	.2878	.2900	.2923	.2945	.2967	.2989
2.0	.3010	.3032	.3054	.3075	.3096	.3118	.3139	.3160	.3181	.3201
2.1	.3222	.3243	.3263	.3284	.3304	.3324	.3345	.3365	.3385	.3404
2.2	.3424	.3444	.3464	.3483	.3502	.3522	.3541	.3560	.3579	.3598
2.3	.3617	.3636	.3655	.3674	.3692	.3711	.3729	.3747	.3766	.3784
2.4	.3802	.3820	.3838	.3856	.3874	.3892	.3909	.3927	.3945	.3962
2.5	.3979	.3997	.4014	.4031	.4048	.4065	.4082	.4099	.4116	.4133
2.6	.4150	.4166	.4183	.4200	.4216	.4232	.4249	.4265	.4281	.4298
2.7	.4314	.4330	.4346	.4362	.4378	.4393	.4409	.4425	.4440	.4456
2.8	.4472	.4487	.4502	.4518	.4533	.4548	.4564	.4579	.4594	.4609
2.9	.4624	.4639	.4654	.4669	.4683	.4698	.4713	.4728	.4742	.4757
3.0	.4771	.4786	.4800	.4814	.4829	.4843	.4857	.4871	.4886	.4900
3.1	.4914	.4928	.4942	.4955	.4969	.4983	.4997	.5011	.5024	.5038
3.2	.5051	.5065	.5079	.5092	.5105	.5119	.5132	.5145	.5159	.5172
3.3	.5185	.5198	.5211	.5224	.5237	.5250	.5263	.5276	.5289	.5302
3.4	.5315	.5328	.5340	.5353	.5366	.5378	.5391	.5403	.5416	.5428
3.5	.5441	.5453	.5465	.5478	.5490	.5502	.5514	.5527	.5539	.5551
3.6	.5563	.5575	.5587	.5599	.5611	.5623	.5635	.5647	.5658	.5670
3.7	.5682	.5694	.5705	.5717	.5729	.5740	.5752	.5763	.5775	.5786
3.8	.5798	.5809	.5821	.5832	.5843	.5855	.5866	.5877	.5888	.5899
3.9	.5911	.5922	.5933	.5944	.5955	.5966	.5977	.5988	.5999	.6010
4.0	.6021	.6031	.6042	.6053	.6064	.6075	.6085	.6096	.6107	.6117
4.1	.6128	.6138	.6149	.6160	.6170	.6180	.6191	.6201	.6212	.6222
4.2	.6232	.6243	.6253	.6263	.6274	.6284	.6294	.6304	.6314	.6325
4.3	.6335	.6345	.6355	.6365	.6375	.6385	.6395	.6405	.6415	.6425
4.4	.6435	.6444	.6454	.6464	.6474	.6484	.6493	.6503	.6513	.6522
4.5	.6532	.6542	.6551	.6561	.6571	.6580	.6590	.6599	.6609	.6618
4.6	.6628	.6637	.6646	.6656	.6665	.6675	.6684	.6693	.6702	.6712
4.7	.6721	.6730	.6739	.6749	.6758	.6767	.6776	.6785	.6794	.6803
4.8	.6812	.6821	.6830	.6839	.6848	.6857	.6866	.6875	.6884	.6893
4.9	.6902	.6911	.6920	.6928	.6937	.6946	.6955	.6964	.6972	.6981
5.0	.6990	.6998	.7007	.7016	.7024	.7033	.7042	.7050	.7059	.7067
5.1	.7076	.7084	.7093	.7101	.7110	.7118	.7126	.7135	.7143	.7152
5.2	.7160	.7168	.7177	.7185	.7193	.7202	.7210	.7218	.7226	.7235
5.3	.7243	.7251	.7259	.7267	.7275	.7284	.7292	.7300	.7308	.7316
5.4	.7324	.7332	.7340	.7348	.7356	.7364	.7372	.7380	.7388	.7396
N	0	1	2	3	4	5	6	7	8	9

APPENDIX 1. LOGARITHMS OF NUMBERS (Cont.)

N	0	1	2	3	4	5	6	7	8	9
5.5	.7404	.7412	.7419	.7427	.7435	.7443	.7451	.7459	.7466	.7474
5.6	.7482	.7490	.7497	.7505	.7513	.7520	.7528	.7536	.7543	.7551
5.7	.7559	.7566	.7574	.7582	.7589	.7597	.7604	.7612	.7619	.7627
5.8	.7634	.7642	.7649	.7657	.7664	.7672	.7679	.7686	.7694	.7701
5.9	.7709	.7716	.7723	.7731	.7738	.7745	.7752	.7760	.7767	.7774
6.0	.7782	.7789	.7796	.7803	.7810	.7818	.7825	.7832	.7839	.7846
6.1	.7853	.7860	.7868	.7875	.7882	.7889	.7896	.7903	.7910	.7917
6.2	.7924	.7931	.7938	.7945	.7952	.7959	.7966	.7973	.7980	.7987
6.3	.7993	.8000	.8007	.8014	.8021	.8028	.8035	.8041	.8048	.8055
6.4	.8062	.8069	.8075	.8082	.8089	.8096	.8102	.8109	.8116	.8122
6.5	.8129	.8136	.8142	.8149	.8156	.8162	.8169	.8176	.8182	.8189
6.6	.8195	.8202	.8209	.8215	.8222	.8228	.8235	.8241	.8248	.8254
6.7	.8261	.8267	.8274	.8280	.8287	.8293	.8299	.8306	.8312	.8319
6.8	.8325	.8331	.8338	.8344	.8351	.8357	.8363	.8370	.8376	.8382
6.9	.8388	.8395	.8401	.8407	.8414	.8420	.8426	.8432	.8439	.8445
7.0	.8451	.8457	.8463	.8470	.8476	.8482	.8488	.8494	.8500	.8506
7.1	.8513	.8519	.8525	.8531	.8537	.8543	.8549	.8555	.8561	.8567
7.2	.8573	.8579	.8585	.8591	.8597	.8603	.8609	.8615	.8621	.8627
7.3	.8633	.8639	.8645	.8651	.8657	.8663	.8669	.8675	.8681	.8686
7.4	.8692	.8698	.8704	.8710	.8716	.8722	.8727	.8733	.8739	.8745
7.5	.8751	.8756	.8762	.8768	.8774	.8779	.8785	.8791	.8797	.8802
7.6	.8808	.8814	.8820	.8825	.8831	.8837	.8842	.8848	.8854	.8859
7.7	.8865	.8871	.8876	.8882	.8887	.8893	.8899	.8904	.8910	.8915
7.8	.8921	.8927	.8932	.8938	.8943	.8949	.8954	.8960	.8965	.8971
7.9	.8976	.8982	.8987	.8993	.8998	.9004	.9009	.9015	.9020	.9025
8.0	.9031	.9036	.9042	.9047	.9053	.9058	.9063	.9069	.9074	.9079
8.1	.9085	.9090	.9096	.9101	.9106	.9112	.9117	.9122	.9128	.9133
8.2	.9138	.9143	.9149	.9154	.9159	.9165	.9170	.9175	.9180	.9186
8.3	.9191	.9196	.9201	.9206	.9212	.9217	.9222	.9227	.9232	.9238
8.4	.9243	.9248	.9253	.9258	.9263	.9269	.9274	.9279	.9284	.9289
8.5	.9294	.9299	.9304	.9309	.9315	.9320	.9325	.9330	.9335	.9340
8.6	.9345	.9350	.9355	.9360	.9365	.9370	.9375	.9380	.9385	.9390
8.7	.9395	.9400	.9405	.9410	.9415	.9420	.9425	.9430	.9435	.9440
8.8	.9445	.9450	.9455	.9460	.9465	.9469	.9474	.9479	.9484	.9489
8.9	.9494	.9499	.9504	.9509	.9513	.9518	.9523	.9528	.9533	.9538
9.0	.9542	.9547	.9552	.9557	.9562	.9566	.9571	.9576	.9581	.9586
9.1	.9590	.9595	.9600	.9605	.9609	.9614	.9619	.9624	.9628	.9633
9.2	.9638	.9643	.9647	.9652	.9657	.9661	.9666	.9671	.9675	.9680
9.3	.9685	.9689	.9694	.9699	.9703	.9708	.9713	.9717	.9722	.9727
9.4	.9731	.9736	.9741	.9745	.9750	.9754	.9759	.9763	.9768	.9773
9.5	.9777	.9782	.9786	.9791	.9795	.9800	.9805	.9809	.9814	.9818
9.6	.9823	.9827	.9832	.9836	.9841	.9845	.9850	.9854	.9859	.9863
9.7	.9868	.9872	.9877	.9881	.9886	.9890	.9894	.9899	.9903	.9908
9.8	.9912	.9917	.9921	.9926	.9930	.9934	.9939	.9943	.9948	.9952
9.9	.9956	.9961	.9965	.9969	.9974	.9978	.9983	.9987	.9991	.9996
N	0	1	2	3	4	5	6	7	8	9

APPENDIX 2. VALUES OF TRIGONOMETRIC FUNCTIONS

Degrees	Radians	Sine	Tangent	Cotangent	Cosine		
0° 00′	.0000	.0000	.0000		1.0000	1.5708	90° 00′
10′	.0029	.0029	.0029	343.77	1.0000	1.5679	50′
20′	.0058	.0058	.0058	171.89	1.0000	1.5650	40′
30′	.0087	.0087	.0087	114.59	1.0000	1.5621	30′
40′	.0116	.0116	.0116	85.940	.9999	1.5592	20′
50′	.0145	.0145	.0145	68.750	.9999	1.5563	10′
1° 00′	.0175	.0175	.0175	57.290	.9998	1.5533	89° 00′
10′	.0204	.0204	.0204	49.104	.9998	1.5504	50′
20′	.0233	.0233	.0233	42.964	.9997	1.5475	40′
30′	.0262	.0262	.0262	38.188	.9997	1.5446	30′
40′	.0291	.0291	.0291	34.368	.9996	1.5417	20′
50′	.0320	.0320	.0320	31.242	.9995	1.5388	10′
2° 00′	.0349	.0349	.0349	28.636	.9994	1.5359	88° 00′
10′	.0378	.0378	.0378	26.432	.9993	1.5330	50′
20′	.0407	.0407	.0407	24.542	.9992	1.5301	40′
30′	.0436	.0436	.0437	22.904	.9990	1.5272	30′
40′	.0465	.0465	.0466	21.470	.9989	1.5243	20′
50′	.0495	.0494	.0495	20.206	.9988	1.5213	10′
3° 00′	.0524	.0523	.0524	19.081	.9986	1.5184	87° 00′
10′	.0553	.0552	.0553	18.075	.9985	1.5155	50′
20′	.0582	.0581	.0582	17.169	.9983	1.5126	40′
30′	.0611	.0610	.0612	16.350	.9981	1.5097	30′
40′	.0640	.0640	.0641	15.605	.9980	1.5068	20′
50′	.0669	.0669	.0670	14.924	.9978	1.5039	10′
4° 00′	.0698	.0698	.0699	14.301	.9976	1.5010	86° 00′
10′	.0727	.0727	.0729	13.727	.9974	1.4981	50′
20′	.0756	.0756	.0758	13.197	.9971	1.4952	40′
30′	.0785	.0785	.0787	12.706	.9969	1.4923	30′
40′	.0814	.0814	.0816	12.251	.9967	1.4893	20′
50′	.0844	.0843	.0846	11.826	.9964	1.4864	10′
5° 00′	.0873	.0872	.0875	11.430	.9962	1.4835	85° 00′
10′	.0902	.0901	.0904	11.059	.9959	1.4806	50′
20′	.0931	.0929	.0934	10.712	.9957	1.4777	40′
30′	.0960	.0958	.0963	10.385	.9954	1.4748	30′
40′	.0989	.0987	.0992	10.078	.9951	1.4719	20′
50′	.1018	.1016	.1022	9.7882	.9948	1.4690	10′
6° 00′	.1047	.1045	.1051	9.5144	.9945	1.4661	84° 00′
10′	.1076	.1074	.1080	9.2553	.9942	1.4632	50′
20′	.1105	.1103	.1110	9.0098	.9939	1.4603	40′
30′	.1134	.1132	.1139	8.7769	.9936	1.4573	30′
40′	.1164	.1161	.1169	8.5555	.9932	1.4544	20′
50′	.1193	.1190	.1198	8.3450	.9929	1.4515	10′
7° 00′	.1222	.1219	.1228	8.1443	.9925	1.4486	83° 00′
10′	.1251	.1248	.1257	7.9530	.9922	1.4457	50′
20′	.1280	.1276	.1287	7.7704	.9918	1.4428	40′
30′	.1309	.1305	.1317	7.5958	.9914	1.4399	30′
40′	.1338	.1334	.1346	7.4287	.9911	1.4370	20′
50′	.1367	.1363	.1376	7.2687	.9907	1.4341	10′
8° 00′	.1396	.1392	.1405	7.1154	.9903	1.4312	82° 00′
10′	.1425	.1421	.1435	6.9682	.9899	1.4283	50′
20′	.1454	.1449	.1465	6.8269	.9894	1.4254	40′
30′	.1484	.1478	.1495	6.6912	.9890	1.4224	30′
40′	.1513	.1507	.1524	6.5606	.9886	1.4195	20′
50′	.1542	.1536	.1554	6.4348	.9881	1.4166	10′
9° 00′	.1571	.1564	.1584	6.3138	.9877	1.4137	81° 00′
		Cosine	Cotangent	Tangent	Sine	Radians	Degrees

APPENDIX 2. VALUES OF TRIGONOMETRIC FUNCTIONS (Cont.)

Degrees	Radians	Sine	Tangent	Cotangent	Cosine		
9° 00′	.1571	.1564	.1584	6.3138	.9877	1.4137	81° 00′
10′	.1600	.1593	.1614	6.1970	.9872	1.4108	50′
20′	.1629	.1622	.1644	6.0844	.9868	1.4079	40′
30′	.1658	.1650	.1673	5.9758	.9863	1.4050	30′
40′	.1687	.1679	.1703	5.8708	.9858	1.4021	20′
50′	.1716	.1708	.1733	5.7694	.9853	1.3992	10′
10° 00′	.1745	.1736	.1763	5.6713	.9848	1.3963	80° 00′
10′	.1774	.1765	.1793	5.5764	.9843	1.3934	50′
20′	.1804	.1794	.1823	5.4845	.9838	1.3904	40′
30′	.1833	.1822	.1853	5.3955	.9833	1.3875	30′
40′	.1862	.1851	.1883	5.3093	.9827	1.3846	20′
50′	.1891	.1880	.1914	5.2257	.9822	1.3817	10′
11° 00′	.1920	.1908	.1944	5.1446	.9816	1.3788	79° 00′
10′	.1949	.1937	.1974	5.0658	.9811	1.3759	50′
20′	.1978	.1965	.2004	4.9894	.9805	1.3730	40′
30′	.2007	.1994	.2035	4.9152	.9799	1.3701	30′
40′	.2036	.2022	.2065	4.8430	.9793	1.3672	20′
50′	.2065	.2051	.2095	4.7729	.9787	1.3643	10′
12° 00′	.2094	.2079	.2126	4.7046	.9781	1.3614	78° 00′
10′	.2123	.2108	.2156	4.6382	.9775	1.3584	50′
20′	.2153	.2136	.2186	4.5736	.9769	1.3555	40′
30′	.2182	.2164	.2217	4.5107	.9763	1.3526	30′
40′	.2211	.2193	.2247	4.4494	.9757	1.3497	20′
50′	.2240	.2221	.2278	4.3897	.9750	1.3468	10′
13° 00′	.2269	.2250	.2309	4.3315	.9744	1.3439	77° 00′
10′	.2298	.2278	.2339	4.2747	.9737	1.3410	50′
20′	.2327	.2306	.2370	4.2193	.9730	1.3381	40′
30′	.2356	.2334	.2401	4.1653	.9724	1.3352	30′
40′	.2385	.2363	.2432	4.1126	.9717	1.3323	20′
50′	.2414	.2391	.2462	4.0611	.9710	1.3294	10′
14° 00′	.2443	.2419	.2493	4.0108	.9703	1.3265	76° 00′
10′	.2473	.2447	.2524	3.9617	.9696	1.3235	50′
20′	.2502	.2476	.2555	3.9136	.9689	1.3206	40′
30′	.2531	.2504	.2586	3.8667	.9681	1.3177	30′
40′	.2560	.2532	.2617	3.8208	.9674	1.3148	20′
50′	.2589	.2560	.2648	3.7760	.9667	1.3119	10′
15° 00′	.2618	.2588	.2679	3.7321	.9659	1.3090	75° 00′
10′	.2647	.2616	.2711	3.6891	.9652	1.3061	50′
20′	.2676	.2644	.2742	3.6470	.9644	1.3032	40′
30′	.2705	.2672	.2773	3.6059	.9636	1.3003	30′
40′	.2734	.2700	.2805	3.5656	.9628	1.2974	20′
50′	.2763	.2728	.2836	3.5261	.9621	1.2945	10′
16° 00′	.2793	.2756	.2867	3.4874	.9613	1.2915	74° 00′
10′	.2822	.2784	.2899	3.4495	.9605	1.2886	50′
20′	.2851	.2812	.2931	3.4124	.9596	1.2857	40′
30′	.2880	.2840	.2962	3.3759	.9588	1.2828	30′
40′	.2909	.2868	.2994	3.3402	.9580	1.2799	20′
50′	.2938	.2896	.3026	3.3052	.9572	1.2770	10′
17° 00′	.2967	.2924	.3057	3.2709	.9563	1.2741	73° 00′
10′	.2996	.2952	.3089	3.2371	.9555	1.2712	50′
20′	.3025	.2979	.3121	3.2041	.9546	1.2683	40′
30′	.3054	.3007	.3153	3.1716	.9537	1.2654	30′
40′	.3083	.3035	.3185	3.1397	.9528	1.2625	20′
50′	.3113	.3062	.3217	3.1084	.9520	1.2595	10′
18° 00′	.3142	.3090	.3249	3.0777	.9511	1.2566	72° 00′
		Cosine	Cotangent	Tangent	Sine	Radians	Degrees

(Cont.)

APPENDIX 2. VALUES OF TRIGONOMETRIC FUNCTIONS (Cont.)

Degrees	Radians	Sine	Tangent	Cotangent	Cosine		
18° 00′	.3142	.3090	.3249	3.0777	.9511	1.2566	72° 00′
10′	.3171	.3118	.3281	3.0475	.9502	1.2537	50′
20′	.3200	.3145	.3314	3.0178	.9492	1.2508	40′
30′	.3229	.3173	.3346	2.9887	.9483	1.2479	30′
40′	.3258	.3201	.3378	2.9600	.9474	1.2450	20′
50′	.3287	.3228	.3411	2.9319	.9465	1.2421	10′
19° 00′	.3316	.3256	.3443	2.9042	.9455	1.2392	71° 00′
10′	.3345	.3283	.3476	2.8770	.9446	1.2363	50′
20′	.3374	.3311	.3508	2.8502	.9436	1.2334	40′
30′	.3403	.3338	.3541	2.8239	.9426	1.2305	30′
40′	.3432	.3365	.3574	2.7980	.9417	1.2275	20′
50′	.3462	.3393	.3607	2.7725	.9407	1.2246	10′
20° 00′	.3491	.3420	.3640	2.7475	.9397	1.2217	70° 00′
10′	.3520	.3448	.3673	2.7228	.9387	1.2188	50′
20′	.3549	.3475	.3706	2.6985	.9377	1.2159	40′
30′	.3578	.3502	.3739	2.6746	.9367	1.2130	30′
40′	.3607	.3529	.3772	2.6511	.9356	1.2101	20′
50′	.3636	.3557	.3805	2.6279	.9346	1.2072	10′
21° 00′	.3665	.3584	.3839	2.6051	.9336	1.2043	69° 00′
10′	.3694	.3611	.3872	2.5826	.9325	1.2014	50′
20′	.3723	.3638	.3906	2.5605	.9315	1.1985	40′
30′	.3752	.3665	.3939	2.5386	.9304	1.1956	30′
40′	.3782	.3692	.3973	2.5172	.9293	1.1926	20′
50′	.3811	.3719	.4006	2.4960	.9283	1.1897	10′
22° 00′	.3840	.3746	.4040	2.4751	.9272	1.1868	68° 00′
10′	.3869	.3773	.4074	2.4545	.9261	1.1839	50′
20′	.3898	.3800	.4108	2.4342	.9250	1.1810	40′
30′	.3927	.3827	.4142	2.4142	.9239	1.1781	30′
40′	.3956	.3854	.4176	2.3945	.9228	1.1752	20′
50′	.3985	.3881	.4210	2.3750	.9216	1.1723	10′
23° 00′	.4014	.3907	.4245	2.3559	.9205	1.1694	67° 00′
10′	.4043	.3934	.4279	2.3369	.9194	1.1665	50′
20′	.4072	.3961	.4314	2.3183	.9182	1.1636	40′
30′	.4102	.3987	.4348	2.2998	.9171	1.1606	30′
40′	.4131	.4014	.4383	2.2817	.9159	1.1577	20′
50′	.4160	.4041	.4417	2.2637	.9147	1.1548	10′
24° 00′	.4189	.4067	.4452	2.2460	.9135	1.1519	66° 00′
10′	.4218	.4094	.4487	2.2286	.9124	1.1490	50′
20′	.4247	.4120	.4522	2.2113	.9112	1.1461	40′
30′	.4276	.4147	.4557	2.1943	.9100	1.1432	30′
40′	.4305	.4173	.4592	2.1775	.9088	1.1403	20′
50′	.4334	.4200	.4628	2.1609	.9075	1.1374	10′
25° 00′	.4363	.4226	.4663	2.1445	.9063	1.1345	65° 00′
10′	.4392	.4253	.4699	2.1283	.9051	1.1316	50′
20′	.4422	.4279	.4734	2.1123	.9038	1.1286	40′
30′	.4451	.4305	.4770	2.0965	.9026	1.1257	30′
40′	.4480	.4331	.4806	2.0809	.9013	1.1228	20′
50′	.4509	.4358	.4841	2.0655	.9001	1.1199	10′
26° 00′	.4538	.4384	.4877	2.0503	.8988	1.1170	64° 00′
10′	.4567	.4410	.4913	2.0353	.8975	1.1141	50′
20′	.4596	.4436	.4950	2.0204	.8962	1.1112	40′
30′	4625	.4462	.4986	2.0057	.8949	1.1083	30′
40′	.4654	.4488	.5022	1.9912	.8936	1.1054	20′
50′	.4683	.4514	.5059	1.9768	.8923	1.1025	10′
27° 00′	.4712	.4540	.5095	1.9626	.8910	1.0996	63° 00′
		Cosine	Cotangent	Tangent	Sine	Radians	Degrees

APPENDIX 2. VALUES OF TRIGONOMETRIC FUNCTIONS (Cont.)

Degrees	Radians	Sine	Tangent	Cotangent	Cosine		
27° 00′	.4712	.4540	.5095	1.9626	.8910	1.0996	63° 00′
10′	.4741	.4566	.5132	1.9486	.8897	1.0966	50′
20′	.4771	.4592	.5169	1.9347	.8884	1.0937	40′
30′	.4800	.4617	.5206	1.9210	.8870	1.0908	30′
40′	.4829	.4643	.5243	1.9074	.8857	1.0879	20′
50′	.4858	.4669	.5280	1.8940	.8843	1.0850	10′
28° 00′	.4887	.4695	.5317	1.8807	.8829	1.0821	62° 00′
10′	.4916	.4720	.5354	1.8676	.8816	1.0792	50′
20′	.4945	.4746	.5392	1.8546	.8802	1.0763	40′
30′	.4974	.4772	.5430	1.8418	.8788	1.0734	30′
40′	.5003	.4797	.5467	1.8291	.8774	1.0705	20′
50′	.5032	.4823	.5505	1.8165	.8760	1.0676	10′
29° 00′	.5061	.4848	.5543	1.8040	.8746	1.0647	61° 00′
10′	.5091	.4874	.5581	1.7917	.8732	1.0617	50′
20′	.5120	.4899	.5619	1.7796	.8718	1.0588	40′
30′	.5149	.4924	.5658	1.7675	.8704	1.0559	30′
40′	.5178	.4950	.5696	1.7556	.8689	1.0530	20′
50′	.5207	.4975	.5735	1.7437	.8675	1.0501	10′
30° 00′	.5236	.5000	.5774	1.7321	.8660	1.0472	60° 00′
10′	.5265	.5025	.5812	1.7205	.8646	1.0443	50′
20′	.5294	.5050	.5851	1.7090	.8631	1.0414	40′
30′	.5323	.5075	.5890	1.6977	.8616	1.0385	30′
40′	.5352	.5100	.5930	1.6864	.8601	1.0356	20′
50′	.5381	.5125	.5969	1.6753	.8587	1.0327	10′
31° 00′	.5411	.5150	.6009	1.6643	.8572	1.0297	59° 00′
10′	.5440	.5175	.6048	1.6534	.8557	1.0268	50′
20′	.5469	.5200	.6088	1.6426	.8542	1.0239	40′
30′	.5498	.5225	.6128	1.6319	.8526	1.0210	30′
40′	.5527	.5250	.6168	1.6212	.8511	1.0181	20′
50′	.5556	.5275	.6208	1.6107	.8496	1.0152	10′
32° 00′	.5585	.5299	.6249	1.6003	.8480	1.0123	58° 00′
10′	.5614	.5324	.6289	1.5900	.8465	1.0094	50′
20′	.5643	.5348	.6330	1.5798	.8450	1.0065	40′
30′	.5672	.5373	.6371	1.5697	.8434	1.0036	30′
40′	.5701	.5398	.6412	1.5597	.8418	1.0007	20′
50′	.5730	.5422	.6453	1.5497	.8403	.9977	10′
33° 00′	.5760	.5446	.6494	1.5399	.8387	.9948	57° 00′
10′	.5789	.5471	.6536	1.5301	.8371	.9919	50′
20′	.5818	.5495	.6577	1.5204	.8355	.9890	40′
30′	.5847	.5519	.6619	1.5108	.8339	.9861	30′
40′	.5876	.5544	.6661	1.5013	.8323	.9832	20′
50′	.5905	.5568	.6703	1.4919	.8307	.9803	10′
34° 00′	.5934	.5592	.6745	1.4826	.8290	.9774	56° 00′
10′	.5963	.5616	.6787	1.4733	.8274	.9745	50′
20′	.5992	.5640	.6830	1.4641	.8258	.9716	40′
30′	.6021	.5664	.6873	1.4550	.8241	.9687	30′
40′	.6050	.5688	.6916	1.4460	.8225	.9657	20′
50′	.6080	.5712	.6959	1.4370	.8208	.9628	10′
35° 00′	.6109	.5736	.7002	1.4281	.8192	.9599	55° 00′
10′	.6138	.5760	.7046	1.4193	.8175	.9570	50′
20′	.6167	.5783	.7089	1.4106	.8158	.9541	40′
30′	.6196	.5807	.7133	1.4019	.8141	.9512	30′
40′	.6225	.5831	.7177	1.3934	.8124	.9483	20′
50′	.6254	.5854	.7221	1.3848	.8107	.9454	10′
36° 00′	.6283	.5878	.7265	1.3764	.8090	.9425	54° 00′
		Cosine	Cotangent	Tangent	Sine	Radians	Degrees

(Cont.)

APPENDIX 2. VALUES OF TRIGONOMETRIC FUNCTIONS (Cont.)

Degrees	Radians	Sine	Tangent	Cotangent	Cosine		
36° 00′	.6283	.5878	.7265	1.3764	.8090	.9425	54° 00′
10′	.6312	.5901	.7310	1.3680	.8073	.9396	50′
20′	.6341	.5925	.7355	1.3597	.8056	.9367	40′
30′	.6370	.5948	.7400	1.3514	.8039	.9338	30′
40′	.6400	.5972	.7445	1.3432	.8021	.9308	20′
50′	.6429	.5995	.7490	1.3351	.8004	.9279	10′
37° 00′	.6458	.6018	.7536	1.3270	.7986	.9250	53° 00′
10′	.6487	.6041	.7581	1.3190	.7969	.9221	50′
20′	.6516	.6065	.7627	1.3111	.7951	.9192	40′
30′	.6545	.6088	.7673	1.3032	.7934	.9163	30′
40′	.6574	.6111	.7720	1.2954	.7916	.9134	20′
50′	.6603	.6134	.7766	1.2876	.7898	.9105	10′
38° 00′	.6632	.6157	.7813	1.2799	.7880	.9076	52° 00′
10′	.6661	.6180	.7860	1.2723	.7862	.9047	50′
20′	.6690	.6202	.7907	1.2647	.7844	.9018	40′
30′	.6720	.6225	.7954	1.2572	.7826	.8988	30′
40′	.6749	.6248	.8002	1.2497	.7808	.8959	20′
50′	.6778	.6271	.8050	1.2423	.7790	.8930	10′
39° 00′	.6807	.6293	.8098	1.2349	.7771	.8901	51° 00′
10′	.6836	.6316	.8146	1.2276	.7753	.8872	50′
20′	.6865	.6338	.8195	1.2203	.7735	.8843	40′
30′	.6894	.6361	.8243	1.2131	.7716	.8814	30′
40′	.6923	.6383	.8292	1.2059	.7698	.8785	20′
50′	.6952	.6406	.8342	1.1988	.7679	.8756	10′
40° 00′	.6981	.6428	.8391	1.1918	.7660	.8727	50° 00′
10′	.7010	.6450	.8441	1.1847	.7642	.8698	50′
20′	.7039	.6472	.8491	1.1778	.7623	.8668	40′
30′	.7069	.6494	.8541	1.1708	.7604	.8639	30′
40′	.7098	.6517	.8591	1.1640	.7585	.8610	20′
50′	.7127	.6539	.8642	1.1571	.7566	.8581	10′
41° 00′	.7156	.6561	.8693	1.1504	.7547	.8552	49° 00′
10′	.7185	.6583	.8744	1.1436	.7528	.8523	50′
20′	.7214	.6604	.8796	1.1369	.7509	.8494	40′
30′	.7243	.6626	.8847	1.1303	.7490	.8465	30′
40′	.7272	.6648	.8899	1.1237	.7470	.8436	20′
50′	.7301	.6670	.8952	1.1171	.7451	.8407	10′
42° 00′	.7330	.6691	.9004	1.1106	.7431	.8378	48° 00′
10′	.7359	.6713	.9057	1.1041	.7412	.8348	50′
20′	.7389	.6734	.9110	1.0977	.7392	.8319	40′
30′	.7418	.6756	.9163	1.0913	.7373	.8290	30′
40′	.7447	.6777	.9217	1.0850	.7353	.8261	20′
50′	.7476	.6799	.9271	1.0786	.7333	.8232	10′
43° 00′	.7505	.6820	.9325	1.0724	.7314	.8203	47° 00′
10′	.7534	.6841	.9380	1.0661	.7294	.8174	50′
20′	.7563	.6862	.9435	1.0599	.7274	.8145	40′
30′	.7592	.6884	.9490	1.0538	.7254	.8116	30′
40′	.7621	.6905	.9545	1.0477	.7234	.8087	20′
50′	.7650	.6926	.9601	1.0416	.7214	.8058	10′
44° 00′	.7679	.6947	.9657	1.0355	.7193	.8029	46° 00′
10′	.7709	.6967	.9713	1.0295	.7173	.7999	50′
20′	.7738	.6988	.9770	1.0235	.7153	.7970	40′
30′	.7767	.7009	.9827	1.0176	.7133	.7941	30′
40′	.7796	.7030	.9884	1.0117	.7112	.7912	20′
50′	.7825	.7050	.9942	1.0058	.7092	.7883	10′
45° 00′	.7854	.7071	1.0000	1.0000	.7071	.7854	45° 00′
		Cosine	Cotangent	Tangent	Sine	Radians	Degrees

APPENDIX 3. WEIGHTS AND MEASURES

UNITED STATES SYSTEM

LINEAR MEASURE

Inches	Feet	Yards	Rods	Furlongs	Miles
1.0 =	.08333 =	.02778 =	.0050505 =	.00012626 =	.00001578
12.0 =	1.0 =	.33333 =	.0606061 =	.00151515 =	.00018939
36.0 =	3.0 =	1.0 =	.1818182 =	.00454545 =	.00056818
198.0 =	16.5 =	5.5 =	1.0 =	.025 =	.003125
7920.0 =	660.0 =	220.0 =	40.0 =	1.0 =	.125
63360.0 =	5280.0 =	1760.0 =	320.0 =	8.0 =	1.0

SQUARE AND LAND MEASURE

Sq. Inches	Square Feet	Square Yards	Sq. Rods	Acres	Sq. Miles
1.0 =	.006944 =	.000772			
144.0 =	1.0 =	.111111			
1296.0 =	9.0 =	1.0 =	.03306 =	.000207	
39204.0 =	272.25 =	30.25 =	1.0 =	.00625 =	.0000098
	43560.0 =	4840.0 =	160.0 =	1.0 =	.0015625
		3097600.0 =	102400.0 =	640.0 =	1.0

AVOIRDUPOIS WEIGHTS

Grains	Drams	Ounces	Pounds	Tons
1.0 =	.03657 =	.002286 =	.000143 =	.0000000714
27.34375 =	1.0 =	.0625 =	.003906 =	.00000195
437.5 =	16.0 =	1.0 =	.0625 =	.00003125
7000.0 =	256.0 =	16.0 =	1.0 =	.0005
14000000.0 =	512000.0 =	32000.0 =	2000.0 =	1.0

DRY MEASURE

Pints	Quarts	Pecks	Cubic Feet	Bushels
1.0 =	.5 =	.0625 =	.01945 =	.01563
2.0 =	1.0 =	.125 =	.03891 =	.03125
16.0 =	8.0 =	1.0 =	.31112 =	.25
51.42627 =	25.71314 =	3.21414 =	1.0 =	.80354
64.0 =	32.0 =	4.0 =	1.2445 =	1.0

LIQUID MEASURE

Gills	Pints	Quarts	U. S. Gallons	Cubic Feet
1.0 =	.25 =	.125 =	.03125 =	.00418
4.0 =	1.0 =	.5 =	.125 =	.01671
8.0 =	2.0 =	1.0 =	.250 =	.03342
32.0 =	8.0 =	4.0 =	1.0 =	.1337
			7.48052 =	1.0

METRIC SYSTEM

UNITS

Length—Meter : Mass—Gram : Capacity—Liter

for pure water at 4°C. (39.2°F.)

1 cubic decimeter or 1 liter = 1 kilogram

1000 Milli {*meters* (mm), *grams* (mg), *liters* (ml)} = 100 Centi {*meters* (cm), *grams* (cg), *liters* (cl)} = 10 Deci {*meters* (dm), *grams* (dg), *liters* (dl)} = 1 {meter, gram, liter}

1000 {meters, grams, liters} = 100 Deka {*meters* (dkm), *grams* (dkg), *liters* (dkl)} = 10 Hecto {*meters* (hm), *grams* (hg), *liters* (hl)} = 1 Kilo {*meter* (km), *gram* (kg), *liter* (kl)}

1 Metric Ton	=	1000 Kilograms
100 Square Meters	=	1 Are
100 Ares	=	1 Hectare
100 Hectares	=	1 Square Kilometer

(Courtesy of the American Institute of Steel Construction.)

APPENDIX 4. DECIMAL EQUIVALENTS AND TEMPERATURE CONVERSION

DECIMAL EQUIVALENTS—INCH-MILLIMETER CONVERSION TABLE

½	¼	⅛	1/16	1/32	1/64	Decimals	Millimeters	½	¼	⅛	1/16	1/32	1/64	Decimals	Millimeters
					1	.015625	.396875						33	.515625	13.096875
				1		.031250	.793750					17		.531250	13.493750
					3	.046875	1.190625						35	.546875	13.890625
			1			.062500	1.587500				9			.562500	14.287500
					5	.078125	1.984375						37	.578125	14.684375
				3		.093750	2.381250					19		.593750	15.081250
					7	.109375	2.778125						39	.609375	15.478125
		1				.125000	3.175000			5				.625000	15.875000
					9	.140625	3.571875						41	.640625	16.271875
				5		.156250	3.968750					21		.656250	16.668750
					11	.171875	4.365625						43	.671875	17.065625
			3			.187500	4.762500				11			.687500	17.462500
					13	.203125	5.159375						45	.703125	17.859375
				7		.218750	5.556250					23		.718750	18.256250
					15	.234375	5.953125						47	.734375	18.653125
	1					.250000	6.350000		3					.750000	19.050000
					17	.265625	6.746875						49	.765625	19.446875
				9		.281250	7.143750					25		.781250	19.843750
					19	.296875	7.540625						51	.796875	20.240625
			5			.312500	7.937500				13			.812500	20.637500
					21	.328125	8.334375						53	.828125	21.034375
				11		.343750	8.731250					27		.843750	21.431250
					23	.359375	9.128125						55	.859375	21.828125
		3				.375000	9.525000			7				.875000	22.225000
					25	.390625	9.921875						57	.890625	22.621875
				13		.406250	10.318750					29		.906250	23.018750
					27	.421875	10.715625						59	.921875	23.415625
			7			.437500	11.112500				15			.937500	23.812500
					29	.453125	11.509375						61	.953125	24.209375
				15		.468750	11.906250					31		.968750	24.606250
					31	.484375	12.303125						63	.984375	25.003125
1						.500000	12.700000	2	4	8	16	32	64	1.000000	25.400000

TEMPERATURE CONVERSION

−210 to 0			1 to 25			26 to 50			51 to 75			76 to 100			101 to 340			341 to 490			491 to 750		
C.	C. or F.	F.	C.	C. or F.	F.	C.	C. or F.	F.	C.	C. or F.	F.	C.	C. or F.	F.	C.	C. or F.	F.	C.	C. or F.	F.	C.	C. or F.	F.
-134	**-210**	-346	-17.2	**1**	33.8	-3.33	**26**	78.8	10.6	**51**	123.8	24.4	**76**	168.8	43	**110**	230	177	**350**	662	260	**500**	932
-129	**-200**	-328	-16.7	**2**	35.6	-2.78	**27**	80.6	11.1	**52**	125.6	25.0	**77**	170.6	49	**120**	248	182	**360**	680	266	**510**	950
-123	**-190**	-310	-16.1	**3**	37.4	-2.22	**28**	82.4	11.7	**53**	127.4	25.6	**78**	172.4	54	**130**	266	188	**370**	698	271	**520**	968
-118	**-180**	-292	-15.6	**4**	39.2	-1.67	**29**	84.2	12.2	**54**	129.2	26.1	**79**	174.2	60	**140**	284	193	**380**	716	277	**530**	986
-112	**-170**	-274	-15.0	**5**	41.0	-1.11	**30**	86.0	12.8	**55**	131.0	26.7	**80**	176.0	66	**150**	302	199	**390**	734	282	**540**	1004
-107	**-160**	-256	-14.4	**6**	42.8	-0.56	**31**	87.8	13.3	**56**	132.8	27.2	**81**	177.8	71	**160**	320	204	**400**	752	288	**550**	1022
-101	**-150**	-238	-13.9	**7**	44.6	0	**32**	89.6	13.9	**57**	134.6	27.8	**82**	179.6	77	**170**	338	210	**410**	770	293	**560**	1040
-95.6	**-140**	-220	-13.3	**8**	46.4	0.56	**33**	91.4	14.4	**58**	136.4	28.3	**83**	181.4	82	**180**	356	216	**420**	788	299	**570**	1058
-90.0	**-130**	-202	-12.8	**9**	48.2	1.11	**34**	93.2	15.0	**59**	138.2	28.9	**84**	183.2	88	**190**	374	221	**430**	806	304	**580**	1076
-84.4	**-120**	-184	-12.2	**10**	50.0	1.67	**35**	95.0	15.6	**60**	140.0	29.4	**85**	185.0	93	**200**	392	227	**440**	824	310	**590**	1094
-78.9	**-110**	-166	-11.7	**11**	51.8	2.22	**36**	96.8	16.1	**61**	141.8	30.0	**86**	186.8	99	**210**	410	232	**450**	842	316	**600**	1112
-73.3	**-100**	-148	-11.1	**12**	53.6	2.78	**37**	98.6	16.7	**62**	143.6	30.6	**87**	188.6	100	**212**	413	238	**460**	860	321	**610**	1130
-67.8	**-90**	-130	-10.6	**13**	55.4	3.33	**38**	100.4	17.2	**63**	145.4	31.1	**88**	190.4	104	**220**	428	243	**470**	878	327	**620**	1148
-62.2	**-80**	-112	-10.0	**14**	57.2	3.89	**39**	102.2	17.8	**64**	147.2	31.7	**89**	192.2	110	**230**	446	249	**480**	896	332	**630**	1166
-56.7	**-70**	-94	-9.44	**15**	59.0	4.44	**40**	104.0	18.3	**65**	149.0	32.2	**90**	194.0	116	**240**	464	254	**490**	914	338	**640**	1184
-51.1	**-60**	-76	-8.89	**16**	60.8	5.00	**41**	105.8	18.9	**66**	150.8	32.8	**91**	195.8	121	**250**	482				343	**650**	1202
-45.6	**-50**	-58	-8.33	**17**	62.6	5.56	**42**	107.6	19.4	**67**	152.6	33.3	**92**	197.6	127	**260**	500				349	**660**	1220
-40.0	**-40**	-40	-7.78	**18**	64.4	6.11	**43**	109.4	20.0	**68**	154.4	33.9	**93**	199.4	132	**270**	518				354	**670**	1238
-34.4	**-30**	-22	-7.22	**19**	66.2	6.67	**44**	111.2	20.6	**69**	156.2	34.4	**94**	201.2	138	**280**	536				360	**680**	1256
-28.9	**-20**	-4	-6.67	**20**	68.0	7.22	**45**	113.0	21.1	**70**	158.0	35.0	**95**	203.0	143	**290**	554				366	**690**	1274
-23.3	**-10**	14	-6.11	**21**	69.8	7.78	**46**	114.8	21.7	**71**	159.8	35.6	**96**	204.8	149	**300**	572				371	**700**	1292
-17.8	**0**	32	-5.56	**22**	71.6	8.33	**47**	116.6	22.2	**72**	161.6	36.1	**97**	206.6	154	**310**	590				377	**710**	1310
			-5.00	**23**	73.4	8.89	**48**	118.4	22.8	**73**	163.4	36.7	**98**	208.4	160	**320**	608				382	**720**	1328
			-4.44	**24**	75.2	9.44	**49**	120.2	23.3	**74**	165.2	37.2	**99**	210.2	166	**330**	626				388	**730**	1346
			-3.89	**25**	77.0	10.0	**50**	122.0	23.9	**75**	167.0	37.8	**100**	212.0	171	**340**	644				393	**740**	1364
																					399	**750**	1382

NOTE:—The numbers in bold face type refer to the temperature either in degrees Centigrade or Fahrenheit which it is desired to convert into the other scale. If converting from Fahrenheit degrees to Centigrade degrees the equivalent temperature will be found in the left column, while if converting from degrees Centigrade to degrees Fahrenheit, the answer will be found in the column on the right.

$$°F = \frac{9}{5}(°C) + 32$$

$$°C = \frac{5}{9}(°F - 32)$$

INTERPOLATION FACTORS

C.		F.	C.		F.
0.56	**1**	1.8	3.33	**6**	10.8
1.11	**2**	3.6	3.89	**7**	12.6
1.67	**3**	5.4	4.44	**8**	14.4
2.22	**4**	7.2	5.00	**9**	16.2
2.78	**5**	9.0	5.56	**10**	18.0

(Courtesy of Stephens–Adamson Manufacturing Co.)

APPENDIX 5. WEIGHTS AND SPECIFIC GRAVITIES

Substance	Weight Lb. per Cu. Ft.	Specific Gravity
METALS, ALLOYS, ORES		
Aluminum, cast, hammered	165	2.55-2.75
Brass, cast, rolled	534	8.4-8.7
Bronze, 7.9 to 14% Sn	509	7.4-8.9
Bronze, aluminum	481	7.7
Copper, cast, rolled	556	8.8-9.0
Copper ore, pyrites	262	4.1-4.3
Gold, cast, hammered	1205	19.25-19.3
Iron, cast, pig	450	7.2
Iron, wrought	485	7.6-7.9
Iron, spiegel-eisen	468	7.5
Iron, ferro-silicon	437	6.7-7.3
Iron ore, hematite	325	5.2
Iron ore, hematite in bank	160-180	....
Iron ore, hematite loose	130-160	....
Iron ore, limonite	237	3.6-4.0
Iron ore, magnetite	315	4.9-5.2
Iron slag	172	2.5-3.0
Lead	710	11.37
Lead ore, galena	465	7.3-7.6
Magnesium, alloys	112	1.74-1.83
Manganese	475	7.2-8.0
Manganese ore, pyrolusite	259	3.7-4.6
Mercury	849	13.6
Monel Metal	556	8.8-9.0
Nickel	565	8.9-9.2
Platinum, cast, hammered	1330	21.1-21.5
Silver, cast, hammered	656	10.4-10.6
Steel, rolled	490	7.85
Tin, cast, hammered	459	7.2-7.5
Tin ore, cassiterite	418	6.4-7.0
Zinc, cast, rolled	440	6.9-7.2
Zinc ore, blende	253	3.9-4.2
VARIOUS SOLIDS		
Cereals, oats bulk	32	....
Cereals, barley bulk	39	....
Cereals, corn, rye bulk	48	....
Cereals, wheat bulk	48	....
Hay and Straw bales	20	....
Cotton, Flax, Hemp	93	1.47-1.50
Fats	58	0.90-0.97
Flour, loose	28	0.40-0.50
Flour, pressed	47	0.70-0.80
Glass, common	156	2.40-2.60
Glass, plate or crown	161	2.45-2.72
Glass, crystal	184	2.90-3.00
Leather	59	0.86-1.02
Paper	58	0.70-1.15
Potatoes, piled	42	....
Rubber, caoutchouc	59	0.92-0.96
Rubber goods	94	1.0-2.0
Salt, granulated, piled	48	....
Saltpeter	67	....
Starch	96	1.53
Sulphur	125	1.93-2.07
Wool	82	1.32

Substance	Weight Lb. per Cu. Ft.	Specific Gravity
TIMBER, U. S. SEASONED		
Moisture Content by Weight:		
Seasoned timber 15 to 20%		
Green timber up to 50%		
Ash, white, red	40	0.62-0.65
Cedar, white, red	22	0.32-0.38
Chestnut	41	0.66
Cypress	30	0.48
Fir, Douglas spruce	32	0.51
Fir, eastern	25	0.40
Elm, white	45	0.72
Hemlock	29	0.42-0.52
Hickory	49	0.74-0.84
Locust	46	0.73
Maple, hard	43	0.68
Maple, white	33	0.53
Oak, chestnut	54	0.86
Oak, live	59	0.95
Oak, red, black	41	0.65
Oak, white	46	0.74
Pine, Oregon	32	0.51
Pine, red	30	0.48
Pine, white	26	0.41
Pine, yellow, long-leaf	44	0.70
Pine, yellow, short-leaf	38	0.61
Poplar	30	0.48
Redwood, California	26	0.42
Spruce, white, black	27	0.40-0.46
Walnut, black	38	0.61
VARIOUS LIQUIDS		
Alcohol, 100%	49	0.79
Acids, muriatic 40%	75	1.20
Acids, nitric 91%	94	1.50
Acids, sulphuric 87%	112	1.80
Lye, soda 66%	106	1.70
Oils, vegetable	58	0.91-0.94
Oils, mineral, lubricants	57	0.90-0.93
Water, 4°C. max. density	62.428	1.0
Water, 100°C.	59.830	0.9584
Water, ice	56	0.88-0.92
Water, snow, fresh fallen	8	.125
Water, sea water	64	1.02-1.03
GASES		
Air, 0°C. 760 mm.	.08071	1.0
Ammonia	.0478	0.5920
Carbon dioxide	.1234	1.5291
Carbon monoxide	.0781	0.9673
Gas, illuminating	.028-.036	0.35-0.45
Gas, natural	.038-.039	0.47-0.48
Hydrogen	.00559	0.0693
Nitrogen	.0784	0.9714
Oxygen	.0892	1.1056

The specific gravities of solids and liquids refer to water at 4°C., those of gases to air at 0°C. and 760 mm. pressure. The weights per cubic foot are derived from average specific gravities, except where stated that weights are for bulk, heaped or loose material, etc.

(Courtesy of the American Institute of Steel Construction.)

APPENDIX 5. WEIGHTS AND SPECIFIC GRAVITIES (CONT.)

Substance	Weight Lb. per Cu. Ft.	Specific Gravity
ASHLAR MASONRY		
Granite, syenite, gneiss	165	2.3-3.0
Limestone, marble	160	2.3-2.8
Sandstone, bluestone	140	2.1-2.4
MORTAR RUBBLE MASONRY		
Granite, syenite, gneiss	155	2.2-2.8
Limestone, marble	150	2.2-2.6
Sandstone, bluestone	130	2.0-2.2
DRY RUBBLE MASONRY		
Granite, syenite, gneiss	130	1.9-2.3
Limestone, marble	125	1.9-2.1
Sandstone, bluestone	110	1.8-1.9
BRICK MASONRY		
Pressed brick	140	2.2-2.3
Common brick	120	1.8-2.0
Soft brick	100	1.5-1.7
CONCRETE MASONRY		
Cement, stone, sand	144	2.2-2.4
Cement, slag, etc.	130	1.9-2.3
Cement, cinder, etc.	100	1.5-1.7
VARIOUS BUILDING MATERIALS		
Ashes, cinders	40-45	....
Cement, portland, loose	90	....
Cement, portland, set	183	2.7-3.2
Lime, gypsum, loose	53-64	....
Mortar, set	103	1.4-1.9
Slags, bank slag	67-72	....
Slags, bank screenings	98-117	....
Slags, machine slag	96	....
Slags, slag sand	49-55	....
EARTH, ETC., EXCAVATED		
Clay, dry	63	....
Clay, damp, plastic	110	....
Clay and gravel, dry	100	....
Earth, dry, loose	76	....
Earth, dry, packed	95	....
Earth, moist, loose	78	....
Earth, moist, packed	96	....
Earth, mud, flowing	108	....
Earth, mud, packed	115	....
Riprap, limestone	80-85	....
Riprap, sandstone	90	....
Riprap, shale	105	....
Sand, gravel, dry, loose	90-105	....
Sand, gravel, dry, packed	100-120	....
Sand, gravel, dry, wet	118-120	....
EXCAVATIONS IN WATER		
Sand or gravel	60	....
Sand or gravel and clay	65	....
Clay	80	....
River mud	90	....
Soil	70	....
Stone riprap	65	....

Substance	Weight Lb. per Cu. Ft.	Specific Gravity
MINERALS		
Asbestos	153	2.1-2.8
Barytes	281	4.50
Basalt	184	2.7-3.2
Bauxite	159	2.55
Borax	109	1.7-1.8
Chalk	137	1.8-2.6
Clay, marl	137	1.8-2.6
Dolomite	181	2.9
Feldspar, orthoclase	159	2.5-2.6
Gneiss, serpentine	159	2.4-2.7
Granite, syenite	175	2.5-3.1
Greenstone, trap	187	2.8-3.2
Gypsum, alabaster	159	2.3-2.8
Hornblende	187	3.0
Limestone, marble	165	2.5-2.8
Magnesite	187	3.0
Phosphate rock, apatite	200	3.2
Porphyry	172	2.6-2.9
Pumice, natural	40	0.37-0.90
Quartz, flint	165	2.5-2.8
Sandstone, bluestone	147	2.2-2.5
Shale, slate	175	2.7-2.9
Soapstone, talc	169	2.6-2.8
STONE, QUARRIED, PILED		
Basalt, granite, gneiss	96	....
Limestone, marble, quartz	95	....
Sandstone	82	....
Shale	92	....
Greenstone, hornblende	107	....
BITUMINOUS SUBSTANCES		
Asphaltum	81	1.1-1.5
Coal, anthracite	97	1.4-1.7
Coal, bituminous	84	1.2-1.5
Coal, lignite	78	1.1-1.4
Coal, peat, turf, dry	47	0.65-0.85
Coal, charcoal, pine	23	0.28-0.44
Coal, charcoal, oak	33	0.47-0.57
Coal, coke	75	1.0-1.4
Graphite	131	1.9-2.3
Paraffine	56	0.87-0.91
Petroleum	54	0.87
Petroleum, refined	50	0.79-0.82
Petroleum, benzine	46	0.73-0.75
Petroleum, gasoline	42	0.66-0.69
Pitch	69	1.07-1.15
Tar, bituminous	75	1.20
COAL AND COKE, PILED		
Coal, anthracite	47-58	....
Coal, bituminous, lignite	40-54	....
Coal, peat, turf	20-26	....
Coal, charcoal	10-14	....
Coal, coke	23-32	....

The specific gravities of solids and liquids refer to water at 4°C., those of gases to air at 0°C. and 760 mm. pressure. The weights per cubic foot are derived from average specific gravities, except where stated that weights are for bulk, heaped or loose material, etc.

WIRE AND SHEET METAL GAGES

IN DECIMALS OF AN INCH

Name of Gage	United States Standard Gage*		The United States Steel Wire Gage	American or Brown & Sharpe Wire Gage	New Birmingham Standard Sheet & Hoop Gage	British Imperial or English Legal Standard Wire Gage	Birmingham or Stubs Iron Wire Gage	Name of Gage
Principal Use	Uncoated Steel Sheets and Light Plates		Steel Wire except Music Wire	Non-Ferrous Sheets and Wire	Iron and Steel Sheets and Hoops	Wire	Strips, Bands, Hoops and Wire	Principal Use
Gage No.	Weight Oz. per Sq. Ft.	Approx. Thickness Inches	Thickness, Inches					Gage No.
7/0's			.4900		.6666	.500		7/0's
6/0's			.4615	.5800	.625	.464		6/0's
5/0's			.4305	.5165	.5883	.432	.500	5/0's
4/0's			.3938	.4600	.5416	.400	.454	4/0's
3/0's			.3625	.4096	.500	.372	.425	3/0's
2/0's			.3310	.3648	.4452	.348	.380	2/0's
0			.3065	.3249	.3964	.324	.340	0
1			.2830	.2893	.3532	.300	.300	1
2			.2625	.2576	.3147	.276	.284	2
3	160	.2391	.2437	.2294	.2804	.252	.259	3
4	150	.2242	.2253	.2043	.250	.232	.238	4
5	140	.2092	.2070	.1819	.2225	.212	.220	5
6	130	.1943	.1920	.1620	.1981	.192	.203	6
7	120	.1793	.1770	.1443	.1764	.176	.180	7
8	110	.1644	.1620	.1285	.1570	.160	.165	8
9	100	.1495	.1483	.1144	.1398	.144	.148	9
10	90	.1345	.1350	.1019	.1250	.128	.134	10
11	80	.1196	.1205	.0907	.1113	.116	.120	11
12	70	.1046	.1055	.0808	.0991	.104	.109	12
13	60	.0897	.0915	.0720	.0882	.092	.095	13
14	50	.0747	.0800	.0641	.0785	.080	.083	14
15	45	.0673	.0720	.0571	.0699	.072	.072	15
16	40	.0598	.0625	.0508	.0625	.064	.065	16
17	36	.0538	.0540	.0453	.0556	.056	.058	17
18	32	.0478	.0475	.0403	.0495	.048	.049	18
19	28	.0418	.0410	.0359	.0440	.040	.042	19
20	24	.0359	.0348	.0320	.0392	.036	.035	20
21	22	.0329	.0318	.0285	.0349	.032	.032	21
22	20	.0299	.0286	.0253	.0313	.028	.028	22
23	18	.0269	.0258	.0226	.0278	.024	.025	23
24	16	.0239	.0230	.0201	.0248	.022	.022	24
25	14	.0209	.0204	.0179	.0220	.020	.020	25
26	12	.0179	.0181	.0159	.0196	.018	.018	26
27	11	.0164	.0173	.0142	.0175	.0164	.016	27
28	10	.0149	.0162	.0126	.0156	.0148	.014	28
29	9	.0135	.0150	.0113	.0139	.0136	.013	29
30	8	.0120	.0140	.0100	.0123	.0124	.012	30
31	7	.0105	.0132	.0089	.0110	.0116	.010	31
32	6.5	.0097	.0128	.0080	.0098	.0108	.009	32
33	6	.0090	.0118	.0071	.0087	.0100	.008	33
34	5.5	.0082	.0104	.0063	.0077	.0092	.007	34
35	5	.0075	.0095	.0056	.0069	.0084	.005	35
36	4.5	.0067	.0090	.0050	.0061	.0076	.004	36
37	4.25	.0064	.0085	.0045	.0054	.0068		37
38	4	.0060	.0080	.0040	.0048	.0060		38
39			.0075	.0035	.0043	.0052		39
40			.0070	.0031	.0039	.0048		40

* U. S. Standard Gage is officially a weight gage, in oz. per sq. ft. as tabulated. The Approx. Thickness shown is the "Manufacturers' Standard" of the American Iron and Steel Institute, based on steel as weighing 501.81 lbs. per cu. ft. (489.6 true weight plus 2.5 percent for average over-run in area and thickness). The A.I.S.I. standard nomenclature for flat rolled carbon steel is as follows:

Widths, Inches	Thicknesses, Inch							
	0.2500 and thicker	0.2499 to 0.2031	0.2030 to 0.1875	0.1874 to 0.0568	0.0567 to 0.0344	0.0343 to 0.0255	0.0254 to 0.0142	0.0141 and thinner
To 3½ incl.	Bar	Bar	Strip	Strip	Strip	Strip	Sheet	Sheet
Over 3½ to 6 incl.	Bar	Bar	Strip	Strip	Strip	Sheet	Sheet	Sheet
" 6 to 12 "	Plate	Strip	Strip	Strip	Sheet	Sheet	Sheet	Sheet
" 12 to 32 "	Plate	Sheet	Sheet	Sheet	Sheet	Sheet	Sheet	Black Plate
" 32 to 48 "	Plate	Sheet	Sheet	Sheet	Sheet	Sheet	Sheet	Sheet
" 48	Plate	Plate	Plate	Sheet	Sheet	Sheet	Sheet	—

(Courtesy of the American Institute of Steel Construction.)

APPENDIX 7. AMERICAN STANDARD GRAPHICAL SYMBOLS FOR ELECTRONIC DIAGRAMS

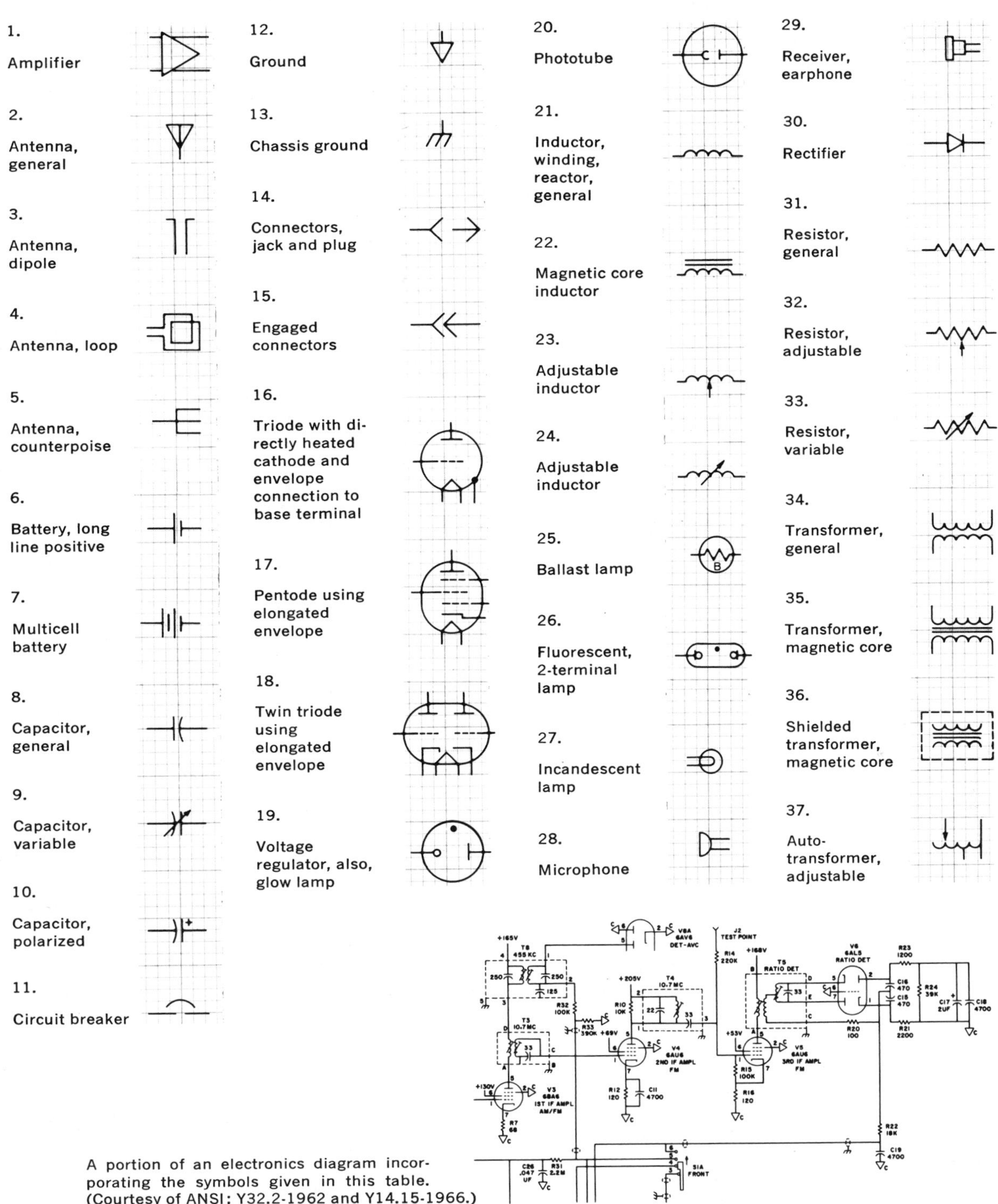

A portion of an electronics diagram incorporating the symbols given in this table. (Courtesy of ANSI; Y32.2-1962 and Y14.15-1966.)

APPENDIX 8. PIPING SYMBOLS

TYPE OF FITTING		DOUBLE LINE CONVENTION					SINGLE LINE CONVENTION					FLOW DIAGRAM
		FLANGED	SCREWED	B & S	WELDED	SOLDERED	FLANGED	SCREWED	B & S	WELDED	SOLDERED	
1	Joint											
2	Joint - Expansion											
3	Union											
4	Sleeve											
5	Reducer											
6	Reducer - Eccentric											
7	Reducing Flange											
8	Bushing											
9	Elbow - 45°											
10	Elbow - 90°											
11	Elbow - Long radius	L.R.	L.R.		L.R.	L.R.	L.R.	L.R.		L.R.	L.R.	
12	Elbow - (turned up)											
13	Elbow - (turned down)											
14	Elbow - Side outlet (outlet up)											
15	Elbow - Side outlet (outlet down)											
16	Elbow - Base											
17	Elbow - Double branch											
18	Elbow - Reducing											
19	Lateral											
20	Tee											
21	Tee - Single sweep											

APPENDIX 8. PIPING SYMBOLS (Cont.)

	TYPE OF FITTING	DOUBLE LINE CONVENTION					SINGLE LINE CONVENTION					FLOW DIAGRAM
		FLANGED	SCREWED	B & S	WELDED	SOLDERED	FLANGED	SCREWED	B & S	WELDED	SOLDERED	
22	Tee-Double sweep											
23	Tee-(outlet up)											
24	Tee-(outlet down)											
25	Tee-Side outlet (outlet up)											
26	Tee-Side outlet (outlet down)											
27	Cross											
28	Valve-Globe											
29	Valve-Angle											
30	Valve-Motor operated globe											Motor operated
31	Valve-Gate											
32	Valve-Angle gate											
33	Valve-Motor operated gate											Motor operated
34	Valve-Check											
35	Valve-Angle check											
36	Valve-Safety											
37	Valve-Angle safety											
38	Valve-Quick opening											
39	Valve-Float operating											
40	Stop Cock											

APPENDIX 9. AMERICAN WELDING SOCIETY STANDARD WELDING SYMBOLS

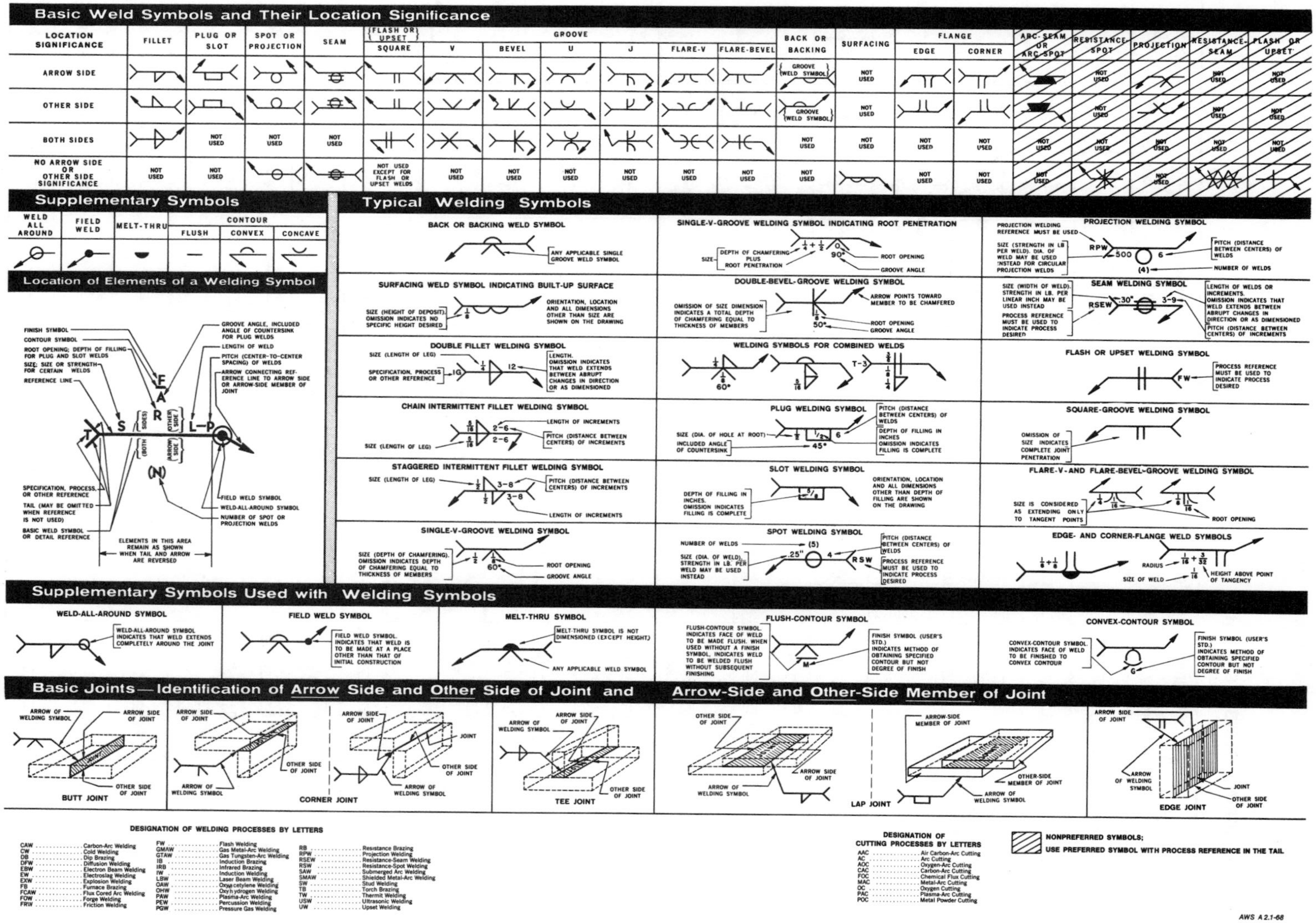

Basic Weld Symbols and Their Location Significance

LOCATION SIGNIFICANCE	FILLET	PLUG OR SLOT	SPOT OR PROJECTION	SEAM	GROOVE: SQUARE {FLASH OR UPSET}	GROOVE: V	GROOVE: BEVEL	GROOVE: U	GROOVE: J	GROOVE: FLARE-V	GROOVE: FLARE-BEVEL	BACK OR BACKING	SURFACING	FLANGE: EDGE	FLANGE: CORNER	ARC-SEAM OR ARC-SPOT	RESISTANCE-SPOT	PROJECTION	RESISTANCE-SEAM	FLASH OR UPSET
ARROW SIDE												GROOVE WELD SYMBOL	NOT USED				NOT USED		NOT USED	NOT USED
OTHER SIDE												GROOVE WELD SYMBOL	NOT USED				NOT USED		NOT USED	NOT USED
BOTH SIDES		NOT USED	NOT USED	NOT USED								NOT USED	NOT USED	NOT USED	NOT USED	NOT USED	NOT USED	NOT USED	NOT USED	NOT USED
NO ARROW SIDE OR OTHER SIDE SIGNIFICANCE	NOT USED	NOT USED			NOT USED EXCEPT FOR FLASH OR UPSET WELDS	NOT USED	NOT USED	NOT USED	NOT USED	NOT USED	NOT USED	NOT USED		NOT USED	NOT USED	NOT USED		NOT USED		

Supplementary Symbols

WELD ALL AROUND	FIELD WELD	MELT-THRU	CONTOUR: FLUSH	CONTOUR: CONVEX	CONTOUR: CONCAVE

Location of Elements of a Welding Symbol

FINISH SYMBOL
CONTOUR SYMBOL
ROOT OPENING; DEPTH OF FILLING FOR PLUG AND SLOT WELDS
SIZE; SIZE OR STRENGTH FOR CERTAIN WELDS
REFERENCE LINE
SPECIFICATION, PROCESS, OR OTHER REFERENCE
TAIL (MAY BE OMITTED WHEN REFERENCE IS NOT USED)
BASIC WELD SYMBOL OR DETAIL REFERENCE
GROOVE ANGLE, INCLUDED ANGLE OF COUNTERSINK FOR PLUG WELDS
LENGTH OF WELD
PITCH (CENTER-TO-CENTER SPACING) OF WELDS
ARROW CONNECTING REFERENCE LINE TO ARROW SIDE OR ARROW-SIDE MEMBER OF JOINT
FIELD WELD SYMBOL
WELD-ALL-AROUND SYMBOL
NUMBER OF SPOT OR PROJECTION WELDS
ELEMENTS IN THIS AREA REMAIN AS SHOWN WHEN TAIL AND ARROW ARE REVERSED
F A R S T L-P (N) (BOTH SIDES) (OTHER SIDE) (ARROW SIDE)

Typical Welding Symbols

BACK OR BACKING WELD SYMBOL
ANY APPLICABLE SINGLE GROOVE WELD SYMBOL

SURFACING WELD SYMBOL INDICATING BUILT-UP SURFACE
SIZE (HEIGHT OF DEPOSIT). OMISSION INDICATES NO SPECIFIC HEIGHT DESIRED
ORIENTATION, LOCATION AND ALL DIMENSIONS OTHER THAN SIZE ARE SHOWN ON THE DRAWING

DOUBLE FILLET WELDING SYMBOL
SIZE (LENGTH OF LEG)
SPECIFICATION, PROCESS OR OTHER REFERENCE
LENGTH. OMISSION INDICATES THAT WELD EXTENDS BETWEEN ABRUPT CHANGES IN DIRECTION OR AS DIMENSIONED

CHAIN INTERMITTENT FILLET WELDING SYMBOL
SIZE (LENGTH OF LEG)
LENGTH OF INCREMENTS
PITCH (DISTANCE BETWEEN CENTERS) OF INCREMENTS

STAGGERED INTERMITTENT FILLET WELDING SYMBOL
SIZE (LENGTH OF LEG)
PITCH (DISTANCE BETWEEN CENTERS) OF INCREMENTS
LENGTH OF INCREMENTS

SINGLE-V-GROOVE WELDING SYMBOL
SIZE (DEPTH OF CHAMFERING). OMISSION INDICATES DEPTH OF CHAMFERING EQUAL TO THICKNESS OF MEMBERS
ROOT OPENING
GROOVE ANGLE

SINGLE-V-GROOVE WELDING SYMBOL INDICATING ROOT PENETRATION
SIZE — DEPTH OF CHAMFERING PLUS ROOT PENETRATION
ROOT OPENING
GROOVE ANGLE

DOUBLE-BEVEL-GROOVE WELDING SYMBOL
OMISSION OF SIZE DIMENSION INDICATES A TOTAL DEPTH OF CHAMFERING EQUAL TO THICKNESS OF MEMBERS
ARROW POINTS TOWARD MEMBER TO BE CHAMFERED
ROOT OPENING
GROOVE ANGLE

WELDING SYMBOLS FOR COMBINED WELDS

PLUG WELDING SYMBOL
SIZE (DIA. OF HOLE AT ROOT)
INCLUDED ANGLE OF COUNTERSINK
PITCH (DISTANCE BETWEEN CENTERS) OF WELDS
DEPTH OF FILLING IN INCHES. OMISSION INDICATES FILLING IS COMPLETE

SLOT WELDING SYMBOL
DEPTH OF FILLING IN INCHES. OMISSION INDICATES FILLING IS COMPLETE
ORIENTATION, LOCATION AND ALL DIMENSIONS OTHER THAN DEPTH OF FILLING ARE SHOWN ON THE DRAWING

SPOT WELDING SYMBOL
NUMBER OF WELDS
SIZE (DIA. OF WELD). STRENGTH IN LB. PER WELD MAY BE USED INSTEAD
PITCH (DISTANCE BETWEEN CENTERS) OF WELDS
PROCESS REFERENCE MUST BE USED TO INDICATE PROCESS DESIRED

PROJECTION WELDING SYMBOL
PROJECTION WELDING REFERENCE MUST BE USED
SIZE (STRENGTH IN LB PER WELD). DIA. OF WELD MAY BE USED INSTEAD FOR CIRCULAR PROJECTION WELDS
PITCH (DISTANCE BETWEEN CENTERS) OF WELDS
NUMBER OF WELDS

SEAM WELDING SYMBOL
SIZE (WIDTH OF WELD). STRENGTH IN LB. PER LINEAR INCH MAY BE USED INSTEAD
PROCESS REFERENCE MUST BE USED TO INDICATE PROCESS DESIRED
LENGTH OF WELDS OR INCREMENTS. OMISSION INDICATES THAT WELD EXTENDS BETWEEN ABRUPT CHANGES IN DIRECTION OR AS DIMENSIONED
PITCH (DISTANCE BETWEEN CENTERS) OF INCREMENTS

FLASH OR UPSET WELDING SYMBOL
PROCESS REFERENCE MUST BE USED TO INDICATE PROCESS DESIRED

SQUARE-GROOVE WELDING SYMBOL
OMISSION OF SIZE INDICATES COMPLETE JOINT PENETRATION

FLARE-V-AND FLARE-BEVEL-GROOVE WELDING SYMBOL
SIZE IS CONSIDERED AS EXTENDING ONLY TO TANGENT POINTS
ROOT OPENING

EDGE- AND CORNER-FLANGE WELD SYMBOLS
RADIUS
SIZE OF WELD
HEIGHT ABOVE POINT OF TANGENCY

Supplementary Symbols Used with Welding Symbols

WELD-ALL-AROUND SYMBOL
WELD-ALL-AROUND SYMBOL INDICATES THAT WELD EXTENDS COMPLETELY AROUND THE JOINT

FIELD WELD SYMBOL
FIELD WELD SYMBOL INDICATES THAT WELD IS TO BE MADE AT A PLACE OTHER THAN THAT OF INITIAL CONSTRUCTION

MELT-THRU SYMBOL
MELT-THRU SYMBOL IS NOT DIMENSIONED (EXCEPT HEIGHT)
ANY APPLICABLE WELD SYMBOL

FLUSH-CONTOUR SYMBOL
FLUSH-CONTOUR SYMBOL INDICATES FACE OF WELD TO BE MADE FLUSH. WHEN USED WITHOUT A FINISH SYMBOL, INDICATES WELD TO BE WELDED FLUSH WITHOUT SUBSEQUENT FINISHING
FINISH SYMBOL (USER'S STD.) INDICATES METHOD OF OBTAINING SPECIFIED CONTOUR BUT NOT DEGREE OF FINISH

CONVEX-CONTOUR SYMBOL
CONVEX-CONTOUR SYMBOL INDICATES FACE OF WELD TO BE FINISHED TO CONVEX CONTOUR
FINISH SYMBOL (USER'S STD.) INDICATES METHOD OF OBTAINING SPECIFIED CONTOUR BUT NOT DEGREE OF FINISH

Basic Joints—Identification of Arrow Side and Other Side of Joint and Arrow-Side and Other-Side Member of Joint

BUTT JOINT — ARROW OF WELDING SYMBOL; ARROW SIDE OF JOINT; OTHER SIDE OF JOINT
CORNER JOINT — ARROW SIDE OF JOINT; OTHER SIDE OF JOINT; ARROW OF WELDING SYMBOL; JOINT
TEE JOINT — ARROW OF WELDING SYMBOL; ARROW SIDE OF JOINT; OTHER SIDE OF JOINT
LAP JOINT — OTHER SIDE OF JOINT; ARROW SIDE OF JOINT; ARROW OF WELDING SYMBOL; ARROW-SIDE MEMBER OF JOINT; OTHER-SIDE MEMBER OF JOINT
EDGE JOINT — ARROW SIDE OF JOINT; ARROW OF WELDING SYMBOL; JOINT; OTHER SIDE OF JOINT

DESIGNATION OF WELDING PROCESSES BY LETTERS

CAW	Carbon-Arc Welding	FW	Flash Welding	RB	Resistance Brazing
CW	Cold Welding	GMAW	Gas Metal-Arc Welding	RPW	Projection Welding
DB	Dip Brazing	GTAW	Gas Tungsten-Arc Welding	RSEW	Resistance-Seam Welding
DFW	Diffusion Welding	IB	Induction Brazing	RSW	Resistance-Spot Welding
EBW	Electron Beam Welding	IRB	Infrared Brazing	SAW	Submerged Arc Welding
EW	Electroslag Welding	IW	Induction Welding	SMAW	Shielded Metal-Arc Welding
EXW	Explosion Welding	LBW	Laser Beam Welding	SW	Stud Welding
FB	Furnace Brazing	OAW	Oxyacetylene Welding	TB	Torch Brazing
FCAW	Flux Cored Arc Welding	OHW	Oxyhydrogen Welding	TW	Thermit Welding
FOW	Forge Welding	PAW	Plasma-Arc Welding	USW	Ultrasonic Welding
FRW	Friction Welding	PEW	Percussion Welding	UW	Upset Welding
		PGW	Pressure Gas Welding		

DESIGNATION OF CUTTING PROCESSES BY LETTERS

AAC	Air Carbon-Arc Cutting
AC	Arc Cutting
AOC	Oxygen-Arc Cutting
CAC	Carbon-Arc Cutting
FOC	Chemical Flux Cutting
MAC	Metal-Arc Cutting
OC	Oxygen Cutting
PAC	Plasma-Arc Cutting
POC	Metal Powder Cutting

NONPREFERRED SYMBOLS;
USE PREFERRED SYMBOL WITH PROCESS REFERENCE IN THE TAIL

AWS A2.1-68

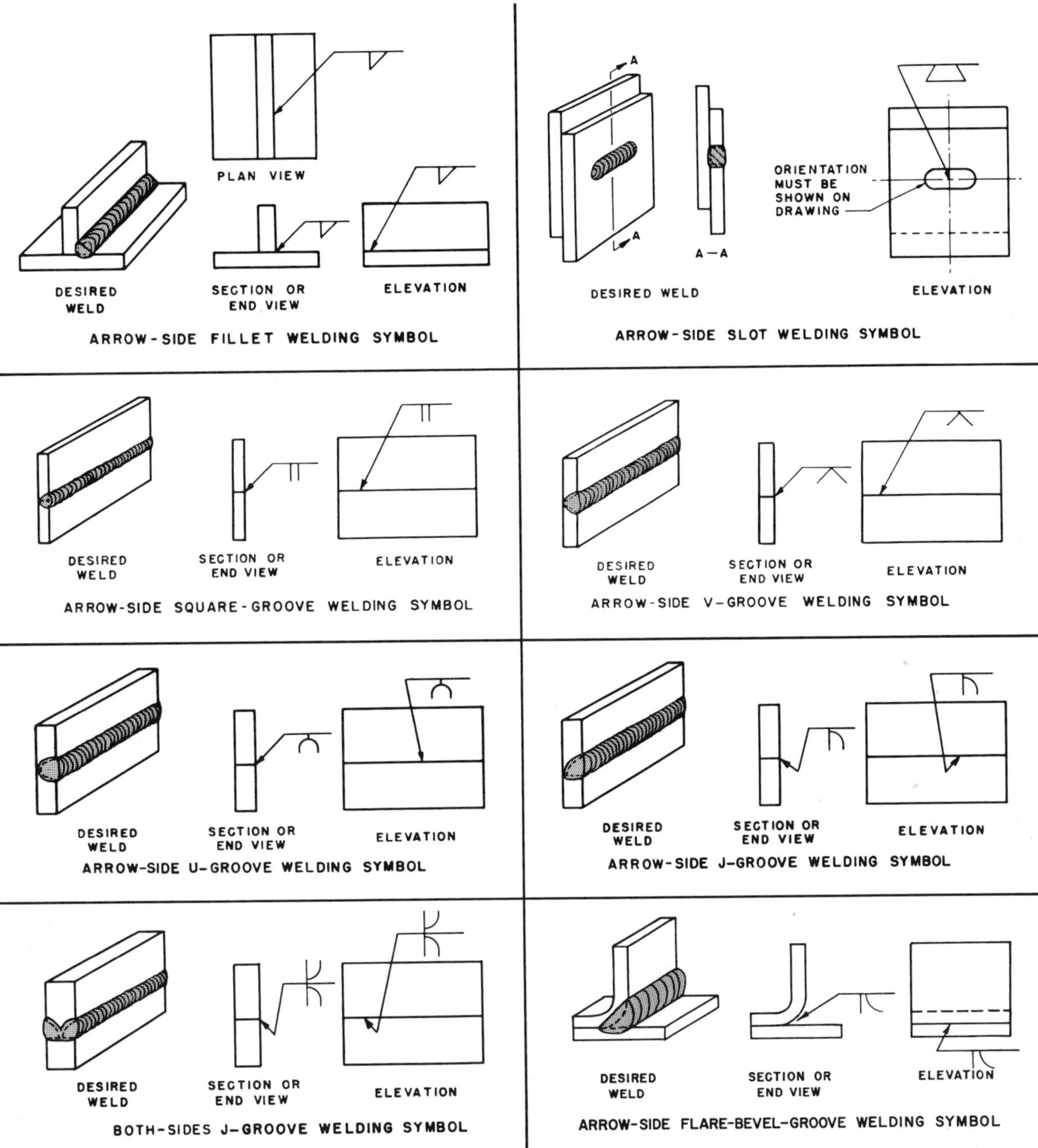

(Courtesy of ANSI; Y32.3-1959.)

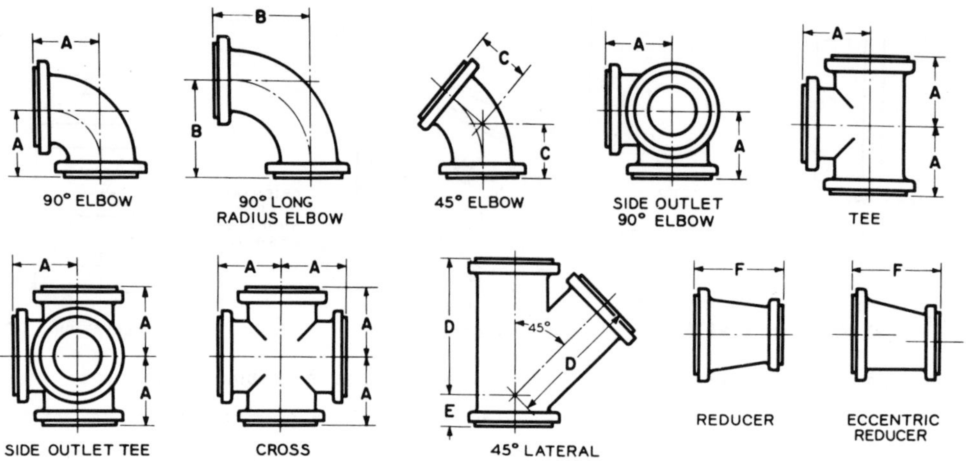

Dimensions of 250-lb Cast Iron Flanged Fittings

Nominal Pipe Size	Flanges			Fittings		Straight					
	Dia of Flange	Thickness of Flange (Min)	Dia of Raised Face	Inside Dia of Fittings (Min)	Wall Thickness	Center to Face 90 Deg Elbow Tees, Crosses and True "Y" A	Center to Face 90 Deg Long Radius Elbow B	Center to Face 45 Deg Elbow C	Center to Face Lateral D	Short Center to Face True "Y" and Lateral E	Face to Face Reducer F
1	$4\frac{7}{8}$	$\frac{11}{16}$	$2\frac{11}{16}$	1	$\frac{7}{16}$	4	5	2	$6\frac{1}{2}$	2	....
$1\frac{1}{4}$	$5\frac{1}{4}$	$\frac{3}{4}$	$3\frac{1}{16}$	$1\frac{1}{4}$	$\frac{7}{16}$	$4\frac{1}{4}$	$5\frac{1}{2}$	$2\frac{1}{2}$	$7\frac{1}{4}$	$2\frac{1}{4}$	....
$1\frac{1}{2}$	$6\frac{1}{8}$	$\frac{13}{16}$	$3\frac{9}{16}$	$1\frac{1}{2}$	$\frac{7}{16}$	$4\frac{1}{2}$	6	$2\frac{3}{4}$	$8\frac{1}{2}$	$2\frac{1}{2}$	....
2	$6\frac{1}{2}$	$\frac{7}{8}$	$4\frac{3}{16}$	2	$\frac{7}{16}$	5	$6\frac{1}{2}$	3	9	$2\frac{1}{2}$	5
$2\frac{1}{2}$	$7\frac{1}{2}$	1	$4\frac{15}{16}$	$2\frac{1}{2}$	$\frac{1}{2}$	$5\frac{1}{2}$	7	$3\frac{1}{2}$	$10\frac{1}{2}$	$2\frac{1}{2}$	$5\frac{1}{2}$
3	$8\frac{1}{4}$	$1\frac{1}{8}$	$5\frac{11}{16}$	3	$\frac{9}{16}$	6	$7\frac{3}{4}$	$3\frac{1}{2}$	11	3	6
$3\frac{1}{2}$	9	$1\frac{3}{16}$	$6\frac{5}{16}$	$3\frac{1}{2}$	$\frac{9}{16}$	$6\frac{1}{2}$	$8\frac{1}{2}$	4	$12\frac{1}{2}$	3	$6\frac{1}{2}$
4	10	$1\frac{1}{4}$	$6\frac{15}{16}$	4	$\frac{5}{8}$	7	9	$4\frac{1}{2}$	$13\frac{1}{2}$	3	7
5	11	$1\frac{3}{8}$	$8\frac{5}{16}$	5	$\frac{11}{16}$	8	$10\frac{1}{4}$	5	15	$3\frac{1}{2}$	8
6	$12\frac{1}{2}$	$1\frac{7}{16}$	$9\frac{11}{16}$	6	$\frac{3}{4}$	$8\frac{1}{2}$	$11\frac{1}{2}$	$5\frac{1}{2}$	$17\frac{1}{2}$	4	9
8	15	$1\frac{5}{8}$	$11\frac{15}{16}$	8	$\frac{13}{16}$	10	14	6	$20\frac{1}{2}$	5	11
10	$17\frac{1}{2}$	$1\frac{7}{8}$	$14\frac{1}{16}$	10	$\frac{15}{16}$	$11\frac{1}{2}$	$16\frac{1}{2}$	7	24	$5\frac{1}{2}$	12
12	$20\frac{1}{2}$	2	$16\frac{7}{16}$	12	1	13	19	8	$27\frac{1}{2}$	6	14
14	23	$2\frac{1}{8}$	$18\frac{15}{16}$	$13\frac{1}{4}$	$1\frac{1}{8}$	15	$21\frac{1}{2}$	$8\frac{1}{2}$	31	$6\frac{1}{2}$	16
16	$25\frac{1}{2}$	$2\frac{1}{4}$	$21\frac{1}{16}$	$15\frac{1}{4}$	$1\frac{1}{4}$	$16\frac{1}{2}$	24	$9\frac{1}{2}$	$34\frac{1}{2}$	$7\frac{1}{2}$	18
18	28	$2\frac{3}{8}$	$23\frac{5}{16}$	17	$1\frac{3}{8}$	18	$26\frac{1}{2}$	10	$37\frac{1}{2}$	8	19
20	$30\frac{1}{2}$	$2\frac{1}{2}$	$25\frac{9}{16}$	19	$1\frac{1}{2}$	$19\frac{1}{2}$	29	$10\frac{1}{2}$	$40\frac{1}{2}$	$8\frac{1}{2}$	20
24	36	$2\frac{3}{4}$	$30\frac{5}{16}$	23	$1\frac{5}{8}$	$22\frac{1}{2}$	34	12	$47\frac{1}{2}$	10	24
30	43	3	$37\frac{3}{16}$	29	2	$27\frac{1}{2}$	$41\frac{1}{2}$	15	....	....	30

All dimensions given in inches.

(Courtesy of ANSI; B16.1-1967.)

SCREW THREAD SERIES

Size	Basic Major Dia	Threads Per Inch						Size
		Coarse (UNC or NC)*	Fine (UNF or NF)*	Extra Fine (UNEF or NEF)*	8 Thread Series (UN, N or NS)*	12 Thread Series (UN or N)*	16 Thread Series (UN or N)*	
0	0.0600		80	–	–	–	–	0
1	0.0730	64	72	–	–	–	–	1
2	0.0860	56	64	–	–	–	–	2
3	0.0990	48	56	–	–	–	–	3
4	0.1120	40	48	–	–	–	–	4
5	0.1250	40	44	–	–	–	–	5
6	0.1380	32	40	–	–	–	–	6
8	0.1640	32	36	–	–	–	–	8
10	0.1900	24	32	–	–	–	–	10
12	0.2160	24	28	32	–	–	–	12
1/4	0.2500	20	28	32	–	–	–	1/4
5/16	0.3125	18	24	32	–	–	–	5/16
3/8	0.3750	16	24	32	–	–	–	3/8
7/16	0.4375	14	20	28	–	–	–	7/16
1/2	0.5000	13	20	28	–	12	–	1/2
9/16	0.5625	12	18	24	–	12	–	9/16
5/8	0.6250	11	18	24	–	12	–	5/8
11/16	0.6875	–	–	24	–	12	–	11/16
3/4	0.7500	10	16	20	–	12	16	3/4
13/16	0.8125	–	–	20	–	12	16	13/16
7/8	0.8750	9	14	20	–	12	16	7/8
15/16	0.9375	–	–	20	–	12	16	15/16
1	1.0000	–	14 **	–	–	–	–	1
1	1.0000	8	12	20	8	12	16	1
1 1/16	1.0625	–	–	18	–	12	16	1 1/16
1 1/8	1.1250	7	12	18	8	12	16	1 1/8
1 3/16	1.1875	–	–	18	–	12	16	1 3/16
1 1/4	1.2500	7	12	18	8	12	16	1 1/4
1 5/16	1.3125	–	–	18	–	12	16	1 5/16
1 3/8	1.3750	6	12	18	8	12	16	1 3/8
1 7/16	1.4375	–	–	18	–	12	16	1 7/16
1 1/2	1.5000	6	12	18	8	12	16	1 1/2
1 9/16	1.5625	–	–	18	–	–	16	1 9/16
1 5/8	1.6250	–	–	18	8	12	16	1 5/8
1 11/16	1.6875	–	–	18	–	–	16	1 11/16
1 3/4	1.7500	5	–	16	8	12	16	1 3/4
1 13/16	1.8125	–	–	–	–	–	16	1 13/16
1 7/8	1.8750	–	–	–	8	12	16	1 7/8
1 15/16	1.9375	–	–	–	–	–	16	1 15/16
2	2.0000	4 1/2	–	16	8	12	16	2
2 1/16	2.0625	–	–	–	–	–	16	2 1/16
2 1/8	2.1250	–	–	–	8	12	16	2 1/8
2 3/16	2.1875	–	–	–	–	–	16	2 3/16
2 1/4	2.2500	4 1/2	–	–	8	12	16	2 1/4
2 5/16	2.3125	–			–	–	16	2 5/16
2 3/8	2.3750	–			–	12	16	2 3/8
2 7/16	2.4375	–			–	–	16	2 7/16
2 1/2	2.5000	4			8	12	16	2 1/2
2 5/8	2.6250	–			–	12	16	2 5/8
2 3/4	2.7500	4			8	12	16	2 3/4
2 7/8	2.8750	–			–	12	16	2 7/8
3	3.0000	4			8	12	16	3
3 1/8	3.1250	–			–	12	16	3 1/8
3 1/4	3.2500	4			8	12	16	3 1/4
3 3/8	3.3750	–			–	12	16	3 3/8
3 1/2	3.5000	4			8	12	16	3 1/2
3 5/8	3.6250	–			–	12	16	3 5/8
3 3/4	3.7500	4			8	12	16	3 3/4
3 7/8	3.8750	–			–	12	16	3 7/8
4	4.0000	4			8	12	16	4
4 1/4	4.2500	–			8	12	16	4 1/4
4 1/2	4.5000	–			8	12	16	4 1/2
4 3/4	4.7500	–			8	12	16	4 3/4
5	5.0000	–	–	–	8	12	16	5
5 1/4	5.2500	–	–	–	8	12	16	5 1/4
5 1/2	5.5000	–	–	–	8	12	16	5 1/2
5 3/4	5.7500	–	–	–	8	12	16	5 3/4
6	6.0000	–	–	–	8	12	16	6

* For Series Symbols applying to a particular thread, see dimensional tables ASA B1.1

** NS

(Courtesy of ANSI; Y14.6-1957.)

APPENDIX 13. AMERICAN STANDARD 125-LB CAST IRON FLANGED FITTINGS

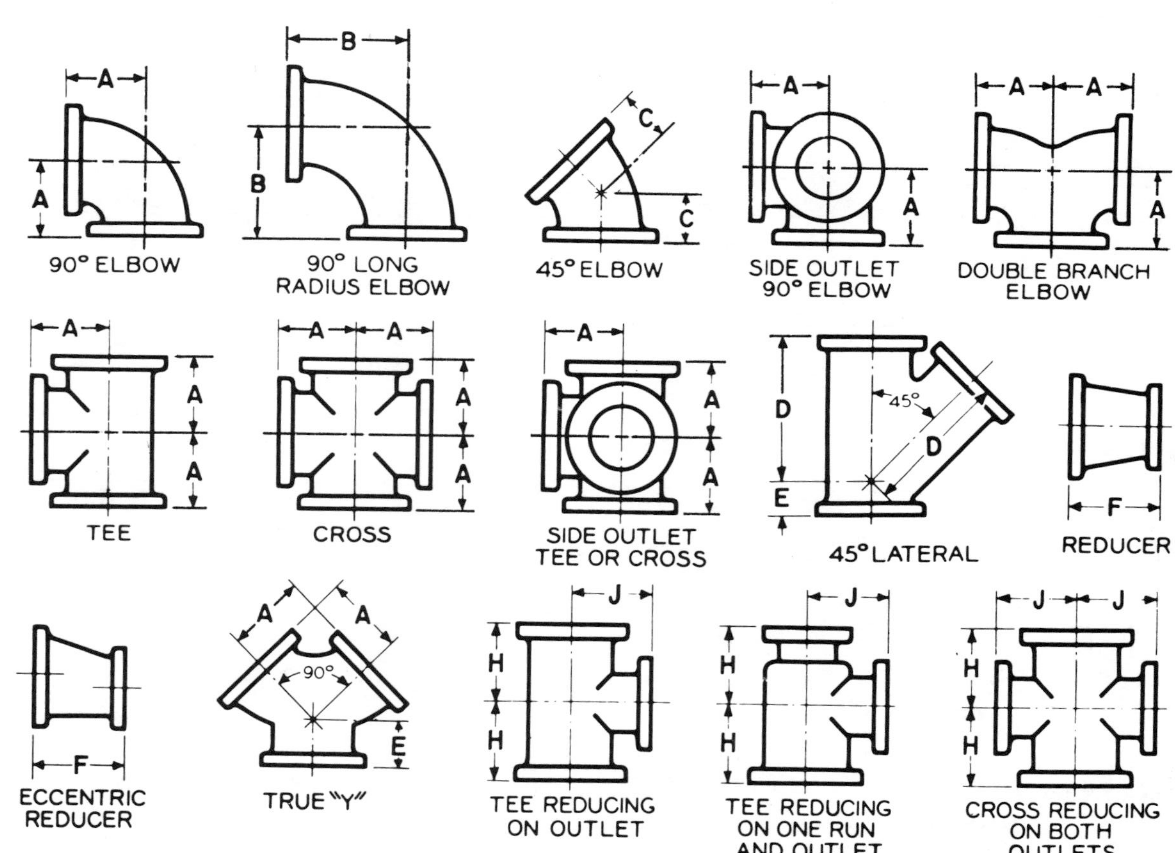

Dimensions of 125-lb Cast Iron Flanged Fittings

Nominal Pipe Size	Flanges		General		Straight Fittings						Reducing Fittings (Short Body Patterns)		
											Tees and Crosses		
	Dia of Flange	Thickness of Flange (Min)	Inside Dia of Flange Fittings	Wall Thickness	Center to Face 90 deg Elbow Tees, Crosses True "Y" and Double Branch Elbow A	Center to Face 90 deg Long Radius El-bow B	Center to Face 45 deg Elbow C	Center to Face Lateral D	Short Center to Face True "Y" and Lateral E	Face to Face Reducer F	Size of Outlet and Smaller	Center to Face Run H	Center to Face Outlet or Side Outlet J
1	4¼	7/16	1	5/16	3½	5	1¾	5¾	1¾	. . .			
1¼	4 5/8	½	1¼	5/16	3¾	5½	2	6¼	1¾	. . .			
1½	5	9/16	1½	5/16	4	6	2¼	7	2				
2	6	5/8	2	5/16	4½	6½	2½	8	2½	5			
2½	7	11/16	2½	5/16	5	7	3	9½	2½	5½			
3	7½	¾	3	3/8	5½	7¾	3	10	3	6			
3½	8½	13/16	3½	7/16	6	8½	3½	11½	3	6½			
4	9	15/16	4	½	6½	9	4	12	3	7			
5	10	15/16	5	½	7½	10¼	4½	13½	3½	8	All reducing tees and crosses, sizes 16 in. and smaller, shall have same center to face dimensions as straight size fittings, corresponding to the size of the largest opening.		
6	11	1	6	9/16	8	11½	5	14½	3½	9			
8	13½	1 1/8	8	5/8	9	14	5½	17½	4½	11			
10	16	1 3/16	10	¾	11	16½	6½	20½	5	12			
12	19	1¼	12	13/16	12	19	7½	24½	5½	14			
14	21	1 3/8	14	7/8	14	21½	7½	27	6	16			
16	23½	1 7/16	16	1	15	24	8	30	6½	18			
18	25	1 9/16	18	1 1/16	16½	26½	8½	32	7	19	12	13	15½
20	27½	1 11/16	20	1 1/8	18	29	9½	35	8	20	14	14	17
24	32	1 7/8	24	1¼	22	34	11	40½	9	24	16	15	19
30	38¾	2 1/8	30	1 7/16	25	41½	15	49	10	30	20	18	23
36	46	2 3/8	36	1 5/8	28*	49	18	. . .	. . .	36	24	20	26
42	53	2 5/8	42	1 13/16	31*	56½	21	. . .	. . .	42	24	23	30
48	59½	2¾	48	2	34*	64	24	. . .	. . .	48	30	26	34

All dimensions given in inches.

(Courtesy of ANSI; B16.1-1967.)

APPENDIX 14. SQUARE AND ACME THREADS

Size	Threads per inch	Size	Threads per inch	Size	Threads per inch	Size	Threads per inch
$\frac{3}{8}$	12	$\frac{7}{8}$	5	2	$2\frac{1}{2}$	$3\frac{1}{2}$	$1\frac{1}{3}$
$\frac{7}{16}$	10	1	5	$2\frac{1}{4}$	2	$3\frac{3}{4}$	$1\frac{1}{3}$
$\frac{1}{2}$	10	$1\frac{1}{8}$	4	$2\frac{1}{2}$	2	4	$1\frac{1}{3}$
$\frac{9}{16}$	8	$1\frac{1}{4}$	4	$2\frac{3}{4}$	2	$4\frac{1}{4}$	$1\frac{1}{3}$
$\frac{5}{8}$	8	$1\frac{1}{2}$	3	3	$1\frac{1}{2}$	$4\frac{1}{2}$	1
$\frac{3}{4}$	6	$1\frac{3}{4}$	$2\frac{1}{2}$	$3\frac{1}{4}$	$1\frac{1}{2}$	over $4\frac{1}{2}$	1

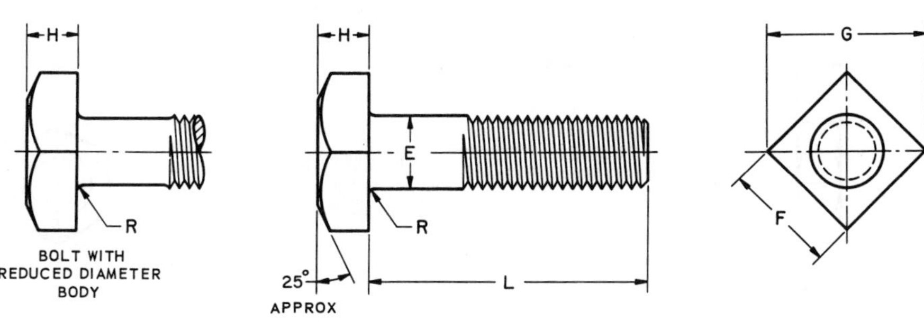

Dimensions of Square Bolts

Nominal Size or Basic Product Dia		Body Dia E	Width Across Flats F			Width Across Corners G		Height H			Radius of Fillet R
		Max	Basic	Max	Min	Max	Min	Basic	Max	Min	Max
1/4	0.2500	0.260	3/8	0.3750	0.362	0.530	0.498	11/64	0.188	0.156	0.031
5/16	0.3125	0.324	1/2	0.5000	0.484	0.707	0.665	13/64	0.220	0.186	0.031
3/8	0.3750	0.388	9/16	0.5625	0.544	0.795	0.747	1/4	0.268	0.232	0.031
7/16	0.4375	0.452	5/8	0.6250	0.603	0.884	0.828	19/64	0.316	0.278	0.031
1/2	0.5000	0.515	3/4	0.7500	0.725	1.061	0.995	21/64	0.348	0.308	0.031
5/8	0.6250	0.642	15/16	0.9375	0.906	1.326	1.244	27/64	0.444	0.400	0.062
3/4	0.7500	0.768	1 1/8	1.1250	1.088	1.591	1.494	1/2	0.524	0.476	0.062
7/8	0.8750	0.895	1 5/16	1.3125	1.269	1.856	1.742	19/32	0.620	0.568	0.062
1	1.0000	1.022	1 1/2	1.5000	1.450	2.121	1.991	21/32	0.684	0.628	0.093
1 1/8	1.1250	1.149	1 11/16	1.6875	1.631	2.386	2.239	3/4	0.780	0.720	0.093
1 1/4	1.2500	1.277	1 7/8	1.8750	1.812	2.652	2.489	27/32	0.876	0.812	0.093
1 3/8	1.3750	1.404	2 1/16	2.0625	1.994	2.917	2.738	29/32	0.940	0.872	0.093
1 1/2	1.5000	1.531	2 1/4	2.2500	2.175	3.182	2.986	1	1.036	0.964	0.093

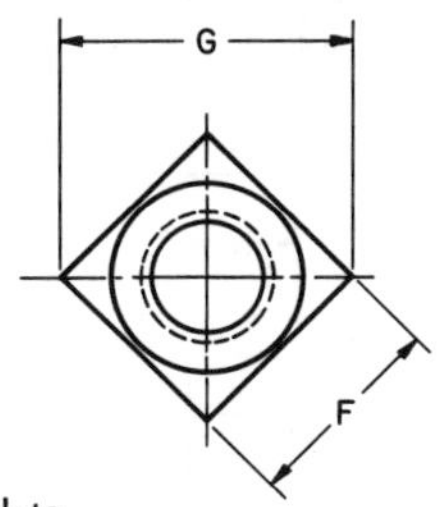

Dimensions of Square Nuts

Nominal Size or Basic Major Dia of Thread		Width Across Flats F			Width Across Corners G		Thickness H		
		Basic	Max	Min	Max	Min	Basic	Max	Min
1/4	0.2500	7/16	0.4375	0.425	0.619	0.584	7/32	0.235	0.203
5/16	0.3125	9/16	0.5625	0.547	0.795	0.751	17/64	0.283	0.249
3/8	0.3750	5/8	0.6250	0.606	0.884	0.832	21/64	0.346	0.310
7/16	0.4375	3/4	0.7500	0.728	1.061	1.000	3/8	0.394	0.356
1/2	0.5000	13/16	0.8125	0.788	1.149	1.082	7/16	0.458	0.418
5/8	0.6250	1	1.0000	0.969	1.414	1.330	35/64	0.569	0.525
3/4	0.7500	1 1/8	1.1250	1.088	1.591	1.494	21/32	0.680	0.632
7/8	0.8750	1 5/16	1.3125	1.269	1.856	1.742	49/64	0.792	0.740
1	1.0000	1 1/2	1.5000	1.450	2.121	1.991	7/8	0.903	0.847
1 1/8	1.1250	1 11/16	1.6875	1.631	2.386	2.239	1	1.030	0.970
1 1/4	1.2500	1 7/8	1.8750	1.812	2.652	2.489	1 3/32	1.126	1.062
1 3/8	1.3750	2 1/16	2.0625	1.994	2.917	2.738	1 13/64	1.237	1.169
1 1/2	1.5000	2 1/4	2.2500	2.175	3.182	2.986	1 5/16	1.348	1.276

(Courtesy of ANSI; B18.2.1-1965 and B18.2.2-1965.)

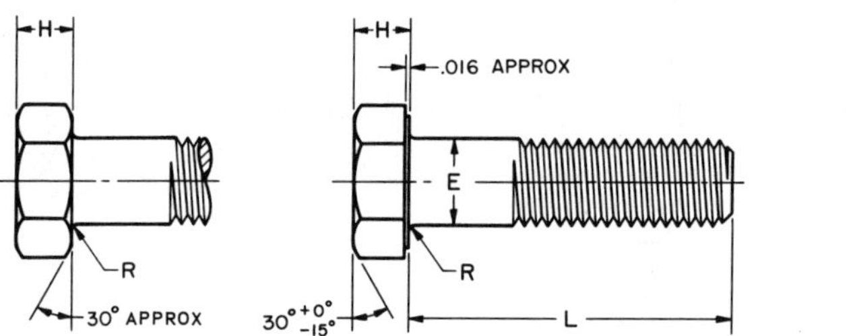

Dimensions of Hex Cap Screws (Finished Hex Bolts)

Nominal Size or Basic Product Dia		Body Dia E		Width Across Flats F			Width Across Corners G		Height H			Radius of Fillet R	
		Max	Min	Basic	Max	Min	Max	Min	Basic	Max	Min	Max	Min
1/4	0.2500	0.2500	0.2450	7/16	0.4375	0.428	0.505	0.488	5/32	0.163	0.150	0.025	0.015
5/16	0.3125	0.3125	0.3065	1/2	0.5000	0.489	0.577	0.557	13/64	0.211	0.195	0.025	0.015
3/8	0.3750	0.3750	0.3690	9/16	0.5625	0.551	0.650	0.628	15/64	0.243	0.226	0.025	0.015
7/16	0.4375	0.4375	0.4305	5/8	0.6250	0.612	0.722	0.698	9/32	0.291	0.272	0.025	0.015
1/2	0.5000	0.5000	0.4930	3/4	0.7500	0.736	0.866	0.840	5/16	0.323	0.302	0.025	0.015
9/16	0.5625	0.5625	0.5545	13/16	0.8125	0.798	0.938	0.910	23/64	0.371	0.348	0.045	0.020
5/8	0.6250	0.6250	0.6170	15/16	0.9375	0.922	1.083	1.051	25/64	0.403	0.378	0.045	0.020
3/4	0.7500	0.7500	0.7410	1 1/8	1.1250	1.100	1.299	1.254	15/32	0.483	0.455	0.045	0.020
7/8	0.8750	0.8750	0.8660	1 5/16	1.3125	1.285	1.516	1.465	35/64	0.563	0.531	0.065	0.040
1	1.0000	1.0000	0.9900	1 1/2	1.5000	1.469	1.732	1.675	39/64	0.627	0.591	0.095	0.060
1 1/8	1.1250	1.1250	1.1140	1 11/16	1.6875	1.631	1.949	1.859	11/16	0.718	0.658	0.095	0.060
1 1/4	1.2500	1.2500	1.2390	1 7/8	1.8750	1.812	2.165	2.066	25/32	0.813	0.749	0.095	0.060
1 3/8	1.3750	1.3750	1.3630	2 1/16	2.0625	1.994	2.382	2.273	27/32	0.878	0.810	0.095	0.060
1 1/2	1.5000	1.5000	1.4880	2 1/4	2.2500	2.175	2.598	2.480	15/16	0.974	0.902	0.095	0.060
1 3/4	1.7500	1.7500	1.7380	2 5/8	2.6250	2.538	3.031	2.893	1 3/32	1.134	1.054	0.095	0.060
2	2.0000	2.0000	1.9880	3	3.0000	2.900	3.464	3.306	1 7/32	1.263	1.175	0.095	0.060
2 1/4	2.2500	2.2500	2.2380	3 3/8	3.3750	3.262	3.897	3.719	1 3/8	1.423	1.327	0.095	0.060
2 1/2	2.5000	2.5000	2.4880	3 3/4	3.7500	3.625	4.330	4.133	1 17/32	1.583	1.479	0.095	0.060
2 3/4	2.7500	2.7500	2.7380	4 1/8	4.1250	3.988	4.763	4.546	1 11/16	1.744	1.632	0.095	0.060
3	3.0000	3.0000	2.9880	4 1/2	4.5000	4.350	5.196	4.959	1 7/8	1.935	1.815	0.095	0.060

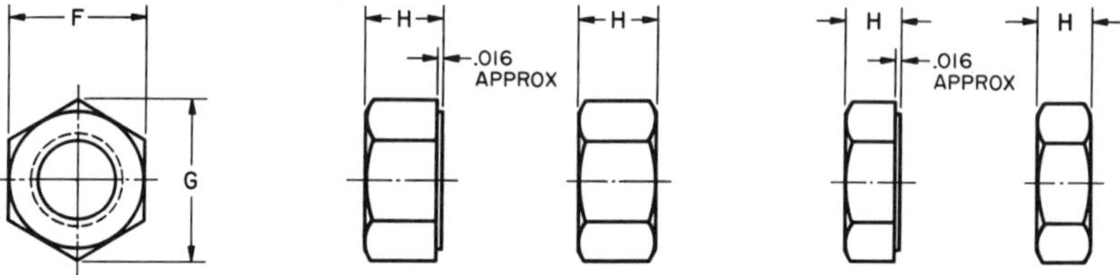

Dimensions of Hex Nuts and Hex Jam Nuts

Nominal Size or Basic Major Dia of Thread		Width Across Flats F			Width Across Corners G		Thickness Hex Nuts H			Thickness Hex Jam Nuts H		
		Basic	Max	Min	Max	Min	Basic	Max	Min	Basic	Max	Min
1/4	0.2500	7/16	0.4375	0.428	0.505	0.488	7/32	0.226	0.212	5/32	0.163	0.150
5/16	0.3125	1/2	0.5000	0.489	0.577	0.557	17/64	0.273	0.258	3/16	0.195	0.180
3/8	0.3750	9/16	0.5625	0.551	0.650	0.628	21/64	0.337	0.320	7/32	0.227	0.210
7/16	0.4375	11/16	0.6875	0.675	0.794	0.768	3/8	0.385	0.365	1/4	0.260	0.240
1/2	0.5000	3/4	0.7500	0.736	0.866	0.840	7/16	0.448	0.427	5/16	0.323	0.302
9/16	0.5625	7/8	0.8750	0.861	1.010	0.982	31/64	0.496	0.473	5/16	0.324	0.301
5/8	0.6250	15/16	0.9375	0.922	1.083	1.051	35/64	0.559	0.535	3/8	0.387	0.363
3/4	0.7500	1 1/8	1.1250	1.088	1.299	1.240	41/64	0.665	0.617	27/64	0.446	0.398
7/8	0.8750	1 5/16	1.3125	1.269	1.516	1.447	3/4	0.776	0.724	31/64	0.510	0.458
1	1.0000	1 1/2	1.5000	1.450	1.732	1.653	55/64	0.887	0.831	35/64	0.575	0.519
1 1/8	1.1250	1 11/16	1.6875	1.631	1.949	1.859	31/32	0.999	0.939	39/64	0.639	0.579
1 1/4	1.2500	1 7/8	1.8750	1.812	2.165	2.066	1 1/16	1.094	1.030	23/32	0.751	0.687
1 3/8	1.3750	2 1/16	2.0625	1.994	2.382	2.273	1 11/64	1.206	1.138	25/32	0.815	0.747
1 1/2	1.5000	2 1/4	2.2500	2.175	2.598	2.480	1 9/32	1.317	1.245	27/32	0.880	0.808

(Courtesy of ANSI; B18.2.1-1965 and B18.2.2-1965.)

Fillister Head Cap Screws

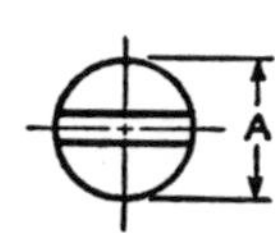

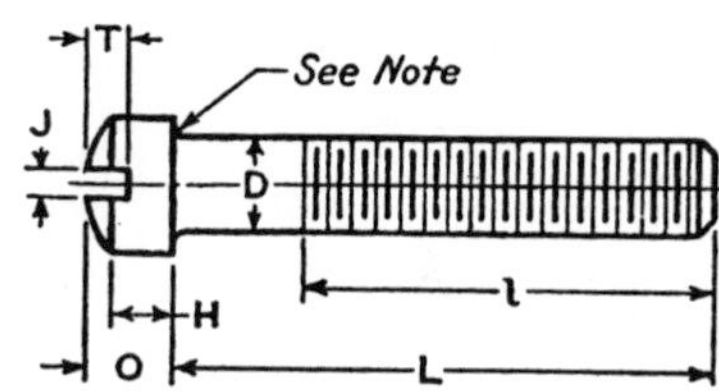

Nominal Size	D		A		H		O		J		T	
	Body Diameter		Head Diameter		Height of Head		Total Height of Head		Width of Slot		Depth of Slot	
	Max	Min	Max	Min	Max	Min	Max	Min	Max	Min	Max	Min
1/4	0.250	0.245	0.375	0.363	0.172	0.157	0.216	0.194	0.075	0.064	0.097	0.077
5/16	0.3125	0.307	0.437	0.424	0.203	0.186	0.253	0.230	0.084	0.072	0.115	0.090
3/8	0.375	0.369	0.562	0.547	0.250	0.229	0.314	0.284	0.094	0.081	0.142	0.112
7/16	0.4375	0.431	0.625	0.608	0.297	0.274	0.368	0.336	0.094	0.081	0.168	0.133
1/2	0.500	0.493	0.750	0.731	0.328	0.301	0.413	0.376	0.106	0.091	0.193	0.153
9/16	0.5625	0.555	0.812	0.792	0.375	0.346	0.467	0.427	0.118	0.102	0.213	0.168
5/8	0.625	0.617	0.875	0.853	0.422	0.391	0.521	0.478	0.133	0.116	0.239	0.189
3/4	0.750	0.742	1.000	0.976	0.500	0.466	0.612	0.566	0.149	0.131	0.283	0.223
7/8	0.875	0.866	1.125	1.098	0.594	0.556	0.720	0.668	0.167	0.147	0.334	0.264
1	1.000	0.990	1.312	1.282	0.656	0.612	0.803	0.743	0.188	0.166	0.371	0.291

All dimensions are given in inches.

The radius of the fillet at the base of the head:
For sizes 1/4 to 3/8 in. incl. is 0.016 min and 0.031 max,
7/16 to 9/16 in. incl. is 0.016 min and 0.047 max,
5/8 to 1 in. incl. is 0.031 min and 0.062 max.

Round Head Cap Screws

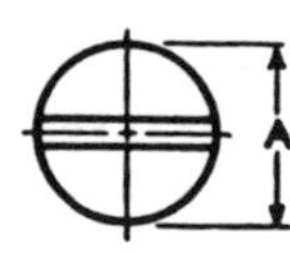

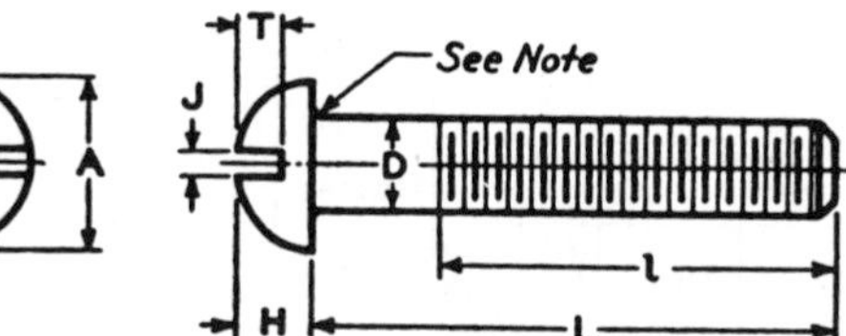

Nominal Size	D		A		H		J		T	
	Body Diameter		Head Diameter		Height of Head		Width of Slot		Depth of Slot	
	Max	Min	Max	Min	Max	Min	Max	Min	Max	Min
1/4	0.250	0.245	0.437	0.418	0.191	0.175	0.075	0.064	0.117	0.097
5/16	0.3125	0.307	0.562	0.540	0.245	0.226	0.084	0.072	0.151	0.126
3/8	0.375	0.369	0.625	0.603	0.273	0.252	0.094	0.081	0.168	0.138
7/16	0.4375	0.431	0.750	0.725	0.328	0.302	0.094	0.081	0.202	0.167
1/2	0.500	0.493	0.812	0.786	0.354	0.327	0.106	0.091	0.218	0.178
9/16	0.5625	0.555	0.937	0.909	0.409	0.378	0.118	0.102	0.252	0.207
5/8	0.625	0.617	1.000	0.970	0.437	0.405	0.133	0.116	0.270	0.220
3/4	0.750	0.742	1.250	1.215	0.546	0.507	0.149	0.131	0.338	0.278

All dimensions are given in inches.

Radius of the fillet at the base of the head:
For sizes 1/4 to 3/8 in. incl. is 0.016 min and 0.031 max,
7/16 to 9/16 in. incl..is 0.016 min and 0.047 max,
5/8 to 1 in..incl. is 0.031 min and 0.062 max.

(Courtesy of ANSI; B18.6.2-1956.)

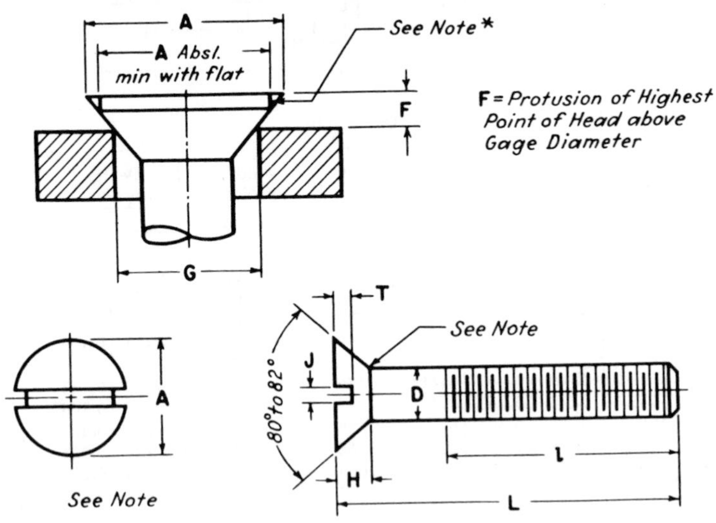

Nominal Size	D		A			G	H	J		T		F	
	Body Diameter		Head Diameter			Gaging Diameter	Height of Head	Width of Slot		Depth of Slot		Protrusion Above Gaging Diameter	
	Max	Min	Max	Min	Absolute Min with Flat		Average	Max	Min	Max	Min	Max	Min
1/4	0.250	0.245	0.500	0.477	0.452	0.4245	0.140	0.075	0.064	0.068	0.045	0.0452	0.0307
5/16	0.3125	0.307	0.625	0.598	0.567	0.5376	0.177	0.084	0.072	0.086	0.057	0.0523	0.0354
3/8	0.375	0.369	0.750	0.720	0.682	0.6507	0.210	0.094	0.081	0.103	0.068	0.0594	0.0401
7/16	0.4375	0.431	0.8125	0.780	0.736	0.7229	0.210	0.094	0.081	0.103	0.068	0.0649	0.0448
1/2	0.500	0.493	0.875	0.841	0.791	0.7560	0.210	0.106	0.091	0.103	0.068	0.0705	0.0495
9/16	0.5625	0.555	1.000	0.962	0.906	0.8691	0.244	0.118	0.102	0.120	0.080	0.0775	0.0542
5/8	0.625	0.617	1.125	1.083	1.020	0.9822	0.281	0.133	0.116	0.137	0.091	0.0846	0.0588
3/4	0.750	0.742	1.375	1.326	1.251	1.2085	0.352	0.149	0.131	0.171	0.115	0.0987	0.0682
7/8	0.875	0.866	1.625	1.568	1.480	1.4347	0.423	0.167	0.147	0.206	0.138	0.1128	0.0776
1	1.000	0.990	1.875	1.811	1.711	1.6610	0.494	0.188	0.166	0.240	0.162	0.1270	0.0870
1 1/8	1.125	1.114	2.062	1.992	1.880	1.8262	0.529	0.196	0.178	0.257	0.173	0.1401	0.0964
1 1/4	1.250	1.239	2.312	2.235	2.110	2.0525	0.600	0.211	0.193	0.291	0.197	0.1542	0.1056
1 3/8	1.375	1.363	2.562	2.477	2.340	2.2787	0.665	0.226	0.208	0.326	0.220	0.1684	0.1151
1 1/2	1.500	1.488	2.812	2.720	2.570	2.5050	0.742	0.258	0.240	0.360	0.244	0.1825	0.1245

All dimensions are given in inches.

The maximum and minimum head diameters, A, are extended to the theoretical sharp corners.

The radius of the fillet at the base of the head shall not exceed 0.4 Max. D.

*Edge of head may be flat as shown or slightly rounded.

(Courtesy of ANSI; B18.6.2-1956.)

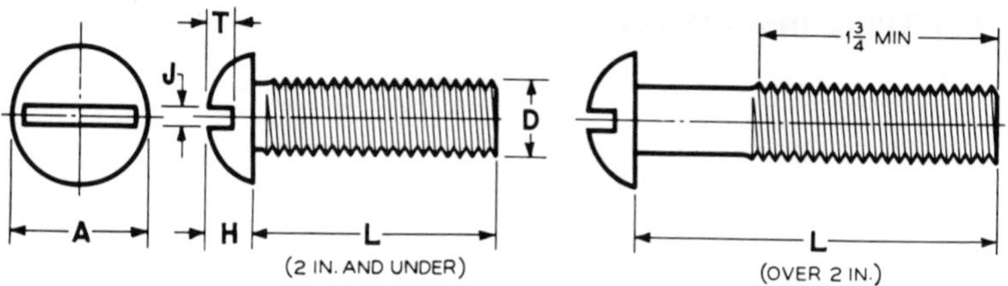

Dimensions of Slotted Round Head Machine Screws

Nominal Size	D	A		H		J		T	
	Diameter of Screw	Head Diameter		Head Height		Width of Slot		Depth of Slot	
	Basic	Max	Min	Max	Min	Max	Min	Max	Min
0	0.0600	0.113	0.099	0.053	0.043	0.023	0.016	0.039	0.029
1	0.0730	0.138	0.122	0.061	0.051	0.026	0.019	0.044	0.033
2	0.0860	0.162	0.146	0.069	0.059	0.031	0.023	0.048	0.037
3	0.0990	0.187	0.169	0.078	0.067	0.035	0.027	0.053	0.040
4	0.1120	0.211	0.193	0.086	0.075	0.039	0.031	0.058	0.044
5	0.1250	0.236	0.217	0.095	0.083	0.043	0.035	0.063	0.047
6	0.1380	0.260	0.240	0.103	0.091	0.048	0.039	0.068	0.051
8	0.1640	0.309	0.287	0.120	0.107	0.054	0.045	0.077	0.058
10	0.1900	0.359	0.334	0.137	0.123	0.060	0.050	0.087	0.065
12	0.2160	0.408	0.382	0.153	0.139	0.067	0.056	0.096	0.073
1/4	0.2500	0.472	0.443	0.175	0.160	0.075	0.064	0.109	0.082
5/16	0.3125	0.590	0.557	0.216	0.198	0.084	0.072	0.132	0.099
3/8	0.3750	0.708	0.670	0.256	0.237	0.094	0.081	0.155	0.117
7/16	0.4375	0.750	0.707	0.328	0.307	0.094	0.081	0.196	0.148
1/2	0.5000	0.813	0.766	0.355	0.332	0.106	0.091	0.211	0.159
9/16	0.5625	0.938	0.887	0.410	0.385	0.118	0.102	0.242	0.183
5/8	0.6250	1.000	0.944	0.438	0.411	0.133	0.116	0.258	0.195
3/4	0.7500	1.250	1.185	0.547	0.516	0.149	0.131	0.320	0.242

All dimensions are given in inches.

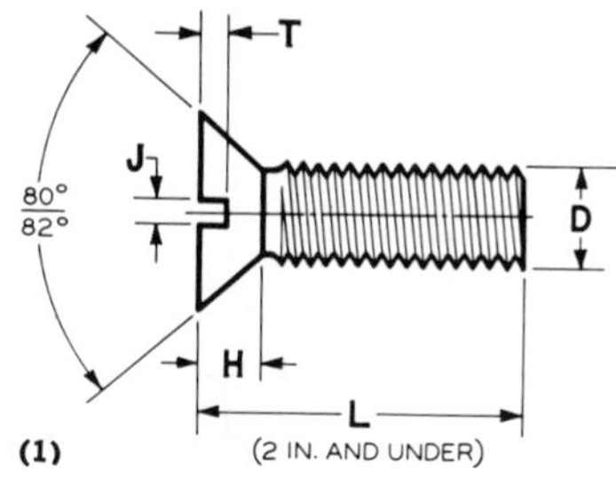

(1)

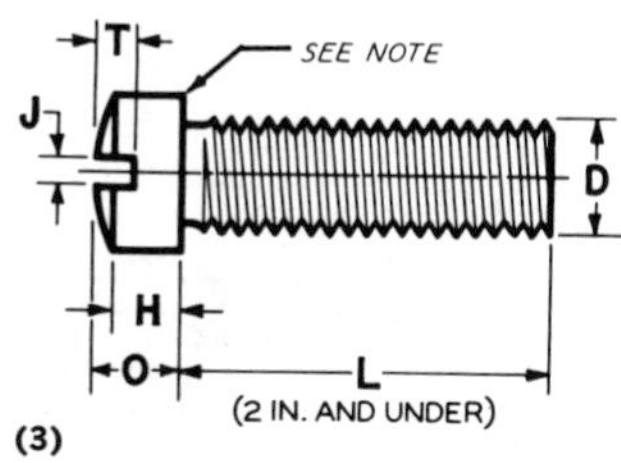

(3)

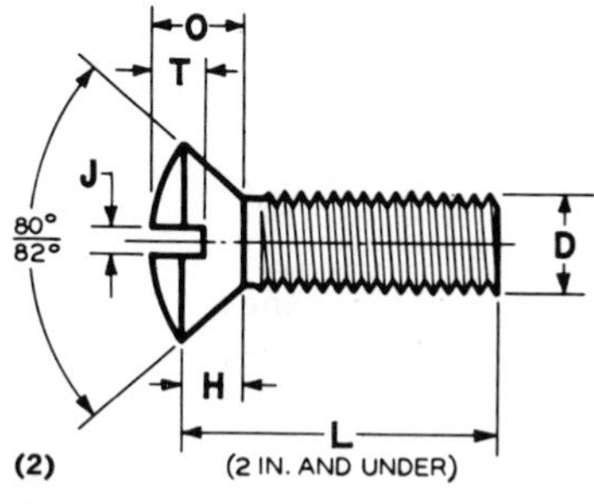

(2)

(Courtesy of ANSI; B18.6.3-1962.)

Three other common forms of machine screws are shown at the left and above: (1) flat head, (2) oval head, and (3) fillister head. Although dimension tables are not given for these three types of machine screws in this text, their general dimensions are closely related to those shown in the table above. Additional information on these screws can be obtained from the ANSI standard B18.6.3-1962.

APPENDIX 20. LETTERING INSTRUMENTS

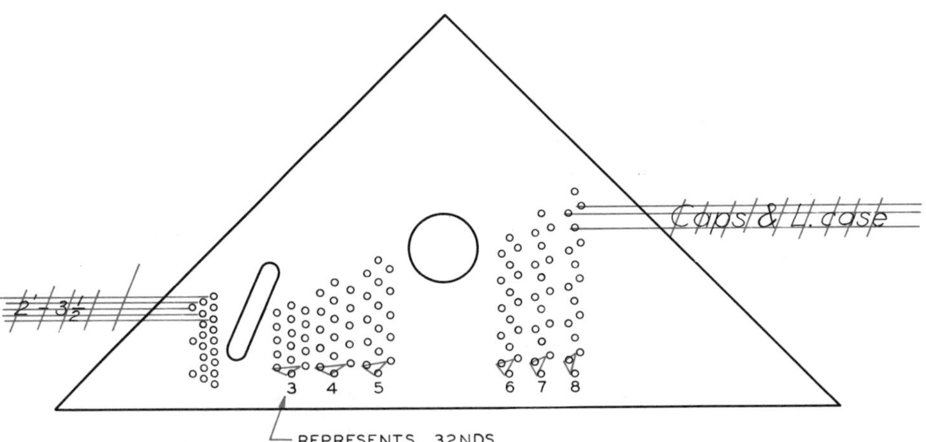

The Braddock-Rowe triangle serves a dual role as a 45° triangle and a lettering instrument. Guidelines are drawn lightly by inserting the pencil point in the guide holes and sliding the triangle along a stationary edge of a drafting machine or T-square. The numbers under the holes represent 32nds of an inch. *Example:* 4 represents $\frac{4}{32}''$ or $\frac{1}{8}''$. A slot is provided for constructing guide lines for slanted lettering. (Courtesy of Braddock Instrument Company.)

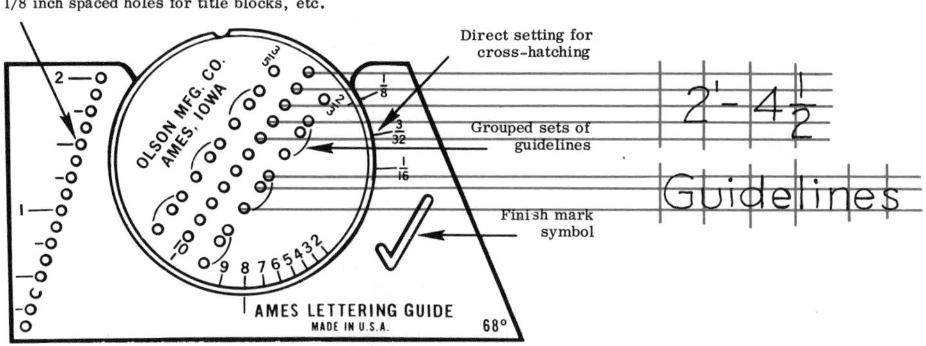

The Ames lettering instrument can be used for the construction of guidelines in much the same manner as the Braddock-Rowe triangle. An adjustable disc can be set on the letter height desired as seen at the bottom of the disc, where the numbers given represent 32nds of an inch. The disc is shown set at $\frac{8}{32}''$ or $\frac{1}{4}''$. (Courtesy of Olson Manufacturing Co.)

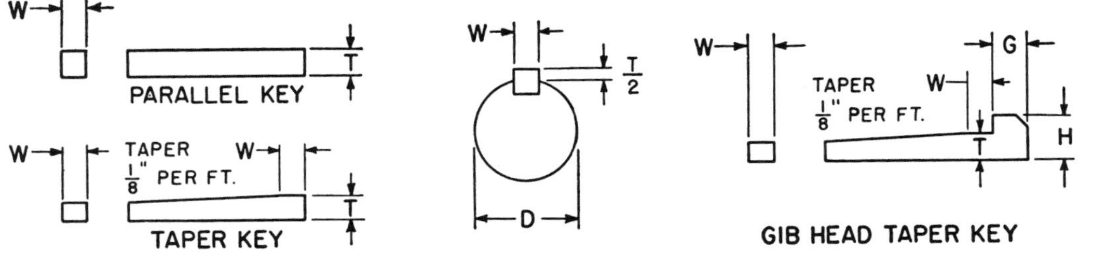

Sprocket Bore (= Shaft Diam.)	Keyway Dimensions — Inches				Key Dimensions — Inches					Gib Head Dimensions — Inches				Key Tolerances Taper and Gib Head	
	For Square Key		For Flat Key		Square		Flat		Tolerance on W and T	Square Key		Flat Key			
Inches D	Width W	Depth T/2	Width W	Depth T/2	Width W	Height T	Width W	Height T	(−)	H	G	H	G	W (−)	T (+)
1/2 — 9/16	1/8 x	1/16	1/8 x	3/64	1/8 x	1/8	1/8 x	3/32	0.002	1/4	7/32	3/16	1/8	0.002	0.002
5/8 — 7/8	3/16 x	3/32	3/16 x	1/16	3/16 x	3/16	3/16 x	1/8	0.002	5/16	9/32	1/4	3/16	0.002	0.002
15/16 — 1 1/4	1/4 x	1/8	1/4 x	3/32	1/4 x	1/4	1/4 x	3/16	0.002	7/16	11/32	5/16	1/4	0.002	0.002
1 5/16 — 1 3/8	5/16 x	5/32	5/16 x	1/8	5/16 x	5/16	5/16 x	1/4	0.002	9/16	13/32	3/8	5/16	0.002	0.002
1 7/16 — 1 3/4	3/8 x	3/16	3/8 x	1/8	3/8 x	3/8	3/8 x	1/4	0.002	11/16	15/32	7/16	3/8	0.002	0.002
1 13/16 — 2 1/4	1/2 x	1/4	1/2 x	3/16	1/2 x	1/2	1/2 x	3/8	0.0025	7/8	19/32	5/8	1/2	0.0025	0.0025
2 5/16 — 2 3/4	5/8 x	5/16	5/8 x	7/32	5/8 x	5/8	5/8 x	7/16	0.0025	1 1/16	23/32	3/4	5/8	0.0025	0.0025
2 7/8 — 3 1/4	3/4 x	3/8	3/4 x	1/4	3/4 x	3/4	3/4 x	1/2	0.0025	1 1/4	7/8	7/8	3/4	0.0025	0.0025
3 3/8 — 3 3/4	7/8 x	7/16	7/8 x	5/16	7/8 x	7/8	7/8 x	5/8	0.003	1 1/2	1	1 1/16	7/8	0.003	0.003
3 7/8 — 4 1/2	1 x	1/2	1 x	3/8	1 x	1	1 x	3/4	0.003	1 3/4	1 3/16	1 1/4	1	0.003	0.003
4 3/4 — 5 1/2	1 1/4 x	5/8	1 1/4 x	7/16	1 1/4 x	1 1/4	1 1/4 x	7/8	0.003	2	1 7/16	1 1/2	1 1/4	0.003	0.003
5 3/4 — 7 3/8	1 1/2 x	3/4	1 1/2 x	1/2	1 1/2 x	1 1/2	1 1/2 x	1	0.003	2 1/2	1 3/4	1 3/4	1 1/2	0.003	0.003
7 1/2 — 9 7/8	1 3/4 x	7/8	..	..	1 3/4 x	1 3/4	..	..	0.004	3	2	..	..	0.004	0.004
10 — 12 1/2	2 x	1	..	..	2 x	2	..	..	0.004	3 1/2	2 3/8	..	..	0.004	0.004

Standard Keyway Tolerances: Straight Keyway — Width (W) $^{+.005}_{-.000}$ Depth (T/2) $^{+.010}_{-.000}$

Taper Keyway — Width (W) $^{+.005}_{-.000}$ Depth (T/2) $^{+.000}_{-.010}$

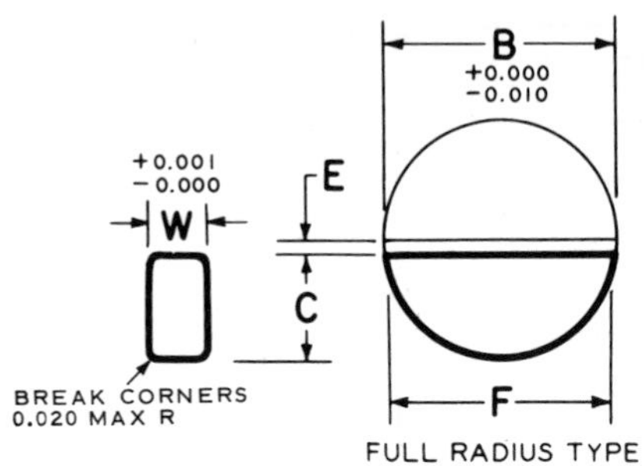

FULL RADIUS TYPE

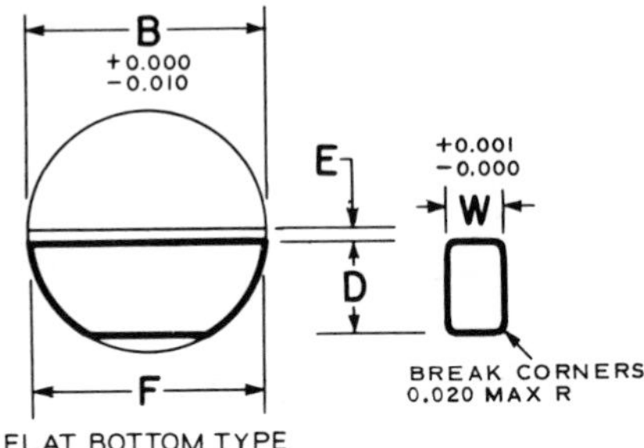

FLAT BOTTOM TYPE

Woodruff Keys

Key No.	Nominal Key Size W × B	Actual Length F +0.000-0.010	Height of Key C Max	Height of Key C Min	Height of Key D Max	Height of Key D Min	Distance Below Center E
202	1/16 × 1/4	0.248	0.109	0.104	0.109	0.104	1/64
202.5	1/16 × 5/16	0.311	0.140	0.135	0.140	0.135	1/64
302.5	3/32 × 5/16	0.311	0.140	0.135	0.140	0.135	1/64
203	1/16 × 3/8	0.374	0.172	0.167	0.172	0.167	1/64
303	3/32 × 3/8	0.374	0.172	0.167	0.172	0.167	1/64
403	1/8 × 3/8	0.374	0.172	0.167	0.172	0.167	1/64
204	1/16 × 1/2	0.491	0.203	0.198	0.194	0.188	3/64
304	3/32 × 1/2	0.491	0.203	0.198	0.194	0.188	3/64
404	1/8 × 1/2	0.491	0.203	0.198	0.194	0.188	3/64
305	3/32 × 5/8	0.612	0.250	0.245	0.240	0.234	1/16
405	1/8 × 5/8	0.612	0.250	0.245	0.240	0.234	1/16
505	5/32 × 5/8	0.612	0.250	0.245	0.240	0.234	1/16
605	3/16 × 5/8	0.612	0.250	0.245	0.240	0.234	1/16
406	1/8 × 3/4	0.740	0.313	0.308	0.303	0.297	1/16
506	5/32 × 3/4	0.740	0.313	0.308	0.303	0.297	1/16
606	3/16 × 3/4	0.740	0.313	0.308	0.303	0.297	1/16
806	1/4 × 3/4	0.740	0.313	0.308	0.303	0.297	1/16
507	5/32 × 7/8	0.866	0.375	0.370	0.365	0.359	1/16
607	3/16 × 7/8	0.866	0.375	0.370	0.365	0.359	1/16
707	7/32 × 7/8	0.866	0.375	0.370	0.365	0.359	1/16
807	1/4 × 7/8	0.866	0.375	0.370	0.365	0.359	1/16
608	3/16 × 1	0.992	0.438	0.433	0.428	0.422	1/16
708	7/32 × 1	0.992	0.438	0.433	0.428	0.422	1/16
808	1/4 × 1	0.992	0.438	0.433	0.428	0.422	1/16
1008	5/16 × 1	0.992	0.438	0.433	0.428	0.422	1/16
1208	3/8 × 1	0.992	0.438	0.433	0.428	0.422	1/16
609	3/16 × 1 1/8	1.114	0.484	0.479	0.475	0.469	5/64
709	7/32 × 1 1/8	1.114	0.484	0.479	0.475	0.469	5/64
809	1/4 × 1 1/8	1.114	0.484	0.479	0.475	0.469	5/64
1009	5/16 × 1 1/8	1.114	0.484	0.479	0.475	0.469	5/64

(Courtesy of ANSI; B17.2-1967.)

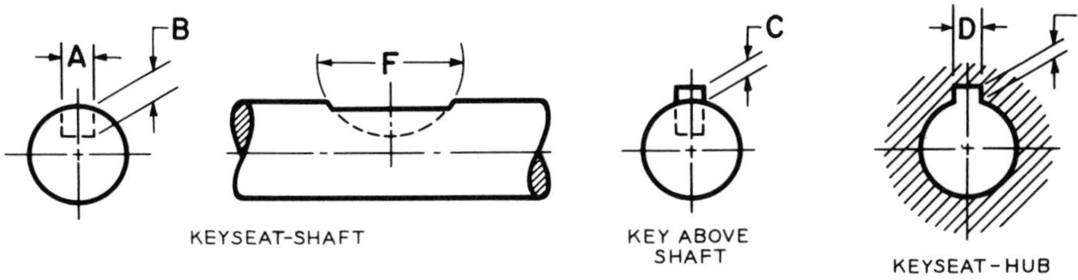

Keyseat Dimensions

Key Number	Nominal Size Key	Keyseat – Shaft					Key Above Shaft	Keyseat – Hub	
		Width A*		Depth B	Diameter F		Height C	Width D	Depth E
		Min	Max	+0.005 -0.000	Min	Max	+0.005 -0.005	+0.002 -0.000	+0.005 -0.000
202	1/16 × 1/4	0.0615	0.0630	0.0728	0.250	0.268	0.0312	0.0635	0.0372
202.5	1/16 × 5/16	0.0615	0.0630	0.1038	0.312	0.330	0.0312	0.0635	0.0372
302.5	3/32 × 5/16	0.0928	0.0943	0.0882	0.312	0.330	0.0469	0.0948	0.0529
203	1/16 × 3/8	0.0615	0.0630	0.1358	0.375	0.393	0.0312	0.0635	0.0372
303	3/32 × 3/8	0.0928	0.0943	0.1202	0.375	0.393	0.0469	0.0948	0.0529
403	1/8 × 3/8	0.1240	0.1255	0.1045	0.375	0.393	0.0625	0.1260	0.0685
204	1/16 × 1/2	0.0615	0.0630	0.1668	0.500	0.518	0.0312	0.0635	0.0372
304	3/32 × 1/2	0.0928	0.0943	0.1511	0.500	0.518	0.0469	0.0948	0.0529
404	1/8 × 1/2	0.1240	0.1255	0.1355	0.500	0.518	0.0625	0.1260	0.0685
305	3/32 × 5/8	0.0928	0.0943	0.1981	0.625	0.643	0.0469	0.0948	0.0529
405	1/8 × 5/8	0.1240	0.1255	0.1825	0.625	0.643	0.0625	0.1260	0.0685
505	5/32 × 5/8	0.1553	0.1568	0.1669	0.625	0.643	0.0781	0.1573	0.0841
605	3/16 × 5/8	0.1863	0.1880	0.1513	0.625	0.643	0.0937	0.1885	0.0997
406	1/8 × 3/4	0.1240	0.1255	0.2455	0.750	0.768	0.0625	0.1260	0.0685
506	5/32 × 3/4	0.1553	0.1568	0.2299	0.750	0.768	0.0781	0.1573	0.0841
606	3/16 × 3/4	0.1863	0.1880	0.2143	0.750	0.768	0.0937	0.1885	0.0997
806	1/4 × 3/4	0.2487	0.2505	0.1830	0.750	0.768	0.1250	0.2510	0.1310
507	5/32 × 7/8	0.1553	0.1568	0.2919	0.875	0.895	0.0781	0.1573	0.0841
607	3/16 × 7/8	0.1863	0.1880	0.2763	0.875	0.895	0.0937	0.1885	0.0997
707	7/32 × 7/8	0.2175	0.2193	0.2607	0.875	0.895	0.1093	0.2198	0.1153
807	1/4 × 7/8	0.2487	0.2505	0.2450	0.875	0.895	0.1250	0.2510	0.1310
608	3/16 × 1	0.1863	0.1880	0.3393	1.000	1.020	0.0937	0.1885	0.0997
708	7/32 × 1	0.2175	0.2193	0.3237	1.000	1.020	0.1093	0.2198	0.1153
808	1/4 × 1	0.2487	0.2505	0.3080	1.000	1.020	0.1250	0.2510	0.1310
1008	5/16 × 1	0.3111	0.3130	0.2768	1.000	1.020	0.1562	0.3135	0.1622
1208	3/8 × 1	0.3735	0.3755	0.2455	1.000	1.020	0.1875	0.3760	0.1935
609	3/16 × 1 1/8	0.1863	0.1880	0.3853	1.125	1.145	0.0937	0.1885	0.0997
709	7/32 × 1 1/8	0.2175	0.2193	0.3697	1.125	1.145	0.1093	0.2198	0.1153
809	1/4 × 1 1/8	0.2487	0.2505	0.3540	1.125	1.145	0.1250	0.2510	0.1310
1009	5/16 × 1 1/8	0.3111	0.3130	0.3228	1.125	1.145	0.1562	0.3135	0.1622

APPENDIX 23. AMERICAN STANDARD RUNNING AND SLIDING FITS

Nominal Size Range Inches		Class RC 1			Class RC 2			Class RC 3			Class RC 4		
		Limits of Clearance	Standard Limits		Limits of Clearance	Standard Limits		Limits of Clearance	Standard Limits		Limits of Clearance	Standard Limits	
Over	To		Hole H5	Shaft g4		Hole H6	Shaft g5		Hole H7	Shaft f6		Hole H8	Shaft f7
0	– 0.12	0.1 0.45	+ 0.2 0	– 0.1 – 0.25	0.1 0.55	+ 0.25 0	– 0.1 – 0.3	0.3 0.95	+ 0.4 0	– 0.3 – 0.55	0.3 1.3	+ 0.6 0	– 0.3 – 0.7
0.12	– 0.24	0.15 0.5	+ 0.2 0	– 0.15 – 0.3	0.15 0.65	+ 0.3 0	– 0.15 – 0.35	0.4 1.12	+ 0.5 0	– 0.4 – 0.7	0.4 1.6	+ 0.7 0	– 0.4 – 0.9
0.24	– 0.40	0.2 0.6	0.25 0	– 0.2 – 0.35	0.2 0.85	+ 0.4 0	– 0.2 – 0.45	0.5 1.5	+ 0.6 0	– 0.5 – 0.9	0.5 2.0	+ 0.9 0	– 0.5 – 1.1
0.40	– 0.71	0.25 0.75	+ 0.3 0	– 0.25 – 0.45	0.25 0.95	+ 0.4 0	– 0.25 – 0.55	0.6 1.7	+ 0.7 0	– 0.6 – 1.0	0.6 2.3	+ 1.0 0	– 0.6 – 1.3
0.71	– 1.19	0.3 0.95	+ 0.4 0	– 0.3 – 0.55	0.3 1.2	+ 0.5 0	– 0.3 – 0.7	0.8 2.1	+ 0.8 0	– 0.8 – 1.3	0.8 2.8	+ 1.2 0	– 0.8 – 1.6
1.19	– 1.97	0.4 1.1	+ 0.4 0	– 0.4 – 0.7	0.4 1.4	+ 0.6 0	– 0.4 – 0.8	1.0 2.6	+ 1.0 0	– 1.0 – 1.6	1.0 3.6	+ 1.6 0	– 1.0 – 2.0
1.97	– 3.15	0.4 1.2	+ 0.5 0	– 0.4 – 0.7	0.4 1.6	+ 0.7 0	– 0.4 – 0.9	1.2 3.1	+ 1.2 0	– 1.2 – 1.9	1.2 4.2	+ 1.8 0	– 1.2 – 2.4
3.15	– 4.73	0.5 1.5	+ 0.6 0	– 0.5 – 0.9	0.5 2.0	+ 0.9 0	– 0.5 – 1.1	1.4 3.7	+ 1.4 0	– 1.4 – 2.3	1.4 5.0	+ 2.2 0	– 1.4 – 2.8
4.73	– 7.09	0.6 1.8	+ 0.7 0	– 0.6 – 1.1	0.6 2.3	+ 1.0 0	– 0.6 – 1.3	1.6 4.2	+ 1.6 0	– 1.6 – 2.6	1.6 5.7	+ 2.5 0	– 1.6 – 3.2
7.09	– 9.85	0.6 2.0	+ 0.8 0	– 0.6 – 1.2	0.6 2.6	+ 1.2 0	– 0.6 – 1.4	2.0 5.0	+ 1.8 0	– 2.0 – 3.2	2.0 6.6	+ 2.8 0	– 2.0 – 3.8
9.85	–12.41	0.8 2.3	+ 0.9 0	– 0.8 – 1.4	0.8 2.9	+ 1.2 0	– 0.8 – 1.7	2.5 5.7	+ 2.0 0	– 2.5 – 3.7	2.5 7.5	+ 3.0 0	– 2.5 – 4.5
12.41	–15.75	1.0 2.7	+ 1.0 0	– 1.0 – 1.7	1.0 3.4	+ 1.4 0	– 1.0 – 2.0	3.0 6.6	+ 0	– 3.0 – 4.4	3.0 8.7	+ 3.5 0	– 3.0 – 5.2
15.75	–19.69	1.2 3.0	+ 1.0 0	– 1.2 – 2.0	1.2 3.8	+ 1.6 0	– 1.2 – 2.2	4.0 8.1	+ 1.6 0	– 4.0 – 5.6	4.0 10.5	+ 4.0 0	– 4.0 – 6.5
19.69	–30.09	1.6 3.7	+ 1.2 0	– 1.6 – 2.5	1.6 4.8	+ 2.0 0	– 1.6 – 2.8	5.0 10.0	+ 3.0 0	– 5.0 – 7.0	5.0 13.0	+ 5.0 0	– 5.0 – 8.0
30.09	–41.49	2.0 4.6	+ 1.6 0	– 2.0 – 3.0	2.0 6.1	+ 2.5 0	– 2.0 – 3.6	6.0 12.5	+ 4.0 0	– 6.0 – 8.5	6.0 16.0	+ 6.0 0	– 6.0 –10.0
41.49	–56.19	2.5 5.7	+ 2.0 0	– 2.5 – 3.7	2.5 7.5	+ 3.0 0	– 2.5 – 4.5	8.0 16.0	+ 5.0 0	– 8.0 –11.0	8.0 21.0	+ 8.0 0	– 8.0 –13.0
56.19	–76.39	3.0 7.1	+ 2.5 0	– 3.0 – 4.6	3.0 9.5	+ 4.0 0	– 3.0 – 5.5	10.0 20.0	+ 6.0 0	–10.0 –14.0	10.0 26.0	+10.0 0	–10.0 –16.0
76.39	–100.9	4.0 9.0	+ 3.0 0	– 4.0 – 6.0	4.0 12.0	+ 5.0 0	– 4.0 – 7.0	12.0 25.0	+ 8.0 0	–12.0 –17.0	12.0 32.0	+12.0 0	–12.0 –20.0
100.9	–131.9	5.0 11.5	+ 4.0 0	– 5.0 – 7.5	5.0 15.0	+ 6.0 0	– 5.0 – 9.0	16.0 32.0	+10.0 0	–16.0 –22.0	16.0 36.0	+16.0 0	–16.0 –26.0
131.9	–171.9	6.0 14.0	+ 5.0 0	– 6.0 – 9.0	6.0 19.0	+ 8.0 0	– 6.0 –11.0	18.0 38.0	+ 8.0 0	–18.0 –26.0	18.0 50.0	+20.0 0	–18.0 –30.0
171.9	–200	8.0 18.0	+ 6.0 0	– 8.0 –12.0	8.0 22.0	+10.0 0	– 8.0 –12.0	22.0 48.0	+16.0 0	–22.0 –32.0	22.0 63.0	+25.0 0	–22.0 –38.0

(Courtesy of ANSI; B4.1-1955.)

Limits are in thousandths of an inch.
Limits for hole and shaft are applied algebraically to the basic size to obtain the limits of size for the parts.
Data in bold face are in accordance with ABC agreements.
Symbols H5, g5, etc., are Hole and Shaft designations used in ABC System.

Class RC 5			Class RC 6			Class RC 7			Class RC 8			Class RC 9			Nominal Size Range Inches	
Limits of Clearance	Standard Limits		Limits of Clearance	Standard Limits		Limits of Clearance	Standard Limits		Limits of Clearance	Standard Limits		Limits of Clearance	Standard Limits			
	Hole H8	Shaft e7		Hole H9	Shaft e8		Hole H9	Shaft d8		Hole H10	Shaft c9		Hole H11	Shaft	Over	To
0.6 **1.6**	**+ 0.6** **− 0**	**− 0.6** **− 1.0**	**0.6** **2.2**	**+ 1.0** **− 0**	**− 0.6** **− 1.2**	**1.0** **2.6**	**+ 1.0** **0**	**− 1.0** **− 1.6**	**2.5** **5.1**	**+ 1.6** **0**	**− 2.5** **− 3.5**	4.0 8.1	**+ 2.5** **0**	− 4.0 − 5.6	0	− 0.12
0.8 **2.0**	**+ 0.7** **− 0**	**− 0.8** **− 1.3**	**0.8** **2.7**	**+ 1.2** **− 0**	**− 0.8** **− 1.5**	**1.2** **3.1**	**+ 1.2** **0**	**− 1.2** **− 1.9**	**2.8** **5.8**	**+ 1.8** **0**	**− 2.8** **− 4.0**	4.5 9.0	**+ 3.0** **0**	− 4.5 − 6.0	0.12−	0.24
1.0 **2.5**	**+ 0.9** **− 0**	**− 1.0** **− 1.6**	**1.0** **3.3**	**+ 1.4** **− 0**	**− 1.0** **− 1.9**	**1.6** **3.9**	**+ 1.4** **0**	**− 1.6** **− 2.5**	**3.0** **6.6**	**+ 2.2** **0**	**− 3.0** **− 4.4**	5.0 10.7	**+ 3.5** **0**	− 5.0 − 7.2	0.24−	0.40
1.2 **2.9**	**+ 1.0** **− 0**	**− 1.2** **− 1.9**	**1.2** **3.8**	**+ 1.6** **− 0**	**− 1.2** **− 2.2**	**2.0** **4.6**	**+ 1.6** **0**	**− 2.0** **− 3.0**	**3.5** **7.9**	**+ 2.8** **0**	**− 3.5** **− 5.1**	6.0 12.8	**+ 4.0** − **0**	− 6.0 − 8.8	0.40−	0.71
1.6 **3.6**	**+ 1.2** **− 0**	**− 1.6** **− 2.4**	**1.6** **4.8**	**+ 2.0** **− 0**	**− 1.6** **− 2.8**	**2.5** **5.7**	**+ 2.0** **0**	**− 2.5** **− 3.7**	**4.5** **10.0**	**+ 3.5** **0**	**− 4.5** **− 6.5**	7.0 15.5	**+ 5.0** **0**	− 7.0 − 10.5	0.71−	1.19
2.0 **4.6**	**+ 1.6** **− 0**	**− 2.0** **− 3.0**	**2.0** **6.1**	**+ 2.5** **− 0**	**− 2.0** **− 3.6**	**3.0** **7.1**	**+ 2.5** **0**	**− 3.0** **− 4.6**	**5.0** **11.5**	**+ 4.0** **0**	**− 5.0** **− 7.5**	8.0 18.0	**+ 6.0** **0**	− 8.0 − 12.0	1.19−	1.97
2.5 **5.5**	**+ 1.8** **− 0**	**− 2.5** **− 3.7**	**2.5** **7.3**	**+ 3.0** **− 0**	**− 2.5** **− 4.3**	**4.0** **8.8**	**+ 3.0** **0**	**− 4.0** **− 5.8**	**6.0** **13.5**	**+ 4.5** **0**	**− 6.0** **− 9.0**	9.0 20.5	**+ 7.0** **0**	− 9.0 − 13.5	1.97−	3.15
3.0 **6.6**	**+ 2.2** **− 0**	**− 3.0** **− 4.4**	**3.0** **8.7**	**+ 3.5** **− 0**	**− 3.0** **− 5.2**	**5.0** **10.7**	**+ 3.5** **0**	**− 5.0** **− 7.2**	**7.0** **15.5**	**+ 5.0** **0**	**− 7.0** **− 10.5**	10.0 24.0	**+ 9.0** **0**	− 10.0 − 15.0	3.15−	4.73
3.5 **7.6**	**+ 2.5** **− 0**	**− 3.5** **− 5.1**	**3.5** **10.0**	**+ 4.0** **− 0**	**− 3.5** **− 6.0**	**6.0** **12.5**	**+ 4.0** **0**	**− 6.0** **− 8.5**	**8.0** **18.0**	**+ 6.0** **0**	**− 8.0** **− 12.0**	12.0 28.0	**+ 10.0** **0**	− 12.0 − 18.0	4.73−	7.09
4.0 **8.6**	**+ 2.8** **− 0**	**− 4.0** **− 5.8**	**4.0** **11.3**	**+ 4.5** **0**	**− 4.0** **− 6.8**	**7.0** **14.3**	**+ 4.5** **0**	**− 7.0** **− 9.8**	**10.0** **21.5**	**+ 7.0** **0**	**− 10.0** **− 14.5**	15.0 34.0	**+ 12.0** **0**	− 15.0 − 22.0	7.09−	9.85
5.0 10.0	**+ 3.0** **0**	− 5.0 − 7.0	5.0 13.0	**+ 5.0** **0**	− 5.0 − 8.0	8.0 16.0	**+ 5.0** **0**	− 8.0 − 11.0	**12.0** **25.0**	**+ 8.0** **0**	**− 12.0** **− 17.0**	18.0 38.0	**+ 12.0** **0**	− 18.0 − 26.0	9.85−	12.41
6.0 11.7	**+ 3.5** **0**	− 6.0 − 8.2	6.0 15.5	**+ 6.0** **0**	− 6.0 − 9.5	10.0 19.5	**+ 6.0** **0**	− 10.0 13.5	**14.0** **29.0**	**+ 9.0** **0**	**− 14.0** **− 20.0**	22.0 45.0	**+ 14.0** **0**	− 22.0 − 31.0	12.41−	15.75
8.0 14.5	**+ 4.0** **0**	− 8.0 −10.5	8.0 18.0	**+ 6.0** **0**	− 8.0 −12.0	12.0 22.0	**+ 6.0** **0**	− 12.0 − 16.0	**16.0** **32.0**	**+10.0** **0**	**− 16.0** **− 22.0**	25.0 51.0	**+ 16.0** **0**	− 25.0 − 35.0	15.75−	19.69
10.0 18.0	+ 5.0 0	−10.0 −13.0	10.0 23.0	+ 8.0 0	−10.0 −15.0	16.0 29.0	+ 8.0 0	− 16.0 − 21.0	20.0 40.0	+12.0 0	− 20.0 − 28.0	30.0 62.0	+ 20.0 0	− 30.0 − 42.0	19.69−	30.09
12.0 22.0	+ 6.0 0	−12.0 −16.0	12.0 28.0	+10.0 0	−12.0 −18.0	20.0 36.0	+10.0 0	− 20.0 − 26.0	25.0 51.0	+16.0 0	− 25.0 − 35.0	40.0 81.0	+ 25.0 0	− 40.0 − 56.0	30.09−	41.49
16.0 29.0	+ 8.0 0	−16.0 −21.0	16.0 36.0	+12.0 0	−16.0 −24.0	25.0 45.0	+12.0 0	− 25.0 − 33.0	30.0 62.0	+20.0 0	− 30.0 − 42.0	50.0 100	+ 30.0 0	− 50.0 − 70.0	41.49−	56.19
20.0 36.0	+10.0 0	−20.0 −26.0	20.0 46.0	+16.0 0	−20.0 −30.0	30.0 56.0	+16.0 0	− 30.0 − 40.0	40.0 81.0	+25.0 0	− 40.0 − 56.0	60.0 125	+ 40.0 0	− 60.0 − 85.0	56.19−	76.39
25.0 45.0	+12.0 0	−25.0 −33.0	25.0 57.0	+20.0 0	−25.0 −37.0	40.0 72.0	+20.0 0	− 40.0 − 52.0	50.0 100	+30.0 0	− 50.0 − 70.0	80.0 160	+ 50.0 0	− 80.0 −110	76.39−	100.9
30.0 56.0	+16.0 0	−30.0 −40.0	30.0 71.0	+25.0 0	−30.0 −46.0	50.0 91.0	+25.0 0	− 50.0 − 66.0	60.0 125	+40.0 0	− 60.0 − 85.0	100 200	+ 60.0 0	−100 −140	100.9 −	131.9
35.0 67.0	+20.0 0	−35.0 −47.0	35.0 85.0	+30.0 0	−35.0 −55.0	60.0 110.0	+30.0 0	− 60.0 − 80.0	80.0 160	+50.0 0	− 80.0 −110	130 260	+ 80.0 0	−130 −180	131.9 −	171.9
45.0 86.0	+25.0 0	−45.0 −61.0	45.0 110.0	+40.0 0	−45.0 −70.0	80.0 145.0	+40.0 0	− 80.0 −105.0	100 200	+60.0 0	−100 −140	150 310	+100 0	−150 −210	171.9 −	200

APPENDIX 24. AMERICAN STANDARD CLEARANCE LOCATIONAL FITS

Nominal Size Range Inches		Class LC 1			Class LC 2			Class LC 3			Class LC 4			Class LC 5		
		Limits of Clearance	Standard Limits		Limits of Clearance	Standard Limits		Limits of Clearance	Standard Limits		Limits of Clearance	Standard Limits		Limits of Clearance	Standard Limits	
Over	To		Hole H6	Shaft h5		Hole H7	Shaft h6		Hole H8	Shaft h7		Hole H10	Shaft h9		Hole H 7	Shaft g6
0 –	0.12	0 0.45	+ 0.25 − 0	+ 0 −0.2	0 0.65	+ 0.4 − 0	+ 0 −0.25	0 1	+ 0.6 − 0	+ 0 − 0.4	0 2.6	+ 1.6 − 0	+ 0 −1.0	0.1 0.75	+ 0.4 − 0	− 0.1 − 0.35
0.12–	0.24	0 0.5	+ 0.3 − 0	+ 0 −0.2	0 0.8	+ 0.5 − 0	+ 0 − 0.3	0 1.2	+ 0.7 − 0	+ 0 − 0.5	0 3.0	+ 1.8 − 0	+ 0 − 1.2	0.15 0.95	+ 0.5 − 0	− 0.15 − 0.45
0.24–	0.40	0 0.65	+ 0.4 − 0	+ 0 −0.25	0 1.0	+ 0.6 − 0	+ 0 − 0.4	0 1.5	+ 0.9 − 0	+ 0 − 0.6	0 3.6	+ 2.2 − 0	+ 0 − 1.4	0.2 1.2	+ 0.6 − 0	− 0.2 − 0.6
0.40–	0.71	0 0.7	+ 0.4 − 0	+ 0 −0.3	0 1.1	+ 0.7 − 0	+ 0 − 0.4	0 1.7	+ 1.0 − 0	+ 0 − 0.7	0 4.4	+ 2.8 − 0	+ 0 − 1.6	0.25 1.35	+ 0.7 − 0	− 0.25 − 0.65
0.71–	1.19	0 0.9	+ 0.5 − 0	+ 0 −0.4	0 1.3	+ 0.8 − 0	+ 0 − 0.5	0 2	+ 1.2 − 0	+ 0 − 0.8	0 5.5	+ 3.5 − 0	+ 0 − 2.0	0.3 1.6	+ 0.8 − 0	− 0.3 − 0.8
1.19–	1.97	0 1.0	+ 0.6 − 0	+ 0 −0.4	0 1.6	+ 1.0 − 0	+ 0 − 0.6	0 2.6	+ 1.6 − 0	+ 0 − 1	0 6.5	+ 4.0 − 0	+ 0 − 2.5	0.4 2.0	+ 1.0 − 0	− 0.4 − 1.0
1.97–	3.15	0 1.2	+ 0.7 − 0	+ 0 −0.5	0 1.9	+ 1.2 − 0	+ 0 − 0.7	0 3	+ 1.8 − 0	+ 0 − 1.2	0 7.5	+ 4.5 − 0	+ 0 − 3	0.4 2.3	+ 1.2 − 0	− 0.4 − 1.1
3.15–	4.73	0 1.5	+ 0.9 − 0	+ 0 −0.6	0 2.3	+ 1.4 − 0	+ 0 − 0.9	0 3.6	+ 2.2 − 0	+ 0 − 1.4	0 8.5	+ 5.0 − 0	+ 0 − 3.5	0.5 2.8	+ 1.4 − 0	− 0.5 − 1.4
4.73–	7.09	0 1.7	+ 1.0 − 0	+ 0 −0.7	0 2.6	+ 1.6 − 0	+ 0 − 1.0	0 4.1	+ 2.5 − 0	+ 0 − 1.6	0 10	+ 6.0 − 0	+ 0 − 4	0.6 3.2	+ 1.6 − 0	− 0.6 − 1.6
7.09–	9.85	0 2.0	+ 1.2 − 0	+ 0 −0.8	0 3.0	+ 1.8 − 0	+ 0 − 1.2	0 4.6	+ 2.8 − 0	+ 0 − 1.8	0 11.5	+ 7.0 − 0	+ 0 − 4.5	0.6 3.6	+ 1.8 − 0	− 0.6 − 1.8
9.85–	12.41	0 2.1	+ 1.2 − 0	+ 0 −0.9	0 3.2	+ 2.0 − 0	+ 0 − 1.2	0 5	+ 3.0 − 0	+ 0 − 2.0	0 13	+ 8.0 − 0	+ 0 − 5	0.7 3.9	+ 2.0 − 0	− 0.7 − 1.9
12.41–	15.75	0 2.4	+ 1.4 − 0	+ 0 −1.0	0 3.6	+ 2.2 − 0	+ 0 − 1.4	0 5.7	+ 3.5 − 0	+ 0 − 2.2	0 15	+ 9.0 − 0	+ 0 − 6	0.7 4.3	+ 2.2 − 0	− 0.7 − 2.1
15.75–	19.69	0 2.6	+ 1.6 − 0	+ 0 −1.0	0 4.1	+ 2.5 − 0	+ 0 − 1.6	0 6.5	+ 4 − 0	+ 0 − 2.5	0 16	+10.0 − 0	+ 0 − 6	0.8 4.9	+ 2.5 − 0	− 0.8 − 2.4
19.69–	30.09	0 3.2	+ 2.0 − 0	+ 0 −1.2	0 5.0	+ 3 − 0	+ 0 − 2	0 8	+ 5 − 0	+ 0 − 3	0 20	+12.0 − 0	+ 0 − 8	0.9 5.9	+ 3.0 − 0	− 0.9 − 2.9
30.09–	41.49	0 4.1	+ 2.5 − 0	+ 0 −1.6	0 6.5	+ 4 − 0	+ 0 − 2.5	0 10	+ 6 − 0	+ 0 − 4	0 26	+16.0 − 0	+ 0 −10	1.0 7.5	+ 4.0 − 0	− 1.0 − 3.5
41.49–	56.19	0 5.0	+ 3.0 − 0	+ 0 −2.0	0 8.0	+ 5 − 0	+ 0 − 3	0 13	+ 8 − 0	+ 0 − 5	0 32	+20.0 − 0	+ 0 −12	1.2 9.2	+ 5.0 − 0	− 1.2 − 4.2
56.19–	76.39	0 6.5	+ 4.0 − 0	+ 0 −2.5	0 10	+ 6 − 0	+ 0 − 4	0 16	+10 − 0	+ 0 − 6	0 41	+25.0 − 0	+ 0 −16	1.2 11.2	+ 6.0 − 0	− 1.2 − 5.2
76.39–	100.9	0 8.0	+ 5.0 − 0	+ 0 −3.0	0 13	+ 8 − 0	+ 0 − 5	0 20	+12 − 0	+ 0 − 8	0 50	+30.0 − 0	+ 0 −20	1.4 14.4	+ 8.0 − 0	− 1.4 − 6.4
100.9 –	131.9	0 10.0	+ 6.0 − 0	+ 0 −4.0	0 16	+10 − 0	+ 0 − 6	0 26	+16 − 0	+ 0 −10	0 65	+40.0 − 0	+ 0 −25	1.6 17.6	+10.0 − 0	− 1.6 − 7.6
131.9 –	171.9	0 13.0	+ 8.0 − 0	+ 0 −5.0	0 20	+12 − 0	+ 0 − 8	0 32	+20 − 0	+ 0 −12	0 8	+ 50.0 − 0	+ 0 −30	1.8 21.8	+12.0 − 0	− 1.8 − 9.8
171.9 –	200	0 16.0	+10.0 − 0	+ 0 −6.0	0 26	+16 − 0	+ 0 −10	0 41	+25 − 0	+ 0 −16	0 100	+60.0 − 0	+ 0 −40	1.8 27.8	+16.0 − 0	− 1.8 −11.8

(Courtesy of ANSI; B4.1-1955.)

Limits are in thousandths of an inch.
Limits for hole and shaft are applied algebraically to the basic size to obtain the limits of size for the parts.
Data in bold face are in accordance with ABC agreements.
Symbols H9, f8, etc., are Hole and Shaft designations used in ABC System[1].

Class LC 6			Class LC 7			Class LC 8			Class LC 9			Class LC 10			Class LC 11			Nominal Size Range Inches	
Limits of Clearance	Standard Limits		Limits of Clearance	Standard Limits		Limits of Clearance	Standard Limits		Limits of Clearance	Standard Limits		Limits of Clearance	Standard Limits		Limits of Clearance	Standard Limits			
	Hole H9	Shaft f8		Hole H10	Shaft e9		Hole H10	Shaft d9		Hole H11	Shaft c10		Hole H12	Shaft		Hole H13	Shaft	Over	To
0.3 1.9	+ 1.0 0	− 0.3 − 0.9	0.6 3.2	+ 1.6 0	− 0.6 − 1.6	1.0 3.6	+ 1.6 − 0	− 1.0 − 2.0	2.5 6.6	+ 2.5 − 0	− 2.5 − 4.1	4 12	+ 4 − 0	− 4 − 8	5 17	+ 6 − 0	− 5 − 11	0	0.12
0.4 2.3	+ 1.2 0	− 0.4 − 1.1	0.8 3.8	+ 1.8 0	− 0.8 − 2.0	1.2 4.2	+ 1.8 − 0	− 1.2 − 2.4	2.8 7.6	+ 3.0 − 0	− 2.8 − 4.6	4.5 14.5	+ 5 − 0	− 4.5 − 9.5	6 20	+ 7 − 0	− 6 − 13	0.12	0.24
0.5 2.8	+ 1.4 0	− 0.5 − 1.4	1.0 4.6	+ 2.2 0	− 1.0 − 2.4	1.6 5.2	+ 2.2 − 0	− 1.6 − 3.0	3.0 8.7	+ 3.5 − 0	− 3.0 − 5.2	5 17	+ 6 − 0	− 5 − 11	7 25	+ 9 − 0	− 7 − 16	0.24	0.40
0.6 3.2	+ 1.6 0	− 0.6 − 1.6	1.2 5.6	+ 2.8 0	− 1.2 − 2.8	2.0 6.4	+ 2.8 − 0	− 2.0 − 3.6	3.5 10.3	+ 4.0 − 0	− 3.5 − 6.3	6 20	+ 7 − 0	− 6 − 13	8 28	+ 10 − 0	− 8 − 18	0.40	0.71
0.8 4.0	+ 2.0 0	− 0.8 − 2.0	1.6 7.1	+ 3.5 0	− 1.6 − 3.6	2.5 8.0	+ 3.5 − 0	− 2.5 − 4.5	4.5 13.0	+ 5.0 − 0	− 4.5 − 8.0	7 23	+ 8 − 0	− 7 − 15	10 34	+ 12 − 0	− 10 − 22	0.71	1.19
1.0 5.1	+ 2.5 0	− 1.0 − 2.6	2.0 8.5	+ 4.0 0	− 2.0 − 4.5	3.0 9.5	+ 4.0 − 0	− 3.0 − 5.5	5 15	+ 6 − 0	− 5 − 9	8 28	+ 10 − 0	− 8 − 18	12 44	+ 16 − 0	− 12 − 28	1.19	1.97
1.2 6.0	+ 3.0 0	− 1.2 − 3.0	2.5 10.0	+ 4.5 0	− 2.5 − 5.5	4.0 11.5	+ 4.5 − 0	− 4.0 − 7.0	6 17.5	+ 7 − 0	− 6 − 10.5	10 34	+ 12 − 0	− 10 − 22	14 50	+ 18 − 0	− 14 − 32	1.97	3.15
1.4 7.1	+ 3.5 0	− 1.4 − 3.6	3.0 11.5	+ 5.0 0	− 3.0 − 6.5	5.0 13.5	+ 5.0 − 0	− 5.0 − 8.5	7 21	+ 9 − 0	− 7 − 12	11 39	+ 14 − 0	− 11 − 25	16 60	+ 22 − 0	− 16 − 38	3.15	4.73
1.6 8.1	+ 4.0 0	− 1.6 − 4.1	3.5 13.5	+ 6.0 0	− 3.5 − 7.5	6 16	+ 6 − 0	− 6 −10	8 24	+ 10 − 0	− 8 − 14	12 44	+ 16 − 0	− 12 − 28	18 68	+ 25 − 0	− 18 − 43	4.73	7.09
2.0 9.3	+ 4.5 0	− 2.0 − 4.8	4.0 15.5	+ 7.0 0	− 4.0 − 8.5	7 18.5	+ 7 − 0	− 7 −11.5	10 29	+ 12 − 0	− 10 − 17	16 52	+ 18 − 0	− 16 − 34	22 78	+ 28 − 0	− 22 − 50	7.09	9.85
2.2 10.2	+ 5.0 0	− 2.2 − 5.2	4.5 17.5	+ 8.0 0	− 4.5 − 9.5	7 20	+ 8 − 0	− 7 −12	12 32	+ 12 − 0	− 12 − 20	20 60	+ 20 − 0	− 20 − 40	28 88	+ 30 − 0	− 28 − 58	9.85	12.41
2.5 12.0	+ 6.0 0	− 2.5 − 6.0	5.0 20.0	+ 9.0 0	− 5 −11	8 23	+ 9 − 0	− 8 −14	14 37	+ 14 − 0	− 14 − 23	22 66	+ 22 − 0	− 22 − 44	30 100	+ 35 − 0	− 30 − 65	12.41	15.75
2.8 12.8	+ 6.0 0	− 2.8 − 6.8	5.0 21.0	+ 10.0 0	− 5 −11	9 25	+10 − 0	− 9 −15	16 42	+ 16 − 0	− 16 − 26	25 75	+ 25 − 0	− 25 − 50	35 115	+ 40 − 0	− 35 − 75	15.75	19.69
3.0 16.0	+ 8.0 0	− 3.0 − 8.0	6.0 26.0	+12.0 − 0	− 6 −14	10 30	+12 − 0	−10 −18	18 50	+ 20 − 0	− 18 − 30	28 88	+ 30 − 0	− 28 − 58	40 140	+ 50 − 0	− 40 − 90	19.69	30.09
3.5 19.5	+10.0 0	− 3.5 − 9.5	7.0 33.0	+16.0 − 0	− 7 −17	12 38	+16 − 0	−12 −22	20 61	+ 25 − 0	− 20 − 36	30 110	+ 40 − 0	− 30 − 70	45 165	+ 60 − 0	− 45 −105	30.09	41.49
4.0 24.0	+12.0 0	− 4.0 −12.0	8.0 40.0	+20.0 − 0	− 8 −20	14 46	+20 − 0	−14 −26	25 75	+ 30 − 0	− 25 − 45	40 140	+ 50 − 0	− 40 − 90	60 220	+ 80 − 0	− 60 −140	41.49	56.19
4.5 30.5	+16.0 0	− 4.5 −14.5	9.0 50.0	+25.0 − 0	− 9 −25	16 57	+25 − 0	−16 −32	30 95	+ 40 − 0	− 30 − 55	50 170	+ 60 − 0	− 50 110	70 270	+100 − 0	− 70 −170	56.19	76.39
5.0 37.0	+20.0 0	− 5 −17	10.0 60.0	+30.0 − 0	−10 −30	18 68	+30 − 0	−18 −38	35 115	+ 50 − 0	− 35 − 65	50 210	+ 80 − 0	− 50 −130	80 330	+125 − 0	− 80 −205	76.39	100.9
6.0 47.0	+25.0 0	− 6 −22	12.0 67.0	+40.0 − 0	−12 −27	20 85	+40 − 0	−20 −45	40 140	+ 60 − 0	− 40 − 80	60 260	+100 − 0	− 60 −160	90 410	+160 − 0	− 90 −250	100.9	131.9
7.0 57.0	+30.0 0	− 7 −27	14.0 94.0	+50.0 − 0	−14 −44	25 105	+50 − 0	−25 −55	50 180	+ 80 − 0	− 50 −100	80 330	+125 − 0	− 80 −205	100 500	+200 − 0	−100 −300	131.9	171.9
7.0 72.0	+40.0 0	− 7 −32	14.0 114.0	+60.0 − 0	−14 −54	25 125	+60 − 0	−25 −65	50 210	+100 − 0	− 50 − 110	90 410	+160 − 0	− 90 −250	125 625	+250 − 0	−125 −375	171.9	200

APPENDIX 25. AMERICAN STANDARD TRANSITION LOCATIONAL FITS

Limits are in thousandths of an inch.
Limits for hole and shaft are applied algebraically to the basic size to obtain the limits of size for the mating parts.
Data in bold face are in accordance with ABC agreements.
"Fit" represents the maximum interference (minus values) and the maximum clearance (plus values).
Symbols H7, js6, etc., are Hole and Shaft designations used in ABC System.

Nominal Size Range Inches	Class LT 1			Class LT 2			Class LT 3			Class LT 4			Class LT 5			Class LT 6		
	Fit	Standard Limits		Fit	Standard Limits		Fit	Standard Limits		Fit	Standard Limits		Fit	Standard Limits		Fit	Standard Limits	
Over To		Hole H7	Shaft js6		Hole H8	Shaft js7		Hole H7	Shaft k6		Hole H8	Shaft k7		Hole H7	Shaft n6		Hole H7	Shaft n7
0 – 0.12	−0.10 +0.50	+0.4 −0	+0.10 −0.10	−0.2 +0.8	+0.6 −0	+0.2 −0.2							−0.5 +0.15	+0.4 −0	+0.5 +0.25	−0.65 +0.15	+0.4 −0	−0.65 +0.25
0.12 – 0.24	−0.15 +0.65	+0.5 −0	+0.15 −0.15	−0.25 +0.95	+0.7 −0	+0.25 −0.25							−0.6 +0.2	+0.5 −0	+0.6 +0.3	−0.8 +0.2	+0.5 −0	+0.8 +0.3
0.24 – 0.40	−0.2 +0.8	+0.6 −0	+0.2 −0.2	−0.3 +1.2	+0.9 −0	+0.3 −0.3	−0.5 +0.5	+0.6 −0	+0.5 +0.1	−0.7 +0.8	+0.9 −0	+0.7 +0.1	−0.8 +0.2	+0.6 −0	+0.8 +0.4	−1.0 +0.2	+0.6 −0	+1.0 +0.4
0.40 – 0.71	−0.2 +0.9	+0.7 −0	+0.2 −0.2	−0.35 +1.35	+1.0 −0	+0.35 −0.35	−0.5 +0.6	+0.7 −0	+0.5 +0.1	−0.8 +0.9	+1.0 −0	+0.8 +0.1	−0.9 +0.2	+0.7 −0	+0.9 +0.5	−1.2 +0.2	+0.7 −0	+1.2 +0.5
0.71 – 1.19	−0.25 +1.05	+0.8 −0	+0.25 −0.25	−0.4 +1.6	+1.2 −0	+0.4 −0.4	−0.6 +0.7	+0.8 −0	+0.6 +0.1	−0.9 +1.1	+1.2 −0	+0.9 +0.1	−1.1 +0.2	+0.8 −0	+1.1 +0.6	−1.4 +0.2	+0.8 −0	+1.4 +0.6
1.19 – 1.97	−0.3 +1.3	+1.0 −0	+0.3 −0.3	−0.5 +2.1	+1.6 −0	+0.5 −0.5	−0.7 +0.9	+1.0 −0	+0.7 +0.1	−1.1 +1.5	+1.6 −0	+1.1 +0.1	−1.3 +0.3	+1.0 −0	+1.3 +0.7	−1.7 +0.3	+1.0 −0	+1.7 +0.7
1.97 – 3.15	−0.3 +1.5	+1.2 −0	+0.3 −0.3	−0.6 +2.4	+1.8 −0	+0.6 −0.6	−0.8 +1.1	+1.2 −0	+0.8 +0.1	−1.3 +1.7	+1.8 −0	+1.3 +0.1	−1.5 +0.4	+1.2 −0	+1.5 +0.8	−2.0 +0.4	+1.2 −0	+2.0 +0.8
3.15 – 4.73	−0.4 +1.8	+1.4 −0	+0.4 −0.4	−0.7 +2.9	+2.2 −0	+0.7 −0.7	−1.0 +1.3	+1.4 −0	+1.0 +0.1	−1.5 +2.1	+2.2 −0	+1.5 +0.1	−1.9 +0.4	+1.4 −0	+1.9 +1.0	−2.4 +0.4	+1.4 −0	+2.4 +1.0
4.73 – 7.09	−0.5 +2.1	+1.6 −0	+0.5 −0.5	−0.8 +3.3	+2.5 −0	+0.8 −0.8	−1.1 +1.5	+1.6 −0	+1.1 +0.1	−1.7 +2.4	+2.5 −0	+1.7 +0.1	−2.2 +0.4	+1.6 −0	+2.2 +1.2	−2.8 +0.4	+1.6 −0	+2.8 +1.2
7.09 – 9.85	−0.6 +2.4	+1.8 −0	+0.6 −0.6	−0.9 +3.7	+2.8 −0	+0.9 −0.9	−1.4 +1.6	+1.8 −0	+1.4 +0.2	−2.0 +2.6	+2.8 −0	+2.0 +0.2	−2.6 +0.4	+1.8 −0	+2.6 +1.4	−3.2 +0.4	+1.8 −0	+3.2 +1.4
9.85 – 12.41	−0.6 +2.6	+2.0 −0	+0.6 −0.6	−1.0 +4.0	+3.0 −0	+1.0 −1.0	−1.4 +1.8	+2.0 −0	+1.4 +0.2	−2.2 +2.8	+3.0 −0	+2.2 +0.2	−2.6 +0.6	+2.0 −0	+2.6 +1.4	−3.4 +0.6	+2.0 −0	+3.4 +1.4
12.41 – 15.75	−0.7 +2.9	+2.2 −0	+0.7 −0.7	−1.0 +4.5	+3.5 −0	+1.0 −1.0	−1.6 +2.0	+2.2 −0	+1.6 +0.2	−2.4 +3.3	+3.5 −0	+2.4 +0.2	−3.0 +0.6	+2.2 −0	+3.0 +1.6	−3.8 +0.6	+2.2 −0	+3.8 +1.6
15.75 – 19.69	−0.8 +3.3	+2.5 −0	+0.8 −0.8	−1.2 +5.2	+4.0 −0	+1.2 −1.2	−1.8 +2.3	+2.5 −0	+1.8 +0.2	−2.7 +3.8	+4.0 −0	+2.7 +0.2	−3.4 +0.7	+2.5 −0	+3.4 +1.8	−4.3 +0.7	+2.5 −0	+4.3 +1.8

(Courtesy of ANSI; B4.1-1955.)

APPENDIX 26. AMERICAN STANDARD INTERFERENCE LOCATIONAL FITS

Limits are in thousandths of an inch.
Limits for hole and shaft are applied algebraically to the basic size to obtain the limits of size for the parts.
Data in bold face are in accordance with ABC agreements,
Symbols H7, p6, etc., are Hole and Shaft designations used in ABC System.

Nominal Size Range Inches	Class LN 1			Class LN 2			Class LN 3		
	Limits of Interference	Standard Limits		Limits of Interference	Standard Limits		Limits of Interference	Standard Limits	
Over – To		Hole H6	Shaft n5		Hole H7	Shaft p6		Hole H7	Shaft r6
0 – 0.12	0 0.45	+ 0.25 – 0	+0.45 +0.25	0 0.65	+ 0.4 – 0	+ 0.65 + 0.4	0.1 0.75	+ 0.4 – 0	+ 0.75 + 0.5
0.12 – 0.24	0 0.5	+ 0.3 – 0	+0.5 +0.3	0 0.8	+ 0.5 – 0	+ 0.8 + 0.5	0.1 0.9	+ 0.5 0	+ 0.9 + 0.6
0.24 – 0.40	0 0.65	+ 0.4 – 0	+0.65 +0.4	0 1.0	+ 0.6 – 0	+ 1.0 + 0.6	0.2 1.2	+ 0.6 – 0	+ 1.2 + 0.8
0.40 – 0.71	0 0.8	+ 0.4 – 0	+0.8 +0.4	0 1.1	+ 0.7 – 0	+ 1.1 + 0.7	0.3 1.4	+ 0.7 – 0	+ 1.4 + 1.0
0.71 – 1.19	0 1.0	+ 0.5 – 0	+1.0 +0.5	0 1.3	+ 0.8 – 0	+ 1.3 + 0.8	0.4 1.7	+ 0.8 – 0	+ 1.7 + 1.2
1.19 – 1.97	0 1.1	+ 0.6 – 0	+1.1 +0.6	0 1.6	+ 1.0 – 0	+ 1.6 + 1.0	0.4 2.0	+ 1.0 – 0	+ 2.0 + 1.4
1.97 – 3.15	0.1 1.3	+ 0.7 – 0	+1.3 +0.7	0.2 2.1	+ 1.2 – 0	+ 2.1 + 1.4	0.4 2.3	+ 1.2 – 0	+ 2.3 + 1.6
3.15 – 4.73	0.1 1.6	+ 0.9 – 0	+1.6 +1.0	0.2 2.5	+ 1.4 – 0	+ 2.5 + 1.6	0.6 2.9	+ 1.4 – 0	+ 2.9 + 2.0
4.73 – 7.09	0.2 1.9	+ 1.0 – 0	+1.9 +1.2	0.2 2.8	+ 1.6 – 0	+ 2.8 + 1.8	0.9 3.5	+ 1.6 – 0	+ 3.5 + 2.5
7.09 – 9.85	0.2 2.2	+ 1.2 – 0	+2.2 +1.4	0.2 3.2	+ 1.8 – 0	+ 3.2 + 2.0	1.2 4.2	+ 1.8 – 0	+ 4.2 + 3.0
9.85 – 12.41	0.2 2.3	+ 1.2 – 0	+2.3 +1.4	0.2 3.4	+ 2.0 – 0	+ 3.4 + 2.2	1.5 4.7	+ 2.0 – 0	+ 4.7 + 3.5
12.41 – 15.75	0.2 2.6	+ 1.4 – 0	+2.6 +1.6	0.3 3.9	+ 2.2 – 0	+ 3.9 + 2.5	2.3 5.9	+ 2.2 – 0	+ 5.9 + 4.5
15.75 – 19.69	0.2 2.8	+ 1.6 – 0	+2.8 +1.8	0.3 4.4	+ 2.5 – 0	+ 4.4 + 2.8	2.5 6.6	+ 2.5 – 0	+ 6.6 + 5.0
19.69 – 30.09		+ 2.0 – 0		0.5 5.5	+ 3 – 0	+ 5.5 + 3.5	4 9	+ 3 – 0	+ 9 + 7
30.09 – 41.49		+ 2.5 – 0		0.5 7.0	+ 4 – 0	+ 7.0 + 4.5	5 11.5	+ 4 – 0	+11.5 + 9
41.49 – 56.19		+ 3.0 – 0		1 9	+ 5 – 0	+ 9 + 6	7 15	+ 5 – 0	+15 +12
56.19 – 76.39		+ 4.0 – 0		1 11	+ 6 – 0	+11 + 7	10 20	+ 6 – 0	+20 +16
76.39 – 100.9		+ 5.0 – 0		1 14	+ 8 – 0	+14 + 9	12 25	+ 8 – 0	+25 +20
100.9 – 131.9		+ 6.0 – 0		2 18	+10 – 0	+18 +12	15 31	+10 – 0	+31 +25
131.9 – 171.9		+ 8.0 – 0		4 24	+12 – 0	+24 +16	18 38	+12 – 0	+38 +30
171.9 – 200		+10.0 – 0		4 30	+16 – 0	+30 +20	24 50	+16 – 0	+50 +40

(Courtesy of ANSI; B4.1-1955.)

Limits are in thousandths of an inch.
Limits for hole and shaft are applied algebraically to the basic size to obtain the limits of size for the parts.
Data in bold face are in accordance with ABC agreements.
Symbols H7, s6, etc., are Hole and Shaft designations used in ABC System.

Nominal Size Range Inches	Class FN 1			Class FN 2			Class FN 3			Class FN 4			Class FN 5		
Over – To	Limits of Interference	Standard Limits Hole H6	Standard Limits Shaft	Limits of Interference	Standard Limits Hole H7	Standard Limits Shaft s6	Limits of Interference	Standard Limits Hole H7	Standard Limits Shaft t6	Limits of Interference	Standard Limits Hole H7	Standard Limits Shaft u6	Limits of Interference	Standard Limits Hole H8	Standard Limits Shaft x7
0 – 0.12	0.05 0.5	+0.25 − 0	+ 0.5 + 0.3	0.2 0.85	+0.4 − 0	+ 0.85 + 0.6				0.3 0.95	+0.4 − 0	+ 0.95 + 0.7	0.3 1.3	+0.6 − 0	+ 1.3 + 0.9
0.12 – 0.24	0.1 0.6	+0.3 − 0	+ 0.6 + 0.4	0.2 1.0	+0.5 − 0	+ 1.0 + 0.7				0.4 1.2	+0.5 − 0	+ 1.2 + 0.9	0.5 1.7	+ 0.7 − 0	+ 1.7 + 1.2
0.24 – 0.40	0.1 0.75	+0.4 − 0	+ 0.75 + 0.5	0.4 1.4	+0.6 − 0	+ 1.4 + 1.0				0.6 1.6	+0.6 − 0	+ 1.6 + 1.2	0.5 2.0	+ 0.9 − 0	+ 2.0 + 1.4
0.40 – 0.56	0.1 0.8	−0.4 − 0	+ 0.8 + 0.5	0.5 1.6	+0.7 − 0	+ 1.6 + 1.2				0.7 1.8	+ 0.7 − 0	+ 1.8 + 1.4	0.6 2.3	+ 1.0 − 0	+ 2.3 + 1.6
0.56 – 0.71	0.2 0.9	+0.4 − 0	+ 0.9 + 0.6	0.5 1.6	+0.7 − 0	+ 1.6 + 1.2				0.7 1.8	+ 0.7 − 0	+ 1.8 + 1.4	0.8 2.5	+ 1.0 − 0	+ 2.5 + 1.8
0.71 – 0.95	0.2 1.1	+0.5 − 0	+ 1.1 + 0.7	0.6 1.9	+0.8 − 0	+ 1.9 + 1.4				0.8 2.1	+0.8 − 0	+ 2.1 + 1.6	1.0 3.0	+ 1.2 − 0	+ 3.0 + 2.2
0.95 – 1.19	0.3 1.2	+0.5 − 0	+ 1.2 + 0.8	0.6 1.9	+0.8 − 0	+ 1.9 + 1.4	0.8 2.1	+0.8 − 0	+ 2.1 + 1.6	1.0 2.3	+0.8 − 0	+ 2.3 + 1.8	1.3 3.3	+ 1.2 − 0	+ 3.3 + 2.5
1.19 – 1.58	0.3 1.3	+0.6 − 0	+ 1.3 + 0.9	0.8 2.4	+1.0 − 0	+ 2.4 + 1.8	1.0 2.6	+1.0 − 0	+ 2.6 + 2.0	1.5 3.1	+1.0 − 0	+ 3.1 + 2.5	1.4 4.0	+ 1.6 − 0	+ 4.0 + 3.0
1.58 – 1.97	0.4 1.4	+0.6 − 0	+ 1.4 + 1.0	0.8 2.4	+1.0 − 0	+ 2.4 + 1.8	1.2 2.8	+1.0 − 0	+ 2.8 + 2.2	1.8 3.4	+1.0 − 0	+ 3.4 + 2.8	2.4 5.0	+ 1.6 − 0	+ 5.0 + 4.0
1.97 – 2.56	0.6 1.8	+0.7 − 0	+ 1.8 + 1.3	0.8 2.7	+1.2 − 0	+ 2.7 + 2.0	1.3 3.2	+1.2 − 0	+ 3.2 + 2.5	2.3 4.2	+1.2 − 0	+ 4.2 + 3.5	3.2 6.2	+ 1.8 − 0	+ 6.2 + 5.0
2.56 – 3.15	0.7 1.9	+0.7 − 0	+ 1.9 + 1.4	1.0 2.9	+1.2 − 0	+ 2.9 + 2.2	1.8 3.7	+1.2 − 0	+ 3.7 + 3.0	2.8 4.7	+1.2 − 0	+ 4.7 + 4.0	4.2 7.2	+ 1.8 − 0	+ 7.2 + 6.0
3.15 – 3.94	0.9 2.4	+0.9 − 0	+ 2.4 + 1.8	1.4 3.7	+1.4 − 0	+ 3.7 + 2.8	2.1 4.4	+1.4 − 0	+ 4.4 + 3.5	3.6 5.9	+1.4 − 0	+ 5.9 + 5.0	4.8 8.4	+ 2.2 − 0	+ 8.4 + 7.0
3.94 – 4.73	1.1 2.6	+0.9 − 0	+ 2.6 + 2.0	1.6 3.9	+1.4 − 0	+ 3.9 + 3.0	2.6 4.9	+1.4 − 0	+ 4.9 + 4.0	4.6 6.9	+1.4 − 0	+ 6.9 + 6.0	5.8 9.4	+ 2.2 − 0	+ 9.4 + 8.0
4.73 – 5.52	1.2 2.9	+1.0 − 0	+ 2.9 + 2.2	1.9 4.5	+1.6 − 0	+ 4.5 + 3.5	3.4 6.0	+1.6 − 0	+ 6.0 + 5.0	5.4 8.0	+1.6 − 0	+ 8.0 + 7.0	7.5 11.6	+ 2.5 − 0	+11.6 +10.0
5.52 – 6.30	1.5 3.2	+1.0 − 0	+ 3.2 + 2.5	2.4 5.0	+1.6 − 0	+ 5.0 + 4.0	3.4 6.0	+1.6 − 0	+ 6.0 + 5.0	5.4 8.0	+1.6 − 0	+ 8.0 + 7.0	9.5 13.6	+ 2.5 − 0	+13.6 +12.0
6.30 – 7.09	1.8 3.5	+1.0 − 0	+ 3.5 + 2.8	2.9 5.5	+1.6 − 0	+ 5.5 + 4.5	4.4 7.0	+1.6 − 0	+ 7.0 + 6.0	6.4 9.0	+1.6 − 0	+ 9.0 + 8.0	9.5 13.6	+ 2.5 − 0	+13.6 +12.0
7.09 – 7.88	1.8 3.8	+1.2 − 0	+ 3.8 + 3.0	3.2 6.2	+1.8 − 0	+ 6.2 + 5.0	5.2 8.2	+1.8 − 0	+ 8.2 + 7.0	7.2 10.2	+1.8 − 0	+10.2 + 9.0	11.2 15.8	+ 2.8 − 0	+15.8 +14.0
7.88 – 8.86	2.3 4.3	+1.2 − 0	+ 4.3 + 3.5	3.2 6.2	+1.8 − 0	+ 6.2 + 5.0	5.2 8.2	+1.8 − 0	+ 8.2 + 7.0	8.2 11.2	+1.8 − 0	+11.2 +10.0	13.2 17.8	+ 2.8 − 0	+17.8 +16.0
8.86 – 9.85	2.3 4.3	+1.2 − 0	+ 4.3 + 3.5	4.2 7.2	+1.8 − 0	+ 7.2 + 6.0	6.2 9.2	+1.8 − 0	+ 9.2 + 8.0	10.2 13.2	+1.8 − 0	+13.2 +12.0	13.2 17.8	+ 2.8 − 0	+17.8 +16.0
9.85 – 11.03	2.8 4.9	+1.2 − 0	+ 4.9 + 4.0	4.0 7.2	+2.0 − 0	+ 7.2 + 6.0	7.0 10.2	+2.0 − 0	+10.2 + 9.0	10.0 13.2	+2.0 − 0	+13.2 +12.0	15.0 20.0	+ 3.0 − 0	+20.0 +18.0
11.03 – 12.41	2.8 4.9	+1.2 − 0	+ 4.9 + 4.0	5.0 8.2	+2.0 − 0	+ 8.2 + 7.0	7.0 10.2	+2.0 − 0	+10.2 + 9.0	12.0 15.2	+2.0 − 0	+15.2 +14.0	17.0 22.0	+ 3.0 − 0	+22.0 +20.0
12.41 – 13.98	3.1 5.5	+1.4 − 0	+ 5.5 + 4.5	5.8 9.4	+2.2 − 0	+ 9.4 + 8.0	7.8 11.4	+2.2 − 0	+11.4 +10.0	13.8 17.4	+2.2 − 0	+17.4 +16.0	18.5 24.2	+ 3.5 + 0	+24.2 +22.0
13.98 – 15.75	3.6 6.1	+1.4 − 0	+ 6.1 + 5.0	5.8 9.4	+2.2 − 0	+ 9.4 + 8.0	9.8 13.4	+2.2 − 0	+13.4 +12.0	15.8 19.4	+2.2 − 0	+19.4 +18.0	21.5 27.2	+ 3.5 − 0	+27.2 +25.0
15.75 – 17.72	4.4 7.0	+1.6 − 0	+ 7.0 + 6.0	6.5 10.6	+2.5 − 0	+10.6 + 9.0	9.5 13.6	+2.5 − 0	+13.6 +12.0	17.5 21.6	+2.5 − 0	+21.6 +20.0	24.0 30.5	+ 4.0 − 0	+30.5 +28.0
17.72 – 19.69	4.4 7.0	+1.6 − 0	+ 7.0 + 6.0	7.5 11.6	+2.5 − 0	+11.6 +10.0	11.5 15.6	+2.5 − 0	+15.6 +14.0	19.5 23.6	+2.5 − 0	+23.6 +22.0	26.0 32.5	+ 4.0 − 0	+32.5 +30.0

(Courtesy of ANSI; B4.1-1955.)

APPENDIX 28. ENGINEERING FORMULAS

Motion

S = distance (inches, feet, miles)
t = time (seconds, minutes, hours)
v = average velocity (feet per second, miles per hour, etc.
v_1 = initial velocity
v_2 = final velocity
a = acceleration (feet per second per second)

(1) $S = vt$

(2) $V(\text{avg.}) = \dfrac{v_2 + v_1}{2}$

(3) $S = \left(\dfrac{v_1 + v_2}{2}\right) \dfrac{\text{ft}}{\text{sec}} (t \text{ sec})$

(4) $a = \dfrac{v_2 - v_1}{t}$

(5) $S = V_1 t + \frac{1}{2}at^2$

Angular Motion

V = linear velocity
N = number of revolutions per min
θ = angular distance in radians
1 radian = $360°/2\pi = 57.3°$
ω (omega) = average angular velocity
= θ/t (rad per sec, rev per min)
ω_1 = initial velocity
ω_2 = final velocity
α (alpha) = angular acceleration = rad per sec^2
S = length of arc
r = radius of arc
D = diameter

(6) $\theta = (\text{avg. } \omega)t$

(7) $\omega(\text{avg}) = \dfrac{\omega_2 + \omega_1}{2}$

(8) $\alpha = \dfrac{\omega_2 - \omega_1}{t}$

(9) $\omega_2 = \omega_1 + \alpha t$

(10) $\theta = \omega_1 t + \dfrac{\alpha t^2}{2}$

(11) $V = \pi DN$ or $V = r\omega$ (ft per sec, ft per min, etc.)

(12) $\omega = \dfrac{2\pi rn}{r} = 2\pi N$

Force and Acceleration

F = force (pounds)
M = mass
a = acceleration (ft per sec^2)
g = gravitational acceleration = 32.2 ft/sec^2
W = weight (pounds)
$M = F/a = W/g$ (units of mass in slugs)

Work

W = work (ft·lb)
F = force (lb)
d = distance
$W = Fd$

Power

W = work
t = time

1 horsepower = $550 \dfrac{\text{ft·lb}}{\text{sec}}$

Avg. power = $\dfrac{W}{t} = \dfrac{\text{ft·lb}}{\text{sec}}$ or $\dfrac{\text{ft·lb}}{\text{min}}$ etc.

Kinetic Energy

W = weight
V = velocity
g = 32.2 ft per sec^2
K.E. = $WV^2/2g$

APPENDIX 29. GRADING GRAPH

This graph can be used for determining the individual grades of members of a team and for computing grade averages for those who do extra assignments.

The percent of participation of each team member should be determined by the team as a whole (see Chapter 18 Problems).

Example: written or oral report grades

Overall team grade: 82

Team members $N = 5$	Contribution $C = \%$	$F = CN$	Grade (graph)
J. Doe	20%	100	82.0
H. Brown	16%	80	76.4
L. Smith	24%	120	86.0
R. Black	20%	100	82.0
T. Jones	20%	100	82.0
	100%		

Example: quiz or problem sheet grades

Number assigned: 30
Number extra: 6
Total 36

Average grade for total (36): 82

$$F = \frac{\text{No. completed} \times 100}{\text{No. assigned}} = \frac{36 \times 100}{30} = 120$$

Final grade (from graph): 86.0

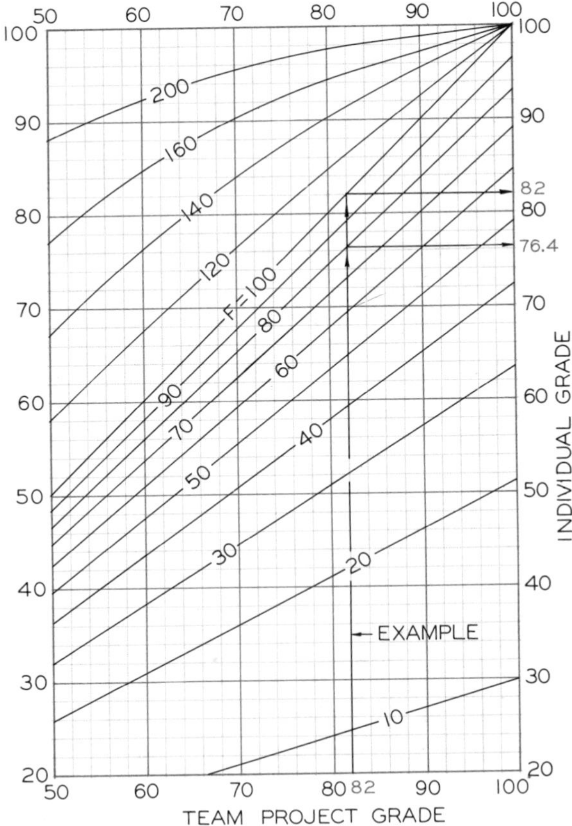

APPENDIX 30. CASE STUDIES IN ENGINEERING DESIGN

Case studies are historical summaries of the procedures used to arrive at a particular solution to a design problem. For significant projects introducing new methods and principles applied in a unique manner, a comprehensive case study is usually prepared for company files as a record of the total design effort. Design summaries of this type provide a reference for future projects involving similar applications. Knowledge gained from each project is equally valuable whether the results were positive or negative. The ability gained from experience to recognize methods that are not applicable to a given situation can save effort and money that would be wasted if an attempt were made to duplicate these methods on projects for which they are poorly suited.

Case studies can be used to suggest class problems and to depict examples of industrial solutions. Cases can be developed from local situations. Alternative solutions may be apparent that would be improvements over those actually used. The recognition of design problems and the analysis of the probable method of solution is a valuable experience to the student engineer or designer.

Two case studies are included in this appendix to illustrate two types of problems encountered in engineering.

The Guy F. Atkinson Company case describes an industrial situation in which the problem to be solved is a component of a total system. The case describes the company's operation and the circumstances surrounding the problem that was solved. As in many industrial problems, graphical methods were used to arrive at a solution. The drawings and photographs included can be used as a class assignment to review the method of arriving at the solution through the application of descriptive geometry techniques.

The electric slicing knife case study reviews the design process applied to a recently developed appliance for the general market. The process of evaluating the market appeal of this project and the engineering of its mechanism are reviewed in general terms.

THE GUY F. ATKINSON COMPANY

A Case History in Engineering Design*

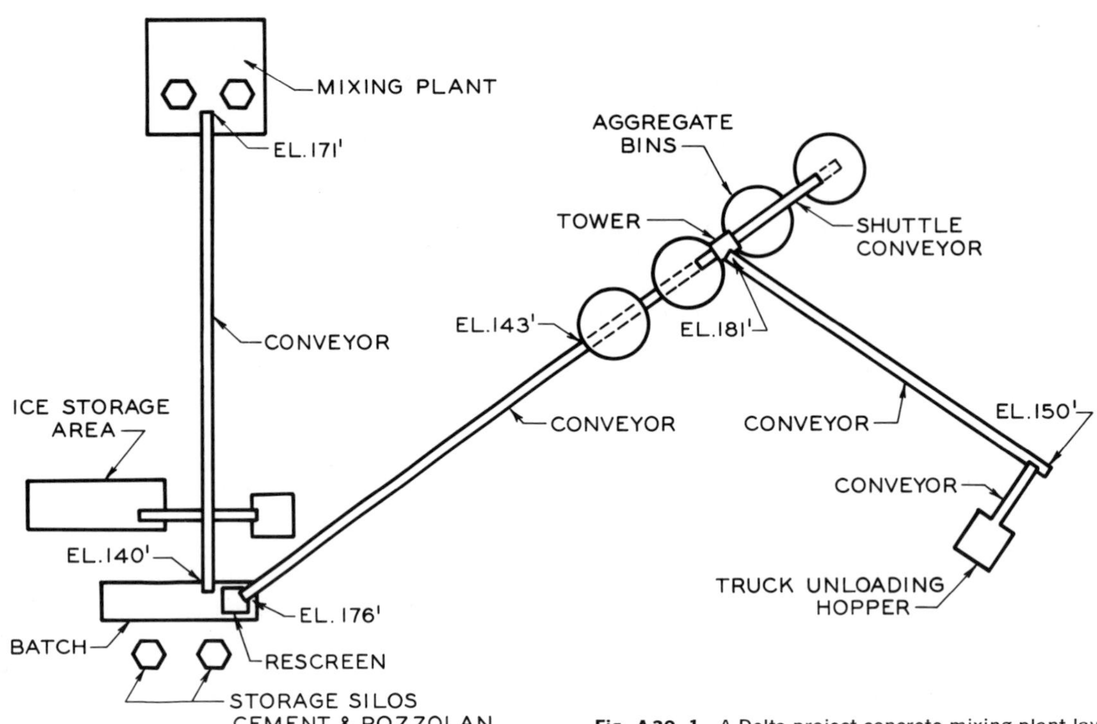

Fig. A30–1. A Delta project concrete mixing plant layout.

CLEARANCE BETWEEN A CONVEYOR AND SUPPORT TOWER

Mr. Atkins,† a civil engineer at the Guy F. Atkinson Company, was considering the design of a conveyor for a new concrete plant. The conveyor was one of several to be used in a plant which would mix sand, rock, cement, and water in correct proportions to produce concrete ready for pouring. Concrete would be taken from the plant by trucks over a 2-mile dirt road to the site of the new Delta Pumping Station, part of a major canal network to distribute irrigation water to Northern California farms. The Delta Pumping station, started in October, 1965, would be completed in February, 1966, after which the concrete plant would be dismantled.

The conveyor being designed was to move rock and sand from ground level to the top of a storage bin, and would be similar in construction to many which the company had used before. Mr. Atkins wanted to be sure that the conveyor

---

* Prepared in the Design Division, Department of Mechanical Engineering, Stanford University, by Robert Regier under the direction of Henry O. Fuchs with support from the National Science Foundation. Copyright © 1965. Reprinted by permission from Stanford University.

† Disguised names are used throughout this case.

was properly adapted to the peculiarities of this situation. Mr. Atkins commented, "We use a lot of standard equipment in our work but a mark of a competent engineer is that he can sense small differences in each situation." He was particularly concerned that a suitable clearance be provided between the conveyor and its supporting tower. The conveyor rested on the tower at a skew angle, making it somewhat difficult to determine the clearances.

GUY F. ATKINSON COMPANY

The Guy F. Atkinson Company is a "heavy construction" contracting organization. Most of its work has been on large projects such as dams, highways, bridges, and harbors, although it contracts smaller jobs as well. Currently its largest project is the construction of two dams and powerhouses in Pakistan for a cost of approximately $354 million. The Delta Pumping Station was, in the opinion of Mr. Atkins, typical of a medium-sized job. Most Atkinson projects have been in the Western United States. Major projects are bid and coordinated from head offices in South San Francisco.

Usually construction projects originate by a customer's invitation to several construction companies for submission of bids. If Atkinson Company enters bidding competition, a bid is formulated based on the estimated costs of required material, labor, and equipment necessary for the project, as well as management's appraisal of an appropriate profit. Of approximately 500 permanent employees in the Atkinson Company about 20% are engineers, and most cost estimating is done within this group. If a contract is awarded, the company engineers determine a work schedule, often with the aid of mathematical scheduling techniques such as CPM.* They also consider the depreciation, maintenance, and income tax implications of any additional equipment which must be purchased or rented for the project, and hire more employees if necessary.

The Delta Project Concrete Mixing Plant. The Delta Pumping Station was to be part of the San Luis Canal system which distributes water to northern and central California for use in agricultural irrigation. It would pump water from one canal to another 240 feet higher. The land around the pumping plant slopes upward in the direction of water flow, and water is pumped to a higher elevation to allow a slight downward slope of the canal. The five 66,000 horsepower pumps in the plant would have a total capacity of 2,500 cu. ft/sec.

Atkinson Company engineers decided that the most economical means of furnishing the large amount of concrete required for the pumping station was to mix it in a specially built plant near the job site. The plant they designed would mix sand; 3″, $1\frac{1}{2}$″, or $\frac{3}{4}$″, aggregate;† cement; and pozzolan‡ to yield structurally useful concrete. A schematic layout of the mixing plant is given in Fig. A30–1. Before dumping material into the unloading hopper, the truck driver locates one end of the shuttle conveyor over the aggregate bin which is to receive the material by selecting an appropriate switch. The shuttle conveyor is shown atop the four aggregate bins (after construction) in Fig. A 30–2. Each bin has a capacity of 180 tons and stores sand or one of the three sizes of aggregates. After unloading, a conveyor, shown in Fig. A30–3, conveys material from the drive-over hopper to the bottom of the aggregate bin conveyor. After being elevated, material falls through a chute onto the shuttle conveyor and is dumped into an aggregate bin. Either sand or a blend of aggregates, depending on plant requirements, is drawn from the aggregate bins by variable speed belt feeders and deposited on a conveyor beneath

* A construction project using CPM (Critical Path Method) is divided into small components, and the time necessary to complete each component is specified. After considering the priority of all components, a minimum completion time for the job is determined. Also, those components whose prompt completion is necessary for attaining this minimum are ascertained.

† After aggregate is passed through a square mesh screen, its size is said to be equal to the length of sides of the mesh squares.

‡ A fine, silica-like powder used to reduce the amount of cement.

Fig. A30–2. Aggregate bins and conveyors.

Fig. A30–3. An unloading Hopper conveyor.

the aggregate bins for transfer to the rescreen plant. This conveyor moves up to 600 tons per hour of sand or 100 tons per hour of aggregate, the aggregate capacity being limited by the rescreen plant. The rescreen provides a check on aggregate size and disposes of any undersize rock. Approximately 90% of all concrete in the pumping station will use 3″ aggregate. However, thin walled sections and inaccessible places often use $1\frac{1}{2}''$ or $\frac{3}{4}''$.

The batch plant, identified in Fig. A30–1, has four bins, one for each aggregate, one for sand, and a two-compartment horizontal silo which separately stores cement and pozzolan. Sand and aggregate are conveyed to a weighing hopper, cement and pozzolan are weighed in another hopper, and ice is conveyed from the ice storage area to an ice-weighing hopper.* Contents of the weigh hoppers are then discharged onto a conveyor for transfer to a holding hopper above the mixing plant. Material in the holding hopper is dumped into a 2 cu. yd rotating drum and mixed with water. The resulting product is discharged into trucks and transported to the pumping station for placing.

* Ice is used to lower the temperature of mixed concrete to minimize cracking.

DETERMINING THE DELTA PLANT LAYOUT

After the Delta Pumping Station job was contracted on August 25, 1964, it was necessary to design a concrete mixing plant which would supply concrete for construction of the pumping station. The plant was to be operative by December 5, 1964, with a mixing capacity of 60 cu. yd/hr. One of the first steps in preparing a specific plant design was to select and arrange the conveyors, bins, and roads so as to achieve low construction and operating costs. As in the design of most plants of this type, an economical layout was not obvious. The cost of any necessary excavation, which is generally large, had to be considered. Also to keep the cost low, support towers, conveyors and components from previous construction projects were used whenever possible. For the same reason conveyors used to elevate material are made as short as possible. Their steepness is limited, however, by the tendency of material to roll down the conveyor. Adjacent structures may also limit the choice of conveyor location.

Factors such as these were considered when initially establishing locations of the aggregate bins and unloading hopper. The arrangement of conveyors and bins shown in Figs. A30–1 and A30–2 appeared to be well-balanced from the

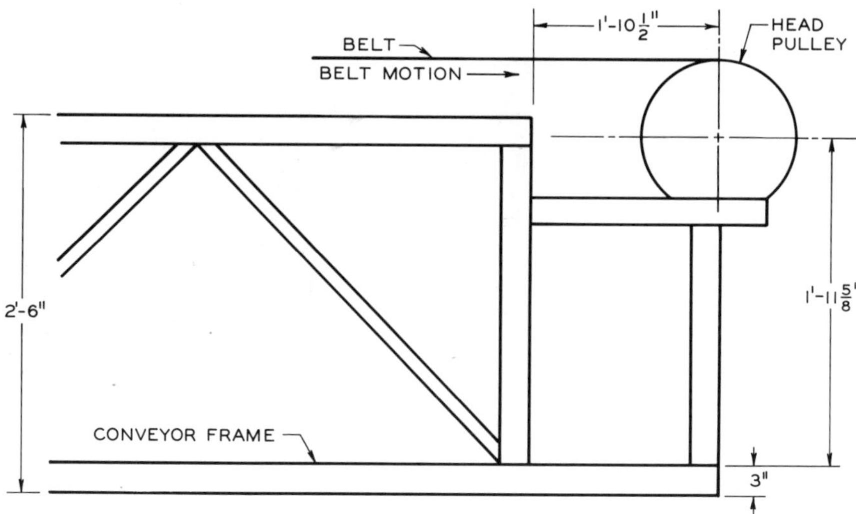

Fig. A30-4. A schematic profile of a conveyor frame and head pulley.

point of view of bin accessibility, conveyor length, characteristics of transported material, cost of excavation, etc. This general plant layout was used as a basis for further design of the specific plant components.

DESIGNING THE AGGREGATE BIN FEED CONVEYOR

In choosing the general Delta plant layout, company engineers had established locations for the unloading hopper and the aggregate bins. The next major task was to design the aggregate bins and a conveyor which would move material from the unloading hopper to the bins. Several concrete mixing plants had been designed to furnish concrete for past Atkinson Company projects and were dismantled upon completion of the projects. Although each mixing plant was different, certain components, such as bins and conveyors, were reused in several plants. In this way a stockpile of mixing plant components was created and, whenever possible, these components were used instead of newly-purchased equipment. After considering the desired output capacity of the Delta plant and checking the availability of used components, four bins from a previous project would be suitable as aggregate bins in the Delta plant.

In specifying the conveyor, the designers were constrained by the locations of the unloading hopper and aggregate bins, i.e. the bottom of the conveyor had to be underneath the unloading hopper conveyor and the top of the conveyor had to be properly positioned above the aggregate bins. In the mixing plant components stockpile Mr. Atkins found a conveyor which he thought was usable as an aggregate bin feed conveyor. Although the conveyor would have to be shortened for the Delta plant, its other specifications, such as belt width, distance between belt support rollers, and belt speed (400 feet per minute), were satisfactory. A portion of this conveyor may be seen in Fig. A30-2. Figures A30-4 and A30-5 give some dimensions of the basic conveyor framework and its position relative to the top belt pulley or head pulley.

Next, the engineers explored means of supporting the conveyor and securing it to the aggregate bins. Several conveyor support towers had previously been designed for other projects and they thought that one of these might be usable with little or no modification for supporting the aggregate bin feed conveyor. This support tower, if used, would be mounted above the aggregate bins as in Fig. A30-2. In determining the proper position of the head pulley

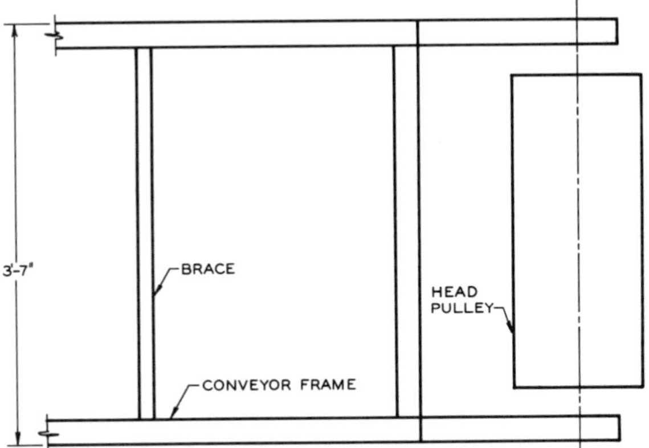

Fig. A30-5. A schematic plan view of a conveyor frame and head pulley.

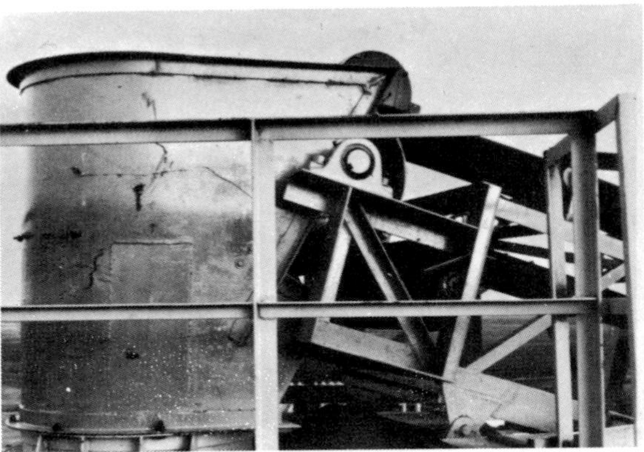

Fig. A30-6. A discharge chute.

relative to the support tower, the discharge characteristics of sand and aggregate as well as dimensions of the discharge chute (shown in Fig. A30-6) were considered. It was concluded that the head pulley should be located as described by Fig. A30-7.

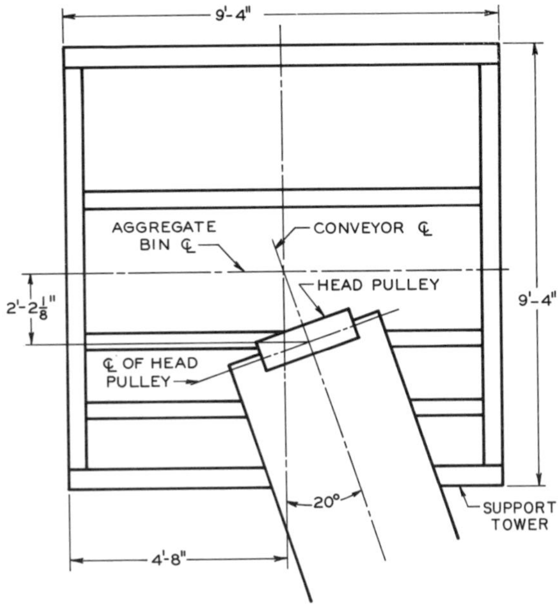

Fig. A30-7. A schematic plan view of a support tower.

The next factor to determine was the clearance between the conveyor, with its head pulley positioned as shown in Fig. A30-4, A30-5, and A30-7, and the support tower. The support tower and conveyor are not completely rigid, and, consequently, the positions of conveyor and support tower after construction may deviate somewhat from the design values. Therefore, the design clearance must be greater than the minimum tolerable clearance. It was felt that a design clearance of $\frac{1}{2}$" was necessary to assure absence of contact after construction. If the clearance was at least $\frac{1}{2}$", Mr. Atkins would design a means of securing the conveyor to the support tower. Otherwise, he would have to find a way of providing necessary clearance, possibly by modifying the support tower or relocating the conveyor.

He assigned the clearance problem to Mr. Smith, another engineer working on the Delta project. Mr. Smith was busy preparing drawings for the Delta plant, but began working on the clearance problem, thinking he would find the answer within about two hours. He first tried to find the clearance using a numerical analysis. The skewed orientation of the conveyor made this difficult, however, and three hours later he had not yet solved for the clearance. He took the problem to Mr. Atkins who then suggested the use of descriptive geometry techniques.

Fig. A30-8. Conveyor mounting brackets.

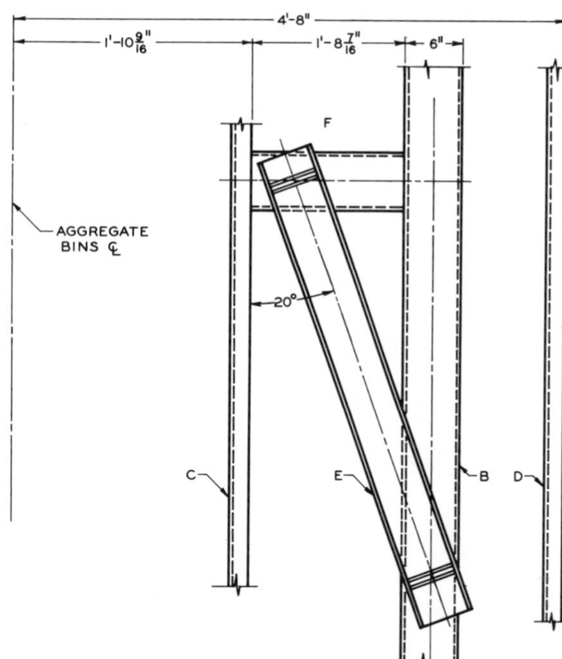

Fig. A30-9. A plan view of support tower members.

Having found that the conveyor, located as shown in Fig. A30-7, would clear the support tower, Mr. Atkins looked for a means of securing the conveyor to the support tower. In the past Mr. Atkins had successfully mounted aggregate conveyors with pins and brackets as in Fig. A30-8, and he chose to secure the Delta conveyor similarly. Using this method two brackets are welded to a piece of channel iron which is bolted to the support tower. These brackets are pinned to similar brackets which are welded to the conveyor. Bracket A of Fig. A30-8 is a type commonly used and was available from the used equipment stockpile. This bracket is welded to a piece of angle iron which is bolted onto the conveyor frame. The position of the brackets and angle iron along the length of the conveyor is chosen to align the pin holes. The size of these brackets is such that the perpendicular distance between the bottom of the conveyor frame and the center of the pin holes is 6".

Beneath the steel plate floor of Fig. A30-8 are the steel members which appear in Figs. A30-7 and A30-9. Since *B* of Fig. A30-9 was stronger than members *C* or *D*, Mr. Atkins wanted one end of support channel *E* to be bolted to *B* and the other end bolted to channel *F*, which would be welded between members *B* and *C*. The position of members *E* and *F* and height of the support tower brackets would be varied to permit pinning of the conveyor and support tower brackets. Mr. Atkins considered writing algebraic equations to find the proper location and size of these brackets. However, because of the geometrical complexity of the problem he chose to use drawings instead.

THE ELECTRIC SLICING KNIFE

A Case History in Engineering Design*

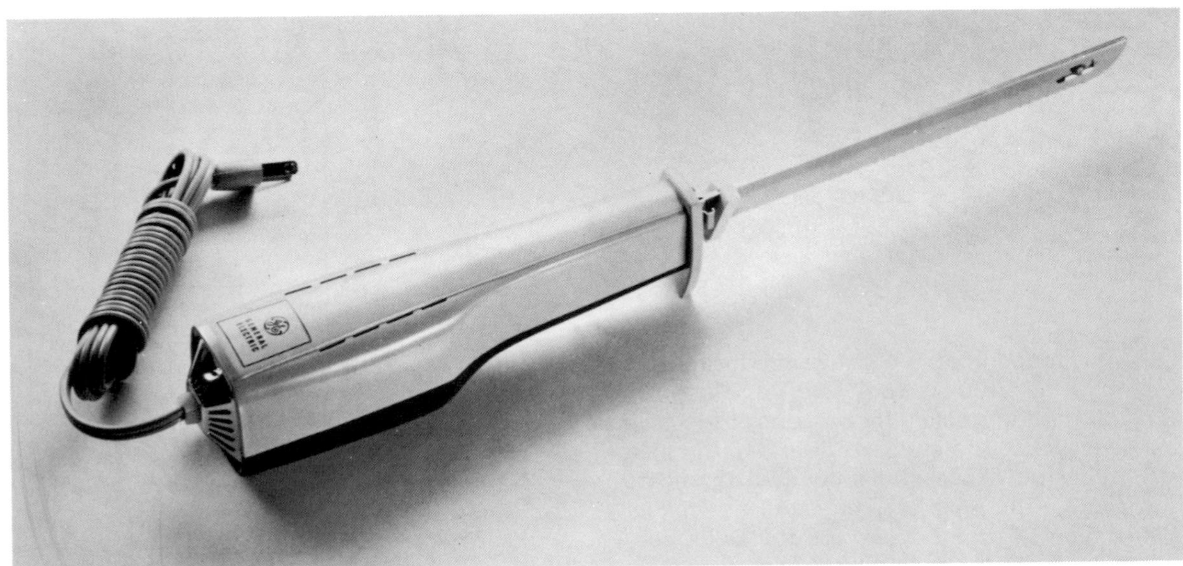

Fig. A30-10. An electric slicing knife.

DEFINITION AND OBJECTIVES

As a project engineer, your assignment is to develop a hand-held electric slicing knife. The concept, without benefit of models, has been market researched, and consumer interest appears to be very high.

As a housewares engineer at the Brockport Plant, you have worked with allied products such as portable mixers, stand mixers, can openers, blenders, knife sharpeners, and even cookware. Some of these products were new lines to the housewares industry, others new to the General Electric Company, while some could be classified as redesigns. These products were probably conceived by you or someone in your Engineering Section, but might have come from Marketing or a myriad of other sources both within and outside the company.

Early electric knife development was started in your Advance Engineering group in Bridgeport and the project is particularly intriguing to you as an engineer, not only because it is a totally new product for the housewares division, but because Marketing requirements permit only 13 months from engineering start to production. To place this timing in its perspective, the design engineering, tooling, manufacturing development, and pilot phases of a typical houseware product require approximately 9 months, leaving you only 4 months for your

* Reprinted by permission from A. H. Freeman of the General Electric Housewares Division, Brockport Plant.

engineering development activity. This engineering development will be considered complete upon proof of feasibility of performance and cost. The device is to retail at $24.95 or less.

Initial development in Advance Engineering has been primarily interested in cutting methods, and tests indicate that a two-blade counter-reciprocating system operating at 2000 operations/minute and $\frac{3}{16}$ inch stroke yields excellent cutting performance. Scalloping the cutting surfaces in this design permits the blades to overcome fibre compliance of the material to be cut, therefore requiring that the knife need only be guided during any slicing operation.

The unit, being hand held, must weigh less than 3 lb, be reasonably well balanced and, of course, be comfortable for the average housewife to manipulate. Average daily/yearly usage must be established as part of your engineering development program and the device must be designed to provide a minimum of 10 years trouble-free, average usage. As with all other housewares products, appearance, ease of cleanability, safety, and Underwriters' Laboratories standards, among other things, must be adhered to rigidly.

SOLUTION

With this background, the schedule is reassessed and felt to be attainable if you:

design using known methods where possible,

understand that all alternatives cannot be tested for optimization of costs,

take some chances.

Many areas require in-depth consideration and evaluation before the design can proceed, such as:

What kind of motor to use. Power? Make or buy?

How to transmit the rotary into reciprocal motion. Spur gears, helical gears, wobble plate, barrel cam?

What kind of reciprocating mechanism to give the required stroke and speed.

Temperature considerations, fan design.

Blade detail, material, hardness, clamping and latching means.

Housing structure, materials, shape—this list could continue *ad infinitum.*

Let us review a few of the major parameters which require resolution before putting together the *first* operating prototype unit.

By fixture testing, motor power can be established at 40–60 maximum watts out and at 1–1.5 in-lb maximum torque to minimize stall conditions when cutting cold beef and fibrous fruits and vegetables (squash, pineapple). Rewinding both the portable mixer armature and field provides this required output and, while this lamination is not as small as desired, its size is adequate. Economic advantages in using an existent lamination are obvious.

A 10/1 crossed helical gear reduction will provide 1950 rpm no load output with this motor, and although an inherent axial thrust component must now be dealt with, the system offers an extremely compact, economical, single-stage gear reduction. Efficiency is not as high as precision spur gearing but is satisfactory, for the application and rundown of the system can be kept to a minimum providing a desirable safety advantage. The factory is well equipped and experienced to hob the armature shaft and gear blank. Gear reaction thrust is handled by a closed rear-end armature journal bearing. The gear carrying two eccentrics, 180 degrees opposed, and operating in a classical scotch yoke mechanism, will provide simple harmonic motion to the counter-reciprocating mechanism at the desired $\frac{3}{16}$ stroke.

In order to provide minimum handle size and weight and offer maximum electrical protection, it is decided to combine the lower case, motor mounting and transmission housing means into a single plastic-handle body component. This design is a radical departure from any then existing portable appliance construction and provides manufacturing a further advantage by permitting the mechanism to be operated and tested before assembly is complete (half shell). See Fig. A30–11.

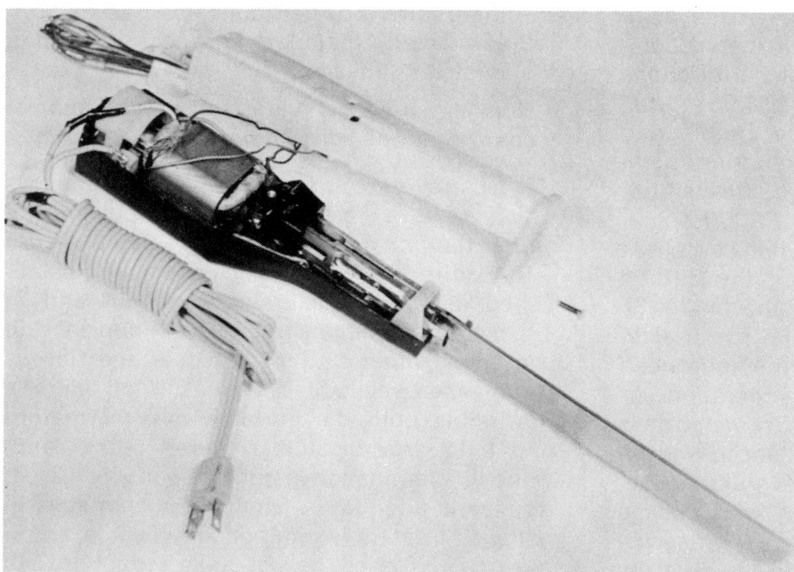

Fig. A30–11. Combining the motor mount and transmission housing into the body component allowed the mechanism to be tested before assembly was completed.

To expedite the prototype completion, initial layout is prepared directly onto a nylon-filled phenolic block prior to machining the handle body part in the engineering sample shop. This material is selected because of its excellent temperature characteristics, dimensional rigidity, and improved impact strength.

The first prototype is completed and ready for test nine weeks from start of development and you now have a similar period of time left to test, redesign, and freeze the design for release to the engineering design unit.

Performance tests out well, but coil temperatures run too high. Armature rear bearing support and brush boxes are then revised to minimize air flow restrictions and the brush boxes are further modified by incorporating into a fan shroud component (Fig. A30-11). The pitch and number of axial fan blades are also modified to provide an increased volume of cooling air. These modifications result in a Brockport* input watt rating sufficiently greater than the motor input requirement for normal and most abnormal cutting chores.

The machined housing behaves admirably during test. However, impact data with a single machined phenolic part are next to meaningless. To test in numbers, a 10–12 week period is needed to single cavity compression mold sufficient parts. This time requirement will overshoot the scheduled release date. What is needed therefore is greater assurance in a shorter period of time.

After much study, it is decided to use a new polycarbonate material called Lexan. Decision is based upon the material's reputed impact (20 filled phenolic), rigidity, and dimensional properties. Additional weight and size savings can also be realized by molding thinner wall sections with this material. Injection molded parts from a single cavity temporary aluminum mold can be ready for test in six weeks.

Acrylonitrile-Butadiene-Styrene handle cover parts from a similar temporary mold are also expected at the same time as the Lexan components.

Tests with the new design reveal the following shortcomings; the reduced tensile modulus of

---

* Input wattage which results in the curve of the highest recorded coil temperature to become asymptotic to 200° F when plotted against time.

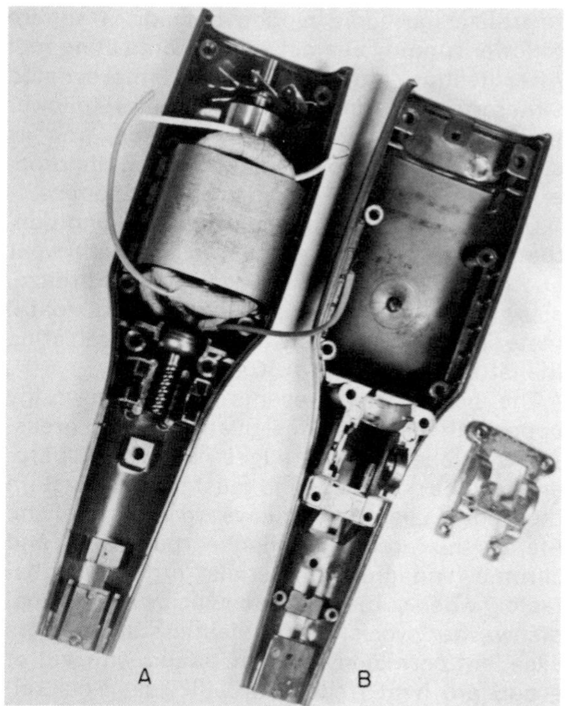

Fig. A30–12. The addition of a zinc transmission housing corrected gear mesh difficulties.

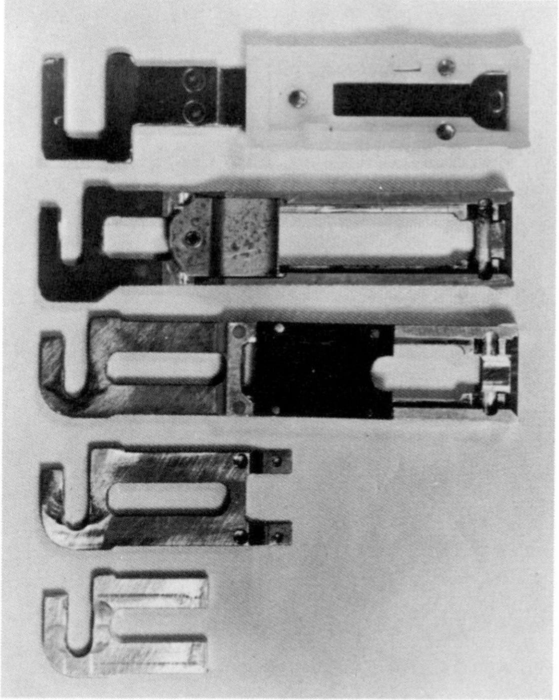

Fig. A30–13. Different materials were tested to determine the most durable with which to make the slider.

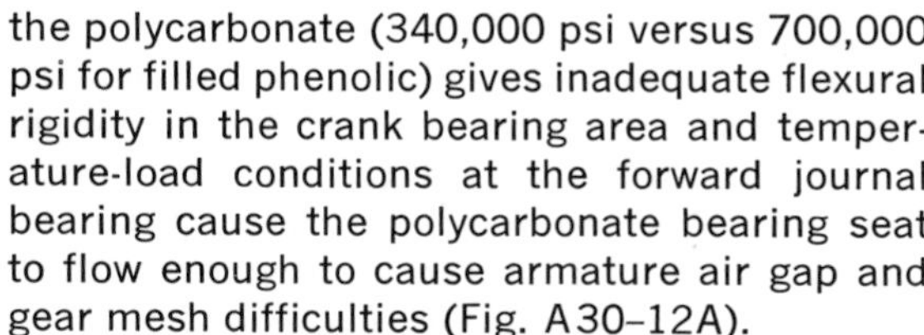

the polycarbonate (340,000 psi versus 700,000 psi for filled phenolic) gives inadequate flexural rigidity in the crank bearing area and temperature-load conditions at the forward journal bearing cause the polycarbonate bearing seat to flow enough to cause armature air gap and gear mesh difficulties (Fig. A30–12A).

Addition of an intermediate die cast zinc transmission housing incorporating the front bearing and crank bearing seats successfully corrects both conditions (Fig. A30–12B).

The reciprocating slide mechanism is originally planned as a powder metal part because of the required functional complexity and dimensional accuracy, and is designed open constructed at the eccentrics for ease of assembly and space considerations. The part functions also to provide support and latching for the blade members at its other extremity and is guided in a nylon forward bearing and against a steel wear plate in the zinc transmission housing.

The sintered construction is unacceptable because of insufficient bending strength at the open portion. Simulated die cast zinc and aluminum running against the forward nylon bearing show abnormal wear, and the part is then redesigned into a metallic rear member and a nylon forward blade retaining portion. The blade spring latch pin is assembled to the metal portion to eliminate cold flow under load.

In decreasing order of magnitude, aluminum, brass and steel rear portions of the slide show extreme impacting when run against mild steel eccentrics. Case hardening both eccentric and slider surfaces improves the condition but does not eliminate it (Fig. A30–13).

Other displacement motions (e.g. parabolic, cycloidal) are investigated to minimize the impacting, but the most promising direction is

Fig. A30-14. The final gear design.

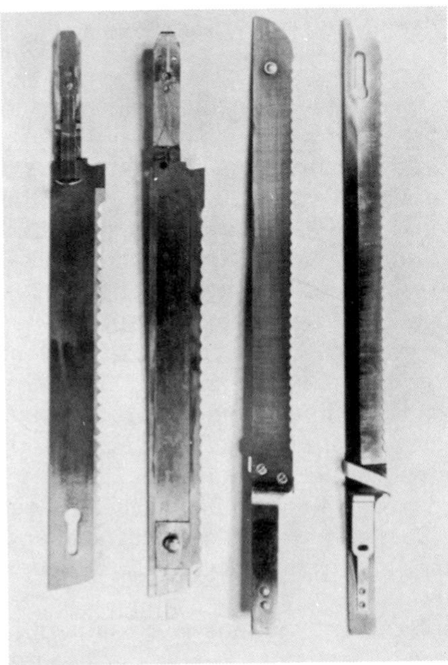

Fig. A30-15. The original and final designs for the blades.

to utilize harmonic motion but add a square follower running against a steel connecting rod. After testing nitrided steel, oil impregnated sintered nylon and powdered metal follower materials, oil impregnated sintered iron is selected because of wear and strength properties, dimensional tolerance and economics.

Despite an initial tooth point contact condition, the gear design proves out well in both wear and tooth strength. Powdered iron and bronze, along with linen based phenolic (textolite) materials, are rigorously tested before selecting the latter design (Fig. A30-14).

The blade area presents some noteworthy opportunities in both design and material areas. The scalloped cutting edges cannot be sharpened by the consumer and must therefore retain their edge, even with abusive treatment, for the life of the product. High carbon steel and chrome vanadium materials prove unsatisfactory when subjected to food acids and normal dishwasher cycles. 440A stainless steel offers excellent corrosion resistance, and with aid of a subzero heat treatment, will yield Rockwell C60-62 hardness. The blade is then tempered by drawing back to RC57-59. Addition of tungsten carbide to the cutting surfaces provides a rugged, long lasting cutting edge.

The original blade design, as received from Advance Engineering, is modified in length, height and cutting wedge angle to improve appearance, maneuverability and cutting performance. Revised means for coupling the two blades together results in improved manufacturability and reduced cost (Fig. A30-15).

Additional blade engineering activity includes the design of a reliable, low cost, simply actuated blade spring latching system and a novel configuration to prevent meat and other cutting juices from entering the handle body via the two tight rubbing blade surfaces.

This brief resume has depicted *some* of the *development* engineering thinking which goes into a housewares product. Once the project is released to the Design Engineering Unit, this same engineer, or more probably another product engineer, becomes concerned with similar problems and many other different ones.

The design is tested and retested and modified where necessary to improve performance, durability, manufacturability and costs. Appearance aspects of the design must be finalized, tolerance studies are prepared and finished drawings released for high volume production tooling.

The design engineer is also responsible, among other things, for packaging design, achieving Underwriters' Laboratory approval and even product service details.

Creativity is of major importance to the success of a product and eight patents have been issued by the U.S. Patent Office covering this knife design. Other patent applications are pending.

As a development or design engineer in our group, you are assigned total project responsibility as opposed to narrow specialization. The responsibility will include electrical, mechanical, thermal, material, and human engineering activities since all these technologies are found in each product engineered at Brockport. Motor technology will encompass series, shaded pole, and permagnet design. We have an important requirement in nickel cadmium and other battery know how, charging and switch circuitry, motor speed control, semiconductors, force balancing governors and the like, gear design, bearings, linkages, cams, and mechanisms. The list could go on and on. Technical know how and creativity however, though mighty important, are not enough. The product must be designed for cost and under the tightest schedules to enable a housewares plant to remain competitive. The consumer market in our business has and will always demand value received and the ability to provide this commodity is the challenge you face as an electric housewares design engineer.

REFERENCES

A selected bibliography of engineering cases is available from Stanford University. This bibliography lists the available case studies of engineering projects that could be used as a basis for design problems for use in engineering design and graphics courses. The bibliography is available from:

Case Program
Design Division
Mechanical Engineering Department
Stanford University
Stanford, California 94305

INDEX

ABCDEFGH79876543

Harnessing the world's surging rivers for irrigation and power—a challenge met by engineers and construction men with many notable achievements. The first great masonry dam—the first Aswan—was constructed on the Nile, and completed in 1902. The Hoover Dam (726.4 feet high, 1200 feet long) was started in 1928, dedicated in 1935 and became one of the largest hydroelectric suppliers in the world.

Probing and observing, engineers begin to chart the course of a fabulous voyage—the penetration of outer space. To accomplish it, engineering on a massive scale, to unprecedented degrees of accuracy and reliability, produced the first manned satellites (1961), Telstar (1962), the first photographs of the moon and Mars. Giant radio telescopes now "see" to the outer edges of the universe.